Larry

W9-CBS-699

Bennett C. Moulder

$5.05

TAXONOMY OF FLOWERING PLANTS

A SERIES OF BOOKS IN BIOLOGY

Editors: Douglas M. Whitaker, Ralph Emerson, Donald Kennedy,
George W. Beadle (1946-1961)

A flowering branch of the Tulip-tree, or Yellow Poplar, *Liriodendron tulipifera* L. The Magnolia Family, of which this plant is a member, is often regarded as one of the most primitive of all families of flowering plants. The scientific name, meaning "the lily tree that bears tulips," is highly descriptive.

Taxonomy of
Flowering Plants

by C. L. PORTER *University of Wyoming*

 W. H. Freeman and Company
San Francisco and London

PRINTED IN THE UNITED STATES OF AMERICA

LIBRARY OF CONGRESS CATALOGUE CARD NUMBER: 59–11828

PREFACE

WHILE MOST branches of botany have long been adequately served by an array of suitable texts, plant taxonomy, the oldest branch, has not been so fortunate. Until quite recently it has been necessary to improvise text material for class work; and even now we are faced, for the most part, with a choice between texts that are really reference books for advanced students and much abbreviated texts that have had much of the meat of the subject deleted from them. It is my hope that this book will help to fill that gap.

To this end I have attempted to put together such a factual and simplified account of basic principles as is needed by students in a beginning course in taxonomy, together with illustrated descriptions of more than a hundred families of flowering plants representative of the North American flora. Only the flowering plants, or angiosperms, are included, for the vascular crypto-gams (ferns and fern allies) and the gymnosperms are often dealt with in separate courses in morphology and dendrology, and for those groups ex-cellent texts are available. In my experience, a study of the basic principles and of selected angiosperm families alone provides ample material for the average beginning course in taxonomy, which is given for a minimum of one semester but preferably extends throughout one school year.

The content of the text is based on the assumption that the students have had at least some introduction to plant science, such as that provided by the usual beginning course in botany. It is particularly aimed at under-graduate students in such practical fields of study as agronomy, range man-agement, forestry, and wildlife management and conservation. This has necessitated a short, concise treatment and the omission of the detailed dis-cussion and elaboration that are found in the published research of many taxonomic experts of the past century. Perhaps I have been guilty of over-simplification in attempting to get at the essence of a complex subject. Those who feel that this is true, as well as more advanced students, will find numerous references to pertinent literature. By delving into at least some of it, the student will gain a better and more detailed knowledge of some of the classical work accomplished in this field.

The text has been divided into three major parts: Part I, dealing with historical and theoretical aspects and with terminology and morphology; Part II, dealing with orders and families of monocotyledons; and Part III, dealing with orders and families of dicotyledons. In practice I have used Parts I and II as the basis of one semester's work and Part III as the basis of a second semester's work. The instructor may or may not wish to follow this sequence.

One method of learning families, proved by a goodly number of classes over the years, is the study of floral diagrams and flower sections, together with other illustrative material, such as habit sketches or photographs and illustrations of fruits. This has called for the development of a system of diagrams not usually found in texts of this sort. These pictorial aids impress the minds of students with the varied floral morphology of plant families much better than conventional descriptions do. It is generally possible to identify a family by its floral diagram alone. In attempting to become acquainted with the flora of any region, one must first learn to recognize *families* rather than a great diversity of genera and species. These may come later with added field experience.

These pages have had a slow evolution. In the beginning they were merely outlines that I used as guides when conducting classes in taxonomy some twenty-five years ago; but at the insistence of the suffering students, who had difficulty in taking down notes from the blackboard, they gradually took the form of mimeographed notes distributed to classes in lieu of a textbook. These notes have been revised repeatedly as need arose until they now form the basis for this text. In drafting the final manuscript, I have incorporated numerous suggestions of my colleagues and have added original photographic illustrations to supplement the simple drawings.

I shall welcome comments and suggestions from students and fellow teachers.

May 1959   C. L. PORTER

TABLE OF CONTENTS

Part II

SELECTED ORDERS AND FAMILIES OF MONOCOTYLEDONS

Part III

SELECTED ORDERS AND FAMILIES OF DICOTYLEDONS

Part I

HISTORY, PRINCIPLES, AND METHODS

CHAPTER 1

The Aims of Taxonomy

"It has been already suggested, and forcibly enough, that plant taxonomy was not invented in any school, or by any philosopher; that it is everywhere as old as language; that no plant name is the name of an individual plant, but is always the name of some group of individuals, and that all grouping is classifying."—Edward Lee Greene in *Landmarks of Botanical History* (1909), page 106.

Plant taxonomy has two aims: (1) to identify all the kinds of plants; (2) to arrange the kinds of plants into a scheme of classification that will show their true relations.

The first aim requires us to make a complete inventory of all the plants on the face of the earth. This is not an insurmountable task, but—largely because our knowledge of many tropical regions is far from complete—it is still a long way from accomplishment. But even the fully explored and more civilized parts of the globe still present problems in plant identification, particularly in such perplexing groups as the genus *Lupinus* (Lupines) of western North America.

Anyone can learn, with a little practice, to identify a goodly number of things, be they people, dogs, rocks, or plants. The ancient civilizations produced people who could recognize and name many hundreds of stars and even arrange them into constellations. This was pure taxonomy. People have always needed to name things in order to have a means of communication. In scientific work it is essential that we be able to apply names with precision, for the validity of much research hinges on the identification of the materials involved. For botanists it is often necessary to identify materials beyond the species level, for minor differences in the kinds of plant under investigation may mean a major difference in the results. By furnishing such identification to others, the taxonomist serves other branches of science in a basic way. *All specialists and all botanical laboratory scientists should realize the importance of accurate identification of the materials with which they work.*

The second aim of the taxonomist is to seek out the evidence that will enable him to understand the relationships among groups of plants —among the lesser groups, or taxa, such as species and their subdivisions, and among the larger groups such as genera, families, and orders. To do this effectively, the taxonomist must utilize the methods and resources of all the major fields of botanical investigation. The *morphologist* gives him an understanding of form and structure, including such refinements as comparative anatomy and embryology. The *physiologist* can point out requirements for existence (such things as "physiological species" seem to occur in plants—groups that appear to be identical but differ in their requirements). The *ecologist* can furnish information about the relationships between plants and their environment, about how environment may affect form and structure, and about the selective action of the environment in determining which plants will survive. The *geneticist* and the *cytologist* contribute information concerning inheritance and reproduction as well as chromosome number and morphology, enabling the taxonomist to judge better whether he is dealing with distinct species or with lesser categories.

In cultivating these fields of investigation, the taxonomist must be able to call on others for assistance. *Geology* (particularly historical geology) furnishes information about past life, climates, and changing land forms, and this enables the taxonomist to interpret plant distribution and to understand something of the long history and evolution of plant life on the earth. A knowledge of *physical geography* is useful when he studies plant distribution and migration, whether local or world-wide, and it also points out what physical barriers to interbreeding may be present.

All this does not imply that the taxonomist is always an expert in all the fields mentioned; but it indicates the diversified knowledge that may be useful to the student.

Taxonomists are sometimes criticized for continually changing the names of plants. It should be remembered that taxonomy, though it is the oldest of the botanical sciences, is still in the learning process, and that we are continually adding to the great fund of information that will eventually enable us to name and classify all plants to the general satisfaction of everyone. That day is still a long way off. New techniques, new discoveries, and a continually expanding fund of information all demand revisions in taxonomic treatment even though these revisions may inconvenience the users of our product. It should also be remembered that we are dealing with living, dynamic, and often fluctuating populations, which will not always be interpreted by all workers, however expert, in exactly the same manner.

The science of taxonomy may be thought of as a synthesis of the four interrelated fields[1] outlined below:

1. *Systematic botany,* the fact-finding field, which includes genetic and cytological studies as well as any other techniques applicable to the problem.
2. *The taxonomic system,* based on the facts that were found, and including:
    (a) Taxonomic concepts of plant groups, or taxa.
    (b) Concepts of the evolutionary sequence of characters.
    (c) Classification and arrangement of taxa.
    (d) Description of taxa, or phytography.
3. *Nomenclature,* a method of naming plants based on international rules that botanists have agreed upon in order to promote a uniform and reasonably stable system. This permits only a single valid scientific name for each kind of plant, discarded names being known as *synonyms.*
4. *Documentation,* which includes the preservation of living or fossil floras in a museum or herbarium, including *type specimens* (those on which names and concepts of species and lesser taxa were originally based) and *illustrations* (which may sometimes be used in lieu of type materials).

By utilizing all four fields of taxonomy we are building up a mass of information that has already thrown much light on plant populations, their units, their means of perpetuation and dispersal, their interrelationships, distribution, and evolutionary tendencies. There remains, however, much more still to be done.

[1] See Mason, H. L., in the list of references at the end of this chapter.

REFERENCES

ARNOLD, CHESTER A.: "Fossil Dicotyledons" in A. Gunderson, *Families of Dicotyledons* (Waltham, Mass., 1950), pp. 3–6.

CAMP, W. H.: "Plant Geography" in A. Gunderson, *Families of Dicotyledons* (Waltham, Mass., 1950), pp. 25–30.

CAMP, W. H.: "Biosystematy," Brittonia 7: 113–127 (1951).

CONSTANCE, LINCOLN: "The Versatile Taxonomist," Brittonia 7: 225–231 (1951).

COPELAND, H. F.: "Embryology" in A. Gunderson, *Families of Dicotyledons* (Waltham, Mass., 1950), pp. 18–19.

FERRIS, G. F.: "The Place of the Systematist in Modern Biology," Sci. Monthly 16: 514–520 (1923).

FERRIS, G. F.: "The Content of Systematic Biology," Sci. Monthly 20: 653–658 (1925).

GATES, R. R.: "The Taxonomic Units in Relation to Cytogenetics and Gene Ecology," Am. Nat. 85: 31–50 (1951).

GLEASON, H. A.: "Some Fundamental Concepts in Taxonomy," Phytologia 4: 1–20 (1952).

GOLDSCHMIDT, R. B.: "Evolution, as Viewed by One Geneticist," Am. Scientist 40: 84–98 (1952).

JUST, THEODOR: "Carpels and Ovules" in A. Gunderson, *Families of Dicotyledons* (Waltham, Mass., 1950), pp. 12–17.

MASON, H. L.: "Taxonomy, Systematic Botany, and Biosystematics," Madroño 10: 193–208 (1950).

MERRILL, E. D.: "Some Economic Aspects of Taxonomy," Torreya 43: 50–64 (1943).

ROLLINS, R. C.: "Taxonomy of the Higher Plants," Am. Jour. Bot. 44: 188–196 (1957).

TIPPO, OSWALD: "Wood Anatomy" in A. Gunderson, *Families of Dicotyledons* (Waltham, Mass., 1950), pp. 6–11.

CHAPTER 2

Historical Summary

The beginnings of taxonomy undoubtedly antedate recorded history. It has always been one of man's characteristics that he likes to have names for things and to arrange things in a somewhat orderly manner. To say that taxonomy started with Aristotle, Dioscorides, or Pliny, or with anyone else now known, is erroneous. The early cultures of China, Egypt, and Assyria were based, to a certain degree, on cultivated plants, and there is evidence that such plants were studied and described by the scholars of those times. Much interest was also shown in plants reputed to have medicinal value. The pre-Columbian Aztec culture of Central America was likewise based on cultivated plants, and to this culture, and probably to people with a knowledge of plant breeding, we may owe the origin of certain modern crop plants, such as Maize. Even among uncivilized races of the present day we find evidence that a sort of taxonomy of plants is practiced, for such people have what are equivalent to concepts of species, genera, and families.

The attempts to classify all known plants have gradually shifted from purely *artificial systems* to *natural, or phylogenetic, systems.* An artificial system of classification is based on mere ease of identification; it uses convenient and readily observed characters of plants regardless of their evolutionary or genetic significance—as, for example, the grouping into herbs, undershrubs, shrubs, and trees (see under Theophrastus below) or the sexual system of Linnaeus, which was based on the number of stamens and styles. A natural, or phylogenetic, system, on the other hand, attempts to classify plants according to their evolutionary sequence and relationships inferred from indirect evidence or proved by genetic experimentation. The gradual growth of botanical terminology and a better understanding of the structure and function of reproductive parts resulted in greater precision in the definition of the various categories, or taxa, such as the species and its subdivisons, the genus, the family, and the order. Though great advances are being made in these fields of study at the present time, we are still a long way from achieving the ultimate goal of a completely phylogenetic system of classification and a complete understanding of all the parts of plants.

The Ancient Greeks and Romans

Among the first persons to leave us a written record of attempts at classification of the plants known to them were the early philosophers and medical practitioners of the Greek and Roman civilizations.

Theophrastus (370–287 B.C.), an outstanding Greek naturalist, was a pupil of Plato and Aristotle. In his *History of Plants,* the oldest botanical work in existence, he described some five hundred species of plants, mostly cultivated. These he classified into four groups, herbs, undershrubs, shrubs, and trees, considering trees to be the most highly developed of all. He also laid the foundations for the study of floral morphology.

Pliny the Elder (23–79 A.D.), a Roman naturalist and scholar, mentioned nearly a thousand plants in his *Historia Naturalis.* This series of thirty-seven books, sixteen of which dealt largely with plants, treated such topics as medicinal properties, timber trees, plant anatomy, and the practice of horticulture. Pliny read, or had read to him, most of the available literature of his time. His publications were therefore encyclopedic in scope; though they perpetuated many of the errors of his predecessors, they also included much factual information. His must be considered one of the most significant contributions to early botanical knowledge. It is unfortunate that his studies were cut short by his death during an eruption of Mount Vesuvius.

Dioscorides (first century A.D.) was a military physician under Emperor Nero of Rome. His chief contribution, *Materia Medica,* was a description of about six hundred species, mainly Mediterranean, used for medicinal purposes. Another manuscript, the *Anicia Juliana Codex,* was prepared for the daughter of a Byzantine emperor about 512 A.D. from material originally compiled by Dioscorides. It contained colored illustrations of plants and is still in existence.

The Herbalists

During the Middle Ages, following the decline of the Greek and Roman civilizations, little significant botanical progress was made. The early herbals, such as the *Codex* of Dioscorides, were copied and recopied for centuries with few additions or improvements. In the first half of the sixteenth century, however, a botanical renaissance developed, and it was greatly stimulated by the still young art of printing. Woodcuts were employed in printing illustrations of plants, and these often show a remarkable degree of fidelity, originality, and skill in execution. The herbals of **Brunfels, Bock, Fuchs** (see Fig. 1), **Cordus,** and others, men sometimes referred to as the "German fathers of botany," are representative of this period. A significant contribution to taxonomy was made at this time by **Kaspar Bauhin,** a pupil of Fuchs. In Bauhin's *Prodromus Theatri Botanici* (1620) and *Pinax Theatri Botanici* (1623) we find one of the first attempts to utilize a *binomial system of nomenclature*—which, however, Bauhin did not use exclusively.

Handed down from the ancients, and elaborated on by the herbalists, was the *doctrine of signatures,* which was based upon the belief that plants or plant parts that resembled portions of the human body must have been so created for the purpose of furnishing remedies for the ailments of those portions. Many plants were given common names that referred to supposed remedial properties, and many scientific names that are still in use today trace their origin to this doctrine—for example, the generic name *Hepatica,* the shape of the leaves in that genus being thought to resemble the shape of the liver and the leaves therefore to be a remedy for diseases of that organ.

The Transition Period

The transition from the Renaissance to the modern period produced many notable workers and much literature, which can be only hinted at in this brief discussion. Botanists gradually broke away from the traditional doctrines of the ancients and developed new systems of classification, a new terminology of description, and a system of nomenclature that was to become a permanent part of taxonomy. Since the concept of evolution had not yet been developed, the arrangement of plant groups in the various systems of classification was still more artificial than phylogenetic. We can, however, sense a groping toward a more natural arrangement of plant groups.

The geographical explorations of this period brought a great influx

1 Page from the herbal *De historia stirpium* of Leonhard Fuchs, published in 1542. The illustration is of *Zea mays* L., or what Fuchs called *Turcicum Frumentum* or "Türckisch korn," stating that it was brought into Germany from Asia by the Turks. Actually maize is of American origin and was unknown in the Old World until after the time of Columbus. The original size of the plate was 8 by 13 inches. [Ann. Mo. Bot. Gard. 35: 158 (1948); used by permission.]

of new species and genera, which soon became burdensome to the struggling taxonomists.

Andrea Cesalpino (1519–1603), an Italian physician, became director of the botanical garden at Bologna and later professor of botany. His herbarium, assembled in 1563 and still preserved in the Museum of Natural History at Florence, contains 768 dried and mounted plants with Latin or Italian names. Cesalpino's contribution to literature was *De Plantis,* consisting of sixteen books: the first a general exposition of the whole of theoretical botany, the others concerned with descriptions, without synonymy or illustration, of some 1,520 species of plants. He recognized a system of phyllotaxy in plants. His classification was based on the ancient grouping into herbs and trees, but within these groups he recognized the significance of fruit and seed characters. He had a good concept of genera, and he thereby exerted considerable influence on later botanists, such as Tournefort and Linnaeus. A copy of *De Plantis* once owned and annotated by Linnaeus is preserved in the library of the Linnaean Society. Cesalpino is commemorated by the name *Caesalpinia,* a genus of handsome legumes including the Poinciana Tree.

Joachin Jung (1587–1657), trained in both mathematics and medicine, and a brilliant teacher in Germany, is sometimes referred to as "the first terminologist." He left us no publications of his own writing, but two of his pupils left a record of his teachings that clearly reveals his concepts. He succeeded in clearing up some of the confusion that had existed between homologous and analogous structures. He believed that the old classification into trees, shrubs, and herbs was not fundamental.

Among the terms that he clearly defined for the first time are the following: *nodes* and *internodes;* the leaf consisting of *blade* and *petiole,* the blade being *simple* or *compound,* and compound leaves *pinnate* or *digitate; perianth* for the calyx instead of for the combined calyx and corolla, as now; *stamens* and *styles* as understood today, although Jung was not aware of their functions; *capitulum,* or head of flowers of the *Asteraceae,* as composed of *disk* and *ray florets.*

John Ray (1627–1705), the son of a British blacksmith, was a graduate of Trinity College. In his *Historia Plantarum* (1686–1704) we find some of the first indications of a natural system of classification. This work was an odd mixture of the old and the new. The old grouping into herbs and trees was retained as of primary significance, but within these groups we find a division into *dicotyledons* and *mono-*

cotyledons, which represented a notable advance in thinking. His classification of the major groups was as follows:

I. Herbae (herbs)
   A. Imperfectae (essentially the cryptogams)
   B. Perfectae (flowering plants)
      Dicotyledones
      Monocotyledones
II. Arborae (trees and shrubs)
   A. Monocotyledones
   B. Dicotyledones

Pierre Magnol (1638–1715) was a French contemporary of John Ray. Finding Ray's system too difficult, he divided plants into what he called *families,* listing some seventy-six of these in his *Prodromus historiae generalis, in qua familiae per tabulas disponuntur* (1689), and construing them as incorporating certain over-all striking characteristics of roots, stems, flowers, and seeds. It is to Magnol, then, that we owe the first concept of modern families, although not all of the families he listed were groups original with him. His name is commemorated by the generic name *Magnolia.*

Joseph Pitton de Tournefort (1656–1708), a pupil of Magnol, was professor of botany at the Jardin du Roi under Louis XIV. Before his time most botanical descriptions were confined to the level of the species, and genera were merely listed. From Magnol Tournefort must have acquired a concept of natural groups, for he reversed this procedure and for the first time gave a *characterization of genera,* merely listing the species under each. He recognized petaliferous and apetalous flowers, corollas with separate and with united petals, and regular and irregular corollas; but he refused to recognize sexuality in plants, and he also retained the ancient basic classification into trees and herbs. Among his contributions to the literature are *Éléments de botanique* (1694), illustrated with 450 copper plates and including 698 genera and 10,146 species, which he enlarged and published in Latin as *Institutiones Rei Herbariae* (1700), and a *Flora of the Environs of Paris* (1698).

Tournefort traveled widely in Europe, and in 1700–1703 he journeyed to Asia Minor, where he succeeded in climbing Mount Ararat. He died of injuries sustained when he was struck in the chest by the tongue of a carriage while crossing the street near the garden where he worked.

Rudolf Camerarius (1665–1721), though not strictly a taxonomist, influenced later workers in that field. He was made professor extraordinary and director of the botanical garden at Tübingen, Germany, in 1688. He experimented with certain plants in which the stamens and pistils were produced in separate flowers, reporting his findings in letters to scientists in other universities. One such letter, entitled *De sexu plantarum epistola,* dated August 25, 1694, and addressed to a professor at Giessen, described his experiments and the failure of the pistillate flowers to set seed in the absence of the staminate flowers. He concluded that the stamens were the male sex organs, that pollen was necessary for seed formation, and that the style and ovary constituted the female parts of the flower. Camerarius thus *established the fact of sexuality in flowering plants.*

Carolus Linnaeus (1707–1778), great Swedish naturalist and classifier, was born at Råshult, Sweden, where his father was a clergyman. Young Linnaeus started out to become a churchman also, but he gave that up at an early age to study natural history under the guidance of a local physician, who befriended him and introduced him to the writings of Tournefort. He attended the university at Uppsala, where he encountered the literature that first suggested to him the artificial *sexual system of classification,* which he later elaborated. His obvious interest in the university garden endeared him to Olof Rudbeck, an elderly professor, who helped him financially and used him as an assistant.

Under the sponsorship of the Academy of Sciences of Uppsala, and at a cost of about $125, Linnaeus undertook in 1732 a botanical exploration of Lapland. He covered about 4,800 miles in five months, and returned with 537 specimens, among them one he named *Campanula serpyllifolia,* which turned out to be not a *Campanula* at all and was renamed *Linnaea borealis* by the Dutch botanist Grovonius in honor of Linnaeus. The results of the Lapland expedition were later published as the *Flora Lapponica* (1737).

Linnaeus, having been urged to study medicine abroad, traveled in 1735 to the Netherlands, where after some time he received his degree in medicine at Harderwijk. While in the Netherlands he met the two eminent Dutch botanists J. F. Gronovius and Hermann Boerhaave, and it was Gronovius who financed the publication of his *Systema Naturae* (1735), a tabular outline consisting of eight folio sheets. He continued his stay in the Netherlands, with short visits to England and France, until 1742, when, at the age of thirty-five, and because of the death of his former teacher, Rudbeck, he returned to Uppsala to fill the chair of medicine and later that of botany.

As a tribute to his success as a teacher, the enrollment at Uppsala soon rose from 500 to 1,500; and through his industry the number of species of plants cultivated in the botanical garden was augmented by more than a thousand. Among his students were such notables as Peter Forskål, Fredrik Hasselquist, Peter Kalm, Carl Thunberg, and Daniel Solander, all explorers of renown who brought back plants from distant lands.

With the publication of his *Species Plantarum* (1753) we have the starting point for the system of priority that is used in our present-day nomenclature of the higher plants (see Figs. 2 and 3). Some 7,300 species were described therein, synonyms and countries of origin were included, and the groups were arranged according to the *sexual system* proposed earlier in the *Systema Naturae*. Here, for the first time, we find a consistent use of the binomial system of nomenclature, and this was one of Linnaeus' greatest contributions even though he was not the first to suggest its use. Linnaeus accepted many of Tournefort's genera, citing his descriptions and figures.

The system of classification divided all plants into twenty-four classes as follows:

1. *Monandria*—stamen 1.
2. *Diandria*—stamens 2.
3. *Triandria*—stamens 3.
4. *Tetrandria*—stamens 4.
5. *Pentandria*—stamens 5.
6. *Hexandria*—stamens 6.
7. *Heptandria*—stamens 7.
8. *Octandria*—stamens 8.
9. *Enneandria*—stamens 9.
10. *Decandria*—stamens 10.
11. *Dodecandria*—stamens 12.
12. *Icosandria*—stamens more than 12, attached to the calyx.
13. *Polyandria*—stamens more than 12, attached to the receptacle
14. *Didynamia*—stamens didynamous (2 long, 2 short).
15. *Tetradynamia*—stamens tetradynamous (4 long, 2 short).
16. *Monadelphia*—stamens monadelphous (in 1 bundle).
17. *Diadelphia*—stamens diadelphous (in 2 bundles).
18. *Polyadelphia*—stamens polyadelphous (in several bundles).
19. *Syngenesia*—stamens syngenesious (with united anthers).
20. *Gynandria*—stamens gynandrous (adnate to the pistil).

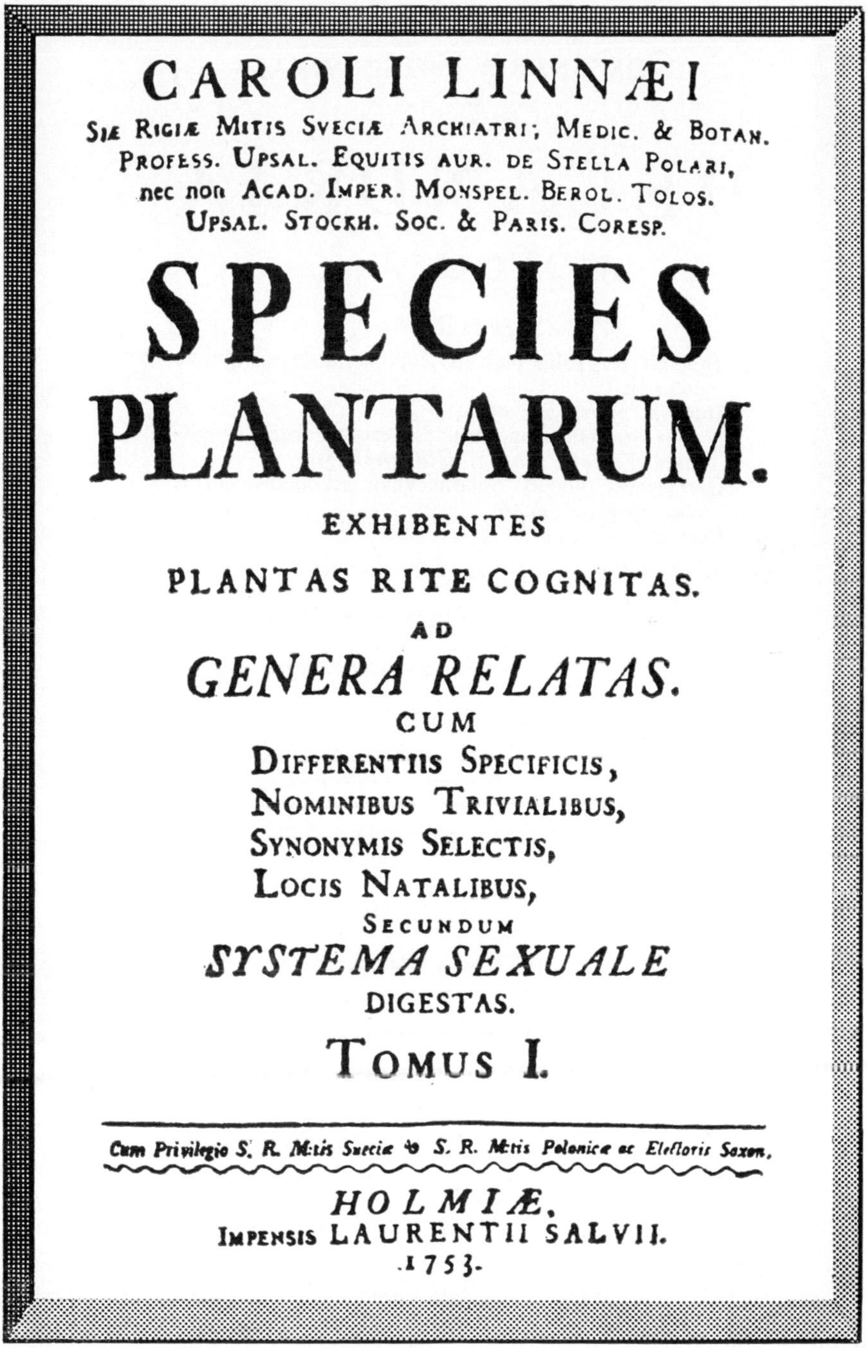

CAROLI LINNÆI

SIÆ RIGIÆ MITIS SVECIÆ ARCHIATRI; MEDIC. & BOTAN.
PROFESS. UPSAL. EQUITIS AUR. DE STELLA POLARI,
nec non ACAD. IMPER. MONSPEL. BEROL. TOLOS.
UPSAL. STOCKH. SOC. & PARIS. CORESP.

SPECIES PLANTARUM.

EXHIBENTES

PLANTAS RITE COGNITAS.

AD

GENERA RELATAS.

CUM

DIFFERENTIIS SPECIFICIS,
NOMINIBUS TRIVIALIBUS,
SYNONYMIS SELECTIS,
LOCIS NATALIBUS,
SECUNDUM

SYSTEMA SEXUALE

DIGESTAS.

TOMUS I.

Cum Privilegio S. R. M:tis Sueciæ & S. R. M:tis Polonicæ ac Electoris Saxon.

HOLMIÆ,
IMPENSIS LAURENTII SALVII.
.1753.

2 Title page of Linnaeus' *Species Plantarum*.

DECANDRIA MONOGYNIA.   373

Claffis X.

DECANDRIA

MONOGYNIA.

SOPHORA.

1. SOPHORA foliis pinnatis. foliolis numerofis villofis *alopecuroi-des.* oblongis.
Sophora. *Hort. cliff.* 156.
Ervum orientale alopecuroides perenne, fructu longis-fimo. *Tonrnef. cor.* 27. *Dill. eltb.* 136.
Glycyrrhiza filiquis nodofis quafi articulatis. *Buxb. cent.* 3. *p.* 25. *t.* 46
Habitat in Oriente. 2

2. SOPHORA foliis pinnatis: foliolis numerofis fubro- *tomentofa* tundis.
Sophora tomentofa, foliolis fubrotundis *Fl. zeyl.* 163. *
Indigophora foliis tomentofis. *Hort. cliff.* 487.
Colutea zeylanica argentea tota. *Herm. lugdb.* 169. *t.* 171. *Raj. bift.* 1720.
Habitat in Zeylona. ♄

3. SOPHORA foliis pinnatis, foliolis feptenis glabris. *heptaphylla.*
Sophora glabra, foliolis feptenis. *Fl. zeyl.* 104.
Fruticulus finenfis, fennæ fylveftris folio anguftiore, nodofa filiqua roftro longiore donata *Pluk. amaltb.* 18. *t.* 451. *f.* 10.?
Habitat in India. ♄

4. SOPHORA foliis ternatis feffilibus: foliolis lineari- *Geniftoides.* bus.
Geniftra africana, foliis galii. *Old. afr.* 31.
Habitat ad Cap. b. Spei.

5. SOPHORA foliis ternatis fubfeffilibus: foliolis fubro- *tinftoria.* tundis glabris.
Cytifus foliis fere feffilibus, calycibus bractea triplici auctis. *Gron. virg.* 82.
Cytifus procumbens americanus, flore luteo, ramofiffi-mus, qui Anil fuppeditat. *Pluk. alm.* 129. *t.* 86. *f.* 2 *Ehret. t.* 1. *f.* 3.
Habitat in Barbados, Virginia.
A a 3   6. SO-

3 Sample page from Linnaeus' *Species Plantarum*. This is the beginning of the treatment of the legumes.

21. *Monoecia*—plant monoecious (unisexual flowers on the same plant).
22. *Dioecia*—plant dioecious (unisexual flowers on separate plants).
23. *Polygamia*—plants polygamous.
24. *Cryptogamia*—flowers concealed (the cryptogams).

These primary divisions, or classes, were subdivided by Linnaeus into orders, which were usually based on the number of styles of the pistil, the ordinal names being *Monogynia, Digynia, Trigynia,* etc. The tremendous increase, during this period, in the number of known plants rendered such a simple classification very popular with the botanists who were called upon to deal with all the new material; but Linnaeus himself realized the limitations of the system and knew that it was more convenient than natural. He suggested that an increased knowledge of relationships among plants would some day permit a more natural grouping.

In 1753 Linnaeus was made a Knight of the Polar Star, the first scientist in Sweden to be knighted. In 1761 he was granted a patent of nobility, and from this date he became known as Carl von Linné.

His personal herbarium and library were sold by his widow, after his death, to Dr. James Edward Smith, the founder and first president of the Linnaean Society of London, for the sum of £1,000. After Smith's death they were purchased by subscription among the Fellows of the Society for presentation to the Linnaean Society, where they are preserved today.

The Modern Period

There is no sharp line of demarcation between the transition period, marked by various attempts at classification, all of which were more or less artificial, and the modern period, which progressed steadily in the development of a system based on natural affinities. Progress is still being made in this direction, the ultimate and as yet distant goal being an arrangement that will reflect the true phylogenetic relationships of the whole plant kingdom.

Bernard de Jussieu (1699–1777), a French contemporary of Linnaeus, attempting to lay out the Royal Gardens at Versailles according to a natural system and finding that the Linnaean system was unsatisfactory, proceeded gradually to modify it into a more natural arrangement. Never being completely satisfied with his groupings, he did not publish his results; but his nephew, **Antoine Laurent de Jussieu** (1748–1836), published his uncle's plan along with his own in *Genera Plantarum secundum Ordines naturales disposita* (1789).

This first attempt at a natural classification included a hundred orders (now mostly recognized as families), all described and classified in fifteen classes as follows:

1. *Acotyledones.*
2. *Monocotyledones*—stamens hypogynous.
3. *Monocotyledones*—stamens perigynous.
4. *Monocotyledones*—stamens epigynous.
5. *Dicotyledones, Apetalae*—stamens epigynous.
6. *Dicotyledones, Apetalae*—stamens perigynous.
7. *Dicotyledones, Apetalae*—stamens hypogynous.
8. *Dicotyledones, Monopetalae*—corolla hypogynous.
9. *Dicotyledones, Monopetalae*—corolla perigynous.
10. *Dicotyledones, Monopetalae*—corolla epigynous, anthers united.
11. *Dicotyledones, Monopetalae*—corolla epigynous, anthers distinct.
12. *Dicotyledones, Polypetalae*—stamens epigynous.
13. *Dicotyledones, Polypetalae*—stamens hypogynous.
14. *Dicotyledones, Polypetalae*—stamens perigynous.
15. *Diclines irregulares.*

According to this system, the *Acotyledones* included mainly the cryptogams, as we know them today, but also included some aquatic flowering plants whose reproduction was not understood at that time. The *Monocotyledones* and *Dicotyledones,* as defined, represented essentially the modern concepts of those groups. (The *Apetalae,* however, were construed as related groups; they are now considered to represent widely divergent lines of evolution and to be reduced forms of the *Polypetalae,* and they are still something of a puzzle to taxonomists.) The term "perigynous," as used by de Jussieu, is likewise at variance with our interpretation of that term; and his *Diclines irregulares* were an odd assortment of gymnosperms, *Amentiferae,* Nettles, and Euphorbias.

Augustin Pyrame de Candolle (1778–1841), the senior member of a notable French-Swiss family, following in the footsteps of de Jussieu, further developed the morphological approach to classification and recognized the significance of vestigial organs. His views were expressed in his *Théorie élémentaire de la botanique* (1813), in which 135 orders (or families as now treated) were delimited, that number being raised to 213 in a revision edited by his son **Alphonse** in 1844. The de Candolles, father and son, and later the grandson **Casimir,** collaborated on the preparation of the monumental *Prodromus systematis naturalis regni vegetabilis* (1824–1873). This series of volumes included nearly all the dicotyledons and probably would have included other groups had the complexity of the problem and the number of known species not increased to such an extent that the project as originally conceived got somewhat out of hand. A later series of monographs resulted in the revision of a number of families. The Candollean herbarium and library are now located at Geneva, Switzerland, where the members of the family did much of their work.

Robert Brown (1773–1858), a Scottish botanist, broke with the British tradition of following the Linnaean system and followed that of the de Candolles. He published no system of his own, but through his studies of seeds he *proved conclusively that the gymnosperms were a discrete group with naked ovules and seeds.* He established several families, among them the *Asclepiadaceae* and *Santalaceae;* and he proposed that the orders then recognized (families as we know them) should be grouped into larger categories (which would be equivalent to the modern orders).

Adolphe Théodore Brongniart (1801–1876), a French botanist, proposed a system of classification in which the *Apetalae* were treated as reduced members of the *Polypetalae.* This represents a distinctly modern trend, which was to be taken up later by Bessey.

George Bentham (1800–1884) and **Sir Joseph Hooker** (1817–1911), British botanists associated with the Royal Botanic Gardens at Kew, contributed an outstanding system of classification in their *Genera Plantarum* (1862–1883), which described some 202 orders (families as now understood) grouped into cohorts (orders as now understood). A combination of the systems of Bentham and Hooker and of the de Candolles was adopted by **Asa Gray** (1810–1888), Harvard botanist, during the formative period of American taxonomy.

The Bentham-Hooker system may be summarized as follows:

Dicotyledones.
  Polypetalae. Petals separate.
      Series 1. *Thalamiflorae.* Petals and stamens hypogynous. (Includes 6 cohorts, and families now known as the *Ranunculaceae, Brassicaceae, Caryophyllaceae,* and *Malvaceae.*)
      Series 2. *Disciflorae.* Stamens usually definite, inserted on or near a disk surrounding the base of the ovary. Ovary superior. (Includes 4 cohorts, and families now known as the *Geraniaceae, Rutaceae, Rhamnaceae, Sapindaceae,* and *Anacardiaceae.*)
      Series 3. *Calyciflorae.* Petals and stamens perigynous, and the gynoecium often enclosed by the development of the floral axis, the ovary sometimes inferior. (Includes 5 cohorts, and

families such as the *Rosaceae, Leguminosae, Onagraceae, Loasaceae, Cactaceae,* and *Apiaceae* or *Umbelliferae.*)

Gamopetalae. Petals united.

     Series 1. *Inferae.* Ovary inferior, stamens the same number as the lobes of the corolla or fewer. (Includes 3 cohorts, and families such as the *Caprifoliaceae, Rubiaceae, Campanulaceae,* and *Asteraceae* or *Compositae.*)

     Series 2. *Heteromerae.* Ovary usually superior; stamens as many as the lobes of the corolla, or more, on the corolla tube or free; carpels more than 2. (Includes 3 cohorts, and families such as the *Ericaceae* and *Primulaceae.*)

     Series 3. *Bicarpellatae.* Ovary usually superior; stamens the same number as the lobes of the corolla or fewer, on the corolla tube; carpels usually 2. (Includes 4 cohorts, and families such as the *Gentianaceae, Asclepiadaceae, Polemoniaceae, Boraginaceae, Solanaceae, Scrophulariaceae,* and *Menthaceae* or *Labiatae.*)

Monochlamydeae. Petals lacking. (No subdivision into cohorts.)

     Series 1. *Curvembryeae.* Embryo curved round the endosperm; ovules usually single; flowers usually perfect; stamens the same number as the sepals or fewer. (Includes *Chenopodiaceae, Polygonaceae,* and *Nyctaginaceae.*)

     Series 2. *Multiovulatae aquaticae.* Aquatics with syncarpous ovary and numerous ovules. (Includes *Podostemaceae.*)

     Series 3. *Multiovulatae terrestres.* Terrestrial herbs or shrubs with syncarpous ovary and numerous ovules. (Includes *Nepenthaceae, Cytinaceae,* and *Aristolochiaceae.*)

     Series 4. *Micrembryeae.* Embryo very small in copious endosperm. Ovary apocarpous or syncarpous, ovules usually single. (Includes *Piperaceae, Chloranthaceae, Myristicaceae,* and *Monimiaceae.*)

     Series 5. *Daphanales.* Ovary usually with 1 carpel, ovules single or paired; perianth sepaloid, in 1 or 2 series; woody plants; flowers perfect. (Includes *Lauraceae, Elaeagnaceae,* etc.)

     Series 6. *Achlamydosporeae.* Ovary 1-celled, 1–3-ovuled; seeds without a seed coat; perianth sepaloid or petaloid; plants often parasitic. (Includes *Santalaceae, Loranthaceae,* etc.)

     Series 7. *Unisexuales.* Flowers unisexual; ovary syncarpous or of 1 carpel; ovules solitary or in pairs; perianth sometimes lacking. (Includes *Euphorbiaceae, Urticaceae, Juglandaceae,* etc.)

     Series 8. *Ordines anomali.* Flowers often unisexual; not closely related to other orders. (Includes *Salicaceae,* etc.)

Gymnospermae. (Includes *Gnetaceae, Pinaceae,* etc., and *Cycadaceae.*)

Monocotyledones.

Series 1. *Microspermae.* At least the inner perianth petaloid; ovary inferior, 1-celled, with 3 parietal placentae; seeds very small, numerous, and without endosperm. (Includes *Orchidaceae, Burmanniaceae,* etc.)

Series 2. *Epigynae.* At least the inner perianth petaloid; ovary usually inferior; seeds with endosperm. (Includes *Bromeliaceae, Iridaceae, Amaryllidaceae,* etc.)

Series 3. *Coronarieae.* At least the inner perianth petaloid; ovary superior; endosperm present. (Includes *Liliaceae, Xyridaceae, Commelinaceae,* etc.)

Series 4. *Calycinae.* Perianth small, sepaloid, stiff or herbaceous; ovary superior; endosperm present. (Includes *Juncaceae, Arecaceae,* etc.)

Series 5. *Nudiflorae.* Perianth lacking or reduced to scales or bristles; ovary superior; carpels united or single, with from 1 to many ovules; endosperm usually present. (Includes *Typhaceae, Araceae, Lemnaceae,* etc.)

Series 6. *Apocarpeae.* Perianth in 1 or 2 series, or lacking; ovary superior; carpels 1 or else free; endosperm lacking. (Includes *Alismaceae, Najadaceae,* etc.)

Series 7. *Glumaceae.* Flowers in heads or spikelets, subtended by usually imbricated bracts; perianth small, scale-like, or chaffy, or lacking; ovary with 1 ovule in each cell or 1-celled and 1-seeded; endosperm present. (Includes *Poaceae* or *Gramineae, Cyperaceae,* etc.)

During this period in the development of botanical science, much of the confusion in the various systems of classification was due to a lack of understanding of the method of reproduction in the lower plants. **Wilhelm Hofmeister** (1824–1877), a German botanist and music dealer of Leipzig, clearly established the fact of *alternation of generations* and demonstrated the essential similarities running through various plant groups. His research focused attention on *resemblances,* whereas earlier workers had emphasized arbitrary *differences.* Hofmeister's findings, coupled with the revolutionary *Origin of Species* (1859) by **Charles Darwin** (1809–1882), stimulated much thought and many publications and controversies, the result of which was a better understanding of relationships. Gradually there emerged a concept of continuity in the plant kingdom, from the lowest forms to the highest, with numerous gaps in the record remaining to be filled.

It is worth mentioning in passing that Darwin, realizing the difficulties and complexities involved in nomenclature, provided in his will for the cost of compiling an index to the names, authorities, and countries of origin of all known flowering plants. This work, carried out under the direction of Joseph Hooker, produced the famous and useful *Index Kewensis,* which has been kept up to date by supplements to the present time.

August Wilhelm Eichler (1839–1887), professor of botany at the University of Kiel, Germany, modified previous systems to place the gymnosperms in their proper sequence as follows:

> *Cryptogamae*
> > *Thallophyta*
> > *Bryophyta*
> > *Pteridophyta*
> *Phanaerogamae*
> > *Gymnospermae*
> > *Angiospermae*
> > > *Monocotyleae*
> > > *Dicotyleae*
> > > > *Choripetalae* (petals separate or none)
> > > > *Sympetalae* (petals united)

Adolf Engler (1844–1930), professor of botany at the University of Berlin, adopted the main features of the Eichler classification, and in collaboration with **Karl Prantl** (1849–1893) and others published *Die natürlichen Pflanzenfamilien,* a comprehensive world treatment of the plant kingdom, the first edition being completed in 1909 and some revisions being added more recently. Herein were given details concerning the morphology, anatomy, and economic aspects of the various families, profuse illustrations, and keys to the genera, which were dealt with in synoptical fashion. Engler's system is still followed in the arrangement of families of flowering plants in nearly all manuals and floras and in most herbaria. For details of the system the student is referred to Engler and Diels' *Syllabus der Pflanzenfamilien,* eleventh edition (Berlin, 1936). The significant feature of the system is that it places the monocotyledons ahead of the dicotyledons, and the apetalous and catkin-bearing dicotyledons ahead of the others, indicating that the authors considered these last to be primitive rather than derived groups.

Richard von Wettstein (1862–1931), an Austrian systematist, produced a classification that was similar in most respects to that of Engler. He also considered the unisexual, naked flower to be primitive and derived perfect flowers with a perianth from such a source. But he took into account more background information than Engler did, and this resulted in some realignment and a more nearly phylogenetic arrangement of groups, for he considered the dicotyledons to be primitive and the monocotyledons to be derived from them through the *Ranales*.

Charles Edwin Bessey (1845–1915), a student of Asa Gray and thereafter professor of botany at the University of Nebraska, introduced some new ideas concerning primitive and advanced characters in plants. After trial flights into the field of classification in 1894 and 1897, at which time he followed rather closely the Bentham-Hooker system, and again in 1907 and 1909, he finally evolved what is now known as the Besseyan System under the title "The Phylogenetic Taxonomy of Flowering Plants" (Ann. Mo. Bot. Gard. 2: 108–164, 1915). Portions of this are given below through the courtesy of the Missouri Botanical Garden.

Bessey's system was based on a series of "dicta," or statements of the guiding principles he used in determining the degree of primitiveness or evolutionary advancement of a plant group. According to these principles he constructed a chart (Fig. 4) showing the relationships as well as the approximate sizes of the relatively few orders of flowering plants he recognized. He took the *Ranales* (or Buttercup order) as the basal group—a feature of the Bentham-Hooker system—from which both monocotyledons and other groups of dicotyledons have evolved. He also believed that all flowering plants originated from strobiliferous cycad ancestors, probably from the *Bennettitales*.

Following are Bessey's dicta:

A. GENERAL DICTA

1. Evolution is not always upward, but often it involves degradation and degeneration.
2. In general, homogeneous structures (with many and similar parts) are lower, and heterogeneous structures (with fewer and dissimilar parts) are higher.
3. Evolution does not necessarily involve all organs of the plant equally in any particular period, and one organ may be advancing while another is retrograding.
4. Upward development is sometimes through an increase in complexity, and sometimes by a simplification of an organ or a set of organs.
5. Evolution has generally been consistent, and when a particular progression or retrogression has set in, it is persisted in to the end of the phylum.
6. In any phylum the holophytic (chlorophyll-green) plants precede

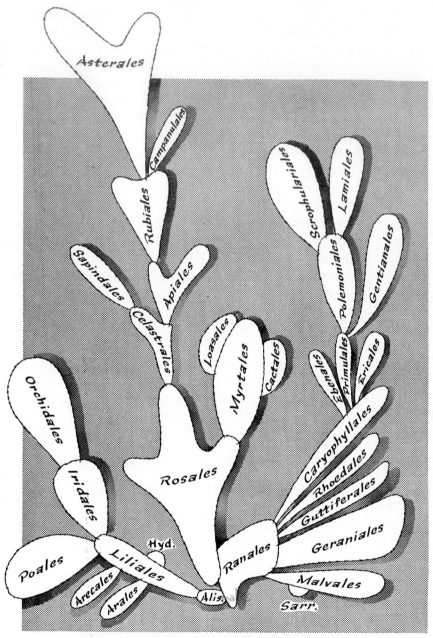

4 Bessey's chart showing relationships of orders he recognized. The areas are approximately proportional to the number of species in the orders. To the left are the monocotyledons, in the center are perigynous and epigynous dicotyledons, and to the right are hypogynous dicotyledons. [Ann. Mo. Bot. Gard. 2: 118 (1915); used by permission, and slightly modified.]

the colorless (hysterophytic) plants, and the latter are derived from the former.

7. Plant relationships are *up and down* the genetic lines, and must constitute the framework of phylogenetic taxonomy.

B. DICTA HAVING SPECIAL REFERENCE TO THE GENERAL STRUCTURE OF THE FLOWERING PLANTS

8. The stem structure with collateral vascular bundles arranged in a cylinder is more primitive than that with scattered bundles, and the latter are to be regarded as derived from the former.
9. Woody stems (as of trees) are more primitive than herbaceous stems, and herbs are held to have been derived from trees.
10. The simple, unbranched stem is an earlier type, from which branching stems have been derived.
11. Historically the arrangement of leaves in pairs on the stem is held to have preceded the spiral arrangement in which the leaves are solitary at the nodes.
12. Historically simple leaves preceded branched ("compound") leaves.
13. Historically leaves were first persistent ("evergreen") and later deciduous.
14. The reticulated venation of leaves is the normal structure, and the parallel venation of some leaves is a special modification derived from it.

C. DICTA HAVING REFERENCE TO THE FLOWERS OF FLOWERING PLANTS

15. The polymerous flower structure precedes, and the oligomerous structure follows from it, and this is accompanied by a progressive sterilization of sporophylls.
16. Petaly is the normal perianth structure, and apetaly is the result of perianth reduction (aphanisis).
17. The apochlamydeous perianth is earlier and the gamochlamydeous perianth is derived from it by symphysis of the members of perianth whorls.
18. Actinomorphy is an earlier structure than zygomorphy, and the latter results from a change from similar to a dissimilar growth of the members of the perianth whorls.
19. Hypogyny is the more primitive structure, and from it epigyny was derived later.
20. Apocarpy is the primitive structure, and from it syncarpy was derived later.
21. Polycarpy is the earlier condition, and oligocarpy was derived from it later.

22. The endospermous seed is primitive and lower, while the seed without endosperm is derived and higher.
23. Consequently, the seed with a small embryo (in endosperm) is more primitive than the seed with a large embryo (in scanty or no endosperm).
24. In earlier (primitive) flowers there are many stamens (polystemonous) while in later flowers there are fewer stamens (oligostemonous).
25. The stamens of primitive flowers are separate (apostemonous), while those of derived flowers are often united (synstemonous).
26. The condition of powdery pollen is more primitive than that with coherent or massed pollen.
27. Flowers with both stamens and carpels (monoclinous) precede those in which these occur on separate flowers (diclinous).
28. In diclinous plants the monoecious condition is the earlier, and the dioecious later.

Hans Hallier (1868–1932) was a German systematist who attempted to develop a phylogenetic system. It is significant that, although the two developed independently, Hallier's system closely resembled that of Bessey. Hallier made much more use of ovule structure and position than other workers had.

John Hutchinson (born in 1884), a British botanist associated with the Royal Botanic Gardens at Kew, has proposed a system somewhat like that of Bessey in his *Families of Flowering Plants:* Vol. I, *Dicotyledons* (1926), and Vol. II, *Monocotyledons* (1934). Hutchinson, however, considering the woody versus the herbaceous habit as of fundamental importance, maintained that the predominantly woody orders stemmed from the Magnolias and their relatives in the *Ranales* as we know them, and that the chiefly herbaceous orders originated from the Buttercups and their relatives, these two lines developing independently but in a more or less parallel fashion. He also proposed many more than the generally accepted number of orders, with fewer families in each. In the following treatment, Hutchinson's scheme has been the basis for the arrangement of monocotyledons, and Bessey's scheme has been the basis for the arrangement of the dicotyledons.

Recent Developments

Much new information has come to light since the above attempts to produce a phylogenetic classification. This information is derived mainly from additional knowledge of certain plant groups found in the Pacific area, from comparative anatomical studies of various organs, particularly of flowers and embryos, and from cytological studies of many aberrant groups.

I. W. Bailey has pointed out that new genera, which are apparently relics of an ancient, woody, dicotyledonous flora, and most of which are represented by one or only a few species, are being discovered in the southwest Pacific area (Fiji, New Caledonia, New Guinea, northern Australia, and northward to China and India). Investigations centering on these plants may in time unravel the great mystery of the origin of angiosperms.

Arthur J. Eames and others have studied a number of families of flowering plants with particular attention to the comparative anatomy of the flowers and secondary wood. Such research has indicated both that a number of genera are misplaced in the traditional treatments of families and also that certain genera and species, despite various unusual characteristics, properly belong where they have been placed by conservative taxonomists. In the future it will probably be necessary to establish several additional families to take care of aberrant genera.

The detailed studies of comparative embryology made by **John R. Reeder** and others substantiate some elements of our traditional system of classification but also point out places where it is probably at fault.

Many cytogenetic studies of a wide range of plant groups have contributed to a better understanding of relationships among the higher plants. At first this research was aimed mainly at infraspecific problems, but as it broadened it began to take on significance in higher levels of classification, even at the family level.

Since evolution has resulted in a branching system of relationships, perhaps even in a reticulate one, any linear sequence, such as must be followed in a book, or any numbered sequence of families, such as that used in many herbaria, must of necessity be artificial. Furthermore, though a broad general pattern of evolution in the flowering plants has emerged from the various studies made of them through the years, many unsolved riddles still exist. As someone has said, "We stand on the wrong side of the tapestry—a confusion of colors, knots, and loose ends. But, be assured, on the other side there is the pattern." It has even been suggested that a science of "systematic physiology" should be developed as an aid in the formulation of phylogenetic systems. In the meantime the "family tree" type of arrangement serves a useful purpose in that it helps us visualize possible relationships—even though some eminent workers have ridiculed the diagrams as "deformed hatracks." Such diagrams, of course, are subject to the modifications that new information may suggest. And it should be remembered that an order or a family, having been clearly differentiated by the evolution of its members, is not likely to have given rise to other orders or families as pictured in these diagrams. But the more plastic and primitive progenitors of such groups could have had this possibility in their germ plasm.

REFERENCES

ARBER, AGNES: *Herbals: Their Origin and Evolution* (Cambridge, England, 1938).

BAILEY, I. W.: "The Anatomical Approach to the Study of Genera," Chron. Bot. 14: 121–125 (1953).

BLAKE, S. F.: "Systems of Plant Classification: A Review," Jour. Heredity 26: 463–467 (1935).

EAMES, A. J.: "Floral Anatomy as an Aid in Generic Limitation," Chron. Bot. 14: 126–132 (1953).

FERNALD, M. L.: "Some Historical Aspects of Plant Taxonomy," Rhodora 44: 21–43 (1942).

FINAN, JOHN J.: "Maize in the Great Herbals," Ann. Mo. Bot. Gard. 35: 149–191 (1948).

GREENE, E. L.: "Landmarks of Botanical History," Smithsonian Inst., Wash., Misc. Coll. 54: 1–329 (1909).

GUNDERSON, ALFRED: "A Sketch of Plant Classification from Theophrastus to the Present," Torreya 18: 213–219, 231–239 (1918).

GUNDERSON, ALFRED: "World Families for Angiosperms," Bull. Torr. Club 81: 210–214 (1954).

HALLIER, H.: "Provisional Scheme of the Natural (Phylogenetic) System of Flowering Plants," New Phytol. 4: 151–162 (1905).

HARSHBERGER, J. W.: "Taxonomic Charts of the Monocotyledons and the Dicotyledons," Proc. Am. Philos. Soc. 46: 313–321 (1907).

HARVEY-GIBSON, R. J.: *Outlines of the History of Botany* (New York, 1919).

HAWKS, ELLISON, & G. S. BOULGER: *Pioneers of Plant Study* (London, 1928).

JACKSON, B. D.: *Linnaeus: The Story of His Life,* adapted from the Swedish of T. M. Fries (London, 1923).

JESSEN, KARL F. W.: *Botanik der Gegenwart und Vorzeit in culturhistorischer Entwickelung* (1864), reprinted by Hafner Publishing Company (New York, 1948).

MAXON, W. R.: "Systematic Botany: Its Development and Contacts," Old and New Plant Lore, Smithsonian Scientific Series 11: 133–164 (1931).

REED, HOWARD S.: *A Short History of the Plant Sciences* (Waltham, Mass., 1942).

REEDER, J. R.: "The Embryo in Grass Systematics," Am. Jour. Bot. 44: 756–768 (1957).

RENDLE, A. B.: *The Classification of Flowering Plants,* Vol. I (Cambridge, England, 1904), pp. 1–31.

ROLLINS, R. C.: "Cytogenetical Approaches to the Study of Genera," Chron. Bot. 14: 133–139 (1953).

SACHS, J. VON: *History of Botany,* English edition by Garnsey & Balfour (Oxford, England, 1890).

SINGER, CHARLES: *A History of Biology,* revised edition (New York, 1950).

SINGER, CHARLES: *From Magic to Science* (New York, 1928).

TIPPO, O.: "A Modern Classification of the Plant Kingdom," Chron. Bot. 7: 203–206 (1942).

TIPPO, O.: "The Role of Wood Anatomy in Phylogeny," Am. Midl. Nat. 36: 367–372 (1946).

TRELEASE, WILLIAM: "Four Generations of Memorable Botanists," Sci. Monthly 19: 53–62 (1924).

TURRILL, W. B.: "Taxonomy and Phylogeny," II, Bot. Rev. 8: 473–532 (1942).

WETTSTEIN, R.: *Handbuch der systematischen Botanik,* 4th edition (Leipzig & Wien, 1935).

CHAPTER 3

Taxonomic Literature

The literature of taxonomy is tremendous, varied in scope, and diverse in purpose. It runs the gamut from ponderous volumes to obscure notes in periodicals and even letters of correspondence between workers. Because of this great volume and diversity, one of the vexing problems of the research worker and teacher is that of keeping abreast of recent publications and developing a knowledge of past publications in his field of special interest. To facilitate this task he may consult the lists of publications that have been issued for many years in the *Bulletin of the Torrey Botanical Club* and in the *Taxonomic Index,* the latter recently published as a supplement to issues of *Brittonia,* the publication of the American Society of Plant Taxonomists. Abstracts of published papers and texts can also be found in *Biological Abstracts,* published by the University of Pennsylvania and including works under the heading "General and Systematic Botany." Other fertile sources of pertinent literature will be found at the end of research papers in the form of bibliographies. Most serious workers gradually accumulate such information by the simple expedient of making card files, each card keyed to subject matter or author, or variously cross-indexed. A very satisfactory file of this sort, used by the author, is based on an arrangement of subject matter by families, the breakdown within the family being an alphabetical sequence by genus. Within the genus, the file is alphabetical by author and chronological by date. Other major files, besides the one by family, are used for more general subjects. Such a file, kept up to date, will yield desired information with a minimum of time and effort, because the system is much the same as that employed by many herbaria for the filing of plant specimens.

It is difficult to classify satisfactorily the major kinds of taxonomic literature, but the following will give some indication of the variety of publications that is to be found in most large libraries.

Comprehensive Publications

These are wide, even world-wide, in scope and often comprise a series of large volumes. Because of the tremendous amount of labor involved in their preparation, the cost of publication, and their limited sale, such publications are almost a thing of the past. But they were formerly the mainstay of the taxonomist, and they are still invaluable to the serious student. In Linnaeus' *Species Plantarum* (1753), de Candolle's *Prodromus Systematis Naturalis Regni Vegetabilis* (1824–1887), and the more recent Engler and Prantl's *Die natürlichen Pflanzenfamilien* (1887–1909, a second edition being unfinished), we have some of the most monumental taxonomic work of all time.

Manuals and Floras

These regional treatments include keys, and usually descriptions, of families, genera, and species. Early publications of this type usually included large areas, but the increasing complexity of the problems involved has led to floras of smaller regions. A modern manual for a single state in the United States may be just as voluminous as one for the whole of North America published many years ago.

Manuals and floras may be illustrated or not; they may vary in the amount of descriptive matter; and some give citations to original publications of taxonomic groups and fairly complete synonymy, but others do not. Here, again, the high cost of publication, and the limited sale, have limited the scope.

In addition to the larger, regional floras, many *local floras* have been published. These are generally treatments of small areas such as valleys, islands, counties, or other more or less natural physiographic provinces. They serve a very useful purpose and make a very worth-while project for the local botanist.

Following is a list of the more commonly consulted major floras of North America north of Mexico:

ABRAMS, LEROY: *An Illustrated Flora of the Pacific States,* Vols. I–III (Stanford University, 1923, 1944, 1951), with more to follow by other authors, Dr. Abrams having died in 1956.

ANDERSON, J. P.: *Flora of Alaska and Adjacent Parts of Canada,* Iowa State Jour. Sci. (1944–1952).

BAILEY, L. H.: *Manual of Cultivated Plants,* 2nd edition (New York, 1949).

BAILEY, V. L., & H. E. BAILEY: *Woody Plants of the Western National Parks* (Notre Dame, Indiana, 1949).

BENSON, LYMAN, & R. A. DARROW: *A Manual of Southwestern Desert Trees and Shrubs,* Univ. Ariz. Biol. Sci. Bull. No. 6 (1944).

CHAPMAN, A. W.: *Flora of the Southern United States,* 3rd edition (Cambridge, Mass., 1897).

COULTER, J. M., & AVEN NELSON: *New Manual of Botany of the Central Rocky Mountains* (New York, 1909).

DAVIS, R. J.: *Flora of Idaho* (Dubuque, Iowa, 1952).

DEAM, C. C.: *Flora of Indiana* (Indianapolis, Indiana, 1940).

FERNALD, M. L.: *Gray's Manual of Botany,* 8th edition (New York, 1950).

GLEASON, H. A.: *New Britton and Brown Illustrated Flora of the Northeastern States and Adjacent Canada,* 3 vols. (New York, 1952).

GRAY, ASA: *Synoptical Flora of North America:* Vol. 2, *Gamopetalae,* 2 parts, 2nd edition (New York, 1886).

GRAY, ASA, SERENO WATSON, & B. L. ROBINSON: *Synoptical Flora of North America:* Vol. 1, *Polypetalae,* 2 parts (New York, 1895–1897).

HARRINGTON, H. D.: *Manual of the Plants of Colorado* (Denver, Colorado, 1954).

HITCHCOCK, C. L., et al.: *Vascular Plants of the Pacific Northwest* (a projected 5-vol. illustrated flora, as yet incomplete): Vol. 5, *Compositae,* by Arthur Cronquist (Seattle, Washington, 1955).

HOOKER, W. J.: *Flora Boreali-Americana* (London, 1829–1834). An account of the plants of northern British America, including collections of such notable explorers as Richardson, Drummond, Franklin, and Douglas.

HULTÉN, ERIC: *Flora of the Aleutian Islands* (Stockholm, 1937).

HULTÉN, ERIC: *Flora of Alaska and Yukon* (Lund, 1941–1950).

JEPSON, W. L.: *A Manual of the Flowering Plants of California* (Berkeley, California, 1923–1925).

JEPSON, W. L.: *A Flora of California,* 3 vols., incomplete (San Francisco and Berkeley, California, 1909–1943).

JONES, G. N.: *Flora of Illinois,* 2nd edition (Notre Dame, Indiana, 1950).

JONES, G. N., & G. D. FULLER: *Vascular Plants of Illinois* (Urbana, Illinois, 1955).

KEARNEY, T. H., & R. H. PEEBLES: *Flowering Plants and Ferns of Arizona,* U. S. Dept. Agr. Miscel. Publ. 423 (1942).

KEARNEY, T. H., & R. H. PEEBLES: *Arizona Flora* (Berkeley and Los Angeles, California, 1951).

MUNZ, P. A.: *A Manual of Southern California Botany* (Claremont, California, 1935).

NUTTALL, THOMAS: *The Genera of North American Plants,* 2 vols. (Philadelphia, Penna., 1818).

PECK, M. E.: *A Manual of the Higher Plants of Oregon* (Portland, Oregon, 1941).

PIPER, C. V., & R. K. BEATTIE: *Flora of Southeastern Washington and Adjacent Idaho* (Lancaster, Penna., 1914).

PIPER, C. V., & R. K. BEATTIE: *Flora of the Northwest Coast* (Lancaster, Penna., 1915).

PURSH, FREDERICK: *Flora Americae Septentrionalis,* 2 vols. (London, 1814; 2nd edition, 1816).

REHDER, ALFRED: *Manual of Cultivated Trees and Shrubs Hardy in North America,* 2nd edition (New York, 1940).

RYDBERG, P. A.: *Flora of the Rocky Mountains and Adjacent Plains* (New York, 1917; 2nd edition, 1922).

RYDBERG, P. A.: *Flora of the Prairies and Plains of Central North America* (New York, 1932).

SCHAFFNER, J. H.: *Field Manual of the Flora of Ohio and Adjacent Territory* (Columbus, Ohio, 1928).

SMALL, J. K.: *Flora of the Southeastern United States* (New York, 1903).

SMALL, J. K.: *Manual of the Southeastern Flora* (New York, 1933).

STEVENS, O. A.: *Handbook of North Dakota Plants* (Fargo, N. D., 1950).

TIDESTROM, IVAR: *Flora of Utah and Nevada,* Contr. U. S. Nat. Herb. 25: 1–665 (1925).

TIDESTROM, IVAR, & SISTER TERESITA KITTELL: *A Flora of Arizona and New Mexico* (Washington, D. C., 1941).

TORREY, JOHN, & ASA GRAY: *A Flora of North America,* 2 vols (New York, 1838–1840).

WOOTON, E. O., & P. C. STANDLEY: *Flora of New Mexico,* Contr. U. S. Nat. Herb. 19: 1–794 (1915).

Various authors: *North American Flora,* published by the New York Botanical Garden at irregular intervals, starting in 1905. Incomplete at present, but eventually to comprise about 34 volumes.

Various authors: *Contributions Toward a Flora of Nevada.* A series prepared through the cooperation of the National Arboretum and the U. S. Department of Agriculture, edited by W. Andrew Archer, and issued as mimeographed parts. The series was started in 1940, and to date some 45 numbers have been issued.

Popular Treatments

These "flower books" are the delight of the novice and of persons wishing to consult non-technical works. They also have their proper place in taxonomic literature and are frequently consulted by experts. Their chief characteristic is that they enable almost anyone to identify many of the common or more ornamental flowering plants by means of pictures alone. There are a number of such books, but perhaps the most sumptuously illustrated and beautiful volumes are *The Macmillan Wild Flower Book* by C. J. Hylander and E. F. Johnston (New York, 1954) and *Wild Flowers of America* by H. W. Rickett, with illustrations by Mary Vaux Walcott and Dorothy Falcon Platt. Both of these contain full-page illustrations in color, supplemented by brief text descriptions.

Treatments of Special Groups

The special interests of experts result in volumes on such subjects as grasses, trees, aquatic plants, forage plants, poisonous plants, and weeds. Most of these are well illustrated, and they are often semi-popular or non-technical in treatment. Some, however, are aimed at serving the needs of experts and professional botanists. Many such publications are issued as bulletins by federal and state agencies.

Of particular interest to persons interested in cultivated plants is *The Standard Cyclopedia of Horticulture* by L. H. Bailey (three volumes, 1947), in which the plants are treated in alphabetical order according to their generic names. The first volume includes a synopsis of the plant kingdom, keys to the families and genera of cultivated plants, English equivalents of Latin names, and an excellent glossary of botanical terms. This work is copiously illustrated. A smaller publication by the same author, *Manual of Cultivated Plants,* second edition (New York, 1949), is a handy reference book for the identification of cultivated plants by means of keys and descriptions, but it has few illustrations.

Those interested in trees are well served by a large array of books, from the eleven-volume, beautifully illustrated set by C. S. Sargent entitled *The Silva of North America* (reprinted in 1947) to the pocket-sized manuals such as that of Richard J. Preston called *North American Trees* (1948, reprinted in 1950), which has good illustrations and a distribution map for each species. Many states have published useful bulletins on the local trees. The U. S. Department of Agriculture's *Yearbook of Agriculture* for 1949, called *Trees,* is another useful source. Many other references will be found in W. A. Dayton's *Bibliography of Tree Identification* (see the reference at the end of the chapter).

Persons concerned with identification of grasses may consult the *Manual of the Grasses of the United States* by A. S. Hitchcock, the second edition revised by Agnes Chase (1950) and published as Miscellaneous Publication No. 200 by the U. S. Department of Agriculture. Here will be found illustrations of most of the species and maps showing their distribution.

Aquatic plants have been treated satisfactorily on a nation-wide basis by two authors: N. C. Fassett, *A Manual of Aquatic Plants* (1940, revised by E. C. Ogden in 1957), and W. C. Muenscher, *Aquatic Plants of the United States* (1944). Both are well illustrated and contain keys for the identification of the species included. *A Flora of the Marshes of California* by H. L. Mason (1957) is another useful source book in this category.

Poisonous plants have been described and illustrated in *Poisonous Plants of the United States* by W. C. Muenscher (1939); and many of the states, particularly those in the West, have issued bulletins on the poisonous plants of their areas.

The literature dealing with weeds is very extensive, and nearly every state is served by agricultural bulletins dealing with this subject. The chief general reference is *Weeds* by W. C. Muenscher (1936).

Those interested in orchids may refer to the beautifully illustrated and very complete treatment by D. S. Correll, *Native Orchids of North America* (1950), illustrated by Blanche Ames and Gordon Dillon, with cultural notes by E. T. Wherry and J. V. Watkins.

Monographic Treatments

These are detailed studies of limited scope and most often deal with single genera or groups of species. The author attempts to bring up to date all the available information concerning the group, and he usually includes detailed keys, citations to original publications, lists of synonyms, descriptions of the taxa, and lists of specimens examined. Included, also, will be attempts to interpret the phylogeny of the group and in recent years a discussion of the cytology involved. Such publications often represent years of painstaking research and constitute the chief bases for our understanding of perplexing groups of plants. It is usually this sort of research that is undertaken by graduate students in taxonomy when working toward an advanced degree. Once having developed an interest in a certain group of plants in this way, a student will often continue the study for many years and eventually become known as the expert on that group of plants. Monographs commonly appear from time to time in the recognized journals and are a valuable supplement to the more meager information contained in floras and manuals.

Notes and Observations

Throughout the literature one will find numerous short papers dealing with such matters as new or noteworthy species, minor variations, and range extensions. This type of publication, because of its varied nature and often inadequate titling, is often difficult to incorporate into a filing system, but the information contained in it may be of considerable significance.

Index, Catalogue, and Dictionary

A few such reference books are essential to the taxonomist. Apart from the usual English dictionaries, which are of general usefulness, and the foreign-language or classical dictionaries, certain more specialized botanical reference books are frequently consulted by the taxonomist. One of these is the *Index Kewensis* (1893–1895 and supplements to date), in which an attempt has been made to list all the scientific names of families, genera, and species of flowering plants, their countries of origin, their authors, and their places of publication. Synonyms, as interpreted by the staff of the Herbarium of the Royal Botanic Gardens at Kew, England, are also included, together with an indication of the valid name to which each applies. A portion of a page of this work is shown in Figure 5.

Of particular interest to workers in North America is the *Gray Herbarium Card Index,* which lists all new names and combinations, including infraspecific names, for the flowering plants and vascular cryptogams of the western hemisphere. Thousands of cards are found in this index, and more are being added each year.

Another very helpful index is the one, previously mentioned, published in each issue of the *Bulletin of the Torrey Botanical Club* and reprinted by the American Society of Plant Taxonomists as the *Taxonomic Index* in the journal *Brittonia.*

In *Taxon,* the official news bulletin of the International Association for Plant Taxonomy, will be found announcements of significant floras as they are published, as well as other information of general interest to taxonomists.

For a listing of recent publications in taxonomy and related fields, the taxonomist will profit by reference to *Biological Abstracts,* also mentioned earlier, in which summaries of published research will be found.

AMBROSIA—AMERIMNON.

'6.—	AMEBIA, Regel, Pl. Nov. Fedsch. 58 (1882) err. typ.= **Arnebia**, Forsk. (Boragin.).
	AMECARPUS, Benth. in Lindl. Veg. Kingd. 554 (1847) =**Indigofera**, Linn. (Legumin.).
'hys. 57 =	AMECHANIA, DC. Prod. vii. 578 (1839)=**Agarista**, D. Don (Ericac.). *hispidula*, DC. l. c. 579 (= *Leucothoë hispidula*). *subcanescens*, DC. l. c. (= *Leucothoë subcanescens*).
77 = a. 16 = 'olia. da. 156 :nui- . vii. 'olia. Afr. 'nisi-) 99 −82) '840) misi- seria	**AMELANCHIER**, Medic. Phil. Bot. i. 135 (1789). *ROSACEAE*, Benth. & Hook. f. i. 628. ARONIA, Pers. Syn. ii. 39 (1807). PERAPHYLLUM, Nutt. in Torr. & Gray, Fl. N. Am. i. 474 (1840). XEROMALON, Rafin. New Fl. Am. iii. 11 (1836). alnifolia, *Nutt. in Journ. Acad. Phil.* vii. (1834) 22.— Am. bor. *asiatica*, Endl. in Walp. Rep. ii. 55 = canadensis. *Bartramiana*, M. Roem. Syn. Rosifl. 145 = cana- densis. *Botryapium*, DC. Prod. ii. 632 = canadensis. canadensis, *Medic. Gesch.* 79 ; *Torr. & Gray, Fl. N. Am. i. 473.* Am. bor. : As. or. *chinensis*, Hort. ex C. Koch, Dendrol. i. 186 = Sorbus arbutifolia. *cretica*, DC. Prod. ii. 632 = vulgaris. *denticulata*, C. Koch, Dendrol. i. 183 = Cotoneaster denticulata. *florida*, Lindl. Bot. Reg. t. 1589 = alnifolia. *grandiflora*, Dougl. ex M. Roem. Syn. Rosifl. 145 = canadensis. *integrifolia*, Boiss. & Hohen. Diagn. Ser. I. iii. 8 = vulgaris. *intermedia*, Spach, Hist. Vég. Phan. ii. 85 = canadensis ? *japonica*, Hort. ex C. Koch, Dendrol. i. 179 = canadensis. *melanocarpa*, Decne. in Nouv. Arch. Mus. Par. Sér. I. x. (1874) 136.—Hab. ? *oblongifolia*, M. Roem. Syn. Rosifl. 147 = canadensis. *oligocarpa*, M. Roem. l. c. 145 = canadensis. *orbicularis*, Borck. ex Steud. Nom. ed. II. i. 76 = vulgaris. *ovalis*, Medic. Gesch. 78 = canadensis. parviflora, *Boiss. Diagn.* Ser. I. iii. 9.—As. Min. *parviflora*, Hort. ex Loud. Arb. Brit. ii. 877 = alnifolia. *pisidica*, Boiss. & Heldr. Diagn. Ser. I. x. 2 = parvi- flora. *pumila*, Nutt. ex Torr. & Gray, Fl. N. Am. i. 474 = alnifolia.

AMELIA :—
media. Al
media.
minor, Ale

AMELINA,
26 (1874)
Wallichii,
aequinoc

AMELLUS,
thera, 1

AMELLU
POSITAi
HAENEI
KRAUSS
alternifoli
anisatus, *C*
austr.
annuus, *W*
carolinian
coilopodiu
diffusus,
Chiliotri
divaricatu
Belgii.
floribundu
igniariur
flosculosus
hispidus, *E*
Lychnitis,
Lychnitis,
tenuifoli
microgloss
mutabilis,
nanus, *DC*
officinalis,
pallidus, S
peduncula
916 = Tr
rosmarinj
Chiliotr
scabridus,
speciosus,
spinulosus,
strigosus,
tenuifolius,
tridactylus
umbellatu
1225) =

5 Portion of a page of the *Index Kewensis*. Note the considerable amount of information given concerning genera and species.

Among the commonly consulted compendia of major publications are the following: *Thesaurus Literaturae Botanicae* by G. A. Pritzel, originally published in Berlin in 1871, and republished in Italy in 1950, which lists both by author and by subject the chief botanical publications preceding it; *Index Londinensis to Illustrations of Flowering Plants, Ferns, and Fern Allies* by Otto Stapf and O. C. Worsdell (1921–1935); and the *Catalogue of the Library of the Royal Botanic Gardens, Kew,* Bulletin of Miscellaneous Information (Kew Bulletin), Additional Series III, 1899, with supplement 1898–1915 (London, 1919).

Specialized dictionaries and glossaries giving the meanings and often the derivations of technical terms are an essential part of any taxonomist's library. Some of these are listed here:

Gray's Lessons in Botany (New York, 1887) has long been known as one of the best-illustrated sources of information on the terminology of structural botany. It was prepared by Asa Gray, and despite its age it is still exceedingly useful at an elementary level. *A Dictionary of Flowering Plants and Ferns* by J. C. Willis (6th edition, Cambridge, England, 1931) contains alphabetically listed and described families and genera. *A Glossary of Botanic Terms* by B. D. Jackson (4th edition, London, 1949) is a standard work in this category. On the practical side we have the *Glossary of Botanical Terms Commonly Used in Range Research* by W. A. Dayton (U. S. Dept. Agr. Miscel. Publ. 110, Washington, D. C., 1931). *Vocabularium Botanicum (Plant Terminology)* by E. F. Steinmetz (2nd edition, Amsterdam, 1953) contains about 4,000 scientific terms in English, Dutch, German, French, Latin, and Greek, and is a useful source of equivalents in various languages. For the average student with a need for a small but practical dictionary of terms there are *Taxonomic Terminology of the Higher Plants* by H. I. Featherly (Ames, Iowa, 1954), *Scientific Terminology* by J. N. Hough (New York, 1953), and the more complete *Composition of Scientific Words* by R. W. Brown (Baltimore, Md., 1954). Practically all regional manuals and floras also include glossaries.

Finally, since it is general practice in taxonomic publications to use abbreviations for publications cited, a very useful reference book dealing with standard abbreviations is *Abbreviations Used in the Department of Agriculture for Titles of Publications* by Carolyn Whitlock (U. S. Dept. Agr. Miscel. Publ. 337, Washington, D. C., 1939). A similar list is *Abbreviations of Periodicals* by Lazella Schwarten and H. W. Rickett (Bull. Torr. Club 74: 348–356, 1947).

Regulations

Legislation agreed upon by representatives at International Botanical Congresses, which have met more or less regularly since 1867, is contained in the *International Code of Botanical Nomenclature*. These rules and recommendations are subject to revision at each International Congress, after which new editions are prepared. A Congress was held at Paris in 1954, and the latest edition of the *Code* was published in 1956 under the editorship of J. Lanjouw. The most recent Congress was held in Montreal, Canada, in 1959, and further revisions were then taken up.

REFERENCES

BLAKE, S. F., & ALICE C. ATWOOD: *Geographical Guide to Floras of the World: I, Africa, Australia, North America, South America, and Islands of the Atlantic, Pacific, and Indian Oceans,* U. S. Dept. Agr. Miscel. Publ. 401 (Washington, D. C., 1942). Includes an appendix of abbreviations of periodicals cited.

DAYTON, W. A.: *United States Tree Books: A Bibliography of Tree Identification,* U. S. Dept. Agr. Bibliogr. Bull. No. 20 (1952).

RENNER, F. G., *et al.*: *A Selected Bibliography on Management of Western Ranges, Livestock, and Wildlife,* U. S. Dept. Agr. Miscel. Publ. No. 281 (Washington, D. C., 1938).

SENN, H. A.: *A Bibliography of Canadian Plant Geography,* Trans. Royal Canad. Instit. 1946–1947, Vol. 26, Parts 1–2; Publ. 863, Dept. Agr. Ottawa (1951; to be continued).

CHAPTER 4

Field and Herbarium Methods

All persons actively engaged in taxonomic work have occasion to study actual plants—plants living in the field or garden, or specimens preserved in a herbarium, or both. There is no substitute for the first-hand information gained through observation of living populations in diverse situations and localities; and if some of this information is to become a part of the permanent record, for others to examine, it is essential that selected material be carefully prepared and preserved in a herbarium.

Objectives

The ultimate goal of collecting in the field and preserving in the herbarium is very simple: it is to preserve for all time a series of specimens and notes that will yield the maximum of information about the plants concerned.

The following details regarding field and herbarium techniques are applicable to a study of flowering plants, ferns, and conifers. Special methods are usually required for preserving such plants as fungi and algae, and directions applicable to those groups will be found in the references at the end of this chapter.

Field Equipment and Methods

The essential items of equipment for field collecting are few (see Fig. 6), and they are subject to modification to meet diversified field conditions and the individual requirements of the collector. The

40

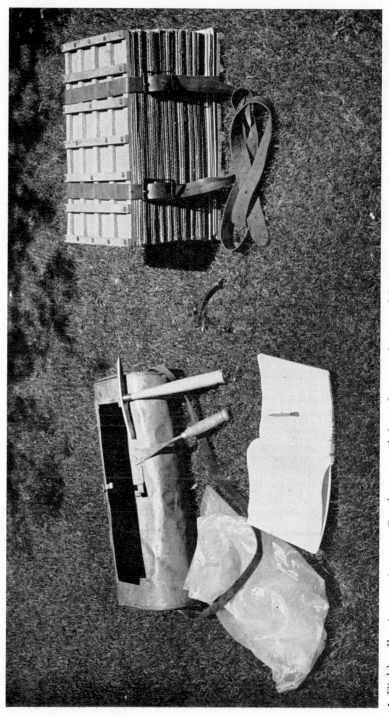

6 Field collecting equipment On the upper left is the vasculum, and below it are plastic bags, notebook, and pencil. Two kinds of diggers are leaning against the vasculum. On the right is a plant press containing alternating layers of corrugated cardboard ventilators and newspaper pressing sheets, the latter being folded to contain the plant specimens.

amount and exact kind of equipment will depend upon the limitations imposed on space and weight by the means of transportation, upon the nature of the terrain, upon the nature of the plant groups to be collected, and upon the individual preferences of the collector.

THE PLANT PRESS.   This is a device by means of which fresh specimens are pressed flat and quickly dried.

The top and bottom frames of the press, usually 12 by 18 inches, are composed of thin, strong pieces of wood laid at right angles to one another so as to form a lattice work, the joints being securely screwed or riveted. Between the frames are driers, or sheets of moisture-absorbing material, also 12 by 18 inches, which may be in the form of blotters or smooth-faced corrugated cardboards, and between these are folded newsprint sheets, in each of which the collector places one kind of plant. The assembled press is tightly bound together by a pair of heavy straps or ropes, these being long enough to allow for expansion as more specimens are added.

Good specimens should include either the flowering or the fruiting phase of the plant, preferably both. They should be carefully displayed on the pressing sheet without unnecessary folding or hiding of parts. If a specimen is too large to fit easily on the sheet, it should be bent into a V shape or a W shape, this shape being maintained, if necessary, by slotted strips of heavy paper or cards slipped over the bent portions.

The press containing the specimens is placed in the hot sun or suspended over moderate heat, and the driers (but not the papers) are changed or dried at least daily until the plants are dry. This task becomes arduous at times, but it must not be neglected, or poor and discolored specimens with poor color preservation will result.

THE FIELD NOTEBOOK.   The notebook, another essential, should preferably be permanently bound, pocket-sized, and with horizontal rulings. It is used for data recorded at the time of collection: the field number of the specimen, the locality, the habitat, the date of collection, the name of the plant if that is known, the flower color, the size of the plant if it is too large to be preserved complete, its abundance, the variations observed, the associated plants, the elevation, and so on. *A number series, once started, should be continuous* throughout the life of the collector so that no confusion will arise when specimens are referred to by the collector's number. If several specimens of the same kind are taken at the same time and place, these duplicates will, of course, be given the same number; otherwise numbers should never be duplicated. Numbers corresponding to those in the field notebook should be *written on the papers containing the specimens* in the field, never on separate slips of paper, which might drop out or become detached from the specimens. Careful and farsighted workers sometimes keep duplicate records: one book for field use, the other remaining at home and containing the same data copied from the field book as soon as possible. Such a system insures against loss of older records should anything happen to the field book.

THE VASCULUM.   This is a container that will somewhat preserve the freshness of specimens until it is convenient to place them in the press. No specimens are likely to be improved by postponement of pressing, but it is not always convenient to press plants as they are collected. Standard vascula are made of sheet metal, are somewhat oval on the ends, are from 18 to 24 inches long, and have on one side a hinged door that is provided with a secure fastener to keep the interior as air-tight as possible.

Recently it has been found that plastic bags make excellent containers for fresh plants; they prevent loss of moisture when closed securely, and each collection may be kept separate in the general container or vasculum. When light weight and compactness are at a premium, as in mountain collecting on foot, such a system, combined with a light pack-basket or back-pack, will be found quite satisfactory.

THE DIGGER.   When one is collecting herbaceous plants, it is essential that the underground parts be made a part of the specimen. The kind of root system, and the presence or absence of rhizomes, bulbs, or other subterranean parts, constitute valuable diagnostic characters for identification. For this reason it is necessary for the collector to carry some sort of substantial digger—a heavy sheath-knife, a dandelion digger, a geologist's pick, a bricklayer's hammer with chisel blade, or any similar suitable tool. And in order to avoid loss in the field one should paint the handle a bright orange or yellow.

The Herbarium

The herbarium, which becomes the repository of the specimens and notes, permanently preserved, is a growing source of information about the vegetation of an area. It may contain millions of specimen vouchers, gradually accumulated by a large institution, and may represent the flora of a continent or more; or it may be a very modest personal and local collection.

As the herbarium grows, it is necessary that the material in it be systematically filed so as to be quickly accessible to all who use it. It is equally important that the specimens be adequately prepared for handling and filing. All of this has led to some standardization of herbarium equipment and methods, but much individuality still remains in the various large collections.

MOUNTING. This is the process by which specimens are prepared for the permanent files. The pressed and dried plants or plant parts are securely attached to one side of a sheet of mounting paper, and a label is attached at the lower right-hand corner.

The mounting paper used in most American herbaria measures 11½ by 16½ inches (European institutions often use a longer sheet); it should be fairly stiff and of an all-rag content for permanence. Various supply houses and paper companies can supply suitable mounting sheets.

Specimens are attached to the sheets in various ways, but the commonest method involves the use of strips of white gummed cloth (known as Holland cloth), supplemented by a non-staining glue, which one applies to the flat surfaces by means of a spatula or by laying the specimen on a glue-coated glass plate and then transferring it to the mounting sheet. The strips should not obscure critical parts, which may need to be studied. Cellulose tape is to be avoided because it is not permanent. One should place thick parts of specimens in different regions of the sheets in order to avoid bulkiness at one spot or at one end. Loose valuable parts, such as seeds, fruits, or dissected parts, are placed in paper packets or envelopes, which are glued to the mounting paper.

In recent years many herbaria have adopted the plastic method of mounting specimens, described by W. Andrew Archer in 1950 and elaborated on by R. C. Rollins in 1955 (see the references and Fig. 7). This method is based on the use of ethyl cellulose and a resin dissolved in a mixture of toluene and methyl alcohol to give a thick, syrupy, adhesive liquid, which is applied by means of a pressure oil gun or a slim-nosed squeeze bottle of the type used to dispense catsup or mustard. One disadvantage of this method was that it was necessary to purchase large quantities of the ingredients, but lately small quantities have been offered for sale, mixed and ready, by the Carolina Biological Supply Company, Elon College, North Carolina. The big advantage of the method lies in the rapidity with which specimens can be mounted and the permanence and pleasing appearance of the mounted plants.

THE LABEL.   The label, usually glued by one edge at the lower right-hand corner of the sheet, supplies information taken from the field book. It varies in size and format, but is usually about 3 by 5 inches or a little less. It should include at least the following: (1) a heading that indicates the state, province, or country of the collection, and usually the name of the person or institution with which the specimen originated; (2) the genus and species, with authority (some include the family as well); (3) the locality of collection (some workers even

7 Mounting herbarium specimens by the plastic method, using a pressure oil gun to dispense the plastic. The sheets at the left are stacked up to dry.

include a small printed map with a spot on it to indicate the locality); (4) the habitat; (5) the date of collection; (6) the name of the collector; (7) the collector's field number; (8) the name of the person who identified the specimen, if not the collector. Additional information might include: the names of associated plants found growing in the immediate vicinity, the color of the flowers or other information about flower parts not readily seen in pressed specimens, the height of the plant if the specimen is not complete, the abundance of the plant in the area, the altitude of the locality, and, if the plant is a large shrub or a tree, the nature of the bark.

Labels, above all, should be legible, neat, and permanent. A specimen without an adequate label is practically worthless, however well it was pressed and mounted. The best labels are printed, but clear type-written labels or even carefully handwritten ones are quite satisfactory. Large printed forms to be filled out are seldom satisfactory, but this kind is used by several governmental agencies. Examples of several sorts of labels are shown in Figure 8.

FILING. This is the process of placing mounted material in a systematic arrangement for storage until needed. In major herbaria the

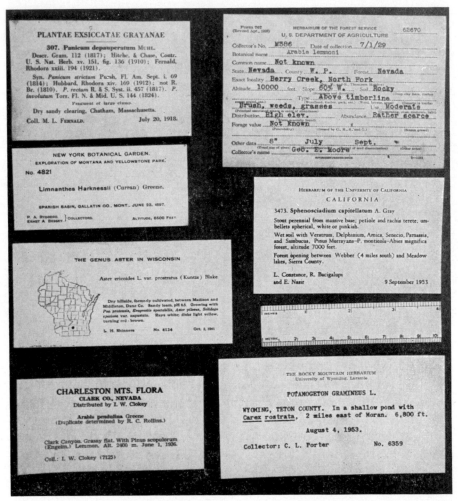

8 Some examples of herbarium labels. The more modern labels generally give more detailed information than the older labels.

specimens are housed in steel filing cases, compartmented into pigeon-holes, and provided with tight-fitting doors. A card on the outside designates the nature of the contents. In small collections the filing system may be entirely alphabetical by genus and species, but in most herbaria the filing system follows a phylogenetic sequence so as to bring closely related things together, in which case the sequence employed is often that of C. G. Dalla Torre and H. Harms in their *Genera Siphonogamarum* (1900–1907). According to this system, each family and each genus has a place in a numbered sequence based on supposed relationships. At the end of this reference is an index of generic names and the families to which they are assigned.

In all major herbaria the specimen sheets are filed inside manila folders slightly larger than the sheets. Each of these folders has written on it, on the front edge, the scientific name of the included specimens. There may be a single folder for an entire genus of rare plants, or there may be several folders for a single commoner species. In some herbaria

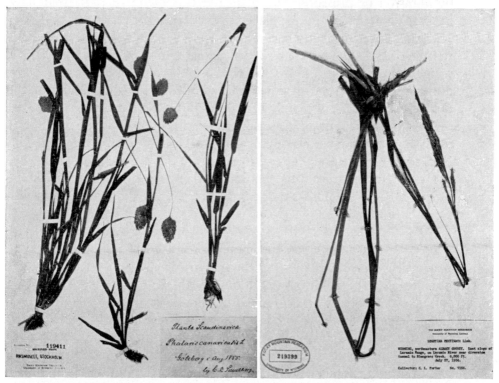

9 Two herbarium specimens, the left-hand one collected in 1855, that on the right collected in 1956. Specimens should last indefinitely if not abused.

the folders, and the specimens with them, are segregated geographically, and various color schemes for folders are employed by some to indicate political or physiographic areas.

CARE OF SPECIMENS.   A properly cared-for specimen should last indefinitely (Fig. 9), but carelessness or abuse can ruin valuable collections very quickly. This does not mean that the resources of a herbarium should not be used, for that is its purpose.

In most areas some precautions must be taken to safeguard against insect damage; these usually consist of fumigation with chemicals such as paradichlorobenzene or of poisoning the specimens by brushing them with a solution of bichloride of mercury. Cabinet doors should be kept tightly closed when specimens are not in use, and a fumigant should be kept inside each cabinet. Care and judgment should be exercised in the examination and handling of specimens: they should not be bent, turned over like leaves in a book, or subjected to injury by abrasion or pressure. Any dissected fragments or parts that have become detached should be placed in small packets.

If corrections in name become necessary, these notations should be written or typed on separate slips of paper, known as *annotation labels,* which are then affixed to the sheets above the regular labels or at some other near-by place. An annotation should include the name of the person making it (not merely his initials) and the date.

In order to prevent undue wear and possible abuse to type specimens, many herbaria have them segregated from the general collection. This is a very desirable practice.

Finally, every precaution should be taken to prevent loss or damage due to fire. This entails storage in fire-resistant cabinets and in a fireproof building.

LOANS.   Specimens are lent by the curators of major herbaria to responsible persons requesting them. This service to research workers also benefits the lending institution, for those workers are often able to make corrections and revisions in nomenclature and identification. Loans are generally made for a specified period of time, and the borrower usually pays the costs of transportation both ways. Borrowers should be meticulously careful to adhere to all the provisions of loans and to supply adequate and carefully prepared annotations.

EXCHANGES.   Exchanges of specimens among scientific institutions and collectors are a standard means of augmenting a collection at little cost. As a rule, the exchanges are conducted on a specimen-for-specimen basis, the shipper paying transportation costs. Specimens for exchange are unmounted, but they should be supplied with adequate labels.

REFERENCES

ALLARD, H. A.: "Drying Herbarium Specimens Slowly or Rapidly," Castanea 16: 129–134 (1951).

ANDREWS, F. M.: "Preservation of Dry Plant Material," Ind. Acad. Sci. Proc. 41: 80–81 (1932).

ARCHER, W. A.: "New Plastic Aid in Mounting Herbarium Specimens," Rhodora 52: 298–299 (1950).

BAILEY, L. H.: "The Palm Herbarium," Gentes Herb. 7: 153–180 (1946).

BAILEY, W. W.: *The Botanical Collector's Handbook* (Salem, Mass., 1881).

BAILEY, W. W.: "Collecting Plants for Identification," Am. Bot. 7: 9–11 (1904).

BENSON, LYMAN: "Notes on Taxonomic Techniques," Torreya 39: 73–75 (1939).

BLAKE, S. F.: *Directions for the Preparation of Plant Specimens for Identification*, U. S. Bur. Plant Indus., Office Econ. and System. Bot. (Circ. 1), 2 pp. (1919).

BLAKE, S. F.: *Directions for Collecting Flowering Plants and Ferns*, U.S.D.A. Dept. Circular 76, pp. 1–7 (1920).

BLUMER, J. C.: "A Simple Plan for Collectors of Ecological Sets of Plants," Plant World 10: 40–42 (1907).

BUCHHOLZ, J. T.: "A Practical Drier for Botanical Specimens," Ill. Acad. Sci. Trans. 24: 103–107 (1931).

CAMP, W. H.: "On the Use of Artificial Heat in the Preparation of Herbarium Specimens," Bull. Torr. Club 73: 235–243 (1946).

CHAMBERLAIN, E. B.: "Mounting Moss Specimens," Bryologist 6: 75–76 (1903).

CLARK, C. S.: "Mounting Mosses," Bryologist 6: 102–103 (1903).

CLEMENTS, F. E.: "Formation and Succession Herbaria," Nebr. Univ. Studies 4: 329–355 (1904).

COLLINS, J. F.: "Mounting Mosses—Some Hints," Bryologist 9: 60–63 (1906).

COLLINS, J. F.: "The Use of Corrugated Paper Boards in Drying Plants," Rhodora 12: 221–224 (1910).

COLLINS, J. F.: "Better Herbarium Specimens," Rhodora 34: 247–249 (1932).

COVILLE, F. V.: *Directions for Collecting Specimens and Information Illustrating the Aboriginal Uses of Plants*, U. S. Nat. Mus. Bull. 39, 8 pp. (1895).

CURTIS, A. H.: "Hints on Herborizing," Plant World 4: 61–66, 81–87 (1901).

DERR, H. B., & C. H. LANE: *Collection and Preservation of Plant Material for Use in the Study of Agriculture,* U.S.D.A. Farmers' Bull. 586, 24 pp. (1914).

ENGELMANN, BEBB, BAILEY, SCRIBNER, MORONG, *et al.*: "How to Collect Certain Plants," Bot. Gaz. 11: 135–150 (1886).

FERNALD, M. L.: "Injury to Herbarium Specimens by Extreme Heat," Rhodora 47: 258–260 (1945).

FOGG, J. M., JR.: "Suggestions for Collectors," Rhodora 42: 145–157 (1940).

FOSBERG, F. R.: *Plant Collecting Manual for Field Anthropologists* (Philadelphia, 1939).

FOSBERG, F. R.: "Formaldehyde in Plant Collecting," Science 106: 250–251 (1947).

GATES, B. N.: "An Electrical Drier for Herbarium Specimens," Rhodora 52: 129–134 (1950).

GATES, F. C.: "Paradichlorobenzene, an Effective Herbarium Insecticide," Science 81: 438–439 (1935).

GENTRY, H. S.: "The Belt Plant Press," Bull. Torr. Club 79: 84–86 (1952).

GILBERT, B. D.: "Mounting Mosses," Bryologist 7: 61–62 (1904).

GLEASON, H. A.: "Annotations on Herbarium Sheets," Rhodora 35: 41–43 (1933).

GLEASON, H. A., & A. C. SMITH: "Methods of Preserving and Arranging Herbarium Specimens," Jour. N. Y. Bot. Gard. 31: 112–125 (1930).

GRIFFITHS, D.: "Preparation of Specimens of *Opuntia,*" Plant World 9: 278–284 (1907).

HEDGECOCK, G. G., & P. SPAULDING: "A New Method of Mounting Fungi Grown in Cultures for the Herbarium," Jour. Myc. 12: 147 (1906).

HITCHCOCK, A. S.: "Collecting Sets of Plants for Exchange," Plant World 3: 148–151 (1900).

HITCHCOCK, A. S.: *Methods of Descriptive Systematic Botany* (New York, 1925).

HITCHCOCK, A. S.: *Field Work for the Local Botanist* (Washington, D. C., 1931).

HITCHCOCK, A. S., & AGNES CHASE: *Directions for Preparing Herbarium Specimens of Grasses,* U.S.D.A., Bur. Plant Ind. Doc. 442, 4 pp. (1909).

HODGE, W. H.: "The Use of Alcohol in Plant Collecting," Rhodora 49: 207–210 (1947).

HOLZINGER, J. M.: "Some Notes on Collecting," Bryologist 6: 37–38 (1903).

HOWARD, R. A.: "The Use of DDT in the Preparation of Botanical Specimens," Rhodora 49: 286–288 (1947).

JOHNSTON, I. M.: *The Preparation of Botanical Specimens for the Herbarium,* 33 pp. (The Arnold Arboretum, Jamaica Plain, Mass., 1939).

LITTLE, E. L.: "Preparing Specimens of *Picea* and *Tsuga,*" Rhodora 54: 232–234 (1952).

LUNDELL, C. L.: "A Useful Method for Drying Plant Specimens in the Field," Wrightia 1: 145, 161–162 (1946).

LUNELL, J.: "Collecting, Drying and Mounting of Plant Specimens," Am. Midl. Nat. 5: 191–195 (1918).

MARTIN, G. W.: "Paradichlorobenzene in the Herbarium," Bot. Gaz. 79: 450 (1925).

MERRILL, E. D.: "An Economical Herbarium Case," Torreya 26: 50–54 (1926).

MERRILL, E. D.: "An Efficient and Economical Herbarium Paste," Torreya 26: 63–65 (1926).

MERRILL, E. D.: "The Significance of the Compiler's Data in Field Work," Bull. Torr. Club 61: 71–74 (1934).

MERRILL, E. D.: "On the Technique of Inserting Published Data in the Herbarium," Jour. Arnold Arbor. 18: 173–182 (1937).

MILLSPAUGH, C. F.: "Herbarium Organization," Field Mus. Nat. Hist. Publ., Mus. Tech. Ser. 1: 1–18 (1925).

MOORE, H. E., JR.: "A Substitute for Formaldehyde and Alcohol in Plant Collecting," Rhodora 52: 123–124 (1950).

NICHOLS, G. E., & H. ST. JOHN: "Pressing Plants with Double-faced Corrugated Paper Boards," Rhodora 20: 153–160 (1918).

NIEUWLAND, J. A.: "The Mounting of Algae," Bot. Gaz. 47: 237–238 (1909).

OGDEN, E. C.: "Display Pocket for Cryptogams," Bryologist 48: 194 (1945).

RICHARDS, H. M.: "New Methods of Drying Plants," Torreya 1: 145–146 (1901).

RICKER, P. L.: "Directions for Collecting Plants," U.S.D.A., Bur. Pl. Indus. Circ. 126: 27–35 (1913).

ROBINSON, B. L.: "Insecticides Used at the Gray Herbarium," Rhodora 5: 237–247 (1903).

ROLLINS, R. C.: "The Archer Method for Mounting Herbarium Specimens," Rhodora 57: 294–299 (1955).

SANFORD, S. N. F.: *The Collection and Preservation of Flowering Plants*, Boston Soc. Nat. Hist. Bull. 79, 23 pp. (1936).

SCHRENK, J.: "Schweinfurth's Method of Preserving Plants for Herbaria," Bull. Torr. Club 15: 292–293 (1888).

SCHULTES, R. E.: "The Use of Formaldehyde in Plant Collecting," Rhodora 49: 54–60 (1947).

SCULLY, F. J.: "Preservation of Plant Material in Natural Colors," Rhodora 39: 16–19 (1937).

SHARP, A. J.: "An Improvement in the Method of Preparing Certain Gymnosperms for the Herbarium," Rhodora 37: 267–268 (1935).

SHOPE, P. F.: "Paradichlorobenzene as a Herbarium Insecticide," Science 83: 19 (1936).

SMITH, MARTINDALE, CHICKERING, BESSEY, *et al.*: "Specimens and Specimen Making," Bot. Gaz. 11: 129–134 (1886).

SPAULDING, V. M.: "Suggestions to Plant Collectors," Plant World 10: 40 (1907).

STANDLEY, P. C.: "Herbarium Notes," Torreya 9: 74–77 (1909).

STEVENS, O. A.: "A Simple Plastic Collecting Bag," Rhodora 51: 393 (1949).

STEYERMARK, J. A.: "Notes on Drying Plants," Rhodora 49: 220–227 (1947).

STONE, G. E.: "Formalin as a Preservative for Botanical Specimens," Jour. Applied Microscopy 2: 537–540 (1900).

SWINGLE, C. F.: "Oxyquinoline Sulphate as a Preservative for Plant Tissue," Bot. Gaz. 90: 333–334 (1930).

TEMPLETON, B. C.: "Methods of Preserving Cacti for Herbarium Use," Desert 3: 127 (1932).

TRAUB, H. P.: "PDB in Plastic Envelopes for Pest Control in the Small Herbarium," Taxon 3: 84–88 (1954).

U. S. DEPARTMENT OF AGRICULTURE, FOREST SERVICE: *Suggestions for the Collection of Range Plant Specimens on National Forests,* U. S. Forest Service, unnumbered leaflet, 4 pp. (1915).

U. S. DEPARTMENT OF AGRICULTURE, FOREST SERVICE: *Instructions for National Forest Range Plant Work,* U. S. Forest Service, unnumbered circular, 4 pp. (1925).

WALKER, E.: "Recording Localities on Specimen Labels," Chron. Bot. 7: 70–71 (1942).

WHERRY, E. T.: "A Plastic Spray for Coating Herbarium Specimens," Bartonia 25: 86 (1949).

WILLIAMS, R. S.: "On Collecting Mosses," Bryologist 13: 56–57 (1910).

WOLLEY-DOD, A. H.: "On Collecting Roses," Jour. Bot. 58: 23–24 (1920).

CHAPTER 5

Nomenclature

As the number of plants known to man increased, it became apparent that some uniform and generally acceptable set of principles had to be adopted if confusion in names was to be avoided. Professional botanists have therefore gradually adopted a system of naming plants and plant groups according to international agreements reached at meetings. Such meetings, held periodically, are known as *International Congresses*, and the rules adopted and published by them are known as the *International Code of Botanical Nomenclature*. These meetings and rules deal only with the use and application of scientific names.

The same degree of accord, unfortunately, has not been attained for the use of common names of plants, among which there is great confusion. It is well known that many a plant has several common names in general use in various parts of the country; and often the same common name is used for quite different plants. Examples of this are the use of the name "Cedar" for quite different groups of trees and the use of the name "Foxtail" for various different grasses. Some plants, furthermore, have no common names, and that is confusing to the layman. An attempt to reduce this confusion was made by a Joint American Committee on Horticultural Nomenclature, which published a list of *Standardized Plant Names* (1923), but few persons outside governmental agencies have adopted this list. It is practically impossible to legislate on common names as on scientific names.

Nomenclature may be defined as the *system of naming* plants, animals, or other objects, or groups of plants, animals, or objects. In botanical nomenclature the names given to plants either are Latin names or are names taken from some other language and Latinized.

The Binomial System

The scientific name of any plant is in two parts: (1) the name of the genus, or *generic name;* (2) the *specific epithet.* For example, the scientific name of the White Oak is *Quercus alba,* and the scientific name of the White Poplar is *Populus alba.* (Scientific names should always be given in italics when printed, or underlined when typed or written by hand.) The scientific name of any species of plant consists, then, of two Latin or Latinized words. The first, or generic, name is sometimes given merely as an abbreviation consisting of the capital initial (followed by a period) if the context makes its meaning clear.

According to the International Code, there can be only one group of plants (one genus) with the name *Quercus,* reserved for the Oak group, and only one with the name *Populus,* reserved for the Poplar group, and within each genus there can be only one valid specific epithet *alba;* but the same specific epithet may be applied to plants that are not members of the same genus.

Should duplicate names arise, one of them (the more recent usually) must be discarded. Should additional names for a validly named plant arise through misconceptions, by errors of one kind or another, or for whatever reason, they must be discarded in favor of the one *legitimate name,* the others becoming *synonyms.*

THE GENERIC NAME.   This is always a noun, in the singular, nominative case, and it is always written with a capital initial letter. It may be (1) descriptive, with reference to some characteristic prominent in the included species, such as *Xanthoxylum* (yellow wood), *Liriodendron* (lily or tulip tree), or *Cercocarpus* (coiled fruit); (2) the aboriginal name of the plant, such as *Quercus, Fagus,* and *Betula,* which were old Greek names for Oak, Beech, and Birch; (3) a name in honor of a person, such as *Jeffersonia* for Thomas Jefferson, *Linnaea* for Linnaeus, *Grayia* for Asa Gray, one of the fathers of American botany, and *Lewisia* for Captain Meriwether Lewis, leader of the Lewis and Clark expedition.

THE SPECIFIC EPITHET.   This may be any of the following:

1. An adjective, agreeing with the generic name in gender, and usually indicating a distinguishing characteristic of the species, or

sometimes referring to a locality where the species was first discovered: *Rosa alba*, the White Rose; *Ulmus americana*, the American Elm; *Erigeron peregrinus*, the Wandering Daisy; *Ranunculus jovis*, a Buttercup first collected on the Thunderer, in Yellowstone National Park, the name referring to the God of Thunder. Sometimes, when botanists find that a certain species is particularly difficult to define or distinguish, the epithet *perplexus* is used.

2. A noun in apposition, hence always in the nominative case to agree with the generic name, but not necessarily agreeing with it in gender, as in *Pyrus malus*, the Apple, in which the epithet is another generic name used as a specific epithet and, according to present rules, either capitalized or not at the discretion of the person using it.

3. A noun in the genitive singular, such as occurs when the species is named in honor of a person, and thus of either masculine or feminine gender: *Carex davisii*, named for a Mr. Davis; *Gilia piersonae*, named for a Miss Pierson. The specific epithet taken from the name of a person may be capitalized or not at the discretion of the user.

4. A common name in the genitive plural, usually indicating something about the habitat of the species: *Polygonum dumetorum*, meaning "of the thickets"; *Convolvulus sepium*, meaning "of the hedges"; *Carex paludosum*, meaning "of the swamps."

Names of taxa superior to the genus, such as orders, families, and subdivisions of such groups, are also formed in accordance with generally accepted principles. Some of these are given below.

The Order

This is the major taxon immediately superior to the family and is often referred to in taxonomic literature. There is still some disagreement among botanists, unfortunately, as to its interpretation and application. We form the name of the order, or the ordinal name, by adding *ales* to the stem of an included generic name: *Poales*, from *Poa*, for the order including grasses and sedges; *Liliales*, from *Lilium*, for the order that includes the lilies. A few ordinal names, still in use by some botanists, are exceptions to this general rule, the exceptions being of the sort that will be explained below in the discussion of family names.

The Family

A family consists of a group of related genera, rarely of a single genus, and it is usually a fairly clear-cut taxon agreed upon by most botanists. (Even here, however, we may find some disagreement as to just what should be included in a single family.) We form its name, except for a few that antedate the standardized system, by adding *aceae* to the stem of an included generic name: *Rosaceae*, from *Rosa*, for the Rose Family; *Ranunculaceae*, from *Ranunculus*, for the Buttercup Family.

A few families have long been designated by names that antedate this system, and such names are often merely the common names used by the ancients and are not based upon generic names. Since a uniform system has certain advantages, however, it has been agreed that substitute names, formed in accordance with the method explained above, may be used in place of the older names at the discretion of the users. Some of these are the following:

Old name:	New name:
Gramineae (Grass Family)	*Poaceae*
Cruciferae (Mustard Family)	*Brassicaceae*
Leguminosae (Pea Family)	*Fabaceae*
Umbelliferae (Parsnip Family)	*Apiaceae*
Labiatae (Mint Family)	*Lamiaceae*
Compositae (Sunflower Family)	*Asteraceae*

THE SUBFAMILY. This is a major subdivision of a family and is sometimes used when the size of the family justifies it and when the included genera may be naturally so grouped. We form the name by adding *oideae* to the stem of an included generic name, such as *Festucoideae*, from *Festuca*, and *Panicoideae*, from *Panicum*, for the two subfamilies of the Grass Family.

THE TRIBE. A tribe is a subdivision of a family, subordinate to the subfamily when that taxon is employed. We form the name by adding *eae* to the stem of an included generic name, such as *Festuceae*, from *Festuca*, for the Fescue Tribe of the Grass Family.

The Authority

Since some person, or occasionally two or more persons, originally published an account of and described each taxon, whether family, genus, or species, and gave it a name, the name of the person or persons written after the scientific name is known as the authority of the name. The author's name may be written out, but more commonly it is indicated by a standardized abbreviation. Since, for example, *Poa pratensis* (Kentucky Bluegrass) was first named and described by Linnaeus, he becomes the authority for that name, and it is written as *Poa pratensis* L. Similarly, *Erythronium grandiflorum* Pursh, for the Glacier Lily, shows that Pursh first named the species. *Lomatium montanum* C. & R., a member of the Parsnip Family, was first named and described by two men, Coulter and Rose, working together on a revision of that group of plants. Supplying the authority for a scientific name is a standard procedure in all serious work; it pins down the name with greater certainty and avoids the misunderstanding that might arise if two or more persons, unknown to each other, publish the same name.

THE PARENTHETICAL AUTHORITY. When the rank of a plant or plant group is changed, or when a species is transferred from one genus to another, or whenever similar changes in nomenclature are made, the name of the original author is placed in parenthesis and is followed by the name of the person making the change. Thus *Medicago polymorpha* L., variety *orbicularis* L., originally so designated by Linnaeus, is raised to specific rank by Allioni, and then becomes *Medicago orbicularis* (L.) All. And when *Ferula foeniculacea* Nutt., first described by Nuttall, is transferred to the genus *Lomatium* by Coulter and Rose, it becomes *Lomatium foeniculaceum* (Nutt.) C. & R.

The Principle of Priority

In order to avoid confusion in the application of scientific names and to eliminate duplication, botanists have agreed that there will be a system of priority. This means, in general, that names published earlier take precedence over names of the same rank published later; the first validly published name of a species or other taxon becomes its valid name. If other names are subsequently published for the same taxon, they shall become *synonyms*, or invalid names. In order to have a definite starting point for such a system of priority, botanists have agreed that for the flowering plants the starting point shall be Linnaeus' *Species Plantarum*, published in 1753. Exceptions to this rule, applying only to generic names at present, are agreed upon from time to time and are listed in the *International Code of Botanical Nomenclature* as *nomina generica conservanda et rejicienda,* a list of conserved and rejected names.

Thus, as stated earlier, there can be only one legitimate name for any plant, but it may have many synonyms in the literature. For this reason it is also common practice, at least in detailed treatments, to cite the publication and date for each name. This is known as the *citation*. For example, "*Cypripedium knightae* A. Nels., Bot. Gaz. 42: 48 (1906)" means that the species was proposed by Aven Nelson in the Botanical Gazette, volume 42, page 48, in 1906.

Summary of Taxa Used in Classification
(Applied to *Poa pratensis*, Kentucky Bluegrass)

> KINGDOM—*Plantae*, the plant kingdom.
>> DIVISION—*Embryophyta*, the embryo plants.
>>> SUBDIVISION—*Phanaerogama*, the seed plants.
>>>> BRANCH—*Angiospermae*, the angiosperms, seeds enclosed in an ovary.
>>>>> CLASS—*Monocotyledoneae*, the monocotyledons.
>>>>>> SUBCLASS—*Glumiflorae*, those with chaffy flowers.
>>>>>>> ORDER—*Poales*, the grasses and sedges.
>>>>>>>> FAMILY—*Poaceae*, the Grass Family.
>>>>>>>>> SUBFAMILY—*Festucoideae*, those resembling *Festuca*.
>>>>>>>>>> TRIBE—*Festuceae*, the Fescue Tribe.
>>>>>>>>>>> GENUS—*Poa*, the Bluegrasses.
>>>>>>>>>>>> SECTION—*Pratenses*, those with rhizomes.
>>>>>>>>>>>>> SPECIES—*Poa pratensis*, Kentucky Bluegrass.

Infrageneric Taxa

Sometimes the taxon *subgenus* is used between the genus and the section, particularly if the genus is naturally divisible into only a few major groups. The name of a subgenus is a substantive resembling the generic name, such as *Trifoliastrum* in the genus *Trifolium*, or *Drabella* in the genus *Draba*. But the rules also provide that the subgenus containing the type of a generic name (see below for the meaning of types) must bear that name unaltered; the subgenus of *Astragalus* that includes the type of that genus (*Astragalus christanus* L.) is therefore named *Astragalus*, not, as formerly, *Euastragalus*.

If there are several or more fairly equal subdivisions of a genus, the taxon *section* is applied to each. Or the genus may be first divided into subgenera and each of these divided into sections. Names of sections are formed in the same manner as names of subgenera.

If a section is large, containing many species, it may be found desirable to divide it into *subsections*, in which case the names are preferably plural adjectives agreeing with the generic name in gender, and written with a capital initial letter.

Infraspecific Taxa

When it is desired to show subdivisions of a species, several designations are possible. These are, in descending order of magnitude, the *subspecies*, the *variety*, and the *forma*, or form. Unfortunately, clear distinctions are not always drawn between subspecies and varieties, and the two categories are used more or less interchangeably. Subspecies and varieties are usually associated with inheritable differences, races, etc., and their scientific names are formed in the same way as those of species, being trinomials with the appropriate designation interposed between the last two epithets. The forma is usually associated with environmentally caused differences of a minor nature, and its name also is formed in the same way as the specific epithet.

The typical phase of the species is now designated by a trinomial that repeats the specific epithet exactly. The typical phase of *Sidalcea candida* Gray is *Sidalcea candida* Gray var. (or subsp.) *candida*, without the addition of any author's name for the second epithet. The typical phase of the species, of course, is the one that includes the type specimen of the species, whether or not this happens to be the commonest or the best-known phase. Trinomials of other phases than the typical one should be followed by an author's name, as in *Sidalcea candida* var. *glabrata* Hitchcock.

The Type Method

In order to stabilize the concepts of taxa from species and their subdivisions upward through orders, botanists have generally adopted the type method. Above the rank of order this method, it is felt, cannot be applied with profit at the present time.

The method requires, briefly, that the author of a species must designate a certain specimen (or an acceptable substitute for a specimen) as the type of that species. This thereafter becomes the nomenclatural type of that species, permanently associated with it in fixing the application of the name given it. The nomenclatural type of a genus then becomes the species on which the generic name was based; the nomenclatural type of a family is the genus on which the family name was based; and the nomenclatural type of an order is the family on which the ordinal name was based. It follows that, if the type of a name is excluded from a taxon for any reason, the name of the taxon must be changed. It also follows that the type of a taxon is not necessarily its most characteristic or representative phase; it is merely that element on which the name was originally based. For example, a certain specimen carefully preserved in a herbarium is the type of the species *Poa pratensis* L. This specimen fixes definitely the strict concept of that species and the application of its name; the genus *Poa* is typified by the species *Poa pratensis* L.; the family *Poaceae* is typified by the genus *Poa;* and the order *Poales* is typified by the family *Poaceae.*

Since catastrophes such as bombings, or fires or other accidents, may damage or destroy preserved botanical specimens (including types, which are the most valuable of all specimens), and in order to put the system into effect in groups not recently revised, botanists have devised a system for the designation of acceptable substitutes. The following terminology of type materials will indicate these and other procedures:

> *holotype (type):* the particular specimen or element designated by the author, which automatically fixes the application of the name.
>
> *lectotype:* a specimen or element selected by a competent worker from the original material studied by the author to serve as a substitute for the holotype if the latter was not designated in the original publication or is missing. A lectotype takes precedence over the following type.
>
> *neotype:* a specimen selected to serve as a substitute for the holotype when all material on which the name was based is missing.
>
> *isotype:* any specimen, other than the holotype, that duplicates the holotype (from the same collection, with the same locality, date, and number as the holotype).
>
> *paratype:* any specimen, other than the holotype, referred to in the original publication of the taxon. Earlier workers often referred to these as "co-types."
>
> *syntype:* one of two or more specimens or elements used by the author of a taxon if no holotype was designated; or one of two or more specimens designated as types simultaneously in the original publication.

REFERENCES

BAILEY, L. H.: "Problems in Taxonomy" (Symposium on Botanical Nomenclature, VII), Am. Jour. Bot. 36: 22–24 (1949).

BLAKE, S. F.: "Cotype, Syntype, and Other Terms Referring to Type Material," Rhodora 45: 481–485 (1943).

BLAKE, S. F.: "Byways of Nomenclature" (Symposium on Botanical Nomenclature, III), Am. Jour. Bot. 36: 8–10 (1949).

BLAKE, S. F.: "Terms Used to Designate Type Material," Madroño 13: 207 (1956).

CROIZAT, LEON: "History and Nomenclature of the Higher Units of Classification," Bull. Torr. Club 72: 52–75 (1945).

CROIZAT, LEON: "On Nomenclature: The 'Type Method,'" Taxon 2: 105–107, 124–130 (1953).

DRESS, W. J.: "On the Gender of Scientific Plant Names," Baileya 3: 59–63 (1955).

EPLING, CARL: "An Approach to Classification," Sci. Monthly 49: 360–367 (1939).

FRIZZELL, D. L.: "Terminology of Types," Am. Midl. Nat. 14: 637–668 (1933).

HALL, H. M.: "The Taxonomic Treatment of Units Smaller than Species," Proc. Int. Bot. Congr. 2: 1461–1468 (1926).

HITCHCOCK, A. S.: "The Type Concept in Systematic Botany," Am. Jour. Bot. 8: 251–255 (1921).

HITCHCOCK, A. S.: "The Relation of Nomenclature to Taxonomy," Proc. Int. Bot. Congr. 2: 1434–1439 (1926).

LANJOUW, J. (editor)· *International Code of Botanical Nomenclature* (Utrecht, Netherlands, 1956).

MERRILL, E. D.: "Adventures in Locating Validly Published but Unlisted Binomials" (Symposium on Botanical Nomenclature, V), Am. Jour. Bot. 36: 14–19 (1949).

PENNELL, F. W.: "Concerning Duplicate Types," Torreya 19: 14 (1919).

PENNELL, F. W.: "Toward a Simple and Clear Nomenclature" (Symposium on Botanical Nomenclature, VI), Am. Jour. Bot. 36: 19–22 (1949).

RICKETT, H. W.: "Orthography in Botanical Nomenclature," Brittonia 6: 365–368 (1948).

RICKETT, H. W.: "Expediency vs. Priority in Nomenclature," Taxon 2: 117–124 (1953).

RICKETT, H. W., & W. H. CAMP: "The Nomenclature of Hybrids," Bull. Torr. Club 75: 496–501 (1948).

RICKETT, H. W., & W. H. CAMP: "The Application and Use of Botanical Names," Bull. Torr. Club 77: 245–261 (1950).

ROSENDAHL, C. O.: "The Problem of Subspecific Categories" (Symposium on Botanical Nomenclature, VIII), Am. Jour. Bot. 36: 24–28 (1949).

SMITH, A. C.: "The Principle of Priority in Biological Nomenclature," Chron. Bot. 9: 114–119 (1945).

SMITH, A. C.: "Fifty Years of Botanical Nomenclature," Brittonia 9: 2–8 (1957).

WEATHERBY, C. A.: "Botanical Nomenclature since 1867" (Symposium on Botanical Nomenclature, II), Am. Jour. Bot. 36: 5–8 (1949).

CHAPTER 6

Concepts of Taxa

If our systems of classification and nomenclature are to be meaning-ful and stable, we must arrive at a reasonable interpretation of the various taxa, or units of classification, and these concepts must be widely acceptable. Much work has been done in recent years to crys-tallize our thinking along these lines, most of it aimed at the inter-pretation of the species and its subdivisions. Far less thought has gone into the understanding of the larger taxa, such as the order.

The Concept of the Species

Before the doctrine of evolution was accepted, it was generally believed that the different kinds of organisms owed their origin to *special creation,* and that these discrete and immutable entities, or species, were incapable of change or intergradation by hybridization or other means. This early concept of the species, a simple, arbitrary, and comforting one, was summarized by the youthful Linnaeus in his *Classes Plantarum* (1738) in the following words: "There are as many species as there were originally created diverse forms."

In his more mature years, however, Linnaeus radically revised his earlier concept in accord with his discovery that distinct species of plants could be hybridized, and in his *Systema Vegetabilium* (1774) he stated:

"Let us suppose that the Divine Being in the beginning progressed from the simpler to the complex; from few to many; similarly that He in the beginning of the plant kingdom created as many plants as there were natural orders. These plant orders He himself, therefrom producing, mixed among themselves until from them originated those plants which today exist as genera.

"Nature then mixed up these plant genera among themselves through generations of double origin and multiplied them into the existing species, as many as possible (whereby the flower structures were not changed), excluding from the number of species the almost sterile hybrids, which are produced by the same mode of origin."

This theory of evolution, proposed by Linnaeus almost a hundred years before that of Darwin, was overlooked by most investigators, who were preoccupied with naming and describing all the new plants being discovered at that time. The significance of Linnaeus' hybridization experiments, as well as those of J. G. Koelreuter in 1761–1766 and C. F. Gaertner in 1849, lies in the establishment of the fact that hybridization can occur, that species hybrids are mostly sterile (but not always completely so), and that varieties of a single species may be crossed to produce fertile offspring.

The next step in the evolution of the concept of species was the observation by Alexis Jordan, a French botanist who published his findings in 1846, that races of one Linnaean species of *Viola* (Violets and Pansies) remained distinct and recognizable when grown under standard conditions in a garden. He interpreted these local races as species, however, and named them accordingly; but what he had really discovered was the fact that *many species consist of local populations* whose members are interfertile yet maintain themselves as recognizable units, often occupying separate ecological niches.

Charles Darwin, in *The Origin of Species* (1859), also called attention to the considerable degree of variation that exists in living things, and brought out *the significance of natural selection and its effect upon survival.*

A major contribution to our understanding of the problem of species was the research by Gregor Mendel, an Austrian monk, who in 1865 discovered the *basic principles governing inheritance,* although his studies did not come to the attention of biologists until 1900. Mendel's work provided a working basis for understanding the mechanism of inheritance as well as a partial explanation of the great variation that was known to occur in various organisms.

Wilhelm Johannsen, experimenting with cultivated beans (1903–1911), showed that *two kinds of variation occurred within a species* and jointly determined its outward appearance (phenotype): (1)

variation due to inheritance, which could be transmitted to the off-spring; (2) variation caused by the environment, which was not inheritable. It naturally followed that the forces of natural selection could act effectively only on inheritable variations.

The studies of W. A. Cannon, W. S. Sutton, and M. F. Guyer in 1902, and those of T. H. Morgan in 1911, gave us our knowledge of the behavior of chromosomes at the time of formation of gametes, of *how chromosomes pair* (enter into synapsis) during reduction division and are then redistributed to the sex cells. This knowledge was most significant, for inability to pair (asynapsis), due to the coming together of different numbers of chromosomes, to differences in the size and shape of chromosomes, or to any genetic dissimilarity, might account, in part, for the sterility barrier that usually exists between species. And a little later, in 1917, Öjvind Winge showed that related plant species might differ cytologically by having various multiples of a basic chromosome number, thus *establishing the fact of polyploidy*, now known to occur very commonly in plants. Polyploid populations are ranked as species in some instances, as varieties in others, and sometimes they are not even assigned any taxonomic rank.

The *discovery of mutations* about 1900 opened up a new avenue of attack on the problem of speciation. These spontaneous and unpredictable changes sometimes resulted in striking inheritable differences in the outward appearance of plants and animals. We now know that mutations may involve invisible characteristics as well. Examples of mutations in flowering plants are double-flowered and cut-leaved individuals, and white-flowered plants of species normally having colored flowers. These mutations would, of course, come under the selective influence of the environment; so they might or might not have survival value. In more recent years we have learned that gene mutations can sometimes be induced or accelerated by artificial means, such as exposure of the organism to X-radiation, ultraviolet rays, variations in temperature, and mustard gas. At present we are all concerned about the possible effects of radioactive fallout.

We also know, through cytological examination of thousands of plants and animals in various species, genera, and families, that *the basic chromosome number and morphology frequently vary* considerably among the species as well as among the larger taxa. In some genera the evolutionary tendency has been toward a reduction in chromosome number, in others toward an increase. One genus in which the species have different somatic numbers is *Nymphaea* (Pond Lily), some of whose species and chromosome numbers are *stellata*

28, *lotus* 56, *odorata* 84, *candida* 112, and *gigantea* about 224. Such studies enable the taxonomist to work out a system of classification that reflects the true relationships of the plants more closely than gross morphological criteria alone do. They may also validate systematic arrangements and relationships that had been inferred by other means. It is important, of course, that cytological investigations be backed up by specimen vouchers of the plants investigated, and that these specimens be deposited in permanent collections where anyone may consult them if any doubt should arise as to their true identity.

Göte Turesson, in 1921–1931, pointed out that *the survival of a plant depends on its physiological fitness to its environment* rather than on its morphological characteristics. He showed that *species occupying large geographic areas are composed of ecological races, or what he called ecotypes.* Many taxonomists had recognized the existence of such races but had often interpreted them as species.

In recent years it has been found that a goodly number of plants are capable of reproducing not only sexually, in the normal manner, but also by the development of an embryo without fertilization. Such reproduction is termed *apomixis,* and the resulting plants are called *apomicts.* This method of reproduction is common in such genera as *Festuca* (Fescue grasses), *Poa* (Bluegrasses), *Crepis* (Hawksbeard), *Hieracium* (Hawkweeds), and *Taraxacum* (Dandelions), to name only a few. It is also known that there are many degrees of apomixis, some plants being obligate apomicts and incapable of sexual reproduction, others being facultative apomicts and capable of sexual reproduction as well. It will be readily seen that in facultative apomicts the sterility barrier that usually accompanies hybridization between sexual species could be completely removed by apomixis, and that the apomicts resulting from any one of these hybrids would be genetically uniform. It seems logical, therefore, that apomicts, reproducing asexually, as plants do from cuttings, can hardly be classified as species in the same sense as plants of normal sexual origin. Some of the "species" we know are definitely of this type. The recommendations of the *International Code* for the designation of apomicts are as follows: (1) if the group is considered to be a species, the abbreviation "ap." is placed between the generic name and the specific epithet; (2) if the group is below the rank of species, the abbreviation "ap." is placed before the final infraspecific epithet.

Much experimentation on several groups of plants has been carried on in California by Jens Clausen, D. D. Keck, and W. M. Hiesey

(1936–1952), who have gone into the problems of speciation from the standpoints of the morphologist, the ecologist, the cytologist, the geneticist, and the physiologist. Their findings they have summarized as follows:

". . . plants are organized into groups, the members of each of which are able to interchange their genes freely in all proportions without detriment to the offspring. Such groups are separated from one another by internal barriers that are of a genetic-physiologic nature (including chromosomal barriers) [and] that prevent such free interchange. These natural groups correspond fairly closely to the species of the moderately conservative taxonomists working with plants that reproduce sexually.

"This criterion for species, now substantiated by experiment, is the same that Turesson (1922) previously applied to the ecospecies. Consequently, we use his terminology to distinguish species whose status has been determined by experiment. The ecospecies becomes the experimental homologue of the taxonomic species. Also Dobzhansky (1937) has recently called attention to the importance of the internal ('physiologic') barriers separating species, noting that commonly they coincide with the delimitations of the species as accepted by systematists." [Am. Jour. Bot. 26: 104 (1939).]

The same workers have condensed the concept of the species into tabular form as follows:[1]

Degree of separation			
Internal → ↓ External	Hybrids fertile, second generation vigorous	Hybrids partially sterile, second generation weak	Hybrids sterile or none
In different environments	Distinct *subspecies* ECOTYPES	Distinct *species* ECOSPECIES	Distinct *species complexes*, CENOSPECIES
In the same environment	*Local variations* of one species BIOTYPES	Species overlapping in common territory (with hybrid swarms)	

In the foregoing tabular form, the systematic units based on experimental evidence are in capitals, their homologues based on external characteristics in italics. It should be emphasized that the terms BIOTYPES, ECOTYPES, ECOSPECIES, and CENOSPECIES should be used only when experimental evidence is at hand to validate their use; otherwise the commonly used terms *variety, subspecies, species,* and *species*

---

[1] The quotation and the table are used with the kind permission of the Editor-in-Chief of the American Journal of Botany and of Dr. Jens Clausen, the senior author.

complex should be employed. Two kinds of barriers to interbreeding are recognized: (1) internal barriers, which are of a genetic-physiologic nature expressed through incompatibility and intersterility or through weakness of the hybrid offspring; (2) external barriers, which are environmental and ecologic-geographic. The internal barriers are the more enduring, for the external barriers may be broken down by changes in the earth's surface.

It must be apparent that no universal definition of species is likely to be forthcoming even though a definite concept may be formulated for any group of plants. When plants reproduce by purely sexual means, in the usual fashion, the problem is more easily resolved on the basis of sterility barriers and over-all morphology and geography. But when plants reproduce asexually, by apomixis or other means, only experience and judgment can bring about a reasonable working system of classification. Perhaps it is reasonable, for practical purposes, to interpret a species as a recognizable and self-perpetuating population that is more or less isolated genetically as well as by its geographic distribution and its environment.

The Concept of the Genus

Perhaps the oldest of all concepts of taxa developed by man is the generic one. Even a cursory examination of the literature of all languages shows that all have words that express well-known generic concepts: in English such words as Oak, Pine, Buttercup, Violet, Maple, and Clover. Even primitive races have fairly sound concepts of natural groups of plants, which are roughly (and sometimes exactly) equivalent to genera, and words to identify them. In fact, whatever the culture of the people, and whatever their language— Chinese, Malay, Egyptian, Greek, Eskimo, or Aztec—all types of ancient and modern civilizations were aware of the group, or generic, idea, with subdivisions to indicate kinds, or species. In a sense, this idea has brought about the development of our present system of nomenclature. When we name people, the surname takes on the generic sense and indicates the group, while the given name indicates the individual. (In our civilization, however, the sequence of names is the reverse of that used in science, wherein the generic name precedes the specific epithet.)

The modern, Latinized, single words for genera are usually thought of as dating back to Tournefort (about 1700), who is also credited with giving the first consistent characterization of genera, although Brunfels' herbal (1532) had previously contained many such generic names. Linnaeus merely adopted Tournefort's generic concepts and enlarged upon them. He also adopted the generic names proposed by Charles Plumier (1703), a contemporary of Tournefort, who named more than 900 American plants and assigned each to a definite genus. Linnaeus did believe, however, that a genus should be a *natural* entity whose species show close genetic affinities.

The criteria for valid genera, then, should be morphological similarity and genetic affinity of the included species. No rule of thumb that will always apply can be set down; but, as suggested by Tournefort, a *similarity of flowers and fruits* often makes the best criterion. Similarities of other organs, such as roots, stems, and leaves, may also be used; and the characteristics of seeds, seedlings, and embryos are often generically diagnostic, as in the *Chenopodiaceae* and *Brassicaceae*. The form and arrangement of the leaves of various conifers, for example, yield generic distinctions into Pine, Spruce, Fir, and so on, whereas the reproductive structures would unite these into one genus. Linnaeus held much the same view, believing that *morphological combinations* furnished the best clues to generic segregation. Anatomy, as pointed out by I. W. Bailey (1953) and others, may also yield clues to the proper disposition of misfit genera in certain families; it has been used quite effectively, in fact, in the disposition of recently discovered relic genera whose affinities are in doubt. The presence, for example, of vesselless xylem in certain primitive angiosperms found in the Southwest Pacific region seems to indicate that these plants are what is left of an ancient, diversified, woody, dicotyledonous flora. Similar studies have been made of the anatomy of other parts of plants, including flowers. Much more work of this nature needs to be done in order to clear up some of the confusion in various parts of our classification system. Just as cytological investigations have become an almost routine part of monographic studies, so should anatomical studies be made with the same ultimate goal of establishing a sound basis for delimiting families, genera, and species.

There has been a tendency in modern times to narrow down the generic concepts of Linnaeus when research has shown that certain groups were not natural entities. Some workers even take a numerical approach and split genera that contain unusually large numbers of species, forgetting that *large genera may be just as natural as small genera.*

In order to comprehend a genus fully, one should study it throughout its entire range; otherwise misconceptions are likely to arise through provinciality of knowledge. Persons familiar with *Senecio*

(Old Man) in the northern part of its range, where the plants are herbaceous and sometimes only a few inches high, might form a quite different concept of that genus than those knowing it in tropical regions, where the plants may become tree-like; and the arborescent *Cornus florida* (Flowering Dogwood), which extends into the southern United States, is quite different in habit from the diminutive and herbaceous *Cornus canadensis* (Bunchberry), which extends into the Arctic. The tropical and northern counterparts of many genera are often, in fact, very unlike in growth form; but transitional forms often connect them.

Convenience is also to be reckoned with when we delimit genera; it is desirable to be able to assign at least a generic name to a plant that is unknown. If, for example, generic distinctions hinge largely or entirely on fruit characters, and if a plant does not produce flowers and fruits at about the same time, specimens in flower alone could not be placed in a genus with certainty, and we should have no name at all to give the plant. A situation such as this has arisen in the large and diversified genus *Astragalus* (Vetch), the American species of which were once divided among twenty-eight genera. Other genera that were once dismembered but have been reunited are *Oenothera* (*Anogra, Onagra, Lavauxia, Pachylophis, Galpinsia, Meriolix, Taraxia, Sphaerostigma, Chylismia,* etc. for various Evening Primroses) and *Haplopappus* (*Oonopsis, Pyrrocoma, Stenotus, Macronema, Isocoma, Oreochrysum, Isopappus, Ericameria,* etc. for a large group of Asteraceae).

Cytological investigations have yielded some useful information concerning relationships at the generic level as well as at the level of the species. In the *Ranunculaceae* (Buttercup Family), for instance, the following basic numbers and relative sizes of chromosomes have been determined, showing that a combination of chromosome number and size provides evidence in support of the integrity of the genera listed:

Ranunculus 7 or 8, medium	*Coptis* 9, small
Paeonia 5, large	*Thalictrum* 14, small
Anemone 8, large	*Aquilegia* 7, small
Hepatica 7, large	*Nigella* 6, large
Caltha 16, medium	*Aconitum* 8, medium

Since the modern tendency, and a good one, is to take a rather conservative view of generic concepts, it should not be difficult to give any plant at least a generic name, a convenient handle for the non-specialist, and at least a temporary home among its relatives in the herbarium. The desirability of a reasonably stable generic concept is further emphasized by the fact that every change from established usage involves creating a new set of binomials for the species.

The Concept of the Family

What has been said about the concept of the genus also applies in large part to that of the family. The common human habit of grouping things, involving categories larger than the genus, may embrace the family as well, as is illustrated by such well-known concepts and terms as *grasses, legumes,* and *orchids.*

The delimitation of families of flowering plants has been fairly well worked out by taxonomists, leaving only a few disagreements here and there—whether, for example, to unite or keep as discrete families the various elements of the *Liliaceae* (Lily Family), the *Fabaceae* (Pea Family), the *Ericaceae* (Heath Family), and the *Asteraceae* (Aster Family).

The characteristics forming the basis of family distinctions are as diverse as those used to distinguish genera, and in general are of the same sort—namely, *combinations of morphological features,* particularly those of flowers and fruits. Because of the frequent diversity of things included within a single family, and since hard-and-fast definitions frequently necessitate an allowance for exceptions, it is often profitable to think of family characteristics as *tendencies.* As examples of combinations of morphological features we might consider the following: *Brassicaceae* (Mustard Family), mostly herbs with pungent watery juice and alternate exstipulate leaves, the flowers often produced in ebracteate racemes, hypogynous, polypetalous, 4-merous, regular, the pistil of 2 united carpels separated by a persistent septum, the stamens usually 2 short and 4 long, the fruit a silique or silicle; or the *Lamiaceae* (Mint Family), plants aromatic, with square stems and opposite leaves, the flowers hypogynous, sympetalous, with irregular corolla, the stamens 2 long and 2 shorter, or only 2, the ovary deeply 4-lobed, and the fruit of 4 seed-like nutlets.

Again it should be emphasized that the ultimate goal in developing concepts of families is to recognize *natural groups,* or combinations of genera that express separate evolutionary trends and relationships. Some families may be very small; others may be huge but may nevertheless be natural groups.

The Concept of the Order

Just as the genus is a natural group of species, and the family a natural group of genera (occasionally these taxa may consist of single components), so the order, ideally, includes one or more families that show definite affinities and similar evolutionary trends. At this point, however, we find the greatest degree of disagreement among the classifiers. The generalization that an order should be a natural group of families is agreeable to all, but many different ideas have been expressed about the setting of ordinal limits. Should we have a few large orders, as suggested by Bessey, or many smaller orders, each containing only one or a few families, as proposed by Hutchinson?

In either case, it is again combinations of morphological characters that determine the limits. The *Rosales* (Rose Order), for example, might be thought of as including a large segment of the perigynous *Polypetalae*, the *Rosaceae, Saxifragaceae, Fabaceae*, etc.; or the *Fabaceae* (Pea Family) may be excluded from this group to make a separate order, based on the leguminous fruit character and a tendency toward irregular corollas and diadelphous stamens.

As the amplitude of a taxon increases beyond that of the genus, the scope of the problem often becomes too great for solution by any one person. A lifetime of research may result in a working knowledge of a genus, if it is not excessively large, or one may become well versed in the intricacies of a family, again if it is not too large; but the chances are slight that one person could become an expert on a large order. Through cooperation between experts, however, and by use of all the information available, a reasonably good understanding of the larger taxa may be achieved. The most recent effort of this sort is Arthur Cronquist's *Outline of a New System of Families and Orders of Dicotyledons*, which presents some realignments, circumscribes the orders the author recognizes, gives the evolutionary trends of each, and offers a distinguishing key to the orders.

REFERENCES

ALLEN, J. A.: "Another Aspect of the Species Question," Am. Nat. 42: 592–600 (1908).

ANDERSON, EDGAR: "Supra-specific Variation in Nature and in Classification—from the Viewpoint of Botany," Am. Nat. 71: 223–235 (1937).

ANDERSON, EDGAR: "The Technique and Use of Mass Collections in Plant Taxonomy," Ann. Mo. Bot. Gard. 28: 287–292 (1941).

ANDERSON, EDGAR, & E. C. ABBE: "A Quantitative Comparison of Specific and Generic Differences in the *Betulaceae*," Jour. Arn. Arbor. 15: 43–49 (1934).

ANDERSON, EDGAR, & T. W. WHITAKER: "Speciation in *Uvularia*," Jour. Arn. Arbor. 15: 28–42 (1934).

ANDERSON, EDGAR, & G. L. STEBBINS: "Hybridization as an Evolutionary Mechanism," Evolution 8: 378–388 (1954).

BABCOCK, E. B.: "Cytogenetics and the Species Concept," Proc. 5th Int. Bot. Cong. 216–218 (1930).

BABCOCK, E. B.: "Basic Chromosome Numbers in Plants with Special Reference to the *Compositae*," New Phytol. 33: 386–388 (1934).

BAILEY, I. W.: "The Anatomical Approach to the Study of Genera," Chron. Bot. 14: 121–125 (1953).

BAILEY, L. H.: "Statements on the Systematic Study of Variables," Proc. 5th Int. Bot. Cong. 1427–1433 (1930).

BARTLETT, H. H., EDGAR ANDERSON, J. M. GREENMAN, E. E. SHERFF, & W. H. CAMP: "The Concept of the Genus," Bull. Torr. Club 67: 349–389 (1940).

BESSEY, C. E., N. L. BRITTON, J. C. ARTHUR, D. T. MACDOUGAL, F. E. CLEMENTS, & H. C. COWLES: "Aspects of the Species Question," Am. Nat. 42: 218–281 (1908).

CAMP, W. H.: "Biosystematy," Brittonia 7: 113-127 (1951).

CAMP, W. H., & C. L. GILLY: "The Structure and Origin of Species," Brittonia 4: 323–385 (1943).

CASPARI, ERNST: "Cytoplasmic Inheritance," Advances in Genetics 2: 1–66 (1948).

CLAUSEN, JENS: *Stages in the Evolution of Plant Species* (Ithaca, N. Y., 1951).

CLAUSEN, JENS, D. D. KECK, & W. M. HIESEY: *Experimental Taxonomy*, Carnegie Inst. Wash. Yearbooks 35–40 (1936–1941).

CLAUSEN, JENS, D. D. KECK, & W. M. HIESEY: "The Concept of the Species Based on Experiment," Am. Jour. Bot. 26: 103–106 (1939).

CLAUSEN, JENS, D. D. KECK, & W. M. HIESEY: "Regional Differentiation in Plant Species," Am. Nat. 75: 231–250 (1941).

CLAUSEN, JENS, D. D. KECK, & W. M. HIESEY: "Heredity of Geographically and Ecologically Isolated Races," Am. Nat. 81: 114–133 (1947).

CLAUSEN, JENS, D. D. KECK, & W. M. HIESEY: *Experimental Studies on the Nature of Species: I, Effect of Varied Environments on Western North American Plants*, Carnegie Inst. Wash. Publ. 520 (second printing, 1950).

CRONQUIST, ARTHUR: "Outline of a New System of Families and Orders of Dicotyledons," Bull. Jard. Bot. (Bruxelles) 27: 13–40 (1957).

DARLINGTON, C. D., & A. P. WYLIE: *Chromosome Atlas of Flowering Plants,* 2nd edition (New York, 1956).

DAVIDSON, J. F.: "The Polygonal Graph for Simultaneous Portrayal of Several Variables in Population Analysis," Madroño 9: 105–110 (1947).

DOBZHANSKY, T.: *Genetics and the Origin of Species,* 2nd edition (New York, 1941).

DU RIETZ, G. E.: "The Fundamental Units of Biological Taxonomy," Svensk. Bot. Tidskr. 24: 333–428 (1930).

EAMES, A. J.: "Floral Anatomy as an Aid in Generic Limitation," Chron. Bot. 14: 126–132 (1953).

EARNSHAW, F.: "The Nature of Ecotypes," Proc. Int. Cong. Plant Sci. 1950: 269–271 (1953).

ERDTMAN, G.: *Pollen Morphology and Plant Taxonomy* (Waltham, Mass., 1952).

FOSBERG, F. R.: "For an Open-minded Taxonomy," Chron. Bot. 6: 368–370 (1941).

GATES, R. R.: "The Taxonomic Units in Relation to Cytogenetics and Gene Ecology," Am. Nat. 85: 31–50 (1951).

GRANT, VERNE: "The Plant Species in Theory and Practice" in *The Species Problem,* pp. 39–80 (A.A.A.S., Washington, D. C., 1957).

GUSTAFSON, A.: "Apomixis in the Higher Plants," I–III, Lunds Univ. Arsskr. N.F. 42, n. 3; 43, n. 3 & 12; 370 pp. (1946–1947).

HALL, H. M., & F. E. CLEMENTS: *The Phylogenetic Method in Taxonomy,* Carnegie Inst. Wash. Publ. 326 (1923).

HARPER, R. A.: "Significance of Taxonomic Units and Their Natural Basis," Proc. Int. Cong. Plant Sci. 1926, 2: 1588–1589 (1929).

HEILBORN, O.: "Significance of Taxonomic Units and Their Natural Basis from the Point of View of Cytology," Proc. Int. Cong. Plant Sci. 1926, 2: 1576–1577 (1929).

HESLOP-HARRISON, J.: *New Concepts in Flowering Plant Taxonomy* (Cambridge, Mass., 1956).

HESLOP-HARRISON, J.: "The Species Concept," Proc 5th Int. Cong. Plant Sci. 1926, 2: 1576–1577 (1929).

HURST, C. C.: "The New Species Concept," Proc. 5th Int. Bot. Cong. 222–223 (1930).

HUXLEY, JULIAN (editor): *The New Systematics* (Oxford, 1940).

JORDAN, ALEXIS: "Observations sur plusieurs plantes nouvelles, rares ou critiques de la France," II, Ann. Soc. Linnéenne de Lyon (1846).

LAWRENCE, G. H. M., *et al.*: "Plant Genera," Chron. Bot. 14: 89–160 (1953). (Some of the parts of this symposium are also listed separately in this bibliography.)

LÖVE, Á.: "Taxonomical Evaluation of Polyploids," Caryologia 3: 263–284 (1951).

MAYR, ERNST: *Systematics and the Origin of Species* (New York, 1942).

MCNAIR, J. B.: "The Evolutionary Status of Plant Families in Relation to Some Chemical Properties," Am. Jour. Bot. 21: 427–452 (1934).

NYGREN, AXEL: "Apomixis in the Angiosperms," II, Bot. Rev. 20: 577–649 (1954).

ROBINSON, B. L.: "The Generic Concept in the Classification of the Flowering Plants," Science n.s. 23: 81–92 (1906).

ROLLINS, R. C.: "Taxonomy Today and Tomorrow," Rhodora 54: 1–19 (1952).

ROLLINS, R. C.: "Cytogenetic Approaches to the Study of Genera," Chron. Bot. 14: 133–139 (1953).

SENN, H. A.: "Chromosome Number Relationships in the Leguminosae," Bibliog. Genet. 12: 175–336 (1938).

SHARP, L. W.: *Fundamentals of Cytology* (New York, 1943), especially Chap. XVII, "Cytology and Taxonomy," pp. 234–250.

SHULL, G. H.: "Significance of Taxonomic Units and Their Natural Basis from the Point of View of Genetics," Proc. Int. Cong. Plant Sci. 1926, 2: 1578–1586 (1929).

SIMPSON, G. G.: "The Species Concept," Evolution 5: 285–298 (1951).

SINNOTT, E. W., L. C. DUNN, & T. DOBZHANSKY: *Principles of Genetics,* 4th edition (New York, 1950).

STEBBINS, G. L., JR.: "Polyploid Complexes in Relation to Ecology and the History of Floras," Am. Nat. 76: 36–45 (1942).

STEBBINS, G. L., JR.: "The Role of Isolation in the Differentiation of Plant Species," Biol. Symposia 1 (1942).

STEBBINS, G. L., JR.: "Types of Polyploids: Their Classification and Significance" in C. Demerec, Advances in Genetics 1: 403–429 (1947).

STEBBINS, G. L., JR.: *Variation and Evolution in Plants* (New York, 1950).

STEBBINS, G. L., JR., & E. B. BABCOCK: "The Effect of Polyploidy and Apomixis on the Evolution of Species in Crepis," Jour. Heredity 30: 519–530 (1939).

TISCHLER, G.: "On Some Problems of Cytotaxonomy and Cytoecology," Jour. Indian Bot. Soc. 16: 165–169 (1937).

TURESSON, G.: "The Genotypical Response of the Plant Species to the Habitat," Hereditas 3: 341–347 (1922).

TURESSON, G.: "The Plant Species in Relation to Habitat and Climate," Hereditas 6: 147–236 (1925).

TURRILL, W. B.: "Contacts Between Plant Classification and Experimental Botany," Nature 137: 563–566 (1936).

VALENTINE, D. H.: "The Units of Experimental Taxonomy," Acta Biotheoretica 9: 75–88 (1949).

VAVILOV, N. I.: "Law of Homologous Series in Variation," Jour. Genetics 12: 47 (1922).

WANSCHER, J. H.: "The Basic Chromosome Number of the Higher Plants," New Phytol. 33: 101–126 (1934).

WHITE, O. E.: "Temperature Reaction, Mutation, and Geographical Distribution in Plant Groups," Proc. 8th Amer. Sci. Cong. 3: 287–294 (1940).

CHAPTER 7

The Construction and Use of Keys

A key is a device for easily and quickly identifying an unknown object. The user is presented with a sequence of choices, usually between two statements but occasionally among more, and by always taking the correct choice he arrives at the name of his unknown object. The statements in the choices are based on the characteristics of the unknown object and, if the object is a flowering plant, are usually concerned with flowers, fruits, seeds, stems, leaves, and roots.

Keys based on successive choices between only two statements, known as *dichotomous* (forking) keys, are preferred to those that offer several equal statements to choose from. In using keys, however, one should be on the lookout for occasional places where three or even four equal choices occur and not overlook some of them.

Using such a key may be likened to traveling a well-marked road that forks repeatedly, each fork bearing directions; if the traveler is correctly informed and follows directions carefully, he will always arrive at his destination. If either his information or the directions along the way are inaccurate, he will, naturally, become lost.

Two general types of construction are used in the preparation of botanical keys, the *indented* type and the *bracket* type. Most botanists prefer the indented type, and most zoologists prefer the bracket type. The plants used in the following examples are common genera of the *Ranunculaceae* (Buttercup Family): *Anemone* (Anemone or Windflower), *Aquilegia* (Columbine), *Clematis* (Clematis), *Delphinium* (Larkspur), and *Ranunculus* (Buttercup).

76

Indented Key

Fruit a group of akenes; flowers not spurred
  Petals none
    Sepals usually 4; involucre none .... CLEMATIS
    Sepals usually 5; involucre present .... ANEMONE
  Petals present .... RANUNCULUS
Fruit a group of follicles; flowers spurred
  Flowers regular; spurs 5 .... AQUILEGIA
  Flowers irregular; spur 1 .... DELPHINIUM

The first choice, if we are concerned only with the genera above, is between "Fruit a group of akenes; flowers not spurred" and "Fruit a group of follicles; flowers spurred," these paired statements being given the same indention. If the latter choice is taken, the next choice, as shown by the indention, is between "Flowers regular; spurs 5" and "Flowers irregular; spur 1." Thus, if the plant in question has follicles and irregular flowers with a single spur, it must be a *Delphinium*.

The bracket type of key is based on the same principle of contrasting choices, but these are always placed in adjacent lines of the key, not separated by intervening lines. Such a key requires less room on a page and has the advantage of keeping coordinate choices together, but it does not show relationships as well. An example follows:

Bracket Key

(1) Fruit a group of akenes; flowers not spurred ..... (2)
(1) Fruit a group of follicles; flowers spurred .... (4)
  (2) Petals none .... (3)
  (2) Petals present .... RANUNCULUS
(3) Sepals usually 4; involucre none .... CLEMATIS
(3) Sepals usually 5; involucre present .... ANEMONE
  (4) Flowers regular; spurs 5 .... AQUILEGIA
  (4) Flowers irregular; spur 1 .... DELPHINIUM

The number at the right end of a line in the bracket key indicates the next numbered pair of choices to be considered. A similar numbering system may be employed in indented keys if they are long enough to warrant it, particularly when they extend over more than a single page. But in a short indented key the indention, and usually the first words of the lines, will indicate which are equivalent lines of the key.

General Suggestions

1. Always read both choices even if the first seems to be the logical one to take. The second may be even better.
2. Be sure you understand the meaning of the terms involved. Do not guess.
3. When measurements are given, use a calibrated scale. Do not guess.
4. When minute objects are concerned, use a lens of sufficient magnifying power to show clearly the feature you need to see.
5. Since living things are always somewhat variable, do not base your conclusion on a single observation, but arrive at an average by studying several parts or specimens. It is surprising how often students will find the one unusual or aberrant sample in a large assortment of normal things!
6. As in traveling a forking road, if the choice of division is not clear, or if you have no way of making a choice because you do not have sufficient information, try both divisions, arrive at two possible answers by doing so, and then read descriptions of each in order to make a choice. A key is only a shortcut to identification; it is not essential if descriptions are available.
7. In constructing keys, keep the following in mind:
    a. Use constant characteristics rather than variable ones.
    b. Use measurements rather than terms such as "large" and "small."
    c. Use characteristics that are generally available to the user of the key rather than seasonal characteristics or those seen only in the field.
    d. When possible, group to show relationships rather than construct an entirely artificial key.
    e. If possible, start both choices of a pair with the same word, and always capitalize the first word. And, if possible, start different pairs of choices with different words.
    f. Precede the descriptive terms by the name of the part to which they apply. For example:

GOOD:	POOR:
Flowers red or purple	Red or purple flowers
Leaves toothed	Toothed leaves

    g. Construct a comparison chart of the objects to be keyed before proceeding with the key itself. This forces one to make complete comparisons and to avoid mentioning a character in one statement and not in the corresponding one. The heavy vertical lines in the following comparison chart indicate possible key characters or important differences.

COMPARISON CHART

	Clematis	*Anemone*	*Ranunculus*	*Aquilegia*	*Delphinium*
Fruits	akenes	akenes	akenes	follicles	follicles
Flowers regular or irregular	regular	regular	regular	regular	irregular
Number of spurs	none	none	none	5	1
Flowers with or without petals	without	without	with	with	with
Usual number of sepals	4	5	5	5	5
Involucre present	no	yes	no	no	no

8. Finally, having arrived at an answer in a key, do not accept this as absolutely reliable, but check a description of the plant to see if it agrees with the unknown specimen. If not, an error has been made somewhere, either in the key or in its use. The ultimate check on identifications is a comparison of the unknown with an authentically named specimen in a herbarium.

CHAPTER 8

Phytography and the Terminology of Plant Description

Phytography is that part of taxonomy which deals with descriptions of plants and their various organs. Its two chief objectives are accuracy and completeness of description without undue wordiness.

Because the space available in taxonomic publications is necessarily limited, it is common practice to limit descriptions to the characters deemed necessary for recognition. Complete descriptions, consequently, are rarely found. Only within the last generation of botanists, in fact, were detailed descriptions felt to be necessary, the earlier workers often having been content to give only a few words of description when publishing accounts of species and genera. The early accounts of vegetation were often profusely illustrated, however, by highly accurate drawings, which indicated that the taxonomists of years gone by were keen observers.

Some of the basic features of the organs of flowering plants—those that are important in the formulation of descriptions—are described below, and the terms commonly used are introduced. The *vegetative organs* (roots, stems, and leaves) are treated first, and then the *reproductive organs* (inflorescences, flowers, fruits, and seeds).

Roots

Root systems are seldom used extensively in the classification of flowering plants. Too often, indeed, they are ignored completely, perhaps because adequate and generally accepted methods of classification of root systems are lacking.

Roots may be thought of as belonging to two general types: (1) those derived from the primary, or seminal (seed), root; (2) adventitious roots, which are derived in some other way. Root systems then fall into three broad classifications: (1) those in which the primary, or seminal, root is maintained; (2) those in which the adventitious root system originates from the lower portion of a vertical unmodified stem, this root system early replacing the primary root; (3) those in which adventitious roots involve various kinds of modified stems, such as rhizomes, stolons, tubers, corms, and bulbs.

In addition to these types, which are characteristically subterranean, there are various types of aerial roots, such as the climbing, or hold-fast, roots of certain vines, and the pendent aerial roots of many epiphytes, or "air plants."

Certain plants, notably some forest trees and members of the Heath Family, have root systems that are characteristically associated with fungi in a more or less symbiotic relationship. This fungus-root association is known as a *mycorhiza*.

Figures 10–13 illustrate some of these characteristics of roots.

Stems

The stems of flowering plants may be quite varied in size, duration, position above or below the ground level, and direction in which they grow. They are sometimes modified for special functions.

Differences in size and duration are indicated by the general terms *herb, shrub,* and *tree,* following a distinction that was made in the earliest writings. More precisely, however, we recognize the following terms:

> *herbaceous:* dying down to the ground every year, the stems containing very little woody tissue, and the duration *annual* if for one year only; *biennial* if the plant blooms the second year, after preliminary vegetative growth the first year, and is short-lived; *perennial* if the plant continues to live for an indefinite period of years and blooms ordinarily every year after the first.
>
> *suffrutescent:* semi-shrubby, the lowest parts of the stems becoming woody and remaining alive over the winter when the higher parts die back (such plants are also referred to as semi-shrubs).
>
> *shrubby,* or *fruticose:* woody more or less throughout, and large, commonly with several main stems but no main trunk.

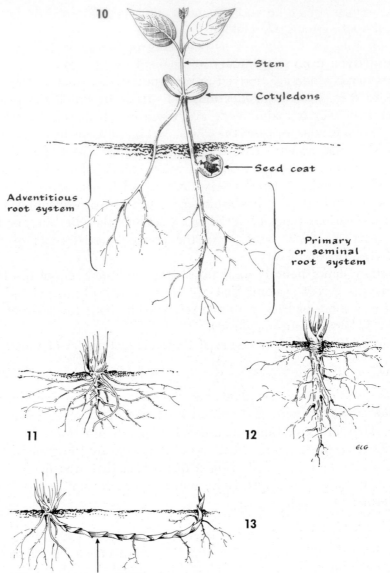

10 Diagram of a hypothetical plant to illustrate the two principal types of root systems.

11 Adventitious root system originating from a vertical, unmodified stem. (Annual Bluegrass, *Poa annua.*)

12 Root system in which the primary root is maintained. (Dandelion, *Taraxacum.*)

13 Adventitious root system involving a modified stem. (Kentucky Bluegrass, *Poa pratensis.*)

arborescent: becoming tree-like in size, and woody, usually with a single main trunk.

Most plants produce ordinary leafy stems, with appendages such as leaves, buds, and flowers from their nodes. Such plants with leafy stems are termed *caulescent* (having a *caulis,* or true stem); when there is no evident aerial stem, the leaves being all basal (actually

14 Basal portion of plant of the grass *Calamovilfa longifolia* (Hook.) Scribn., showing strong creeping rhizomes. This makes the plant an excellent sand-binder.

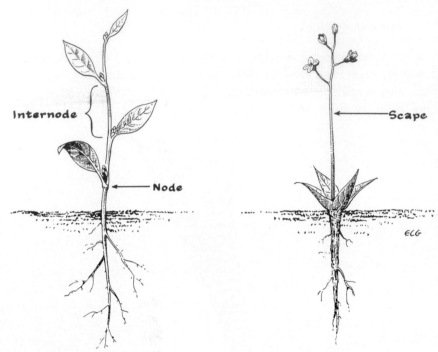

15 Caulescent plant.   **16** Acaulescent or scapose plant.

on a shortened stem at the base), and the flower stalk, or *scape*, is leafless, the plants are termed *acaulescent* (stemless) or *scapose* (with a scape), as Dandelions and some kinds of Violets. These forms are shown in Figs. 15 and 16.

There are many modifications of stem structure, among them the following, which are quite common:

> *stolons*, or *runners:* stems trailing above ground, which often root at their nodes and thus tend to produce new plants when the connection with the parent plant is broken, as in the Strawberry.
>
> *rhizomes*, or *rootstocks:* underground stems, often creeping horizontally and producing new shoots at their tips, as in Kentucky Bluegrass.
>
> *tubers:* thickened and fleshy subterranean stems that serve as organs for food storage and reproduction, as in the Irish Potato.
>
> *corms:* fleshy, upright, subterranean stems that bear papery modified leaves or scales, as in the Crocus.
>
> *bulbs:* upright, subterranean stems, the stem part of which is much smaller than in the corm and is surrounded by thickened, fleshy leaves or scales, as in the Onion.

> *tendrils:* may be slender, twining branches used for support by climbing plants such as Grapes, or, in other plants, may be of leaf origin.
> *spines,* or *thorns:* are often sharp and stunted branches, but may be modified leaves or parts of leaves.

Leaves

Most stems of flowering plants produce leaves from their nodes, usually of a form and in an arrangement peculiar to the species, which one can often recognize by the leaves alone. A few species, such as many cactus plants, are leafless, and a few, such as Sassafras and Mulberry trees and many aquatic plants, show considerable variation in the shape of the leaves.

LEAF ARRANGEMENT.   If the leaves are arranged singly on the stem, one leaf at a node, they are *alternate* in arrangement, but the angle between the leaf and the one directly above it may vary considerably and may be expressed by a numerical fraction indicating the degree of rotation of the internode before the next leaf is reached. If the leaves are paired on the stem, two at each node, they are *opposite*. If three or more leaves occur at a single node, they are *whorled*. Most plants maintain a single kind of arrangement, or *phyllotaxy*, of their leaves throughout; but occasionally a plant may be variable in this characteristic, having perhaps alternate leaves below and opposite leaves higher on the stem.

LEAF PARTS.   A leaf may consist of three main parts: the *blade*, or expanded portion, the *petiole*, or leaf stalk, and the *stipules*, which are a pair of appendages at the base of the petiole. Any of these parts may be lacking: infrequently a blade is reduced to only a midrib or is completely lacking, and the leaf is then *bladeless;* if the blade is present but much reduced, the leaves may be called *phyllodia;* the petiole may be lacking and the blade attached directly to the branch, such leaves being called *sessile;* often stipules are not produced, and such leaves are *exstipulate*. In some plants the stipules may be modified into thorn-like structures, which are then called *stipular spines*.

SIMPLE AND COMPOUND LEAVES.   A leaf with a single blade (which may be variously indented or deeply cut) is a *simple leaf*. A leaf with more than one blade is a *compound leaf,* and its blades are called *leaflets*. The leaflets of a compound leaf may be arranged like the spokes of a wheel or the fingers of a hand when the leaf is *palmately* or *digitately compound;* or they may be arranged on either side of an elongated axis, or *rachis,* when the leaf is *pinnately compound,* resembling a feather. When the leaflets are in threes, as in most Clover leaves, the leaf is usually termed a *trifoliolate* leaf; if the leaf blade is divided more than once into threes, as in some members of the Parsnip Family, it is called a *ternate* leaf. Compound leaves are sometimes twice divided or even thrice divided, in which case they are *twice-compound* or *decompound,* the latter term generally designating very numerous and fine divisions. Some of these terms are illustrated by Figures 17–20.

LEAF MARGINS. The edge of the leaf blade is its *margin,* and there is a great diversity in the margins of the leaves of different kinds of plants. The illustrations (Fig. 21) show some of the common types of margins and their terminology.

LEAF VENATION. The system of principal veins in the leaf blade constitutes its *venation.* The illustration (Fig. 22) shows the three chief types, which are *parallel* (sometimes called *nerved*), *pinnate,* and *palmate,* the second and third being *reticulate,* or *net-veined,* types. Occasionally we find combinations of these types, as in the Buckthorn (*Rhamnus*), in which some species have three principal veins from the base but each is pinnate above.

LEAF SHAPES. The general outline of the blade, or of all the leaflets of a compound leaf, constitutes the *shape* of the leaf. Usually the shape is described as including only the blade, omitting the petiole. We approximate the general shape of lobed leaves and compound leaves by drawing an imaginary line round all projecting parts, ignoring the indentions and the areas between leaflets. *The student should be careful to discriminate between the shape of a compound leaf and the shape of its leaflets.*

The illustrations (Fig. 23) show some of the common terms describing leaf shapes. It is common practice to use two or more terms to describe intermediate shapes, hyphenating the terms used; thus a leaf that is intermediate between ovate and lanceolate in outline may be termed ovate-lanceolate. The prefix *ob* means that the shape is inverted: a heart-shaped leaf upside down is thus *obcordate.*

LEAF SURFACES. The presence or absence of hairs, the kind of hairs, and the presence or absence of other surface features, such as glands,

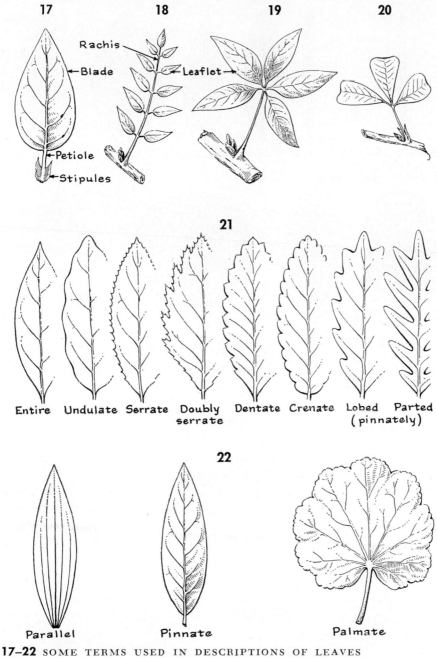

17–22 SOME TERMS USED IN DESCRIPTIONS OF LEAVES

17 Simple leaf and its parts.

18 Pinnately compound leaf.

19 Palmately or digitately
compound leaf.

20 Trifoliolate leaf.

21 Leaf margins.

22 Leaf venation.

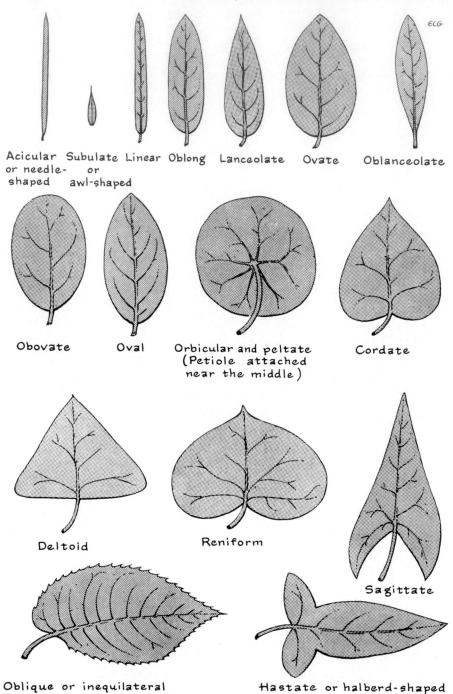

Acicular or needle-shaped   Subulate or awl-shaped   Linear   Oblong   Lanceolate   Ovate   Oblanceolate

Obovate   Oval   Orbicular and peltate (Petiole attached near the middle)   Cordate

Deltoid   Reniform   Sagittate

Oblique or inequilateral   Hastate or halberd-shaped

23 Some common leaf shapes.

all offer the taxonomist useful recognition characters. These are best examined through a good hand lens or microscope. The following terms are commonly used to describe the surfaces of leaves and other parts of plants:

barbellate: barbed down the sides (applied to hairs).
canescent: covered or becoming covered with grayish hairs.
ciliate: with soft hairs on the margin forming a fringe.
comose: having a tuft of hair, as many seeds.
fimbriate: with a fringe.
floccose: with tufts of woolly hairs that rub off easily.
glabrescent or *glabrate:* becoming glabrous (hairless) in age.
glabrous: without hairs.
glandular: with glands (usually hairs having enlarged cells at the tip).
glaucous: covered with a bloom, a whitish substance that rubs off.
glochidiate: having hairs that are barbed at the tip.
hirsute: having moderately stiff separate hairs.
hispid: with stiff or bristly hairs.
lanate: covered with woolly, tangled hairs.
pilose: covered with soft, rather long, shaggy hairs.
puberulent: with very soft, minute, downy hairs.
pubescent: covered with short, soft hairs (the term *pubescence* refers to any kind of hairiness).
punctate: having dots or pits, these often waxy or glandular.
rugose: wrinkled.
scabrous: with very short, stiff hairs or projections that one can feel by lightly passing the fingers over the surface.
scurfy: covered with minute scales.
sericeus: silky.
stellate: like a star (hairs having radiating branches).
strigose: with sharp-pointed, straight, appressed hairs.
tomentose: densely woolly, with matted hairs.
uncinate: with a hook at the tip, as some hairs or spines.
villous: with long, soft, shaggy hairs that are not matted.
viscid: sticky (usually from glandular hairs exuding a sticky liquid).

The student will find it profitable to get good, typical, representative parts of various plants, showing these and other surface features, and to make small, permanent mounts of them so that he will have examples to refer to when in doubt about the application of terms. Fragments of leaves or other parts may be mounted on cards and protected by an overlay of clear plastic, the edges of the mount being bound with tape.

MODIFIED LEAVES.   Most plants produce modified leaves that are somewhat different from the ordinary foliage leaves. Buds are covered by *bud scales;* bulbs are surrounded by *bulb scales;* some *tendrils* are modified leaves or parts of leaves serving as thread-like attachment organs; *bracts* are more or less modified leaves in an inflorescence or flower cluster; scale-like leaves occur on rhizomes; and sometimes leaves are modified into contrivances for capturing insects, as in the Pitcher Plant (*Sarracenia*), whose leaves are tabular and hold water. Some plants have their leaves reduced to spines. And, as will be pointed out later, the parts of a flower—sepals, petals, stamens, and carpels—are generally believed to have evolved from leaves.

Inflorescences

An inflorescence is the arrangement of flowers on a plant, or the mode of flowering. It may be very simple and readily distinguishable, or it may be a highly complex structure whose precise nature is not evident at a glance. We may try to force all flower arrangements into a set of rigidly defined types, but it should be remembered that it is not always possible to make variable plants fit such a system.

An old concept of inflorescences was based on the sequence of blooming and the position occupied by the oldest flower. Inflorescences were classified by this method into *determinate* types, in which the oldest flower terminated the main axis and the general progression of blooming was downward or outward, and *indeterminate* types, in which the youngest flower was terminal or central and the progression of blooming was upward or inward. Careful observation has shown, however, that, though the sequence of blooming may be significant in some instances, it may be quite irregular in others. The flowers of some inflorescences appear to open almost simultaneously; and sometimes the terminal flower aborts.

The main supporting stalk of the whole inflorescence is called a *peduncle.* The stalks supporting single flowers are called *pedicels.* These parts are indicated in Figure 26.

An inflorescence may have *bracts* (Fig. 26), which are modified leaves or scales from the axils of which flowers or flowering branches are produced. If there are no bracts, the inflorescence is said to be *ebracteate.* Bracts are generally unlike the foliage leaves, often being smaller or of a different shape or texture. Clusters or whorls of bracts make up an *involucre* (Figs. 37 and 39); if secondary involucres occur (as in compound umbels), these are known as *involucels of bractlets*

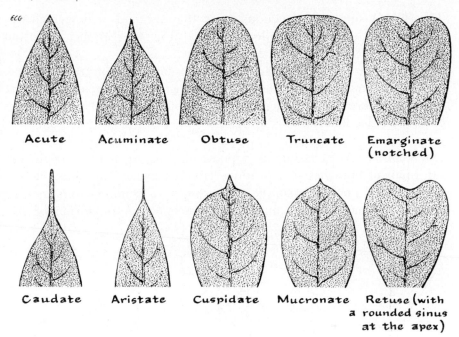

Acute   Acuminate   Obtuse   Truncate   Emarginate (notched)

Caudate   Aristate   Cuspidate   Mucronate   Retuse (with a rounded sinus at the apex)

24 Leaf apices.

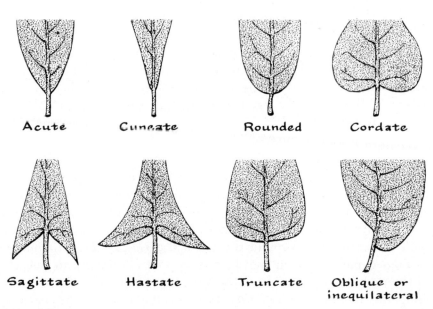

Acute   Cuneate   Rounded   Cordate

Sagittate   Hastate   Truncate   Oblique or inequilateral

25 Leaf bases.

(Fig. 39). A single, conspicuous bract that subtends a flower cluster (usually a fleshy spike) is called a *spathe* (Fig. 41); spathes are often ornamental.

Following are descriptions of the common kinds of inflorescence. Each is illustrated by a diagram in which small circles represent flowers; if there is a significant order of blooming, the larger circles represent older flowers.

DICHASIUM.   A dichasium is a peduncle bearing a terminal flower and a pair of branches that produce lateral flowers. The oldest flower is the central one. This *simple dichasium* is a common unit making up parts of many more complex inflorescences. A repetition of this

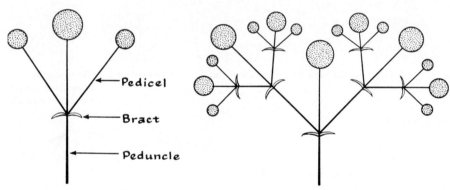

26 Simple dichasium.   **27** Compound dichasium (cyme).

on a lateral pair of branches produces a *compound dichasium*. A dichasium may be called a *cyme*, but that term has been loosely applied to any compound, more or less flat-topped inflorescence, particularly if the oldest flowers terminate the main axes. Dichasia are shown in Figures 26 and 27.

MONOCHASIUM.   A monochasium is a peduncle bearing a terminal flower and, below it, one branch that produces a single lateral flower. The terminal flower is older. This is a *simple monochasium*. A repetition of this on the lateral branches produces a *compound monochasium*, which may be of four types: (1) the *bostryx*, or helicoid cyme, which is spirally coiled round the vertical axis; (2) the *cincinnus*, or scorpioid cyme, in which the flowers appear alternately to one side and the other along one side of the axis, the whole inflorescence often coiling downward; (3) the *rhipidium*, which is a bostryx flattened in one plane, the inflorescence often being fan-shaped; (4) the

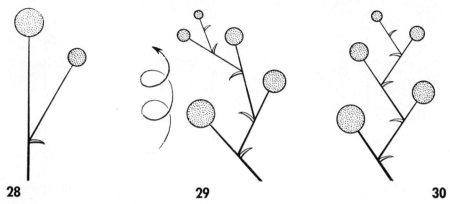

28 Simple monochasium.

29 Bostryx (the direction of coiling indicated by the arrow).

30 Cincinnus (often coiled downward).

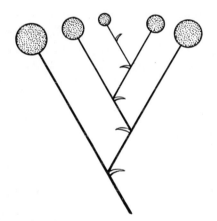

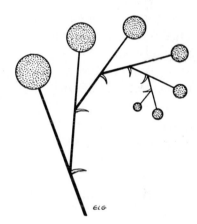

31 Rhipidium (flattened in the plane of the paper).

32 Drepanium (flattened in the plane of the paper and coiled to one side).

drepanium, which is a cincinnus having all the branches on one side, the inflorescence thus being flattened in one plane and usually coiled to one side and downward. This last is one of the commonest forms of the monochasium and is also a kind of scorpioid cyme. Monochasia are illustrated by Figures 28–32.

PANICLE. A panicle is a more or less elongated inflorescence with a central axis along which there are branches that are themselves branched. There may be a sequence of blooming from the base up-

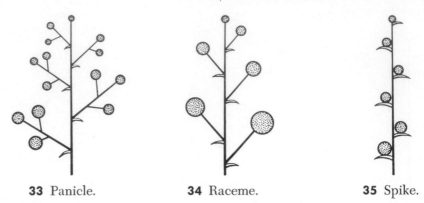

33 Panicle.   **34** Raceme.   **35** Spike.

ward, but some panicles are made up wholly of small dichasia. A congested, more or less cylindrical panicle is sometimes called a *thyrse*. A typical panicle is shown in Figure 33.

RACEME.   A raceme is an elongated inflorescence with a central axis along which are simple pedicels of more or less equal length. There is usually an order of blooming from the base upward, but some racemes have flowers opening almost simultaneously or irregularly. A raceme is shown in Figure 34.

SPIKE.   A spike is an elongated inflorescence with a central axis along which are sessile or subsessile flowers. The usual order of blooming is from the base upward. Very small spikes, particularly in grasses and sedges, are known as *spikelets*. These may be grouped into various arrangements such as panicles, racemes, or spikes. See Figure 35.

CORYMB. A corymb is a more or less flat-topped inflorescence having a main vertical axis and pedicels or branches of unequal length produced along it. The side branches may branch, or they may be simple pedicels as shown in Figure 36. The blooming sequence is usually from the outside toward the center, but it may be irregular.

HEAD.   A head, or *capitulum,* is a rounded or flat-topped cluster of sessile flowers. Many heads show a progression of blooming from the outside toward the center. Heads may be solitary, or they may be aggregated into various arrangements, such as panicles, racemes, spikes, or corymbs. Heads such as those found in *Aster* and other

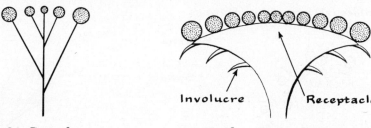

36 Corymb.   **37** Head in longitudinal section.

members of the Aster Family may resemble flowers, for they often consist of two kinds of flowers, the outer more ornamental and resembling petals. Figure 37 shows such a head in longitudinal section.

UMBEL.   An umbel is an inflorescence having several branches arising from a common point at the summit of the peduncle. If these branches end in flowers, we have a *simple umbel* (Fig. 38); if they end in secondary *umbellets,* we have a *compound umbel* (Fig. 39). The blooming sequence is generally from the outside toward the center. An umbel may have a group or whorl of bracts, collectively called an *involucre,* at the summit of the peduncle. If there are similar bracts in groups at the base of an umbellet, they are called an *involucel* and the individual members are called *bractlets.* The main branches of a compound umbel are called *rays,* and the corresponding members of the umbellet are called *pedicels.*

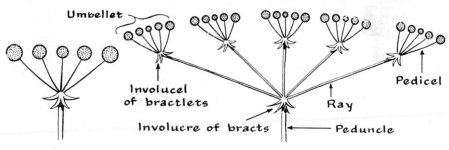

38 Simple umbel.   **39** Compound umbel.

CATKIN.   A catkin, or *ament,* is a spike, raceme, or dichasium composed of unisexual flowers without petals and falling as a whole. It may be erect or pendent, and it may be long or short. The flowers are usually very small, and usually each is subtended by a little bract, or *scale.*

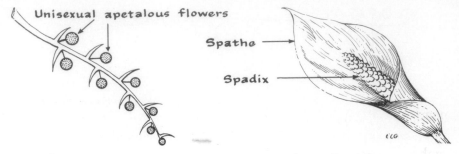

40 Catkin, or ament.   **41** Spathe and spadix.

Sometimes one or two leaf-like bracts (perhaps true leaves) occur at the base of the catkin and fall with it. This type of inflorescence is shown in Figure 40.

SPADIX.   A spadix is a spike with a thickened, fleshy axis, usually enveloped by a conspicuous or colored bract called a *spathe*. The flowers are often very minute and frequently unisexual. See Figure 41.

Flowers

What we might think of as a typical, unmodified flower, such as that of a Lily or Flax, is made up of four sets of flower parts: sepals, petals, stamens, and pistil or pistils.

SEPALS.   Sepals, collectively called the *calyx*, are the outermost parts and are commonly leaf-like and green, but they may be colored like the petals and have a thinner texture, in which case they are described as being *petaloid*. In the unmodified flower they are all alike in size and shape. The sepals enclose the flower in bud and may or may not persist for the life of the flower.

PETALS.   Petals, collectively called the *corolla*, normally occupy a position in the flower between the sepals and the stamens. Petals are commonly delicate in texture and are often colored. They are often larger than the sepals, and they may be shed soon after the flower opens. Their color or fragrance may attract insects. The sepals and petals together make up the *perianth*, or floral envelope, a term that is especially useful when the distinction between sepals and petals is not obvious.

STAMENS.   Stamens, collectively called the *androecium*, are the male reproductive parts of the flower and occupy a position inward from the perianth. They vary widely in size and number. Each stamen usually consists of two parts: the *anther,* the sac-like part, which contains the pollen; and the *filament,* or stalk, which connects the anther to the floral axis or some other part.

PISTILS.   Pistils, collectively called the *gynoecium,* are the female reproductive parts of the flower and occupy a central position. The gynoecium may consist of a single pistil, as in the Lily, of several or many pistils, as in the Buttercup. Each pistil usually consists of three parts: the *stigma,* the pollen-receptive part at the summit, which may be single or variously lobed or branched; the *style,* the stalk-like portion below the stigma; and the *ovary,* the enlarged portion at the base, which contains one or more ovules or immature seeds. In some pistils the style may be lacking, but the stigma and the ovary are essential to the functioning of the organ.

The basic unit of construction of a pistil is the *carpel,* which is a single megasporophyll, or modified seed-bearing leaf. A pistil may consist of a single carpel, as in the Sweet Pea, or of two or more carpels partly or completely joined together, as in the Lily (three carpels) or the Mustard (two carpels). One can usually determine the number of carpels in a pistil by sectioning the ovary and counting the number of partitions or rows of ovules or seeds, or by counting the number of styles or stigmas.

If a flower contains two or more separate carpels, it is called an *apocarpous* flower; if it contains a single pistil that consists of two or more united carpels, it is called a *syncarpous* flower.

A more detailed account of the androecium and the gynoecium will be found farther along in this chapter.

FLORAL DIAGRAMS.   A floral diagram represents a cross-section of a flower as it would appear if all parts were at the same level. It might also be thought of as a sort of aerial view of a flower in diagrammatic form. For uniformity and convenience, the various parts are represented in diagrams by standardized symbols, those used in this text being shown in Figures 42–62.

In general, lines connecting parts of a flower in the diagram indicate that those parts are connected. This and other features of floral diagrams are shown in Figures 57–62.

NUMERICAL PLAN OF THE FLOWER.   Most flowers are constructed upon a definite numerical plan. In the monocotyledons the flowers

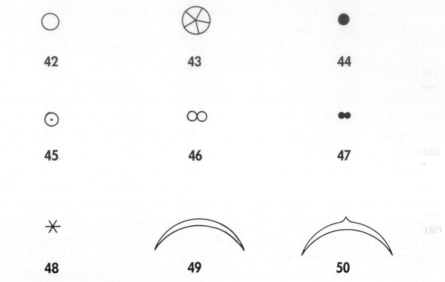

42 Carpel, a small circle.

43 United carpels, five in this case.

44 Vestigial carpel, a small black circle.

45 Axis of inflorescence, a small circle with a dot in the center.

46 Stamen.

47 Vestigial stamen, or staminodium.

48 A part that is lacking completely, in its normal position.

49 Sepal.

50 Petal.

usually have a numerical plan of three: 3 sepals, 3 petals, and usually 3 or a multiple of 3 stamens. These are called *3-merous* flowers. Dicotyledon flowers are usually constructed on a numerical plan of four or five and are then referred to as *4-merous* or *5-merous* flowers. The numerical plan of the flower is most evident in the sepals and petals, and to some extent it is carried through to the stamens; but this feature of the construction very often does not apply to carpels or pistils.

ALTERNATION OF PARTS.   The parts of a flower are usually arranged in such a manner that the petals alternate with the sepals, and the stamens alternate with the petals (inner sets of stamens may alternate with outer sets). The pistils or carpels, however, are often op-

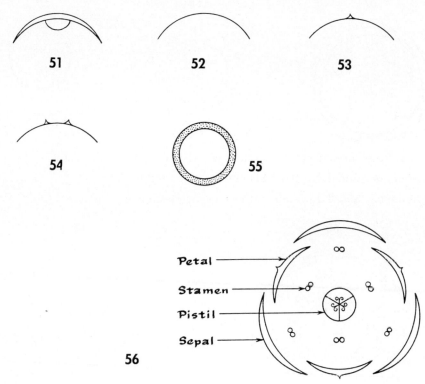

51 Nectar pit, gland, or spur on a sepal.

52 Bract, or glume, of grasses.

53 Lemma of grasses.

54 Palea of grasses.

55 Hypanthium. This structure is discussed in the text on page 102.

56 Floral diagram of a hypogynous flower having separate parts except for the three united carpels of the pistil. The term "hypogynous" is explained in the text on pages 102 and 103.

posite the sepals. This feature of alternation of parts gives us a valuable clue to the location of vestigial or missing flower parts in certain groups. If, for example, a single set of stamens is placed so that each stamen comes opposite a petal, as in the Primrose Family, we assume that an outer set of stamens has been lost in the process of evolution.

COMPLETE AND INCOMPLETE FLOWERS.   When all the characteristic parts—sepals, petals, stamens, and pistils—are present, the flower is

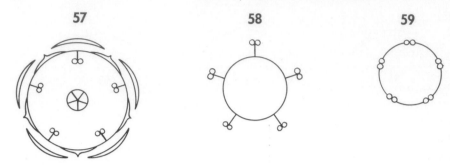

57 Corolla of united petals; stamens inserted on the corolla tube.

58 Stamens united by their filaments (monadelphous).

59 Stamens united by their anthers (syngenesious).

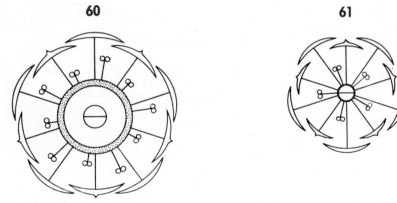

60 Floral diagram of a perigynous flower, the stamens, petals, and sepals inserted on the hypanthium.

61 Floral diagram of an epigynous flower without a hypanthium, the floral parts inserted directly on the ovary.

62 Floral diagram of an epigynous flower with a tubular hypanthium, the hypanthium inserted on the ovary and the other flower parts inserted on the hypanthium. Note: in epigynous flowers the ovary wall is represented by a heavier line than in hypogynous or perigynous flowers. The symbol for the ovary is an approximation of the cross section of the ovary, usually omitting the ovules. The text (p. 102) explains the terms "hypogynous," "perigynous," and "epigynous."

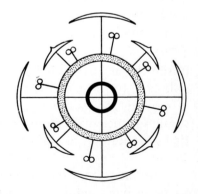

complete. But we frequently find that one or more of these parts may be lacking, in which case the flower is *incomplete.* Should the whole perianth of sepals and petals be lacking, the flower is *naked,* as in Willows. If only the petals are lacking, the flower is *apetalous,* and then the sepals frequently take on the aspect of petals, as in Anemones.

Flowers having both stamens and pistils, regardless of the presence or absence of other parts, are *perfect* flowers. If a flower has only one kind of sexual organ, either stamens or pistils but not both, it is a *unisexual* flower; male flowers, or those having stamens, are called *staminate* flowers, and female flowers, or those having pistils, are called *pistillate* flowers. When the flowers are unisexual and both sexes occur on the same plant, as in Oaks and Birches, the plants are known as *monoecious* plants; when unisexual flowers occur on separate plants, as in Willows and Poplars, the plants are *dioecious.* Intermediate conditions of sexuality also occur in some plants, such as species of the Rhubarb Family, some flowers being perfect while others are unisexual, and such a condition is known as *polygamous.* Carrying this a little further, we may designate the sexual condition as either *polygamo-monoecious* or *polygamo-dioecious,* depending on the placement of the different kinds of flowers.

REGULAR AND IRREGULAR FLOWERS. These terms apply to the perianth, as a rule, and rarely involve the reproductive parts. *Regular flowers* (sometimes called *actinomorphic* flowers) are those in which the perianth parts of each kind are similar in size and shape, so that the flower may be divided into equal halves by a vertical plane in various directions, the flower being radially symmetrical. Lilies and Buttercups, for example, have regular flowers. *Irregular flowers* (sometimes called *zygomorphic* flowers) are those in which the perianth parts of each kind are dissimilar in size and shape, some petals being unlike other petals, or some of the sepals being dissimilar in size or shape to others. Irregularity usually involves the petals, but it may involve the sepals or the whole perianth. Sweetpeas and Pansies have irregular flowers, which may be divided into equal halves only by a single vertical plane.

SPIRAL AND CYCLIC ARRANGEMENTS OF FLOWER PARTS. In what are usually regarded as more primitive flower types, the various parts may be inserted on the floral axis in a spiral manner, as the scales of a pine cone and the reproductive parts of a Buttercup flower. In a floral diagram this is shown by a dotted spiral line. In more advanced flower types, such as found in the Lily, the various parts are inserted in whorls, each whorl at a slightly different level, and this is known as a cyclic arrangement.

HYPOGYNOUS, PERIGYNOUS, AND EPIGYNOUS FLOWERS.   Flowers may be hypogynous, perigynous, or epigynous, depending on the way the flower parts are inserted in relation to one another.

Hypogynous flowers have the sepals, petals, and stamens inserted round the base of the gynoecium and free from it; or the stamens may be inserted on the petals, which are inserted below the base of the gynoecium but free from it. Hypogynous flowers never have a hypanthium.

Perigynous flowers have the sepals, petals, and stamens inserted on the rim of a shallow or deep saucer-like or cup-like structure called the hypanthium, which arises at the base of the gynoecium and may be free from it or adnate to it. The gynoecium, then, is situated inside the hypanthium and above its base, never beneath it. Perigynous flowers always have a hypanthium, whether it is large and conspicuous or abbreviated and inconspicuous. If the hypanthium becomes adnate to the ovary, as in the Apple, the flower takes on the appearance of being epigynous, but a section of the flower across the ovary and hypanthium will always show a band of tissue (the hypanthium) surrounding the ovary. The term "hypanthium" is a recent one, older treatments having often confused the structure with a calyx-tube. As must be evident, the hypanthium is more than a calyx-tube, for it also gives rise to petals and stamens. In apetalous and unisexual flowers, however, it is often difficult or impossible to determine the true nature of this kind of structure, whether calyx-tube or hypanthium, and the best clues lie in anatomical features such as vasculature.

Epigynous flowers have a single ovary, which is beneath the flower parts, and these arise directly from its summit. According to some workers, epigynous flowers must have an external tissue or sleeve connecting the sepals, petals, and stamens to the base of the ovary; but in the writer's experience this cannot be demonstrated by a section across the ovary, and we must assume that those flower parts are attached directly to the ovary. It seems likely, however, that a perigynous flower with an adnate hypanthium might have given rise to an epigynous flower by losing the hypanthium.

Hypogynous flowers are believed to have originated first and to have been followed in evolution by perigynous and epigynous types. In a few families, however, such as the Heath Family, both hypogynous

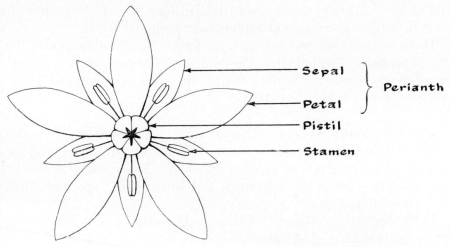

63 Viewed from above, a 5-merous, regular, complete flower.

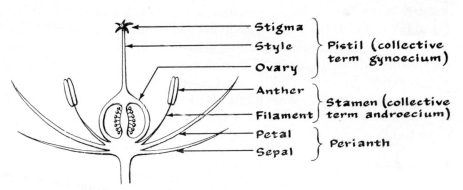

64 Longitudinal section, showing the flower to be hypogynous.

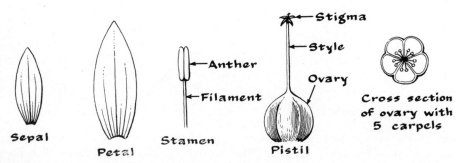

65 Flower parts represented individually.

and epigynous flower types occur; this feature, therefore, cannot always be used as a criterion of evolutionary position.

These flower types are discussed in greater detail below under the title of Six Basic Morphological Flower Types. The parts of an ordinary, hypogynous, regular, complete flower, their arrangement and insertion, are shown in Figures 63–65.

SIX BASIC MORPHOLOGICAL FLOWER TYPES. The flowers of angiosperms, while showing great diversity of form and structure, may be considered as fitting into six basic morphological types. These represent increasing degrees of specialization, and within each type additional specialization may occur.

1. *The hypogynous flower.* Although this is the basic type, without much specialization, it includes advanced groups in which some parts, such as the corolla and stamens, are greatly modified. Hypogynous flowers of a simple type occur in Buttercups and Lilies, of an advanced type in Snapdragons and Mints. The sepals, petals, and stamens are inserted at the base of the gynoecium axis (or the stamens may be on the petals), and this renders the gynoecium superior in position. In primitive types the carpels and stamens are indefinite in number, often numerous, and often spirally arranged, becoming fewer and cyclic in higher types. In some plants, such as the Lotus (*Nelumbo*), the axis may be expanded. The parts of the perianth may be separate (*distinct*) or united, and they may be regular or irregular. There is no hypanthium. Figure 66 illustrates this type.

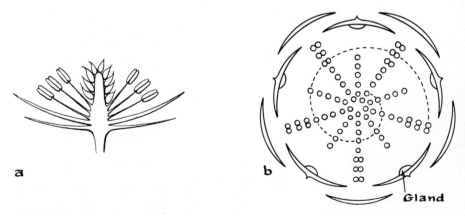

66 Hypogynous flower of a Buttercup (*Ranunculus*): (a) longitudinal section; (b) floral diagram. The dotted spiral line indicates that the stamens and carpels are spirally arranged.

2. *The perigynous flower with free hypogynous hypanthium.* Here there has been an outgrowth of tissue, apparently from a primordium surrounding the base of the gynoecium axis. This is undifferentiated at first, but it eventually gives rise to stamens, petals, and sepals. This outgrowth, called the *hypanthium,* is free from the gynoecium and forms a cup-like or saucer-shaped structure. The gynoecium may consist of a single pistil, as in the Cherry (*Prunus*); or it may consist of several or numerous pistils (carpels), as in the Cinquefoil (*Potentilla*) or in the Strawberry (*Fragaria*), the latter having a fleshy gynoecium axis in fruit. The number of stamens may also vary from few to many. In most flowers of this type the corolla is regular, but in some groups, as in many members of the Pea Family, it is irregular. Perigynous flowers are believed to have been derived from hypogynous types and to manifest a higher degree of specialization. They are especially well represented in the *Rosales.* Figure 67 illustrates this type.

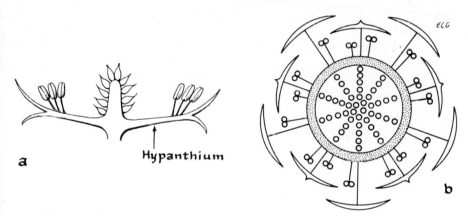

67 Cinquefoil flower (*Potentilla*): (a) longitudinal section; (b) floral diagram.

3. *The perigynous flower with the floral axis expanded continuously.* The floral organs are produced on a cup-like structure, and often there is a transition zone, near the middle of the cup, at which the female portion gives way to the male portion. The transition zone often produces sterile carpels and stamens. This uncommon floral type is best illustrated by the Calycanthus Family (*Calycanthaceae*) and, in more advanced condition, by the Rose (*Rosa*) in the *Rosaceae.* In the latter the transition zone is completely sterile and produces no organs. Figure 68 illustrates this type.

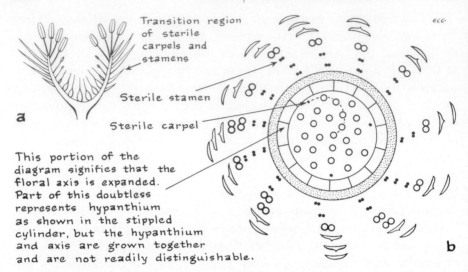

68 Calycanthus flower (*Calycanthus*): (a) longitudinal section; (b) floral diagram. When floral parts are numerous, it is better to omit connecting lines to the hypanthium to avoid confusion. The sepals, petals, and stamens must always be on the hypanthium if it is present; there can be no other place of insertion.

4. *The perigynous flower with adnate hypogynous hypanthium.* This is similar to the preceding type, but the hypanthium grows up round the ovary and is adnate to it, often becoming fleshy in fruit. This gives the flower the appearance of epigyny, the ovary appearing to be inferior, but the appearance is due to the adnation of the hypanthium, inside which the ovary is situated. This occurs in Apple

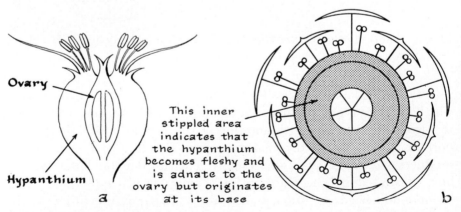

69 Apple flower (*Pyrus*): (a) longitudinal section; (b) floral diagram.

and Pear (*Pyrus*) flowers and in the Walnut (*Juglans*). The flesh of the apple fruit is hypanthium, and the husk round the nut of walnuts is also hypanthium. An interesting indication of the manner in which this type may have originated is shown by the Russian Olive (*Elaeagnus*): the flowering stage has a free hypanthium, but with the enlargement of the ovary in fruit the hypanthium-cup becomes completely filled and adnate to the ovary. Figure 69 illustrates this morphological type.

5. *The epigynous flower without a hypanthium.* Here the ovary is inferior in position to the rest of the flower parts, the sepals, petals, and stamens being inserted near the summit of the ovary. There is no hypanthium. This rather common type is illustrated by the Parsnip Family (*Apiaceae*), the Dogwood Family (*Cornaceae*), and the Orchid Family (*Orchidaceae*). It represents a somewhat higher de-

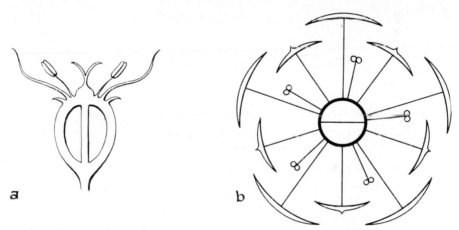

70 Parsnip flower (*Pastinaca*): (a) longitudinal section; (b) floral diagram.

velopment than the hypogynous and perigynous types. Figure 70 illustrates this type.

6. *The epigynous flower with an epigynous hypanthium.* This is similar to the preceding type but differs in having a hypanthium which originates from near the summit of the ovary and extends above it as a funnel, tube, or rod. This hypanthium may be very short or may be several inches long. In many members of the Evening Primrose Family (*Onagraceae*) the hypanthium is tubular or funnelform; in the Iris (*Iris*) it is solid and rod-shaped. This condition of epigyny with

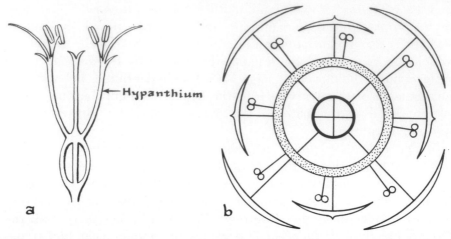

71 Evening Primrose flower (*Oenothera*): (a) longitudinal section: (b) floral diagram.

a hypanthium somewhat parallels the condition in No. 5 in evolution, some families having both types. Figure 71 illustrates this type.

THE ANDROECIUM.   The androecium of a flower is made up of the male reproductive parts—that is, the microsporophylls, or stamens. It occupies a position outward from the gynoecium and inward from the corolla, but the stamens are sometimes inserted on the corolla (*epipetalous*), and infrequently, as in Orchids, they are attached to the pistil (*gynandrous*). In all perigynous flowers the stamens are inserted on a hypanthium.

Stamens are attached to one another in two general ways: by union of their filaments into one group (*monadelphous*), two groups (*diadelphous*), etc., and by union of their anthers into a ring (*syngenesious*).

When the stamens are of unequal lengths, two long and two shorter,

72 Epipetalous stamens of the Olive flower.

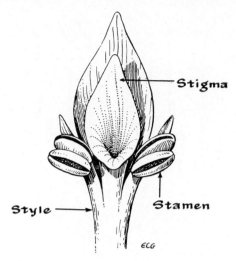

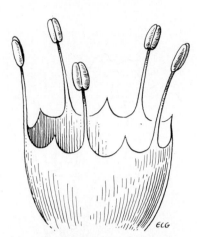

73 Gynandrous stamens of an Orchid.

74 Monadelphous stamens of a Flax flower. The alternating points on the tube are probably the remnants of what were formerly stamens.

they are termed *didynamous*. When there are four long and two shorter stamens, they are termed *tetradynamous*.

Attachment of the anther to the filament is of three general sorts: *innate* when the anther sacs are chiefly terminal and do not face inward or outward in the flower; *adnate* when the anther sacs are elongated and attached lengthwise to the filament, facing either inward (*introrse*) or outward (*extrorse*) in the flower; and *versatile* when the anther is

75 Diadelphous stamens of a Sweet Pea flower, nine in one group and one in the other.

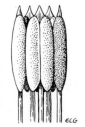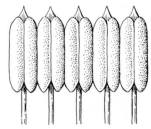

76 Syngenesious stamens of a member of the Sunflower Family. At the left they are shown as they would be in the flower; at the right they are shown spread out flat.

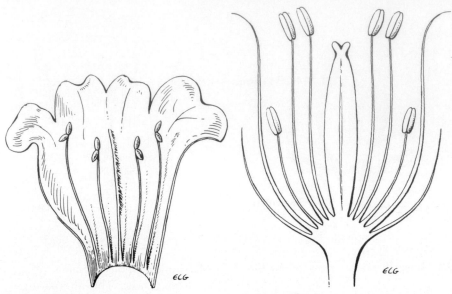

77 Didynamous fertile stamens of *Penstemon*.

78 Tetradynamous stamens of a Mustard flower.

attached by its middle with both ends free. The portion of the stamen that represents a continuation of the filament between the anther sacs is termed the *connective*.

All parts of the stamen are subject to modification. The filament is variously elongated, often dilated and petaloid, or, infrequently, lacking. The connective sometimes becomes greatly broadened transversely so that the anther sacs are widely separated (see *Salvia* in the Mint Family). Either or both of the anther sacs may be reduced and

79 Sterile stamens (staminodia) of a *Catalpa* flower.

sterile; if both, we have sterile stamens, or *staminodia,* which are frequently very elaborate and much unlike the normal stamens. It is believed that glands in some flowers may represent much reduced stamens.

Primitive flowers, in general, are believed to have had numerous and more or less spirally arranged stamens, and from this condition flowers with progressively fewer and often more elaborate stamens have evolved. Irregular flowers usually have their stamens modified or reduced from the normal number (less than the number of sepals or

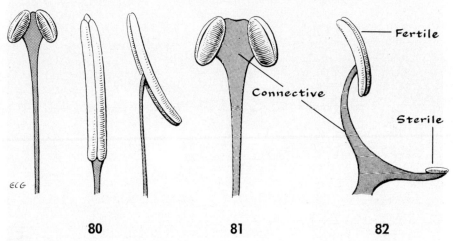

80 Innate (left), adnate (middle), and versatile (right) anthers.

81 Anther with a moderately broadened connective.

82 Stamen of *Salvia* with an elongated connective between the anther sacs, one fertile and the other sterile.

petals). Figures 72–83 illustrate these terms and features of the androecium.

THE GYNOECIUM.   The gynoecium of a flower is made up of the female reproductive parts—that is, the carpels or pistils. It occupies a central position in the flower.

When the pistil is composed of a single megasporophyll, or *carpel,* it is termed a *simple pistil.* When it is composed of two or more carpels that are more or less united, it is a *compound pistil.*

Each carpel has two ribs, seams, or *sutures,* one representing the midrib of the leaf and called the *dorsal suture* (not really a seam), the other representing the joined edges of the leaf and called the *ventral*

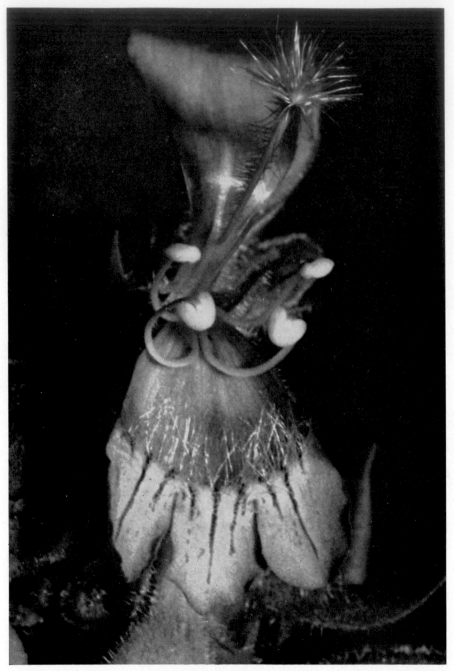

83 Flower of *Penstemon eriantherus* Pursh, with the corolla torn open to show the didynamous fertile stamens and the fifth and bearded stamen, or staminodium.

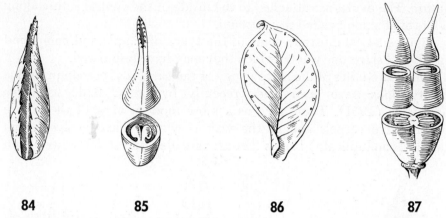

84   **85**   **86**   **87**

84 Inrolled leaf.

85 Simple pistil of *Isopyrum*.

86 Pistil of *Caltha* after shedding its seeds; one carpel.

87 Compound pistil of two carpels of *Saxifraga*.

(Figs. 84–87 are redrawn from Gray's *Lessons*.)

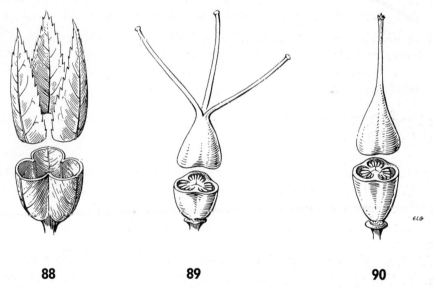

88   **89**   **90**

88 Three leaves forming a compound pistil.

89 Compound pistil of three carpels of *Hypericum*.

90 Compound pistil of three carpels of *Hypericum*.

(Figs. 88–90 are redrawn from Gray's *Lessons*.)

suture. The ovules are attached to the inside of the ventral suture along a line or at a point called the *placenta.*

Figures 84–90 illustrate some of the types of simple and compound pistils and show one way in which they may have originated.

Detailed studies of the morphology of the carpels of certain primitive dicotyledons have been made recently by I. W. Bailey and his associates (1951). These give us a more modern view of the nature of primitive carpels and of the way they may have evolved from folded (conduplicate) blades that are unsealed and styleless, as shown

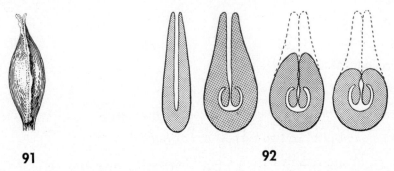

91   **92**

91 Primitive conduplicate carpel in ventral view. [Redrawn from I. W. Bailey and B. G. L. Swamy in Am. Jour. Bot. 38: 374 (1951).]

92 Transverse sections of primitive carpels showing the development of a locule and stages in the closure of conduplicate carpels. [Redrawn from I. W. Bailey and B. G. L. Swamy in Am. Jour. Bot. 38: 377 1951).]

in Figure 91. Stages in the formation of such simple pistils are shown in Figure 92.

PLACENTATION TYPES. When cross-sections of various ovaries are examined, it is found that the position of the ovules and placentae nearly always conforms to one of the three main patterns shown in Figures 93–97. Variations of these basic patterns are known but are uncommon.

Parietal and marginal placentation. Here the ovules are attached to the inner wall of the ovary on one or more placentae. This type occurs in simple pistils, where it is often referred to as *marginal*, and in many compound pistils, where it is called *parietal*. With rare exceptions, as in the Mustard Family, the ovary is not compartmented. This type of placentation is generally regarded as primitive. It is illustrated in Figures 93–95.

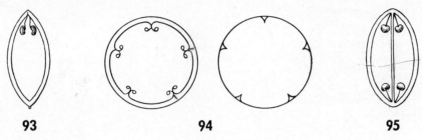

93   **94**   **95**

93 Cross section of ovary of a simple pistil (Pea).

94 Cross section of ovary of a compound pistil of five carpels with five parietal placentae (Poppy); at right as shown diagrammatically in a floral diagram.

95 Cross section of ovary of a two-carpeled pistil with two parietal placentae (Mustard).

Axillary (axile) placentation. Here the ovules are attached near the center of the ovary at the junction or axis of the partitions that divide the ovary into compartments. This can occur only in compound pistils and is regarded as an intermediate stage in evolution. It is illustrated by Figure 96.

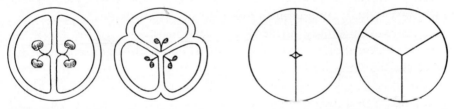

96 Two examples of axillary placentation. The left-hand figure of each pair is from a Morning-glory, that on the right from a Lily. The two right-hand figures show how these might be represented in floral diagrams.

Free-central and basal placentation. Here the ovules are produced on a projection from the base of the ovary of a compound pistil, this placenta being free from the ovary wall laterally and the ovary one-celled. *Basal placentation* is restricted to the reduced condition in which a single ovule is produced. By dissolution of the partitions in the axillary type we can derive this one, illustrated by Figures 97 and 98.

Fruits

The fruit of a flowering plant may be defined as a matured ovary and its contents together with other flower parts that may sometimes

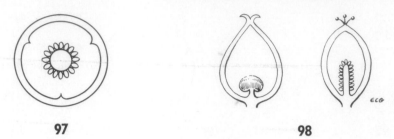

97   **98**

97 Cross section of an ovary of three carpels showing free-central placentation (Chickweed).

98 Longitudinal sections of ovaries showing basal placentation (left) and free-central placentation (right).

adhere to it. The fruit is often an important diagnostic feature of a family or genus: the legume of the Pea Family, for example, or the aggregate of drupelets of the Blackberry and Raspberry (genus *Rubus*). We should keep in mind that for the taxonomist the saying "By their fruits ye shall know them" takes on real meaning!

The ovary wall, known as the *pericarp,* consists of three layers in fruits: the *exocarp,* or outer layer, which is often the skin; the *mesocarp,* or middle layer, which may become fleshy; and the *endocarp,* or inner layer, which is sometimes modified in various ways.

As yet we have only an artificial classification of fruits, based on their gross morphology rather than on their mode of origin. Until a better classification and a better nomenclature of fruits are forthcoming, the following key will distinguish the commonly recognized kinds. (It should be pointed out that the term "pod," while meaning some sort of dry and dehiscent fruit, has no precise meaning to the taxonomist.)

Key to Types of Fruits

1. Fruit derived from several flowers . . . . MULTIPLE FRUIT
(Pineapple, Mulberry, Fig)
1. Fruit derived from a single flower
  2. Derived from more than one pistil . . . . AGGREGATE FRUIT
(Raspberry, Strawberry)
  2. Derived from a single pistil . . . . SIMPLE FRUITS
(see below)
    3. Fruit fleshy, usually indehiscent (not splitting)
      4. Flesh of fruit derived from a hypanthium that surrounds the papery carpels . . . . POME
(Apple, Pear, Quince)

    4. Flesh of fruit derived from the ovary wall
      5. Pericarp with an outer fleshy layer and an inner bony layer (the stone) . . . . .DRUPE
                            (Peach, Cherry)
      5. Pericarp without an inner bony layer, more or less fleshy throughout . . . . , ...BERRY
                            (Tomato, Grape)
      Modifications of the berry type of fruit may be defined as follows:
      6. Septae evident in cross section; the outer layer leathery
. . . . .HESPERIDIUM
                            (Orange, Lemon)
      6. Septae lacking; the outer layer leathery to hard and woody
. . . . .PEPO
           (Cucumber, Watermelon, Cantaloupe)
3. Fruit dry at maturity, dehiscent or indehiscent
    7. Fruit indehiscent (not splitting open)
      8. With one or more wings . . . . .SAMARA
                          (Maple, Ash, Elm)
      8. Without wings
        9. From a compound pistil, becoming hard and bony-shelled
. . . . .NUT (or NUTLET if small)
                    (Oak, Walnut, Hazelnut)
        9. From a simple pistil, often with a thin shell but not bony
          10. Pericarp fused to the seed . . . . .GRAIN (CARYOPSIS)
                      (Wheat, Rice, Corn)
          10. Pericarp separable from the seed . . . . .AKENE
               (Sedges, Sunflower, Aster)
    7. Fruit dehiscent (splitting open)
      11. From a simple pistil (1 carpel)
        12. Splitting on two sutures . . . . .LEGUME
                  (Pea, Bean, Alfalfa)
        12. Splitting on one suture . . . . .FOLLICLE
              (Milkweed, Larkspur)
      11. From a compound pistil (carpels 2 or more, united)
        13. Carpels separating from each other but each retaining its seed . . . . : .SCHIZOCARP
                    (Parsnip, Carrot)
        13. Carpels splitting, releasing 1 or more seeds
          14. Fruit 2-celled, the two valves splitting away from a persistent, thin partition or septum (replum) . . . .
              SILIQUE (or SILICLE if short)
                        (Mustard)

99 Three types of capsules: on the left below is a septicidal capsule of *Yucca*, in the middle above is a pair of loculicidal capsules of *Iris*, and on the right below is a poricidal capsule of *Papaver*, a Poppy.

14. Fruit 1–several-celled, the partition not persistent if fruit 2-celled . . . . CAPSULE
(Willow, Iris, Yucca)
There are modifications of the capsular type of fruit (see Fig. 99) as follows:
15. Opening by a lid (circumscissile capsules)

16. With a single seed .... UTRICLE
(Pigweed)
16. With several seeds .... PYXIS
(Portulaca)
15. Opening by holes near the top .. PORICIDAL CAPSULE
(Poppy)
15. Opening by splitting lengthwise
17. Splitting on the septae .... SEPTICIDAL CAPSULE
(Yucca)
17. Splitting between the septae and in the locules
or chambers .... LOCULICIDAL CAPSULE
(Glacier Lily)

Ovules and Seeds

A seed is a matured ovule. It should not be confused with a fruit, which, though it may resemble a seed, is really a matured ovary containing one or more seeds. The typical seed consists of an *embryo* surrounded and protected by a *seed coat,* with or without a quantity of stored food, known as the *endosperm,* in which the embryo is embedded. Figures 100 and 101 illustrate the principal parts of seeds, one with and the other without endosperm.

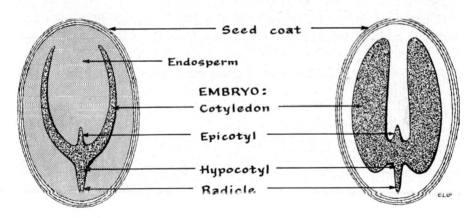

Seed coat

Endosperm

EMBRYO:
Cotyledon

Epicotyl

Hypocotyl

Radicle

100 Longitudinal section of a seed containing endosperm. (Diagrammatic.)

101 Longitudinal section of a seed without endosperm. (Diagrammatic.)

The *embryo* is the young plant within the seed. It may be very much smaller than the seed, in which case it is likely to be surrounded by a quantity of endosperm, upon which it draws for nourishment until it is independent. It may be large enough to fill the seed cavity, in which case it usually contains reserve food within itself. The principal parts of the embryo are the *cotyledons,* which are a pair of leaf-like organs in the dicotyledons, a single one in the monocotyledons, a whorl of several in the gymnosperms; the *epicotyl,* projecting above the point of attachment of the cotyledons, which will become stem and leaf; the *hypocotyl,* a transitional stem-like portion between the attachment of the cotyledons and the root-forming part; and the *radicle,* or root-forming part. The hypocotyl may be poorly developed in some embryos and well defined in others.

Since embryos show varying degrees of specialization, they may be useful in the delimitation of genera and families, as will be seen in such families as the *Chenopodiaceae* (Goosefoot Family) and the *Brassicaceae* (Mustard Family). The primitive embryo was probably straight; more advanced types are curved or bent in the middle, and some are even spirally coiled.

The *seed coat* may be either a single or a double structure derived from the integument or integuments of the ovule. When there are two seed coats, the outer one (*testa*) is usually hard and tough, and the inner one (*tegumen*) is thin and delicate. Variations in the structure and markings of the seed coat may furnish useful taxonomic characters for distinguishing groups of plants. Commonly used features of this sort are the wings on the seeds of the *Bignoniaceae* (Trumpet-vine Family) and the tufts of hair on the seeds of the *Salicaceae* (Willow Family) and *Asclepiadaceae* (Milkweed Family). The seed hairs of the genus *Gossypium* (Cotton) are of great economic importance.

The *endosperm* is present in the immature stages of the formation of seeds and may persist, as a cellular food mass in which the embryo is embedded, when the seed is ripe. In many plants, however, the endosperm is used up, and its space is occupied by the embryo when the seed is mature, the food stored in the endosperm tissue having been assimilated by the embryo and re-elaborated, in part, as food stored in the cotyledons. The presence or absence of endosperm in mature seeds is a useful diagnostic character, usually at the family level.

Some seeds have an additional feature known as an *aril,* which is an outgrowth from the seed stalk (*funiculus*) or sometimes from the placenta. It is often of a mucilaginous or gelatinous texture and some-times brightly colored. Examples of arillate seeds are the Litchi (*Sapindaceae*), the aril of which is eaten, the Yew (*Taxaceae*), in which it is red, and the spice known as mace, which is the aril of the Nutmeg (*Myristicaceae*).

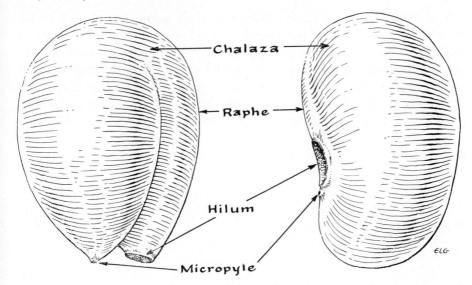

102 Side views of seeds of Violet (left) and Bean (right) showing external features.

External features of the seed, in addition to those mentioned above, are the *hilum*, the scar left on the seed at the point where the funiculus was detached; the *raphe*, the ridge formed by the fusion of the funiculus with the seed when the funiculus is bent; the *chalaza*, the upper portion of the raphe where the funiculus merges with the base of the ovule; and the *micropyle*, the minute pore through which the pollen tube once entered the ovule. These features are illustrated in Figure 102.

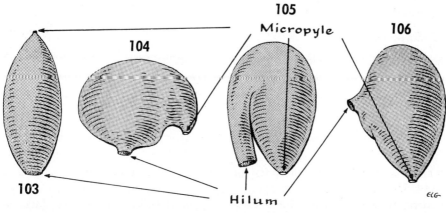

103 Orthotropous ovule.

104 Campylotropous ovule.

105 Anatropous ovule.

106 Amphitropous ovule.

The *direction*, the way in which the ovule points in relation to its attachment to the ovary, is sometimes used as an aid in defining taxa. This direction or condition may take four forms. If the ovule is *orthotropous*, it is straight, and the micropylar end is directly opposite the hilum, as in Figure 103. If the ovule is *campylotropous*, it is curved, so that the micropylar end is close to the hilum, but the ovule as a whole is more or less horizontal, as in Figure 104. If the ovule is *anatropous*, it is inverted, the funiculus being curved at the apex and the body of the ovule lying against it. This is one of the commonest types and is illustrated by Figure 105. If the ovule is *amphitropous*, the funiculus and the raphe are short, and the ovule is attached laterally. This condition, intermediate between the campylotropous and the anatropous, is illustrated by Figure 106.

REFERENCES

Vegetative organs

ARBER, AGNES: "Root and Shoot in the Angiosperms: A Study of Morphological Categories," New Phytol. 29: 297–315 (1930).

CANDOLLE, A. P. DE: *Organographie végétale*, I (Paris, 1827).

CANDOLLE, C. DE: "Théorie de la feuille," Arch. d. Sci. de la Bibl. Universelle 32: 32–64 (1868).

GOEBEL, K.: *Organography of Plants, Especially of the* Archegoniatae *and* Spermatophyta (authorized English edition by Isaac Bayley Balfour), Part II (Oxford, 1905).

Inflorescences

CROIZAT, LEON: "The Concept of the Inflorescence," Bull. Torr. Club 70: 496–509 (1943).

PARKIN, J.: "The Evolution of the Inflorescence," Proc. Linn. Soc. 42: 511–562 (1914).

PHILIPSON, W. R.: "Studies in the Development of the Inflorescence," Ann. Not. n.s. 10: 257–270 (1946), 11: 285–297, 409–416 (1947), 12: 65–75, 147–156 (1948).

RICKETT, H. W.: "The Classification of Inflorescences," Bot. Rev. 10: 187–231 (1944).

RICKETT, H. W.: "Materials for a Dictionary of Botanical Terms: III, Inflorescences," Bull. Torr. Club 82: 419–445 (1955).

WOODSON, R. E., JR.: "Observations on the Inflorescence of *Apocynaceae*," Ann. Mo. Bot. Gard. 22: 1–48 (1935).

Floral diagrams

EICHLER, A. W.: *Blüthendiagramme,* 2 vols. (Leipzig, 1875–1878).

SCHAFFNER, J. H.: "A General System of Floral Diagrams," Ohio Jour. Sci. 16: 360–364 (1916).

Floral morphology

ARBER, AGNES: "The Interpretation of the Flower: A Study of Some Aspects of Morphological Thought," Biol. Rev. 12: 57–84 (1937).

BAILEY, I. W., & B. G. L. SWAMY: "The Conduplicate Carpel of Dicotyledons and Its Initial Trends of Specialization," Am. Jour. Bot. 38: 373–379 (1951).

BAILEY, I. W., & C. G. NAST: "The Comparative Morphology of the *Winteraceae:* II, Carpels," Jour. Arnold Arb. 24: 472–481 (1943).

BANCROFT, H.: "A Review of Researches Concerning Floral Morphology," Bot. Rev. 1: 77–99 (1935).

DOUGLAS, G. E.: "The Inferior Ovary," Bot. Rev. 10: 125–186 (1944).

EAMES, A. J.: "The Role of Flower Anatomy in the Determination of Angiosperm Phylogeny," Proc. Int. Congr. Plant Sci. 1926, 1: 423–427 (1929).

EAMES, A. J.: "The Vascular Anatomy of the Flower with a Refutation of the Theory of Carpel Polymorphism," Am. Jour. Bot. 18: 147–188 (1931).

GAUTHIER, ROGER: "The Nature of the Inferior Ovary in the Genus *Begonia,*" Contr. Inst. Bot. Univ. Montreal 66: 1–91 (1950).

GUNDERSON, A.: "Flower Structures of Dicotyledons," Torreya 28: 70–73 (1928).

HENSLOW, G.: *The Origin of Floral Structures Through Insect and Other Agencies* (New York, 1888).

HENSLOW, G.: "On the Vascular Systems of Floral Organs and Their Importance in the Interpretation of the Morphology of Flowers," Jour. Linn. Soc. 28: 151–197 (1891).

HUNT, K. W.: "A Study of the Style and Stigma, with Reference to the Nature of the Carpel," Am. Jour. Bot. 24: 288–295 (1937).

JACKSON, G.: "The Morphology of Flowers of *Rosa* and Certain Closely Related Genera," Am. Jour. Bot. 21: 453–466 (1934).

SAUNDERS, E. R.: *Floral Morphology,* I, II (Cambridge, England, 1937, 1939).

SCHAFFNER, J. H.: "The Fundamental Nature of the Flower," Bull. Torr. Club 64: 576–582 (1937).

THOMAS, H. H.: "The Nature and Origin of the Stigma," New Phytol. 33: 173–198 (1934).

VAN TIEGHEM, P.: "Recherches sur la structure du pistil," Ann. Sci. Nat. Ser. V, 12: 127–226 (1868).

VAN TIEGHEM, P.: *Recherches sur la structure du pistil et sur l'anatomie comparée de la fleur* (Paris, 1868).

WERNHAM, H. F.: "Floral Evolution: with Particular Reference to the Sympetalous Dicotyledons," New Phytol. 10: 293–305 (1911).

WILSON, C. L.: "The Phylogeny of the Stamen," Am. Jour. Bot. 24: 686–699 (1937).

WILSON, C. L.: "The Telome Theory and the Origin of the Stamen," Am. Jour. Bot. 29: 759–765 (1942).

WILSON, C. L., & THEODOR JUST: "The Morphology of the Flower," Bot. Rev. 5: 97–131 (1939).

WODEHOUSE, R. P.: "Pollen Grains in the Identification and Classification of Plants," Bull. Torr. Club 55: 181–198, 449–462 (1928), 56: 123–138 (1929), 57: 21–46 (1930), 63: 495–514 (1936); Am. Jour. Bot. 16: 297–312 (1929), 18: 749–764 (1931).

Fruits

CHUTE, HETTIE M.: "The Morphology and Anatomy of the Achene," Am. Jour. Bot. 17: 703–723 (1930).

EGLER, F. E.: "The Fructus and the Fruit," Chron. Bot. 7: 391–395 (1943).

MACDANIELS, L. H.: *The Morphology of the Apple and Other Pome Fruits*, Mem. Cornell Univ. Agr. Exp. Sta. 230 (1940).

MASTERS, M. T.: "Classification of Fruits," Nature 5: 6 (1871).

Ovules and seeds

JOHANSEN, D. A.: *Plant Embryology* (Waltham, Mass., 1950).

General

BROWN, R. W.: *Composition of Scientific Words* (Baltimore, Md., 1954).

FEATHERLY, H. I.: *Taxonomic Terminology of the Higher Plants* (Ames, Iowa, 1954).

GRAY, ASA: *Gray's Lessons in Botany*, revised edition (New York, 1887).

HOUGH, J. N.: *Scientific Terminology* (New York, 1953).

JACKSON, B. D.: *A Glossary of Botanic Terms, with Their Derivation and Accent*, 4th edition (London, 1949).

LAWRENCE, G. H. M.: *Taxonomy of Vascular Plants* (New York, 1951).

CHAPTER 9

Angiosperms

The angiosperms, or *Angiospermae,* which are generally known as the flowering plants, constitute that subdivision of the seed plants (*Spermatophyta, Phanaerogamae,* or *Embryophyta Siphonogama*) whose members characteristically have stems with xylem tissue composed in part of vessels and bear their seeds within one or more closed carpels.

The angiosperms are usually called "flowering plants" because they produce what are commonly thought of as true flowers (some of which, however, are much reduced). But the gymnosperms (*Gymnospermae*), also, often produce flower-like structures, such as the male and female cones, or "flowers," of pines. Without a more precise definition of the term "flower," therefore, this feature is not entirely distinctive and reliable.

Phylogeny

Fossil evidence indicates that the angiosperms originated in the Mesozoic era, probably in the Jurassic period, of geologic time, roughly 165 million years ago and perhaps even earlier than that. But the fossil record is so incomplete that to date it has not been possible to ascertain much concerning the origin and true relationships, or phylogeny, of this vast assemblage of plants that now dominates the vegetation of the earth, including perhaps a quarter of a million species and about three hundred families.

Among the earliest fossil angiosperms we find members of the *Ranales,* or Buttercup Order, such as relatives of the modern *Lirioden-*

125

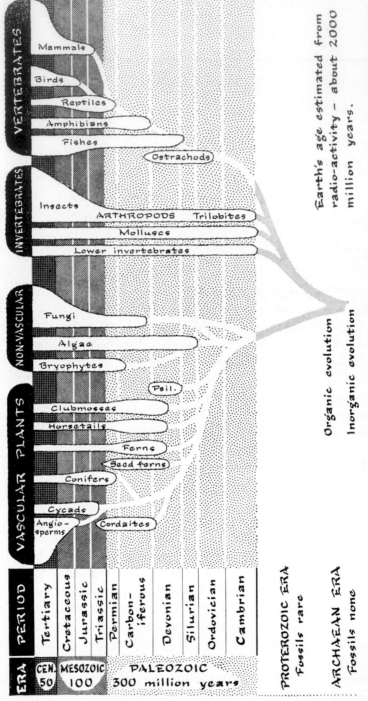

107 Diagram illustrating the dominance of plant and animal groups in the geologic periods and their relationships. [Modified from Alfred Gunderson in Brooklyn Botanic Garden Leaflets, Ser. 18, No. 4 (1930); used by permission.]

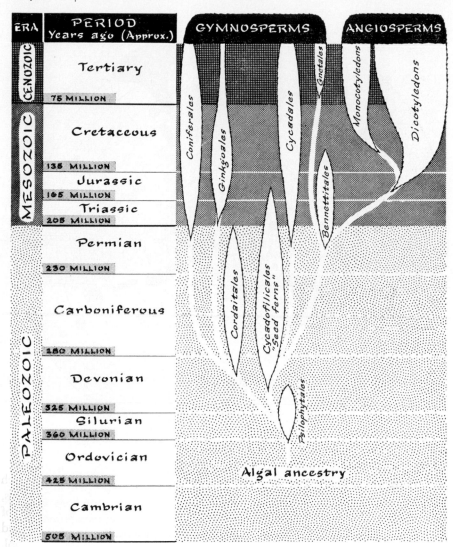

108 More detailed chart of possible relationships and evolutionary history of the seed plants.

dron and *Magnolia*, as well as members of the *Amentiferae*, or catkin-bearers, like our modern willows. This has led to the supposition by some workers that the *Ranales* should be considered as the basal group in the evolution of the angiosperms, and by others that the *Amentiferae* should be considered as among the most primitive angiosperms. Nor are we able to do more than make an educated guess as to the ancestral group that produced the angiosperms: whether it was the extinct group

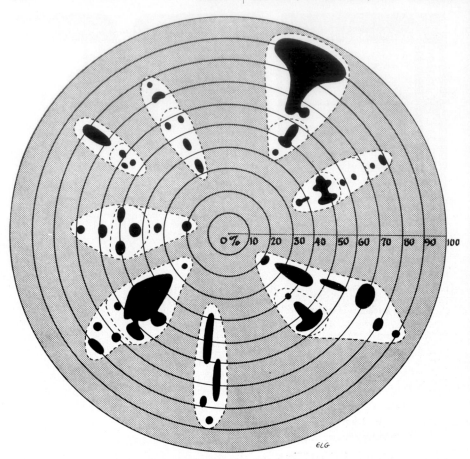

109 Scheme for showing phylogenetic relationships within a group such as the flowering plants. The black areas represent hypothetical families, and the broken lines enclosing groups of families represent areas of affinity. The concentric circles represent degrees of advancement based on a percentage. This is the sort of scheme proposed by Sporne [Biol. Rev. 31: 1–29 (1956)].

of ancient seed ferns, some group of the cycads, or even some group of as yet undiscovered fossil gymnosperms. All we know is that suddenly, in Upper Cretaceous time, there appeared a great outburst of angiosperms and that these were already so far advanced in evolution as to be generally assignable to living genera. Figures 107 and 108 illustrate some possible relationships and details of the fossil records of various groups: the first a generalized picture of plant and animal groups, the second a more detailed chart of inferred relationships among modern and fossil seed plants.

The ultimate goal of taxonomists is to achieve a phylogenetic classification of living plants. To reach this goal, we must understand the past history of each group and must know which characters of the group are primitive and which are advanced. Because so little is known of the past history of angiosperms, we must rely on an assessment of primitive and advanced characters if we are to produce a reasonably objective and phylogenetic classification. Though this part of the problem is not easily solved, there are certain means of drawing conclusions. As pointed out by Sporne (1956) and others, certain characters, including anatomical ones, are undoubtedly primitive, as indicated by the fossil record and as determined by other means. These primitive characters, furthermore, seem to be statistically correlated with certain other characters, which therefore seem also to be primitive. It follows, then, that the absence of such primitive characters indicates an advanced condition, and that by analyzing the degree of advancement we may place various groups in a phylogenetic arrangement, each group being located by a calculated advancement index. The resulting phylogenetic scheme, as suggested by Sporne, would resemble a target with concentric rings representing degrees of advancement from center to periphery. Groups, such as families or orders, could then be pictured as variously shaped areas on the target, their radial extent indicating the range of advancement within the group, and the shape of the area indicating the distribution of the included plants (genera or species) according to their advancement. Such a scheme is shown in Figure 109, which is a hypothetical representation of this sort.

It has long been customary to represent phylogenetic classifications by a "family tree" diagram, modern groups being assigned places on the trunk and branches of the tree, as was done by Bessey (Fig. 2). But in reality we are dealing with living groups that are represented by only the twig ends of such a tree, and it is pure speculation to fill in the trunk and branches without a full knowledge of the past history. Speculation of this sort, nevertheless, is not entirely fruitless, and it does help to suggest possible ancestral relationships. Furthermore, while lacking positive proof in all cases, and while admitting that single characters may be criteria of advancement or primitiveness in one group and not in another, taxonomists generally agree that certain criteria can be used in a phylogenetic classification. Some of these are listed below.

Criteria Used in Classification

1. *The presence or absence of petals, and, when present, whether separate or united.* This gives the primary subdivisions of dicotyledons: *apetalae*, without petals; *polypetalae*, with separate petals; and *sympetalae*, with united petals. These groups, though somewhat artificial, are extremely useful. Separate petals seem to have come first, historically, and from this condition the derived conditions of apetaly and sympetaly have been evolved.

2. *The hypogynous, perigynous, or epigynous nature of the flower.* The sequence here seems to have been from hypogynous through perigynous to epigynous types. But we occasionally find epigyny in otherwise hypogynous groups, as in the Huckleberries in the otherwise hypogynous family *Ericaceae*. And perigyny seems to be totally lacking in the sympetalous groups.

3. *The number of parts.* It is believed that primitive flowers, in general, had indefinite numbers of parts, the stamens and carpels often being numerous. The general tendency of evolution has been toward fewer parts.

4. *The union of parts.* Separate parts are generally regarded as ancestral to united parts: separate petals preceded united petals, and separate carpels preceded united carpels. The condition in which the carpels are separate is *apocarpous;* the condition of united carpels is *syncarpous.* The apocarpous condition can occur only in hypogynous or perigynous flowers, all epigynous flowers being syncarpous or else having only a single carpel.

5. *The nature of the perianth.* In the monocotyledons, particularly, the nature of the perianth distinguishes groups of orders. The calyx may be green and the perianth biseriate; these two parts may be similar and all petaloid; or the perianth may be variously reduced to bristles, scales, or hairs.

6. *The nature of the fruit.* To some extent, the nature of the fruit is determined by the nature of the gynoecium. In some families, such as the *Poaceae* (Grass Family), *Brassicaceae* (Mustard Family), and *Fabaceae* (Pea Family), the fruit type is unique and immediately distinguishes the family from all others. On the other hand, partly because of our present unsatisfactory nomenclature for fruits, the nature of the fruit may be a confusing feature to the beginner. For example, we have not distinguished between the akene of the Buckwheat Family (*Polygonaceae*), which comes from a hypogynous

flower, and the fruit of the Sunflower Family (*Asteraceae*), which comes from an epigynous flower.

7. *The type of placentation.* This may be determined by inspection of either the ovary or the fruit, and it often indicates affinities. The free-central and basal placentation types, in particular, have been used to associate whole groups of families.

8. *The morphology of the seed.* Here are included such characteristics as the presence or absence of endosperm (referred to as albumen in older treatments) and the nature of the embryo. The number of cotyledons, of course, is a major means of distinguishing large groups.

9. *Anatomical characters.* One of the most dependable characters used to distinguish monocotyledons from dicotyledons is the gross anatomy of the stem. But occasionally we find peculiarities of stem anatomy that are distinctive of lesser groups, such as the occurrence of bicollateral bundles in the Pumpkin Family (*Cucurbitaceae*) and in the Gentian Order (*Gentianales*). Also included here are such peculiarities as the occurrence of specialized secretory tissue, such as that found in families having milky juice, and the presence of exceptionally long and strong phloem fibers. A fairly long list of correlated characters of vascular tissue is given by Sporne (1956), these being associated with evolutionary stages in the dicotyledons. The vascularization of flower parts, of stem nodes, and of integuments of seeds has also yielded clues to affinities.

10. *Vegetative characters.* These have to do with roots, stems, and leaves, and are sometimes highly useful as indicative of relationships. The woody or herbaceous habit, the presence or absence of stipules, the general morphology of leaves, and the peculiarities of pubescence are included here. Certain groups are well adapted to dry habitats by the succulent nature of the plants. In a few families there are plants with milky juice. All such vegetative characters aid in recognition as well as in classification.

11. *Serum diagnosis.* A technique of determining relationships by the reaction to serum of members of various families has been developed by Karl Mez (see Chester in the references). Adapting the methods of bacteriologists, he based his system on the similarity of the proteins produced by the plants. This was determined by the degree of precipitation produced when the protein extracts were mixed with a serum from an animal. By 1926 enough data had been assembled to enable Mez to draw up a family tree that showed many

similarities to similar schemes proposed by workers who used morphological characters. It seems, however, that a phylogenetic scheme based on serum diagnosis alone is not likely to be any closer to the truth than any other scheme based on a single morphological character. The same proteins are apparently found in very distantly related families.

Classification of Angiosperms

Since John Ray, near the end of the seventeenth century, first established a system of classification that delimited monocotyledons and d'cotyledons, there has been little disagreement with this division into two classes, the *Monocotyledoneae* (one cotyledon) and the *Dicotyledoneae* (two cotyledons). These two groups are distinguished from each other not only by the number of cotyledons, however, but also by combinations of other characters as well, as noted in the following tabular comparison. Exceptions may occur for nearly all the characters enumerated, but the exceptions are few, and they almost never

COMPARISON OF MONOCOTYLEDONS AND DICOTYLEDONS

Monocotyledons	*Dicotyledons*
EMBRYO: with 1 cotyledon, which usually develops underground; endosperm often present in the seed.	EMBRYO: with 2 cotyledons, which often develop above the ground; endosperm present or lacking in the seed.
ROOTS: the primary root of short duration, soon replaced by adventitious roots, which form a fibrous root system or sometimes a fascicle of fleshy roots, but usually without a taproot.	ROOTS: the primary root often persistent and becoming a strong taproot, with smaller secondary roots.
GROWTH FORM: mostly herbaceous, from bulbs, corms, or rhizomes; a few are arborescent, such as Bamboos, Palms, Yuccas, and Dracaenas.	GROWTH FORM: either herbaceous or woody.
VASCULAR SYSTEM: consisting of numerous scattered bundles, without definite arrangement and in a ground parenchyma; no cambium except in a few such as *Dracaena;* no differentiation into cortical and stelar regions in stems.	VASCULAR SYSTEM: usually consisting of a definite number of primary bundles in a ring, with a cambium, and secondary growth in diameter of the stem; differentiation into cortical and stelar regions in stems.
LEAVES: usually parallel-veined, often sheathing at the base, commonly oblong or linear in shape; petiole seldom developed.	LEAVES: usually net-veined (pinnate or palmate), seldom sheathing at the base, usually broader in shape; petiole commonly developed.
FLOWERS: with their parts usually in threes or multiples of three (3-merous).	FLOWERS: with their parts usually in fours or fives (4- or 5-merous).

involve more than a single character in any one plant. The most useful differences are those associated with stem structure, leaf venation, and number of parts in the flower.

CLASSIFICATION OF MONOCOTYLEDONS.   One of the most recent and detailed treatments of this large assemblage of plants is that of Hutchinson, a British botanist: *The Families of Flowering Plants:* II, *Monocotyledons* (London, 1934). In this volume that author has divided all monocotyledons into three groups (which he calls divisions) based on the nature of the perianth. Though not yet recognized by all American taxonomists, these groups seem to form a natural basis for a primary breakdown and apparently consist of families and orders that are rather closely related. Hutchinson's grouping is given below and is followed, with minor modifications, in this text. We shall call his primary groups subclasses of the class *Monocotyledoneae.*

Subclass 1: Calyciferae.   This group includes the most ancient monocotyledons, those believed to have been derived from an early pair of groups in the *Ranales,* one in which the flowers produced small, one-seeded fruits (akenes), and another in which the flowers produced

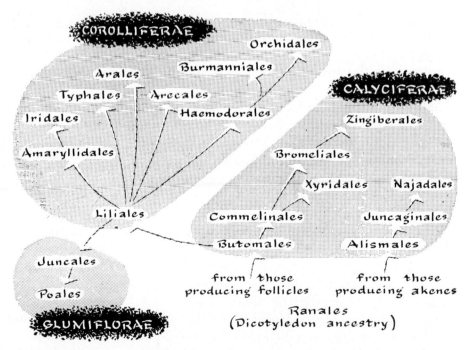

110 Chart to show possible relationships among the chief orders of monocotyledons.

fewer, larger, several-seeded fruits (follicles) with a tendency to split open at maturity. Since these two conditions still exist in the *Ranales*, the earliest monocotyledons evidently came from two sources in that dicotyledonous order, as shown on the chart of the relationships found among the chief orders of monocotyledons (Figure 110).

The *Calyciferae* have a biseriate perianth, the sepals usually being green, and the corolla, when present, is usually colored or white. There is no adnation of the sepals and petals into a common perianth tube, as there sometimes is in the second group below. The plants are usually rhizomatous or annual, and bulbs or corms are never produced. Some of the families are aquatic.

Subclass 2: Corolliferae.   This group is believed to have been de-rived from the *Calyciferae*, and it includes as its basal order the *Liliales*. Here the perianth is uniseriate and often petaloid throughout, but in derived families it may be reduced to hairs or bristles. There is a tendency for the calyx and the corolla to unite into a perianth tube. The plants are predominantly terrestrial, and bulbs and corms are fairly common. One notable exception in regard to the perianth char-acter occurs in the genus *Trillium* (family *Liliaceae*), which has green sepals.

Subclass 3: Glumiflorae.   Here there is a tendency for the perianth to be chaffy or to be reduced to scales or lodicules, and there is a further tendency among the more reduced families (*Cyperaceae* and *Poaceae*) for the flowers to be aggregated into spikelets. The plants of this group, having a general grass-like aspect, are often referred to as "the grasses and grass-like plants." Fibrous roots and rhizomes are common; only a very few plants produce poorly developed bulbs.

Figure 110 illustrates the possible relationships among these three major groups and among the orders within each.

CLASSIFICATION OF DICOTYLEDONS.   In order to arrive at a satisfactory classification of dicotyledons, we must first come to some agreement about the basal or most primitive group and then try to derive other groups from it. As we have noted, there has been much speculation about the way in which the dicotyledons have evolved and about the group or groups within them that should be regarded as primitive and consequently ancestral to the others.

One of the theories, followed by Endlicher, Eichler, Wettstein, and Engler, suggests that the dicotyledons were derived from gnetalian, or conifer-like, ancestors among the gymnosperms. The primitive dicotyle-dons, then, would be woody, without petals, with unisexual, wind-pol-

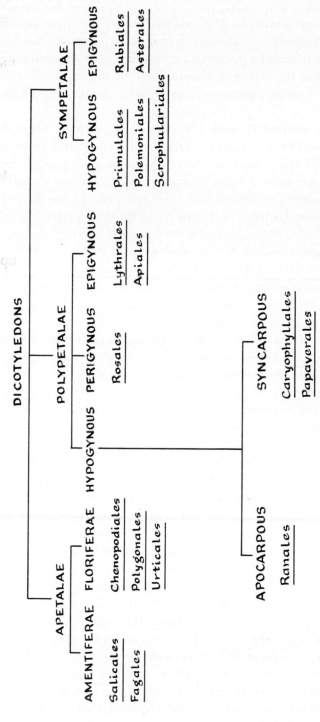

111 Generalized scheme of classification of the dicotyledons, showing some of the characteristic orders represented. The *Ranales*, the most primitive order, or their precursors gave rise to other orders either by reduction or by specialization in various other ways, the *Apetalae* being considered as reduced members, and the *Sympetalae* as members that became specialized by the development of united petals, which is believed to have aided in pollination by insects.

linated flowers having few parts, and those grouped in a cone-like inflorescence such as a catkin. The catkin-bearers, or *Amentiferae,* accordingly, were regarded as primitive and were supposed to have given rise to groups that had a perianth and often had insect-pollinated flowers. This view has the corroboration of some of the fossil evidence, for we find catkin-bearing plants such as willows among the earliest angiosperm fossils.

Another theory, supported and elaborated in various ways by Bentham and Hooker, Bessey, Hallier, Arber and Parkin, and Hutchinson, might be called the "ranalian theory" because it suggested that the dicotyledons were derived from gymnospermous ancestors such as the cycads of the order *Bennettitales,* which gave rise to the *Ranales,* or Magnolia-Buttercup Order. The primitive dicotyledon, then, would have perfect flowers with numerous separate parts spirally arranged on an elongated axis, as in *Magnolia,* and simpler flowers, without a perianth, would be derived by reduction. The fossil evidence also lends support to this view, for relatives of the modern *Magnolia* are also among the earliest dicotyledons known. This is the theory most generally accepted at the present time.

Authorities also differ about the subsequent evolution of the dicotyledons. One useful scheme divides them into three major groups: the *Polypetalae* (those with separate petals), including the *Ranales;* the *Apetalae* (those without petals), which have been derived from various sources in the *Polypetalae* by reduction and consequently are not a natural group; and the *Sympetalae* (those with united petals, also called the *Metachlamydeae*), which have also been derived from the *Polypetalae.* The *Apetalae* are subdivided into the *Amentiferae* (those with catkins) and the *Floriferae* (those without catkins). The *Polypetalae* are subdivided into hypogynous, perigynous, and epigynous groups; and the *Sympetalae* are subdivided into hypogynous and epigynous groups, perigyny being lacking in the *Sympetalae.*

This arrangement, with representative orders of each group, is shown in Figure 111. By utilizing the simple characters on which this chart is based, the student will be able to place any unknown plant known to be a dicotyledon among its near relatives. Most manuals and floras follow the sequence given, from *Apetalae* through *Polypetalae* to *Sympetalae,* and also for the secondary groups within those groups. Monocotyledons precede dicotyledons in most manuals.

Another attempt to show the possible relationships among the dicotyledonous orders is presented in Figure 112. This is based on Bessey's system and retains his ideas about the evolution of a basically hypogynous line, shown on the right, and of a perigynous-epigynous line, shown on the left. The apetalous orders are doubtfully assigned places within this scheme. The orders in the shaded section are sympetalous, and according to this scheme parallel evolution produced

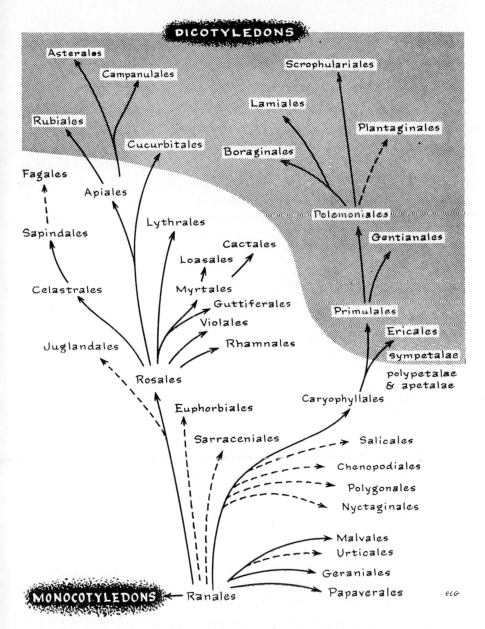

112 Chart showing possible relationships among dicotyledonous orders.

separate hypogynous sympetalous groups and epigynous sympetalous groups. We cannot be sure, however, that this actually took place. The broken lines connecting various orders indicate considerable doubt about the relationships.

REFERENCES

ANDREWS, H. N., JR.: *Ancient Plants and the World They Lived In,* 279 pp. (Ithaca, N. Y., 1947).

ARNOLD, C. A.: *An Introduction to Paleobotany,* 433 pp. (New York, 1947).

AXELROD, DANIEL I.: "A Theory of Angiosperm Evolution," Evolution 6: 29–60 (1952).

BAILEY, I. W.: "Origin of the Angiosperms: Need for a Broadened Outlook," Jour. Arnold Arb. 30: 64–70 (1949).

BAILEY, I. W.: "The Potentialities and Limitations of Wood Anatomy in the Study of Phylogeny and Classification of Angiosperms," Jour. Arnold Arb. 38: 243–254 (1957).

BERTRAND, P., & P. CORSIN: "Phylogénie des végétaux vasculaires," Bull. Soc. Bot. Fr. 85: 331–348 (1938).

BERTRAND, P., & P. CORSIN: "Phylogénie des végétaux vasculaires: Observations complémentaires," Bull. Soc. Bot. Fr. 85: 503–504 (1938).

BESSEY, C. E.: "The Point of Divergence of Monocotyledons and Dicotyledons," Bot. Gaz. 22: 229–232 (1895).

BESSEY, C. E.: "Phylogeny and Taxonomy of the Angiosperms," Bot. Gaz. 24: 145–178 (1897).

BESSEY, C. E.: "The Phylogenetic Taxonomy of Flowering Plants," Ann. Mo. Bot Gard. 2: 109–164 (1915).

BOWER, F. O.: *Primitive Land Plants* (Cambridge, England, 1935).

BROWNE, I. M. P.: "Some Views on the Morphology and Phylogeny of the Leafy Vascular Sporophyte," Bot. Rev. 1: 383–404 (1935).

CAMPBELL, D. H.: "The Phylogeny of the Angiosperms," Bull. Torr. Club 55: 479–497 (1929).

CAMPBELL, D. H.: "The Phylogeny of Monocotyledons," Ann. Bot. 44: 311–331 (1930).

CAMPBELL, D. H.: *The Evolution of the Land Plants* (Embryophyta), 731 pp. (Stanford University, California, 1940).

CHALK, L.: "The Phylogenetic Value of Certain Anatomic Features of Dicotyledonous Plants," Ann. Bot. n.s. 1: 429–437 (1937).

CHAMBERLAIN, C. J.: "An Evaluation of the Structural Evidence for Genetical Relationships in Plants: Some Evidence for Vascular Plants," Proc. Int. Congr. Pl. Sci. 1926, 1: 473–480 (1929).

CHEADLE, V. I.: "The Role of Anatomy in Phylogenetic Studies of the Monocotyledoneae," Chron. Bot. 7: 253–254 (1942).

CHESTER, K. S.: "A Critique of Plant Serology: A Review in English of the Serodiagnostic Work of Karl Mez," Quart. Rev. Biol. 12: 19–46, 165–190, 294–321 (1937).

COPELAND, H. F.: "The Phylogeny of the Angiosperms," Madroño 5: 209–218 (1940).

DARRAH, W. C.: *Principles of Paleobotany,* 239 pp. (Leyden, 1939).

DAVY, J. B.: "On the Primary Groups of Dicotyledons," Ann. Bot. n.s. 1: 429–437 (1937).

DEBEER, C. R.: *Embryology and Evolution,* 116 pp. (Oxford, 1936).

EAMES, A. J.: "On the Origin of the Herbaceous Type in the Angiosperms," Ann. Bot. 25: 215–224 (1911).

EAMES, A. J.: "The Role of Flower Anatomy in the Determination of Angiosperm Phylogeny," Proc. Int. Congr. Pl. Sci. 1926 (Ithaca, N. Y.) 1: 423–427 (1929).

FAEGRI, K.: "Some Fundamental Problems of Taxonomy and Phylogenetics," Bot. Rev. 3: 400–423 (1937).

FOSTER, A. S.: "Leaf Differentiation in the Angiosperms," Bot. Rev. 2: 349–372 (1936).

FOSTER, A. S.: "Foliar Venation in Angiosperms from an Ontogenetic Standpoint," Am. Jour. Bot. 39: 752–766 (1952).

FRENGUELLI, J.: "El origen de las angiospermas," Bol. Soc. Argent. Bot. 1: 169–208 (1946).

GIBBS, R. D.: "Comparative Chemistry and Phylogeny of Flowering Plants," Trans. Roy. Soc. Canada III, 48: 1–47 (1954).

GILBERT, S. G.: "Evolutionary Significance of Ring Porosity in Woody Angiosperms," Bot. Gaz. 102: 105–120 (1940).

GILMOUR, J. S. L., & W. B. TURRILL: "The Aim and Scope of Taxonomy," Chron. Bot. 6: 217–219 (1941).

GUNDERSON, A.: "Flower Buds and Phylogeny of Dicotyledons," Bull. Torr. Club 66: 287–295 (1939).

GUNDERSON, A.: "The Classification of Dicotyledons," Torreya 39: 108–110 (1939).

GUNDERSON, A.: "Flower Structure and the Classification of Dicotyledons," Brooklyn Bot. Gard. Rec. 30: 93–98 (1941).

GUNDERSON, A.: "Flower Forms and Groups of Dicotyledons," Bull. Torr. Club 70: 510–516 (1943).

HALLIER, H.: "Provisional Scheme of the Natural (Phylogenetic) System of Flowering Plants," New Phytol. 4: 151–162 (1905).

HARRIS, T. M.: "The Ancestry of the Angiosperms," Proc. Sixth Int. Congr. Amsterdam 2: 230–231 (1935).

HILL, A. W.: "The Morphology and Seedling Structure of Geophilous Species of *Peperomia*, Together with Some Views on the Origin of Monocotyledons," Ann. Bot. 20: 395–427 (1906).

HOEG, O. A.: "The Devonian Floras and Their Bearing upon the Origin of Vascular Plants," Bot. Rev. 3: 563–592 (1937).

HUTCHINSON, J.: "Contributions Toward a Phylogenetic Classification of Flowering Plants," Kew Bull. 1923: 65–89, 241–261; 1924: 49–66, 114–134.

HUTCHINSON, J.: "The Phylogeny of Flowering Plants," Proc. Int. Congr. Pl. Sci. 1926, 1: 413–421 (1929).

JOHNSON, J., & I. A. HOGGAN: "The Challenge of Plant Virus Differentiation and Classification," Science n.s. 73: 29–32 (1931).

JUST, T.: "Gymnosperms and the Origin of Angiosperms," Bot. Gaz. 110: 91–103 (1948).

KUNKEL, L. C.: "Possibilities in Plant Virus Classification," Bot. Rev. 1: 1–17 (1935).

LEWIS, D.: "The Evolution of Sex in Flowering Plants," Biol. Rev. 17: 46–67 (1942).

LOTSY, P.: "Phylogeny of Plants," Bot. Gaz. 49: 460–461 (1910).

MAHESHWARI, P.: *An Introduction to the Embryology of Angiosperms*, 453 pp. (New York, 1950).

MARTIN, A. C.: "The Comparative Internal Morphology of Seeds," Am. Midl. Nat. 36: 513–660 (1946).

MATTHEWS, J. R.: "Floral Morphology and Its Bearing on the Classification of Angiosperms," Trans. Bot. Soc. Edinb. 23: 60–82 (1941).

MCNAIR, J. B.: "The Evolutionary Status of Plant Families in Relation to Some Chemical Properties," Am. Jour. Bot. 21: 427–452 (1934).

MCNAIR, J. B.: "Angiosperm Phylogeny on a Chemical Basis," Bull. Torr. Club 62: 515–532 (1935).

METCALFE, C. R.: "The Systematic Anatomy of the Vegetative Organs of the Angiosperms," Biol. Rev. 21: 159–172 (1946).

PENNELL, F. W.: "The Taxonomic Significance of an Understanding of Floral Evolution," Brittonia 6: 301–308 (1948).

POPE, M. A.: "Pollen Morphology as an Index to Plant Relationship," Bot. Gaz. 80: 63–73 (1925).

PULLE, A.: "The Classification of the Spermatophytes," Chron. Bot. 4: 109–113 (1938).

REICHERT, E. T.: *A Biochemic Basis for the Study of Problems of Taxonomy, Heredity, Evolution, etc. with Special Reference to the Starches* (Washington, D. C., 1919).

RUSBY, H. H.: "The Value and Limitations of Histology in Vegetable Taxonomy," Proc. Int. Congr. Pl. Sci. 1926, 2: 1356–1360 (1929).

SARGANT, E.: "The Reconstruction of a Race of Primitive Angiosperms," Ann. Bot. 22: 121–186 (1908).

SCHAFFNER, J. H.: "The Importance of Phylogenetic Taxonomy in Systematic Botany," Ecology 19: 296–300 (1938).

SCHUBERT, C.: "The Evolution of Primitive Plants from the Geologist's Point of View," New Phytol. 19: 272–275 (1921).

SINNOTT, E. W.: "Investigations on the Phylogeny of the Angiosperms," Am. Jour. Bot. 1: 303–322 (1914).

SINNOTT, E. W., & I. W. BAILEY: "Investigations on the Phylogeny of the Angiosperms," Am. Jour. Bot. 1: 441–453 (1914); Ann. Bot. 28: 547–600 (1914); Am. Jour. Bot. 2: 1–22 (1915).

SPORNE, K. R.: "A New Approach to the Problem of the Primitive Flower," New Phytol. 48: 259–276 (1949).

SPORNE, K. R.: "The Phylogenetic Classification of the Angiosperms," Biol. Rev. 31: 1–29 (1956).

SPRAGUE, T. A.: "Taxonomic Botany, with Special Reference to the Angiosperms" in J. Huxley, *The New Systematics*, pp. 435–454 (London, 1940).

STEBBINS, G. L.: "Cytological Characteristics Associated with the Different Growth Habits in the Dicotyledons," Am. Jour. Bot. 25: 189–197 (1938).

TAKHTAJAN, A. L.: "Phylogenetic Principles of the System of Higher Plants," Bot. Rev. 19: 1–45 (1953).

THOMAS, H. H.: "The Early Evolution of the Angiosperms," Ann. Bot. 45: 647–672 (1931).

THOMAS, H. H.: "Paleobotany and the Origin of the Angiosperms," Bot. Rev. 2: 397–418 (1936).

TIPPO, O.: "A Modern Classification of the Plant Kingdom," Chron. Bot. 7: 203–206 (1942).

TURRILL, W. B.: "Taxonomy and Phylogeny," Bot. Rev. 8: 247–270, 473–532, 655–707 (1942).

TURRILL, W. B.: "Modern Trends in the Classification of Plants," Taxon 1: 17–19 (1951).

VESTAL, P. A.: "Wood Anatomy as an Aid to Classification and Phylogeny," Chron. Bot. 6: 53–54 (1940).

WEEVERS, T.: "The Relation Between Taxonomy and Chemistry of Plants," Blumea 5: 412–422 (1943).

WERNHAM, H. F.: "Floral Evolution," New Phytol. 10: 78–83, 109–120, 145–159, 217–226, 293–307 (1911).

WIELAND, G. R.: "Antiquity of the Angiosperms," Proc. Int. Congr. Pl. Sci. 1926, 1: 429–456 (1929).

WIELAND, G. R.: "Views of Higher Seed Plant Descent since 1879," Science n.s. 70: 223–228 (1929).

WIELAND, G. R.: "Why the Angiosperms Are Old," Science n.s. 74: 219–221 (1931).

WILSON, C. L.: "The Phylogeny of the Stamen," Am. Jour. Bot. 24: 686–699 (1937).

WODEHOUSE, R. P.: "Evolution of Pollen Grains," Bot. Rev. 2: 67–84 (1936).

YAMPOLSKY, C.: "Origin of Sex in the Phanaerogamic Flora," Genetica 7: 521–532 (1925).

Part II

SELECTED ORDERS AND FAMILIES OF MONOCOTYLEDONS

The Calyciferae

Key to the Principal Families

Fruit 1-seeded, or sometimes 2-seeded

  Plants scapose, the leaves basal

    Leaves broad; inflorescence a bracteate panicle or open raceme; inner perianth segments petaloid .... ALISMATACEAE

    Leaves linear, grass-like; inflorescence a narrow, spike-like, ebracteate raceme; inner perianth segments sepaloid .... JUNCAGINACEAE

    Plants with leafy stems .... NAJADACEAE

Fruit 3–many-seeded

  Gynoecium of separate carpels .... BUTOMACEAE

  Gynoecium of united carpels

    Submerged aquatics with small epigynous flowers and whorled leaves .... HYDROCHARITACEAE

    Plants not submerged aquatics; flowers hypogynous or epigynous; leaves not whorled

      Plants mostly epiphytic or xerophytic, with densely clustered linear and often spiny-toothed leaves; flowers in terminal, spike-like inflorescences (or in *Tillandsia* the leaves entire and well spaced) .... BROMELIACEAE

      Plants terrestrial, seldom xerophytic, their leaves not spiny-toothed

        Flowers hypogynous

          Plants with leafy stems; flowers in cymes .... COMMELINACEAE

          Plants scapose; flowers in heads ... XYRIDACEAE

        Flowers epigynous

          Plants not aromatic; fertile stamens 5–6

Leaves and bracts spirally arranged; fruit fleshy .... MUSACEAE

Leaves and bracts 2-ranked; fruit capsular .... STRELITZIACEAE

Plants aromatic; fertile stamen 1 .. ZINGIBERACEAE

ORDER ALISMATALES

ALISMATACEAE: Water-plantain Family

Scapose marsh or aquatic herbs with large paniculate or racemose and bracteate inflorescences. Flowers perfect or unisexual, hypogynous, regular, 3-merous, the calyx of 3 green sepals, the corolla of 3 white or sometimes lavender petals, which fall early. Stamens 6 or more. Carpels (pistils) usually numerous, forming a head or whorl of akenes in fruit.

The family includes about 13 genera and 50 species, widely distributed in temperate and tropical regions.

EXAMPLES: *Alisma:* Water-plantain.
                    Sagittaria: Arrowhead.
                    Echinodorus: Burhead.

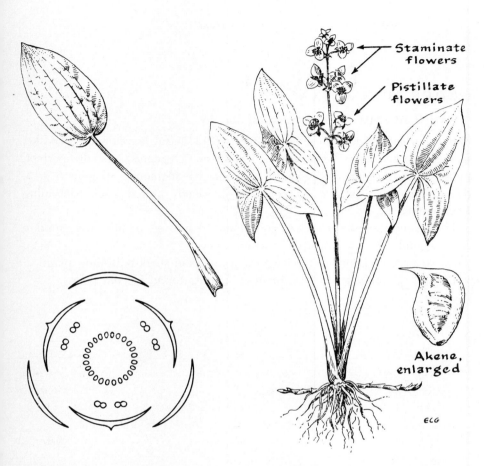

113 Floral diagram and leaf of *Alisma*.

114 Plant of *Sagittaria latifolia*.

ORDER JUNCAGINALES

JUNCAGINACEAE: Arrowgrass Family

Marsh herbs from rhizomes, with long, narrow, basal leaves and spike-like, scapose, ebracteate inflorescences. Flowers small, greenish, usually perfect, hypogynous, regular, the perianth of 6 concave segments. Stamens 6 or 3, the anthers nearly sessile. Carpels 6 or 3, weakly united, each containing 1 or 2 ovules.

The family includes 4 genera and about 10 species, mainly in temperate regions, and often in brackish or saline areas.

EXAMPLES: *Triglochin:* Arrowgrass, a common stock-poisoning plant.

Scheuchzeria: a plant commonly found in cold bogs.

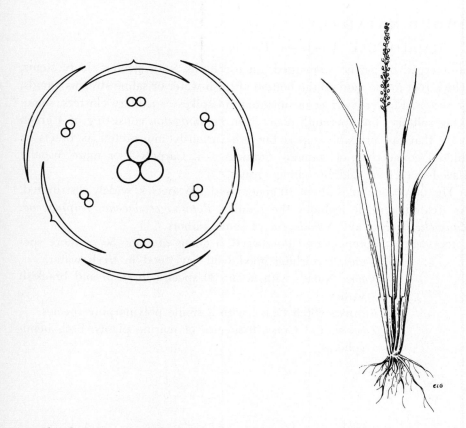

115 Floral diagram of *Triglochin palustris*.

116 Plant of *Triglochin palustris*.

ORDER NAJADALES

NAJADACEAE: Pondweed Family

Submerged or partly submerged aquatic herbs, with slender, leafy stems, which root in the mud on the bottom of fresh-water or saline streams, ponds, or shores. Flowers perfect or unisexual, in spikes or axillary clusters, sometimes solitary. True perianth none, or in *Potamogeton* consisting of 4 green parts that are probably sepals but are variously interpreted as bracts or dilated connectives of stamens. Stamens 1–4. Carpels 1 or more, usually 1-seeded in fruit and becoming akenes.

The family includes about 10 genera and 105 species, widely distributed. As treated here, it includes the families *Potamogetonaceae*, *Ruppiaceae*, *Zannichelliaceae*, and *Najadaceae* of some authors.

EXAMPLES: *Potamogeton:* Pondweed, a genus of some 50 or more species, furnishing good wild-fowl food in fresh water.

Najas: Naiad, with about 30 species in fresh and brackish water.

Ruppia: Ditch Grass, with a single polymorphic species.

Zostera: Eel Grass, 6 species of marine plants, both hemispheres.

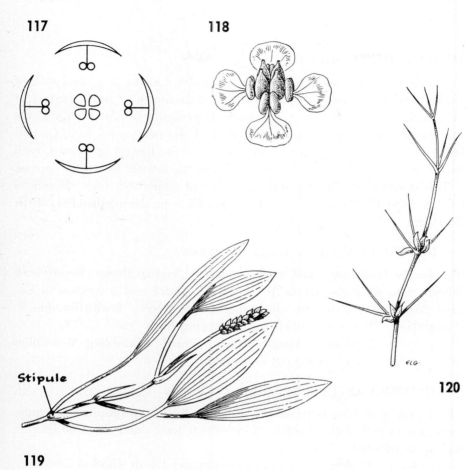

117 Floral diagram of *Potamogeton*.

118 Flower of *Potamogeton*, enlarged.

119 Portion of plant of *Potamogeton nodosus*.

120 Portion of plant of *Zannichellia*.

ORDER BUTOMALES

Perennial aquatic herbs of fresh or salt water. Leaves in a basal tuft, or cauline and then alternate or whorled. Flowers showy or small, perfect or unisexual, hypogynous or epigynous, the perianth mostly biseriate, the outer segments green and the inner petaloid. Stamens many to 3. Carpels free and the flowers hypogynous, or united and the flowers epigynous, each carpel many-ovuled, the ovules scattered over the interior face of the carpel.

This is one of the most primitive groups of monocotyledons, showing a relationship with the dicotyledons through follicle-producing members of the *Ranales.*

BUTOMACEAE: Flowering Rush Family

The family is distinguished in the order by having showy, hypogynous flowers with separate carpels. It includes 4 genera and 6 species, in Europe, Asia, and America, mainly temperate and tropical in distribution.

EXAMPLES: *Butomus umbellatus:* Flowering Rush.

Hydrocleis nymphoides: of Brazil, resembling Waterlilies and sometimes cultivated.

HYDROCHARITACEAE: Frog's Bit Family

The family is distinguished in the order by having inconspicuous, epigynous flowers with united carpels. It includes 6 genera and about 60 species, widely distributed.

EXAMPLES: *Elodea:* a common freshwater weed with whorled leaves.

Vallisneria: Tape Grass, a widely distributed dioecious freshwater plant with ribbon-like leaves.

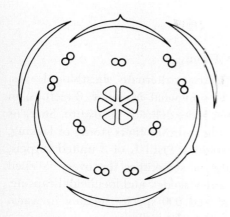

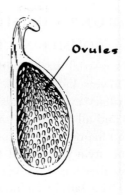

121 Floral diagram of *Butomus*.

122 Longitudinal section of a carpel of *Butomus*.

123 Flower and leaf of *Hydrocleis*.

ORDER COMMELINALES

COMMELINACEAE: Spiderwort Family

Terrestrial herbs with jointed stems bearing alternate sheathing leaves. Flowers hypogynous, perfect, regular to somewhat irregular, 3-merous, in axillary cymes. Sepals green. Petals often blue, delicate in texture. Stamens 6 and all fertile, or sometimes 3 or 2 fertile and the others sterile or lacking, the filaments often hairy and brightly colored. Pistil 1, of 3 united carpels, the style single and the stigma capitate, or sometimes the ovary 2-celled by abortion of one carpel. Fruit usually a few-seeded and loculicidal capsule.

The family includes about 26 genera and 600 species, mainly in warm regions, but extending into north temperate latitudes.

EXAMPLES: *Tradescantia:* Spiderwort, an American genus of some 40 species, often in sandy areas.

Commelina: Dayflower, with about 100 species in warm regions.

Zebrina pendula: Wandering Jew, a commonly cultivated foliage plant for window boxes or hanging baskets.

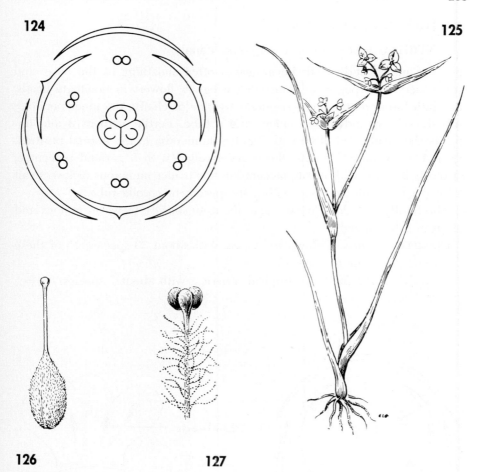

124 Floral diagram of *Tradescantia*.

125 Plant of *Tradescantia occidentalis*.

126 Pistil of *Tradescantia*.

127 Stamen of *Tradescantia*, enlarged.

ORDER XYRIDALES

XYRIDACEAE: Yellow-eyed Grass Family

Scapose marsh herbs with linear leaves often sheathing at the base, and small, perfect, hypogynous, somewhat irregular flowers in bracteate heads. Perianth biseriate, the outer segments hyaline or chaffy, the inner petaloid, usually yellow, and united below into a tube. Fertile stamens 3 and opposite the petals, and often with 3 outer staminodia in the normal position. Pistil 1, of 3 united carpels, the ovary 1-celled with 3 parietal placentae, or partly 3-celled with basal placentation, the ovules numerous or few. Fruit a 3-valved capsule enclosed within the persistent corolla tube.

The family includes 2 genera and about 40 species, in warm regions and often in saline marshes.

EXAMPLES: *Xyris:* Yellow-eyed Grass, with about 33 species, 15 of these in Florida.

Abolboda: of tropical America, with about 7 species.

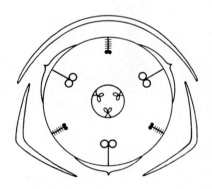

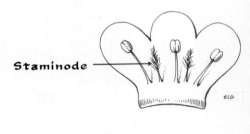

Staminode

128 Floral diagram of *Xyris*.

129 Corolla of *Xyris* opened to show the stamens, enlarged.

ORDER BROMELIALES

BROMELIACEAE: Pineapple Family

Mostly epiphytic, tropical or subtropical, xerophytic plants with densely clustered linear and usually spiny-toothed leaves. Inflorescence terminal, spike-like, often with colored bracts. Perianth of free or united segments, consisting of green sepals and corolline petals, and usually with appendages within forming a corona. Stamens 6, usually inserted on the perianth. Pistil 1, the ovary superior or inferior, 3-celled. Fruit often fleshy.

The family includes 4 tribes, 45 genera, and about 1,000 species, confined to tropical and subtropical America.

EXAMPLES: *Tillandsia usneoides:* Spanish Moss, common on trees in the Gulf states, and used in the upholstering of furniture.

Ananas sativus: Pineapple, a valuable fruit crop, especially in the Hawaiian Islands. The fiber from the leaves is used to make piña cloth.

ORDER ZINGIBERALES

Tropical or subtropical herbs of moist places, with rhizomes and fibrous or tuberous roots. Pseudostems often formed by overlapping sheaths of the leaves. Flowers epigynous, the perianth biseriate, the corolla regular or irregular, often inconspicuous. Stamens 5–6, or reduced to 1 and then with or without staminodia, the staminodia sometimes very conspicuous and petaloid. Fruit a capsule, or indehiscent and fleshy.

The order represents a high degree of specialization within the *Calyciferae* and somewhat parallels that of the Orchids in the *Corolliferae*. The exact interpretation of the morphology of the flowers has been the subject of much discussion.

Six families are included in the order, the following being representative.

MUSACEAE: Banana Family

A small family of 1 genus and some 45 species, in the tropics of the Old World, distinguished in the order by having spirally arranged leaves and bracts, irregular flowers with 5–6 stamens, often unisexual by abortion, and indehiscent fleshy fruits.

EXAMPLES: *Musa paradisiaca* var. *sapientum:* the common Banana.

Musa textilis: Manila Hemp, used in making rope.

STRELITZIACEAE: Strelitzia Family

A small family of 4 genera and about 38 species, in tropical America, South Africa, and Madagascar. It is distinguished in the order by having 2-ranked leaves and bracts, flowers with 3 distinct sepals, 3 irregular petals, 5–6 stamens, and capsular fruits.

EXAMPLES: *Strelitzia reginae:* Bird of Paradise Flower, often cultivated.
Ravenala madagascariensis: Travelers' Tree.

ZINGIBERACEAE: Ginger Family

A family of about 24 genera and 300 species, in tropical and subtropical regions, especially in Asia. It is distinguished in the order by the plants' being aromatic, with flowers having the inner perianth segments regular, but both the inner and outer segments united, and the androecium of 1 fertile stamen, the others being reduced to petaloid staminodia or lacking. The fruit is either a 3-valved capsule or fleshy and indehiscent.

EXAMPLES: *Zingiber officinale:* Ginger, a native of tropical Asia.
Curcuma angustifolia: Arrowroot, of the East Indies, yielding a valuable starch.
Amomum subulatum: Cardamom, of Bengal, a common spice.

The Corolliferae

Key to the Principal Families

Plants thalloid and aquatic, without true stems and leaves .... LEMNACEAE

Plants with stems and leaves, sometimes aquatic

Herbs with minute flowers in a dense spike (spadix), which is usually subtended by a conspicuous bract (spathe) .... ARACEAE

Herbs, shrubs, or trees, if herbaceous the flowers not as above

Trees or shrubs with large pinnate or palmate leaves in a terminal tuft; fruit a large nut, drupe, or berry; flowers mostly unisexual .... ARECACEAE

Mostly herbs, but if woody the leaves simple, the flowers perfect, and the fruit a capsule

Flowers perfect, the perianth petaloid and often showy

Ovary superior, the flowers hypogynous .. LILIACEAE

Ovary inferior, the flowers epigynous

Flowers regular; stamens 6 or 3; placentation axillary

Stamens 6; plants scapose .... AMARYLLIDACEAE

Stamens 3; plants with equitant-leafy stems .... IRIDACEAE

Flowers irregular; stamens 2 or 1; placentation parietal .... ORCHIDACEAE

Flowers unisexual, minute, in dense heads or spikes; perianth not petaloid

Inflorescence a continuous or interrupted and cylindrical spike; fruit disseminated by silky hairs .... TYPHACEAE

Inflorescence of few to many globose heads; fruit without hairs .... SPARGANIACEAE

ORDER LILIALES

LILIACEAE: Lily Family

Perennial herbs, or sometimes woody, from rhizomes, bulbs, or fleshy roots. Flowers often in racemes, regular, hypogynous, usually perfect, 3-merous (except *Maianthemum,* which is 4-merous), and often showy, the perianth usually petaloid (except *Trillium,* which has green sepals). Stamens commonly 6. Pistil 1, of 3 united carpels, with 1 or 3 styles and usually 3 stigmas, the ovary 3-celled, with axillary placentation and an indefinite number of ovules. Fruit a capsule or berry.

The family includes about 200 genera and 2,500 species, world-wide in distribution, including ornamentals and a few poisonous plants. As treated here, it includes the families *Trilliaceae, Smilacaceae, Melanthaceae, Convallariaceae, Dracaenaceae, Calochortaceae,* etc. of various American authors. It thus includes 11 subfamilies for the world.

EXAMPLES: *Lilium:* Lily, with about 45 species.

Calochortus: Mariposa or Sego Lily, with about 57 species.

Allium: Onion, with about 250 species.

Zigadenus: Death Camas, some species being very poisonous.

Yucca: Yucca or Soapweed, a genus of xerophytic shrubs.

Dracaena: Dragon Tree, a genus of small trees of dry warm areas.

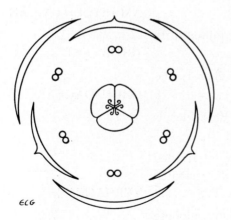

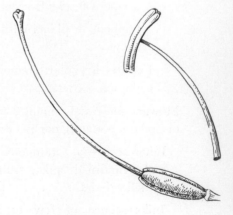

130 Floral diagram of *Lilium.*   **131** Stamen and pistil of *Lilium.*

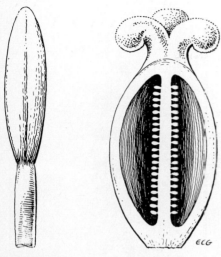

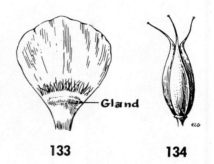

133 Perianth segment of a species of *Calochortus*.

134 Pistil of *Zygadenus*.

133

134

132 Stamen and section of pistil of *Tulipa*.

135 Flower of *Lilium philadelphicum* L. The sepals and petals are all alike and all petaloid, typical of members of the *Corolliferae*.

136 *Yucca glauca* Nutt., a common plant, of western plains and hills, having a woody base.

137 *Yucca glauca* Nutt., detailed view of a fruit, which is a septicidal capsule.

ORDER AMARYLLIDALES

AMARYLLIDACEAE: Amaryllis Family

Perennial scapose herbs or woody plants from bulbs or rhizomes. Flowers solitary, umbellate, or in elongated racemes or panicles, epigynous, with a tubular epigynous hypanthium, regular or nearly so, the perianth petaloid and often with appendages within forming a corona. Stamens 6. Pistil 1, of 3 united carpels, the style single and stigmas 3. Fruit a capsule or berry.

As treated here, the family includes about 65 genera and nearly 900 species, mainly in warm regions and often xerophytic.

As defined by Hutchinson,[1] this family would include those liliaceous groups, such as Onions (*Allium*), that have a scapose habit and umbellate inflorescence subtended by one or more spathaceous bracts. He considers this type of inflorescence to be of greater taxonomic importance than the character of superior or inferior ovary, which is usually used to distinguish the *Liliaceae* from the *Amaryllidaceae*. The Century Plants, moreover, are often treated as a separate family.

EXAMPLES: *Amaryllis:* a South African genus, often cultivated.

Narcissus: Narcissus, Jonquil, Daffodil.

Agave: Century Plant, of desert areas.

[1] J. Hutchinson: *The Families of Flowering Plants:* II, *Monocotyledons* (1934).

138 Floral diagram of *Narcissus.*

139 Flower and longitudinal section of flower of *Narcissus.*

140 *Narcissus pseudo-narcissus* L., the cultivated Daffodil, showing the conspicuous corona.

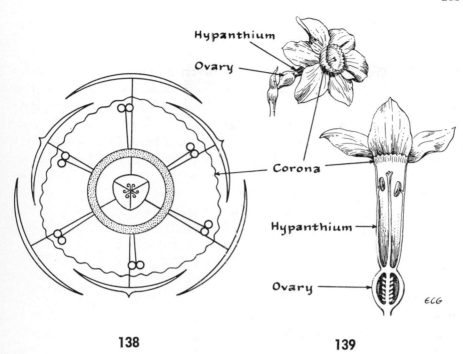

138

139

140

ORDER IRIDALES

IRIDACEAE: Iris Family

Mostly perennial herbs from rhizomes or corms, the leaves equitant and conduplicate (2-ranked and folded lengthwise at the base). Flowers epigynous, 3-merous, regular, with a short or long solid epigynous hypanthium, the perianth petaloid. Stamens 3. Pistil 1, of 3 united carpels, the styles often petaloid, the placentation axillary. Fruit a loculicidal capsule.

The family includes about 57 genera and 800 species, in temperate and tropical regions.

EXAMPLES: *Iris:* Iris, Blue Flag.
Gladiolus: Gladiolus, often cultivated.
Sisyrinchium: Blue-eyed Grass.

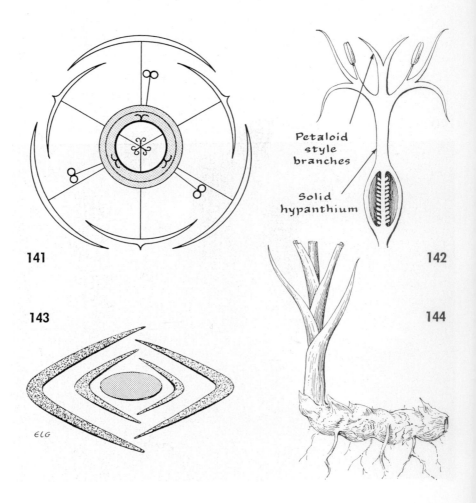

141

Petaloid
style
branches

Solid
hypanthium

142

143

144

ELG

141 Floral diagram of *Iris*.

142 Diagrammatic longitudinal section of an *Iris* flower.

143 Cross section through stem and leaves of *Iris*.

144 Lower portion of an *Iris* plant.

145 *Iris missouriensis* Nutt., flowers and fruit.

145

ORDER TYPHALES

Aquatic herbs from rhizomes, the leaves sheathing at the base. Flowers anemophilous, unisexual, small, produced in dense spikes or heads, the perianth reduced to hairs or scales. The order is probably a reduced group, the culmination of a line of evolution derived from the *Liliales*, and includes the following two families.

TYPHACEAE: Cattail Family

Tall aquatic or marsh herbs from rhizomes, with 2-ranked linear sheathing leaves. Flowers monoecious, in dense terminal spikes in which the upper part is staminate and the lower pistillate. Staminate flowers of 2–5 (usually 3) stamens, each flower surrounded by a hair-like or membranaceous perianth of indefinite parts. Pistillate flowers with a single pistil having a long-stipitate ovary, the stipe bearing numerous perianth hairs. Fruit 1-seeded and dehiscent at maturity.

The family includes the single genus *Typha*, with about 9 species, in temperate and tropical regions but not occurring south of the equator in the Americas and Africa.

EXAMPLES: *Typha latifolia:* Broad-leaved Cattail.

Typha angustifolia: Narrow-leaved Cattail.

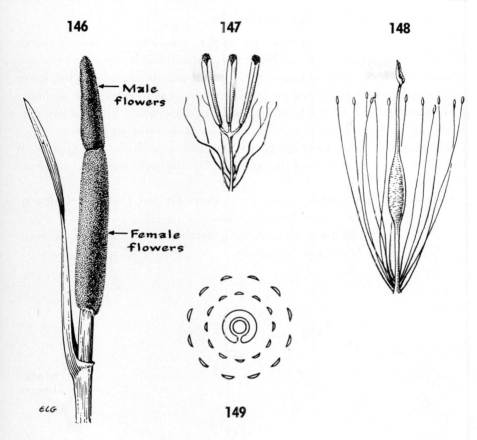

146 Upper part of flowering plant of *Typha*.

147 Male flower of *Typha*, enlarged.

148 Female flower of *Typha*, enlarged.

149 Floral diagram of female flower of *Typha*.

SPARGANIACEAE: Bur-reed Family

Rather low (mostly 1 meter or less high), grass-like, aquatic or marsh herbs from rhizomes, with 2-ranked linear sheathing leaves. Flowers monoecious, in dense globose heads, the upper heads staminate and the lower pistillate. Perianth composed of a few narrow scales. Stamens 3 or more, their filaments free or partly united near the base. Pistil 1, the ovary narrowed at the base, 1-celled or sometimes 2-celled. Fruit an akene.

The family includes the single genus *Sparganium*, with about 15 species, in temperate and cool regions of the Northern Hemisphere, Australia, and New Zealand.

EXAMPLES: *Sparganium eurycarpum:* Broad-fruited Bur-reed, transcontinental in North America.

Sparganium angustifolium: Narrow-leaved Bur-reed, of North America and Australia.

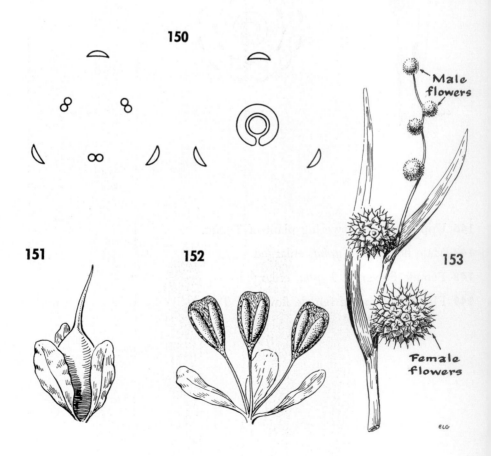

150

151   152   153

Male flowers

Female flowers

154

150 Floral diagrams of staminate (left) and pistillate (right) flowers of *Sparganium*. (The perianth segments are variable.)

151 Pistillate flower of *Sparganium*, enlarged.

152 Staminate flower of *Sparganium*, enlarged.

153 Upper portion of flowering plant of *Sparganium*.

154 *Sparganium multipedunculatum* (Morong) Rydb., showing fruiting heads. The staminate flowers have dropped off.

ORDER ARALES

Terrestrial or sometimes aquatic and mostly herbaceous plants with minute flowers produced on a dense spike (spadix), which is usually subtended by a large and sometimes ornamental bract (spathe). Fruit a berry.

The group probably was derived from the *Liliales*, representing a line of evolution parallel to that of the *Arecales* and *Typhales*.

ARACEAE: Arum Family

Herbs, climbers, or rarely shrubs, of various habit and size, the leaves usually large, simple or compound, net-veined, and with sheathing petioles. Inflorescence characteristically a spathe (a more or less showy or petaloid bract) and spadix (a spike of numerous small flowers, subtended or enclosed by the spathe). Flowers hypogynous, unisexual or perfect, 2–3-merous or naked, crowded, ebracteate, the stamens 1 or more, the anthers opening by terminal pores, the filaments free or united; the pistil 1, of 1 or more carpels, nearly always forming a berry in fruit.

The family is mostly tropical, with only a few representatives in temperate North America. It includes about 100 genera and 1,500 species, some ornamental and others producing food for human consumption.

EXAMPLES: *Zantedeschia aethiopica:* Calla-lily.
Arisaema triphyllum: Jack-in-the-pulpit.
Symplocarpus foetidus: Skunk-cabbage.
Colocasia esculenta: Taro, or Poi.

LEMNACEAE: Duckweed Family

Small to minute, floating or submerged herbs, which are more or less thalloid (without stems or leaves, and the roots, if any, thread-like). Flowers monoecious and naked; stamens 1–2; pistil 1, 1-celled; ovules 1–7.

The family includes 2–3 genera and about 19 species, in fresh water of temperate and tropical regions.

EXAMPLE: *Lemna:* Duckweed, often found in ponds and swamps.

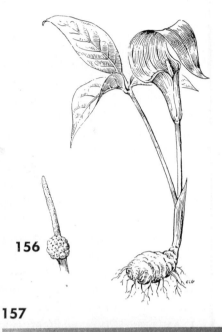

155 *Calla palustris.*

156 *Arisaema triphyllum.* Shown separately is the spadix in fruit.

157 A species of *Aglaonema*, called Chinese Evergreen, often cultivated as a house plant. This shows the characteristic spathe and spadix inflorescence, the spadix with staminate flowers above and pistillate flowers below.

ORDER ARECALES

ARECACEAE: Palm Family

Mostly unbranched shrubs or trees with large persistent leaves in a terminal tuft, the stem often covered by the persistent leaf-bases, the stem sometimes much reduced, and sometimes vine-like or rope-like, with scattered leaves and stout spines. Flowers small, in large and usually paniculate inflorescences, which are sometimes enclosed in a large spathe-like bract, hypogynous, perfect, or, usually, unisexual (polygamous, monoecious, or dioecious), with 3 sepals and 3 petals, these perianth segments distinct or connate. Stamens usually 6, rarely numerous. Gynoecium usually of 3 carpels, which are distinct or connate at the base, each carpel producing a single seed. Fruit berry-like, drupaceous, or nut-like.

The family, of considerable economic importance, is divided into 8 tribes, including about 170 genera and 1,500 species, in tropical and subtropical regions of the world, especially in the Indo-Malayan region and in the Guianas and Brazil. It is probably a terminal evolutionary group derived from woody members of the *Liliales*.

EXAMPLES: *Cocos nucifera:* Coconut Palm. The genus includes some 30 species, the others being entirely American.

Phoenix dactylifera: Date Palm.

Elaeis guineensis: Oil Palm.

Areca catechu: Betel-nut Palm.

Roystonea regia: Royal Palm, often planted in avenues.

Washingtonia filifera: Sentinel Palm of southern California.

Raphia pedunculata: Raffia.

Sabal: Cabbage Palm, or Palmetto, including 8 species, 4 of them in the Gulf states.

Calamus and *Daemonorops:* Rattans. The genus *Calamus* is one of the largest in the family, with some 200 species, mostly in Asia, and having rope-like stems often several hundred feet long, bearing stout spines.

158 Tree of the Coconut Palm, *Cocos nucifera.*

159 *Synechanthus,* floral diagrams of staminate (left) and pistillate (right) flowers. Vestigial carpels and stamens are common in unisexual flowers of the family.

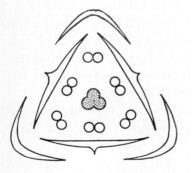

ORDER HAEMODORALES

Perennial herbs, or sometimes woody plants, from rhizomes or corms. Leaves mostly entire, rarely lobed, in a basal tuft in herbaceous members and in tufts at the ends of branches in woody ones (*Velloziaceae*). Flowers perfect, solitary, in panicles, or in umbels, varying from regular to irregular, hypogynous or, usually, epigynous. Stamens numerous to 6, or sometimes reduced to 3, 2, or 1. Pistil 1, of 3 united carpels, the ovary either 3-celled with axillary placentation or 1-celled with parietal placentation.

The order, as defined by Hutchinson,[1] includes 6 families, which are mainly tropical and subtropical in the Southern Hemisphere. It includes plants that are somewhat intermediate in character between the *Liliales* and the *Orchidales*.

ORDER BURMANNIALES

Small annual or perennial herbs, often saprophytic. Leaves usually reduced to scales. Flowers solitary and terminal, or in racemes or cymes, perfect or unisexual, regular to irregular, epigynous. Stamens 6 or 3. Pistil 1, of 3 united carpels, the ovary either 3-celled with axillary placentation or 1-celled with parietal placentation. Ovules and seeds very numerous and small.

The order, as defined by Hutchinson,[1] includes 3 families, which are tropical and subtropical in distribution. It probably represents a development parallel to that of the *Orchidales*, as evidenced by the tendency of the plants to become saprophytic and to produce numerous minute seeds, but the degree of specialization in the flower parts has not equaled that of the Orchids.

ORDER ORCHIDALES

ORCHIDACEAE: Orchid Family

Perennial herbs, often epiphytic and sometimes saprophytic, from rhizomes or fleshy roots. Flowers strikingly irregular, often spurred, epigynous, 3-merous, the axis twisted through a semicircle in anthesis. Stamens 1 or 2, attached to the style (gynandrous), and together with the style and stigmas forming the *column*. Pistil 1, of 3 united carpels, the ovary usually 1-celled with 3 parietal placentae, the style single and the stigmas 3 and all functional or 2 functional and 1 sterile, the latter often produced upward into a beak, or *rostellum*. Fruit a capsule. Seeds very minute and very numerous.

This is one of the largest families of flowering plants, including about 500 genera and perhaps 15,000 species, widely distributed, but mainly in tropical forests.

[1] J. Hutchinson: *The Families of Flowering Plants:* II, *Monocotyledons* (1934).

EXAMPLES: *Cypripedium:* Lady's Slipper.
               Habenaria: Rein Orchis, with about 500 species.
               Corallorhiza: Coral-root, the plants saprophytic.
               Vanilla planifolia: Vanilla Orchid, which yields the extract
                  from immature pods.
               Cattleya: one of the chief horticultural or corsage orchids.
               Bulbophyllum and *Dendrobium:* each with about 1,000
                  species in the Malaysian region alone.

160 Floral diagram of *Orchis*.   **161** Flower of *Orchis*.

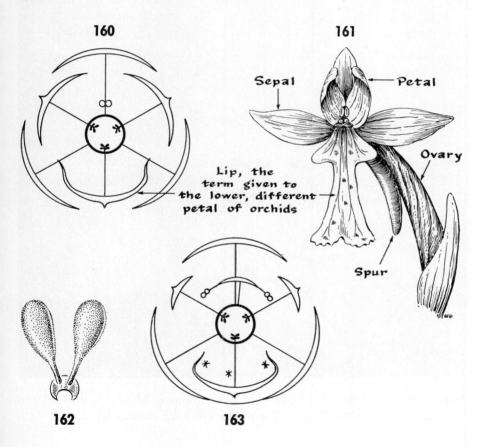

162 Pollinia, or waxy pollen masses, of *Orchis*.

163 Floral diagram of *Cypripedium*. The odd upper stamen is represented
   by a staminodium and connected, with the two fertile stamens, to the
   style, forming the column. Three lower stamens are lacking.

164 *Calypso bulbosa* (L.) Oakes, the Fairy Slipper. The lip is inflated and resembles a little slipper. The plants are 6–22 centimeters tall.

165 Detail of flower of *Calypso bulbosa* (L.) Oakes, the Fairy Slipper. The petaloid part in the center, above the lip, is the column.

The Glumiflorae

Key to the Families

Fruit a 3-valved capsule containing 3–many seeds; perianth of 6 chaffy and similar segments; flowers not associated with scale-like bracts (scales, lemmas, or glumes) . . . .   JUNCACEAE

Fruit an akene or a grain (caryopsis), indehiscent and 1-seeded; perianth inconspicuous, of scales, bristles, or hairs, or sometimes lacking; flowers associated with scale-like bracts (scales, lemmas, or glumes)

    Stems not jointed; leaves when present 3-ranked; fruit a lenticular or trigonous akene . . . .   CYPERACEAE

    Stems jointed; leaves always present and 2-ranked; fruit a grain (caryopsis), seldom angled . . . .   POACEAE

ORDER JUNCALES

Mostly grass-like plants with small and chaffy liliaceous flowers, which are anemophilous.

The order includes 4 families, typified by the following, which is the only one represented in North America.

166 Floral diagram of *Juncus*.

167 Longitudinal section of flower of *Juncus*.

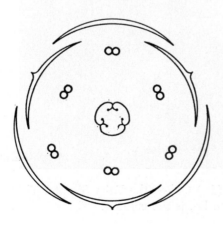

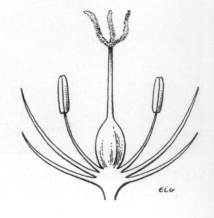

JUNCACEAE: Rush Family

Perennial or annual herbs, rarely shrubby (*Prionium*), usually with fibrous roots and erect or horizontal rhizomes. Stems commonly leafy only at the base, the leaves in a basal tuft or sometimes reduced to sheaths, which may be open or closed, the blades, when present, cylindric to flat and grass-like, mostly linear or filiform. Flowers mostly anemophilous, solitary or usually in panicles, corymbs, or heads, often very small, regular, 3-merous, perfect or unisexual, the perianth usually of 6 segments in two series, rarely of only 3 segments, chaffy, greenish, brownish, or black, rarely white or yellowish. Stamens 6 or 3, the anthers basifixed. Pollen in tetrads. Pistil 1, of 3 united carpels, the ovary superior and 1-celled with parietal placentation or, rarely, 3-celled with axillary placentation (*Prionium*), the style long and single to almost none, the stigmas 3. Fruit a loculicidal capsule with few to many seeds.

The family includes 8 genera and about 300 species, widely distributed in temperate and cold regions but especially well represented in the Andes of South America.

EXAMPLES: *Juncus:* Rush
            Luzula: Wood Rush

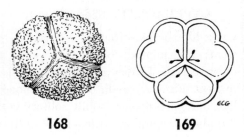

168   **169**

168 Pollen tetrad of *Luzula,*
    greatly magnified.

169 Cross section of ovary of
    Prionium, enlarged.

ORDER POALES

Annual or perennial, mostly grass-like herbs, sometimes woody, with alternate and mostly linear leaves composed of a sheath and a blade. Flowers small, naked or with a scale-like or hair-like perianth, enclosed between scale-like bracts. Stamens 6, 3, or fewer. Pistil 1, the ovary superior, 1-celled and 1-seeded. Fruit a grain (caryopsis) or an akene.

The order probably represents an early modification from the *Liliales* through the *Juncales*. It includes two important families, the Sedges and the Grasses. These two families may be distinguished as follows:

	Cyperaceae: Sedges	*Poaceae:* Grasses
Stems	Herbaceous Not jointed Usually solid Often triangular in cross-section	Herbaceous, or sometimes woody Jointed Usually hollow in internodes Circular in cross-section
Leaves	3-ranked when present Sheaths usually closed Ligule usually not present	2-ranked Sheaths usually open Ligule usually present
Fruit	An akene	A grain (caryopsis)
Habitat	Usually in wet places	Usually in drier places, but some aquatic

CYPERACEAE: Sedge Family

Grass-like herbs, often in wet places, from rhizomes or fibrous roots, the stems not jointed, often with solid pith, and frequently triangular in cross-section. Leaves usually 3-ranked, with a closed sheath; ligule rarely present. Flowers small, perfect, monoecious or dioecious, arranged in spikelets, and each flower usually solitary within a bract (*glume* or *scale*). Bracts 2-ranked or spiral in arrangement in the spikelet, the inflorescence composed of one or more spikelets and commonly subtended by one or more leaf-like bracts. Perianth reduced to hypogynous scales, bristles, or hairs, rarely somewhat petaloid, and often absent. Stamens 3 or fewer, rarely more, the anthers basifixed. Ovary superior, 1-celled, the style with 2 or 3 branches or teeth. Ovule solitary. Fruit a lenticular or trigonous akene.

The family includes 75 genera and about 3,500 species, mostly in temperate and cold regions, many extending into the Artic. It is important as a source of forage and of food for wild fowl.

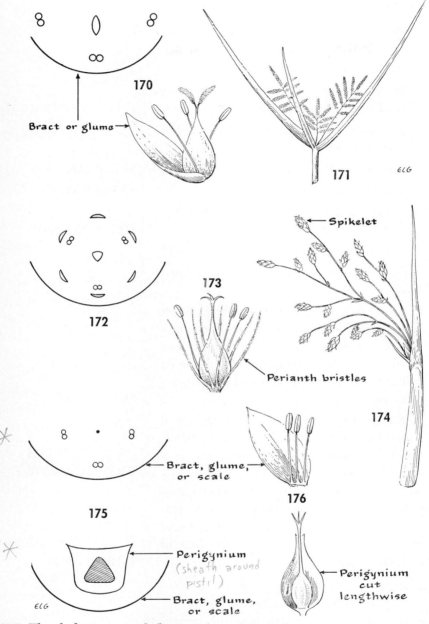

Bract or glume

170

171   ELG

172

173

Spikelet

Perianth bristles

174

175   Bract, glume,
                       or scale

176

Perigynium
(sheath around
pistil)

Bract, glume,
or scale

ELG

Perigynium
cut
lengthwise

170 Floral diagram and flower of *Cyperus*.

171 Inflorescence of *Cyperus*.

172 Floral diagram of *Scirpus*.

173 Flower of *Scirpus*, enlarged.

174 Inflorescence of *Scirpus*.

175 Floral diagrams of male (above) and female (below) flowers of *Carex*.

176 Male (above) and female (below) flowers of *Carex*.

Key to the Tribes

Flowers perfect

Hypogynous scales, when present, filiform, flat, or perianth-like, not folded

Spikelets mostly 1–2-flowered, often 2 or more of the lower glumes empty . . . .   RHYNCHOSPOREAE

Spikelets several–many-flowered, only 1–2 of the lower glumes empty

Glumes not 2-ranked . . . .   SCIRPEAE

Glumes 2-ranked . . . .   CYPEREAE

Hypogynous scales 2, folded or keeled, spikelets several–many-flowered . . . .   HYPOLYTREAE

Flowers unisexual, no hypogynous setae present

Female flower not enclosed by a modified glume

Pistillate flower solitary at the base of an androgynous spikelet or the spikelets unisexual, the female spikelets 1-flowered and in the lower part of the panicle, the male spikelets in the upper part and 2- or more-flowered . . . .   SCLERIEAE

Pistillate flower terminal in a unisexual spikelet or in the upper part of the panicle, the male spikelets produced lower and 2- or more-flowered . . . .   CRYPTANGIEAE

Female flower enclosed by a modified glume (*perigynium*), female spikelets 1-flowered, spicate, male spikelets 2- or more-flowered and terminal or, rarely, continuous at the base of the female spike . . . .   CARICEAE

Rhynchosporeae: cosmopolitan in distribution.
Scirpeae: cosmopolitan in distribution.
Cypereae: chiefly tropical, some in temperate regions.
Hypolytreae: tropical and subtropical; the most primitive group.
Sclerieae: cosmopolitan in distribution.
Cryptangieae: chiefly in tropical America, some in Africa.
Cariceae: chiefly in temperate and cold regions, rare in the tropics, and common in mountainous regions.

EXAMPLES: *Cyperus papyrus:* Papyrus, of the Nile valley (*Cypereae*).
                 Eleocharis: Spike Rush (*Scirpeae*).
                 Scirpus validus: Bulrush (*Scirpeae*).
                 Eriophorum: Cotton Grass (*Scirpeae*).
                 Carex: Sedge, the largest genus, with nearly 800 species, in
                 temperate, alpine, and arctic regions (*Cariceae*).

177 *Carex rostrata* Stokes, a common sedge, showing unisexual spikes, staminate at the top, and below them thicker, pistillate spikes.

POACEAE (GRAMINEAE): Grass Family

Annual or perennial herbs, or sometimes woody in warm regions. Stems often branched at the base, in perennials forming flowering stems (*culms*) and sterile shoots (*innovations*), the culms cylindrical, jointed, usually hollow in the internodes and closed in the nodes. Leaves sometimes crowded at the base of the plants, alternate and 2-ranked, each consisting of *sheath, ligule,* and *blade:* sheaths encircling the stem with the margins free and overlapping or sometimes united; ligule placed at the junction of sheath and blade, membranaceous or reduced to a fringe of hairs, rarely absent; blades usually long and narrow, often involute, parallel-veined. Flowers usually perfect, small and inconspicuous, consisting of stamens and pistil and 2–3 minute, hyaline or fleshy scales (*lodicules*) representing the perianth, each such flower subsessile between two bracts (*lemma* and *palea,* the palea sometimes wanting), the whole forming a *floret,* or false flower. Florets 1–many, 2-ranked, sessile on a short or minute and slender axis (*rachilla*) and bearing at the base 2 empty bracts (the first and second *glumes*), the florets and glumes together forming a *spikelet.* Spikelets pediceled in open or contracted panicles or racemes, or sessile in spikes. Stamens usually 3, sometimes 6, hypogynous, opening by longitudinal slits. Ovary 1-celled, with 1 ovule, which is usually adnate to one side of the carpel; styles 2, stigmas plumose. Fruit a grain, or caryopsis, with a thin pericarp adnate to the seed, with starchy endosperm and a small embryo at the base.

The family, one of the most important in the whole plant kingdom, includes about 525 genera and 5,000 species, world-wide in distribution. It has been subdivided into two subfamilies and as many as 27 tribes. Fourteen tribes, including about 1,500 species, occur in the United States. Of these species, about 140 are important native forage plants, and about 60 are cultivated in the United States.

Comparison of subfamilies

I. *Festucoideae*	II. *Panicoideae*
Spikelets 1–several-flowered, the sterile florets, if any, usually above the fertile florets in the spikelet.	Spikelets with 1 perfect terminal floret and 1 sterile floret below it, the sterile floret usually represented by an empty lemma. Some genera are monoecious, and some produce staminate or empty florets.
Articulation usually above the glumes and between the florets, the glumes remaining on the plant when the seed is shed.	Articulation below the glumes, the whole spikelet (including the glumes) falling when the seed is shed.
Spikelets laterally compressed, the glumes and lemmas usually folded lengthwise, or sometimes the spikelets terete.	Spikelets dorsally compressed, the glumes and lemmas flat, or sometimes the spikelets terete.

Note: Any two of the above three characteristics will place the grass in the proper
   subfamily.

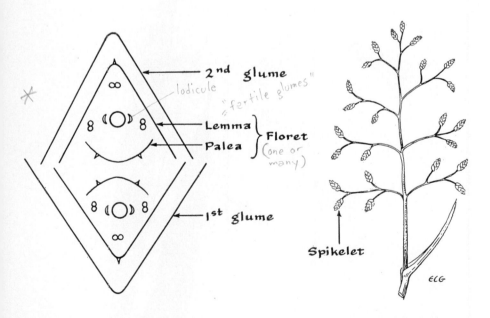

178 Diagram of a spikelet of *Poa* in cross section.

179 Panicle of *Poa*, showing spikelets.

180 *Uniola latifolia* Michx., Broad-leaf Uniola, tribe *Festuceae*. On the ends of the very slender panicle branches are the spikelets, each with several florets. Some of the spikelets have started to disarticulate.

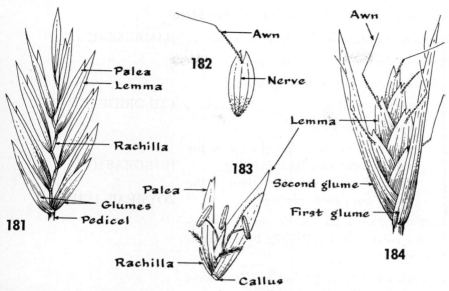

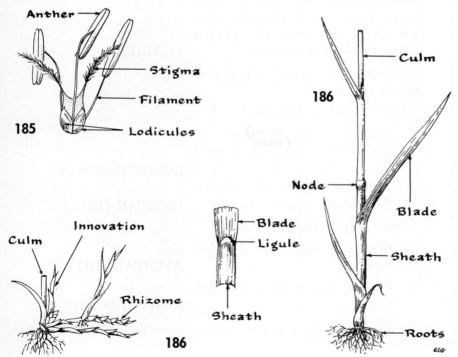

181 Spikelet of bromegrass.

182 Single floret of oat grass.

183 Single floret of a grass at blooming time.

184 Spikelet of oat grass.

185 Reproductive parts of a grass floret.

186 Vegetative parts of grasses.

Key to the Tribes of Subfamily Festucoideae[1]

Plants woody, mostly large trees or shrubs .. BAMBUSEAE (I)

Plants herbaceous, sometimes tall

  Inflorescence of 1 or more spikes

    Spikes 1-sided .... CHLORIDEAE (VI)

    Spikes symmetrical

      Articulation above the glumes, or the rachis sometimes disarticulating ..... HORDEAE (IV)

      Articulation below the glumes, the rachis not disarticulating .... ZOYSIEAE (VII)

  Inflorescence a raceme or panicle, sometimes narrow and spike-like but never a true spike

    Spikelets with 1 perfect terminal floret and 2 sterile or empty lemmas below it .... PHALARIDEAE (VIII)

    Spikelets not as above, the sterile florets, if any, above the fertile

      Spikelets unisexual, falling entire, terete; panicles with pistillate spikelets above and staminate spikelets below, these spikelets unlike .... ZIZANIEAE (X)

      Spikelets usually perfect, if unisexual then not as above

        Spikelets strictly 1-flowered

          Articulation usually above the glumes, the glumes not reduced in size .... AGROSTIDEAE (V)

          Articulation below the glumes, the glumes reduced or lacking .. ORYZEAE (IX)

        Spikelets with 2 or more florets

          Glumes longer than the first lemma .... AVENEAE (III)

          Glumes shorter than the first lemma .... FESTUCEAE (II)

[1] Keys to tribes are for the United States only, and are somewhat simplified. Rare exceptions may occur although not indicated.

Key to the Tribes of Subfamily Panicoideae[1]

Plants with at least some perfect florets, the
inflorescence essentially uniform

Spikelets in pairs, one sessile and fertile,
the other pedicellate and sterile (sometimes obsolete), rarely both pedicellate;
glumes indurate .... ANDROPOGONEAE (XII)

Spikelets not paired, in racemes or in open
or spike-like panicles; glumes herbaceous
or membranaceous, not indurate .... PANICEAE (XI)

Plants monoecious, the male and female
spikelets in separate inflorescences or in different parts of the same inflorescence ...... TRIPSACEAE (XIII)

[1] The tribe *Melinideae* is represented in the United States by two grasses, both introduced: *Melinis minutiflora* Beauv., in southern Florida, and *Thysanolaena maxima* (Roxb.) Kuntze, in southern Florida and southern California. For characteristics of this tribe and these genera see A. S. Hitchcock, *Manual of the Grasses of the United States.* The tribe *Melinideae* has been omitted above for purposes of simplicity and brevity.

Tribe I. *Bambuseae* (Bamboo Tribe): Woody plants with the spikelet characters of the tribe *Festuceae*. Chiefly tropical plants, many of which are of great economic importance. The genus *Arundinaria* (Cane) is a native of the southeastern United States, and several species of various genera of Bamboos are cultivated in the warmer states, the commonest being *Sasa japonica* (Sieb. & Zucc.) Makino.

Tribe II. *Festuceae* (Fescue Tribe): Spikelets 2–several-flowered, in open, narrow, or spike-like panicles, rarely in racemes. Lemmas awnless, awned from the tip, or awned from between two minute teeth near the apex, the awns straight. Glumes shorter than the first lemma. Articulation above the glumes.

A large tribe, chiefly in the cooler parts of the world, including many important forage grasses. There are 37 genera in the United States.

    EXAMPLES: *Poa:* Bluegrasses.

                    Festuca: Fescue grasses.

                    Bromus: Bromegrasses.

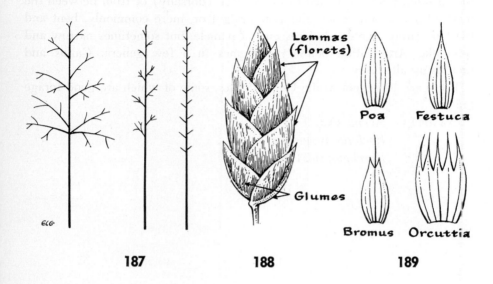

187 Tribe *Festuceae,* inflorescence types.

188 Tribe *Festuceae,* spikelet type.

189 Tribe *Festuceae,* lemma types.

Tribe III. *Aveneae* (Oat Tribe): Spikelets 2–several-flowered, with glumes as long as the first lemma or, usually, equaling or exceeding all the florets in the spikelet. Lemmas awned from the back (dorsally) or from between the teeth of a bidentate apex; the awn straight or, more commonly, bent and twisted; rarely awnless. Inflorescence a panicle, but sometimes narrow and spike-like. Articulation below the glumes in a few genera. Callus and rachilla usually hairy.

There are 10 genera in the United States, some of which are good forage grasses.

    EXAMPLES: *Avena:* Oat.
                 Koeleria: June grass.
                 Deschampsia: Hairgrass.

Tribe IV. *Hordeae* (Barley Tribe): Spikelets 1–several-flowered, sessile on alternate sides of a single symmetrical spike, the articulation above the glumes. The rachis continuous and persistent or readily disarticulating at maturity. Glumes often variously modified into bristles or awns.

A large tribe, including many valuable forage grasses and several common small-grain cereals, such as Wheat, Rye, and Barley. There are 12 genera in the United States.

    EXAMPLES: *Agropyron:* Wheatgrass, one of the large genera.
                 Elymus: Wild-rye.

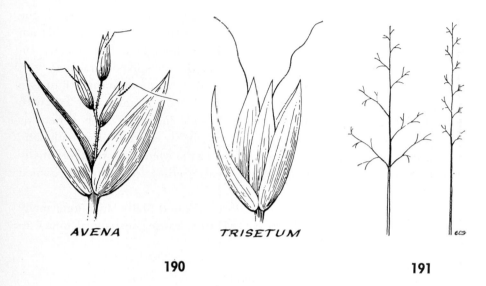

AVENA   TRISETUM

190   **191**

190 Tribe *Aveneae,* spikelet types.

191 Tribe *Aveneae,* inflorescence types.

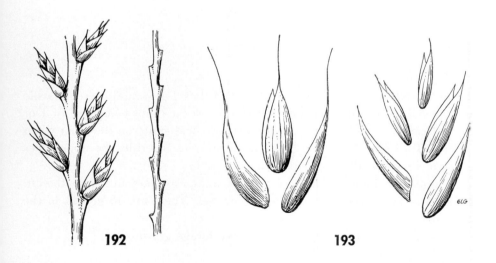

192   **193**

192 Tribe *Hordeae,* portions of spikes showing rachis with and without spikelets.

193 Tribe *Hordeae,* generalized types of spikelets.

Tribe V. *Agrostideae* (Timothy Tribe): Spikelets strictly 1-flowered, the lemmas either awnless or awned from the tip or from the back. Articulation usually above the normal glumes but below them in a few genera. Inflorescence an open or narrow panicle, or sometimes a spikelike raceme.

The tribe, as here defined, has been divided by some authors into two tribes, those members having indurate (hardened) lemmas that fall with the fruit being split off into the tribe *Stipeae*, including such genera as *Stipa* and *Aristida*. The *Agrostideae* are probably a tribe of polyphyletic origin, having been derived in part from the *Festuceae* (those with terminally awned lemmas) and in part from the *Aveneae* (those with dorsally awned lemmas).

A large tribe, with about 25 genera in the United States, including many valuable forage grasses. Some species of *Stipa* cause mechanical injury to grazing animals.

    EXAMPLES: *Phleum:* Timothy.

                Agrostis: Redtop, or Bentgrass.

                Muhlenbergia: Muhly.

                Stipa: Needlegrass.

                Oryzopsis: Indian Ricegrass.

Tribe VI. *Chlorideae* (Grama Tribe): Spikelets 1–several-flowered, sessile on one side of a continuous rachis, the inflorescence thus composed of 1 or more 1-sided spikes, which may be racemose or digitate on the culm when several. Typically the lowest floret in the spikelet is fertile, the upper ones being much reduced in size and sterile.

A large tribe, found chiefly in warm dry areas, especially in the Southwest. It includes many very valuable forage grasses. There are 18 genera in the United States.

    EXAMPLES: *Bouteloua:* Grama, valuable forage grasses.

                Buchloë: Buffalo Grass.

                Beckmannia: Sloughgrass, a source of food for ducks.[1]

[1] See A. E. Porsild in Sargentia 4: 9 (1943).

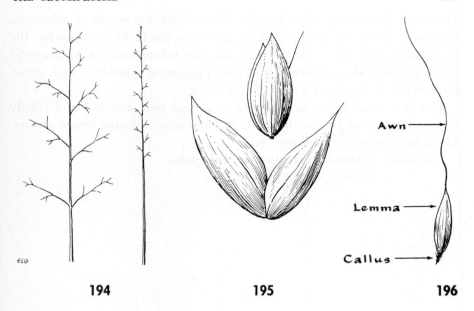

194 Tribe *Agrostideae*, inflorescence types.

195 Tribe *Agrostideae*, spikelet type.

196 Tribe *Agrostideae*, indurate lemma and fruit of *Stipa*.

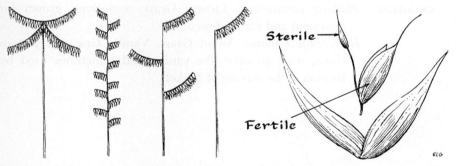

197 Tribe *Chlorideae*, inflorescence types.

198 Tribe *Chlorideae*, spikelet type.

Tribe VII. *Zoysieae* (Curly Mesquite Tribe): Spikelets sessile or subsessile, in groups, the whole group falling entire from the rachis at maturity, the articulation thus below the glumes and the inflorescence a symmetrical spike. The typical arrangement is to have the central spikelet of each group fertile while the two lateral spikelets are sterile.

This is a small tribe, probably not a natural one, and is found chiefly in desert regions of the Southwest. It includes some valuable forage grasses. There are 5 genera in the United States.

    EXAMPLES: *Hilaria belangeri:* Curly Mesquite.
                     Hilaria jamesii: Galleta.

Tribe VIII. *Phalarideae* (Canary Grass Tribe): Spikelets with 1 perfect terminal floret and 2 sterile florets below it (these may be either staminate or empty lemmas, sometimes normal in size and sometimes much reduced). The inflorescence is an open or narrow panicle, sometimes spike-like, but never a true spike. Articulation above the glumes.

A small tribe of 6 genera, 3 of them in the United States. None of the species is abundant enough to furnish much forage.

    EXAMPLES: *Phalaris canariensis:* Canary Grass, sometimes grown for ornament and for bird seed.

                     Hierochloë odorata: Sweet Grass, Vanilla Grass, or Seneca Grass, with an odor like vanilla and sometimes used by Indians in the making of baskets.

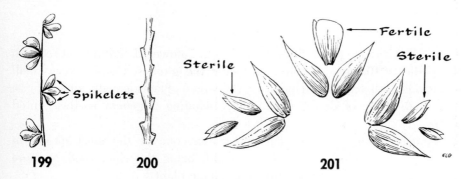

199 Tribe *Zoysieae*, inflorescence.   **201** Tribe *Zoysieae*, spikelet group.

200 Tribe *Zoysieae*, rachis.

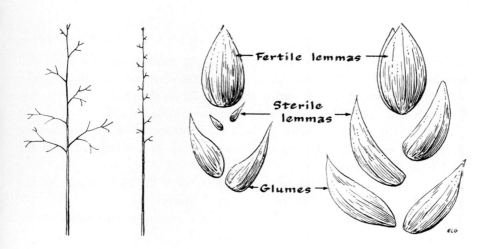

202 Tribe *Phalarideae*, inflores-   **203** Tribe *Phalarideae*, spikelet
cence types.   types.

Tribe IX. *Oryzeae* (Rice Tribe): Spikelets 1-flowered, falling entire from the pedicels, the articulation thus below the glumes. Glumes very small or lacking. Inflorescence a panicle. Stamens 6. Plants chiefly aquatic.

A small tribe, of doubtful affinities, including 2 genera in the United States.

EXAMPLES: *Oryza sativa:* cultivated Rice, one of the most important food plants of the world, being the chief food of more people than any other single plant.

Leersia oryzoides: Rice Cutgrass, a common species of moist places in North America.

Tribe X. *Zizanieae* (Indian Rice Tribe): Plants monoecious, the male and female spikelets on the same plant but in different parts of the panicle. Spikelets 1-flowered, falling entire, the articulation thus below the glumes. Glumes small or obsolete. Plants aquatic, mostly rather tall.

A small tribe, with 5 genera in the United States, of no great economic significance except for the genus *Zizania*, which is a source of food for wild fowl and Indians.

EXAMPLES: *Zizania aquatica:* Indian Rice, or Wild Rice, mainly in the eastern half of the United States.

Hydrochloa caroliniensis: of the southeastern United States, said to be eaten by livestock.

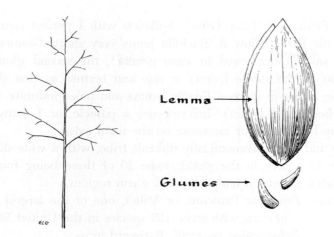

204 Tribe *Oryzeae*, inflorescence type.

205 Tribe *Oryzeae*, spikelet type.

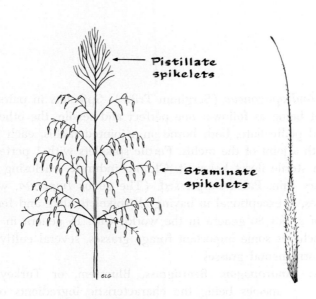

206 Tribe *Zizanieae*, inflorescence of *Zizania*.

207 Tribe *Zizanieae*, pistillate floret of *Zizania*.

Tribe XI. *Paniceae* (Millet Tribe): Spikelets with 1 perfect terminal floret and 1 sterile floret below it. Rachilla joints very short. Glumes thin, the first very small (suppressed in some genera), the second glume normal and similar to the sterile lemma in size and texture so that these often appear like a pair of glumes. Fertile lemma and palea indurate (hardened and attached to the grain). Inflorescence a panicle, or 1–many racemes, which may be digitate or racemose on the main axis.

A large and often taxonomically difficult tribe, with a wide distribution. There are 80 genera in the world, some 20 of these being found in the United States, mainly in temperate and warm regions.

    examples: *Panicum:* Panicum, or Millet, one of the largest genera of grasses, with some 160 species in the United States.

          Echinochloa crusgalli: Barnyard grass.

          Setaria: Bristlegrass.

          Cenchrus: Sandbur, often a troublesome weed.

          Digitaria: Crabgrass, weedy plants, sometimes cut for hay.

Tribe XII. *Andropogoneae* (Sorghum Tribe): Spikelets in pairs, the usual arrangement being as follows: one perfect and sessile, the other sterile or reduced and pedicellate, both borne on a jointed rachis, each pair falling together with a joint of the rachis. Fertile spikelets with 1 perfect terminal floret and a sterile floret below it. Glumes indurate, enclosing the florets. Lemmas very thin. Palea suppressed. (The genus *Imperata*, with narrow silky panicles, is exceptional in having all spikelets alike and fertile.)

A tribe of about 80 genera in the world, with 16 genera in the United States. It includes some important forage grasses, several cultivated crops, and a few ornamental grasses.

    examples: *Andropogon:* Beardgrass, Bluestem, or Turkeyfoot, some species being the characteristic ingredients of tall-grass prairies.

          Saccharum officinarum: Sugar cane.

          Sorghum vulgare: Sorghum.

          Miscanthus sinensis: Eulalia, a cultivated ornamental.

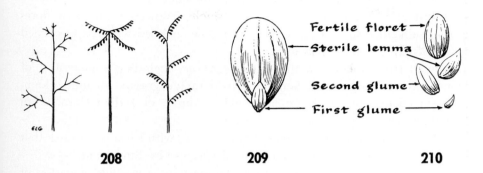

208 Tribe *Paniceae,* inflorescence types.

209 Tribe *Paniceae,* spikelet closed.

210 Tribe *Paniceae,* spikelet opened to show structure.

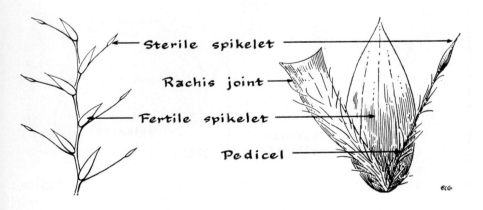

211 Tribe *Andropogoneae,* diagram of arrangement of spikelets of *Andropogon.*

212 Tribe *Andropogoneae,* spike
let pair of *Andropogon.*

Tribe XIII. *Tripsaceae* (Corn Tribe): Plants monoecious. Spikelets unisexual, the male and female spikelets in separate inflorescences or in different parts of the same inflorescence. Staminate spikelets in 2's or 3's, 2-flowered. Pistillate spikelets in 2's or, usually, single, 2-flowered, the lower floret sterile, embedded in a thickened axis (cob) or enclosed within a thickened sheath. Glumes and lemmas awnless.

A small tribe, related to the *Andropogoneae*, including 7 genera, 4 of them in the United States. Some are good forage grasses, though seldom common enough to be of significance, but Maize, or Indian Corn, is an important field crop in the United States.

EXAMPLES: *Zea mays:* Maize, or Indian Corn, with several varieties that are termed "agricultural species" by Sturtevant.[1]

Euchlaena: Teosinte, of interest as a possible ancestor of Indian Corn.[2]

Tripsacum: Gama grass, another possible ancestor of Indian Corn.

Coix lacryma-jobi: Job's-tears, sometimes cultivated for ornament.

[1] E. L. Sturtevant: *Varieties of Corn*, U.S.D.A. Exp. Sta. Bull. 57 (1899).
[2] G. N. Collins: "The Origin of Maize," Jour. Wash. Acad. Sci. 2: 520–530 (1912).

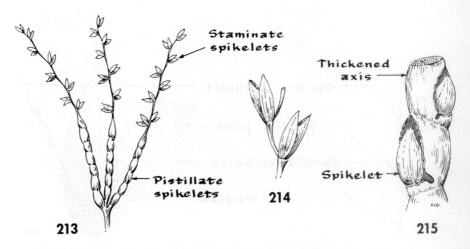

213 Tribe *Tripsaceae*, diagrammatic representation of inflorescence of *Tripsacum*.

214 Tribe *Tripsaceae*, staminate spikelets of *Tripsacum*.

215 Tribe *Tripsaceae*, pistillate spikelets of *Tripsacum*.

Part III

SELECTED ORDERS AND FAMILIES OF DICOTYLEDONS

THE APETALAE

This is generally regarded as an artificial group of orders and families, probably derived from various members of the *Polypetalae*. The flowers have no petals.

The Amentiferae

This group includes all dicotyledons having some or all of their flowers produced in catkins, or aments. The plants are woody, varying from large trees to ordinary or diminutive shrubs.

Key to the Families

Leaves pinnately compound, without stipules; plants aromatic; fruit a bony nut completely enclosed in a leathery husk .... JUGLANDACEAE

Leaves simple and stipulate; plants not aromatic; fruit naked or partly or completely enclosed in an involucre

    Fruit a capsule; seeds hairy; plants dioecious ..... SALICACEAE

    Fruit a nut or nutlet; seeds not hairy; plants monoecious

        Male and female flowers in catkins (in *Corylus* the female catkins very small and bud-like); leaves often thin and often doubly serrate; fruit a nut or nutlet enclosed within or subtended by foliaceous or herbaceous bracts, the nutlets often winged .... BETULACEAE

        Male flowers in catkins, female flowers in clusters or solitary; leaves leathery, not doubly serrate but often lobed; fruit a nut enclosed or partly enclosed within a cup or bur of hard, prickly or scaly bractlets, the nut never winged .... FAGACEAE

ORDER SALICALES

SALICACEAE: Willow Family

Trees or shrubs (rarely herbaceous) with simple, alternate, stipulate leaves. Flowers dioecious, in erect or pendulous catkins (aments), the calyx much reduced or lacking, petals none, and stamens 2 or more. Ovary 1-celled, with parietal placentation and numerous ovules. Seeds covered with long hairs. Fruit a 2–4-valved capsule.

There are 4 genera and some 200 species in the world, widely distributed; common in northern and mountainous areas, but absent from the Malay Archipelago and Australia. Only two genera, *Salix* and *Populus*, occur in North America.

EXAMPLES: *Salix babylonica:* Weeping Willow, an ornamental.
Populus alba: White or Silver Poplar.
Populus nigra var. *italica:* Lombardy Poplar.
Populus tremuloides: Quaking Aspen.

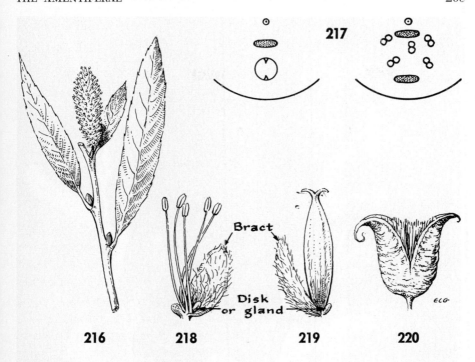

216 *Salix*, twig with catkin.

217 *Salix*, floral diagrams of female and male flowers.

218 *Salix*, male flower.

219 *Salix*, female flower.

220 *Salix*, capsule.

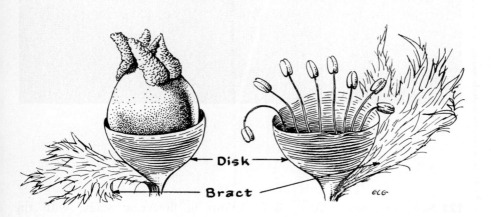

221 *Populus*, female flower.

222 *Populus*, male flower.

223 *Salix ligulifolia* (Ball) Ball, catkins in flowering stage, with the staminate on the left and the pistillate on the right. This is a precocious willow; that is, it blooms before the leaves appear.

224 *Populus tremuloides* Michx., Trembling Aspen, showing pendulous staminate catkins.

ORDER JUGLANDALES

JUGLANDACEAE: Walnut Family

Mostly resinous and aromatic trees with alternate, pinnately compound leaves without stipules. Flowers monoecious, the male in pendulous catkins, the female in few-flowered clusters or, less commonly, in pendulous catkins. Male flower subtended by a bract and a pair of bracteoles, and often there are several scale-like parts that may represent a reduced perianth; the stamens indefinite in number and arrangement, 3–100. Female flowers perigynous, with an adnate hypogynous hypanthium, the sepals 0–4, the pistil single, with a 1–4-celled ovary, short style, and usually 2 plumose stigmas. Fruit a single-seeded nut surrounded by the fleshy or leathery hypanthium husk, which may be indehiscent or may split longitudinally into 4 valves.

The family includes about 6 genera and 60 species, mostly in north temperate regions and in the mountains of the northern tropics, but the fossil record indicates that in the Cretaceous and Tertiary periods the family had a much wider distribution, extending into Greenland and Alaska. Two genera and about 19 species are native to the United States.

EXAMPLES: *Juglans regia:* English Walnut, widely distributed in Eurasia.

Juglans nigra: Black Walnut, native to the United States and a valuable timber tree.

Juglans cinerea: Butternut, or White Walnut.

Carya ovata: Shagbark Hickory.

Carya illinoensis: Pecan, cultivated for the fruit.

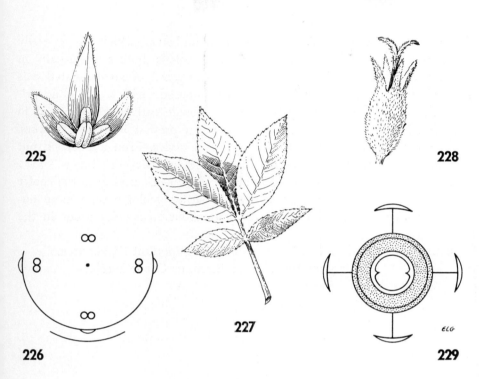

225 *Carya ovata*, male flower.

226 *Carya ovata*, floral diagram of male flower.

227 *Carya ovata*, leaf.

228 *Carya ovata*, female flower.

229 *Carya ovata*, floral diagram of female flower.

ORDER FAGALES

Trees or shrubs with simple, alternate, stipulate leaves. Flowers monoecious, at least the staminate in catkins. Fruit a nut or nutlet.

BETULACEAE: Birch Family

Trees or shrubs with simple, alternate, stipulate leaves, which are generally thin and often doubly serrate. Flowers monoecious, both sexes usually in catkins (the inflorescence is theoretically composed of an elongated axis along which there are spirally arranged condensed dichasia including primary, secondary, and tertiary bracts), the female catkins few-flowered in *Corylus*. Perianth rudimentary or none; when present in female flowers, adnate to the 2-celled, 4-ovuled ovary with 2 styles. Fruit a 1-seeded nut or nutlet, often winged, enclosed or subtended by foliaceous bracts.

The family includes 6 genera and about 110 species, mostly in the cooler parts of the northern hemisphere but in earlier geologic time more numerous and widespread. Five genera and about 25 species occur in the United States.

EXAMPLES: *Betula lutea:* Yellow Birch, an important timber tree.
Betula papyrifera: Paper Birch, or Canoe Birch.
Alnus: Alder.
Corylus: Hazelnut.

230 *Betula lutea*, winged nutlet, primary bract, and leaf.

231 *Ostrya virginiana*, fruiting branchlet.

232 *Corylus cornuta*, pair of fruits inside involucre, and leaf.

233 *Betula occidentalis* Hook. Portion of a branch showing pistillate catkin on left, and pendulous staminate catkins lying on top of another pistillate catkin on the right.

230

231

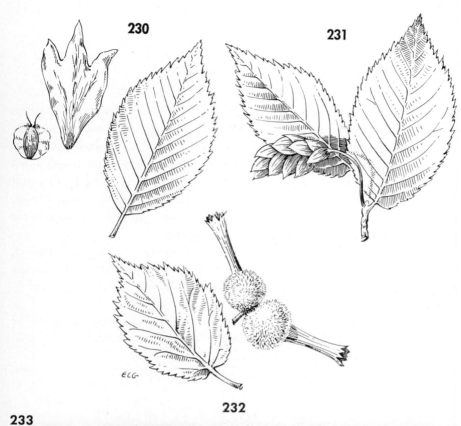

232

233

FAGACEAE: Beech Family

Trees or shrubs with simple, alternate, stipulate leaves, which are often strongly ribbed and may be deeply lobed, the texture usually leathery. Flowers monoecious, the male usually in catkins (in globose heads in *Fagus*), the female in few-flowered clusters. Male flowers with a 4–7-lobed calyx and 4 or more stamens. Female flowers with a 4–8-lobed calyx and a single pistil, usually of 3 carpels, with 3 styles and stigmas. Fruit a nut, 1-seeded by the abortion of the other ovules, and partially or completely enclosed by an involucre of scales or a spiny bur.

The family includes 9 genera and about 600 species, widely distributed, but mostly in temperate regions. Five genera and about 90 species occur in the United States, some of them valuable timber trees.

EXAMPLES: *Fagus:* Beech.

Quercus: Oak, a large and taxonomically difficult genus of over 200 species, some of them of great economic importance for lumber and cork.

Castanea: Chestnut.

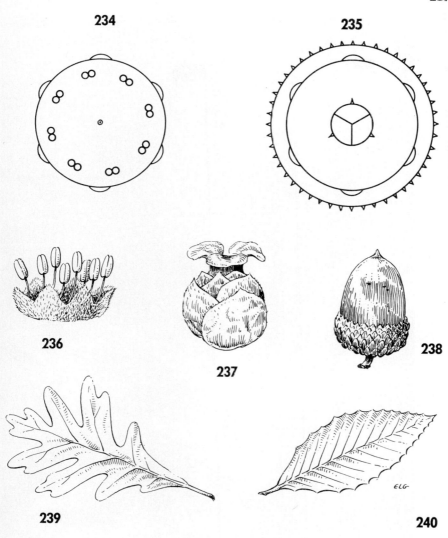

234 *Quercus alba*, floral diagram of male flower.

235 *Quercus alba*, floral diagram of female flower.

236 *Quercus alba*, male flower enlarged.

237 *Quercus alba*, female flower enlarged.

238 *Quercus alba*, fruit.

239 *Quercus alba*, leaf.

240 *Fagus grandifolia*, leaf.

241 *Castanea dentata* Borkh., American Chestnut, showing staminate and pistillate flowers.

The Floriferae

This group includes those members of the *Apetalae* whose flowers are produced, not in catkins, but in various other types of inflorescences. The plants may be herbaceous or woody.

Key to the Families

Juice milky; fruit a multiple .... MORACEAE

Juice not milky; fruit simple

  Trees with unsymmetrical leaves; fruit a samara
  or a drupe .... ULMACEAE

  Herbs, vines, or shrubs with symmetrical leaves;
  fruit otherwise

    Plants aromatic .... CANNABINACEAE

    Plants not aromatic

      With stinging hairs or at least mostly op-
      posite leaves; inflorescence of numerous,
      minute, green flowers, axillary .... URTICACEAE

      Without stinging hairs, the leaves alternate;
      inflorescence sometimes of green flowers
      but not all axillary

        Fruit not an anthocarp, not surrounded
        by the withered remains of the perianth
        tube; stamens mostly opposite the sepals
        or the sepals lacking

          Embryo straight; plants not mealy;
          perianth petaloid or else in two series
          (*Rumex*); stipules sheathing the stem
          or the flowers usually involucrate
          (*Eriogonum*); fruit usually a triangular
          akene, rarely a lenticular akene ..... POLYGONACEAE

          Embryo curved or coiled; plants often
          mealy; perianth green or scarious when
          present, always in 1 series; stipules
          lacking; flowers not involucrate; fruit
          a utricle, pyxis, or rounded akene

            Inflorescence without prickly bracts CHENOPODIACEAE

            Inflorescence with prickly bracts .. AMARANTHACEAE

        Fruit an anthocarp, surrounded by the
        withered remains of the perianth tube;
        stamens alternate with the sepals ...... NYCTAGINACEAE

ORDER URTICALES

Herbs, shrubs, or trees with reduced flowers, which are small, greenish, apetalous or, rarely, naked, perfect to polygamous, monoecious, or dioecious, but not produced in catkins. Stamens variable, but mostly of the same number as the sepals and opposite them. Carpels 1–2, but the fruit with a single seed and becoming a samara, nutlet, akene, or drupe, or sometimes a multiple.

The order includes the following 4 families, of ancient origin and dubious affinities.

COMPARISON OF FAMILIES OF URTICALES

	Ulmaceae	*Urticaceae*	*Cannabinaceae*	*Moraceae*
Growth form	trees and shrubs	herbs, shrubs or trees in the tropics	herbs or vines, not woody	nearly all trees or shrubs, except *Dorstenia*
Plants with milky juice	no	no	no	yes
Plants aromatic	no	no	yes	no
Leaves alternate or opposite	alternate	alternate or opposite	alternate or opposite	alternate, rarely opposite
Flowers *polygamous, monoecious, dioecious,* or *perfect*	perf, pol, mon	mon or di, or sometimes perf	mostly di	mon or di
Fruit type	samara or drupaceous	akene, nutlet, or sometimes drupaceous	akene or nutlet	usually a multiple

Key to the Families of Urticales

Mostly trees or shrubs; fruit not a simple akene or nutlet

    Juice milky; fruit usually multiple .... MORACEAE

    Juice not milky; fruit a samara or a drupe ...... ULMACEAE

Herbs or vines, woody only in the tropics; fruit an akene or nutlet, or sometimes drupaceous

    Plants aromatic, without stinging hairs .... CANNABINACEAE

    Plants not aromatic, often with stinging hairs .... URTICACEAE

ULMACEAE: Elm Family

Trees or shrubs, rarely herbs, with simple, alternate, stipulate leaves having blades that are often inequilateral at the base. Flowers perfect or
polygamo-monoecious, the calyx with a very short or, often, a funnelform
tube below the 4–9 lobes. Petals none. Stamens 4–6. Pistil 1, the ovary
usually 1-celled and 1-seeded, the stigmas 2. Fruit a samara, drupe, or
nutlet.

The family includes about 15 genera and 150 species, mostly in temperate
regions. There are 5 genera in the United States, including some valuable
timber and shade trees.

EXAMPLES: *Ulmus americana:* American, or White, Elm.
             Celtis occidentalis: Hackberry, or Nettle Tree.
             Planera aquatica: Planer Tree.

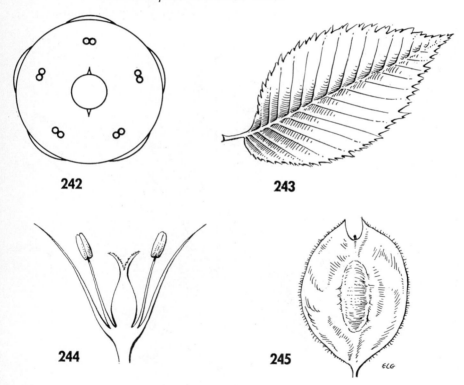

242

243

244

245

242 *Ulmus americana,* floral diagram.

243 *Ulmus americana,* leaf.

244 *Ulmus americana,* longitudinal section of flower, enlarged.

245 *Ulmus americana,* fruit, enlarged.

URTICACEAE: Nettle Family

Annual or perennial herbs in ours, but arborescent in some genera in the tropics, with simple, alternate or (mostly) opposite, stipulate, toothed leaves and watery juice. Stems and leaves often armed with stinging hairs. Flowers small, greenish, variously clustered, often axillary, apetalous, monoecious, dioecious, or polygamous, usually 4–5-merous, the stamens as many as the sepals and opposite them. Pistil 1, with a 1-celled ovary and 1 ovule. Fruit an akene or sometimes drupaceous.

The family is mainly tropical; it includes about 42 genera and 600 species.

EXAMPLES: *Urtica:* Nettle, with about 50 species, widely distributed in both hemispheres.

                Boehmeria nivea: Ramie, grown for its long fibers.

                Laportea: includes Tree Nettles of the tropical Pacific.

                Pilea: Clearweed, a large and mainly tropical genus.

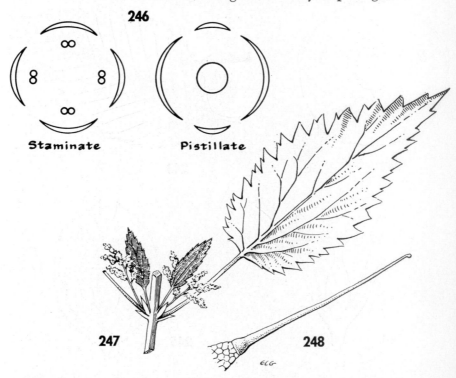

246 *Urtica dioica,* floral diagrams of staminate and pistillate flowers.

247 *Urtica dioica,* portion of plant.

248 *Urtica dioica,* stinging hair, greatly magnified, showing the secretory cells at the base and a minute bulbous tip, which breaks off when touched to release the fluid within.

249 *Urtica dioica* L. var. *procera* (Muhl. ex Willd.) Wedd., a common Nettle, showing the upper part of the plant in bloom.

CANNABINACEAE: Hemp Family

Erect or climbing aromatic herbs with watery juice and alternate or often opposite leaves, which are simple and palmately veined or else palmately compound, the margins coarsely toothed. Stipules present and persistent. Flowers usually dioecious, apetalous, axillary; the staminate flowers in panicles, each with a usually 5-parted calyx and 5 stamens, the pistillate flowers in crowded bracteate spikes, each with a single sepal, which envelops the single 1-celled, 1-ovuled ovary. Fruit an akene, which is surrounded by the persistent perianth.

The family includes 2 genera and 3 species, widely distributed and mostly of considerable economic significance.

EXAMPLES: *Cannabis sativa:* Hemp. The plants are often cultivated for the strong fibers of the stem. It is also the source of marijuana and hashish, which are intoxicants.

Humulus lupulus: Hop Vine, commonly used in the brewing industry. Numerous yellow glandular hairs on the bracteoles secrete lupulin, and to this the plants owe their economic value.

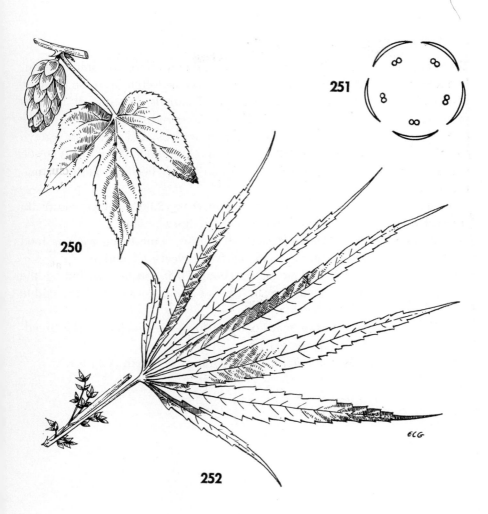

250 *Humulus lupulus*, fruiting branch.

251 *Cannabis sativa*, floral diagram of staminate flower.

252 *Cannabis sativa*, fruiting branch.

MORACEAE: Mulberry Family

Trees or shrubs, rarely herbs, with milky sap, and alternate, simple, stipulate leaves. Flowers small, monoecious or dioecious, often in dense clusters, commonly 4-merous. Petals none. Pistil of 2 carpels, but one of these is often abortive and represented only by a style or rudiment. Fruit an akene or a drupe, invested by a fleshy perianth or axis and variously grown together to form a multiple fruit or a syconium (a hollow floral axis inside which the minute flowers are produced and which becomes fleshy at maturity as in a Fig).

A large family of some 55 genera and perhaps 2,300 species, mostly in tropical regions, but a few extend into the temperate zone.

EXAMPLES: *Morus:* Mulberry, with 10 species, some being used as food for silkworms, and the fruit sweet and edible.

Ficus: Fig, a genus of about 2,000 species,[1] including the well-known Banyan Tree (*F. bengalensis*) and the edible Fig (*F. carica*).

Artocarpus: a genus of some 40 species, including the Breadfruit (*A. incisa*).

Maclura pomifera: Osage Orange of North America.

---

[1] E. D. Merrill: "Some Economic Aspects of Taxonomy," Torreya 43: 50–64 (1943). "Approaching 2,000 species even without splitting hairs on specific differences."

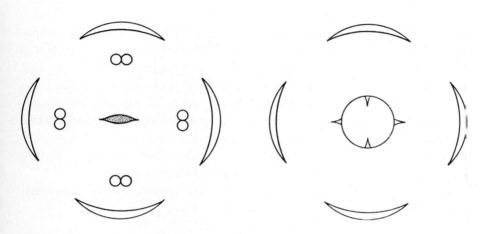

253 *Morus*, floral diagram of staminate flower.

254 *Morus*, floral diagram of pistillate flower.

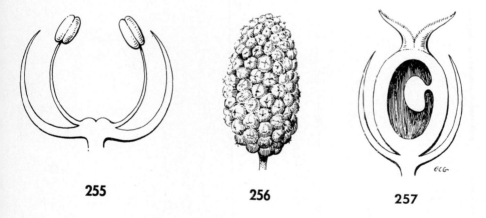

255

256

257

255 *Morus*, longitudinal section of staminate flower.

256 *Morus*, multiple fruit.

257 *Morus*, longitudinal section of pistillate flower.

ORDER POLYGONALES

POLYGONACEAE: Buckwheat Family

Herbs, in ours, often with sour juice, and with mostly alternate, simple, entire leaves, with stipules forming sheaths (ochreae) around the stem at the joints (these lacking in *Eriogonum* and *Brunnichia*). Flowers small, often numerous, mostly perfect but sometimes polygamous or dioecious, the perianth often petaloid and in a single series, or sepaloid and in two series, consisting of 4–6 parts, sometimes persistent, and sometimes tubular or funnelform. Stamens 4–12, free or inserted at the base of the perianth tube. Pistil 1, the ovary 1-celled and 1-ovuled, the styles 2–3. Fruit a lenticular or triangular akene. Seed with a straight embryo.

The family includes about 32 genera and 700 species, widely distributed.

EXAMPLES: *Fagopyrum sagittatum:* Buckwheat.
Rheum rhaponticum: Rhubarb.
Rumex: Dock.
Eriogonum: False Buckwheat.

Knotweed

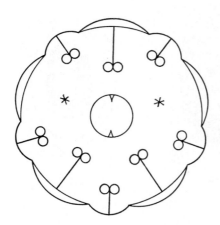

258 *Polygonum pensylvanicum,* floral diagram.

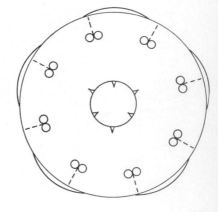

259 *Fagopyrum,* floral diagram.

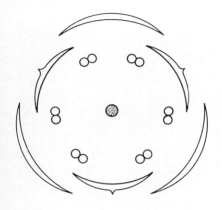

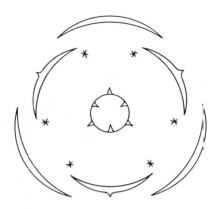

260 *Rumex acetosella*, floral diagram of staminate flower.

261 *Rumex acetosella*, floral diagram of pistillate flower.

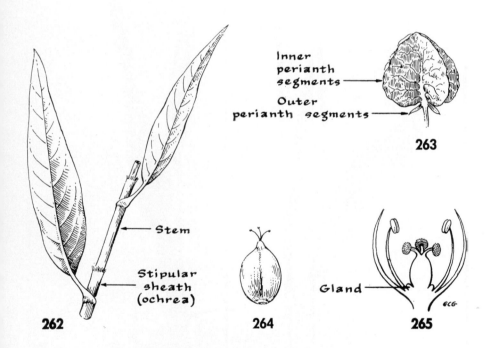

Inner
perianth
segments

Outer
perianth segments

263

Stem

Stipular
sheath
(ochrea)

262

Gland

264

265

262 *Polygonum persicaria*, stem and leaves.

263 *Rumex*, fruiting perianth.

264 *Polygonum*, akene, enlarged.

265 *Rheum*, longitudinal section of flower, enlarged.

266 *Polygonum viviparum* L., a low, circumboreal species. The lower flowers in the spike are modified into bulblets.

267 *Rumex crispus* L., Sour Dock, a common weed. This shows the early fruit stage.

ORDER CHENOPODIALES

Mostly weedy herbs, sometimes shrubs, of dry regions, with alternate or opposite, simple, exstipulate leaves, and small, often densely clustered, greenish flowers without petals. Gynoecium composed of from 1 to several carpels, free or connate, with basal placentation, the seeds from 1 to several, with the embryo usually curved or coiled round the endosperm, rarely with a straight embryo.

The order includes 6 families as here defined: *Phytolaccaceae, Cynocrambaceae, Chenopodiaceae, Batidaceae, Amaranthaceae,* and *Basellaceae,* these being the apetalous members of the group of families often referred to as the *Centrospermae,* which also includes the related order *Caryophyllales* in the polypetalae. This relationship is best shown by the similarity of placentation and seed morphology.

CHENOPODIACEAE: Goosefoot Family

Annual or perennial, often halophytic herbs or shrubs, which are commonly mealy, with mostly alternate, simple, exstipulate leaves and small, greenish, perfect or sometimes unisexual flowers. Calyx usually of 1–5 sepals, which are often fleshy, sometimes lacking. Petals none. Stamens as many as the sepals and opposite them, or fewer. Pistil 1, the ovary 1-celled, the styles 2 or 3. Fruit 1-seeded and circumscissile (a utricle), or indehiscent (an akene). The embryo may be either curved or spirally coiled.

The family includes about 75 genera and 500 species, widely distributed.

EXAMPLES: *Spinacea oleracea:* Spinach.
Beta vulgaris: Beet.
Chenopodium: Goosefoot.
Eurotia lanata: Winterfat.
Atriplex: Saltbush.
Salsola: Russian Thistle.

268
268 *Chenopodium album,* floral diagram.

269
269 *Chenopodium album,* longitudinal section of flower, enlarged.

270
270 *Chenopodium album,* leaf.

271 *Chenopodium*, section of seed, enlarged.

272 *Salsola*, embryo, enlarged.

273 *Chenopodium album* L., Lamb's Quarters, a common weed. Upper part of plants in flower.

AMARANTHACEAE: Pigweed Family

Annual or perennial herbs, rarely undershrubs or climbers, with opposite or alternate, simple, exstipulate leaves. Flowers small and usually crowded, often with scarious or prickly bracts and bracteoles, perfect or unisexual. Sepals usually 5, thin and dry. Petals none. Stamens of the same number as the sepals and opposite them, their filaments often united below into a short tube (monadelphous). Pistil 1, the ovary 1-celled and with 1 or more ovules from the base, the styles short or long, and the stigmas 1, 2, or 3. Fruit a utricle, akene, or pyxis.

The family includes about 50 genera and 500 species, in temperate and warm regions.

EXAMPLES: *Celosia cristata:* Cockscomb, a common ornamental.

Amaranthus retroflexus: Pigweed, a common weed.

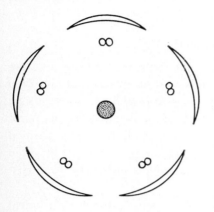
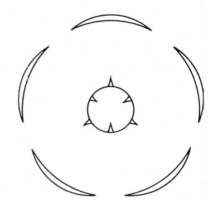

274 *Amaranthus retroflexus*, floral diagram of staminate flower.

275 *Amaranthus retroflexus*, floral diagram of pistillate flower.

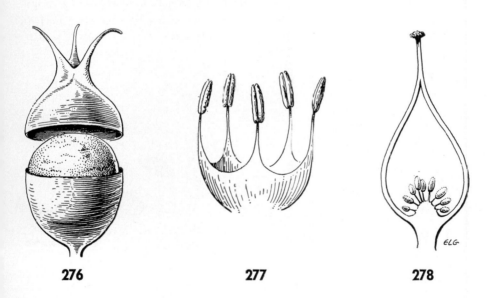

276   **277**   **278**

276 *Amaranthus*, fruit (utricle).

277 *Celosia*, monadelphous stamens.

278 *Celosia*, longitudinal section of pistil.

ORDER NYCTAGINALES

NYCTAGINACEAE: Four O'Clock Family

Herbs, shrubs, vines, or trees with simple, alternate or opposite, exstipulate leaves. Flowers perfect or sometimes unisexual, in cymes that are often dense and head-like, often subtended by prominent or colored bracts. Calyx tubular, salverform, or funnelform, 4–5-lobed, often petaloid. Petals none. Stamens 1 or more, free or connate at the base. Pistil 1, with a 1-celled ovary containing a single ovule, and a slender simple style. Fruit often enclosed in the persistent base of the calyx and indehiscent (an anthocarp), sometimes broadly winged at maturity.

The family includes about 20 genera and 160 species, mainly in tropical America but with some representatives in temperate regions.

EXAMPLES: *Mirabilis jalapa:* Four o'Clock, a commonly cultivated herb native to tropical America.

Bougainvillea glabra: Bougainvillea, a cultivated woody vine commonly growing over buildings in warm regions, having showy magenta or purple bracts, and native to Brazil.

Abronia: Sand Verbena, with several native North American species, usually in dry sandy soil.

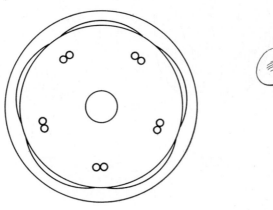

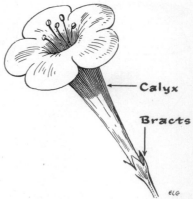

279 *Mirabilis,* floral diagram. Note the abnormal position of the stamens.

280 *Mirabilis,* flower.

281 *Abronia*, portion of plant.
[After Standley in Contr.
U. S. Nat. Herb. 12: pl. 32
(1909).]

282 *Abronia*, flower, enlarged

THE POLYPETALAE

Included in this group are the dicotyledons having flowers with separate petals. A few families contain genera or species that have apetalous flowers, but these are exceptional. Within the *Polypetalae* there is a general progression from hypogynous through perigynous to epigynous flowers, and in the hypogynous and perigynous members from apocarpous to syncarpous flowers.

ORDER CARYOPHYLLALES

Herbaceous or, rarely, shrubby, sometimes succulent plants, with mostly opposite or whorled leaves having stipules reduced or lacking. Flowers hypogynous (partly epigynous in *Portulaca*) and regular, usually with petals. Stamens mostly definite. Pistil 1, with free-central or basal placentation.

This order includes the polypetalous members of the *Centrospermae: Elatinaceae, Caryophyllaceae, Molluginaceae, Aizoaceae,* and *Portulacaceae.* Its connection with the apetalous *Centrospermae* is through the subfamily *Paronychioideae* of the family *Caryophyllaceae.*

CARYOPHYLLACEAE: Chickweed or Pink Family

Annual or perennial herbs with opposite, simple, and mostly exstipulate leaves (scarious stipules present in *Paronychia*). Flowers solitary or in cymes, usually perfect, regular, hypogynous, with or sometimes without petals, 4–5-merous. Stamens 10 or fewer, distinct. Pistil 1, of 2–5 united carpels, the ovary 1-celled and with free-central placentation and 1–many ovules, the styles commonly distinct but sometimes connate. Fruit a utricle or, more commonly, a capsule opening by valves or apical teeth.

The family, named for the pre-Linnaean genus *Caryophyllus*, includes about 80 genera and 2,000 species, mostly in cool or north temperate regions. It includes three clearly defined subfamilies, sometimes treated as families.

Paronychioideae	*Alsinoideae*	*Silenoideae*
Petals lacking.	Petals present.	Petals present.
Sepals distinct or united.	Sepals distinct.	Sepals united.
Fruit a utricle.	Fruit a capsule.	Fruit a capsule.
EXAMPLES:	EXAMPLES:	EXAMPLES:
Paronychia: Whitlow-wort.	*Cerastium:* Chickweed.	*Silene:* Catchfly.
Scleranthus: Knawel.	*Arenaria:* Sandwort.	*Lychnis:* Campion.
		Dianthus: Carnation, or Pink.

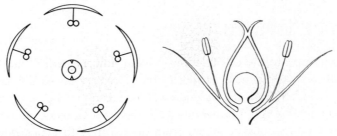

283 *Paronychia*, floral diagram and flower section. The stamens are inserted on the base of the sepals.

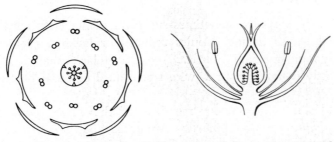

284 *Stellaria pubera*, floral diagram and flower section. The petals are bifid, deeply two-lobed.

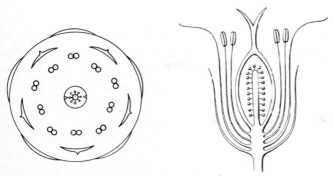

285 *Dianthus plumarius,* floral diagram and flower section.

286 *Cerastium arvense* L., Chickweed. This illustrates the characteristic dichasium inflorescence, the central flower in each group being the oldest, the corolla having withered, while on each side are younger flowers.

PORTULACACEAE: Purslane Family

Herbs or small shrubs with succulent, alternate or opposite leaves and scarious stipules (except *Claytonia*, which is exstipulate). Flowers solitary or in cymes or racemes, regular, perfect, and hypogynous or sometimes partly epigynous. Sepals usually 2, often persistent. Petals usually 4–6, often falling early. Stamens as many as the petals and opposite them, often epipetalous, and sometimes more numerous or fewer. Pistil 1, the ovary 1-celled with free-central placentation, the style variously divided but the branches often 3. Fruit a capsule, which is either circumscissile (a pyxis) or dehiscent by valves.

The family includes about 20 genera and 200 species, chiefly American in distribution.

EXAMPLES: *Portulaca grandiflora:* Portulaca, often grown for ornament.
Portulaca oleracea: Purslane, a succulent weed of cultivated areas.
Claytonia: Spring Beauty.
Lewisia rediviva: Bitter-root, named for Captain Meriwether Lewis, and the state flower of Montana.

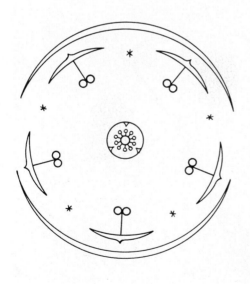

287 *Claytonia,* floral diagram.   **288** *Claytonia,* plant.

289 *Claytonia,* capsule, enlarged.   **290** *Portulaca,* circumscissile capsule (pyxis), enlarged.

291 *Claytonia lanceolata* Pursh, Spring Beauty. The flowers are pink to nearly white, the leaves thick and succulent.

ORDER RANALES

Herbs or woody plants with spiral or cyclic, hypogynous, and regular to irregular flowers. Perianth consisting of sepals and petals, sometimes the petals lacking or reduced and the sepals petaloid. Stamens usually numerous. Carpels numerous and 1-seeded to few and several-seeded, sometimes single.

As treated here, the order includes 12 families according to Rendle[1] and 23 families according to Hutchinson,[2] who divides the group into 5 orders. This is generally regarded as the most primitive order of dicotyledons and is taken as the ancestral group that gave rise to the monocotyledons. The following families are well represented in the North American flora.

MAGNOLIACEAE: Magnolia Family

Shrubs or trees with mostly alternate simple leaves, with or without stipules. Flowers usually solitary and showy, perfect, regular, and hypogynous, the floral axis usually elongated and the floral parts spirally arranged on it. Perianth usually but not always clearly differentiated into calyx and corolla, the sepals or the petals in two or more series. Stamens numerous. Carpels (pistils) usually numerous and distinct, becoming follicles, samaras, or berries in fruit, or sometimes aggregates.

The family includes 10 genera and about 100 species in tropical Asia and tropical America, extending northward into the temperate zone, but with a much wider distribution in the upper Cretaceous and Tertiary periods.

EXAMPLES: *Magnolia:* Magnolia, ornamental small trees and shrubs.
      Liriodendron tulipifera: Tulip-tree, a valuable timber tree, often reaching immense size. (See the frontispiece.)

[1] A. B. Rendle: *The Classification of Flowering Plants* (1925), Vol. II, p. 124.
[2] J. Hutchinson: *The Families of Flowering Plants* (1926), Vol. I, pp. 10–11.

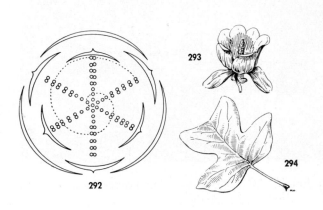

292 *Liriodendron tulipifera,* floral diagram. The dotted spiral indicates that the parts are spirally arranged.

293 *Liriodendron tulipifera,* flower.

294 *Liriodendron tulipifera,* leaf.

NYMPHAEACEAE: Water Lily Family

Perennial aquatic herbs with submerged, floating, or sometimes emersed and often large leaves. Flowers usually solitary and showy, hypogynous or more or less epigynous, the perianth composed of sepals and petals that are often indefinite in number and in two or more series, the calyx and corolla poorly differentiated. Stamens few or usually many. Carpels 2 to many, free or united. Fruit nut-like or berry-like.

As treated here, the family includes 8 genera and about 50 species, in tropical and north temperate regions. Because of the varied floral structure found in this group, some authors have proposed that several families be recognized [1] instead of the one given here.

EXAMPLES: *Nymphaea:* Water Lily, the largest genus, with about 32 species.

Nuphar: Yellow Water Lily, or Spatterdock.

Nelumbo: Lotus Lily.

Victoria amazonica: Giant Water Lily of the Amazon region, with leaves 6–7 feet in diameter, often cultivated.

[1] Five families are recognized by Hui-Lin Li. See Am. Midl. Nat. 54: 33–41 (1955).

295 *Nelumbo,* floral diagram.

296 *Nelumbo,* gynoecium axis and pistils.

297 *Nymphaea,* flower and leaf.

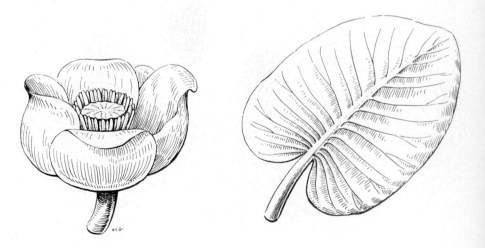

298 *Nuphar,* flower and leaf.

299 *Nuphar luteum* (L.) Sibth. & Sm. subsp. *polysepalum* (Engelm.) Beal, the western Yellow Water Lily, or Spatterdock, shown growing in a lake in about five feet of clear water, rooted in the mud on the bottom and with leaves and flower floating on the surface of the water.

RANUNCULACEAE: Buttercup Family

Mostly perennial herbs with alternate or basal and often divided leaves without stipules, or, in *Clematis*, sometimes soft-woody climbers with opposite leaves. Flowers solitary or in racemes or panicles, hypogynous, usually perfect, quite variable, regular to irregular, sometimes spurred. Sepals 3 or more, sometimes petaloid. Petals none to indefinite, often with a nectariferous claw, the sepals and petals each usually in one series. Stamens usually numerous and spirally arranged. Pistils simple (flowers apocarpous), numerous, spirally arranged, and forming akenes in fruit, or few and cyclic and forming follicles or berries in fruit.

The family includes about 40 genera and 1,500 species, in temperate and cold regions, often circumboreal.

more than 1 pistil

EXAMPLES: *Ranunculus:* Buttercup, with about 300 species, nearly 100 of these in North America.

Delphinium: Larkspur, often cultivated, and some species of western ranges poisonous to livestock.

Aquilegia: Columbine, with both native and cultivated species.

Paeonia: Peony, often cultivated for its large flowers.

Anemone: Anemone, or Windflower, with about 100 species.

Caltha: Marsh Marigold, with about 20 species in cold and north temperate regions.

300 *Ranunculus,* floral diagram.

301 *Ranunculus,* diagrammatic longitudinal section of flower.

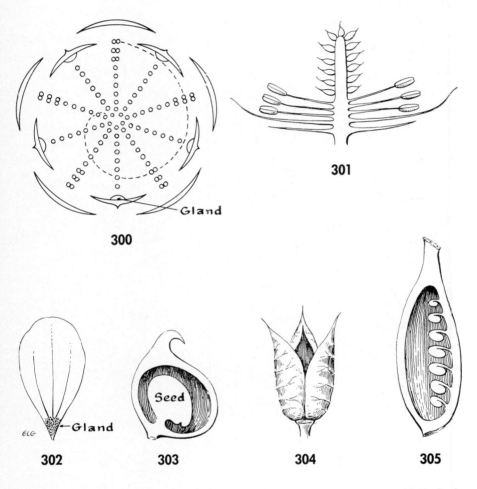

Gland

300

301

Seed

Gland

ELG

302   **303**   **304**   **305**

302 *Ranunculus,* petal.

303 *Ranunculus,* fruit (akene) cut lengthwise.

304 *Delphinium,* fruits (follicles).

305 *Caltha,* follicle cut lengthwise.

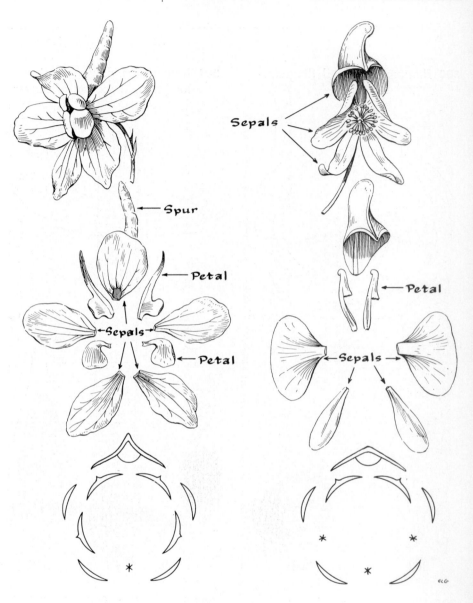

306 *Delphinium*, flower, perianth, and diagram of perianth.

307 *Aconitum*, flower, perianth, and diagram of perianth.

308 *Caltha leptosepala* DC., a species of Marsh Marigold found in cool, moist situations in western North America. It has white flowers.

309 *Ranunculus glaberrimus* Hook., a common early Buttercup of the western United States.

310

310 *Anemone patens* L., Pasque Flower, a circumboreal species with several races. The large sepals are blue and resemble petals, but the flowers have no petals. The leaf-like whorl below the flower is an involucre.

311 *Aquilegia caerulea* James, Columbine, of the Rocky Mountains, and the State Flower of Colorado. The petals have long spurs projecting backward from the flower.

LAURACEAE: Laurel Family

Mainly aromatic woody plants with alternate, simple, entire or lobed, and exstipulate leaves. Flowers numerous, in mixed inflorescences, perfect to unisexual, regular, 3-merous, the perianth of similar parts (probably representing sepals and petals). Stamens definite, the inner often reduced to staminodia, the fertile anthers opening by valves. Pistil 1, with a single style and often 3 stigmas (probably representing 3 carpels but only 1 developing), the ovary with a single ovule. Fruit a drupe.

The family includes about 40 genera and 1,000 species, mainly tropical but with a few representatives in North America.

EXAMPLES: *Laurus nobilis:* Laurel, or Bay Tree, of Europe, often cultivated.

Sassafras: a genus of 3 species, one in the eastern United States, one in China, and one in Taiwan (Formosa).

Cinnamomum zeylandicum: Cinnamon, of southern Asia.

Cinnamomum camphora: Camphor tree, of southern Asia.

Persea gratissima: Avocado, native of tropical America.

Umbellularia californica: Oregon Myrtle, or California Laurel.

BERBERIDACEAE: Barberry Family

Perennial herbs or shrubs with simple or compound, often spiny-toothed, mostly exstipulate leaves. Flowers usually small, solitary or in mixed inflorescences, perfect, hypogynous, 2–3-merous, the sepals and petals often similar and the petals sometimes lacking. Stamens 4–9, opposite the petals, their anthers opening by valves. Pistil 1, of 1 carpel. Fruit usually a berry.

The family includes 9 genera and about 200 species, mainly in north temperate regions.

EXAMPLES: *Berberis:* Barberry, the largest genus, with nearly 200 species. *B. vulgaris* is the alternate host of Wheat Rust and has been largely exterminated in the United States. The Japanese Barberry, *B. thunbergii*, is often cultivated.
Podophyllum peltatum: May Apple.
Mahonia: Oregon Grape.

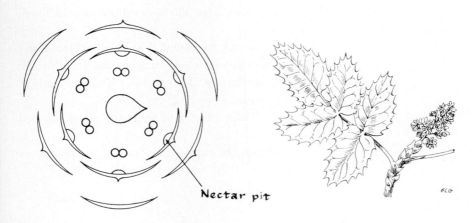

Nectar pit

312 *Berberis*, floral diagram.

313 *Mahonia (Berberis)*, flowering branch.

ORDER PAPAVERALES (RHOEDALES)

Mostly herbaceous plants with alternate exstipulate leaves. Flowers hypogynous, perfect, regular to irregular, with separate petals, mostly 4-merous, the stamens from numerous to 2, the pistil syncarpous, with or without septation in the ovary, the placentation parietal. Fruit a capsule or silique.

The order represents an early modification of the *Ranales* by reduction and specialization of flower parts, and as here treated it includes the families *Papaveraceae, Fumariaceae, Brassicaceae (Cruciferae),* and *Capparidaceae.*

PAPAVERACEAE: Poppy Family

Annual or perennial herbs, rarely shrubs or trees, with milky or colored juice and exstipulate leaves. Flowers usually solitary, often showy, regular, perfect, and hypogynous, or rarely somewhat perigynous. Sepals 2–3, falling as the flowers open. Petals 4–12, in two series, crumpled in the bud. Stamens numerous and distinct. Pistil 1, of 2 or more united carpels; the ovary 1-celled, with parietal placentation, or sometimes becoming several-celled by intrusion of the placentae; the stigmas as many as the placentae, often forming a lobed disk on top of the ovary or on a short style. Fruit a many-seeded capsule opening by a ring of pores under the stigmas, or opening by valves.

The family includes about 24 genera and 450 species, chiefly in north temperate and subtropical regions.

EXAMPLES: *Papaver:* Poppy, a genus of about 100 species, including *P. somniferum,* which yields opium from the latex of the green pods; *P. nudicaule,* the Iceland Poppy; and *P. orientale,* the Oriental Poppy of our gardens.

Argemone: Prickly Poppy, common in the western United States.

Sanguinaria canadensis: Bloodroot, a common spring flower of the wooded areas of the eastern United States.

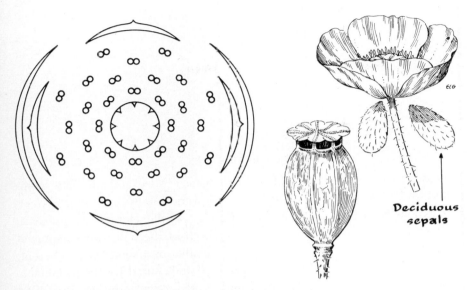

314 *Papaver,* floral diagram.   **315** *Papaver,* flower and capsule.

316 *Argemone hispida* Gray, Prickly Poppy. The petals are white.

FUMARIACEAE: Fumitory Family

Delicate smooth herbs or climbers with watery juice and alternate compound and dissected exstipulate leaves. Flowers usually irregular, perfect, hypogynous. Sepals 2, small and deciduous. Corolla closed, the petals 4, in two pairs, somewhat connivent, one or both of the outer petals spurred or saccate at the base, the two inner ones smaller and sometimes coherent. Stamens 4, free and opposite the petals, or 6 and united by their filaments in two groups (diadelphous). Pistil 1, of 2 united carpels, the ovary 1-celled with 2 parietal placentae and 2 to many ovules, the style single, and the stigma capitate or lobed. Fruit a 2-valved capsule or rarely (in *Fumaria*) indehiscent and nut-like.

The family includes 5 genera and about 150 species, found chiefly in north temperate regions, especially in the Mediterranean basin. It is included with the *Papaveraceae* by some authors.

EXAMPLES: *Dicentra spectabilis:* Bleeding-heart.
Dicentra cucullaria: Dutchman's-breeches.

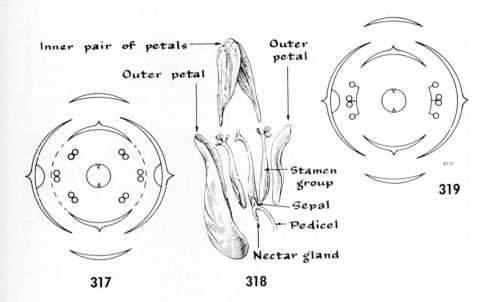

Inner pair of petals

Outer petal

Outer petal

Stamen group

Sepal

Pedicel

Nectar gland

317

318

319

317 *Dicentra*, floral diagram.

318 *Corydalis*, dissected flower. [After Gray, *Genera Florae Americae Boreali-Orientalis Illustrata*, 1: pl. 52 (1848).]

319 *Corydalis*, floral diagram.

CAPPARACEAE: Caper Family

Mostly herbs, in ours, but often arborescent in the tropics, with watery juice, with leaves that are usually alternate, simple or often digitately 3–7-foliolate, and exstipulate or with minute or spiny stipules. Flowers often in bracteate racemes, usually 4-merous, hypogynous, regular or somewhat irregular. Petals usually long-clawed. Stamens 4 or more, usually 6, about equal in length and usually much exserted. Pistil 1, of 2 or more united carpels (usually 2), the ovary usually 1-celled with parietal placentation and often elevated on a long stipe or gynophore, the style short and simple or none, the stigma commonly capitate. Fruit a capsule or less commonly a berry.

The family includes about 40 genera and 450 species, mostly in the tropics. It is generally regarded as the ancestral group to the *Brassicaceae* (*Cruciferae*).

EXAMPLES: *Capparis spinosa:* Capers, the condiment being the flower buds; a Mediterranean shrub.

Cleome spinosa: Spider Plant, often cultivated.

Cleome serrulata: Rocky Mountain Bee Plant, a common roadside weed.

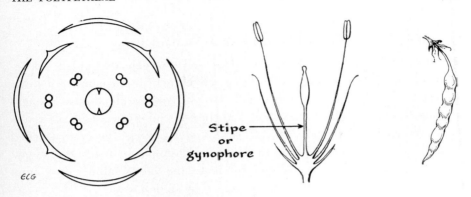

320 *Cleome*, floral diagram and flower section.   **321** *Cleome*, fruit.

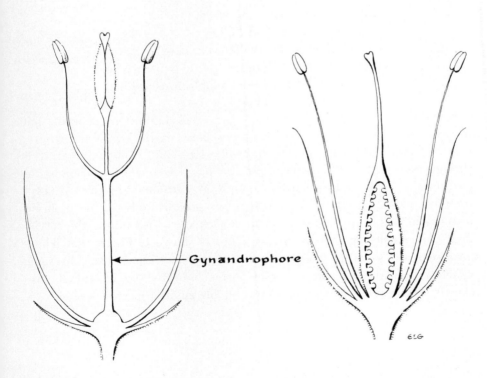

322 *Gynandropsis*, flower section.   **323** *Polanisia*, flower section.

BRASSICACEAE (CRUCIFERAE): Mustard Family

Mostly herbs with pungent watery juice and alternate exstipulate leaves. Flowers in simple or sometimes branched ebracteate racemes, 4-merous, hypogynous and regular. Petals usually long-clawed, rarely absent. Stamens usually 6, the two outer ones short and the four inner ones long, or sometimes reduced to 2, included. Pistil 1, of 2 united carpels, the ovary 2-celled with 1 or more ovules in each cell, the style simple or none, the stigma capitate or 2-lobed. Fruit a silique or silicle, the valves falling away from the persistent partition at maturity, or, rarely, indehiscent.

The family includes about 200 genera and 1,800 species, mostly in temperate and cold regions, including numerous alpine species. Some are noxious weeds, some are ornamentals, and some are common garden vegetables.

EXAMPLES: *Brassica oleracea:* Cabbage, with var. *gemmifera,* Brussels Sprouts; var. *botrytis,* Cauliflower; var. *caulorapa,* Kohlrabi; and var. *italica,* Broccoli.

Brassica rapa: Turnip.

Brassica alba: White Mustard.

Raphanus sativa: Radish.

Cheiranthus cheiri: Wallflower.

Iberis amara: Candytuft.

Sisymbrium altissimum: Tumble Mustard.

Cardaria draba: White-top.

In most members of the family the ovary is sessile on the receptacle, but in some, such as *Stanleya,* there is a *stipe* between the ovary and the receptacle, and this may elongate in fruit (Fig. 327). When the fruit is strongly flattened, the flattening may be parallel to a broad septum or partition; or contrary to a narrow septum or partition (Fig. 328). Except for the genus *Leavenworthia,* which has a straight embryo, the embryos of the members of the family are bent in such a way as to bring the cotyledons and radicle together in various ways, as shown in Figure 329. These arrangements are sometimes used as a basis for classification. In some manuals the arrangement of cotyledons is indicated by a symbol, also shown, which indicates the appearance of the embryo in cross-section.

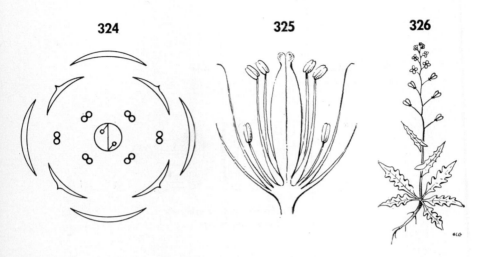

324 *Brassica*, floral diagram.

325 *Brassicaceae*, representative flower section showing all the stamens.

326 *Capsella*, plant.

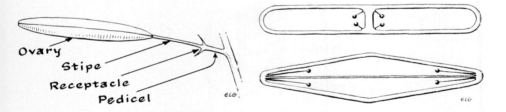

327 *Stanleya*, showing the stipitate pod.

328 Two types of flattening of fruits of the Mustard Family, one flattened contrary to the septum, the other flattened parallel to the septum.

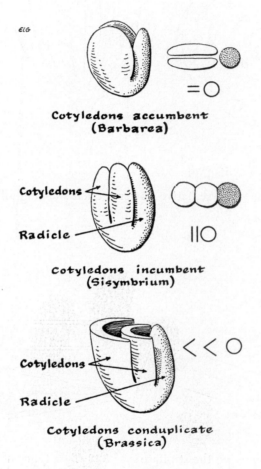

ELG

Cotyledons accumbent
(Barbarea)

Cotyledons

Radicle

Cotyledons incumbent
(Sisymbrium)

Cotyledons

Radicle

Cotyledons conduplicate
(Brassica)

329 Types of embryos: *Barbarea*, with cotyledons accumbent; *Sisymbrium*, with cotyledons incumbent; and *Brassica*, with cotyledons conduplicate. The small figures are diagrams of these structures.

330 *Stanleya pinnata* (Pursh) Britt., var. *integrifolia* (James) Rollins. Plants of this genus indicate seleniferous soils, which often produce plants poisonous to livestock. The flowers are yellow.

ORDER SARRACENIALES

Herbaceous plants, often in bogs, having their leaves variously modified to capture insects. Flowers perfect, regular, hypogynous or somewhat perigynous, polypetalous, the stamens numerous to 4 or 5, the pistil 1, of 3–5 united carpels, the placentation parietal or axillary. Fruit a loculicidal capsule.

The order, as interpreted here, includes the families *Droseraceae* and *Sarraceniaceae*, but not the *Nepenthaceae* or Tropical Pitcher-plant Family of Indo-Malaya and Madagascar, which is sometimes placed in this order. The group represents an early modification, and a terminal one, from the *Ranales* by specialization of the leaves and the adoption of a specialized habitat.

DROSERACEAE: Sundew Family

Mostly bog herbs with a basal rosette of leaves, which are modified to capture insects and are sensitive to touch, the blades commonly covered with large stalked glands (*Drosera*) or provided with a marginal fringe of stiff bristles, which intermesh when the blade folds upward to trap an insect (*Dionaea*). Flowers in racemes or cymes, scapose, hypogynous to somewhat perigynous, mostly 5-merous, regular and perfect. Stamens commonly 5, but sometimes more, the pollen in tetrads. Pistil 1, of mostly 3–5 united carpels, the ovary usually 1-celled, with parietal placentation, the styles commonly free and often divided so as to appear to be twice as many as the carpels. Fruit a loculicidal capsule.

The family includes about 6 genera and nearly 100 species, widely distributed.

EXAMPLES: *Drosera:* Sundew, with about 90 species, temperate and tropical.

Dionaea: Venus'-flytrap, with a single species along the southeastern seacoast of the United States.

Drosophyllum: with a single species in Spain, Portugal, and Morocco.

Aldrovanda: with a single species in Australia, Bengal, northeast Asia, and Europe.

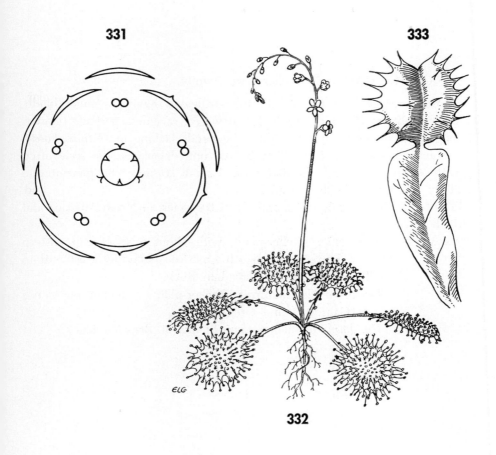

331 *Drosera,* floral diagram.   **332** *Drosera rotundifolia,* plant.

333 *Dionaea,* leaf. The bristle-like hairs near the middle of the upper part of the blade are sensitive to touch and cause the blade to snap shut.

SARRACENIACEAE: Pitcher-plant Family

Scapose perennial bog herbs with tubular leaves having a small blade. Flowers solitary (in ours) or in few-flowered racemes, perfect, regular, hypogynous, 5-merous, polypetalous (the petals lacking in *Heliamphora*), the stamens numerous. Pistil 1, of 3 or 5 united carpels; the style often greatly dilated and umbrella-like, with 5 small stigmas; the placentation axillary. Fruit a loculicidal capsule.

The family includes 3 genera and about 8 species, in North America and British Guiana.

EXAMPLES: *Sarracenia:* Pitcher-plant, with about 6 species in eastern and northeastern North America, extending westward to Texas and to the Canadian Rockies.

Darlingtonia: California Pitcher-plant, a monotypic genus of California and Oregon.

Heliamphora: a monotypic genus of British Guiana.

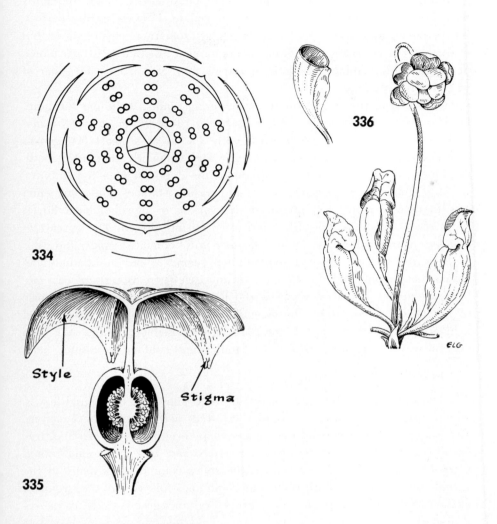

Style

Stigma

334

335

336

334 *Sarracenia,* floral diagram.

335 *Sarracenia,* pistil cut lengthwise.

336 *Sarracenia,* plant and portion of leaf cut transversely.

ORDER ROSALES

Herbs, shrubs, or trees with simple or compound leaves, which frequently have conspicuous stipules but may be exstipulate. Flowers mostly perfect, polypetalous, 5-merous, regular to irregular, sometimes hypogynous but characteristically perigynous. Stamens numerous to definite, distinct, monadelphous or diadelphous. Carpels numerous to 1, free from each other or united. Fruit various.

This is one of the largest orders of flowering plants, including the families *Rosaceae, Saxifragaceae, Hydrangeaceae, Grossulariaceae*,[1] *Crassulaceae*, and *Fabaceae* (*Leguminosae*), with a total of at least 600 genera and 17,000 species. It represents an early and eminently successful modification from the *Ranales* by the frequent development of a hypanthium, which, together with specialization of the corolla, stamens, and gynoecium axis in many groups, has produced the variety of morphological flower types characteristic of the order, and often misinterpreted. The order *Dilleniales*, a tropical group having flowers with connate sepals and thus perhaps the beginnings of a hypanthium, seems to be intermediate between the *Ranales* and the *Rosales*. In any case there is certainly a more than accidental similarity between the flowers of a Buttercup and those of *Potentilla* (Cinquefoil), the essential difference being the presence of a hypanthium in *Potentilla*. Figure 337 shows possible relations and, in a general way, the relative sizes of the families and subfamilies treated here.

ROSACEAE: Rose Family

Trees, shrubs, and herbs, with mostly alternate, simple or compound leaves, which often have prominent stipules. Flowers perfect, regular, 5-merous, and perigynous, the hypanthium saucer-shaped, cup-like, or urn-like, free or adnate to the ovary. Stamens numerous and free from each other. Carpels 1–many, separate or united, the styles commonly as many as the carpels when the latter are united or sometimes joined. Fruit a group of akenes or follicles, a pome, or a drupe, or an aggregate of akenes or drupelets.

The family, as treated here, includes about 100 genera and 3,000 species, cosmopolitan in distribution. There are three subfamilies, well represented in North America, which are treated as families by some.

---

[1] The flowers of the *Grossulariaceae* are epigynous and exceptional in the order. The family is probably misplaced here.

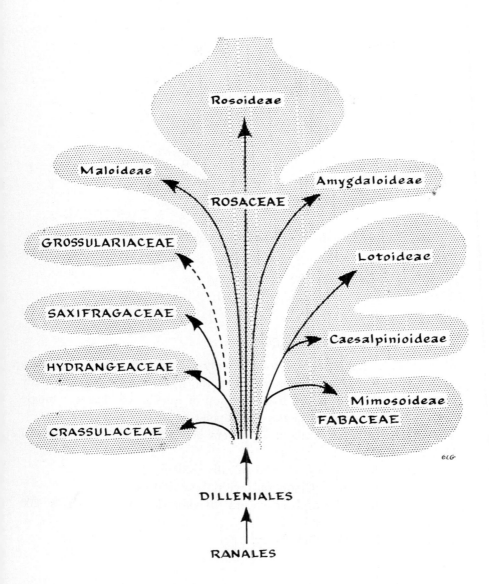

337 Diagram of possible relationships in the *Rosales*. The *Grossulariaceae*, with epigynous flowers, are probably misplaced here.

Key to the Subfamilies

Hypanthium free from the gynoecium; fruit not a pome

    Woody or mostly herbaceous plants, often with persistent stipules; fruit a group of akenes or follicles, or aggregates of akenes or drupelets .... 1. ROSOIDEAE

    Woody plants with deciduous stipules; fruit usually a single drupe .... 2. AMYGDALOIDEAE

Hypanthium adnate to the gynoecium, the flowers thus appearing as if epigynous; fruit a pome .... 3. MALOIDEAE

SUBFAMILY 1. ROSOIDEAE: *Rose Subfamily*

    Mostly herbs, but including some woody plants, the leaves often with persistent stipules. Hypanthium free from the gynoecium. Carpels usually separate and often numerous. Fruit a group of follicles or akenes, a single akene, or an aggregate of akenes or drupelets.

    The subfamily includes about 75 genera and 1,200 species, widely distributed.

    EXAMPLES: *Rosa:* Roses, a taxonomically difficult genus.

                   Potentilla: Cinquefoil, with about 300 species.

                   Rubus: Raspberries and Blackberries, with perhaps 200 species.

                   Fragaria: Strawberry.

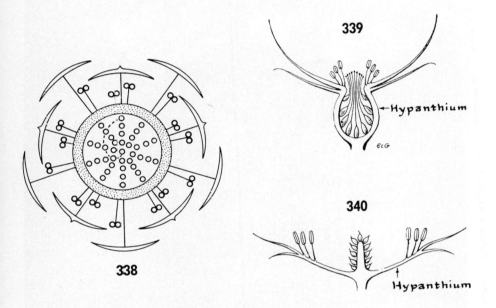

338 *Potentilla*, floral diagram.

339 Longitudinal section of flower of *Rosa*.

340 *Potentilla*, longitudinal section of flower.

341 *Potentilla fissa* Nutt., a species of Cinquefoil (subfamily *Rosoideae*).

342 *Rosa woodsii* Lindl., a common western species with pink flowers.

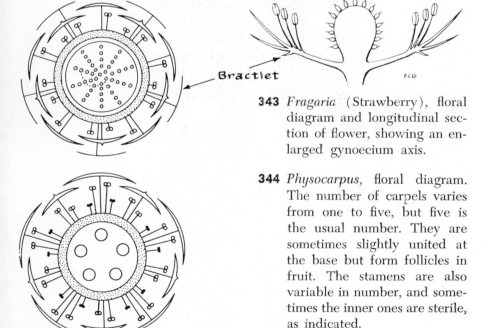

Bractlet

343 *Fragaria* (Strawberry), floral diagram and longitudinal section of flower, showing an enlarged gynoecium axis.

344 *Physocarpus,* floral diagram. The number of carpels varies from one to five, but five is the usual number. They are sometimes slightly united at the base but form follicles in fruit. The stamens are also variable in number, and sometimes the inner ones are sterile, as indicated.

SUBFAMILY 2. AMYGDALOIDEAE: *Peach Subfamily*

Trees and shrubs with alternate simple and serrate or entire leaves, which often have glandular petioles and stipules that are small and deciduous. Hypanthium usually cup-shaped, free from the ovary, deciduous. Pistil usually single, the ovary 1-celled and maturing into a drupe in fruit.[1]

The subfamily includes about 6 genera and 120 species, widely distributed. The leaves, bark, and seeds contain prussic acid and may poison livestock.

EXAMPLES: *Prunus serotina:* Black Cherry, a valuable timber tree of the eastern United States.

Prunus cerasus: Sour Cherry, cultivated for its fruit.

Prunus persica: Peach.

Prunus armeniaca: Apricot.

Prunus domestica: Garden Plum.

[1] The genus *Osmaronia* of the Pacific Northwest is anomalous in having mostly 5 pistils, which mature into 1–5 drupes in fruit.

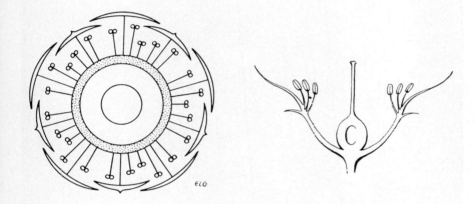

345 *Prunus,* floral diagram and longitudinal section of flower.

346 *Prunus virginiana* L., var. *melanocarpa* (A. Nels.) Sargent, the western dark-fruited Choke Cherry (subfamily *Amygdaloideae*).

347 *Prunus americana* Marsh., Wild Plum, a shrub or small tree with white flowers (subfamily *Amygdaloideae*).

SUBFAMILY 3. MALOIDEAE: *Apple Subfamily*

Trees and shrubs with alternate, simple or pinnately compound leaves having small deciduous stipules. Hypanthium adnate to the ovary throughout. Pistil 1, of 1–5 united carpels and maturing into a more or less fleshy pome, the flesh being derived from the enlarged hypanthium, which encloses the bony, leathery, or papery carpels.

The subfamily includes about 20 genera and 500 species, widely distributed.

EXAMPLES: *Malus pumila:* Common Apple, with many varieties.

Pyrus communis: Common Pear.

Cydonia oblonga: Quince.

Crataegus: Hawthorn, or Thorn-apple, a taxonomically difficult genus of at least 300 species.

Sorbus: Mountain Ash, plants with pinnately compound leaves.

CRASSULACEAE: Stonecrop Family

Mostly succulent herbs or small shrubs with thick, alternate or opposite, usually simple, exstipulate leaves. Flowers in cymes, usually perfect, regular, commonly 5-merous, hypogynous. Sepals free or united into a tube. Petals free or somewhat united. Stamens definite and, in gamopetalous flowers, inserted on the corolla tube. Carpels usually free and 5 in number, sometimes united at the base, each carpel associated with a glandular appendage perhaps representing additional carpels. Fruit usually a group of follicles, rarely a capsule.

The family includes abut 20 genera and 900 species, widely distributed and especially common in South Africa, rare in Australia and the southwest Pacific.

EXAMPLES: *Crassula portulacea:* Japanese Rubber-plant, a common house plant.

Sempervivum tectorum: House-leek or Hen-and-chickens.

Bryophyllum calycinum: Air-plant, often propagated by leaves.

Sedum: Stonecrop, the largest genus, with about 140 species.

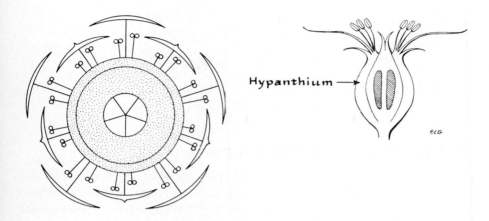

348 *Malus*, floral diagram and longitudinal section of flower. The stippling between the hypanthium and the ovary in the floral diagram indicates adnation and subsequent enlargement.

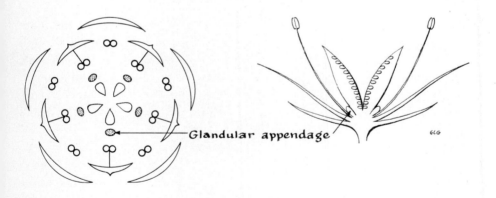

349 *Sedum*, floral diagram and longitudinal section of flower.

HYDRANGEACEAE: Hydrangea Family

Shrubs, vines, or small trees with simple, opposite, exstipulate leaves. Flowers sometimes showy and solitary, but usually small and in corymbose or paniculate cymes, usually perfect and regular (sometimes the marginal flowers sterile and with enlarged sepals), 4–5-merous, perigynous, but the hypanthium somewhat adnate to the lower part of the ovary. Pistil 1, of 2–10 carpels, which are often free at the apex. Fruit usually a many-seeded capsule.

The family includes about 16 genera and 80 species, mainly in North America and eastern Asia, some of the members being handsome ornamentals.

EXAMPLES: *Philadelphus coronarius:* Syringa, or Mock-orange.
Hydrangea paniculata and *H. arborescens:* Hydrangea.

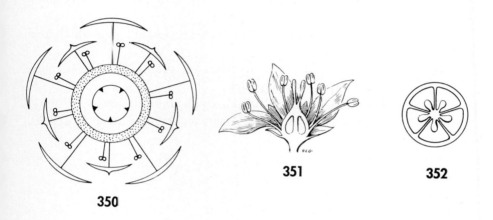

350 *Jamesia*, floral diagram. The number of carpels is variable, five and three carpels often occurring on the same plant.

351 *Whipplea*, longitudinal section of flower. [After Torrey, in Pacific R. R. Rep. 4: pl. 7 (1857).]

352 *Whipplea*, cross section of ovary.

SAXIFRAGACEAE: Saxifrage Family

Herbs with mostly alternate or basal exstipulate leaves, which are often palmately veined, are variously toothed or lobed, and are frequently hirsute. Flowers often scapose, usually racemose or paniculate, perigynous, the hypanthium free or rarely adnate to the ovary, regular, 5-merous, the stamens definite and usually 5 or 10. Pistil 1, of 2 (rarely 3 or 4) united carpels, commonly 2-horned at the apex, with 2 styles or stigmas. Ovary 1-celled with 2 parietal placentae, or 2-celled with axillary placentation. Fruit a many-seeded capsule.

The family includes about 36 genera and 500 species, in temperate, boreal, arctic, and alpine regions.

EXAMPLES: *Saxifraga:* Saxifrage, a genus of about 300 species, some cultivated in rock gardens.

Parnassia: Grass of Parnassus, with about 40 species.

Heuchera: Alumroot, an American genus of about 50 species.

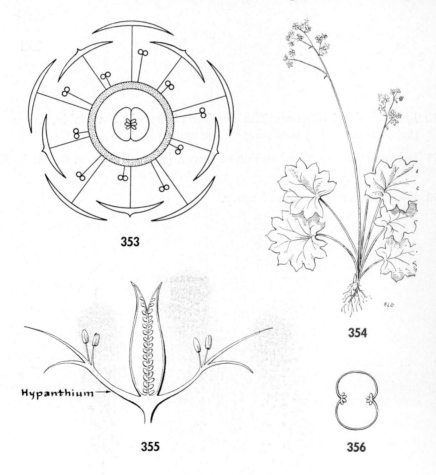

353

354

Hypanthium

355   356

353 *Saxifraga*, floral diagram.

354 *Saxifraga aestivalis*, plant.

355 *Saxifraga*, longitudinal section of flower, enlarged.

356 *Tiarella*, cross section of ovary, enlarged.

357 *Saxifraga rhomboidea* Greene, a species of Saxifrage that ranges from Montana to New Mexico. The scapes are mostly 1–3 decimeters high.

GROSSULARIACEAE: Gooseberry Family

Shrubs, often spiny, with simple alternate leaves, which are palmately veined and often lobed, with or without stipules. Flowers commonly in racemes, usually perfect, 5-merous, regular, with a short or long tubular epigynous hypanthium, this as well as the sepals usually petaloid. Petals smaller than the sepals. Stamens 5, alternate with the petals, inserted on the hypanthium. Pistil 1, of 2 united carpels, the ovary inferior and 1-celled with 2 parietal placentae, the styles and stigmas 1 or 2. Fruit a several-seeded berry.

The family is usually regarded as including the single genus *Ribes*, the Gooseberries and Currants, with some 130 species, in temperate and alpine regions. Affinities seem to lie with the *Rosales*, but the clearly epigynous flowers set the family apart in an anomalous position.

EXAMPLES: *Ribes aureum:* Golden Currant.
Ribes nigrum: Black Currant.
Ribes rubrum: Red Currant.

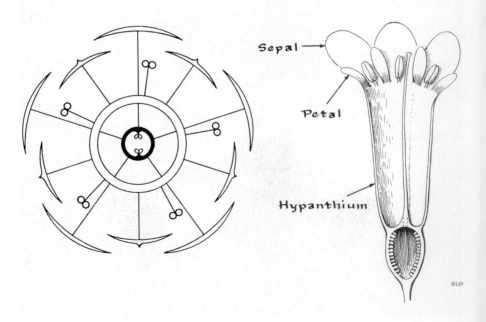

358 *Ribes aureum,* floral diagram.   **359** *Ribes aureum,* longitudinal section of flower, enlarged.

360 *Ribes aureum,* cross section of ovary, enlarged.

361 *Ribes aureum,* leaf.

362 *Ribes cereum* Dougl., Squaw Currant, a shrub with reddish berries. This shows the fruiting stage, with the withered remains cf the hypanthium adhering to the top of the ovary.

FABACEAE (LEGUMINOSAE): Pea Family

Herbs, shrubs, or trees with mostly alternate compound leaves, with or without stipules. Flowers usually perfect, regular or irregular, usually perigynous but the hypanthium often very short, mostly 5-merous, the stamens numerous to 10 or less and often monadelphous or diadelphous. Pistil 1, of 1 carpel, forming a legume in fruit.

The family includes about 500 genera and 14,000 species, world-wide in distribution, and including many valuable food and forage crops, ornamentals, and some poisonous plants.

363–371 SOME TERMS USED IN DESCRIPTIONS OF PLANTS.

363 Even-pinnate leaf with tendrils.

364 Bipinnate leaf.

365 Pinnate leaf.

366 Trifoliolate leaf.

367 Leaf with stipels.

368 Even-pinnate leaf with a bristle.

369 Digitate leaf.

370 Parts of a papilionaceous corolla.

371 Types of keel petals.

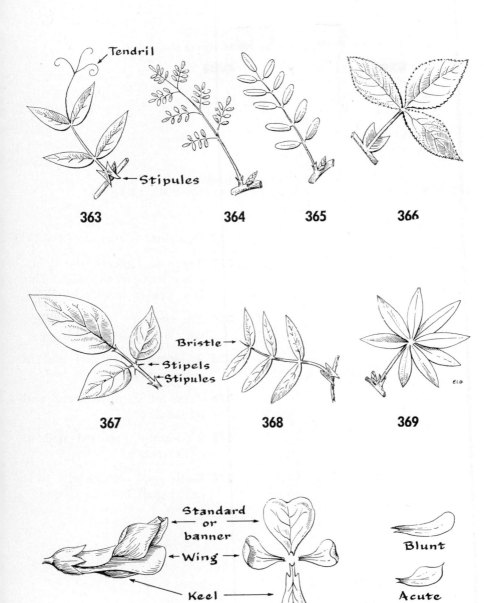

363

364

365

366

367

368

369

370

371

372–378 SOME TERMS USED IN DESCRIPTIONS OF PLANTS.

372 Diadelphous stamens $(9 + 1)$.

373 Types of loments, the dehiscence between the seeds. This is a type of modified legume.

374 The ordinary type of legume with longitudinal dehiscence.

375 A laterally flattened pod in cross section.

376 Types of stigmas, lateral and terminal.

377 A dorsally flattened pod in cross section.

378 Partly and completely two-celled pods in cross section.

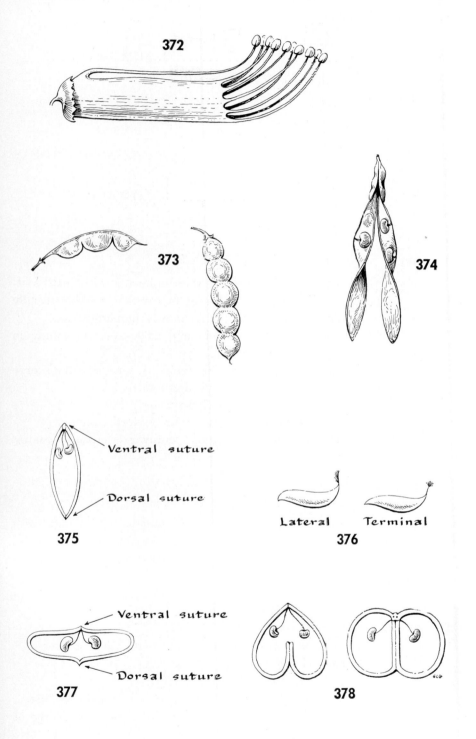

Ventral suture

Dorsal suture

375

Lateral   Terminal

376

Ventral suture

Dorsal suture

377

378

Key to the Subfamilies

Flowers regular; stamens 10 or more; leaves
bipinnate ....   1. MIMOSOIDEAE

Flowers irregular (papilionaceous); stamens 10
or less; leaves mostly pinnate or digitate, rarely
simple

    Lateral petals (wings) covering the upper
    one (standard) in the bud ....   2. CAESALPINIOIDEAE

    Lateral petals (wings) enclosed by the stand-
    ard in the bud ....   3. LOTOIDEAE

SUBFAMILY 1. MIMOSOIDEAE: *Mimosa Subfamily*

Trees or shrubs, rarely herbs. Leaves mostly bipinnate, with small leaflets. Flowers perfect, small, spicate, racemose, or capitate, regular, usually
5-merous. Stamens distinct or monadelphous, mostly numerous.

The subfamily includes about 35 genera and 2,000 species, mainly in
dry, tropical or subtropical regions.

    EXAMPLES: *Acacia:* a genus of about 450 species. *A. senegal* is the source
                of gum arabic, from tropical Africa.
                Mimosa: a genus of about 300 species.
                Schrankia uncinata: Sensitive Briar of North America.
                Prosopis: the Mesquites of the southwestern United States.

SUBFAMILY 2. CAESALPINIOIDEAE: *Senna Subfamily*

Trees, shrubs, or, rarely, herbs. Leaves usually pinnate or bipinnate, with
or without stipules. Flowers showy, racemose or spicate, rarely cymose,
somewhat irregular, usually 5-merous, the stamens mostly 10 or fewer, distinct or monadelphous.

The subfamily includes about 60 genera and 2,200 species, some of them
valuable timber trees. It is mainly tropical.

    EXAMPLES: *Cercis:* Redbud of North America.
                Cassia: Senna, species used for the production of dyes.
                Gleditsia: Honey Locust.
                Gymnocladus: Kentucky Coffee-tree.
                Copaifera pubiflora: Purple-heart Wood of British Guiana.
                Haematoxylon: Logwood, of tropical America, the source of
                a dye often used in microscopy.

379 *Acacia*, floral diagram.

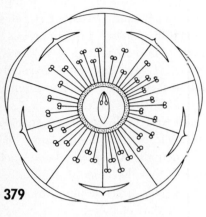

379

380 Flower of *Acacia*, enlarged.

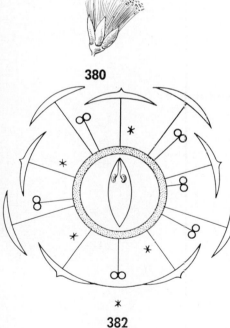

380

382

382 *Gleditsia*, floral diagram. The flowers are polygamo-dioecious, and the stamens, sepals, and petals are variable in number. The two lower petals are sometimes united.

381 Portion of plant and fruit of *Acacia*.

381   ELG

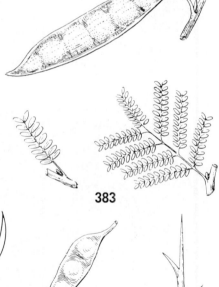

383

383 *Gleditsia*, pinnate and bipinnate leaves, fruit, and branched spine from the trunk.

SUBFAMILY 3. LOTOIDEAE: *Pea Subfamily*

Mostly herbs, but some shrubs and trees. Leaves usually pinnate or digitate, less commonly simple, mostly with prominent and persistent stipules,
and occasionally with tendrils. Flowers strongly irregular (papilionaceous),
perfect, 5-merous, the stamens usually diadelphous (9 united and 1 free)
but sometimes monadelphous or all distinct. Ovary and fruit normally
1-celled, but sometimes partly or completely 2-celled by the intrusion of
one or both of the sutures.

The subfamily includes about 400 genera and at least 10,000 species,
many of which are valuable forage plants, some of them food plants, and
several of them commonly cultivated ornamentals. Some members, such
as the genus *Oxytropis*, are poisonous to livestock because of their alka-
loidal content; others, such as species of *Astragalus*, are selenium absorbers
and poisonous because of the accumulation of that element.

EXAMPLES: *Pisum sativum:* Peas.
            Lathyrus odoratus: Sweet Pea.
            Glycine hispida: Soybean.
            Trifolium: Clover.
            Medicago sativa: Alfalfa.
            Dalbergia: East Indian Rosewood.

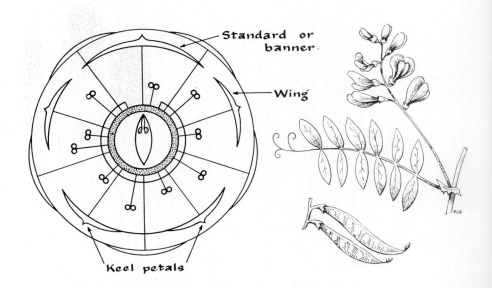

384 *Lathyrus,* floral diagram (stamens diadelphous).

385 *Lathyrus,* portion of plant and
fruit.

386 *Lupinus plattensis* S. Wats., a species of Lupine.

Key to the Tribes[1]

Stamens distinct, not monadelphous or diadelphous

Leaves pinnate or with a single leaflet; trees or shrubs . . . .   SOPHOREAE

Leaves digitate, often 3-foliolate, or with a single leaflet; shrubs or herbs . . . .   PODALYRIEAE

Stamens monadelphous or diadelphous

Leaflets not stipellate

Leaves odd-pinnate, without tendrils

Pod not a loment

Leaves glandular-dotted . . . .   PSORALEAE

Leaves glandless (except *Glycyrrhiza*, which has pods with hooked prickles and small white flowers)

Stamens mostly monadelphous; anthers of 2 kinds, some large and some small . . . .   GENISTEAE

Stamens mostly diadelphous; anthers all alike

Leaves mostly 3–5-foliolate

Leaflets denticulate . . . .   TRIFOLIEAE

Leaflets entire . . . .   LOTEAE

Leaves mostly pinnate

Pod dehiscent; plants chiefly herbaceous . . . .   GALEGEAE

Pod indehiscent; plants woody . . . .   DALBERGIEAE

Pod a loment, dividing transversely into 1-seeded joints or articles . . . .   HEDYSAREAE

Leaves mostly with tendrils or terminated by a bristle, mostly even-pinnate; shrubs or mostly herbs or herbaceous vines . . . .   VICIEAE

Leaflets stipellate; woody or herbaceous vines, or herbs, often twining . . . .   PHASEOLEAE

---

[1] This simplified key will usually produce the correct answer, but it should be remembered that exceptions will occur occasionally.

ORDER GERANIALES

Herbs, undershrubs, shrubs, or trees with hypogynous, perfect, regular to irregular flowers. Corolla of separate and often clawed petals. Stamens typically in two sets, the outer sometimes opposite the petals, or reduced to one set, and sometimes with sterile stamens present. Pistil syncarpous, with axillary placentation, the ovules few or solitary in each carpel.

The order is a large one, of perhaps 20 families, and is treated in different ways by various authors. It may represent an early modification from the *Malvales* by a reduction in stamen number and often by the development of variously modified fruits. The following families are representative.

Key to the Families

Herbage glandular-dotted; plants aromatic; fruit often a hesperidium .... RUTACEAE

Herbage not glandular-dotted; plants sometimes aromatic; fruit not a hesperidium

  Flowers regular, never spurred

    Herbs with sour juice and 3-foliolate leaves .. OXALIDACEAE

    Herbs or shrubs, the leaves not 3-foliolate; juice not sour

      Fruit an elastic capsule with a long beak . GERANIACEAE

      Fruit sometimes elastic but not beaked

        Leaves pinnately compound; stamens distinct; mostly shrubs of the southwestern desert regions, but some annual herbs .. ZYGOPHYLLACEAE

        Leaves simple and entire; stamens monadelphous; mostly herbs of northern and temperate regions .... LINACEAE

  Flowers irregular, with or without a spur

    Flowers not spurred .... POLYGALACEAE

    Flowers spurred

      Fruit an elastic capsule with a long beak (the African genus *Pelargonium*) .... GERANIACEAE

      Fruit often elastic but not beaked

        Leaves peltate; stamens 8; spur straight .. TROPAEOLACEAE

        Leaves not peltate; stamens 5; spur curved .... BALSAMINACEAE

RUTACEAE: Rue Family

Aromatic trees or shrubs, rarely herbs, with simple or compound leaves, which are exstipulate, glabrous, often leathery, and usually glandular-dotted. Flowers perfect or rarely unisexual, usually regular, typically 5-merous, with a fleshy disk between the stamens and the ovary. Stamens numerous and in several bundles (polyadelphous) or 5 or 10, distinct, the outer stamens often opposite the petals. Pistil 1, usually of 4–5 united carpels, the ovary often deeply lobed. Fruit a berry with a leathery pericarp (hesperidium), a drupe, or rarely a capsule or samara.

The family includes 5 subfamilies, about 140 genera, and 1,500 species, widely distributed, mostly in tropical and subtropical regions, and best developed in South Africa and Australia.

EXAMPLES: *Citrus sinensis:* Orange
Citrus limonia: Lemon   citrus fruits, natives
Citrus maxima: Grapefruit   of subtropical Asia.
Citrus media: Citron
Xanthoxylum americanum: Prickly Ash of North America.
Ptelea trifoliata: Wafer-ash of North America.
Ruta graveolens: Rue, a native of Europe and cultivated.

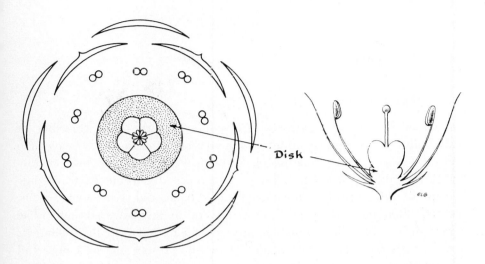

387 *Ruta,* floral diagram of terminal flower, which is 5-merous; the lateral flowers are 4-merous.

388 *Ruta,* generalized longitudinal section of flower.

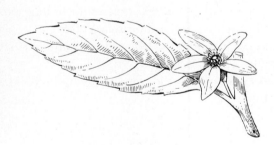

389 *Citrus limonum,* portion of plant.

390 *Citrus,* stamen bundle.

OXALIDACEAE: Wood Sorrel Family

Annual or perennial, scapose or leafy-stemmed herbs from rhizomes or scaly bulbs, the juice sour because of the presence of oxalic acid. Leaves (in ours) 3-foliolate, often long-petioled, the leaflets obcordate and characteristically folding at night. Flowers sometimes dimorphic or trimorphic because of differences in relative lengths of stamens and styles, hypogynous, perfect, often on long peduncles, solitary or in few-flowered umbel-like cymes, the corolla yellow, white, or purple. Stamens united by their filaments at the base (monadelphous), usually 10 and in two sets, one set longer and one set shorter, the outer set opposite the petals, or occasionally with an additional outer set of sterile stamens. Pistil 1, of 5 united carpels, the styles usually distinct. Fruit a loculicidal capsule or (in the Asiatic genus *Averrhoa*) a berry. Seeds 2 or more in each carpel, often discharged by the elastic separation of an outer layer (aril) of the seed coat from an inner harder layer.

The family includes about 7 genera and 900 species, mainly in tropical and subtropical regions, a few extending into temperate regions.

EXAMPLES: *Oxalis:* Wood Sorrel, with about 800 species, including some weeds in North America, and a few ornamentals.

Averrhoa: a tree, cultivated in the tropics for its edible berry, which tastes like a gooseberry.

Biophytum: with 30 species in the tropics, having leaves that are sensitive to touch.

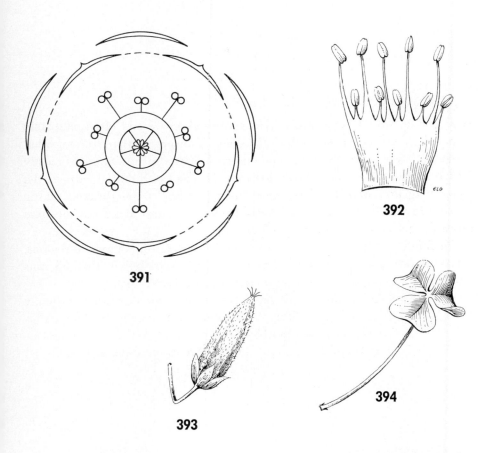

391 *Oxalis*, floral diagram.

392 *Oxalis*, stamens with the tube
    opened up.

393 *Oxalis*, capsule.

394 *Oxalis*, leaf.

GERANIACEAE: Geranium Family

Herbs or soft-woody semishrubs, with mostly alternate and often palmately veined leaves. Pubescence often glandular. Flowers regular to somewhat irregular, hypogynous, perfect, 5-merous, with clawed petals. Stamens mostly 5 or 10, rarely 15, some of them often sterile. Pistil of 5 united carpels, the styles long and united, the stigmas distinct. Fruit a long-beaked elastic capsule in which the styles split away from the central axis from the base upward, each carpel with 1 or 2 seeds.

The family includes 11 genera and about 650 species, in temperate regions.

EXAMPLES: *Geranium:* Wild Geranium, or Crane's-bill, with numerous species in Europe and North America.

Pelargonium: cultivated Geraniums, often grown in window boxes, as house plants, and for borders, with numerous species in South Africa.

Erodium: Stork's-bill, several species of common weeds.

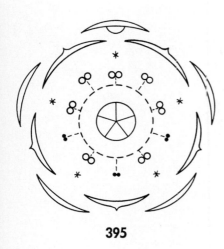

395

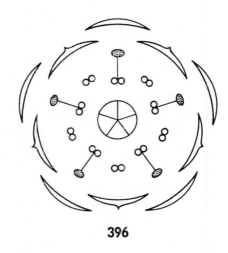

396

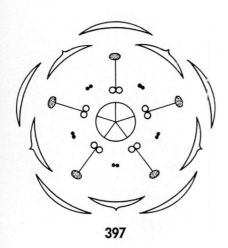

397

395 *Pelargonium,* floral diagram, the upper sepal spurred, and the corolla slightly irregular.

396 *Geranium,* floral diagram, the outer set of stamens reduced to nectar glands, which lie at the base of the filaments of the inner stamens.

397 *Erodium,* floral diagram, showing five sterile stamens and five nectar glands, which probably represent a reduced outer set of stamens, as in *Geranium.*

398   **399**   **400**

398 *Geranium richardsonii*, portion of plant.

399 *Geranium*, fruit before and after dehiscence.

400 *Erodium cicutarium*, fruit.

401 *Erodium cicutarium* (L.) L'Her., Stork's-bill, or Filaria, a common weed. Long-beaked capsules are shown on the left and right.

ZYGOPHYLLACEAE: Caltrop Family

Herbs or shrubs, with mostly opposite, compound, stipulate leaves and entire leaflets. Flowers hypogynous, perfect, and regular, 5-merous, with usually 10 distinct stamens in 2 whorls, and a single pistil of 2–6 united carpels, the styles united into a short column. Fruit a capsule, berry, or drupe, or sometimes (in *Tribulus*) forming a bur-like schizocarp.

The family includes 25 genera and about 160 species, in warm and dry regions.

EXAMPLES: *Guaiacum officinale:* a small tree of tropical America, which furnishes a gum used in medicine.

Tribulus terrestris: Puncture Vine, a weed in dry areas of the Southwest, extending as far north as Wyoming.

Larrea tridentata: the common Creosote Bush of the deserts of the Southwest.

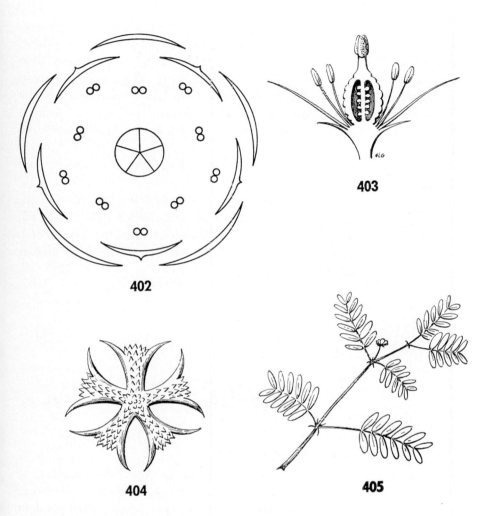

402 *Tribulus*, floral diagram.

403 *Tribulus*, flower section.

404 *Tribulus*, fruit.

405 *Tribulus*, portion of plant.

LINACEAE: Flax Family

Mostly herbs, with alternate entire leaves and perfect, regular, hypogynous, 5-merous flowers. Petals fugacious, clawed, in ours usually blue or yellow, rarely white. Stamens 5, in ours, alternate with the petals, united by their filaments below into a short tube (monadelphous), these fertile stamens often alternating with very short staminodia. Pistil 1, of 5 united carpels, the styles distinct or united below, the ovary 10-celled because of a false septum in each carpel. Ovules and seeds normally 2 in each carpel. Fruit a septicidal capsule.

The family includes 9 genera and about 150 species, in temperate and tropical regions.

EXAMPLES: *Linum usitatissimum:* Flax, cultivated for the stem fibers, which make linen, and for the seeds, which yield linseed oil.

Linum grandiflorum: a red-flowered cultivated ornamental.

Hugonia: a genus of tropical trees and shrubs with flowers having 10–25 stamens.

POLYGALACEAE: Milkwort Family

Herbs, shrubs, woody vines, or trees, with simple, alternate, opposite, or whorled leaves. Flowers appearing as if papilionaceous, perfect, hypogynous, irregular. Calyx of 5 unequal sepals, the 2 inner ones (wings) often petaloid and larger than the 3 smaller outer ones. Corolla of 5 or often 3 petals, which are more or less connate, the lowest one often concave, appearing like a keel, and with or without a fringed crest. Stamens 3–8 (often 8), monadelphous, the tube often split along the upper side, the anthers usually 1-celled and opening by a terminal or subterminal pore. Pistil 1, usually of 2 united carpels, with axillary placentation. Fruit usually a loculicidal capsule with a single seed in each carpel.

The family includes about 12 genera and 1,000 species, cosmopolitan in distribution but not extending into arctic regions.

EXAMPLES: *Polygala senega:* Seneca Snakeroot.

Polygala paucifolia: Flowering Wintergreen.

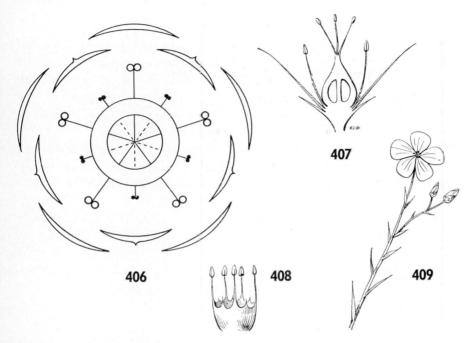

406 *Linum*, floral diagram.

407 *Linum*, longitudinal section of flower.

408 *Linum*, stamen structure.

409 *Linum lewisii*, portion of plant.

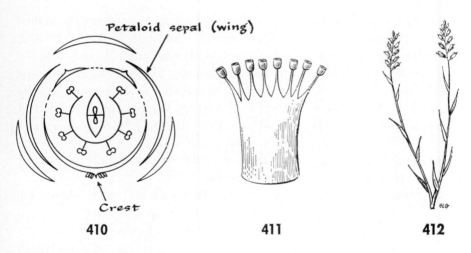

410 *Polygala*, floral diagram.

411 *Polygala*, group of eight stamens and stamen tube.

412 *Polygala alba*, portion of plant.

TROPAEOLACEAE: Nasturtium Family

Annual or perennial, succulent, often twining herbs with pungent juice and orbicular, exstipulate, peltate leaves. Flowers showy, solitary, axillary on long peduncles, irregular, 5-merous, the calyx petaloid, the upper sepal with a long straight spur, the 3 lower petals bearded. Stamens 8. Pistil 1, of 3 weakly united carpels, the ovary 3-lobed, the style single, and stigmas 3. Fruit nut-like, of 1-seeded carpels, one or two often aborting.

The family includes the single genus *Tropaeolum,* ranging from Mexico southwards, in the Andes to Chile, and with 3 species in southern Brazil.

EXAMPLE: *Tropaeolum majus:* Nasturtium, a native of Peru.

BALSAMINACEAE: Jewelweed Family

Herbs with succulent stems, thin, alternate, exstipulate, pinnately veined leaves, and showy, bilabiate, axillary flowers. Dorsal sepal large, petaloid, and with a curved spur, two of the lateral sepals small and greenish, and the two lower lateral sepals much reduced or lacking. Petals 5, the lateral ones united. Stamens 5, often united by their filaments (monadelphous) or by their anthers (syngenesious). Pistil 1, of 5 united carpels, the style short or lacking, the stigma 5-toothed or 5-lobed. Fruit usually an oblong, succulent, elastically dehiscent capsule with several seeds.

The family includes 2 genera and about 400 species, mainly in tropical Asia and Africa, with a few in North America.

EXAMPLES: *Impatiens:* Jewelweed, or Touch-me-not, with about 400 species, chiefly in India, a few species cultivated.

                Hydrocera triflora: of southern Asia, a monotypic genus.

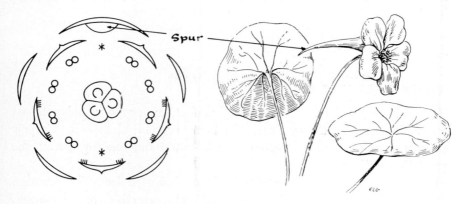

413 *Tropaeolum,* floral diagram.

414 *Tropaeolum,* flower and leaves.

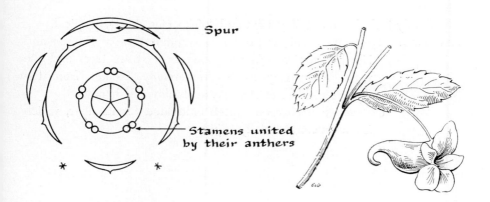

415 *Impatiens balsamina,* floral diagram.

416 *Impatiens biflora,* portion of plant.

ORDER MALVALES

Herbs, shrubs, and trees, with mostly perfect, hypogynous, polypetalous flowers. Stamens numerous, monadelphous or polyadelphous. Carpels numerous or as few as three, often weakly united and forming a ring, the placentation axillary.

The order probably represents an early modification from the *Ranales*, with tendencies toward united stamens and a characteristic ring of carpels. The following families are representative.

TILIACEAE: Basswood Family

Mostly tropical trees, shrubs, or herbs, often with strong phloem fibers. Leaves usually alternate and simple, with stipules, the blade often oblique at the base. Flowers regular, usually perfect, usually 5-merous, in cymes or panicles. Stamens 10 to many, often united by the basal part of their filaments into 5 or 10 bunches (polyadelphous), some of the stamens sometimes modified into petaloid staminodia. Pistil 1, of 2–10 carpels, the ovary 2–10-celled with 1–several ovules in each cell, the placentation usually axillary, the style single. Fruit variable, fleshy or dry, and dehiscent or indehiscent.

The family includes about 40 genera and 400 species, mostly tropical.

EXAMPLES: *Tilia:* Basswood, or Linden, a common tree of Europe and North America, often planted as a street tree, and the wood extensively used commercially. Nectar from the flowers yields a characteristically flavored honey.

Corchorus: herbaceous, often cultivated for its fiber, which is known commercially as jute.

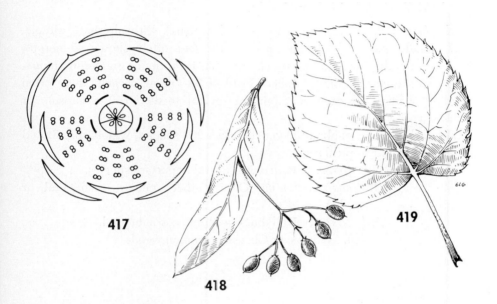

417 *Tilia americana*, floral diagram. The five petaloid structures inside the stamen groups are probably sterile stamens.

418 *Tilia americana*, leaf-like bract and fruit cluster.

419 *Tilia americana*, leaf.

MALVACEAE: Mallow Family

Herbs (some shrubs and trees in tropical regions) with alternate, simple, and usually palmately veined leaves. Flowers often showy, 5-merous, hypogynous, the petals often attached to the tube of the numerous monadelphous stamens. Anthers 1-celled. Pistil of 3 to many carpels, these often forming a ring and each containing 1–several seeds. Fruit a capsule or schizocarp.

The family includes about 50 genera and 1,200 species, widely distributed in temperate and tropical regions.

EXAMPLES: *Gossypium:* Cotton, with several important species.

Hibiscus esculentus: Okra (other species ornamental or weedy).

Althaea rosea: Hollyhock, a common ornamental.

Malva: Mallows, or Cheeses, common weeds.

420 *Malva*, floral diagram.   **421** *Malva*, longitudinal section of flower.

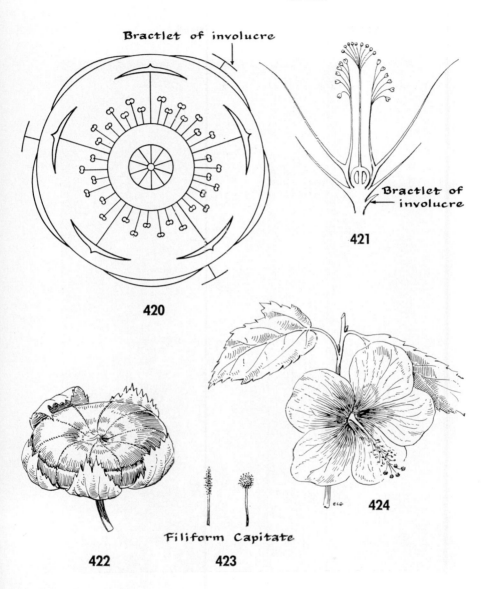

Bractlet of involucre

Bractlet of involucre

421

420

Filiform Capitate

422   **423**

422 *Malva*, fruit and persistent calyx.

423 Two stigma types, filiform and capitate.

424 *Hibiscus*, portion of plant.

425

425 *Iliamna rivularis* (Dougl.) Greene, a common western Mallow. The plants are about one meter high, and have white to pink or lavender flowers.

426 *Iliamna rivularis* (Dougl.) Greene, detail of a single flower showing the characteristic numerous monadelphous stamens, and the style branches protruding beyond them.

ORDER GUTTIFERALES

Herbs, shrubs, or trees, with opposite or whorled, simple leaves, which are often punctate or black-dotted. Flowers hypogynous, polypetalous, regular, 4–5-merous, usually with numerous stamens, which are united in bunches by their filaments (polyadelphous), the single pistil of 3–5 united carpels, and the ovary usually with parietal placentation.

The order, as defined by Hutchinson, includes 4 families and is mainly tropical. By others it is combined with a larger number of families in the order *Parietales*, which is generally regarded as a heterogeneous assemblage and not a natural group. The following family is representative.

HYPERICACEAE: St.-John's-wort Family

Herbs or shrubs with simple, opposite or whorled, entire leaves, which are punctate or black-dotted, without stipules. Flowers usually in cymes (dichasia), usually yellow or orange, 4–5-merous, regular. Stamens often numerous but sometimes definite in *Hypericum*, usually united below by their filaments into 3–5 (6–8) bunches. Pistil 1, of 3–5 carpels, the styles distinct or partly united, the ovary 1-celled and with 3–5 parietal placentae, or 3–5-celled by the intrusion of the placentae, and the placentation then apparently axillary. Fruit usually a septicidal, many-seeded capsule, sometimes a berry.

The family, as defined here, includes 3 genera and about 311 species of temperate and tropical regions.

EXAMPLES: *Hypericum:* St.-John's-wort, a genus of about 300 species, about 40 of which occur in the United States. Some are weeds, some are poisonous to livestock, and some are ornamentals.

Ascyrum hypericoides: St.-Andrew's-cross, an evergreen shrub, sometimes cultivated.

Triadenum: Marsh St.-John's-wort.

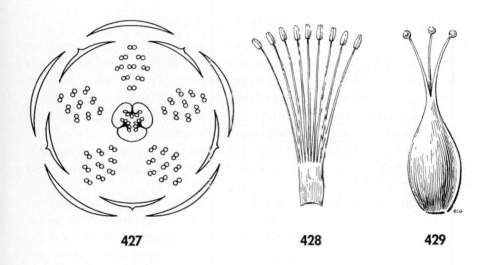

427

428

429

427 *Hypericum,* floral diagram.

429 *Hypericum,* pistil.

428 *Hypericum,* stamen bundle.

ORDER SAPINDALES

Trees or shrubs with simple or compound leaves. Flowers numerous and often small, regular to irregular, hypogynous or perigynous, polypetalous, often with a disk below the ovary. Gynoecium 2–3-carpeled. Fruit often 1-seeded.

The order has been variously regarded by different workers as consisting of from 9 families (Hutchinson) to 23 families (Engler and Diels). Its relationship to other orders is not clear, but the perigynous tendency suggests an ancient connection with the *Rosales*, from which it may have been derived by reduction. The group is mainly tropical. The following families are representative.

ANACARDIACEAE: Cashew or Sumac Family

Resinous shrubs or small trees, sometimes poisonous, the leaves simple or often pinnately compound. Flowers small and numerous, perfect or unisexual, mostly regular, somewhat perigynous, usually 5-merous, but the stamens often of twice the number of the sepals (in *Mangifera* reduced to a single fertile stamen, the others sterile), and the carpels often 3, but only 1 of these functional in most genera. Fruit usually a drupe.

The family includes about 60 genera and 600 species, mostly in tropical regions but with some representatives in temperate Europe, Asia, and America.

EXAMPLES: *Anacardium occidentale:* Cashew nut of tropical America.

Mangifera indica: Mango, of Asia but cultivated in warm regions elsewhere for the large, delicious fruits.

Pistacia vera: Pistachio nuts of the Mediterranean region.

Rhus toxicodendron and *R. radicans:* Poison Ivy and Poison Oak.

Rhus vernix: Poison Sumac.

Cotinus obovatus: Smoke tree of southern and southeastern United States.

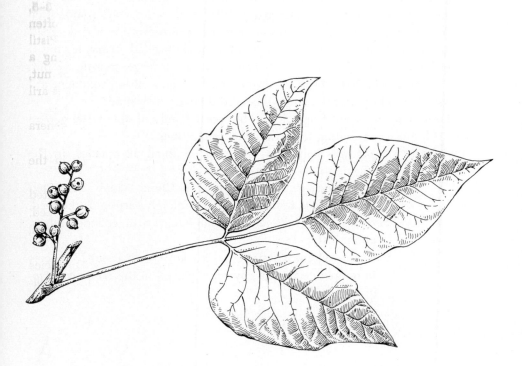

430 *Rhus radicans,* Poison Ivy. The fruits are pale greenish-white.

SAPINDACEAE: Soapberry Family

Trees, shrubs, or sometimes lianas, with mostly alternate, compound, and usually exstipulate leaves. Flowers commonly numerous and small, often polygamo-dioecious and 5-merous, regular or irregular, the petals 3–5, separate, or often lacking. Stamens usually in 2 series, but some often reduced, giving the flower 8 or fewer stamens, inserted inside a disk. Pistil 1, usually of 3 carpels, with a single style and 3-celled ovary having a single ovule and seed in each cell. Fruit various: a large capsule or nut, often winged, or a fleshy berry or drupe. Seeds often with a prominent aril and without endosperm, the embryo curved, folded, or twisted.

A large and important tropical or subtropical family of about 100 genera and 1,600 species, including some valuable timber trees.

EXAMPLES: *Sapindus:* Soapberry, a genus of about 11 species, in the warmer parts of Asia and America.

Litchi chinensis: Litchi, a native of China, widely cultivated for the sweet, fleshy aril that completely surrounds the seed.

Serjania and *Paullinia:* tropical lianas with coiled tendrils, about 300 species.

Aesculus: Horse Chestnut and Buckeye, with about 13 species in temperate regions, by some placed in the *Hippocastanaceae.*

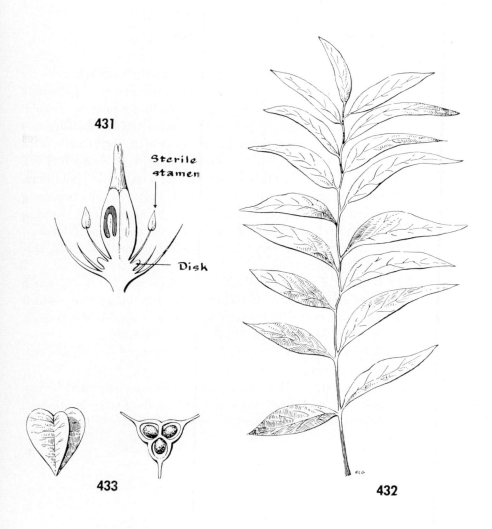

431 *Sapindus,* female flower in longitudinal section.

432 *Sapindus,* leaf.

433 *Urvillea,* fruit, and cross section of fruit.

ACERACEAE: Maple Family

Trees or shrubs with sweetish, watery sap and opposite, exstipulate leaves with long petioles, the blades varying from simple and entire to palmately lobed, trifoliolate, or pinnately compound, usually palmately veined. Flowers regular, dioecious, polygamous, or sometimes perfect, usually on a short, leafy shoot, appearing before the leaves, somewhat perigynous, often with a disk. Sepals 4–5. Petals 4–5 or none. Stamens 4–12 (usually 7–8), attached to the edge of the disk, which may represent a reduced hypanthium. Pistil 1, of 2 united carpels (occasionally 3), each flattened and becoming winged, the placentation axillary, and seeds 1–2 in each carpel. Fruit a winged schizocarp, which splits into 2 single-winged mericarps (the fruit often described as a paired samara), the wing subterminal in *Acer*, surrounding the carpel in *Dipteronia*.

The family includes 2 genera and about 125 species, mostly in north temperate or mountainous regions. It includes valuable timber trees, which may also produce maple sugar, and several species are valuable shade trees.

EXAMPLES: *Acer saccharum:* Sugar Maple, or Hard Maple.

Acer saccharinum: Silver Maple, with several ornamental cut-leaved varieties.

Acer negundo: Box Elder, with pinnately compound leaves.

Acer macrophyllum: Big-leaf Maple of the Pacific Northwest.

Dipteronia: with two species, in central China.

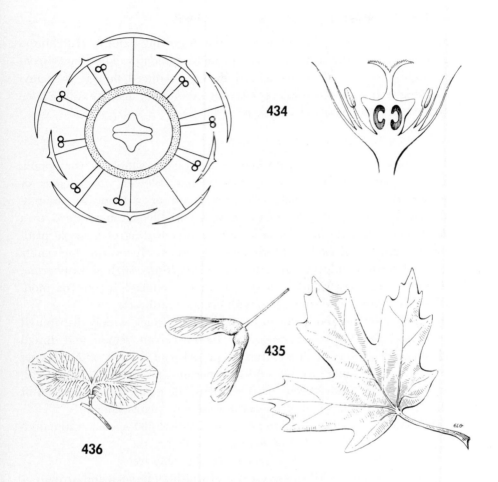

434 *Acer glabrum*, floral diagram and longitudinal section of perfect flower, the latter much enlarged.

435 *Acer grandidentatum*, fruit and leaf.

436 *Dipteronia*, fruit. [After Pax in Engler & Prantl, *Nat. Pflanz.*, 3^5: 269 (1896).]

ORDER EUPHORBIALES

An anomalous group, including only the following family. Hutchinson suggests a possible origin from *Malvales* and *Sapindales*. The plants seem to be highly specialized, as evidenced by very reduced flowers in many, the peculiar and flower-like inflorescence in *Euphorbia,* and the milky juice and attendant complex secretory tissue.

EUPHORBIACEAE: Spurge Family

Herbs, shrubs, or trees, often with milky juice. Leaves simple or compound, usually alternate, sometimes reduced to spines. Flowers monoecious or sometimes dioecious, commonly in cymes, with or without a perianth, sometimes with a corolla. Staminate flowers variable, often reduced to a single stamen. Pistillate flowers rather uniform, consisting of a single pistil of mostly 3 carpels, 3-lobed, and forming a capsule or schizocarp which splits into three 1-seeded nutlets in fruit. In specialized forms, such as *Euphorbia,* the inflorescence may simulate a flower, being reduced to one or more cymules or cyathia, these sometimes with ornamental bracts.

The family includes about 283 genera and 7,300 species, widely distributed in temperate and tropical regions, the Indo-Malayan region and Brazil being the chief centers of distribution. Some African species of *Euphorbia* resemble cactus plants. Economically important products include food, drugs, and rubber. Many species are poisonous, the genus *Toxicodendron* of South Africa including some of the most poisonous plants known.

EXAMPLES: *Euphorbia:* the largest genus, with 1,600 species estimated, including *E. pulcherrima,* the Poinsettia.

Hevea braziliensis: an important rubber tree.

Manihot utilissima: Cassava, furnishing tapioca and arrowroot starch from the tuberous roots.

Ricinus communis: Castor Bean, the source of castor oil.

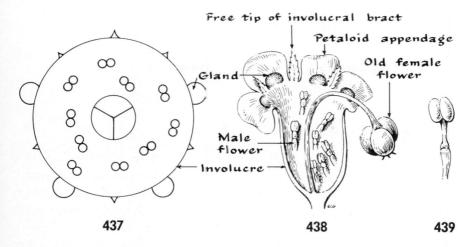

437 *Euphorbia*, diagram of cyathium (cymule).

438 *Euphorbia*, cyathium cut open lengthwise to show structure, enlarged.

439 *Euphorbia*, single staminate flower on a pedicel.

440 *Euphorbia pulcherrima* Willd., Poinsettia, or Christmas Plant. The leaf-like bracts subtending the inflorescence are red.

ORDER RHAMNALES

Trees, shrubs, or lianas, with simple or palmately compound, mostly stipulate, alternate or opposite leaves. Flowers regular, perfect or unisexual, perigynous, the stamens of the same number as the petals and opposite them or in that position if the petals are lacking. Carpels 1–5, rarely more, united.

The order probably represents an early modification from the *Rosales*, being characterized by having perigynous flowers, but the stamens are definite and in an unusual position. The following families are representative.

RHAMNACEAE: Buckthorn Family

Mostly shrubs or trees, sometimes spiny, with simple, alternate or sometimes opposite 3–5-nerved or pinnately veined leaves, which usually have small and deciduous stipules. Flowers small, in cymes, the corolla inconspicuous or 4–5-merous, perfect or polygamous, perigynous, the hypanthium sometimes becoming adnate to the base of the ovary. Stamens of the same number as the sepals and alternate with them (opposite the petals when these are present). Pistil of 2–4 carpels (commonly 3), forming a capsule or a few-seeded berry in fruit.

The family includes about 50 genera and 600 species, widely distributed, and commoner in warm regions.

EXAMPLES: *Rhamnus purshiana:* Cascara, found in the Northwest.

Rhamnus cathartica: often planted for ornament.

Ceanothus: ornamentals and chaparral shrubs in the Southwest.

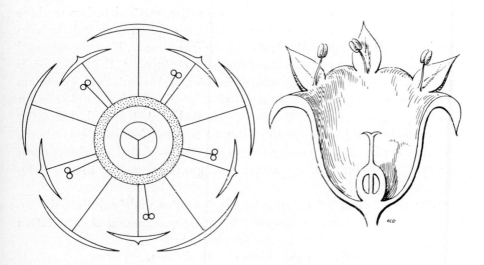

441 *Rhamnus*, floral diagram.

442 *Rhamnus*, longitudinal section of flower, enlarged.

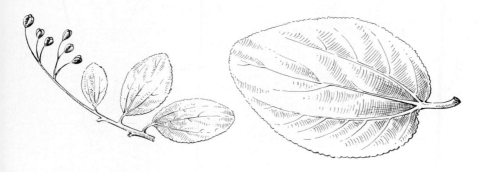

443 *Ceanothus velutinus*, fruiting twig and lower leaf.

ELAEAGNACEAE: Russian Olive Family

Trees or shrubs with alternate or opposite, entire, exstipulate leaves, these as well as the young stems and often the fruit covered with stellate hairs or scales, which often give the plants a silvery appearance. Flowers unisexual or perfect, 4-merous, apetalous, regular, and perigynous, the hypanthium enclosing the ovary, which thus appears inferior, and in fruit the hypanthium adnate to the ovary. Stamens mostly 4 or 8. Pistil 1, with a single slender style and capitate stigma, the ovary 1-celled and 1-seeded, becoming drupaceous in fruit because of the adherent fleshy or leathery hypanthium.

A small family of 3 genera and about 20 species, found chiefly in north temperate and subtropical regions, a few species occurring in the Indo-Malayan region.

EXAMPLES: *Elaeagnus angustifolia:* Russian Olive, widely cultivated.
Elaeagnus commutata: Silver-berry, common along western stream courses at lower elevations.
Hippophae rhamnoides: Sea Buckthorn.
Shepherdia canadensis: Canadian Buffalo-berry, a common shrub in wooded areas of North America.

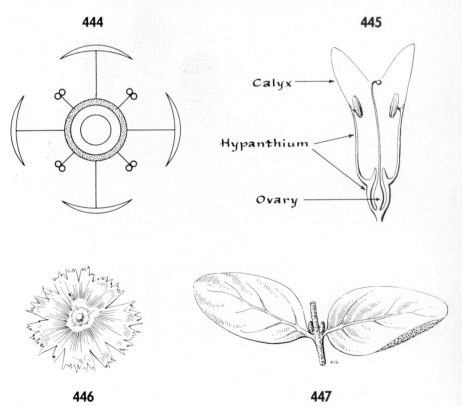

444

445

Calyx

Hypanthium

Ovary

446

447

448

444 *Elaeagnus*, floral diagram.

445 *Elaeagnus*, longitudinal section of flower.

446 *Elaeagnus*, scale from leaf, greatly magnified.

447 *Shepherdia canadensis*, portion of branch.

448 *Elaeagnus commutata* Bernh., Silver-berry, showing flowers and a single fruit from the preceding year.

ORDER VIOLALES

Herbaceous or woody plants with mostly alternate, stipulate leaves, and usually irregular, hypogynous or perigynous, polypetalous flowers. Stamens usually definite (as many as 40 in *Resedaceae*) and free. Carpels 2–6 (often 3), usually united, the ovary with parietal placentation.

The order probably represents an early and terminal development from the *Rosales*. The following family is representative.

VIOLACEAE: Violet Family

Mainly annual or perennial herbs in temperate latitudes, but in tropical regions often shrubs or trees. Leaves usually alternate or basal, with prominent stipules. Flowers solitary or variously clustered, regular or irregular, perigynous (the hypanthium short), 5-merous, the lower petal often spurred. Stamens 5, connivent around the pistil, the lower pair often spurred, the filaments usually dilated and sometimes connate in a short tube. Pistil 1, tricarpellate, the ovary 1-celled with 3 parietal placentae, the style single and terminal, the stigma variously shaped. Fruit an elastic, loculicidal, 3-valved capsule with several to many seeds. Cleistogamous flowers are sometimes found in addition to the normal flowers, or the showy flowers may be sterile.

The family includes about 18 genera and 450 species, widely distributed in temperate and tropical regions.

EXAMPLES: *Viola:* Violet and Pansy, including some 300 species and numerous hybirds. Flowers irregular.

Rinorea: 60 species of tropical trees and shrubs with regular flowers.

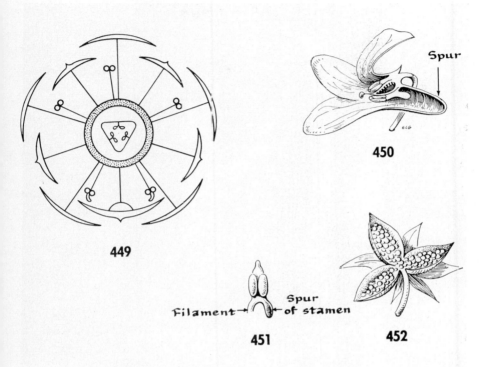

449 *Viola*, floral diagram.

450 *Viola*, longitudinal section of flower, enlarged.

451 *Viola*, single stamen of lower pair, enlarged.

452 *Viola*, open capsule, enlarged.

453 *Viola canadensis* L., a wide-ranging species with leafy stems and white or pale lavender flowers.

454 *Viola nuttallii* Pursh, Yellow Prairie Violet, a common species from the Great Plains westward.

ORDER LOASALES

Mostly herbs with well-developed exstipulate leaves and regular, mostly 5-merous, perigynous or epigynous, polypetalous flowers. Stamens numerous to definite, often in bunches. Pistil 1, usually of 3 carpels, the ovary with parietal or, rarely, axillary placentation.

The order includes the *Turneriaceae* (perigynous) and the *Loasaceae* (epigynous), both characteristically American families. The relationships are rather obscure, but Hutchinson suggests affinities with the *Papaverales*. There may also be relationships with the *Myrtales*.

LOASACEAE: Loasa Family

Mostly herbaceous plants having the herbage covered with rough, bristly, or sometimes stinging hairs. Flowers epigynous, with little or no hypanthium, regular, usually 5-merous. Stamens numerous and in bunches opposite the petals, or sometimes definite, the outer filaments sometimes dilated and petaloid. Ovary usually 1-celled and with parietal placentation. Fruit a many-seeded capsule.

The family includes about 15 genera and 250 species, chiefly in the drier parts of the southwestern United States, and in Mexico and South America, with 1 monotypic genus in South Africa and Arabia.

EXAMPLES: *Mentzelia:* Blazing Star, or Stickleaf, with numerous species, some of them with large, handsome flowers.

Loasa vulcania: an ornamental annual of South America.

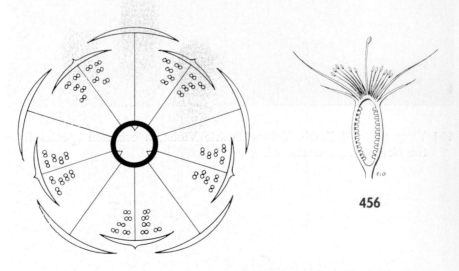

455

455 *Mentzelia,* floral diagram.

456 *Mentzelia,* longitudinal section of flower.

457 *Mentzelia*, hair.

458 *Eucnide*, hair.

459 *Cevallia*, hairs.

457   458   459

460 *Mentzelia decapetala* (Pursh) Urban & Gilg, a large-flowered species of Blazing Star, or Stickleaf, with cream-colored or white flowers.

ORDER CACTALES

The order includes only the following family and therefore has its characteristics. Divergent views have been expressed about the relationship of the *Cactales* to other orders: Bessey and Hutchinson considered the order to be related to the *Cucurbitales* (Pumpkin and Squash Order); Wettstein, Hallier, and others have suggested, because of anatomical and embryological evidence, that it is related to the *Caryophyllales* (Chickweed or Pink Order). On the basis of floral morphology, epidermal structures, and serological evidence gathered by Mez, it might also be related to the *Loasales* and the complex *Parietales*. Proliferation, which results in the development of new flowers on top of old fruits, occurs in some members and suggests the possibility that the ovary is embedded in stem tissue.

CACTACEAE: Cactus Family

Herbs, shrubs, and trees, mostly fleshy and succulent, generally without true leaves on mature stems, the stems often globose, cylindrical, or flattened, and provided with sharp bristles or spines, which emerge from areolae. Flowers solitary, perfect, regular to slightly irregular, epigynous, with or without a hypanthium. Sepals and petals not clearly differentiated, often in several series, and often merging into bracts. Stamens numerous and sometimes thigmotropic. Pistil 1, of 3 or more carpels, the ovary 1-celled and with as many parietal placentae as there are carpels and stigmas. Ovules numerous. Fruit a somewhat dry or fleshy berry.

The family includes about 120 genera and perhaps 1,500 species (there is disagreement on generic limits), and it is chiefly American, being found from Argentina and Chile northward to British Columbia. The genus *Rhipsalis* of tropical America has found its way to Africa and Ceylon; and several species of *Opuntia* occur on the shores of the Mediterranean Sea and in South Africa and Australia.

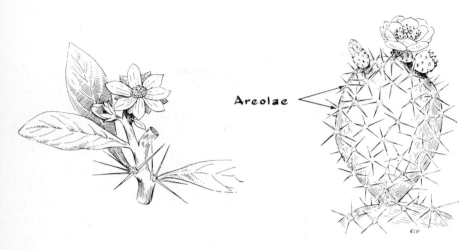

Areolae

461 *Pereskia (Pereskioideae)*, por-
tion of plant. [Redrawn from
Schumann in Engler & Prantl,
Nat. Pflanz., 3⁶: 204 (1894).]

462 *Opuntia (Opuntioideae)*, portion of plant.

463 *Opuntia polyacantha* Haw., a species of semi-desert regions (subfamily *Opuntioideae*).

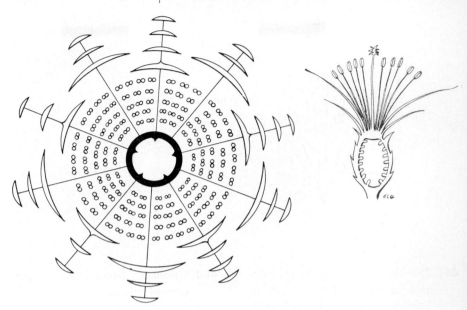

464 *Pereskia* (*Pereskioideae*), floral diagram and longitudinal section of flower. This is also the general situation in the subfamily *Opuntioideae*.

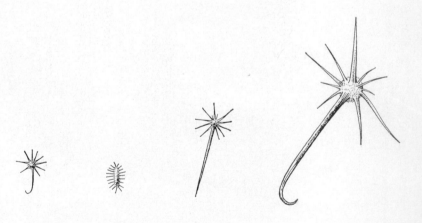

465 Various types of spines of cacti.

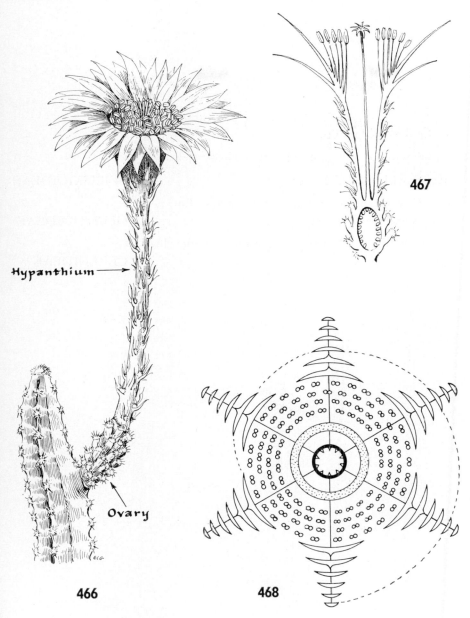

466 *Cereus greggii* (*Cereoideae*), portion of plant. [Modified from Engelmann, *Cactaceae of the Mexican Boundary*, pl. 63 (1859).]

467 *Epiphyllum* (*Cereoideae*), longitudinal section of flower.

468 *Epiphyllum* (*Cereoideae*), floral diagram.

Key to the Subfamilies

Flowers without a hypanthium; plants leafy or leafless

    Plants with normal leaves .... PERESKIOIDEAE

    Plants without leaves on mature stems, but new shoots and seedlings may be leafy .... OPUNTIOIDEAE

Flowers with a tubular hypanthium; plants leafless .... CEREOIDEAE

469 *Mammillaria vivipara* (Nutt.) Haw., a Nipple Cactus with bright
purplish flowers (subfamily *Cereoideae*).

ORDER LYTHRALES

Herbaceous or woody plants, sometimes aquatic, with reduced flowers, with simple and mostly exstipulate leaves. Flowers often 4-merous, regular or nearly so, perigynous or epigynous, the latter with or without a hypanthium. Stamens as many or twice as many as the petals, free. Gynoecium syncarpous, with axillary placentation.

The order, which probably evolved from the *Rosales*, includes 8 families as defined by Hutchinson, the following being representative.

ONAGRACEAE: Evening Primrose Family

Mostly herbs with simple, alternate or opposite, exstipulate leaves. Flowers axillary or in terminal racemes, regular, perfect, 2-merous or usually 4-merous, epigynous, with or without a tubular epigynous hypanthium. Stamens as many or twice as many as the petals. Ovary inferior, mostly 2- or 4-celled, with a single style and a 4-lobed, capitate, or discoid stigma. Fruit usually a capsule, rarely a berry (*Fuchsia*) or indehiscent and nut-like (*Circaea* and *Gaura*). Seeds sometimes with a tuft of silky hairs (comatose).

The family includes about 38 genera and 500 species, mainly in temperate and subtropical regions, the chief center of distribution being western North America.

EXAMPLES: *Oenothera:* Evening Primrose, with about 100 species in North and South America.

Epilobium: Willow-herb or Fire-weed, with about 160 species, widely distributed except in the tropics.

Clarkia and *Godetia:* commonly cultivated ornamentals.

Fuchsia: about 60 species of woody plants in Central and South America and New Zealand.

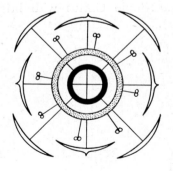 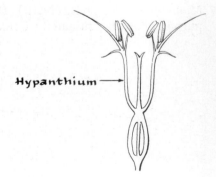

470 *Oenothera,* floral diagram and flower section.

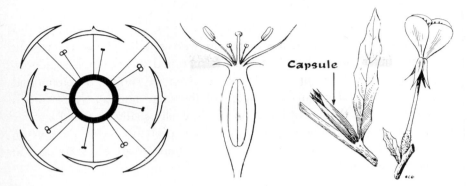

Capsule

472 *Gayophytum*, floral diagram and flower section.

471 *Oenothera*, flower and fruit.

473 *Oenothera caespitosa* Nutt., an Evening Primrose common in the Rocky Mountains. The flowers are white and fade pink.

ORDER APIALES (UMBELLALES)

Woody or herbaceous plants with simple or usually compound or dissected leaves, with or without stipules. Flowers small, epigynous, without a hypanthium, regular (or sometimes the marginal flowers of the inflorescence irregular), in capitate clusters or often in simple or compound umbels. Sepals much reduced. Stamens of the same number as the petals and alternate with them. Pistil of 2–5 carpels, each usually 1-seeded.

This, the highest order of the polypetalae, probably evolved from an ancestral stock near the *Rosales*. The following families are the chief ones in the North American flora.

Key to the Families

Leaves simple and usually opposite; flowers mostly 4-merous; style usually single ....   CORNACEAE

Leaves compound (rarely simple) and alternate or basal; flowers 5-merous; styles usually 2 or 5

    Styles 5; fruit a berry or drupe ....   ARALIACEAE

    Styles 2; fruit a schizocarp (2 mericarps) ....   APIACEAE (UMBELLIFERAE)

CORNACEAE: Dogwood Family

Mostly trees and shrubs, occasionally herbaceous, with opposite or rarely alternate, simple, and usually entire leaves without stipules. Flowers small, in umbels, cymes, or heads, often with a showy involucre of pink or white bracts, epigynous, usually 4-merous, regular, with stamens of the same number as the petals and alternate with them. Pistil 1, mostly of 2 carpels, with a single style and generally a lobed stigma. Fruit a drupe or a few-seeded berry.

The family includes about 11 genera and 90 species, chiefly in the northern hemisphere.

    EXAMPLES: *Cornus florida:* Flowering Dogwood, a small tree.

                Cornus canadensis: Bunchberry, exceptional in being herbaceous.

                Cornus stolonifera: Red Osier Dogwood, a common shrub.

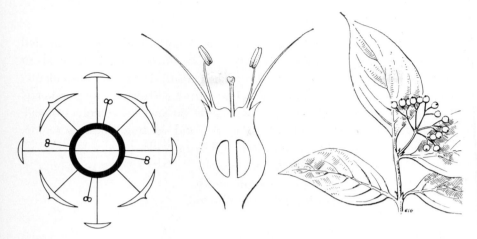

474 *Cornus*, floral diagram and flower section.

475 *Cornus stolonifera*, fruiting branch.

476 *Cornus stolonifera* Michx., Red Osier Dogwood, a common shrub. A portion of the plant is shown in fruiting condition. The fruits are white.

ARALIACEAE: Ginseng Family

Trees, shrubs, or herbs, with mostly alternate and divided or compound leaves, with petioles often sheathing at the base. Flowers small, in heads or umbels, regular, epigynous, with 5 stamens. Pistil 1, of 2–5 (usually 5) carpels, the styles usually as many as the carpels. Fruit a drupe or berry.

The family includes about 65 genera and 750 species, mainly tropical, with distributional centers in tropical America and the Indo-Malayan region.

EXAMPLES: *Hedera helix:* Ivy, often grown on walls.
Panax quinquefolium: Ginseng.
Aralia spinosoa: Hercules'-club.
Oplopanax horridus: Devil's-club.

APIACEAE (UMBELLIFERAE): Celery or Parsnip Family

Aromatic herbs with alternate or basal and usually compound leaves having petioles dilated and sheathing the stem at the nodes. Flowers small, mostly in compound umbels, regular (or the marginal flowers of an umbellet sometimes irregular), epigynous, without a hypanthium, 5-merous, the sepals very small and sometimes obsolete. Stamens 5, alternate with the petals. Pistil 1, of 2 united carpels, with 2 styles, and an inferior 2-celled ovary, which ripens into 2 small 1-seeded fruits, each known as a mericarp and collectively known as a schizocarp, each carpel indehiscent but separating from the other carpel.

The family includes about 200 genera and 3,000 species, found mainly in the temperate regions of the world or in the mountains of the tropics.

EXAMPLES: *Apium graveolens:* Celery.
Petroselinum hortense: Parsley.
Daucus carota: Carrot.
Cicuta: Water Hemlock, a stock-poisoning marsh herb.
Conium maculatum: Poison Hemlock, or Snakeweed, very poisonous.

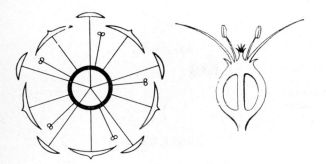

477 *Aralia*, floral diagram and flower section.

478 *Aralia*, fruit, enlarged.

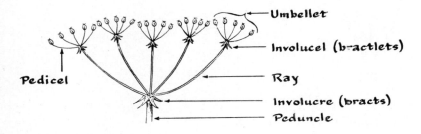

Umbellet

Involucel (bractlets)

Pedicel

Ray

Involucre (bracts)

Peduncle

479 Parts of a typical compound umbel.

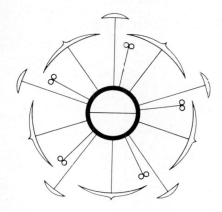

480 Generalized floral diagram and flower section for the *Apiaceae*

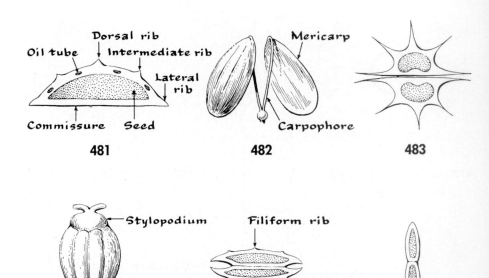

481 Cross section of a mericarp.

482 Fruits from a single flower (two mericarps).

483 *Cymopterus*, cross section of fruit showing winged ribs.

484 Fruit with a stylopodium.

485 *Pastinaca*, cross section of a dorsally flattened fruit.

486 *Hydrocotyle*, cross section of a laterally flattened fruit.

487 *Sium suave* Walt., Water Parsnip, a swamp plant with white flowers. The species is regarded as poisonous to livestock.

THE SYMPETALAE

This group includes all families of dicotyledonous flowering plants whose flowers show a tendency toward united petals. It includes two major lines of development, which are somewhat parallel: one a hypogynous (rarely epigynous) line, probably derived from the *Ranales* and showing relationships to the *Caryophyllales;* the other a strictly epigynous line, probably evolved from the *Rosales* and showing relationships to the *Apiales* and *Lythrales.* The sympetalae are thus probably biphyletic in origin.

The perigynous condition of the flower, which was strongly developed in the polypetalous *Rosales* and a few related orders, does not appear in the sympetalae.

Figures 488–495 illustrate most of the common forms of flowers having united petals and the chief parts of sympetalous corollas.

The Hypogynous Sympetalae

These orders and families, perhaps, have evolved from a hypogynous ancestry, and may have been derived from the *Ranales* through the *Caryophyllales.* The epigynous condition occurs only rarely, as in the subfamily *Vaccinioideae* (Huckleberries) of the family *Ericaceae.*

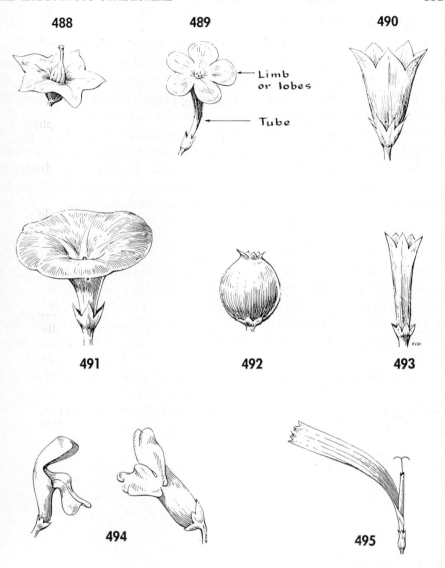

488   489   490

Limb or lobes

Tube

491   492   493

494   495

488 Rotate corolla of *Solanum*.

489 Salverform corolla of *Phlox*.

490 Campanulate corolla of *Campanula*.

491 Funnelform corolla of *Ipomoea*.

492 Urceolate, or urn-shaped, corolla of *Gaultheria*.

493 Tubular corolla of *Nicotiana*.

494 Bilabiate corollas of *Lamium* (left) and *Antirrhinum* (right).

495 Ligulate corolla of *Cichorium*.

ORDER ERICALES

Woody or sometimes herbaceous plants, occasionally saprophytic or parasitic, with simple, alternate, and usually leathery exstipulate leaves. Flowers usually perfect, regular or nearly so, hypogynous or epigynous, the corolla (with a few exceptions) of united petals. Stamens free from the corolla, usually twice as many as its lobes, the anthers often opening by terminal pores and often with awn-like appendages. Pistil 1, of few to several united carpels, the ovary with axillary placentation, the style single.

The order includes the families *Clethraceae, Ericaceae* (with 4 sub-families as treated here), *Epacridaceae,* and *Diapensiaceae.* The following family is representative and well represented in North America.

ERICACEAE: Heath Family

Herbs, shrubs, or trees, sometimes saprophytic, with alternate or sometimes opposite, simple, and often leathery leaves. Flowers perfect, regular or nearly so, hypogynous or epigynous, 4–5-merous, the petals usually united. Stamens as many or twice as many as the lobes of the corolla (petals), the anthers commonly opening by terminal pores and often appendaged. Pistil 1, of 4–5 carpels, with a single style and capitate stigma. Fruit a capsule or berry.

As treated here, the family includes about 90 genera and 1,700 or more species, found chiefly in temperate and cold regions or in the mountains of the tropics. The plants are often bog xerophytes, preferring acid soil.

Key to the Subfamilies

Flowers hypogynous; fruit a capsule or berry

    Plants green, with normal leaves

        Herbs with a somewhat scapose habit; petals distinct or only slighty united ...... 1. PYROLOIDEAE

        Shrubs or trees; petals usually united ..... 2. ERICOIDEAE

    Plants saprophytic, without green leaves .... 3. MONOTROPOIDEAE

Flowers epigynous; plants shrubby, sometimes slender and trailing; fruit a berry .... 4. VACCINIOIDEAE

SUBFAMILY 1. PYROLOIDEAE: *Pyrola Subfamily*

Green leafy herbs with a somewhat scapose habit. Inflorescence usually a raceme or the flowers solitary. Petals 5, distinct or slightly united. Anthers opening by terminal pores, not appendaged, the pollen in tetrads. Ovary superior, incompletely septate. Style commonly declined. Fruit a loculicidal capsule.

The subfamily includes 3 genera and about 30 species, mainly in forested regions of the north temperate and arctic zones.

EXAMPLES: *Pyrola:* Pyrola, or Wintergreen.
              Chimaphila: Pipsissewa, or Prince's-pine.
              Moneses uniflora: Moneses.

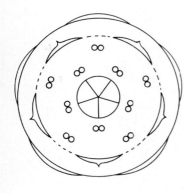

496 *Pyrola,* floral diagram and plant.

SUBFAMILY 2. ERICOIDEAE: *Heath Subfamily*

Shrubs or trees with mostly leathery leaves. Petals united or occasionally distinct. Anthers opening by terminal pores or longitudinal slits, often awned. Ovary superior, completely septate. Fruit a septicidal capsule or sometimes a berry.

The subfamily includes about 54 genera and 1,700 species, in temperate and cold regions and in the mountains of the tropics.

EXAMPLES: *Rhododendron* (including *Azalea*): shrubs and trees, often ornamentals, with about 800 species, many in southern Asia.

Erica: Heath, with about 500 species, mainly in South Africa and the Mediterranean region.

Arbutus menziesii: Madroño tree of the Pacific Coast.

Arctostaphylos: Bearberry and Manzanita, about 20 species, mostly in North and Central America.

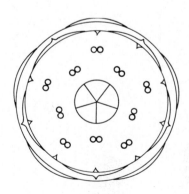

497 *Kalmia,* floral diagram. The corolla has ten pleats lengthwise.

498 *Chamaedaphne,* flowering branch.

499 *Arctostaphylos,* longitudinal section of flower, enlarged.

500 *Erica,* flowers, stamen, and pistil. [Redrawn from Drude in Engler & Prantl, *Nat. Pflanz.,* 4^1: 25 (1897).]

501 *Arctostaphylos uva-ursi* (L.) Spreng., Bearberry, a common sprawling shrub (subfamily *Ericoideae*).

SUBFAMILY 3. MONOTROPOIDEAE: *Indian Pipe Subfamily*

Saprophytic or parasitic fleshy herbs without green color, the leaves reduced to scales. Petals distinct or united. Anthers opening by longitudinal slits, the pollen simple. Ovary superior, incompletely septate, the upper portion commonly 1-celled. Fruit a loculicidal capsule.

The subfamily includes 5 genera and 7 species, found in moist woods of the northern hemisphere.

    EXAMPLES: *Monotropa uniflora:* Indian Pipe.

                   Pterospora andromedea: Pinedrops.

                   Sarcodes sanguinea: Snow Plant of Pacific North America.

SUBFAMILY 4. VACCINIOIDEAE: *Huckleberry Subfamily*

Shrubs, sometimes slender and trailing, with alternate leaves and epigynous flowers. Corolla of united petals, cylindric, urn-shaped, or nearly globose. Anthers opening by terminal pores in their tubular tips. Ovary completely septate and forming a berry in fruit.

The subfamily includes 23 genera and about 330 species, in the north temperate zone and in the mountains of the tropics. Several species are circumpolar, and some are epiphytes in tropical mountains.

    EXAMPLES: *Vaccinium oxycoccos:* Cranberry.

                   Gaylussacia: Huckleberries.

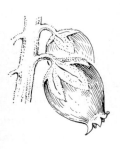

502 *Pterospora*, portion of raceme, enlarged.

503 *Monotropa uniflora*, plants.

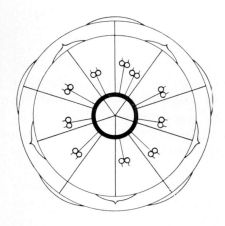

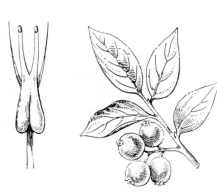

504 *Vaccinium*, floral diagram and stamen, enlarged.

505 *Vaccinium corymbosum*, fruiting branch.

ORDER PRIMULALES

Mostly scapose herbs, sometimes leafy-stemmed, with umbellate or uni-lateral inflorescences, and regular, hypogynous, sympetalous, 5-merous flowers. Stamens of the same number as the lobes of the corolla and op-posite them, adnate to the corolla tube. Pistil 1, of united carpels, the styles united or distinct. Ovules 1–many, from a free-central placenta.

The order includes the families *Primulaceae* and *Plumbaginaceae*. It is generally regarded as a sympetalous development from the *Caryophylla-ceae*, the free-central placentation identifying this order with the *Centro-spermae*. The following family is representative.

PRIMULACEAE: Primrose Family

Mostly scapose but sometimes caulescent herbs with simple leaves. Flowers hypogynous, 5-merous, the corolla regular and of united petals. Stamens 5, attached to the tube of the corolla opposite its lobes. Pistil 1, probably of 5 united carpels, but the style and stigma single and the ovary with free-central placentation. Fruit a capsule, which is usually dehiscent by 5 teeth or valves, less commonly circumscissile.

The family includes about 22 genera and 600 species, cosmopolitan in distribution, but commonest in the temperate and cooler parts of the northern hemisphere, many being found in arctic and alpine regions.

EXAMPLES: *Primula:* Primrose, several species being cultivated house plants.

Cyclamen: with about 20 species of Mediterranean origin.

Dodecatheon: Shooting-star, common in moist meadows.

ORDER GENTIANALES

Herbs, shrubs, or trees, with mostly opposite or whorled, exstipulate, simple or pinnately compound leaves. Flowers hypogynous, sympetalous or occasionally apetalous, 4–5-merous, the corolla limb often convolute. Stamens as many as the lobes of the corolla, inserted on the corolla tube alternate with its lobes, or sometimes the stamens half as many. Gynoecium of 2 carpels, which are weakly or completely united. Internal phloem oc-curs except in *Oleaceae*.

The order may have evolved from a stock ancestral to the *Primulales* and *Polemoniales* and probably represents an offshoot that has terminated a line of evolution, as evidenced by the very specialized floral structures of the *Asclepiadaceae* (Milkweed Family). By some the group is split into three orders.

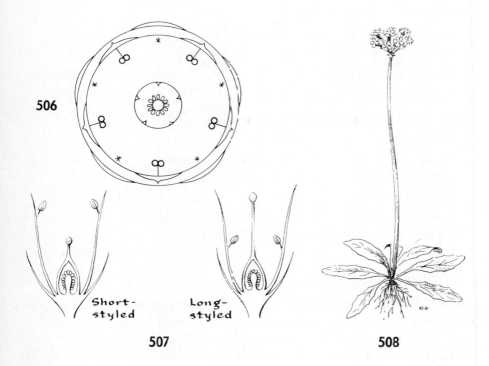

506 *Primula,* floral diagram.

507 Dimorphic flowers of *Primula* in longitudinal section, one short-styled and the other long-styled. This favors cross pollination.

508 *Primula farinosa,* plant.

Key to the Families

Juice not milky; flowers 4–5-merous; fruit not a follicle; seeds not comose

Mostly herbs; stamens 4–5 .... GENTIANACEAE

Mostly trees and shrubs; stamens 2 .... OLEACEAE

Juice milky; flowers 5-merous; fruit a follicle; seeds comose

Stamens free from each other, seldom coherent with the stigma; corona none or inconspicuous; follicles linear .... APOCYNACEAE

Stamens united by their anthers and to the stigma; corona conspicuous; follicles lanceolate .... ASCLEPIADACEAE

GENTIANACEAE: Gentian Family

Mostly glabrous annual or perennial herbs, with opposite or whorled, simple, sessile, entire, and exstipulate leaves. Flowers often showy, perfect, regular, 4–5-merous, the corolla of united petals, and the stamens as many as the lobes of the corolla, alternate with them, and inserted on the corolla tube. Pistil 1, of 2 carpels, the ovary usually 1-celled, with 2 large and often 2-lobed parietal placentae, the style single or none, and the stigma single or commonly 2-lobed. Fruit a 2-valved septicidal capsule with numerous seeds.

The family includes about 70 genera and 800 species, world-wide in distribution, but mainly in temperate regions.

EXAMPLES: *Gentiana:* Gentian, with about 400 species.

Frasera: Elkweed.

Menyanthes: Buckbean, with compound leaves.

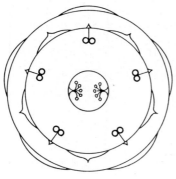

509   510

511

509 *Gentiana*, floral diagram and plant. The flowers may be either 4-merous or 5-merous.

510 *Eustoma*, longitudinal section of flower.

511 *Gentiana thermalis* Kuntze [*Gentianella detonsa* (Rottb.) G. Don, ssp. *elegans* (A. Nels.) Gillett], a common Gentian of the Rocky Mountains. The flowers are deep blue.

OLEACEAE: Olive Family

Trees or shrubs with mostly opposite, simple or odd-pinnate leaves without stipules. Flowers perfect, polygamous, or dioecious, hypogynous, regular, usually 4-merous, the corolla of united petals or lacking. Stamens usually 2. Pistil 1, of 2 carpels, the ovary 2-celled, the style single, and the stigma 2-lobed. Ovules few (generally 2 in each cell, and sometimes only 1 maturing). Fruit a capsule, drupe, berry, or samara.

The family includes 22 genera and about 400 species, in temperate and tropical regions, chiefly in eastern and southern Asia.

EXAMPLES: *Syringa:* Lilac, with 10 species.

Jasminum: Jasmin, with 200 species, some cultivated.

Olea europea: Olive of southeastern Europe and Asia Minor.

Fraxinus: Ash, with about 39 species, several in North America.

Ligustrum: Privet, with about 35 species, some used for hedges.

Forsythia: Golden-bell, an ornamental, early-blooming shrub.

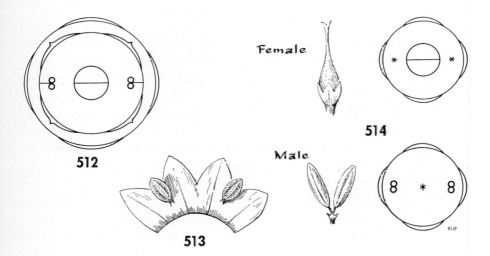

Female

Male

512

513

514

512 *Forsythia,* floral diagram.

513 *Olea,* corolla and stamens, enlarged.

514 *Fraxinus americana,* female and male flowers and floral diagrams, the flowers enlarged.

APOCYNACEAE: Dogbane Family

Herbs, shrubs, or trees, with milky juice and simple, entire, and often opposite leaves, usually without stipules. Flowers hypogynous, perfect, regular, usually 5-merous, the corolla of united petals and salverform, tubular, or funnelform. Stamens of the same number as the corolla lobes, alternate with them, and attached to the corolla tube, the anthers sometimes adhering to the stigma. Carpels 2, the ovaries separate or connate, their styles and stigmas united. Fruit commonly 2 follicles, the seeds often hairy.

The family includes about 155 genera and 1,000 species, mainly in warm regions. The plants are often poisonous to livestock.

EXAMPLES: *Nerium oleander:* Oleander, a large shrub of the Mediterreanean region, often grown for ornament.

Vinca: Periwinkle, an ornamental trailing plant.

Apocynum: Dogbane, or Indian Hemp, with several species in North America.

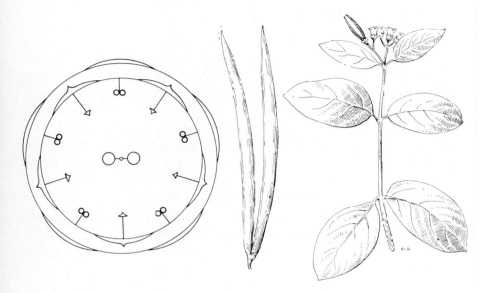

515 *Apocynum,* floral diagram.

516 *Apocynum androsaemifolium,* pair of follicles and flowering shoot.

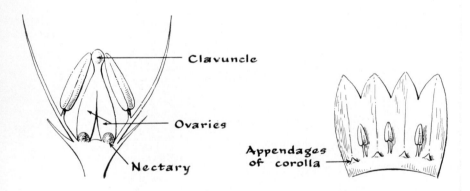

517 *Apocynum,* diagrammatic longitudinal section of flower, enlarged. A *clavuncle* is a thickened fleshy style that is common to the two carpels, whose ovaries are separate at the base.

518 *Apocynum,* part of corolla and stamens, enlarged. A *corona* is a set of appendages on the corolla and may be small and inconspicuous, as in this family, or very conspicuous, as in the following family (*Asclepiadaceae*).

ASCLEPIADACEAE: Milkweed Family

Perennial herbs or shrubby climbers, shrubs, or trees, sometimes succulent, with milky juice and simple, usually entire, mostly opposite or whorled, exstipulate leaves. Flowers usually in umbels or cymes, hypogynous, 5-merous, regular, and perfect. Corolla rotate or salverform, often with a set of appendages arising from the back of the stamens or from the corolla, which form a petaloid corona. Stamens 5, the anthers united to form a cone, which is commonly attached to the stigma, the pollen often united into waxy pollinia. Carpels 2, the ovaries separate but the styles and stigmas united, each carpel forming a follicle in fruit (or sometimes 1 carpel aborting). Seeds numerous and often with a tuft of silky hairs at one end.

The family includes about 280 genera and 1,800 species, mostly in the tropics, but with several representatives in North America.

EXAMPLES: *Asclepias:* Milkweed or Butterfly-weed. Some species are poisonous to livestock.

Hoya carnosa: Wax Plant, a vine of tropical regions often grown as a house plant.

Stapelia: Starfish-flower, succulents often grown as house plants.

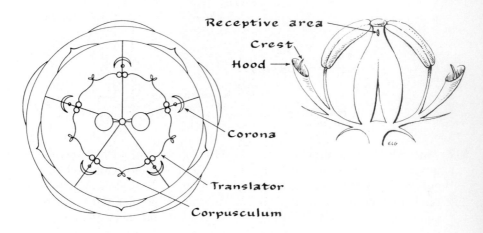

519 *Asclepias,* floral diagram.

520 *Asclepias,* diagrammatic longitudinal section of flower.

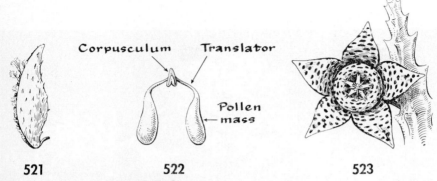

521
522
523

521 *Asclepias speciosa,* follicle.

522 *Asclepias speciosa,* pollinium, enlarged.

523 *Stapelia,* flower and branch.

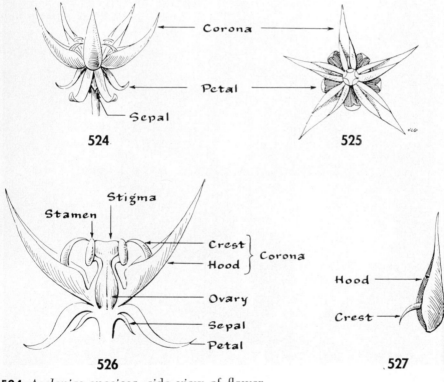

524
525
526
527

524 *Asclepias speciosa,* side view of flower.

525 *Asclepias speciosa,* face view of flower.

526 *Asclepias speciosa,* longitudinal section of flower.

527 *Asclepias speciosa,* side view of a segment of the corona.

528 *Asclepias speciosa* Torr., a Milkweed, showing the conspicuous corona of the flowers.

529 *Asclepias speciosa* Torr., two opened follicles with comose seeds.

The "Tubiflorae"

This series of families and orders is sometimes treated as one large order having the following general tendencies: the development of a deeply 4-lobed ovary with a consequent fruit of 4 nutlets (*Boraginales* and *Lamiales*), and the development of irregular corollas and a simultaneous modification of the stamens by the reduction of 1 or 3 of them (*Lamiales*), and the retention of the capsular type of fruit, with many seeds, and the development of irregular corollas and modified stamens (*Scrophulariales*). The *Plantaginales* may represent an offshoot in which the scapose habit, parallel-veined leaves, and small, spicate flowers with a scarious corolla are the chief distinguishing features.

Key to the Families

Corolla regular; stamens of the same number as the corolla lobes

    Flowers 5-merous; corolla not scarious

        Corolla scarcely lobed or the plants parasitic .... CONVOLVULACEAE

        Corolla definitely lobed; plants green

            Carpels 3, stigmas 3 .... POLEMONIACEAE

            Carpels 2, stigmas 1 or 2

                Ovary deeply 4-lobed .... BORAGINACEAE

                Ovary not deeply 4-lobed

                    Styles 2 or the style 2-cleft .... HYDROPHYLLACEAE

                    Style 1 or the stigma sessile .... SOLANACEAE

        Flowers 4-merous; corolla scarious .... PLANTAGINACEAE

Corolla irregular, sometimes only slightly so; stamens often fewer than the corolla lobes or some of them sterile

    Aromatic herbs with square stems and opposite leaves; ovary usually deeply 4-lobed and fruit 4 nutlets; style arising from between the lobes of the ovary .... LAMIACEAE

Plants seldom aromatic; sometimes with square stems and opposite leaves; ovary not deeply 4-lobed; fruit usually a many-seeded capsule; style arising from the apex of the ovary.

    Plants parasitic, without green color ......   OROBANCHACEAE

    Plants not parasitic, green leaves present

        Stems woody; leaves often compound ...   BIGNONIACEAE

        Stems herbaceous, rarely woody; leaves never compound but sometimes deeply cleft

            Aquatic herbs, often insectivorous, the submerged leaves usually finely divided; flowers with 2 stamens and the ovary with free-central placentation ..   LENTIBULARIACEAE

            Mostly terrestrial plants, sometimes in wet places, the leaves not finely divided; flowers with mostly 4 stamens, the ovary never with free-central placentation

                Flowers in spikes or heads; fruit 2–4 nutlets ....   VERBENACEAE

                Flowers not in spikes or heads but sometimes congested; fruit a many-seeded capsule ....   SCROPHULARIACEAE

ORDER POLEMONIALES

Herbs or low shrubs with alternate or opposite leaves. Flowers sympetalous, hypogynous, regular, 5-merous (rarely 4-merous). Stamens of the same number as the lobes of the corolla, alternate with them, and inserted on the corolla tube. Pistil 1, of 2–3 united carpels, the placentation axillary. Seeds numerous or few. Fruit a capsule.

The order may have evolved from the same ancestral stock as the *Gentianales*, and this same line of development may have given rise to the more advanced *Boraginales, Lamiales, Scrophulariales,* and *Plantaginales*. As defined here, the order includes the following two families.

POLEMONIACEAE: Phlox Family

Mostly annual or perennial herbs, occasionally shrubby, with alternate or opposite leaves without stipules. Flowers often showy, commonly in cymes or solitary, regular, hypogynous, 5-merous, the corolla of united petals and usually salverform or tubular, the lobes contorted in bud. Stamens 5, inserted on the corolla tube alternate with its lobes. Pistil 1, of 3 united carpels, the ovary 3-celled, the style slender and single, the stigmas or style-branches 3. Fruit a loculicidal capsule with several to many seeds.

The family includes about 15 genera and 275 species and is especially well represented in western North America. There are numerous alpine species.

EXAMPLES: *Phlox:* Phlox, with about 50 species, some of them cultivated.
Polemonium: Jacob's-ladder, with about 20 species.
Gilia: Gilia, with about 100 species, but some of these often placed in segregate genera.

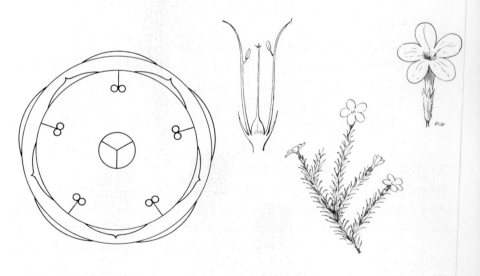

530 *Phlox,* floral diagram.

531 *Phlox hooddii,* flower section, portion of plant, and flower.

532 *Phlox multiflora* A. Nels., a mat-forming species with white to pinkish or lavender flowers, common in the Rocky Mountains.

CONVOLVULACEAE: Morning-glory Family

Mostly annual or perennial herbs, often twining (occasionally shrubby or arborescent in the tropics), with simple or rarely pinnate, alternate, exstipulate leaves; or the plants leafless, twining, parasitic herbs. Flowers often showy, solitary and axillary or in axillary clusters, usually perfect, regular, hypogynous, 5-merous, with a funnelform or tubular corolla, which is usually twisted in the bud. Stamens 5, inserted on the tube of the corolla alternate with its lobes. Pistil 1, of 1–3 (usually 2) carpels, the ovary usually 2-celled with 1–2 ovules in each cell, the style usually single and terminal, and the stigmas 2. Fruit a loculicidal capsule.

The family includes about 47 genera and 1,100 species, mostly in warm regions. A few are troublesome weeds, and a few are cultivated for their flowers or tuberous roots. The parasitic members (the single genus *Cuscuta*, or Dodder) are destructive of certain crops and may spread disease. By some these are treated as a separate family, the *Cuscutaceae*.

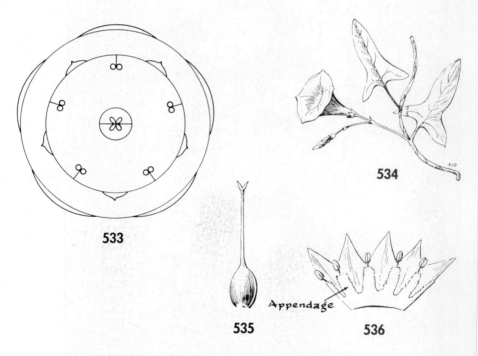

533 *Convolvulus*, floral diagram.

534 *Convolvulus arvensis*, portion of plant.

535 *Convolvulus*, pistil, enlarged.

536 *Cuscuta arvensis*, corolla opened up to show appendages, enlarged.

537 *Convolvulus arvensis* L., a common weedy species with white to pinkish flowers.

Key to the Subfamilies

Plants green, with normal leaves .... 1. CONVOLVULOIDEAE

Plants parasitic and leafless, not green ...... 2. CUSCUTOIDEAE

SUBFAMILY 1. CONVOLVULOIDEAE: *Morning-glory Subfamily*

> EXAMPLES: *Convolvulus:* with about 200 species, includes wild Morning-glory and Bindweed.
>
> *Ipomoea:* with about 400 species, includes *I. purpurea,* the commonly cultivated Morning-glory, and *I. batatas,* the Sweet Potato.

SUBFAMILY 2. CUSCUTOIDEAE: *Dodder Subfamily*

Includes only the genus *Cuscuta,* or Dodder, with about 100 species. In this subfamily the corolla is often very small and appendaged within as shown in Figure 536.

ORDER BORAGINALES

Herbs, or sometimes shrubs or trees, with mostly alternate leaves and more or less coiled inflorescences. Flowers sympetalous, hypogynous, regular, 5-merous. Stamens of the same number as the lobes of the corolla and alternate with them, inserted on the corolla tube. Pistil 1, of 2 carpels, the ovary shallowly lobed and with numerous ovules or deeply lobed and the ovules 4 or less. Fruit a capsule or 1–4 nutlets.

The order shows a progressive development from the *Polemoniales* in the tendency toward a reduction in the number of carpels and ovules and in the specialized inflorescence, while maintaining a regular corolla and isomerous stamens. It includes the following two families.

HYDROPHYLLACEAE: Water-leaf Family

Herbs, or occasionally undershrubs, with various exstipulate leaves, which often form a basal rosette. Flowers small or sometimes showy, often in coiled cymes, perfect, regular, hypogynous, 5-merous, the corolla of united petals and often with scale-like appendages alternate or opposite the lobes. Stamens 5, on the lower part of the corolla tube, alternate with the lobes, usually well exserted. Pistil 1, of 2 united carpels, the ovary not deeply lobed, usually 1-celled with 2 large parietal placentae, or sometimes 2-celled with axillary placentation, the styles 2 and distinct or partly united, usually exserted, the stigmas usually capitate. Fruit commonly a loculicidal capsule or sometimes berry-like.

The family includes about 18 genera and 200 species, mostly in North America.

> EXAMPLES: *Hydrophyllum:* Water-leaf.
>
> *Phacelia:* Phacelia, with more than 100 species.

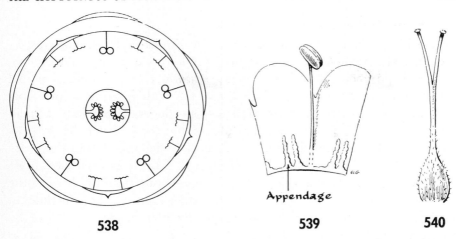

538

539

Appendage

540

538 *Phacelia,* floral diagram.

539 *Phacelia,* portion of corolla and stamens, enlarged.

540 *Phacelia,* pistil, enlarged.

541 *Hydrophyllum fendleri* (A. Gray) Heller, a species of Water-leaf.

BORAGINACEAE: Borage Family

Mostly hispid, bristly or hairy herbs, rarely shrubs or trees, with simple, generally alternate leaves without stipules. Flowers often in coiled cymes, perfect, hypogynous, 5-merous, regular or nearly so, the corolla of united petals, tubular, salverform, or funnelform, the limb commonly spreading, and the throat often closed by petaloid appendages, which form a small corona. Stamens 5, inserted on the tube of the corolla alternate with its lobes. Pistil 1, of 2 united carpels, each usually deeply 2-lobed, the ovary thus 2-celled and usually deeply 4-lobed, with 1 ovule in each lobe. Style single or occasionally the styles 2, usually originating from the base of the ovary between the lobes (gynobasic), the stigmas 1 or 2, or sometimes 4. Fruit commonly consisting of four 1-seeded nutlets, sometimes fewer by abortion, and sometimes a drupe.

The family includes about 88 genera and 1,600 species, mostly in warm and temperate regions, especially in the Mediterranean basin, tropical America, and the western United States.

EXAMPLES: *Borago:* Borage.
    Cynoglossum: Hound's-tongue.
    Lappula: Stickseed.
    Myosotis: Forget-me-not.

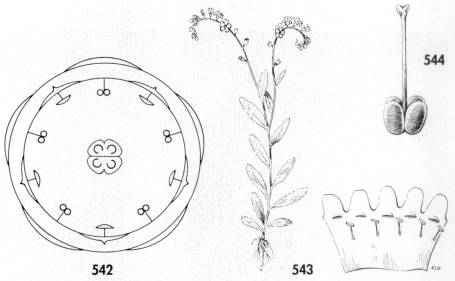

542 *Myosotis,* floral diagram.

543 *Myosotis virginica,* plant, and corolla and stamens, the corolla opened.

544 *Myosotis,* pistil showing gynobasic style.

545 *Cryptantha bradburyana* Payson. Notice the coiling of the inflorescence and the bristly hairs of the plant, both characteristic of the family.

ORDER LAMIALES

Mostly herbs, often aromatic, with opposite or whorled leaves and ir-regular, often 2-lipped flowers. Stamens reduced to 4 or 2, rarely 5; sterile filaments sometimes present. Carpels usually 2, each with 2 ovules. Fruit a drupe, a berry, or, more commonly, four 1-seeded nutlets.

VERBENACEAE: Vervain Family

Herbs, or sometimes shrubs or trees, with opposite or whorled leaves with-out stipules, and mostly small, perfect, 4–5-merous, hypogynous flowers produced in spikes or heads. Corolla of united petals, somewhat irregular. Stamens 4, in two pairs (didynamous), inserted on the corolla tube alter-nate with its lobes. Pistil 1, of 2 united carpels, with a terminal style and 1 or 2 stigmas, the ovary not deeply lobed, and forming 2 or 4 nutlets in fruit or sometimes a drupe or berry.

The family includes about 90 genera and 3,000 species, widely distributed but most abundant in tropical and subtropical regions.

EXAMPLES: *Verbena:* Vervain, with about 270 species, some cultivated.

Lantana: ornamental shrubs and climbers.

Tectona grandis: Teak, of southeastern Asia, a valuable timber tree with very heavy, durable wood.

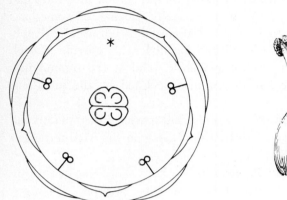

546 *Verbena*, floral diagram, pistil, and flower section.

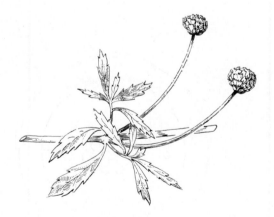

547 *Verbena hastata*, portion of plant.

548 *Phyla cuneifolia*, portion of plant.

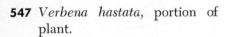

LAMIACEAE (LABIATAE): Mint Family

Mostly aromatic herbs, occasionally shrubs or trees, with square stems and opposite, simple, exstipulate leaves. Flowers perfect, hypogynous, 5-merous, the calyx persistent and from nearly regular to bilabiate, the corolla usually strikingly irregular and bilabiate. Stamens 4 and didynamous (two long and two short) or reduced to 2, inserted on the corolla tube alternate with its lobes, the fifth (upper) stamen usually lacking or sometimes present as a staminodium. Pistil 1, of 2 united carpels, each usually deeply 2-lobed, the ovary thus deeply 4-lobed and 2-celled, with 1 ovule in each lobe. Style single, terminal or usually gynobasic, bifid at the summit into unequal branches. Fruit four 1-seeded nutlets enclosed by the persistent calyx.

The family includes about 160 genera and 3,500 species, in temperate and warm regions, the chief center of distribution being in the Mediterranean basin.

EXAMPLES: *Mentha piperita:* Peppermint.
Mentha spicata: Spearmint.
Salvia officinalis: Sage, often used for seasoning.
Thymus vulgaris: Thyme.
Lavandula spica: Lavender, source of a common perfume.
Lamium: Dead Nettle.

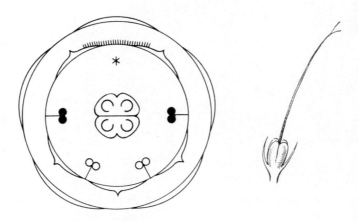

549 *Monarda,* floral diagram and pistil.

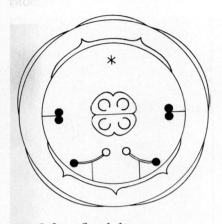

550 *Salvia*, floral diagram.

551 *Scutellaria brittonii*, portion of plant.

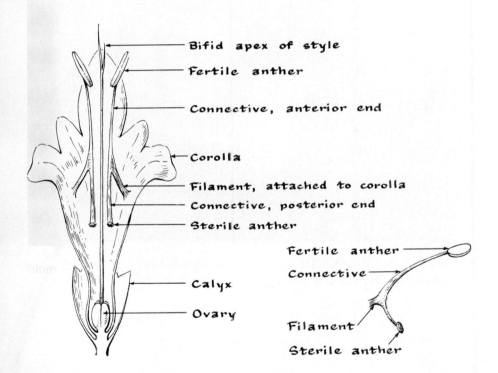

552 *Salvia*, flower opened up to show structure, enlarged. This is a highly specialized flower type, modified for insect pollination.

553 *Salvia*, single stamen, enlarged. Insect visitors receive pollen on their backs by pushing against or stepping on the pedal-like sterile anther.

554 *Stachys palustris* L., Hedge Nettle, a wide-ranging species of moist situations. Notice the two-lipped corollas.

555 *Mentha arvensis* L., a common species of Mint across North America in moist places. The flowers are pale lavender and only slightly irregular.

ORDER SCROPHULARIALES

Plants of various habit but predominantly herbaceous. Leaves various but mostly alternate. Flowers hypogynous, sympetalous, mostly 5-merous, the corolla from nearly or quite regular to mostly strongly irregular or bilabiate. Stamens 5 and all fertile, or more commonly reduced to 4 and didynamous, with or without a fifth sterile stamen, or sometimes with only 2 fertile stamens. Pistil 1, of 2 united carpels, the ovary not deeply lobed, with numerous ovules, 2-celled, or rarely 1-celled with free-central placentation. Fruit commonly a capsule, sometimes a berry.

This, the largest order of the *Tubiflorae*, represents another divergent line of evolution from the *Polemoniales*, which culminates in the *Scrophulariaceae*. The unspecialized gynoecium and fruit are retained, but there is a strong tendency toward irregularity in the corolla and with it a reduction in the number of fertile stamens.

SOLANACEAE: Potato Family

Plants chiefly herbaceous, sometimes climbing, and occasionally woody, the stems with bicollateral bundles. Leaves mostly alternate, without stipules. Flowers hypogynous, 5-merous, regular to somewhat irregular, perfect, the corolla of united petals, usually plicate in bud. Stamens 5, inserted on the tube of the corolla alternate with the lobes, rarely 4 or 2. Pistil 1, of 2 united carpels, the ovary not deeply lobed, usually 2-celled with an oblique placenta, but sometimes nearly 4-celled by the development of additional placental lobes, the style single or none, and the stigma single or slightly 2-lobed. Fruit a capsule or berry.

The family includes about 85 genera and 2,200 species, about half of which are in the large genus *Solanum*. The chief center of distribution is in South America, but the general distribution is world-wide in temperate and warm regions. Many of the plants contain poisonous alkaloids, some are important drug plants, some ornamentals, and some valuable food plants.

EXAMPLES: *Solanum tuberosum:* Potato.

Solanum dulcamara: Nightshade, a plant with poisonous berries.

Lycopersicon esculentum: Tomato.

Nicotiana tabacum: Tobacco.

Capsicum frutescens: Peppers.

Atropa belladonna: source of the drug atropine.

Petunia: species of garden ornamentals.

556 *Solanum*, diagrammatic flower section, flower, and floral diagram.

557 *Hyoscyamus niger* L., Henbane, an introduced weed with some medicinal properties. The greenish-yellow flowers are slightly irregular.

BIGNONIACEAE: Bignonia Family

Mostly woody plants, often lianas in the tropics, with simple or compound and often opposite leaves. Flowers showy, with the general structure of those in the *Scrophulariaceae,* but the ovary either 2-celled with two placentae in each cell or 1-celled and with parietal placentae. Stigma 2-lipped. Fruit a capsule, often elongated, or sometimes fleshy and indehiscent. Seeds often winged.

The family includes about 100 genera and 800 species, widely distributed in tropical or subtropical regions, a few extending into temperate regions. The chief center of distribution is Brazil.

EXAMPLES: *Catalpa:* Catalpa, trees often cultivated for fence posts and as shade trees.

Campsis radicans: Trumpet Creeper, a common ornamental vine.

Chilopsis linearis: Desert Willow, a common shrub of the deserts of the southwestern United States.

OROBANCHACEAE: Broomrape Family

Root parasites with reduced leaves and little or no green color. Flower structure essentially like that in the *Scrophulariaceae,* but the ovary 1-celled and with 2–6 parietal placentae.

The family includes about 14 genera and 170 species, mostly in the northern hemisphere, especially in the Old World.

EXAMPLE: *Orobanche:* Broomrape, with about 100 species, is fairly common in dry sandy areas, attached to roots of various host plants.

LENTIBULARIACEAE: Bladderwort Family

Mostly aquatic, insectivorous herbs, the submerged leaves usually finely divided into capillary divisions and commonly bearing minute bladder-like traps. Flowers essentially like those in the *Scrophulariaceae,* the corolla spurred, the stamens 2, the stigma sessile, and the ovary with free-central placentation.

The family includes 5 genera and about 300 species, widely distributed in temperate and tropical regions.

EXAMPLES: *Utricularia:* Bladderwort, with about 300 species, many tropical.

Pinguicula: Butterwort, with about 45 species, mainly in the north temperate zone and in the mountains of tropical America.

SCROPHULARIACEAE: Figwort Family

Mostly herbs, occasionally shrubby or arborescent, and sometimes partly parasitic, but the leaves green, alternate, opposite, or whorled, without stipules. Flowers in cymes or racemes, or sometimes spicate, hypogynous, perfect, 5-merous, the corolla of united petals (rarely lacking) and from nearly regular to strongly bilabiate. Stamens usually 4 and didynamous, with a sterile upper fifth stamen, but occasionally 5, and sometimes reduced to 2, inserted on the corolla tube alternate with its lobes. Pistil 1, of 2 united carpels, the ovary not deeply lobed, 2-celled, with axillary placentation and numerous ovules. Style 1- or 2-lobed. Fruit usually a capsule, sometimes a berry.

The family includes about 205 genera and 2,600 species, cosmopolitan in distribution, with many species in the western United States.

 EXAMPLES: *Verbascum:* Mullein.
      Scrophularia: Figwort.
      Digitalis: Foxglove, a common drug plant.
      Penstemon: Beardtongue, with about 225 species in North
       America.
      Castilleja: Indian Paintbrush.
      Antirrhinum majus: Snapdragon, a common ornamental.

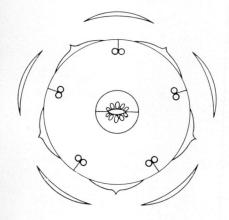

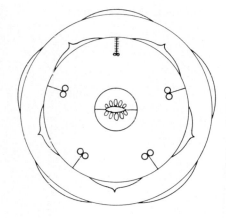

558 *Verbascum,* floral diagram, the corolla nearly regular.

559 *Penstemon,* floral diagram, the upper stamen bearded and the corolla irregular.

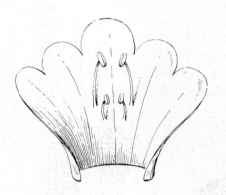

560 *Torenia,* corolla opened up to show the characteristic arrangement of stamens.

561 Pistil type found in the *Scrophulariaceae.*

562 *Penstemon secundiflorus* Benth., a Beardtongue having lavender to pinkish-violet flowers.

563 *Pedicularis groenlandica* Retz., a Lousewort that ranges from Green-land to Alaska, and southward in the western mountains. The flowers are purplish.

564 *Castilleja chromosa* A. Nels., one of many species of Indian Paint-brush. The bracts are brilliant red.

ORDER PLANTAGINALES

PLANTAGINACEAE: Plantain Family

Mostly herbs with prominently parallel-veined basal leaves and scapose, spicate, bracteate inflorescences. Flowers hypogynous, sympetalous, 4-merous, usually perfect, regular, and small. Calyx herbaceous and persistent. Corolla scarious or membranaceous, usually salverform. Stamens mostly 4 or 2, rarely 1, inserted on the corolla tube alternate with its lobes, or sometimes free from the corolla, often long-exserted. Pistil 1, the ovary 1–4-celled, the style single and filiform, longitudinally stigmatic. Fruit a pyxis, or indehiscent and nut-like.

The family includes 3 genera and about 200 species, mainly in temperate regions. It probably represents an offshoot from the *Polemoniales* or perhaps from the *Primulales.*

EXAMPLES:　*Plantago:* Plantain, with about 200 species, some of them noxious weeds.

Littorella: Shore-grass, with 2 species having unisexual flowers, one in Europe and North America, the other in South America.

Bougueria: a monotypic genus of the high Andes.

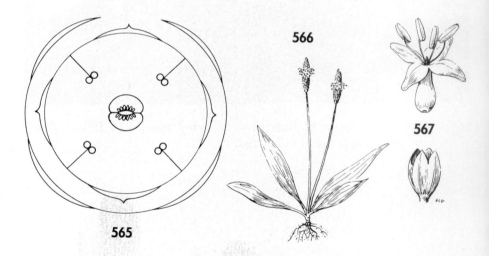

565 *Plantago lanceolata,* floral diagram.

566 *Plantago lanceolata,* plant.

567 *Plantago lanceolata,* calyx, and flower with calyx removed. [After Harms in Engler & Prantl, *Nat. Pflanz.,* 4³ᵇ: 366 (1895).]

568 *Plantago purshii* R. & S., Pursh's Plantain.

The Epigynous Sympetalae

These orders and families, perhaps, have evolved along lines that parallel those of the hypogynous sympetalae. They may have come from a perigynous or epigynous polypetalous ancestry such as that which produced the *Lythrales* and *Apiales,* and not from a hypogynous ancestry, although serodiagnostic evidence indicates a relationship between the *Rubiales* and the *Polemoniales.* Along with the development of a corolla of united petals have gone tendencies toward a reduction in, and often a late development of, the calyx, which eventually becomes an organ of dissemination of the fruit. Irregularity in the corolla occurs in some members, and there is a general tendency toward a reduction in the number of carpels and ovules. In the highest groups there is also a modification of the inflorescence as well, culminating in the well-known involucrate head of flowers that is characteristic of the *Asteraceae (Compositae).* Some of these tendencies had already made their appearance in the *Apiaceae.*

Key to the Principal Families

Tendril-bearing herbs; fruit a pepo (*Cucurbitales*) .... CUCURBITACEAE

Tendrils lacking; fruit not a pepo

  Stamens free from the corolla (*Campanulales*) .. CAMPANULACEAE

  Stamens inserted on the corolla tube

    Ovary 2–several-celled and 2–several-seeded (*Rubiales*)

      Flowers regular; leaves opposite and stipulate or appearing whorled and exstipulate .. RUBIACEAE [1]

      Flowers regular or irregular; leaves opposite or perfoliate and usually exstipulate .... CAPRIFOLIACEAE [1]

    Ovary 1-celled and 1-seeded (*Asterales*)

      Flowers not in an involucrate head; anthers distinct .... VALERIANACEAE

      Flowers in an involucrate head; anthers united or distinct

        Anthers distinct .... DIPSACACEAE

        Anthers united (very few exceptions) ... ASTERACEAE

ORDER RUBIALES

Herbaceous or woody plants with opposite or apparently whorled leaves and mostly cymose inflorescences. Flowers epigynous, sympetalous, typically perfect, regular to irregular, 4–5-merous, the stamens usually of the same number as the lobes of the corolla or sometimes fewer, inserted on the corolla tube alternate with its lobes. Carpels usually few. Seeds numerous to 1 in each carpel.

The order includes the following two families, which are usually treated as separate families but might be better combined.

---

[1] Although it has long been the custom to treat the *Rubiaceae* and *Caprifoliaceae* as distinct families, they can be distinguished only arbitrarily and would be better combined.

RUBIACEAE: Madder Family

Mostly trees or shrubs, occasionally (especially in northern regions) herbs or climbers, with opposite or apparently whorled, simple, entire leaves, the stipules often resembling the leaves and thus giving the whorled appearance. Flowers in cymes or panicles, or sometimes capitate or solitary, epigynous, usually perfect and regular and usually 4–5-merous. Stamens of the same number as the lobes of the corolla and inserted on the corolla tube alternate with its lobes. Pistil 1, usually of 2 united carpels, the ovary usually 2-celled, the style single or divided at the summit. Fruit a capsule, berry, or drupe, or the carpels separating to form mericarps.

The family includes about 400 genera and 7,000 species, mostly in tropical regions but some members extending into temperate regions.

EXAMPLES: *Coffea arabica:* Coffee, an evergreen shrub or small tree of tropical Asia and Africa, widely cultivated.

Cinchona officinalis: Quinine, of the Andes, but grown in Asia and Australia for its valuable bark.

Gardenia florida: Gardenia, an ornamental, native of China.

Galium: Bedstraw, or Cleavers, a common North American genus.

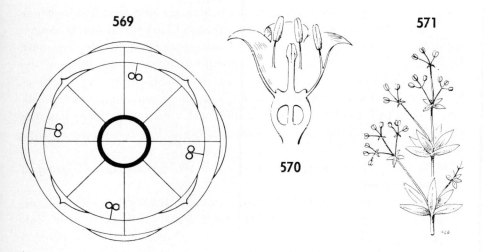

569 *Cephalanthus,* floral diagram.

570 *Rubia,* longitudinal section of flower. The genus has 5-merous flowers.

571 *Galium triflorum,* portion of fruiting plant.

CAPRIFOLIACEAE: Honeysuckle Family

Generally shrubby plants, with opposite, simple or compound leaves, which are exstipulate or with small or reduced stipules. Flowers variously arranged but often in cymes, perfect, regular to irregular, epigynous, usually 5-merous, the corolla of united petals. Stamens usually as many as the lobes of the corolla, inserted on the corolla tube alternate with its lobes, or sometimes the upper (posterior) stamen reduced and the 4 remaining stamens didynamous. Pistil 1, of 2–5 united carpels, the ovary 1–5-celled, and the styles distinct or united. Fruit commonly a berry, but sometimes a drupe or capsule.

The family includes about 11 genera and 350 species, mainly in north temperate regions.

EXAMPLES: *Sambucus:* Elderberries, unusual in having compound leaves.

Lonicera: Honeysuckles, with about 175 species, some cultivated.

Symphoricarpos: Snowberry.

Linnaea: Twinflower, a trailing plant named for Linnaeus.

Viburnum: Arrow-wood, Sheepberry, or Nannyberry.

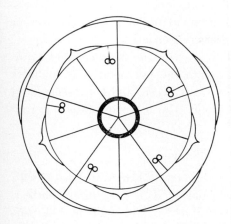

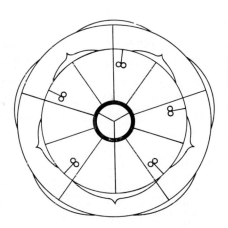

572 *Sambucus canadensis*, floral diagram. Ovary 3–5-celled, and flowers 4-merous. Stamens sometimes six or more. Flowers regular.

573 *Lonicera sempervirens*, floral diagram. Flowers somewhat irregular, with one larger petal.

574 *Lonicera canadensis*, flowering branch.

575 *Symphoricarpos racemosus*, longitudinal section of flower, enlarged.

ORDER CUCURBITALES

Mostly herbs, often climbing, with unisexual, 5-merous, epigynous flowers, the corolla of separate or united petals. Stamens numerous to few, free or variously united. Carpels 2–5, often 3, several-seeded.

The order has somewhat doubtful affinities with the *Myrtales* and *Lythrales*, and it may more properly belong with the polypetalae. It includes the families *Cucurbitaceae, Begoniaceae, Datiscaceae,* and *Caricaceae,* and is an essentially tropical or subtropical group. The following family is representative.

CUCURBITACEAE: Gourd or Pumpkin Family

Coarse, often scabrous, tendril-bearing herbs (rarely shrubs or trees), with palmately veined leaves. Flowers monoecious or dioecious, rarely perfect, epigynous, regular, the corolla of 5 free or united petals. Stamens 1–5, usually 3, often variously united, the anthers often variously folded or curved. Carpels usually 3, united, the ovary with parietal placentation or the placentae often meeting in the center, the style usually single, and stigmas 3. Fruit fleshy, often large, and several–many-seeded, with a leathery or hardened exocarp, and thus a modified berry or pepo.

The family includes about 90 genera and 700–760 species, mainly tropical.

EXAMPLES: *Citrullus lanatus:* Watermelon.
Cucurbita pepo: Pumpkin.
Cucumis melo: Muskmelon.
Cucumis sativus: Cucumber.
Lagenaria: Calabash, the fruit often used to make utensils.
Gurania: of tropical America, a genus of shrubs.
Dendrosicyos: of Africa and Socotra Island in the Indian Ocean, a genus of trees.

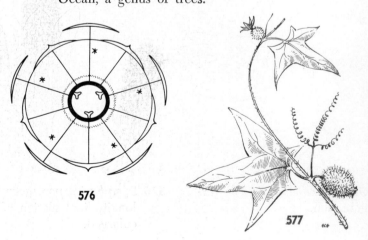

576

577

578

576 *Sicyos* (Star Cucumber), floral diagram of female flower. The number of parts is variable. The stippled area outside the ovary represents a glandular ring that may have originated from reduced stamens.

577 *Echinocystis lobata*, portion of plant showing female flower and fruit.

578 *Echinocystis lobata* (Michx.) T. & G., Wild Cucumber, a common weedy vine with monoecious flowers. The two globose and prickly fruits shown are immature.

ORDER CAMPANULALES

Plants herbaceous to somewhat woody. Flowers regular to strikingly irregular, nearly always epigynous, sympetalous, and 5-merous. Stamens 5, free from the corolla or nearly so, sometimes monadelphous, and the anthers free, connivent, or united (syngenesious). Ovary 1–10-celled (usually 2–3-celled), the placentation usually axillary and the ovules numerous.

The order may be related to the *Rubiales;* but, as suggested by Hutchinson, it may have been derived from the *Gentianales* or *Polemoniales.* The following family is represented in North America; two others, the *Goodeniaceae* and *Stylidiaceae,* are mainly Australian and antarctic in distribution.

CAMPANULACEAE: Bluebell Family

Mostly herbs, rarely woody, often with milky juice, the leaves usually simple, alternate, and exstipulate. Flowers solitary or in racemes, spikes, or heads, often showy, usually perfect and 5-merous, epigynous, regular to very irregular, the calyx often persistent and the corolla of united petals, campanulate, tubular, or bilabiate. Stamens 5, free from the corolla tube or nearly so, alternate with the lobes of the corolla, the filaments commonly dilated and sometimes united, the anthers free, connate, or united. Pistil 1, of 2–5 (commonly 3) united carpels, with a single terminal style, which usually elongates in anthesis and often has a terminal, hairy, brushlike apical portion, which later splits to expose the stigmatic surfaces. Fruit usually a many-seeded capsule.

The family includes about 61 genera and 1,500 species, in temperate and subtropical regions. It is divided into the following three subfamilies, which are sometimes treated as families.

Key to the Subfamilies

Corolla regular .... 1. CAMPANULOIDEAE
Corolla irregular
    Anthers distinct .... 2. CYPHIOIDEAE
    Anthers united (syngenesious) .... 3. LOBELIOIDEAE

SUBFAMILY 1. CAMPANULOIDEAE

Flowers regular, the anthers usually free. Cosmopolitan in distribution.
    EXAMPLES: *Campanula:* Bluebell.
                Platycodon: Balloon-flower.

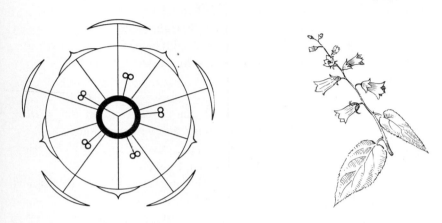

579 *Campanula rapunculoides,* floral diagram and portion of plant.

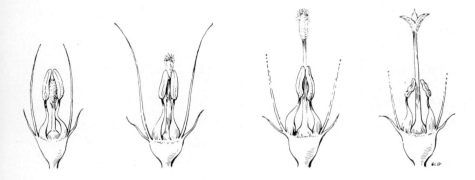

580 Successive stages in the elongation of the style of *Campanula*. Part of the flower has been cut away to show the reproductive parts. The terminal portion of the style acts like a brush to sweep out the pollen grains and carry them upward, after which this portion splits to expose the stigmatic surfaces.

SUBFAMILY 2. CYPHIOIDEAE

Flowers irregular, the stamens sometimes monadelphous but the anthers free. African and western American in distribution.

EXAMPLES: *Cyphia:* with about 20 species in Africa.
Nemacladus: with 2 species in California.
Parishella: with 1 species in California.
Cyphocarpus: with 1 species in Chile.

SUBFAMILY 3. LOBELIOIDEAE

Flowers strikingly irregular and 2-lipped, the anthers united into a tube (syngenesious). Tropical and north and south temperate regions.

EXAMPLES: *Lobelia:* with about 200 species, several in North America. *L. cardinalis* is the Cardinal Flower.
Siphocampylus: a genus with numerous species in tropical America.

581 *Lobelia,* floral diagram.   **582** *Lobelia splendens,* flower.

ORDER ASTERALES

Mainly herbaceous but sometimes woody plants, with alternate or opposite exstipulate leaves. Inflorescence commonly an involucrate head but sometimes cymose or paniculate. Flowers epigynous, sympetalous, regular or irregular, usually perfect and 5-merous, the stamens 1–5 (usually 5), inserted on the corolla tube alternate with the lobes, the anthers free or united. Ovary mostly 1-celled and containing a single ovule. Fruit an akene, which is often crowned by a late-developing calyx of scales or hairs known as the *pappus.*

The order includes the families *Adoxaceae, Valerianaceae, Dipsacaceae, Calyceraceae,* and *Asteraceae* (*Compositae*), and was probably derived from ancestral forms of the *Apiales* and *Campanulales.* The following families are representative.

VALERIANACEAE: Valerian Family

Perennial or annual herbs, rarely shrubs, with strong-smelling rhizomes and opposite or radical, often divided, exstipulate leaves. Flowers usually in cymes, perfect or unisexual by abortion, epigynous. Calyx represented in the flower by an epigynous ring, becoming enlarged and often plumose in fruit. Corolla usually salverform, 5-lobed, often saccate or spurred at the base and somewhat irregular. Stamens 1–4, usually 4, on the tube of the corolla and alternate with its lobes, the anthers free. Pistil of 3 united carpels and typically 3-celled in flower, but only 1 carpel fertile and maturing into a 1-seeded indehiscent fruit (akene) crowned by the pappus, which is the enlarged calyx.

A progressive modification of the flower is found in different genera, from *Patrinia* and *Nardostachys*, in which the corolla is nearly regular, to *Centranthus*, in which the corolla is spurred and the stamens are reduced to one. In extreme cases the corolla tube may be divided into two compartments by a septum which separates the stamens from the style and stigma.

The family includes about 10 genera and 350 species, chiefly in north temperate regions and in the Andes.

EXAMPLES: *Valeriana:* Valerian, with about 200 species.

Nardostachys jatamcnsi: Spikenard, the source of an unguent used especially by the Romans.

583 *Valeriana officinalis,* floral diagram. Two of the carpels abort, leaving only one in fruit.

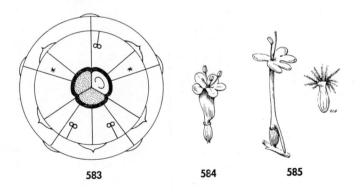

583

584

585

584 *Valeriana,* flower enlarged.

585 *Centranthus,* flower and fruit, enlarged.

DIPSACACEAE: Teasel Family

Annual or perennial, often very scabrous herbs, with opposite or rarely whorled, exstipulate leaves. Flowers small, in dense bracteate heads, perfect, epigynous, sympetalous, mostly irregular, each flower surrounded by an epicalyx or involucel of small bracts. Corolla 4–5-lobed. Stamens 4, 2, or 3, inserted on the base of the corolla tube alternate with its lobes, the anthers free. Ovary 1-celled and with a single ovule, the style filiform and the stigma simple or bifid. Fruit an akene, often crowned by the persistent bristly or spiny calyx, or pappus.

In some genera, such as *Scabiosa*, the flowers show a differentiation into ray and disk flowers, both as to size and as to degree of irregularity of the corolla.

The family includes about 9 genera and 150 species and is world-wide in range, the chief center of distribution being the eastern Mediterranean region.

EXAMPLES: *Dipsacus fullonum:* Teasel, the fruiting heads of which are used commercially for raising the nap of woolen cloth.

Scabiosa atropurpurea: Scabiosa, a common ornamental from southern Europe.

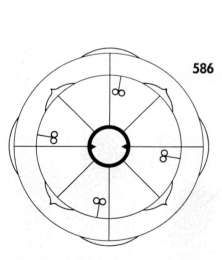

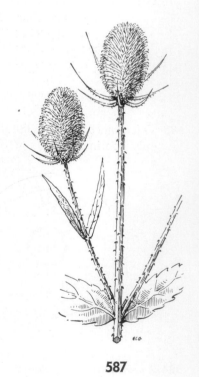

586 *Dipsacus,* floral diagram.

587 *Dipsacus sylvestris,* portion of plant.

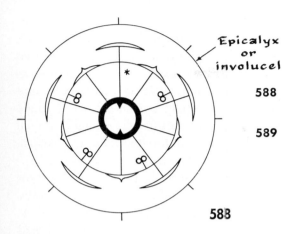

Epicalyx or involucel

588 *Scabiosa atropurpurea,* floral diagram.

589 *Dipsacus sylvestris* Huds., the common Teasel, an introduced European plant now common in the United States. This is a flower head after the flowers have dropped.

588

589

ASTERACEAE (COMPOSITAE): Sunflower Family

Mainly herbaceous, but sometimes woody, plants, with alternate, opposite, or, rarely, whorled leaves, which may be entire to variously dissected, but never truly compound, without stipules. Flowers in dense heads, the common receptacle of each head surrounded below by an involucre of several to many bracts (the *phyllaries*), each such head appearing like a single flower but actually composed of few to many small flowers (*florets*), which are epigynous, mostly 5-merous, all tubular and regular, or the central (*disk flowers*) tubular and regular and the marginal (*ray flowers*) strap-shaped (*ligulate*) and irregular, or all the flowers in the head ligulate or all bilabiate. Stamens 5, inserted on the corolla tube, the filaments usually free but the anthers united in a ring (*syngenesious*), the arrangement alternate with the lobes of the corolla in regular flowers. Pistil 1, of 2 united carpels, the ovary 1-celled and containing a single seed at maturity. Fruit an akene, which is usually crowned by a late-developing calyx (the *pappus*), which may be composed of hairs, bristles, awns, or scales, but may be lacking.

The family includes about 1,000 genera and 23,000 species, ranking as one of the largest families in the plant kingdom and involving about a tenth of the species of flowering plants. It is cosmopolitan in range but especially well adapted to temperate and cooler climates.

The family (see the table on pp. 418–419) is usually divided into 13 tribes, in 2 series, the latter distinguished as follows:

Some of the flowers of the head with tubular or
sometimes bilabiate corollas; juice not milky ....   1. TUBULIFLORAE

All of the flowers of the head ligulate; juice milky ..   2. LIGULIFLORAE

Series 1. *Tubuliflorae:* The larger series, including 12 tribes. Plants of various aspect, the juice never milky; flowers all tubular and regular, sometimes the flowers all bilabiate, and usually the central (disk) flowers tubular and regular and the marginal (ray) flowers ligulate and irregular.

    EXAMPLES: *Aster:* the Asters.
              Solidago: Goldenrod.
              Helianthus: Sunflower.
              Senecio: Old Man, the largest genus, with some 2,300 species
                of herbs, shrubs, climbers, and even a few trees.

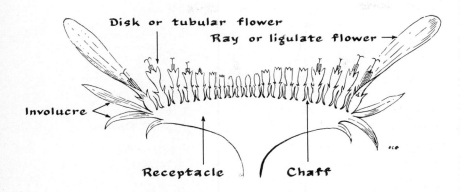

590 Typical composite head cut vertically in half.

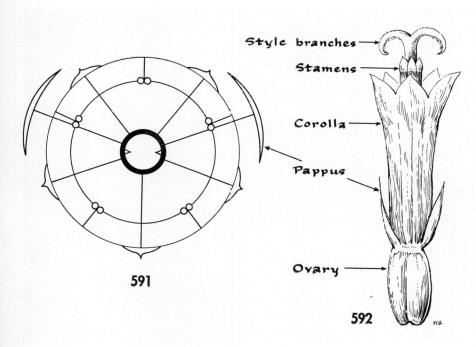

591 *Helianthus annuus,* floral diagram of disk flower.

592 *Helianthus,* disk flower, enlarged.

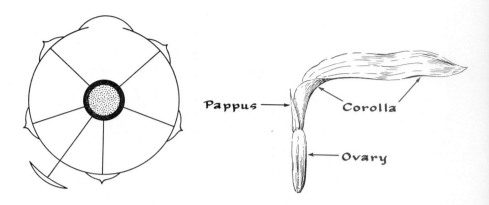

593 *Helianthus annuus,* floral diagram and ray flower, the latter enlarged. Ray flowers are sterile, with a rudimentary pistil.

594 *Balsamorhiza sagittata* (Pursh) Nutt., Balsamroot, of western North America (*Tubuliflorae*).

595 *Balsamorhiza sagittata* (Pursh) Nutt., Balsamroot, three heads, that on the left showing ligulate and tubular flowers, that in the center cut in half to show the typical structure of the inflorescence, and that on the right in side view showing the involucre below the flowers.

Series 2. *Liguliflorae:* The smaller series, including the single tribe *Cichorieae,* and sometimes treated as a separate family. Herbs, rarely shrubs or trees, of various habit. Flowers in the head all ligulate and homogamous. Juice milky.

EXAMPLES: *Cichorium:* Chicory.

Taraxacum: Dandelion.

Lactuca: Lettuce, including 100 species.

Crepis: Hawksbeard, with nearly 200 species.

Hieracium: Hawkweed, with about 400 species.

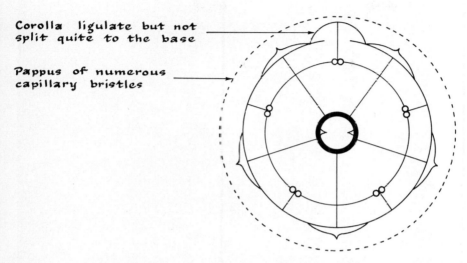

Corolla ligulate but not
split quite to the base

Pappus of numerous
capillary bristles

596 *Taraxacum*, floral diagram of floret. The fruit develops partheno-
genetically.

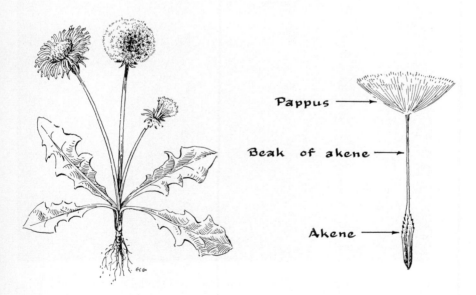

Pappus

Beak of akene

Akene

597 *Taraxacum*, plant.   **598** *Taraxacum*, fruit, enlarged.

599 *Nothocalais cuspidata* (Pursh) Greene, a Dandelion relative having all the flowers in the head with ligulate corollas (*Liguliflorae*).

600 *Tragopogon dubius* Scop., Goatsbeard, a common weed introduced from Europe. On the left is a flower bud, and in the center is a fruiting head of beaked akenes having a plumose pappus (*Liguliflorae*).

TRIBES OF ASTERACEAE	LIGULIFLORAE Chichorieae	TUBULIFLORAE Vernonieae	Eupatorieae	Asterieae	Inuleae	Heliantheae
Juice milky	yes	no	no	no	no	no
Corollas tubular, ligulate, or bilabiate	l	t	t	t or t & l	t except *Inula*, which has t & l	t or t & l
Nature of pappus	simple or plumose	setose and copious	5–many bristles or scales, or none	various	usually simple or plumose bristles	not capillary, usually 2–3 awns or scales
Nature of anthers	sagittate	sagittate, blunt, or short-tailed	blunt and basifixed	blunt and basifixed	tailed	blunt or acute not tailed, basifixed
Receptacle chaffy	yes or no	?	?	no (in ours)	yes or no	yes
Heads *hom*ogamous or *heter*ogamous	hom	hom	hom	het (rarely hom)	hom or het	het (rarely hom)
Plants aromatic	no	no	no	no	no	no
General range	world-wide, chiefly in Old World, many in Mediterranean region	chiefly in tropical America, also Africa, Asia, and Australia, not in Europe	cosmopolitan, especially in Old World and Brazil; *Eupatorium* in N. America	world-wide, but chiefly in temperate zone	widely distributed	mainly American, few in Old World
Some examples, with approximate numbers of species in each, with other notes.	*Cichorium*, 8 *Crepis*, 200 *Hieracium*, 400 *Lactuca*, 100 *Scorzonera*, 100 *Taraxacum*, 25 *Leontodon*, 50 *Dendroseris* and *Fitchia* of the South Seas are tree genera.	*Veronia*, 500, includes herbs and some small trees.	*Eupatorium*, 400 *Mikania*, 150 Mainly herbs, some twiners.	*Aster, Erigeron,* and *Solidago* have numerous species; *Olearia*, 90, in Australia; *Conyza*, 50, in tropics; *Baccharis*, 300, in tropical America.	*Inula*, 90; *Gnaphalium*, 120; *Leontopodium alpinum* is Edelweiss; *Helichrysum*, 300, species of S. African Everlastings.	Includes 10 subtribes. *Zinnia*, 12 *Helianthus*, 55 *Coreopsis*, 70 *Dahlia*, 9 *Rudbeckia*, 30

TUBULIFLORAE (CONTINUED)

Helenieae	Anthemideae	Senecioneae	Calenduleae	Arctotideae	Cynareae	Mutisieae
no	no	no	no	no	no	no
t & l	t or t & l	t or t & l	t & l	t & l	t	b
...ot capillary, ...usually 2–3 ...ns or scales	absent or reduced to a ring or cup	capillary	none	none or not capillary	usually capillary	capillary
...lunt or acute, ...not tailed, ...basifixed	blunt or acute, not tailed, basifixed	blunt or acute, not tailed, basifixed	pointed at the base	blunt-pointed at the base	usually tailed	long-tailed
no	yes or no	usually no	no	?	yes, many bristles	?
...het (rarely ...hom)	het (rarely hom)	hom or het	het	het	hom (rays may be neuter or female)	hom or het
no	yes	no	no	no	no	no
mainly Mexican and Pacific N. American	some in Old World, some world-wide but northern	world-wide	mainly S. Africa, also in Mediterranean region	mainly S. Africa and mountains of tropical Africa	world-wide, with chief center in Mediterranean region	in Andes, also in Africa, Asia, and Tasmania
Helenium, 24 *Gaillardia*, 15	*Anthemis*, 100 *Achillea*, 100 *Chrysanthemum*, 200 *Artemisia*, 200	*Petasites*, 14; *Senecio*, 2,300, including a few trees and shrubs; *Cineraria*, 25, in S. Africa; *Arnica*, 32	*Calendula*, 20	*Arctotis*, 50 *Gazania*, 30	*Arctium*, 6 *Carduus*, 100 *Cirsium*, 200 *Centaurea*, 500	*Mutisia*, 60 *Gerbera*, 40

A-. A prefix meaning without, as in "asepalous," without sepals.

Abaxial. On the side away from the axis.

Acaulescent. Without an evident leafy stem.

Accrescent. Enlarging with age; often applied to the calyx.

Accumbent (cotyledons). Placed with their edges against the radicle.

Achene. See Akene.

Achlamydeous. Without a perianth; naked.

Acicular. Needle-shaped.

Acropetal. Produced in succession toward the apex; usually applied to the order of blooming in an inflorescence. (See Basipetal.)

Actinomorphic. With radial symmetry, the parts similar in size and shape.

Aculeate. Prickly.

Acuminate. Tapering into a long point.

Acute. Pointed; forming less than a right angle.

Adaxial. On the side next to the axis.

Adnate (dissimilar parts). Grown together.

Adventitious. In an unusual place; often applied to roots or buds.

Adventive. Introduced but not well established.

Aestivation. Arrangement of flower parts in the bud.

Aggregate (fruit). A cluster of fruits produced by a single flower, as in the blackberry.

Akene. A small, dry, indehiscent, 1-seeded fruit having a thin pericarp that is free from the seed.

Albumen. An old term largely replaced by the term "endosperm," which see.

Allopatric. Occurring in different areas. (See Sympatric.)

Alternate. Located singly at a node, as leaves on a stem; situated between other parts, as stamens between petals.

Ament (catkin). An elongate, deciduous cluster of unisexual and usually bracteate flowers, as in willows.

Amphitropous (ovule). Attached near its middle; half-inverted.

Amplexicaul. Clasping the stem.

Anatropous (ovule). Inverted, with the micropyle close to the point of attachment.

Androecium. The stamens collectively.

Androgynous. Having staminate flowers above and pistillate flowers below in the same spike.

Androphore. A stalk that supports stamens above the point of attachment of the perianth.

Anemophilous. Pollinated by wind. (See Entomophilous.)

Angiosperm. A plant producing seeds enclosed by an ovary.

Annual. A plant that completes its development in one year or one season and then dies.

Anterior. Away from the axis; in bilabiate flowers the lower lip is anterior and the upper lip is posterior.

Anther. The pollen-containing part of a stamen, usually consisting of two sacs.

Anthesis. The time of blooming.

Apetalous. Without petals.

Apical. Concerning the apex or tip.

Apiculate. With a short and abrupt point.

Apocarpous (polycarpous). With separate carpels.

Apochlamydeous (perianth parts). Not united.

Appressed. Lying against, as hairs lying close to the leaf surface.

Approximate. Close to each other but not united.

Aquatic. Growing in water.

Arachnoid. Cobwebby, with fine tangled hairs.

Arborescent. Becoming almost tree-like in size.

Arcuate. Curved or arched.

Areole. A marked space on a surface or beneath it, as spaces between veins in leaves, or spine-bearing areas on cactus plants.

Aril. An appendage or outgrowth from the hilum or funiculus of a seed, often spongy or gelatinous, and sometimes enveloping the seed.

Aristate. With a stiff bristle or awn.

Armed. Having prickles, spines, or thorns.

Article. One of the segments of a jointed fruit such as a loment.

Articulate. With one or more joints or points of separation.

Ascending. Growing upward at an angle, but not erect.

Assurgent. Ascending; growing upward at an angle, but not erect.

Attenuate. Gradually tapering; drawn out into a narrowed portion.

Auricle. An ear-like lobe or appendage.

Austral. Southern. (See Boreal.)

Autophytic. With chlorophyll and therefore independent, as opposed to saprophytic or parasitic.

Awn. A bristle-like appendage such as occurs on the back or at the tip of glumes and lemmas of many grasses.

Axil. The angle formed between two organs, as between a leaf and a stem.

Axillary (axile). In the axis; designating flowers borne in the axils of leaves, and ovules or seeds produced in the angles formed by partitions in the ovary of a compound pistil.

Baccate. Like a berry.

Banner (standard). The upper petal of a papilionaceous corolla.

Barbed. With rigid points that are reflexed, or directed backward, as in a fish-hook.

Barbellate. Finely barbed.

Basifixed. Attached by the base.

Basipetal. Produced or blooming in succession from the top downward. (See Acropetal.)

Beak. A narrow projection, as on some fruits.

Bearded. With rather long hairs.

Berry. A simple, fleshy, usually indehiscent fruit with one or more seeds, as tomatoes or grapes.

Bi-. A prefix meaning two or twice, as in "bipinnate," twice pinnate.

Biennial. A plant that completes its development in two years, usually blooming the second year.

Bifid. Split about midway into two lobes.

Bilabiate. Two-lipped.

Bipinnate. Twice pinnate.

Bladdery. Thin-walled and inflated.

Blade. The expanded portion of a leaf, sepal, petal, or other part.

Bloom. Whitish powdery covering of a surface, easily rubbed off.

Boreal. Northern. (See Austral.)

Bract. A more or less modified leaf subtending a flower or a flower cluster.

Bracteole (bractlet). A secondary bract, often very small.

Bud. An undeveloped or dormant branch, leaf, or flower, usually enclosed by protective scales.

Bulb. A subterranean bud composed of fleshy scales attached to a central or basal stem.

Bulbil (bulblet). A little bulb or bulb-like body, often produced above ground on stems or in inflorescences.

Caducous. Falling early; often applied to petals.

Caespitose. See Cespitose.

Calcarate. With a spur.

Callus. A hardened projection; in grasses the hardened base of a lemma at the point of its attachment to the rachilla.

Calyculate. Having bracts or an involucre resembling an outer calyx.

Calyx. The outer part of the floral envelope, composed of sepals.

Campanulate. Shaped like a bell.

Campylotropous (ovule). Curved so as to bring the apex and base close together.

Canaliculate. Grooved lengthwise.

Canescent. With close grayish pubescence.

Capillary. Hair-like.

Capitate. Like a head; in a dense, more or less rounded cluster.

Capitulum. A little head.

Capsule. A simple, dry, dehiscent fruit of two or more carpels, and usually several- to many-seeded.

Carinate. Keeled or creased, with a sharp ridge.

Carpel. A megasporophyll; often regarded as a single, modified, seed-bearing leaf.

Carpophore. A slender stalk between the two carpels of Parsnip Family fruits; from its summit the carpels are suspended at maturity.

Caruncle. An appendage or protuberance adjacent to the hilum of some seeds.

Caryopsis. The fruit of grasses, seed-like, with a thin pericarp adherent to the seed; a grain.

Castaneous. Dark brown, with the color of a chestnut.

Catkin (ament). An elongate, deciduous cluster of unisexual, apetalous, and usually bracteate flowers, as in willows.

Caudate. Tailed; with a slender appendage.

Caudex. The thickened and often woody base of a perennial plant.

Caudicle. The thread-like or strap-shaped stalk that connects a mass of pollen to an anther sac in many orchids.

Caulescent. With a leafy stem above ground.

Cauline. Pertaining to the stem, as cauline leaves.

Cell. A unit of which plants and animals are constructed; also a compartment within an ovary.

Ceriferous. Waxy.

Cernuous. Nodding or drooping.

Cespitose. Tufted or matted.

Chaff. Small, dry, scale-like bracts.

Chalaza. The basal portion of an ovule where it joins the funiculus.

Channeled. Grooved lengthwise.

Chartaceous. Papery.

Choripetalous (polypetalous). With separate petals.

Chorisepalous. With separate sepals.

Ciliate. With marginal hairs or bristles.

Cincinnus. A type of monochasial inflorescence; a scorpioid cyme.

Cinereous. Ash-colored.

Circinate. Coiled in the bud.

Circumscissile. Opening by a transverse circular split so as to release a lid.

Cladophyll. A modified stem resembling a leaf in form and function.

Clasping. Partly surrounding another structure at the base.

Clavate. Shaped like a club, tapering a little toward the base.

Claw. The slender, stalk-like basal portion of some petals and sepals.

Cleft. Deeply cut.

Cleistogamous. Descriptive of a flower that does not open and is self-pollinated.

Cleistogene. A plant bearing cleistogamous flowers.

Coetaneous. Producing flowers and leaves at about the same time, as in some willows.

Collar. The outer side of the leaf at the place where the blade and sheath come together in grasses.

Column. In orchids the combined style and stamen structure; in certain grasses the basal portion of awns; in the Mallow Family the stamen tube.

Coma. A tuft of fine hairs, as on some seeds.

Commissure. In the Parsnip Family the flat adjacent faces of the two carpels.

Comose. With a tuft of hairs.

Compound. Composed of two or more parts; compound leaves have two or more leaflets; compound pistils have two or more carpels.

Compressed. Flattened.

Connate. United similar parts, as leaves or anthers.

Connective. The part of a stamen joining the two anther sacs.

Connivent. Coming close together or touching, but not united, as in some stamens.

Contorted. Twisted.

Convolute. Rolled up lengthwise.

Cordate. Heart-shaped, with a basal notch.

Coriaceous. Leathery.

Corm. A modified, usually subterranean stem that is fleshy and thickened, and often bears scale-like leaves.

Corolla. The inner set of floral leaves, consisting of petals.

Corona. A petaloid structure situated between the corolla and the stamens of some flowers.

Corymb. A rounded or flat-topped inflorescence in which the pedicels or branches are attached at intervals on an elongate axis and are of unequal length, the lower ones longer.

Costate. With longitudinal ribs or veins.

Cotyledon. An embryonic leaf of a seedling or in a seed.

Crenate. With rounded teeth.

Crest. A ridge or elevation on a structure; in some milkweed flowers a horn-like projection from a segment (hood) of the corona.

Crisped. A curled leaf-margin; curled hairs.

Cucullate. Hood-shaped.

Culm. The flowering stem of a grass or sedge.

Cuneate. Wedge-shaped.

Cuspidate. With an abrupt, short, sharp, often rigid point.

Cyathium. The small, cup-like, specialized inflorescence of *Euphorbia.*

Cyclic. In circles or whorls, as opposed to a spiral arrangement.

Cyme. An inflorescence in which the central flower of each group is the oldest; in general a loose term for complex flower clusters that are more or less rounded or flat-topped.

Deca-. A prefix meaning ten.

Deciduous. Falling off, as leaves that are shed in the autumn.

Decompound. Two or more times compound, usually meaning with many small divisions.

Decumbent. With the base prostrate but the upper parts erect or ascending.

Decurrent. Extending downward, as leaves having their bases prolonged downward as wings along the stem.

Definite. Usually meaning ten or less, as opposed to numerous.

Deflexed. Bent downward.

Dehiscence. The method or act of opening or splitting.

Dehiscent (fruit). One that splits open.

Deltoid. Broadly triangular, with the base nearly straight and the sides often a little curved toward the apex.

Dentate. Toothed, the teeth acute and directed outward.

Denticulate. The diminutive of "dentate"; with small teeth.

Depauperate. Stunted or poorly developed.

Determinate (inflorescence). Sometimes applied to those in which the terminal or central flower is the oldest.

Di-. A prefix meaning two.

Diadelphous (stamens). United by their filaments in two groups.

Diandrous. Having two stamens.

Dichasium. An inflorescence having a central older flower and a pair of lateral branches bearing younger flowers.

Dichotomous. Forking; branching by pairs.

Diclinous. Having two sexes; unisexual flowers.

Didymous. Paired or twinned.

Didynamous. With four stamens in two pairs.

Diffuse. With many loose or open branches.

Digitate. With parts diverging from a common base, as fingers of a hand.

Dimorphic. Of two forms.

Dioecious. Having unisexual flowers and these produced on separate plants.

Disk. An enlargement of the floral axis, often fleshy or glandular; in the *Asteraceae*, the central part of the head.

Disk flowers. In *Asteraceae*, those produced in the central part of the head and tubular in shape.

Dissected. Cut into many fine segments.

Distal. Toward the apex.

Distichous. In two rows.

Distinct. Separate from each other.

Divaricate. Widely spreading or divergent.

Divided. Cut deeply to or near the base.

Dolabriform. Shaped like a pick, attached near the middle.

Dorsal. Relating to the back, the side away from the axis.

Drepanium. A flattered and coiled or curved monochasial inflorescence.

Drupaceous. Like a drupe in general appearance but not necessarily with its true structure.

Drupe. A simple, fleshy fruit with a single seed enclosed in a bony endocarp or pit; a stone fruit.

Drupelet. A little drupe, usually found in clusters, as in blackberries.

E-. A prefix meaning without.

Ebracteate. Without bracts.

Echinate. Prickly.

Eglandular. Without glands.

Elliptical. Like an ellipse; longer than wide and with rounded ends.

Emarginate. Notched at the apex.

Embryo. The rudimentary plant within a seed.

Emersed. With parts extending above the water.

Endemic. With a very restricted range; confined to a single geographic area.

Endocarp. The innermost of the three layers forming the wall of the pericarp of a fruit.

Endosperm. Nutritive material or tissue in some seeds outside the embryo.

Ensiform. Sword-shaped.

Entire. With an unbroken or even margin; without teeth or other indentations.

Entomophilous. Pollinated by insects.

Envelope. Surrounding part, as the floral envelope, which consists of the perianth; the sepals and petals.

Ephemeral. Lasting for only a short time, usually less than one day.

Epi-. A prefix meaning upon.

Epicalyx. A set of bracts adjacent to and resembling a calyx.

Epigynous. A flower in which the hypanthium or the perianth is attached to the upper part of the ovary, the ovary then appearing inferior in position.

Epipetalous. Regarding stamens that are attached to the corolla.

Epiphyte. An independent plant growing upon another plant and not connected to the ground.

Equitant. Folded lengthwise and in two flat rows, as the leaves of *Iris*.

Erose. With irregular margin, as though chewed.

Excurrent. Running through and out, as a vein extending beyond a leaf blade into a point.

Exfoliating. Scaling off or shedding in plates, as the bark of some trees.

Exocarp. The outermost of the three layers forming the wall or pericarp of a fruit.

Exserted. Projecting beyond, as stamens protruding from the corolla.

Exstipulate. Without stipules.

Extrorse. Facing outward.

Falcate. Curved like a sickle.

Farinose. Mealy; covered with a mealy powder.

Fascicle. A cluster or bundle.

Fastigiate (branches). Erect and closely spaced.

Fertile. Capable of reproducing, as a stamen producing viable pollen or a carpel producing ovules.

Filament. The stalk of a stamen; any thread-like body.

Filiform. Thread-like.

Fimbriate. Fringed.

Fistulose. Hollow and cylindrical, as the leaves of some onions.

Flabellate. Fan-shaped; broadly wedge-shaped.

Flaccid. Limp or flabby.

Flexous. Wavy; curved alternately in opposite directions.

Floccose. With tufts of soft hair.

Floral envelope. The calyx and corolla, or perianth.

Floret. A little flower; in grasses including the lemma.

Floriferous. Flower-bearing.

Foliaceous. Leaf-like, usually meaning with green color.

Foliar. Pertaining to leaves or leaf-like parts.

Follicle. A dry fruit of one carpel that splits on cne side.

Free. Not adnate to other parts. (Compare with Distinct.)

Frond. The leaf of a fern or of some other plants such as palms; sometimes applied to the thallus of certain plants such as duckweeds.

Fruit. A ripened ovary, sometimes including other adherent parts.

Frutescent. Becoming shrubby.

Fruticose. Shrubby.

Fugacious. Falling early, as the sepals or petals of some flowers.

Fulvous. Dull yellow.

Funiculus. The stalk of an ovule or seed.

Funnelform. Shaped like a funnel, with gradually widened tube.

Fuscous. Dusky brown or grayish brown.

Fusiform. Spindle-shaped, thickened in the middle and tapering to the ends.

Galea. The upper, usually concave lip of a bilabiate calyx or corolla.

Gamo-. A prefix meaning united.

Geniculate. Bent at a joint; kneed.

Gibbous. Swollen or with a protuberance on one side, usually near the base.

Glabrate. Becoming glabrous or hairless at maturity.

Glabrescent. Same as glabrate.

Glabrous. Without pubescence; smooth.

Gland. A secretory hair or other part that produces nectar or some other liquid.

Glandular. Having glands.

Glaucous. Grayish or bluish in color because of a coating of minute powdery or waxy particles.

Glochid. A finely barbed bristle or hair, especially those forming a tuft at the areolae of stems in *Opuntia.*

Glomerule. A small, compact, more or less rounded cluster.

Glumes. A pair of empty scale-like bracts at the base of a grass spikelet.

Grain (*caryopsis*). The fruit of grasses, seed-like, with a thin pericarp adherent to the seed. Also a hardened, seed-like protuberance at the base of inner perianth segments in some species of *Rumex.*

Gynandrous. Having the male and female parts of a flower united, as the stamen attached to the style in orchids.

Gynecandrous. In *Carex,* having pistillate flowers above the staminate flowers of a spike.

Gynobasic style. One that originates between the lobes of a deeply lobed ovary, as in mints and borages.

Gynoecium. The collective term for the female parts of a flower, the pistil or pistils.

Gynophore. A stalk or stipe on which an ovary or fruit is elevated above the floral axis.

Halberd-shaped. Shaped somewhat like an arrowhead but with divergent basal lobes.

Halophyte. A plant usually associated with saline soils.

Hastate. Halberd-shaped; like an arrowhead but with divergent lobes at the base.

Head. A dense inflorescence of sessile or subsessile flowers on a short or broadened axis.

Helicoid. In a spiral like a snail shell.

Herb. A plant that dies completely at the end of the growing season, or one that dies to the ground; not woody-stemmed.

Herbaceous. Like an herb, not woody; or having a green color and a leafy texture.

Hesperidium. A kind of berry having a leathery pericarp, as in citrus fruits.

Heterogamous. With two kinds of flowers, as in a daisy. (See Homogamous.)

Hilum. A scar on a seed marking the point of attachment of the funiculus.

Hirsute. With rather stiff or bristly hairs.

Hirtellous. Minutely hirsute.

Hispid. With stiff or rigid, spreading bristles.

Homogamous. With one kind of flower. (See Heterogamous.)

Hood. In the *Asclepiadaceae*, one of the concave segments of the corona.

Hyaline. Thin and translucent.

Hydrophyte. An aquatic plant.

Hypanthium. A saucer-shaped, cup-shaped, tubular, or sometimes rod-shaped expansion of the floral axis that produces floral organs such as sepals, petals, and stamens, from its upper margin.

Hypocotyl. The axis of an embryo or seedling below the cotyledons and above the radicle.

Hypogynous. Having the flower parts attached near the base of the ovary and free from it.

Imbricate. With overlapping edges, as shingles on a roof.

Immersed. Completely submerged in water.

Incised. Cut sharply, irregularly, and rather deeply.

Included. Not protruding beyond the surrounding structure. (See Exserted.)

Incumbent (cotyledons). Placed with their backs to the radicle.

Indefinite (flower parts). Of a number large enough to make an exact count difficult.

Indehiscent. Not splitting open.

Indeterminate (inflorescences). Sometimes applied to those in which the terminal or central flower is the last to open.

Indument. Any covering of a plant surface, especially pubescence.

Indurate. Hardened.

Inequilateral. With sides unequal in length and thus unsymmetrical.

Inferior (ovary). Situated below the point of insertion of the flower parts.

Inflorescence. A flower cluster.

Innate (anther). Attached to the end of the filament.

Innovation. A sterile, basal shoot occurring in some perennial grasses.

Insectivorous. Descriptive of plants that capture insects.

Inserted. Attached to, meaning the point of origin.

Integument. The covering of a body, as the coat of an ovule or seed.

Internode. The portion of a stem between two adjacent nodes.

Interrupted. Having gaps between the parts.

Introrse (anther.) Facing inward.

Involucel. A secondary involucre that subtends a part of an inflorescence.

Involucrate. Having an involucre.

Involucre. A whorl of bracts subtending an inflorescence.

Involute. Rolled lengthwise so as to expose the lower side and conceal the upper side, as in some leaves. (See Revolute.)

Irregular (flower). Having dissimilar parts of the same kind (usually the petals); with bilateral symmetry; zygomorphic.

Jointed. Having swollen or otherwise obvious nodes, as in grass stems.

Keel. A sharp crease or ridge, as in many boats.

Keeled. Sharply creased; with a keel.

Labellum. The lip, or apparently lower petal, of flowers of *Orchidaceae.*

Labiate. Lipped.

Lacerate. With an irregular or ragged margin, as though torn.

Laciniate. Cut deeply into narrow divisions.

Lactiferous. With milky juice.

Lamina. The broad, expanded part of a leaf, sepal, or petal; the blade.

Lanate. Woolly.

Lanceolate. Shaped like the head of a lance, elongate and pointed above, the sides curved, and the broadest part below the middle.

Leaflet. One of the divisions of a compound leaf.

Legume. A simple, dry, dehiscent fruit of one carpel, usually splitting at maturity along two sutures.

Lemma. A bract that usually encloses a flower in the spikelet of grasses.

Lenticel. A corky spot or line on the bark of many woody plants.

Lenticular. Lens-shaped, biconvex with two edges.

Liana. Woody tropical jungle vine.

Ligulate. Tongue-shaped or strap-shaped.

Ligule. A small, often tongue-shaped appendage, as at the junction of blade and sheath of grasses; one of the strap-shaped corollas of *Asteraceae.*

Limb. The upper, expanded portion of a calyx or corolla of united parts, as contrasted with the lower narrow part called the tube.

Linear. Long and narrow with parallel sides, the length generally more than ten times the width.

Lingulate. Strap-shaped.

Lip. One of the two parts of a bilabiate corolla; also the apparently lower and different petal of an orchid.

Lobe. A partial division of a leaf or other organ.

Locule. A cavity within an ovary.

Loculicidal. Splitting along the walls of locules or cavities, as distinct from splitting on the septae or splitting transversely.

Lodicule. One of the two or three minute perianth parts of a grass flower.

Loment. A modified legume having constrictions between the seeds and breaking apart transversely at the constrictions.

Lunate. Shaped like a half-moon, or crescent-shaped.

Lyrate. With relatively small pinnate divisions and a large terminal lobe.

Maculate. Spotted.

Malpighiaceous (hairs). Straight, appressed, and attached near the middle.

Marcescent. Withering but persistent, as flower parts after blooming.

Membranaceous (*membranous*). Thin, soft, flexible, and more or less translucent.

Mericarp. One of the two fruiting carpels of the Parsnip Family.

-merous. A suffix indicating the number of parts or floral organs, as in "3-merous," having the perianth in sets of three.

Mesocarp. The middle layer of the pericarp.

Mesophyte. A plant having medium moisture requirements.

Micropyle. The minute opening into an ovule for the entrance of the pollen-tube, becoming a pit-like mark on the mature seed.

Midrib. The main or central vein of a leaf or other part.

Monadelphous. Stamens that are united into one group by their filaments.

Moniliform. Like a string of beads.

Mono-. A prefix meaning one or once.

Monochasium. A type of inflorescence in which there is a single terminal flower, and below this a single branch bearing one or more younger flowers.

Monoclinous (*perfect*). Having both stamens and pistils in the same flower.

Monoecious. Having separate staminate and pistillate flowers on the same plant.

Mucro. A short, sharp point.

Mucronate. Having a short, sharp point at the apex.

Multi-. A prefix meaning several or many.

Multicipital caudex. A root-crown from which several stems arise.

Multiple (fruit). Derived from several flowers.

Muricate. Having the surface covered with short, sharp projections.

Mycorhiza (*mycorrhiza*). A fungus-root association.

Naked. Lacking organs or parts, a naked flower being one that lacks a perianth.

Nectary. A gland or glands secreting nectar.

Nerve. One of the principal veins of a parallel-veined leaf or other part.

Node. A point on a stem where leaves or branches are attached.

Numerous (stamens or carpels). Usually meaning more than ten. (See Definite.)

Nut. A simple, dry, indehiscent fruit with a bony shell, characteristically derived from a compound pistil, but 1-seeded by abortion.

Nutlet. A small nut. The term is often loosely used to include any small, thick-shelled, seed-like fruit, with or without one or more wings.

Ob-. A prefix meaning inverted, as in "oblanceolate," upside down lanceolate and broadest above the middle.

Oblong. Elongate and with more or less parallel sides, the length usually less than ten times the width.

Obtuse. Blunt, usually forming more than a right angle.

Ocrea. A stipular sheath surrounding the stem.

Odd-pinnate. With a terminal leaflet.

Oligo-. A prefix meaning few.

Oligomerous. Having few parts.

Opposite. (Leaves) in pairs, one on either side of the node; (stamens) inserted in front of petals and thus opposite them.

Orbicular. Circular.

Orthotropous (ovule). Erect, with the micropyle at the upper end.

Oval. Broadly elliptic, the width more than half the length.

Ovary. The bulbous basal portion of a pistil containing one or more ovules.

Ovate. Egg-shaped, the broadest part below the middle.

Ovule. The structure that becomes a seed after fertilization.

Palea (*palet*). The inner and usually smaller of two scaly bracts immediately subtending the grass flower in a spikelet.

Palmate (*digitate*). With parts diverging from a common base, as fingers of a hand.

Panicle. An elongate inflorescence with compound branching.

Papilionaceous. Descriptive of a flower like that of a Sweet Pea, having a standard (banner), two wings, and two keel petals comprising the corolla.

Papillose. Covered with short, rounded projections.

Pappus. The modified and late-maturing calyx of the *Asteraceae,* arising from the summit of the akene, and consisting of hairs, bristles, scales, or awns.

Parasite. A plant that gets its food from another living plant to which it is attached.

Parietal. Produced along the inner side of the ovary wall.

Parted. Cut or lobed more than halfway to the middle or base.

Patent. Spreading.

Pectinate. Like a comb, with many or few, narrow, pinnate divisions.

Pedicel. The stalk of a single flower in an inflorescence.

Peduncle. The stalk supporting a whole inflorescence, or the stalk of a solitary flower.

Peltate. Attached by the lower surface, not by the margin, as the leaves of *Tropaeolum,* the garden Nasturtium.

Perennial. A plant that continues to live year after year.

Perfect (*monoclinous*). A flower having both male and female reproductive parts (stamens and pistils).

Perfoliate. Descriptive of a leaf having the stem apparently passing through it because of a joining of the basal lobes of the blade.

Perianth. The calyx and corolla collectively, or either one when only one is present.

Pericarp. The ovary wall in the fruiting stage.

Perigynous. A type of flower with a hypanthium that arises from the base of the floral axis.

Persistent. Remaining attached rather than falling off.

Petal. One of the parts of the corolla or inner leaf-like parts of a flower.

Petaloid. Resembling a petal in color or texture, usually delicate and not green.

Petiole. The stalk of a leaf.

Phylloclade. A stem that is somewhat broadened and has the function of a leaf.

Phyllode. A broadened petiole without a blade.

Pilose. With rather sparse, soft hairs.

Pinnate. Like a feather; having the parts arranged in two rows along a common axis.

Pinnatifid. Cleft or divided pinnately.

Pistil. The female reproductive part of a flower, occupying a central position; in some flowers single and in others several or many.

Placenta. A point or line of attachment of ovules within an ovary or of seeds within a fruit.

Plumose. Feather-like, having fine, soft hairs along the sides, the hairs divergent from the organ to which they are attached.

Pod. A term often loosely applied to any simple, dry, dehiscent fruit.

Pollen. Microspores; minute spores produced by the anther of a stamen.

Pollinium. A mass of pollen grains adhering together and shed as a unit.

Polycarpous (apocarpous). With separate carpels, each a separate pistil.

Polygamo-dioecious. A sexual condition in which two sorts of plants occur: one having some perfect and some staminate flowers, the other having some perfect and some pistillate flowers.

Polygamo-monoecious. A sexual condition in which some perfect and some staminate flowers are produced on the same plant.

Polygamous. Producing some perfect and some unisexual flowers.

Polypetalous. With separate petals.

Polysepalous. With separate sepals.

Pome. A simple, fleshy fruit like an apple, in which the flesh is derived largely from an adnate hypanthium.

Posterior. Next to the axis; in bilabiate corollas the upper lip is posterior and the lower lip is anterior.

Precocious. Blooming before the leaves are expanded.

Procumbent. Lying on the ground but not rooting at the nodes.

Prostrate. Lying flat on the ground.

Puberulent. Very finely pubescent.

Pubescent. Covered with hairs, especially soft, downy hairs.

Punctate. Covered with dots or pits.

Raceme. A type of inflorescence having an elongate axis and along this simple pedicels, the order of blooming usually from base to apex.

Racemose. Like a raceme; in general any inflorescence capable of indefinite prolongation, having lateral and axillary flowers.

Rachilla. A little rachis, particularly the axis of a spikelet in grasses.

Rachis. The axis of a spike or of a pinnately compound leaf.

-ranked. Preceded by a number, indicating the number of rows.

Raphe. The part of the funiculus that becomes a part of the seed.

Ray. One of the main branches of a compound umbel; a strap-shaped marginal flower in a head when tubular disk flowers are also present.

Receptacle. The floral axis to which the various flower parts are attached; the enlarged summit of the peduncle of a head to which the flowers are attached.

Recurved. Curved downward or backward.

Reflexed. Bent downward or backward.

Regular (actinomorphic). With radial symmetry; the parts of the same sort of similar size and shape.

Reniform. Kidney-shaped; broader than long, with rounded ends, and with a wide basal sinus.

Repand. With a wavy margin.

Replum. The thin partition between the fruiting carpels in mustards.

Reticulate. Like a network,

Retrorse. Directed downward.

Retuse. With a rounded sinus at the apex.

Revolute. Rolled lengthwise so as to expose the upper side and conceal the lower side. (See Involute.)

Rhipidium. A type of monochasial inflorescence that is more or less fan-shaped.

Rhizome. A modified underground stem, usually growing horizontally.

Rib. One of the main veins of a parallel-veined leaf or other organ.

Root. The absorbing, usually underground part of a plant, without nodes.

Rosette. A basal cluster of leaves produced on a very short stem.

Rostrate. With a beak.

Rosulate. With one or more rosettes.

Rotate (corolla). Wheel-shaped; having a short tube and a widely spreading limb, as in a potato flower.

Rugose. Wrinkled.

Runcinate. With jagged lateral indentations, lobes, or teeth that are directed backward.

Runner (stolon). A horizontal, above-ground stem that may root at the nodes or apex and develop new plantlets at those places, as in the Strawberry.

Saccate. Shaped like a bag.

Sagittate. Shaped like an arrowhead.

Salverform. A calyx or corolla with a slender tube and widely spreading limb.

Samara. A simple, dry, indehiscent fruit, usually 1-seeded, and with one or more wings.

Saprophyte. A plant without green color that obtains its food from dead organic matter.

Scabrous. Rough to the touch because of minute stiff hairs or other projections.

Scape. A leafless flowering stalk arising from the ground or from a very short stem bearing basal leaves.

Scapose. Bearing a scape or produced on a scape.

Scaricus. Thin and dry, like tissue paper, not green.

Schizocarp. A fruit that splits apart into 1-seeded carpels or parts.

Sclerophyllous. With leathery or tough leaves.

Scorpioid. Coiled at the tip.

Scurfy. Covered with minute scales.

Secund. Turned to one side.

Seed. A mature ovule, consisting of an embryo, with or without endosperm, and a surrounding protective coat.

Semi-. A prefix meaning half, as in "semi-sagittate," shaped like half an arrowhead.

Seminal root. The first or primary root produced by a seedling.

Sepal. One of the parts of the calyx or outer set of floral leaves.

Septate. Having partitions, as many ovaries and some leaves with obvious, internal cross-thickenings.

Septicidal (capsule). Splitting along the septae or partitions.

Septum. A partition.

Seriate. In series, rows, or rings.

Sericeus. Silky with soft hairs.

Serrate. With fine, sharp teeth that are inclined forward or upward.

Serrulate. Finely serrate.

Sessile. Lacking a stalk, as some leaves and flowers.

Seta. A bristle.

Sheath. A tube-like part surrounding another part, as the lower part of a grass leaf that is wrapped round the stem.

Shrub. A plant that is woody and has several main stems, smaller than a tree in height.

Silicle. A little silique, usually not much longer than wide.

Silique. A simple, dry, dehiscent fruit of two carpels that split apart and leave a thin, persistent partition (replum) remaining on the plant; the characteristic fruit of the *Brassicaceae.*

Simple. (Fruit) derived from a single flower and a single pistil; (leaf) having the blade in one piece; (pistil) consisting of a single carpel.

Sinuate. With a wavy margin.

Sinus. The indentation between two lobes.

Solitary. Single.

Sordid. Dirty, not pure white.

Spadix. A spike of flowers on a fleshy axis.

Spathe. A single, large, often showy bract enclosing or subtending an inflorescence, which is commonly a spadix.

Spatulate. Shaped like a spatula, oblong, sometimes a little broader toward the upper end, and with a rounded apex.

Spicate. Produced in a spike.

Spike. An elongated inflorescence of sessile or subsessile flowers.

Spinescent. Bearing spines, or ending in a spine.

Spinulose. Bearing small spines or thorns.

Sporophyll. A reproductive organ, usually thought to be derived from a leaf, that produces spores, as the stamens and carpels of flowering plants.

Spur. A hollow, more or less pointed projection, usually from the calyx or corolla, commonly producing nectar in its tip.

Squarrose. With parts widely spreading or recurved.

Stamen. A pollen-producing organ of a flower, typically consisting of anther and filament; a microsporophyll.

Staminate. Bearing stamens and consequently male; usually used in reference to unisexual flowers or plants.

Staminodium. A sterile stamen.

Standard (banner). The uppermost, large petal of a papilionaceous corolla, as in the Sweet Pea.

Stellate. Star-shaped; usually used in reference to hairs.

Stem. The major supporting structure in plants, to which buds, leaves, and flowers are attached at regular intervals at points called nodes.

Stigma. The part of a pistil on which pollen adheres and germinates, generally terminal in position, and often enlarged.

Stipe. A stalk supporting a single organ, particularly an ovary; also the petiole of a fern leaf.

Stipel. A stipule-like appendage at the base of a leaflet of a compound leaf.

Stipitate. Having a stipe or stalk.

Stipular. Pertaining to the stipules.

Stipulate. Possessing stipules.

Stipules. A pair of appendages that may be present at the point of attachment of a leaf to a stem.

Stolon. A modified horizontal stem, aboveground, that may root at the nodes and apex, developing new plantlets at those places, as in a Strawberry.

Stoloniferous. Having stolons.

Strigose. Having the surface covered with straight, appressed hairs that usually are directed forward.

Strophiole. An appendage of the hilum in some seeds.

Style. The stalk-like part of some pistils, connecting the stigma and the ovary.

Sub-. A prefix meaning somewhat, as in "suborbicular," nearly round.

Subtend. To occur immediately below, as a bract subtending a flower.

Succulent. With a fleshy or juicy texture or composition that is usually resistant to drying.

Suffrutescent. Woody or shrubby at the base but not throughout.

Sulcate. Longitudinally grooved.

Super-. A prefix meaning above.

Superior (ovary). Having a position above the point of attachment of the other flower parts, as in hypogynous and perigynous flowers.

Supra-. A prefix meaning above.

Suture. A seam or line along which union has occurred or along which splitting may take place.

Syconium. A hollow, multiple fruit, as that of a Fig.

Sym-. A prefix meaning united.

Symmetrical (flower). Having the same number of each kind of part.

Sympatric. Occurring in one area. (See Allopatric.)

Sympetalous. Having the petals partly or completely united to each other.

Syn-. A prefix meaning united.

Syncarpous. With united carpels.

Syngenesious (stamens or anthers). United by the anthers in a ring.

Tawny. Dull yellowish brown.

Tendril. A part of a stem or leaf modified into a slender, twining, holdfast structure.

Terete. Circular in cross section, cylindrical, rod-shaped.

Ternate. In threes.

Terrestrial. Growing on the land. (See Aquatic.)

Testa. The outer seed coat.

Tetra-. A prefix meaning four.

Tetrad. A group of four, particularly the four pollen grains from one pollen mother cell.

Tetradynamous. With six stamens, four of them longer and two of them shorter, as in flowers of most *Brassicaceae.*

Thalloid. Like a thallus, undifferentiated into stems and leaves.

Thallus. A plant body that is not differentiated into stems and leaves.

Throat. The place in a calyx or corolla of united parts where the tube and limb come together.

Thyrse. A term loosely used to describe a compact panicle; more accurately, a complex group of dichasia resembling a panicle.

Tomentose. Woolly, covered with curly, matted hairs.

Tomentulose. Diminutive of "tomentose," finely woolly.

Tomentum. A covering of woolly, matted hairs.

Torose. Thickened, elongate, and having more or less regular constrictions.

Torulose. Diminutive of "torose."

Torus The receptacle or floral axis.

Tree. A large, woody plant usually having a single main stem or trunk.

Tri-. A prefix meaning three.

Trigonous. Three-angled.

Triquetrous. Three-angled.

Truncate. Having the base or apex flattened as though cut off.

Tube. The united, more or less cylindrical

part of a calyx or corolla of united parts. (See Limb.)

Tuber. A thickened, fleshy, modified stem having functions of food storage and propagation, as the Irish Potato.

Tubercle. A small, swollen structure usually different in color from the part to which it is attached, and often with a hardened texture.

Tubular. Shaped like a tube; also descriptive of corollas that have a well-developed tubular portion but little or no limb portion.

Tufted. Forming clumps. (See Cespitose.)

Tunicate (bulb). Having the leaves arranged in circles when viewed in cross section, as an onion.

Turbinate. Top-shaped, thick at the apex and tapering to a basal point.

Turgid. Swollen.

Turion. A short, scaly branch produced from a rhizome.

Umbel. A flat-topped or rounded inflorescence having flowers on pedicels of nearly equal length and attached to the summit of the peduncle, the characteristic order of blooming being from the outside toward the center.

Umbellet. One of the little umbels of a compound umbel.

Unarmed. Without prickles or spines.

Uncinate. Hooked at the end, as some spines or bristles.

Undershrub. A perennial plant having stems that are woody only in the basal part, the upper part dying back.

Undulate. Having a wavy margin.

Uni-. A prefix meaning one or single.

Uniseriate. In one series or whorl.

Unisexual (*diclinous*). Of one sex only, either male or female, staminate or pistillate.

Urceolate. Urn-shaped; descriptive of a corolla of united petals having a bulbous tube, a narrowed neck, and a very small limb.

Utricle. A 1-seeded fruit with a thin wall, often dehiscent by a lid.

Valvate. With the edges coming together but not overlapping. (See Imbricate.)

Valve. A portion of the wall of a fruit or other part that separates from the remaining part or parts at maturity.

Velutinous. Velvety.

Vein. A bundle of externally visible transporting tissue in a leaf or other organ.

Venation. The system or pattern of veins in an organ.

Ventral. The lower side of a flat organ, or the adaxial side of a carpel. The ventral suture of a carpel bears the seeds along its inner edge.

Ventricose. Enlarged on one side, as some bilabiate corollas.

Vernation. The arrangement of parts in a bud.

Verrucose. Warty.

Versatile. Attached by the middle and free to swing, as some anthers.

Verticil. A whorl.

Villose (*villous*). Covered with fine, long hairs that are not tangled.

Virgate. Wand-like; descriptive of a slender, erect, straight, leafy stem bearing only short or no branches.

Viscid. Sticky, causing foreign particles to adhere to it.

Viviparous. Sprouting from seed or bulblets while still attached to the parent plant; sometimes applied to plants that have flowers modified into bulblets.

Whorl. A group of three or more parts at a node.

Wing. A flat, usually thin appendage on a seed or fruit; also each of the two lateral petals of a papilionaceous corolla, as in the Sweet Pea.

Xerophyte. A plant adapted to very dry situations.

Zygomorphic (flower or corolla). Having the parts of the same kind of different sizes or shapes so as to be bilaterally but not radially symmetrical. (See Irregular.)

INDEX

3. SOLVE. We simplify the right side of the equation.

$$A = 10,000\left(1 + \frac{0.05}{4}\right)^{4 \cdot 3}$$

$$A = 10,000(1.0125)^{12} \qquad \text{Simplify } 1 + \frac{0.05}{4} \text{ and write } 4 \cdot 3 \text{ as 12.}$$

$$A \approx 10,000(1.160754518) \qquad \text{Approximate } (1.0125)^{12}.$$

$$A \approx 11,607.55 \qquad \text{Multiply and round to two decimal places.}$$

4. INTERPRET.

Check: Repeat your calculations to make sure that no error was made. Notice that $11,607.55 is a reasonable amount to have in the account after 3 years.

State: In 3 years, the account will contain $11,607.55.   □

PRACTICE

4   Russ placed $8000 into his credit union account paying 6% compounded semi-annually (twice a year). How much will be in Russ's account in 4 years?

Graphing Calculator Explorations

To solve Example 4, we approximated the expression

$$10,000\left(1 + \frac{0.05}{4}\right)^{4 \cdot 3}.$$

Use the keystrokes shown in the accompanying calculator screen to evaluate this expression using a graphing calculator. Notice the use of parentheses.

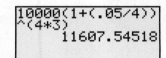

```
10000(1+(.05/4))
^(4*3)
         11607.54518
```

EXAMPLE 5   **Finding Cycling Time**

The fastest average speed by a cyclist across the continental United States is 15.4 mph, by Pete Penseyres. If he traveled a total distance of about 3107.5 miles at this speed, find his time cycling. Write the time in days, hours, and minutes. (*Source: The Guinness Book of World Records*)

Solution

1. UNDERSTAND. Read and reread the problem. The appropriate formula needed is the distance formula

$$d = rt \qquad \text{where}$$
$$d = \text{distance traveled} \quad r = \text{rate} \quad \text{and} \quad t = \text{time}$$

2. TRANSLATE. Use the distance formula and let $d = 3107.5$ miles and $r = 15.4$ mph.

Check: $\qquad\qquad\qquad\qquad d = rt$

State: $\qquad\qquad\qquad\qquad 3107.5 = 15.4t$

3. SOLVE.

$$\frac{3107.5}{15.4} = \frac{15.4t}{15.4} \qquad \text{Divide both sides by 15.4.}$$

$$201.79 \approx t$$

The time is approximately 201.79 hours. Since there are 24 hours in a day, we divide 201.79 by 24 and find that the time is approximately 8.41 days. Now, let's convert the decimal part of 8.41 days back to hours. To do this, multiply 0.41 by 24 and the result is 9.84 hours. Next, we convert the decimal part of 9.84 hours to minutes by multiplying by 60 since there are 60 minutes in an hour. We have $0.84 \cdot 60 \approx 50$ minutes rounded to the nearest whole. The time is then approximately

8 days, 9 hours, 50 minutes.

4. INTERPRET.

Check: Repeat your calculations to make sure that an error was not made.

State: Pete Penseyres's cycling time was approximately 8 days, 9 hours, 50 minutes. ☐

PRACTICE
5 Nearly 4800 cyclists from 36 U.S. states and 6 countries recently rode in the Pan-Massachusetts Challenge recently to raise money for cancer research and treatment. If the riders of a certain team traveled their 192-mile route at an average speed of 7.5 miles per hour, find the time they spent cycling. Write the answer in hours and minutes.

2.3 EXERCISE SET

Solve each equation for the specified variable. See Examples 1–3.

1. $D = rt$; for t

2. $W = gh$; for g

3. $I = PRT$; for R

△ 4. $V = lwh$; for l

📷 5. $9x - 4y = 16$; for y

6. $2x + 3y = 17$; for y

△ 7. $P = 2L + 2W$; for W

8. $A = 3M - 2N$; for N

9. $J = AC - 3$; for A

10. $y = mx + b$; for x

11. $W = gh - 3gt^2$; for g

12. $A = Prt + P$; for P

13. $T = C(2 + AB)$; for B

14. $A = 5H(b + B)$; for b

△ 15. $C = 2\pi r$; for r

△ 16. $S = 2\pi r^2 + 2\pi rh$; for h

17. $E = I(r + R)$; for r

18. $A = P(1 + rt)$; for t

📷 19. $s = \dfrac{n}{2}(a + L)$; for L

20. $C = \dfrac{5}{9}(F - 32)$; for F

21. $N = 3st^4 - 5sv$; for v

22. $L = a + (n - 1)d$; for d

△ 23. $S = 2LW + 2LH + 2WH$; for H

24. $T = 3vs - 4ws + 5vw$; for v

In this exercise set, round all dollar amounts to two decimal places. Solve. See Example 4.

25. Complete the table and find the balance A if \$3500 is invested at an annual percentage rate of 3% for 10 years and compounded n times a year.

n	1	2	4	12	365
A					

26. Complete the table and find the balance A if \$5000 is invested at an annual percentage rate of 6% for 15 years and compounded n times a year.

n	1	2	4	12	365
A					

27. A principal of \$6000 is invested in an account paying an annual percentage rate of 4%. Find the amount in the account after 5 years if the account is compounded

  a. semiannually   **b.** quarterly

  c. monthly

28. A principal of \$25,000 is invested in an account paying an annual percentage rate of 5%. Find the amount in the account after 2 years if the account is compounded

  a. semiannually   **b.** quarterly

  c. monthly

MIXED PRACTICE

Solve. See Examples 4 and 5.

29. The day's high temperature in Phoenix, Arizona, was recorded as 104°F. Write 104°F as degrees Celsius. [Use the formula $C = \dfrac{5}{9}(F - 32)$]

30. The annual low temperature in Nome, Alaska, was recorded as -15°C. Write -15°C as degrees Fahrenheit. [Use the formula $F = \dfrac{9}{5}C + 32$]

31. Omaha, Nebraska, is about 90 miles from Lincoln, Nebraska. Irania must go to the law library in Lincoln to get a document for the law firm she works for. Find how long it takes her to drive round-trip if she averages 50 mph.

32. It took the Selby family $5\frac{1}{2}$ hours round-trip to drive from their house to their beach house 154 miles away. Find their average speed.

△ **33.** A package of floor tiles contains 24 one-foot-square tiles. Find how many packages should be bought to cover a square ballroom floor whose side measures 64 feet.

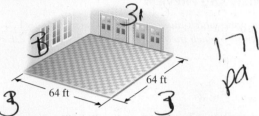

64 ft
64 ft

△ **34.** One-foot-square ceiling tiles are sold in packages of 50. Find how many packages must be bought for a rectangular ceiling 18 feet by 12 feet.

🖩 **35.** If the area of a triangular kite is 18 square feet and its base is △ 4 feet, find the height of the kite.

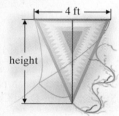

|← 4 ft →|

height

36. Bryan, Eric, Mandy, and Melissa would like to go to Disneyland in 3 years. Their total cost should be $4500. If each invests $1000 in a savings account paying 5.5% interest, compounded semiannually, will they have enough in 3 years?

△ **37.** A gallon of latex paint can cover 500 square feet. Find how many gallon containers of paint should be bought to paint two coats on each wall of a rectangular room whose dimensions are 14 feet by 16 feet (assume 8-foot ceilings).

△ **38.** A gallon of enamel paint can cover 300 square feet. Find how many gallon containers of paint should be bought to paint three coats on a wall measuring 21 feet by 8 feet.

△ **39.** A portion of the external tank of the Space Shuttle *Endeavour* is a liquid hydrogen tank. If the ends of the tank are hemispheres, find the volume of the tank. To do so, answer parts **a** through **c**.

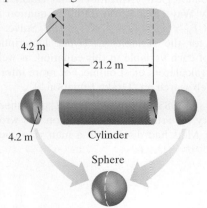

4.2 m

|← 21.2 m →|

4.2 m   Cylinder

Sphere

a. Find the volume of the cylinder shown. Round to 2 decimal places.

b. Find the volume of the sphere shown. Round to 2 decimal places.

c. Add the results of parts **a** and **b**. This sum is the approximate volume of the tank.

△ **40.** In 1945, Arthur C. Clarke, a scientist and science-fiction writer, predicted that an artificial satellite placed at a height of 22,248 miles directly above the equator would orbit the globe at the same speed with which the Earth was rotating. This belt along the equator is known as the Clarke belt. Use the formula for circumference of a circle and find the "length" of the Clarke belt. (*Hint:* Recall that the radius of the Earth is approximately 4000 miles. Round to the nearest whole mile.)

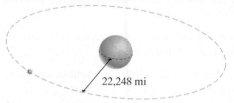

22,248 mi

41. Amelia Earhart was the first woman to fly solo nonstop coast to coast, setting the women's nonstop transcontinental speed record. She traveled 2447.8 miles in 19 hours 5 minutes. Find the average speed of her flight in miles per hour. (Change 19 hours 5 minutes into hours and use the formula $d = rt$.) Round to the nearest tenth of a mile per hour.

△ **42.** The Space Shuttle *Endeavour* has a cargo bay that is in the shape of a cylinder whose length is 18.3 meters and whose diameter is 4.6 meters. Find its volume.

△ **43.** The deepest hole in the ocean floor is beneath the Pacific Ocean and is called Hole 504B. It is located off the coast of Ecuador. Scientists are drilling it to learn more about the Earth's history. Currently, the hole is in the shape of a cylinder whose volume is approximately 3800 cubic feet and whose length is 1.3 miles. Find the radius of the hole to the nearest hundredth of a foot. (*Hint:* Make sure the same units of measurement are used.)

44. The deepest man-made hole is called the Kola Superdeep Borehole. It is approximately 8 miles deep and is located near a small Russian town in the Arctic Circle. If it takes 7.5 hours to remove the drill from the bottom of the hole, find the rate that the drill can be retrieved in feet per second. Round to the nearest tenth. (*Hint:* Write 8 miles as feet, 7.5 hours as seconds, then use the formula $d = rt$.)

△ **45.** Eartha is the world's largest globe. It is located at the headquarters of DeLorme, a mapmaking company in Yarmouth, Maine. Eartha is 41.125 feet in diameter. Find its exact circumference (distance around) and then approximate its circumference using 3.14 for π. (*Source:* DeLorme)

△ **46.** Eartha is in the shape of a sphere. Its radius is about 20.6 feet. Approximate its volume to the nearest cubic foot. (*Source: DeLorme*)

47. Find *how much interest* $10,000 earns in 2 years in a certificate of deposit paying 8.5% interest compounded quarterly.

48. Find how long it takes Mark to drive 135 miles on I-10 if he merges onto I-10 at 10 a.m. and drives nonstop with his cruise control set on 60 mph.

The calorie count of a serving of food can be computed based on its composition of carbohydrate, fat, and protein. The calorie count C for a serving of food can be computed using the formula $C = 4h + 9f + 4p$, where h is the number of grams of carbohydrate contained in the serving, f is the number of grams of fat contained in the serving, and p is the number of grams of protein contained in the serving.

49. Solve this formula for *f*, the number of grams of fat contained in a serving of food.

50. Solve this formula for *h*, the number of grams of carbohydrate contained in a serving of food.

51. A serving of cashews contains 14 grams of fat, 7 grams of carbohydrate, and 6 grams of protein. How many calories are in this serving of cashews?

52. A serving of chocolate candies contains 9 grams of fat, 30 grams of carbohydrate, and 2 grams of protein. How many calories are in this serving of chocolate candies?

53. A serving of raisins contains 130 calories and 31 grams of carbohydrate. If raisins are a fat-free food, how much protein is provided by this serving of raisins?

54. A serving of yogurt contains 120 calories, 21 grams of carbohydrate, and 5 grams of protein. How much fat is provided by this serving of yogurt? Round to the nearest tenth of a gram.

REVIEW AND PREVIEW

Determine which numbers in the set $\{-3, -2, -1, 0, 1, 2, 3\}$ are solutions of each inequality. See Sections 1.3 and 2.1.

55. $x < 0$

56. $x > 1$

57. $x + 5 \leq 6$

58. $x - 3 \geq -7$

59. In your own words, explain what real numbers are solutions of $x < 0$.

60. In your own words, explain what real numbers are solutions of $x > 1$.

CONCEPT EXTENSIONS

61. Solar system distances are so great that units other than miles or kilometers are often used. For example, the astronomical unit (AU) is the average distance between Earth and the Sun, or 92,900,000 miles. Use this information to convert each planet's distance in miles from the Sun to astronomical units. Round to three decimal places. (*Source:* National Space Science Data Center)

Planet	Miles from the Sun	AU from the Sun	Planet	Miles from the Sun	AU from the Sun
Mercury	36 million		Saturn	886.1 million	
Venus	67.2 million		Uranus	1783 million	
Earth	92.9 million		Neptune	2793 million	
Mars	141.5 million		Pluto	3670 million	
Jupiter	483.3 million				

62. An orbit such as Clarke's belt in Exercise 40 is called a geostationary orbit. In your own words, why do you think that communications satellites are placed in geostationary orbits?

63. How much do you think it costs each American to build a space shuttle? Write down your estimate. The space shuttle *Endeavour* was completed in 1992 and cost approximately $1.7 billion. If the population of the United States in 1992 was 250 million, find the cost per person to build the *Endeavour*. How close was your estimate?

64. If you are investing money in a savings account paying a rate of *r*, which account should you choose—an account compounded 4 times a year or 12 times a year? Explain your choice.

65. To borrow money at a rate of *r*, which loan plan should you choose—one compounding 4 times a year or 12 times a year? Explain your choice.

66. The Drake Equation is a formula used to estimate the number of technological civilizations that might exist in our own Milky Way Galaxy. The Drake Equation is given as $N = R^* \times f_p \times n_e \times f_l \times f_i \times f_c \times L$. Solve the Drake Equation for the variable n_e. (*Note:* Descriptions of the meaning of each variable in this equation, as well as Drake Equation calculators, exist online. For more information, try doing a Web search on "Drake Equation.")

67. On April 1, 1985, *Sports Illustrated* published an April Fool's story by writer George Plimpton. He wrote that the New York Mets had discovered a man who could throw a

168-miles-per-hour fast ball. If the distance from the pitcher's mound to the plate is 60.5 feet, how long would it take for a ball thrown at that rate to travel that distance? (*Hint:* Write the rate 168 miles per hour in feet per second. Then use the formula $d = r \cdot t$.)

$$168 \text{ miles per hour} = \frac{168 \text{ miles}}{1 \text{ hour}}$$
$$= \frac{\_\_ \text{ feet}}{\_\_ \text{ seconds}}$$
$$= \frac{\_\_ \text{ feet}}{1 \text{ second}}$$
$$= \_\_ \text{ feet per second}$$

The measure of the chance or likelihood of an event occurring is its **probability**. *A formula basic to the study of probability is the formula for the probability of an event when all the outcomes are equally likely. This formula is*

$$\text{Probability of an event} = \frac{\text{number of ways that the event can occur}}{\text{number of possible outcomes}}$$

For example, to find the probability that a single spin on the spinner will result in red, notice first that the spinner is divided into 8 parts, so there are 8 possible outcomes. Next, notice that there is only one sector of the spinner colored red, so the number of ways that the spinner can land on red is 1. Then this probability denoted by P(red) is

$P(\text{red}) = \frac{1}{8}$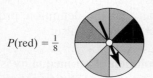

Find each probability in simplest form.

68. $P(\text{green})$

69. $P(\text{yellow})$

70. $P(\text{black})$

71. $P(\text{blue})$

72. $P(\text{green or blue})$

73. $P(\text{black or yellow})$

74. $P(\text{red, green, or black})$

75. $P(\text{yellow, blue, or black})$

76. $P(\text{white})$

77. $P(\text{red, yellow, green, blue, or black})$

78. From the previous probability formula, what do you think is always the probability of an event that is impossible occuring?

79. What do you think is always the probability of an event that is sure to occur?

 STUDY SKILLS BUILDER

How Are Your Homework Assignments Going?

It is very important in mathematics to keep up with homework. Why? Many concepts build on each other. Often your understanding of a day's concepts depends on an understanding of the previous day's material.

Remember that completing your homework assignment involves a lot more than attempting a few of the problems assigned.

To complete a homework assignment, remember these four things:

- Attempt all of it.
- Check it.
- Correct it.
- If needed, ask questions about it.

Take a moment and review your completed homework assignments. Answer the questions below based on this review.

1. Approximate the fraction of your homework you have attempted.

2. Approximate the fraction of your homework you have checked (if possible).

3. If you are able to check your homework, have you corrected it when errors have been found?

4. When working homework, if you do not understand a concept, what do you do?

2.4 LINEAR INEQUALITIES AND PROBLEM SOLVING

Relationships among measurable quantities are not always described by equations. For example, suppose that a salesperson earns a base of $600 per month plus a commission of 20% of sales. Suppose we want to find the minimum amount of sales needed to receive a total income of *at least* $1500 per month. Here, the phrase "at least" implies that an income of $1500 *or more* is acceptable. In symbols, we can write

$$\text{income} \geq 1500$$

This is an example of an inequality, and we will solve this problem in Example 8.

A **linear inequality** is similar to a linear equation except that the equality symbol is replaced with an inequality symbol, such as $<, >, \leq,$ or $\geq$.

Linear Inequalities in One Variable

$3x + 5 \geq 4$	$2y < 0$	$3(x - 4) > 5x$	$\dfrac{x}{3} \leq 5$
↑	↑	↑	↑
is greater than or equal to	is less than	is greater than	is less than or equal to

---

Linear Inequality in One Variable

A linear inequality in one variable is an inequality that can be written in the form

$$ax + b < c$$

where $a, b,$ and c are real numbers and $a \neq 0$.

In this section, when we make definitions, state properties, or list steps about an inequality containing the symbol $<$, we mean that the definition, property, or steps apply to inequalities containing the symbols $>, \leq$ and $\geq$ also.

OBJECTIVE 1 ▶ Using interval notation. A **solution** of an inequality is a value of the variable that makes the inequality a true statement. The **solution set** of an inequality is the set of all solutions. Notice that the solution set of the inequality $x > 2$, for example, contains all numbers greater than 2. Its graph is an interval on the number line since an infinite number of values satisfy the variable. If we use open/closed-circle notation, the graph of $\{x | x > 2\}$ looks like the following.

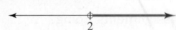

In this text **interval notation** will be used to write solution sets of inequalities. To help us understand this notation, a different graphing notation will be used. Instead of an open circle, we use a parenthesis. With this new notation, the graph of $\{x | x > 2\}$ now looks like

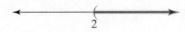

and can be represented in interval notation as $(2, \infty)$. The symbol ∞ is read "infinity" and indicates that the interval includes *all* numbers greater than 2. The left parenthesis indicates that 2 *is not* included in the interval.

In the case where 2 *is* included in the interval, we use a bracket. The graph of $\{x | x \geq 2\}$ is below

and can be represented as $[2, \infty)$.

The following table shows three equivalent ways to describe an interval: in set notation, as a graph, and in interval notation.

Set Notation	Graph	Interval Notation
$\{x \mid x < a\}$	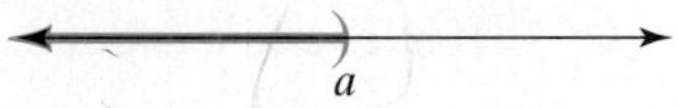	$(-\infty, a)$
$\{x \mid x > a\}$	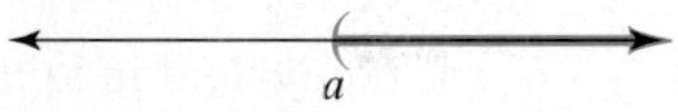	(a, ∞)
$\{x \mid x \leq a\}$	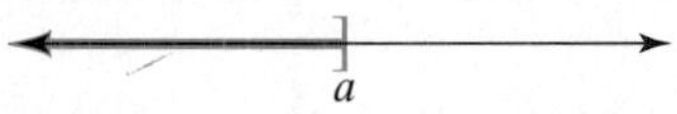	$(-\infty, a]$
$\{x \mid x \geq a\}$	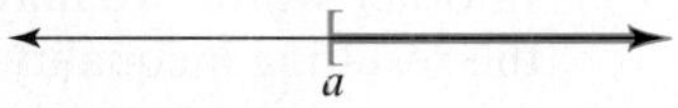	$[a, \infty)$
$\{x \mid a < x < b\}$	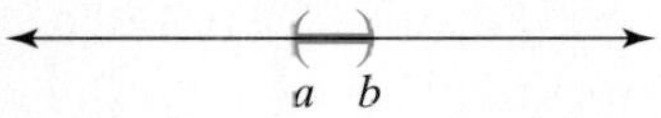	(a, b)
$\{x \mid a \leq x \leq b\}$	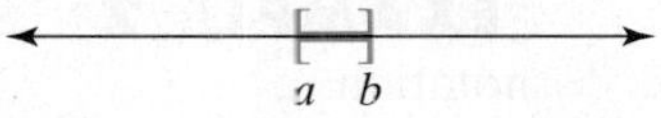	$[a, b]$
$\{x \mid a < x \leq b\}$	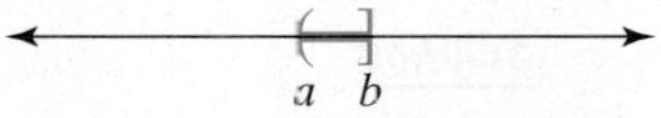	$(a, b]$
$\{x \mid a \leq x < b\}$	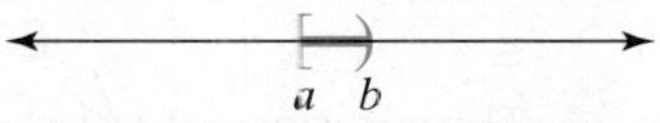	$[a, b)$

> **Helpful Hint**
> Notice that a parenthesis is always used to enclose ∞ and $-\infty$.

Concept Check ☑

Explain what is wrong with writing the interval $(5, \infty]$. $(5, \infty)$

EXAMPLE 1   Graph each set on a number line and then write in interval notation.

a. $\{x \mid x \geq 2\}$ **b.** $\{x \mid x < -1\}$ **c.** $\{x \mid 0.5 < x \leq 3\}$

Solution

a. 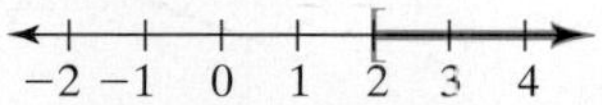 $[2, \infty)$

b. 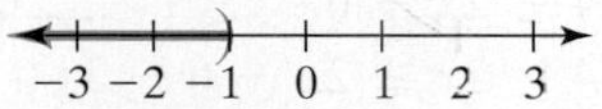 $(-\infty, -1)$

c. 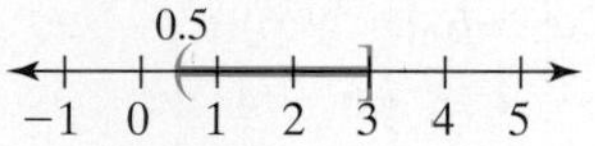 $(0.5, 3]$

PRACTICE

1   Graph each set on a number line and then write in interval notation.

a. $\{x \mid x < 3.5\}$
b. $\{x \mid x \geq -3\}$
c. $\{x \mid -1 \leq x < 4\}$

OBJECTIVE 2 ▶ Solving linear inequalities using the addition property. We will use interval notation to write solutions of linear inequalities. To solve a linear inequality, we use a process similar to the one used to solve a linear equation. We use properties of inequalities to write equivalent inequalities until the variable is isolated.

Answer to Concept Check:
should be $(5, \infty)$ since a parenthesis is always used to enclose ∞

> **Addition Property of Inequality**
> If a, b, and c are real numbers, then
> $$a < b \quad \text{and} \quad a + c < b + c$$
> are equivalent inequalities.

In other words, we may add the same real number to both sides of an inequality and the resulting inequality will have the same solution set. This property also allows us to subtract the same real number from both sides.

EXAMPLE 2 Solve: $x - 2 < 5$. Graph the solution set and write it in interval notation.

Solution
$$x - 2 < 5$$
$$x - 2 + 2 < 5 + 2 \quad \text{Add 2 to both sides.}$$
$$x < 7 \quad \text{Simplify.}$$

The solution set is $\{x | x < 7\}$, which in interval notation is $(-\infty, 7)$. The graph of the solution set is

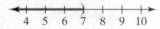

PRACTICE
2 Solve: $x + 5 > 9$. Graph the solution set and write it in interval notation.

> ▶ **Helpful Hint**
> In Example 2, the solution set is $\{x | x < 7\}$. This means that *all* numbers less than 7 are solutions. For example, 6.9, 0, $-\pi$, 1, and -56.7 are solutions, just to name a few. To see this, replace x in $x - 2 < 5$ with each of these numbers and see that the result is a true inequality.

EXAMPLE 3 Solve: $3x + 4 \geq 2x - 6$. Graph the solution set and write it in interval notation.

Solution
$$3x + 4 \geq 2x - 6$$
$$3x + 4 - 2x \geq 2x - 6 - 2x \quad \text{Subtract } 2x \text{ from both sides.}$$
$$x + 4 \geq -6 \quad \text{Combine like terms.}$$
$$x + 4 - 4 \geq -6 - 4 \quad \text{Subtract 4 from both sides.}$$
$$x \geq -10 \quad \text{Simplify.}$$

The solution set is $\{x | x \geq -10\}$, which in interval notation is $[-10, \infty)$. The graph of the solution set is

$$\xleftarrow{\quad\quad}\overset{[}{\underset{-11\;-10\;-9\;-8\;-7\;-6}{\rule{4cm}{0.4pt}}}\xrightarrow{\quad\quad}$$

PRACTICE
3 Solve: $8x + 21 \leq 2x - 3$. Graph the solution set and write it in interval notation.

OBJECTIVE 3 ▶ **Solving linear inequalities using the multiplication and addition properties.** Next, we introduce and use the multiplication property of inequality to solve linear inequalities. To understand this property, let's start with the true statement $-3 < 7$ and multiply both sides by 2.

$$-3 < 7$$
$$-3(2) < 7(2) \quad \text{Multiply by 2.}$$
$$-6 < 14 \qquad \text{True}$$

The statement remains true.

Notice what happens if both sides of $-3 < 7$ are multiplied by -2.

$$-3 < 7$$
$$-3(-2) < 7(-2) \quad \text{Multiply by } -2.$$
$$6 < -14 \qquad \text{False}$$

The inequality $6 < -14$ is a false statement. However, **if the direction of the inequality sign is reversed,** the result is true.

$$6 > -14 \quad \text{True}$$

These examples suggest the following property.

> **Multiplication Property of Inequality**
>
> If a, b, and c are real numbers and c is **positive**, then
>
> $$a < b \quad \text{and} \quad ac < bc$$
>
> are equivalent inequalities.
> If a, b, and c are real numbers and c is **negative**, then
>
> $$a < b \quad \text{and} \quad ac > bc$$
>
> are equivalent inequalities.

In other words, we may multiply both sides of an inequality by the same positive real number and the result is an equivalent inequality.

We may also multiply both sides of an inequality by the same **negative number** and **reverse the direction of the inequality symbol**, and the result is an equivalent inequality. The multiplication property holds for division also, since division is defined in terms of multiplication.

> ❱ **Helpful Hint**
>
> Whenever both sides of an inequality are multiplied or divided by a negative number, the direction of the inequality symbol **must be** reversed to form an equivalent inequality.

EXAMPLE 4   Solve and graph the solution set. Write the solution set in interval notation.

a. $\dfrac{1}{4}x \le \dfrac{3}{8}$ **b.** $-2.3x < 6.9$

Solution

a.
$$\frac{1}{4}x \le \frac{3}{8}$$

$$4 \cdot \frac{1}{4}x \le 4 \cdot \frac{3}{8} \quad \text{Multiply both sides by 4.}$$

$$x \le \frac{3}{2} \quad \text{Simplify.}$$

> ❱ **Helpful Hint**
>
> The inequality symbol is the same since we are multiplying by a *positive* number.

The solution set is $\left\{ x \mid x \leq \dfrac{3}{2} \right\}$, which in interval notation is $\left(-\infty, \dfrac{3}{2} \right]$. The graph of the solution set is

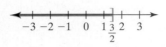

b. $\qquad\qquad -2.3x < 6.9$

$$\dfrac{-2.3x}{-2.3} > \dfrac{6.9}{-2.3} \qquad$$ Divide both sides by -2.3 and reverse the inequality symbol.

$$x > -3 \qquad$$ Simplify.

> ▶ **Helpful Hint**
>
> The inequality symbol is *reversed* since we divided by a *negative* number.

The solution set is $\{ x \mid x > -3 \}$, which is $(-3, \infty)$ in interval notation. The graph of the solution set is

□

PRACTICE

4 Solve and graph the solution set. Write the solution set in interval notation.

a. $\dfrac{2}{5}x \geq \dfrac{4}{15}$

b. $-2.4x < 9.6$

Concept Check ✓

In which of the following inequalities must the inequality symbol be reversed during the solution process?

a. $-2x > 7$ $\qquad\qquad$ **c.** $-x + 4 + 3x < 7$

b. $2x - 3 > 10$ $\qquad\qquad$ **d.** $-x + 4 < 5$

To solve linear inequalities in general, we follow steps similar to those for solving linear equations.

Solving a Linear Inequality in One Variable

STEP 1. Clear the inequality of fractions by multiplying both sides of the inequality by the least common denominator (LCD) of all fractions in the inequality.

STEP 2. Use the distributive property to remove grouping symbols such as parentheses.

STEP 3. Combine like terms on each side of the inequality.

STEP 4. Use the addition property of inequality to write the inequality as an equivalent inequality with variable terms on one side and numbers on the other side.

STEP 5. Use the multiplication property of inequality to isolate the variable.

EXAMPLE 5 Solve: $-(x - 3) + 2 \leq 3(2x - 5) + x$.

Solution $\qquad -(x - 3) + 2 \leq 3(2x - 5) + x$

$$-x + 3 + 2 \leq 6x - 15 + x \qquad$$ Apply the distributive property.

$$5 - x \leq 7x - 15 \qquad$$ Combine like terms.

$$5 - x + x \leq 7x - 15 + x \qquad$$ Add x to both sides.

$$5 \leq 8x - 15 \qquad$$ Combine like terms.

Answer to Concept Check:
a, d

> ▶ **Helpful Hint**
>
> Don't forget that $\frac{5}{2} \le x$ means the same as $x \ge \frac{5}{2}$.

$$5 + 15 \le 8x - 15 + 15 \qquad \text{Add 15 to both sides.}$$
$$20 \le 8x \qquad \text{Combine like terms.}$$
$$\frac{20}{8} \le \frac{8x}{8} \qquad \text{Divide both sides by 8.}$$
$$\frac{5}{2} \le x, \quad \text{or} \quad x \ge \frac{5}{2} \qquad \text{Simplify.}$$

The solution set written in interval notation is $\left[\frac{5}{2}, \infty\right)$ and its graph is

PRACTICE
5   Solve: $-(4x + 6) \le 2(5x + 9) + 2x$. Graph and write the solution set in interval notation.

EXAMPLE 6   Solve: $\frac{2}{5}(x - 6) \ge x - 1$.

Solution

$$\frac{2}{5}(x - 6) \ge x - 1$$

$$5\left[\frac{2}{5}(x - 6)\right] \ge 5(x - 1) \qquad \begin{array}{l}\text{Multiply both sides by} \\ \text{5 to eliminate fractions.}\end{array}$$

$$2(x - 6) \ge 5(x - 1)$$

$$2x - 12 \ge 5x - 5 \qquad \text{Apply the distributive property.}$$

$$-3x - 12 \ge -5 \qquad \text{Subtract } 5x \text{ from both sides.}$$

$$-3x \ge 7 \qquad \text{Add 12 to both sides.}$$

$$\frac{-3x}{-3} \le \frac{7}{-3} \qquad \begin{array}{l}\text{Divide both sides by } -3 \text{ and reverse} \\ \text{the inequality symbol.}\end{array}$$

$$x \le -\frac{7}{3} \qquad \text{Simplify.}$$

The solution set written in interval notation is $\left(-\infty, -\frac{7}{3}\right]$ and its graph is

PRACTICE
6   Solve: $\frac{3}{5}(x - 3) \ge x - 7$. Graph and write the solution set in interval notation.

EXAMPLE 7   Solve: $2(x + 3) > 2x + 1$.

Solution

$$2(x + 3) > 2x + 1$$
$$2x + 6 > 2x + 1 \qquad \text{Distribute on the left side.}$$
$$2x + 6 - 2x > 2x + 1 - 2x \qquad \text{Subtract } 2x \text{ from both sides.}$$
$$6 > 1 \qquad \text{Simplify.}$$

$6 > 1$ is a true statement for all values of x, so this inequality and the original inequality are true for all numbers. The solution set is $\{x \mid x \text{ is a real number}\}$, or $(-\infty, \infty)$ in interval notation, and its graph is

PRACTICE
7 Solve: $4(x - 2) < 4x + 5$. Graph and write the solution set in interval notation.

OBJECTIVE 4 ▶ Solving problems modeled by linear inequalities. Application problems containing words such as "at least," "at most," "between," "no more than," and "no less than" usually indicate that an inequality be solved instead of an equation. In solving applications involving linear inequalities, we use the same procedure as when we solved applications involving linear equations.

EXAMPLE 8   **Calculating Income with Commission**

A salesperson earns $600 per month plus a commission of 20% of sales. Find the minimum amount of sales needed to receive a total income of at least $1500 per month.

Solution

1. UNDERSTAND. Read and reread the problem. Let x = amount of sales
2. TRANSLATE. As stated in the beginning of this section, we want the income to be greater than or equal to $1500. To write an inequality, notice that the salesperson's income consists of $600 plus a commission (20% of sales).

In words: 600   +   commission (20% of sales)   ≥   1500

Translate: 600   + $0.20x$ ≥   1500

3. SOLVE the inequality for x.

$$600 + 0.20x \geq 1500$$
$$600 + 0.20x - 600 \geq 1500 - 600$$
$$0.20x \geq 900$$
$$x \geq 4500$$

4. INTERPRET.

Check: The income for sales of $4500 is

$$600 + 0.20(4500), \text{ or } 1500.$$

Thus, if sales are greater than or equal to $4500, income is greater than or equal to $1500.

State: The minimum amount of sales needed for the salesperson to earn at least $1500 per month is $4500 per month.   □

PRACTICE
8   A salesperson earns $900 a month plus a commission of 15% of sales. Find the minimum amount of sales needed to receive a total income of at least $2400 per month.

EXAMPLE 9   **Finding the Annual Consumption**

In the United States, the annual consumption of cigarettes is declining. The consumption c in billions of cigarettes per year since the year 1990 can be approximated by the formula

$$c = -9.2t + 527.33$$

where t is the number of years after 1990. Use this formula to predict the years that the consumption of cigarettes will be less than 200 billion per year.

Solution

1. UNDERSTAND. Read and reread the problem. To become familiar with the given formula, let's find the cigarette consumption after 20 years, which would be the year $1990 + 20$, or 2010. To do so, we substitute 20 for t in the given formula.

$$c = -9.2(20) + 527.33 = 343.33$$

Thus, in 2010, we predict cigarette consumption to be about 343.3 billion.

Variables have already been assigned in the given formula. For review, they are c = the annual consumption of cigarettes in the United States in billions of cigarettes

$$t = \text{the number of years after 1990}$$

2. TRANSLATE. We are looking for the years that the consumption of cigarettes c is less than 200. Since we are finding years t, we substitute the expression in the formula given for c, or

$$-9.2t - 527.33 < 200$$

3. SOLVE the inequality.

$$-9.2t + 527.33 < 200$$
$$-9.2t < -327.33$$
$$t > \text{approximately } 35.58$$

4. INTERPRET.

Check: Substitute a number greater than 35.58 and see that c is less than 200.

State: The annual consumption of cigarettes will be less than 200 billion more than 35.58 years after 1990, or in approximately $36 + 1990 = 2026$. □

PRACTICE

9 Use the formula given in Example 9 to predict when the consumption of cigarettes will be less than 250 billion per year.

VOCABULARY & READINESS CHECK

Match each graph with the interval notation that describes it.

1.

-7 -6 -5 -4 -3 -2 -1 0

a. $(-5, \infty)$ b. $(-5, -\infty)$
c. $(\infty, -5)$ d. $(-\infty, -5)$

2.

-13 -12 -11 -10 -9 -8

a. $(-\infty, -11]$ b. $(-11, \infty)$
c. $[-11, \infty)$ d. $(-\infty, -11)$

3.

-2.5 $\frac{7}{4}$

-3 -2 -1 0 1 2 3 4

a. $\left[\frac{7}{4}, -2.5\right)$ b. $\left(-2.5, \frac{7}{4}\right]$
c. $\left[-2.5, \frac{7}{4}\right)$ d. $\left(\frac{7}{4}, -2.5\right]$

4.

$-\frac{10}{3}$ 0.2

-4 -3 -2 -1 0 1 2 3

a. $\left[-\frac{10}{3}, 0.2\right)$ b. $\left(0.2, -\frac{10}{3}\right]$
c. $\left(-\frac{10}{3}, 0.2\right]$ d. $\left[0.2, -\frac{10}{3}\right)$

Use the choices below to fill in each blank.

$(-\infty, -0.4)$ $(-\infty, -0.4]$ $[-0.4, \infty)$ $(-0.4, \infty)$ $(\infty, -0.4]$

5. The set $\{x \mid x \geq -0.4\}$ written in interval notation is _____ .

6. The set $\{x \mid x < -0.4\}$ written in interval notation is _____ .

7. The set $\{x \mid x \leq -0.4\}$ written in interval notation is _____ .

8. The set $\{x \mid x > -0.4\}$ written in interval notation is _____ .

Each inequality below is solved by dividing both sides by the coefficient of x. In which inequality will the inequality symbol be reversed during this solution process?

9. $3x > -14$ **10.** $-3x \leq 14$ **11.** $-3x < -14$ **12.** $-x \geq 23$

2.4 EXERCISE SET

PRACTICE   WATCH   DOWNLOAD   READ   REVIEW

Graph the solution set of each inequality and write it in interval notation. See Example 1.

1. $\{x \mid x < -3\}$ **2.** $\{x \mid x > 5\}$

3. $\{x \mid x \geq 0.3\}$ **4.** $\{x \mid x < -0.2\}$

5. $\{x \mid -7 \leq x\}$ **6.** $\{x \mid -7 \geq x\}$

7. $\{x \mid -2 < x < 5\}$ **8.** $\{x \mid -5 \leq x \leq -1\}$

9. $\{x \mid 5 \geq x > -1\}$ **10.** $\{x \mid -3 > x \geq -7\}$

Solve. Graph the solution set and write it in interval notation. See Examples 2 through 4.

11. $x - 7 \geq -9$ **12.** $x + 2 \leq -1$

13. $7x < 6x + 1$ **14.** $11x < 10x + 5$

15. $8x - 7 \leq 7x - 5$ **16.** $7x - 1 \geq 6x - 1$

17. $\frac{3}{4}x \geq 6$ **18.** $\frac{5}{6}x \geq 5$

19. $5x < -23.5$ **20.** $4x > -11.2$

21. $-3x \geq 9$ **22.** $-4x \geq 8$

Solve. Write the solution set using interval notation. See Examples 5 through 7.

23. $-2x + 7 \geq 9$

24. $8 - 5x \leq 23$

25. $15 + 2x \geq 4x - 7$

26. $20 + x < 6x - 15$

27. $4(2x + 1) > 4$

28. $6(2 - 3x) \geq 12$

29. $3(x - 5) < 2(2x - 1)$

30. $5(x + 4) \leq 4(2x + 3)$

31. $\frac{5x + 1}{7} - \frac{2x - 6}{4} \geq -4$

32. $\frac{1 - 2x}{3} + \frac{3x + 7}{7} > 1$

33. $-3(2x - 1) < -4[2 + 3(x + 2)]$

34. $-2(4x + 2) > -5[1 + 2(x - 1)]$

MIXED PRACTICE

Solve. Write the solution set using interval notation. See Examples 1 through 7.

35. $x + 9 < 3$ **36.** $x - 9 < -12$

37. $-x < -4$ **38.** $-x > -2$

39. $-7x \leq 3.5$ **40.** $-6x \leq 4.2$

41. $\frac{1}{2} + \frac{2}{3} \geq \frac{x}{6}$

42. $\frac{3}{4} - \frac{2}{3} \geq \frac{x}{6}$

43. $-5x + 4 \leq -4(x - 1)$

44. $-6x + 2 < -3(x + 4)$

45. $\frac{3}{4}(x - 7) \geq x + 2$

46. $\frac{4}{5}(x + 1) \leq x + 1$

47. $0.8x + 0.6x \geq 4.2$

48. $0.7x - x > 0.45$

49. $4(x - 6) + 2x - 4 \geq 3(x - 7) + 10x$

50. $7(2x + 3) + 4x \leq 7 + 5(3x - 4) + x$

51. $14 - (5x - 6) \geq -6(x + 1) - 5$

52. $13y - (9y + 2) \leq 5(y - 6) + 10$

53. $\frac{1}{2}(3x - 4) \leq \frac{3}{4}(x - 6) + 1$

54. $\frac{2}{3}(x + 3) < \frac{1}{6}(2x - 8) + 2$

55. $\frac{-x + 2}{2} - \frac{1 - 5x}{8} < -1$

56. $\frac{3 - 4x}{6} - \frac{1 - 2x}{12} \leq -2$

57. $\frac{x + 5}{5} - \frac{3 + x}{8} \geq -\frac{3}{10}$

58. $\frac{x - 4}{2} - \frac{x - 2}{3} > \frac{5}{6}$

59. $\frac{x + 3}{12} + \frac{x - 5}{15} < \frac{2}{3}$

60. $\frac{3x + 2}{18} - \frac{1 + 2x}{6} \leq -\frac{1}{2}$

61. $0.4(4x - 3) < 1.2(x + 2)$

62. $0.2(8x - 2) < 1.2(x - 3)$

63. $\frac{2}{5}x - \frac{1}{4} \leq \frac{3}{10}x - \frac{4}{5}$

64. $\frac{7}{12}x - \frac{1}{3} \leq \frac{3}{8}x - \frac{5}{6}$

65. $4(x - 1) \geq 4x - 8$

66. $3x + 1 < 3(x - 2)$

67. $7x < 7(x - 2)$

68. $8(x + 3) \leq 7(x + 5) + x$

Solve. See Examples 8 and 9. For Exercises 69 through 76, **a.** *answer with an inequality, and* **b.** *in your own words, explain the meaning of your answer to part a.*

69. Shureka Washburn has scores of 72, 67, 82, and 79 on her algebra tests.

    a. Use an inequality to find the scores she must make on the final exam to pass the course with an average of 77 or higher, given that the final exam counts as two tests.

    b. In your own words explain the meaning of your answer to part a.

70. In a Winter Olympics 5000-meter speed-skating event, Hans Holden scored times of 6.85, 7.04, and 6.92 minutes on his first three trials.

    a. Use an inequality to find the times he can score on his last trial so that his average time is under 7.0 minutes.

    b. In your own words, explain the meaning of your answer to part a.

71. A small plane's maximum takeoff weight is 2000 pounds or less. Six passengers weigh an average of 160 pounds each. Use an inequality to find the luggage and cargo weights the plane can carry.

72. A shopping mall parking garage charges $1 for the first half-hour and 60 cents for each additional half-hour. Use an inequality to find how long you can park if you have only $4.00 in cash.

73. A clerk must use the elevator to move boxes of paper. The elevator's maximum weight limit is 1500 pounds. If each box of paper weighs 66 pounds and the clerk weighs 147 pounds, use an inequality to find the number of whole boxes she can move on the elevator at one time.

74. To mail an envelope first class, the U.S. Post Office charges 41 cents for the first ounce and 17 cents per ounce for each additional ounce. Use an inequality to find the number of whole ounces that can be mailed for no more than $2.50.

75. Northeast Telephone Company offers two billing plans for local calls.

Plan 1: $25 per month for unlimited calls

Plan 2: $13 per month plus $0.06 per call

Use an inequality to find the number of monthly calls for which plan 1 is more economical than plan 2.

76. A car rental company offers two subcompact rental plans.

Plan A: $36 per day and unlimited mileage

Plan B: $24 per day plus $0.15 per mile

Use an inequality to find the number of daily miles for which plan A is more economical than plan B.

77. At room temperature, glass used in windows actually has some properties of a liquid. It has a very slow, viscous flow. (Viscosity is the property of a fluid that resists internal flow. For example, lemonade flows more easily than fudge syrup. Fudge syrup has a higher viscosity than lemonade.) Glass does not become a true liquid until temperatures are greater than or equal to 500°C. Find the Fahrenheit temperatures for which glass is a liquid. (Use the formula $F = \frac{9}{5}C - 32$.)

78. Stibnite is a silvery white mineral with a metallic luster. It is one of the few minerals that melts easily in a match flame or at temperatures of approximately 977°F or greater. Find the Celsius temperatures for which stibnite melts. [Use the formula $C = \frac{5}{9}(F - 32)$.]

79. Although beginning salaries vary greatly according to your field of study, the equation

$$s = 651.2t + 28,472$$

can be used to approximate and to predict average beginning salaries for candidates with bachelor's degrees. The variable s is the starting salary and t is the number of years after 1990.

    a. Approximate when beginning salaries for candidates will be greater than $42,000.

    b. Determine the year you plan to graduate from college. Use this year to find the corresponding value of t and approximate your beginning salary.

80. a. Use the formula in Example 9 to estimate the years that the consumption of cigarettes will be less than 50 billion per year.

    b. Use your answer to part a to describe the limitations of your answer.

The average consumption per person per year of whole milk w in gallons can be approximated by the equation

$$y = -0.19t + 7.6$$

where t is the number of years after 2000. The average consumption of nonfat milk s per person per year can be approximated by the equation

$$y = -0.07t + 3.5$$

where t is the number of years after 2000. The consumption of whole milk is shown on the graph in red and the consumption of nonfat milk is shown on the graph in blue. Use this information to answer Exercises 81–88.

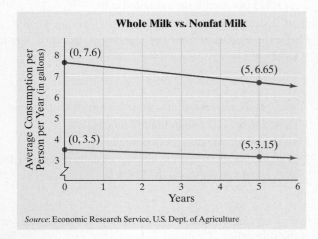

Whole Milk vs. Nonfat Milk

Source: Economic Research Service, U.S. Dept. of Agriculture

81. Is the consumption of whole milk increasing or decreasing over time? Explain how you arrived at your answer.

82. Is the consumption of nonfat milk increasing or decreasing over time? Explain how you arrived at your answer.

83. Predict the consumption of whole milk in the year 2010. (*Hint:* Find the value of *t* that corresponds to the year 2010.)

84. Predict the consumption of nonfat milk in the year 2010. (*Hint:* Find the value of *t* that corresponds to the year 2010.)

85. Determine when the consumption of whole milk will be less than 6 gallons per person per year.

86. Determine when the consumption of nonfat milk will be less than 3 gallons per person per year.

87. For 2000 through 2005 the consumption of whole milk was greater than the consumption of nonfat milk. Explain how this can be determined from the graph.

88. How will the two lines in the graph appear if the consumption of whole milk is the same as the consumption of nonfat milk?

REVIEW AND PREVIEW

List or describe the integers that make both inequalities true. See Section 1.4.

89. $x < 5$ and $x > 1$

90. $x \geq 0$ and $x \leq 7$

91. $x \geq -2$ and $x \geq 2$

92. $x < 6$ and $x < -5$

Solve each equation for x. See Section 2.1.

93. $2x - 6 = 4$

94. $3x - 12 = 3$

95. $-x + 7 = 5x - 6$

96. $-5x - 4 = -x - 4$

CONCEPT EXTENSIONS

Each row of the table shows three equivalent ways of describing an interval. Complete this table by filling in the equivalent descriptions. The first row has been completed for you.

	Set Notation	Graph	Interval Notation
	$\{x \mid x < -3\}$	(← toward −3)	$(-\infty, -3)$
97.		(graph at 2)	
98.		(graph at −4)	
99.	$\{x \mid x < 0\}$		
100.	$\{x \mid x \leq 5\}$		
101.			$(-2, 1.5]$
102.			$[-3.7, 4)$

103. Solve: $2x - 3 = 5$.

104. Solve: $2x - 3 < 5$.

105. Solve: $2x - 3 > 5$.

106. Read the equations and inequalities for Exercises 103, 104, and 105 and their solutions. In your own words, write down your thoughts.

107. When graphing the solution set of an inequality, explain how you know whether to use a parenthesis or a bracket.

108. Explain what is wrong with the interval notation $(-6, -\infty)$.

109. Explain how solving a linear inequality is similar to solving a linear equation.

110. Explain how solving a linear inequality is different from solving a linear equation.

111. Write an inequality whose solution set is $\{x \mid x \leq 2\}$.

THE BIGGER PICTURE   SOLVING EQUATIONS AND INEQUALITIES

This is a special feature that will be repeated and expanded throughout this text. It is very important for you to be able to recognize and solve different types of equations and inequalities. To help you do this, we will begin an outline below and continually expand this outline as different equations and inequalities are introduced. Although suggestions will be given, this outline should be in your own words and you should include at least "how to recognize" and "how to begin to solve" under each letter heading.

For example:

Solving Equations and Inequalities

I. Equations

A. Linear equations: Power on variable is 1 and there are no variables in denominator. (Section 2.1)

$$5(x - 2) = \frac{4(2x + 1)}{3}$$

$$3 \cdot 5(x - 2) = \cancel{3} \cdot \frac{4(2x + 1)}{\cancel{3}} \quad \text{Multiply both sides by the LCD, 3.}$$

$$15(x - 2) = 4(2x + 1) \quad \text{Simplify.}$$

$$15x - 30 = 8x + 4 \quad \text{Multiply.}$$

$$7x = 34 \quad \begin{array}{l}\text{Add 30 and subtract}\\ 8x \text{ from both sides.}\end{array}$$

$$x = \frac{34}{7} \quad \text{Divide both sides by 7.}$$

II. Inequalities

A. Linear Inequalities: Inequality sign and power on x is 1 and there are no variables in denominator. (Section 2.4)

$$-3(x + 2) \geq 6 \quad \text{Linear inequality}$$

$$-3x - 6 \geq 6 \quad \text{Multiply.}$$

$$-3x \geq 12 \quad \text{Add 6 to both sides.}$$

$$\frac{-3x}{-3} \leq \frac{12}{-3} \quad \begin{array}{l}\text{Divide both sides by } -3, \text{ and } change\\ \text{the direction of the inequality sign.}\end{array}$$

$$x \leq -4 \text{ or } (-\infty, -4]$$

Solve. Write inequality solutions in interval notation.

1. $3x - 4 = 3(2x - 1) + 7$

2. $5 + 2x = 5(x + 1)$

3. $\dfrac{x + 3}{2} > 1$

4. $\dfrac{x - 2}{2} - \dfrac{x - 4}{3} = \dfrac{5}{6}$

5. $\dfrac{7}{5} + \dfrac{y}{10} = 2$

6. $5 + 2x = 2(x + 1)$

7. $4(x - 2) + 3x \geq 9(x - 1) - 2$

8. $6(x + 1) - 2 = 6x + 4$

INTEGRATED REVIEW   LINEAR EQUATIONS AND INEQUALITIES

Sections 2.1– 2.4

Solve each equation or inequality. For inequalities, write the solution set in interval notation.

1. $-4x = 20$

2. $-4x < 20$

3. $\dfrac{3x}{4} \geq 2$

4. $5x + 3 \geq 2 + 4x$

5. $6(y - 4) = 3(y - 8)$

6. $-4x \leq \dfrac{2}{5}$

7. $-3x \geq \dfrac{1}{2}$

8. $5(y + 4) = 4(y + 5)$

9. $7x < 7(x - 2)$

10. $\dfrac{-5x + 11}{2} \leq 7$

11. $-5x + 1.5 = -19.5$

12. $-5x + 4 = -26$

13. $5 + 2x - x = -x + 3 - 14$

14. $12x + 14 < 11x - 2$

15. $\dfrac{x}{5} - \dfrac{x}{4} = \dfrac{x - 2}{2}$

16. $12x - 12 = 8(x - 1)$

17. $2(x - 3) > 70$

18. $-3x - 4.7 = 11.8$

19. $-2(b - 4) - (3b - 1) = 5b + 3$

20. $8(x + 3) < 7(x + 5) + x$

21. $\dfrac{3t + 1}{8} = \dfrac{5 + 2t}{7} + 2$

22. $4(x - 6) - x = 8(x - 3) - 5x$

23. $\dfrac{x}{6} + \dfrac{3x - 2}{2} < \dfrac{2}{3}$

24. $\dfrac{y}{3} + \dfrac{y}{5} = \dfrac{y + 3}{10}$

25. $5(x - 6) + 2x > 3(2x - 1) - 4$

26. $14(x - 1) - 7x \leq 2(3x - 6) + 4$

27. $\dfrac{1}{4}(3x + 2) - x \geq \dfrac{3}{8}(x - 5) + 2$

28. $\dfrac{1}{3}(x - 10) - 4x > \dfrac{5}{6}(2x + 1) - 1$

2.5 COMPOUND INEQUALITIES

Two inequalities joined by the words **and** or **or** are called **compound inequalities.**

Compound Inequalities

$$x + 3 < 8 \quad \text{and} \quad x > 2$$

$$\frac{2x}{3} \geq 5 \quad \text{or} \quad -x + 10 < 7$$

OBJECTIVE 1 ▶ Finding the intersection of two sets. The solution set of a compound inequality formed by the word **and** is the **intersection** of the solution sets of the two inequalities. We use the symbol ∩ to represent "intersection."

Intersection of Two Sets

The intersection of two sets, A and B, is the set of all elements common to both sets. A intersect B is denoted by

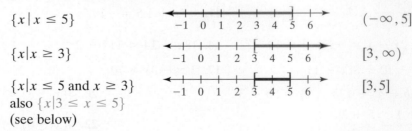

$$A \cap B$$

EXAMPLE 1 If $A = \{x \mid x$ is an even number greater than 0 and less than 10$\}$ and $B = \{3, 4, 5, 6\}$, find $A \cap B$.

Solution Let's list the elements in set A.

$$A = \{2, 4, 6, 8\}$$

The numbers 4 and 6 are in sets A and B. The intersection is $\{4, 6\}$. ☐

PRACTICE

1 If $A = \{x \mid x$ is an odd number greater than 0 and less than 10$\}$ and $B = \{1, 2, 3, 4\}$, find $A \cap B$.

OBJECTIVE 2 ▶ Solving compound inequalities containing "and." A value is a solution of a compound inequality formed by the word **and** if it is a solution of *both* inequalities. For example, the solution set of the compound inequality $x \leq 5$ and $x \geq 3$ contains all values of x that make the inequality $x \leq 5$ a true statement **and** the inequality $x \geq 3$ a true statement. The first graph shown below is the graph of $x \leq 5$, the second graph is the graph of $x \geq 3$, and the third graph shows the intersection of the two graphs. The third graph is the graph of $x \leq 5$ **and** $x \geq 3$.

$\{x \mid x \leq 5\}$	◄─┼─┼─┼─┼─┼─┼─┤─┼─► ‑1 0 1 2 3 4 5 6	$(-\infty, 5]$
$\{x \mid x \geq 3\}$	◄─┼─┼─┼─┼─├─┼─┼─┼─► ‑1 0 1 2 3 4 5 6	$[3, \infty)$
$\{x \mid x \leq 5 \text{ and } x \geq 3\}$ also $\{x \mid 3 \leq x \leq 5\}$ (see below)	◄─┼─┼─┼─┼─├─┼─┤─┼─► ‑1 0 1 2 3 4 5 6	$[3, 5]$

Since $x \geq 3$ is the same as $3 \leq x$, the compound inequality $3 \leq x$ and $x \leq 5$ can be written in a more compact form as $3 \leq x \leq 5$. The solution set $\{x \mid 3 \leq x \leq 5\}$ includes all numbers that are greater than or equal to 3 and at the same time less than or equal to 5.

In interval notation, the set $\{x \mid x \leq 5 \text{ and } x \geq 3\}$ or $\{x \mid 3 \leq x \leq 5\}$ is written as $[3, 5]$.

▶ **Helpful Hint**

Don't forget that some compound inequalities containing "and" can be written in a more compact form.

Compound Inequality	Compact Form	Interval Notation
$2 \leq x$ and $x \leq 6$	$2 \leq x \leq 6$	$[2, 6]$

Graph:

EXAMPLE 2   Solve: $x - 7 < 2$ and $2x + 1 < 9$

Solution   First we solve each inequality separately.

$$x - 7 < 2 \quad \text{and} \quad 2x + 1 < 9$$
$$x < 9 \quad \text{and} \quad 2x < 8$$
$$x < 9 \quad \text{and} \quad x < 4$$

Now we can graph the two intervals on two number lines and find their intersection. Their intersection is shown on the third number line.

$\{x \mid x < 9\}$ $(-\infty, 9)$

$\{x \mid x < 4\}$ $(-\infty, 4)$

$\{x \mid x < 9 \text{ and } x < 4\} = \{x \mid x < 4\}$ $(-\infty, 4)$

The solution set is $(-\infty, 4)$.

PRACTICE
2   Solve: $x + 3 < 8$ and $2x - 1 < 3$. Write the solution set in interval notation.

EXAMPLE 3   Solve: $2x \geq 0$ and $4x - 1 \leq -9$.

Solution   First we solve each inequality separately.

$$2x \geq 0 \quad \text{and} \quad 4x - 1 \leq -9$$
$$x \geq 0 \quad \text{and} \quad 4x \leq -8$$
$$x \geq 0 \quad \text{and} \quad x \leq -2$$

Now we can graph the two intervals and find their intersection.

$\{x \mid x \geq 0\}$ $[0, \infty)$

$\{x \mid x \leq -2\}$ $(-\infty, -2]$

$\{x \mid x \geq 0 \text{ and } x \leq -2\} = \varnothing$ $\varnothing$

There is no number that is greater than or equal to 0 *and* less than or equal to -2. The solution set is $\varnothing$.

PRACTICE
3   Solve: $4x \leq 0$ and $3x + 2 > 8$. Write the solution set in interval notation.

▶ **Helpful Hint**

Example 3 shows that some compound inequalities have no solution. Also, some have all real numbers as solutions.

To solve a compound inequality written in a compact form, such as $2 < 4 - x < 7$, we get x alone in the "middle part." Since a compound inequality is really two inequalities in one statement, we must perform the same operations on all three parts of the inequality.

EXAMPLE 4   Solve: $2 < 4 - x < 7$

Solution   To get x alone, we first subtract 4 from all three parts.

$$2 < 4 - x < 7$$
$$2 - 4 < 4 - x - 4 < 7 - 4 \quad \text{Subtract 4 from all three parts.}$$
$$-2 < -x < 3 \quad \text{Simplify.}$$
$$\frac{-2}{-1} > \frac{-x}{-1} > \frac{3}{-1} \quad \text{Divide all three parts by } -1 \text{ and reverse the inequality symbols.}$$
$$2 > x > -3$$

> ▶ **Helpful Hint**
> Don't forget to reverse both inequality symbols.

This is equivalent to $-3 < x < 2$.

The solution set in interval notation is $(-3, 2)$, and its graph is shown.

PRACTICE

4   Solve: $3 < 5 - x < 9$. Write the solution set in interval notation.

EXAMPLE 5   Solve: $-1 \le \dfrac{2x}{3} + 5 \le 2$.

Solution   First, clear the inequality of fractions by multiplying all three parts by the LCD of 3.

$$-1 \le \frac{2x}{3} + 5 \le 2$$

$$3(-1) \le 3\left(\frac{2x}{3} + 5\right) \le 3(2) \quad \text{Multiply all three parts by the LCD of 3.}$$

$$-3 \le 2x + 15 \le 6 \quad \text{Use the distributive property and multiply.}$$
$$-3 - 15 \le 2x + 15 - 15 \le 6 - 15 \quad \text{Subtract 15 from all three parts.}$$
$$-18 \le 2x \le -9 \quad \text{Simplify.}$$
$$\frac{-18}{2} \le \frac{2x}{2} \le \frac{-9}{2} \quad \text{Divide all three parts by 2.}$$
$$-9 \le x \le -\frac{9}{2} \quad \text{Simplify.}$$

The graph of the solution is shown.

The solution set in interval notation is $\left[-9, -\dfrac{9}{2}\right]$.

PRACTICE

5   Solve: $-4 \le \dfrac{x}{2} - 1 \le 3$. Write the solution set in interval notation.

OBJECTIVE 3 ▶ **Finding the union of two sets.** The solution set of a compound inequality formed by the word **or** is the **union** of the solution sets of the two inequalities. We use the symbol $\cup$ to denote "union."

▶ **Helpful Hint**

The word "either" in this defini-tion means "one or the other or both."

Union of Two Sets

The **union** of two sets, A and B, is the set of elements that belong to *either* of the sets. A union B is denoted by

$$A \cup B$$

EXAMPLE 6   If $A = \{x \mid x$ is an even number greater than 0 and less than 10$\}$ and $B = \{3, 4, 5, 6\}$. Find $A \cup B$.

Solution   Recall from Example 1 that $A = \{2, 4, 6, 8\}$. The numbers that are in either set or both sets are $\{2, 3, 4, 5, 6, 8\}$. This set is the union.   ☐

PRACTICE
6   If $A = \{x \mid x$ is an odd number greater than 0 and less than 10$\}$ and $B = \{2, 3, 4, 5, 6\}$. Find $A \cup B$.

OBJECTIVE 4 ▶ **Solving compound inequalities containing "or."** A value is a solution of a compound inequality formed by the word **or** if it is a solution of **either** inequality. For example, the solution set of the compound inequality $x \leq 1$ **or** $x \geq 3$ contains all numbers that make the inequality $x \leq 1$ a true statement **or** the inequality $x \geq 3$ a true statement.

$\{x \mid x \leq 1\}$ $(-\infty, 1]$

$\{x \mid x \geq 3\}$ $[3, \infty)$

$\{x \mid x \leq 1 \text{ or } x \geq 3\}$ $(-\infty, 1] \cup [3, \infty)$

In interval notation, the set $\{x \mid x \leq 1 \text{ or } x \geq 3\}$ is written as $(-\infty, 1] \cup [3, \infty)$.

EXAMPLE 7   Solve: $5x - 3 \leq 10 \text{ or } x + 1 \geq 5$.

Solution   First we solve each inequality separately.

$$5x - 3 \leq 10 \quad \text{or} \quad x + 1 \geq 5$$
$$5x \leq 13 \quad \text{or} \quad x \geq 4$$
$$x \leq \frac{13}{5} \quad \text{or} \quad x \geq 4$$

Now we can graph each interval and find their union.

$\left\{ x \mid x \leq \dfrac{13}{5} \right\}$ $\left(-\infty, \dfrac{13}{5} \right]$

$\{x \mid x \geq 4\}$ $[4, \infty)$

$\left\{ x \mid x \leq \dfrac{13}{5} \text{ or } x \geq 4 \right\}$ $\left(-\infty, \dfrac{13}{5} \right] \cup [4, \infty)$

The solution set is $\left(-\infty, \dfrac{13}{5} \right] \cup [4, \infty)$.   ☐

PRACTICE
7   Solve: $8x + 5 \leq 8 \text{ or } x - 1 \geq 2$. Write the solution set in interval notation.

EXAMPLE 8 Solve: $-2x - 5 < -3 \text{ or } 6x < 0$.

Solution First we solve each inequality separately.

$$-2x - 5 < -3 \quad \text{or} \quad 6x < 0$$
$$-2x < 2 \quad \text{or} \quad x < 0$$
$$x > -1 \quad \text{or} \quad x < 0$$

Now we can graph each interval and find their union.

$\{x | x > -1\}$ 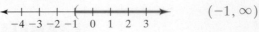 $(-1, \infty)$

$\{x | x < 0\}$  $(-\infty, 0)$

$\{x | x > -1 \text{ or } x < 0\}$ 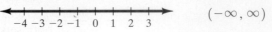 $(-\infty, \infty)$
= all real numbers

The solution set is $(-\infty, \infty)$.

PRACTICE
8 Solve: $-3x - 2 > -8 \text{ or } 5x > 0$. Write the solution set in interval notation.

Concept Check ✓

Which of the following is _not_ a correct way to represent the set of all numbers between -3 and 5?

Answer to Concept Check:
b is not correct

a. $\{x | -3 < x < 5\}$ **b.** $-3 < x \text{ or } x < 5$

c. $(-3, 5)$ **d.** $x > -3 \text{ and } x < 5$

VOCABULARY & READINESS CHECK

Use the choices below to fill in each blank. Some choices may be used more than once.

or $\cup$ $\varnothing$

and $\cap$ compound

1. Two inequalities joined by the words "and" or "or" are called _____ inequalities.

2. The word _____ means intersection.

3. The word _____ means union.

4. The symbol _____ represents intersection.

5. The symbol _____ represents union.

6. The symbol _____ is the empty set.

7. The inequality $-2 \leq x < 1$ means $-2 \leq x$ _____ $x < 1$.

8. $\{x | x < 0 \text{ and } x > 0\} =$ _____

2.5 | EXERCISE SET

MIXED PRACTICE

If $A = \{x | x \text{ is an even integer}\}$, $B = \{x | x \text{ is an odd integer}\}$, $C = \{2, 3, 4, 5\}$, and $D = \{4, 5, 6, 7\}$, list the elements of each set. See Examples 1 and 6.

1. $C \cup D$ **2.** $C \cap D$

3. $A \cap D$ **4.** $A \cup D$

5. $A \cup B$ **6.** $A \cap B$

7. $B \cap D$ **8.** $B \cup D$

9. $B \cup C$ **10.** $B \cap C$

11. $A \cap C$ **12.** $A \cup C$

Solve each compound inequality. Graph the solution set and write it in interval notation. See Examples 2 and 3.

13. $x < 1 \text{ and } x > -3$ **14.** $x \leq 0 \text{ and } x \geq -2$

15. $x \leq -3 \text{ and } x \geq -2$ **16.** $x < 2 \text{ and } x > 4$

17. $x < -1$ and $x < 1$

18. $x \geq -4$ and $x > 1$

Solve each compound inequality. Write solutions in interval notation. See Examples 2 and 3.

19. $x + 1 \geq 7$ and $3x - 1 \geq 5$

20. $x + 2 \geq 3$ and $5x - 1 \geq 9$

21. $4x + 2 \leq -10$ and $2x \leq 0$

22. $2x + 4 > 0$ and $4x > 0$

23. $-2x < -8$ and $x - 5 < 5$

24. $-7x \leq -21$ and $x - 20 \leq -15$

Solve each compound inequality. See Examples 4 and 5.

25. $5 < x - 6 < 11$

26. $-2 \leq x + 3 \leq 0$

27. $-2 \leq 3x - 5 \leq 7$

28. $1 < 4 + 2x < 7$

29. $1 \leq \dfrac{2}{3}x + 3 \leq 4$

30. $-2 < \dfrac{1}{2}x - 5 < 1$

31. $-5 \leq \dfrac{-3x + 1}{4} \leq 2$

32. $-4 \leq \dfrac{-2x + 5}{3} \leq 1$

Solve each compound inequality. Graph the solution set and write it in interval notation. See Examples 7 and 8.

33. $x < 4$ or $x < 5$

34. $x \geq -2$ or $x \leq 2$

35. $x \leq -4$ or $x \geq 1$

36. $x < 0$ or $x < 1$

37. $x > 0$ or $x < 3$

38. $x \geq -3$ or $x \leq -4$

Solve each compound inequality. Write solutions in interval notation. See Examples 7 and 8.

39. $-2x \leq -4$ or $5x - 20 \geq 5$

40. $-5x \leq 10$ or $3x - 5 \geq 1$

41. $x + 4 < 0$ or $6x > -12$

42. $x + 9 < 0$ or $4x > -12$

43. $3(x - 1) < 12$ or $x + 7 > 10$

44. $5(x - 1) \geq -5$ or $5 - x \leq 11$

MIXED PRACTICE

Solve each compound inequality. Write solutions in interval notation. See Examples 1 through 8.

45. $x < \dfrac{2}{3}$ and $x > -\dfrac{1}{2}$

46. $x < \dfrac{5}{7}$ and $x < 1$

47. $x < \dfrac{2}{3}$ or $x > -\dfrac{1}{2}$

48. $x < \dfrac{5}{7}$ or $x < 1$

49. $0 \leq 2x - 3 \leq 9$

50. $3 < 5x + 1 < 11$

51. $\dfrac{1}{2} < x - \dfrac{3}{4} < 2$

52. $\dfrac{2}{3} < x + \dfrac{1}{2} < 4$

53. $x + 3 \geq 3$ and $x + 3 \leq 2$

54. $2x - 1 \geq 3$ and $-x > 2$

55. $3x \geq 5$ or $-\dfrac{5}{8}x - 6 > 1$

56. $\dfrac{3}{8}x + 1 \leq 0$ or $-2x < -4$

57. $0 < \dfrac{5 - 2x}{3} < 5$

58. $-2 < \dfrac{-2x - 1}{3} < 2$

59. $-6 < 3(x - 2) \leq 8$

60. $-5 < 2(x + 4) < 8$

61. $-x + 5 > 6$ and $1 + 2x \leq -5$

62. $5x \leq 0$ and $-x + 5 < 8$

63. $3x + 2 \leq 5$ or $7x > 29$

64. $-x < 7$ or $3x + 1 < -20$

65. $5 - x > 7$ and $2x + 3 \geq 13$

66. $-2x < -6$ or $1 - x > -2$

67. $-\dfrac{1}{2} \leq \dfrac{4x - 1}{6} < \dfrac{5}{6}$

68. $-\dfrac{1}{2} \leq \dfrac{3x - 1}{10} < \dfrac{1}{2}$

69. $\dfrac{1}{15} < \dfrac{8 - 3x}{15} < \dfrac{4}{5}$

70. $-\dfrac{1}{4} < \dfrac{6 - x}{12} < -\dfrac{1}{6}$

71. $0.3 < 0.2x - 0.9 < 1.5$

72. $-0.7 \leq 0.4x + 0.8 < 0.5$

REVIEW AND PREVIEW

Evaluate the following. See Sections 1.2 and 1.3.

73. $|-7| - |19|$

74. $|-7 - 19|$

75. $-(-6) - |-10|$

76. $|-4| - (-4) + |-20|$

Find by inspection all values for x that make each equation true.

77. $|x| = 7$

78. $|x| = 5$

79. $|x| = 0$

80. $|x| = -2$

CONCEPT EXTENSIONS

Use the graph to answer Exercises 81 and 82.

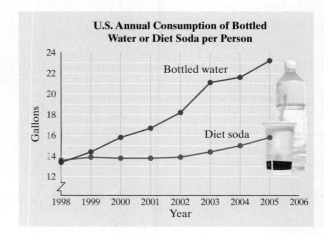

U.S. Annual Consumption of Bottled Water or Diet Soda per Person

Bottled water

Diet soda

Gallons

Year

81. For what years was the consumption of bottled water greater than 20 gallons per person *and* the consumption of diet soda greater than 14 gallons per person?

82. For what years was the consumption of bottled water less than 15 gallons per person *or* the consumption of diet soda greater than 14 gallons per person?

The formula for converting Fahrenheit temperatures to Celsius temperatures is $C = \frac{5}{9}(F - 32)$. Use this formula for Exercises 83 and 84.

83. During a recent year, the temperatures in Chicago ranged from $-29°$ to $35°C$. Use a compound inequality to convert these temperatures to Fahrenheit temperatures.

84. In Oslo, the average temperature ranges from $-10°$ to $18°$ Celsius. Use a compound inequality to convert these temperatures to the Fahrenheit scale.

Solve.

85. Christian D'Angelo has scores of 68, 65, 75, and 78 on his algebra tests. Use a compound inequality to find the scores he can make on his final exam to receive a C in the course. The final exam counts as two tests, and a C is received if the final course average is from 70 to 79.

86. Wendy Wood has scores of 80, 90, 82, and 75 on her chemistry tests. Use a compound inequality to find the range of scores she can make on her final exam to receive a B in the course. The final exam counts as two tests, and a B is received if the final course average is from 80 to 89.

*Solve each compound inequality for x. See the example below. To solve $x - 6 < 3x < 2x + 5$, notice that this inequality contains a variable not only in the middle, but also on the left and the right. When this occurs, we solve by rewriting the inequality using the word **and**.*

$$x - 6 < 3x \quad \text{and} \quad 3x < 2x + 5$$
$$-6 < 2x \quad \text{and} \quad x < 5$$
$$-3 < x$$
$$x > -3 \quad \text{and} \quad x < 5$$

$x > -3$

$x < 5$

$-3 < x < 5$, or $(-3, 5)$

87. $2x - 3 < 3x + 1 < 4x - 5$

88. $x + 3 < 2x + 1 < 4x + 6$

89. $-3(x - 2) \leq 3 - 2x \leq 10 - 3x$

90. $7x - 1 \leq 7 + 5x \leq 3(1 + 2x)$

91. $5x - 8 < 2(2 + x) < -2(1 + 2x)$

92. $1 + 2x < 3(2 + x) < 1 + 4x$

THE BIGGER PICTURE   SOLVING EQUATIONS AND INEQUALITIES

We now continue the outline started in Section 2.4. Although suggestions will be given, this outline should be in your own words. Once you complete this new portion, try the exercises below.

Solving Equations and Inequalities

I. **Equations**

  A. **Linear equations** (Section 2.1)

II. **Inequalities**

  A. **Linear Inequalities** (Section 2.4)

  B. **Compound Inequalities:** Two inequality signs or 2 inequalities separated by "and" or "or." *Or* means *union* and *and* means *intersection.* (Section 2.5)

Solve. Write inequality solutions in interval notation.

1. $x - 2 \leq 1$ and $3x - 1 \geq -4$

2. $-2 < x - 1 < 5$

3. $-2x + 2.5 = -7.7$

4. $-5x > 20$

5. $x \leq -3$ or $x \leq -5$

6. $5x < -10$ or $3x - 4 > 2$

7. $\frac{5t}{2} - \frac{3t}{4} = 7$

8. $5(x - 3) + x + 2 \geq 3(x + 2) + 2x$

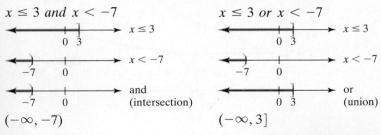

$x \leq 3$ *and* $x < -7$

$x \leq 3$

$x < -7$

and (intersection)

$(-\infty, -7)$

$x \leq 3$ *or* $x < -7$

$x \leq 3$

$x < -7$

or (union)

$(-\infty, 3]$

2.6 ABSOLUTE VALUE EQUATIONS

OBJECTIVE

1 Solve absolute value equations.

OBJECTIVE 1 ▶ Solving absolute equations. In Chapter 1, we defined the absolute value of a number as its distance from 0 on a number line.

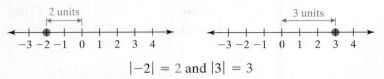

$$|-2| = 2 \text{ and } |3| = 3$$

In this section, we concentrate on solving equations containing the absolute value of a variable or a variable expression. Examples of absolute value equations are

$$|x| = 3 \qquad -5 = |2y + 7| \qquad |z - 6.7| = |3z + 1.2|$$

Since distance and absolute value are so closely related, absolute value equations and inequalities (see Section 2.7) are extremely useful in solving distance-type problems, such as calculating the possible error in a measurement.

For the absolute value equation $|x| = 3$, its solution set will contain all numbers whose distance from 0 is 3 units. Two numbers are 3 units away from 0 on the number line: 3 and -3.

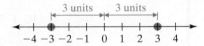

Thus, the solution set of the equation $|x| = 3$ is $\{3, -3\}$. This suggests the following:

Solving Equations of the Form $|X| = a$

If a is a positive number, then $|X| = a$ is equivalent to $X = a$ or $X = -a$.

EXAMPLE 1   Solve: $|p| = 2$.

Solution   Since 2 is positive, $|p| = 2$ is equivalent to $p = 2$ or $p = -2$.

To check, let $p = 2$ and then $p = -2$ in the original equation.

$|p| = 2$	Original equation	$|p| = 2$	Original equation
$|2| = 2$	Let $p = 2$.	$|-2| = 2$	Let $p = -2$.
$2 = 2$	True	$2 = 2$	True

The solutions are 2 and -2 or the solution set is $\{2, -2\}$. □

PRACTICE

1   Solve: $|q| = 7$.

If the expression inside the absolute value bars is more complicated than a single variable, we can still apply the absolute value property.

▶ Helpful Hint

For the equation $|X| = a$ in the box above, X can be a single variable or a variable expression.

EXAMPLE 2   Solve: $|5w + 3| = 7$.

Solution   Here the expression inside the absolute value bars is $5w + 3$. If we think of the expression $5w + 3$ as X in the absolute value property, we see that $|X| = 7$ is equivalent to

$$X = 7 \quad \text{or} \quad X = -7$$

Then substitute $5w + 3$ for X, and we have

$$5w + 3 = 7 \quad \text{or} \quad 5w + 3 = -7$$

Solve these two equations for w.

$$
\begin{aligned}
5w + 3 &= 7 &\text{or}& & 5w + 3 &= -7 \\
5w &= 4 &\text{or}& & 5w &= -10 \\
w &= \frac{4}{5} &\text{or}& & w &= -2
\end{aligned}
$$

Check: To check, let $w = -2$ and then $w = \frac{4}{5}$ in the original equation.

Let $w = -2$

$$
\begin{aligned}
|5(-2) + 3| &= 7 \\
|-10 + 3| &= 7 \\
|-7| &= 7 \\
7 &= 7 \quad \text{True}
\end{aligned}
$$

Let $w = \frac{4}{5}$

$$
\begin{aligned}
\left|5\left(\frac{4}{5}\right) + 3\right| &= 7 \\
|4 + 3| &= 7 \\
|7| &= 7 \\
7 &= 7 \quad \text{True}
\end{aligned}
$$

Both solutions check, and the solutions are -2 and $\frac{4}{5}$ or the solution set is $\left\{-2, \frac{4}{5}\right\}$.   □

PRACTICE
2   Solve: $|2x - 3| = 5$.

EXAMPLE 3   Solve: $\left|\dfrac{x}{2} - 1\right| = 11$.

Solution $\left|\dfrac{x}{2} - 1\right| = 11$ is equivalent to

$$
\frac{x}{2} - 1 = 11 \quad \text{or} \quad \frac{x}{2} - 1 = -11
$$

$$
2\left(\frac{x}{2} - 1\right) = 2(11) \quad \text{or} \quad 2\left(\frac{x}{2} - 1\right) = 2(-11) \quad \text{Clear fractions.}
$$

$$
\begin{aligned}
x - 2 &= 22 &\text{or}& & x - 2 &= -22 &\text{Apply the distributive property.} \\
x &= 24 &\text{or}& & x &= -20
\end{aligned}
$$

The solutions are 24 and -20.   □

PRACTICE
3   Solve: $\left|\dfrac{x}{5} + 1\right| = 15$.

To apply the absolute value rule, first make sure that the absolute value expression is isolated.

> ▶ **Helpful Hint**
>
> If the equation has a single absolute value expression containing variables, isolate the absolute value expression first.

EXAMPLE 4   Solve: $|2x| + 5 = 7$.

Solution   We want the absolute value expression alone on one side of the equation, so begin by subtracting 5 from both sides. Then apply the absolute value property.

$$|2x| + 5 = 7$$
$$|2x| = 2 \qquad \text{Subtract 5 from both sides.}$$
$$2x = 2 \quad \text{or} \quad 2x = -2$$
$$x = 1 \quad \text{or} \quad x = -1$$

The solutions are -1 and 1. ☐

PRACTICE
4   Solve: $|3x| + 8 = 14$.

EXAMPLE 5   Solve: $|y| = 0$.

Solution   We are looking for all numbers whose distance from 0 is zero units. The only number is 0. The solution is 0. ☐

PRACTICE
5   Solve: $|z| = 0$.

The next two examples illustrate a special case for absolute value equations. This special case occurs when an isolated absolute value is equal to a negative number.

EXAMPLE 6   Solve: $2|x| + 25 = 23$.

Solution   First, isolate the absolute value.

$$2|x| + 25 = 23$$
$$2|x| = -2 \qquad \text{Subtract 25 from both sides.}$$
$$|x| = -1 \qquad \text{Divide both sides by 2.}$$

The absolute value of a number is never negative, so this equation has no solution. The solution set is $\{\ \}$ or $\varnothing$. ☐

PRACTICE
6   Solve: $3|z| + 9 = 7$.

EXAMPLE 7   Solve: $\left|\dfrac{3x-1}{2}\right| = -2$.

Solution   Again, the absolute value of any expression is never negative, so no solution exists. The solution set is $\{\ \}$ or $\varnothing$. ☐

PRACTICE
7   Solve: $\left|\dfrac{5x+3}{4}\right| = -8$.

Given two absolute value expressions, we might ask, when are the absolute values of two expressions equal? To see the answer, notice that

$$|2| = |2|, \quad |-2| = |-2|, \quad |-2| = |2|, \quad \text{and} \quad |2| = |-2|$$

$$\underbrace{\quad\quad}_{\text{same}} \quad \underbrace{\quad\quad}_{\text{same}} \quad \underbrace{\quad\quad}_{\text{opposites}} \quad \underbrace{\quad\quad}_{\text{opposites}}$$

Two absolute value expressions are equal when the expressions inside the absolute value bars are equal to or are opposites of each other.

EXAMPLE 8   Solve: $|3x + 2| = |5x - 8|$.

Solution   This equation is true if the expressions inside the absolute value bars are equal to or are opposites of each other.

$$3x + 2 = 5x - 8 \quad \text{or} \quad 3x + 2 = -(5x - 8)$$

Next, solve each equation.

$$
\begin{aligned}
3x + 2 &= 5x - 8 \quad &\text{or} \quad 3x + 2 &= -5x + 8 \\
-2x + 2 &= -8 \quad &\text{or} \quad 8x + 2 &= 8 \\
-2x &= -10 \quad &\text{or} \quad 8x &= 6 \\
x &= 5 \quad &\text{or} \quad x &= \frac{3}{4}
\end{aligned}
$$

The solutions are $\frac{3}{4}$ and 5. □

PRACTICE
8   Solve: $|2x + 4| = |3x - 1|$.

EXAMPLE 9   Solve: $|x - 3| = |5 - x|$.

Solution

$$
\begin{aligned}
x - 3 &= 5 - x \quad &\text{or} \quad x - 3 &= -(5 - x) \\
2x - 3 &= 5 \quad &\text{or} \quad x - 3 &= -5 + x \\
2x &= 8 \quad &\text{or} \quad x - 3 - x &= -5 + x - x \\
x &= 4 \quad &\text{or} \quad -3 &= -5 \quad \text{False}
\end{aligned}
$$

Recall from Section 2.1 that when an equation simplifies to a false statement, the equation has no solution. Thus, the only solution for the original absolute value equation is 4. □

PRACTICE
9   Solve: $|x - 2| = |8 - x|$.

Concept Check ☑

True or false? Absolute value equations always have two solutions. Explain your answer.

The following box summarizes the methods shown for solving absolute value equations.

Absolute Value Equations

$|X| = a$
$\begin{cases} \text{If } a \text{ is positive, then solve } X = a \text{ or } X = -a. \\ \text{If } a \text{ is } 0, \text{ solve } X = 0. \\ \text{If } a \text{ is negative, the equation } |X| = a \text{ has no solution.} \end{cases}$

$|X| = |Y|$ Solve $X = Y$ or $X = -Y$.

Answer to Concept Check:
false; answers may vary

VOCABULARY & READINESS CHECK

Match each absolute value equation with an equivalent statement.

1. $|x - 2| = 5$

2. $|x - 2| = 0$

3. $|x - 2| = |x + 3|$

4. $|x + 3| = 5$

5. $|x + 3| = -5$

A. $x - 2 = 0$

B. $x - 2 = x + 3 \text{ or } x - 2 = -(x + 3)$

C. $x - 2 = 5 \text{ or } x - 2 = -5$

D. $\varnothing$

E. $x + 3 = 5 \text{ or } x + 3 = -5$

2.6 | EXERCISE SET

Solve each absolute value equation. See Examples 1 through 7.

1. $|x| = 7$

2. $|y| = 15$

3. $|3x| = 12.6$

4. $|6n| = 12.6$

5. $|2x - 5| = 9$

6. $|6 + 2n| = 4$

7. $\left|\dfrac{x}{2} - 3\right| = 1$

8. $\left|\dfrac{n}{3} + 2\right| = 4$

9. $|z| + 4 = 9$

10. $|x| + 1 = 3$

11. $|3x| + 5 = 14$

12. $|2x| - 6 = 4$

13. $|2x| = 0$

14. $|7z| = 0$

15. $|4n + 1| + 10 = 4$

16. $|3z - 2| + 8 = 1$

17. $|5x - 1| = 0$

18. $|3y + 2| = 0$

19. Write an absolute value equation representing all numbers x whose distance from 0 is 5 units.

20. Write an absolute value equation representing all numbers x whose distance from 0 is 2 units.

Solve. See Examples 8 and 9.

21. $|5x - 7| = |3x + 11|$

22. $|9y + 1| = |6y + 4|$

23. $|z + 8| = |z - 3|$

24. $|2x - 5| = |2x + 5|$

25. Describe how solving an absolute value equation such as $|2x - 1| = 3$ is similar to solving an absolute value equation such as $|2x - 1| = |x - 5|$.

26. Describe how solving an absolute value equation such as $|2x - 1| = 3$ is different from solving an absolute value equation such as $|2x - 1| = |x - 5|$.

MIXED PRACTICE

Solve each absolute value equation. See Examples 1 through 9.

27. $|x| = 4$

28. $|x| = 1$

29. $|y| = 0$

30. $|y| = 8$

31. $|z| = -2$

32. $|y| = -9$

33. $|7 - 3x| = 7$

34. $|4m + 5| = 5$

35. $|6x| - 1 = 11$

36. $|7z| + 1 = 22$

37. $|4p| = -8$

38. $|5m| = -10$

39. $|x - 3| + 3 = 7$

40. $|x + 4| - 4 = 1$

41. $\left|\dfrac{z}{4} + 5\right| = -7$

42. $\left|\dfrac{c}{5} - 1\right| = -2$

43. $|9v - 3| = -8$

44. $|1 - 3b| = -7$

45. $|8n + 1| = 0$

46. $|5x - 2| = 0$

47. $|1 + 6c| - 7 = -3$

48. $|2 + 3m| - 9 = -7$

49. $|5x + 1| = 11$

50. $|8 - 6c| = 1$

51. $|4x - 2| = |-10|$

52. $|3x + 5| = |-4|$

53. $|5x + 1| = |4x - 7|$

54. $|3 + 6n| = |4n + 11|$

55. $|6 + 2x| = -|7|$

56. $|4 - 5y| = -|-3|$

57. $|2x - 6| = |10 - 2x|$

58. $|4n + 5| = |4n + 3|$

59. $\left|\dfrac{2x - 5}{3}\right| = 7$

60. $\left|\dfrac{1 + 3n}{4}\right| = 4$

61. $2 + |5n| = 17$

62. $8 + |4m| = 24$

63. $\left|\dfrac{2x - 1}{3}\right| = |-5|$

64. $\left|\dfrac{5x + 2}{2}\right| = |-6|$

65. $|2y - 3| = |9 - 4y|$

66. $|5z - 1| = |7 - z|$

67. $\left|\dfrac{3n + 2}{8}\right| = |-1|$

68. $\left|\dfrac{2r - 6}{5}\right| = |-2|$

69. $|x + 4| = |7 - x|$

70. $|8 - y| = |y + 2|$

71. $\left|\dfrac{8c - 7}{3}\right| = -|-5|$

72. $\left|\dfrac{5d + 1}{6}\right| = -|-9|$

73. Explain why some absolute value equations have two solutions.

74. Explain why some absolute value equations have one solution.

REVIEW AND PREVIEW

The circle graph shows the U.S. Cheese consumption for 2005. Use this graph to answer Exercises 75–77. See Section 2.2. (Source: National Agriculture Statistics Service, USDA)

U.S. Cheese Consumption

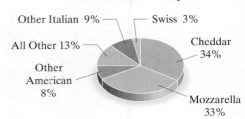

Other Italian 9% Swiss 3%
All Other 13% Cheddar 34%
Other American 8% Mozzarella 33%

75. What percent of cheese consumption came from chedder cheese?

76. A circle contains 360°. Find the number of degrees in the 3% sector for swiss cheese.

77. If a family consumed 120 pounds of cheese in 2005, find the amount of mozzarella we might expect they consumed.

List five integer solutions of each inequality. See Sections 1.2 through 1.4.

78. $|x| \leq 3$

79. $|x| \geq -2$

80. $|y| > -10$

81. $|y| < 0$

CONCEPT EXTENSIONS

82. Write an absolute value equation representing all numbers x whose distance from 1 is 5 units.

83. Write an absolute value equation representing all numbers x whose distance from 7 is 2 units.

Write each as an equivalent absolute value.

84. $x = 6$ or $x = -6$

85. $2x - 1 = 4$ or $2x - 1 = -4$

86. $x - 2 = 3x - 4$ or $x - 2 = -(3x - 4)$

87. For what value(s) of c will an absolute value equation of the form $|ax + b| = c$ have

  a. one solution?
  b. no solution?
  c. two solutions?

2.7 ABSOLUTE VALUE INEQUALITIES

OBJECTIVE 1 ▶ Solving absolute value inequalities of the form $|x| < a$. The solution set of an absolute value inequality such as $|x| < 2$ contains all numbers whose distance from 0 is less than 2 units, as shown below.

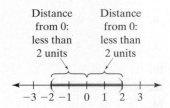

The solution set is $\{x | -2 < x < 2\}$, or $(-2, 2)$ in interval notation.

EXAMPLE 1   Solve: $|x| \leq 3$.

Solution   The solution set of this inequality contains all numbers whose distance from 0 is less than or equal to 3. Thus 3, -3, and all numbers between 3 and -3 are in the solution set.

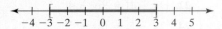

The solution set is $[-3, 3]$.

1   Solve: $|x| < 2$ and graph the solution set.

In general, we have the following.

> **Solving Absolute Value Inequalities of the Form $|X| < a$**
> If a is a positive number, then $|X| < a$ is equivalent to $-a < X < a$.

This property also holds true for the inequality symbol $\leq$.

EXAMPLE 2   Solve for m: $|m - 6| < 2$.

Solution   Replace X with $m - 6$ and a with 2 in the preceding property, and we see that

$$|m - 6| < 2 \quad \text{is equivalent to} \quad -2 < m - 6 < 2$$

Solve this compound inequality for m by adding 6 to all three parts.

$$\begin{aligned} -2 &< m - 6 < 2 \\ -2 + 6 &< m - 6 + 6 < 2 + 6 \quad \text{Add 6 to all three parts.} \\ 4 &< m < 8 \quad\quad\quad\quad\quad \text{Simplify.} \end{aligned}$$

The solution set is $(4, 8)$, and its graph is shown.

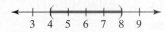

2   Solve for b: $|b + 1| < 3$. Graph the solution set.

> ▶ **Helpful Hint**
> Before using an absolute value inequality property, isolate the absolute value expression on one side of the inequality.

EXAMPLE 3   Solve for x: $|5x + 1| + 1 \le 10$.

Solution   First, isolate the absolute value expression by subtracting 1 from both sides.

$$|5x + 1| + 1 \le 10$$

$$|5x + 1| \le 10 - 1 \quad \text{Subtract 1 from both sides.}$$

$$|5x + 1| \le 9 \quad \text{Simplify.}$$

Since 9 is positive, we apply the absolute value property for $|X| \le a$.

$$-9 \le 5x + 1 \le 9$$

$$-9 - 1 \le 5x + 1 - 1 \le 9 - 1 \quad \text{Subtract 1 from all three parts.}$$

$$-10 \le 5x \le 8 \quad \text{Simplify.}$$

$$-2 \le x \le \frac{8}{5} \quad \text{Divide all three parts by 5.}$$

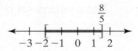

The solution set is $\left[-2, \dfrac{8}{5}\right]$, and the graph is shown above.

PRACTICE
3   Solve for x: $|3x - 2| + 5 \le 9$. Graph the solution set.

EXAMPLE 4   Solve for x: $\left|2x - \dfrac{1}{10}\right| < -13$.

Solution   The absolute value of a number is always nonnegative and can never be less than -13. Thus this absolute value inequality has no solution. The solution set is $\{ \ \}$ or $\varnothing$.

PRACTICE
4   Solve for x: $\left|3x + \dfrac{5}{8}\right| < -4$.

OBJECTIVE 2 ▶ **Solving absolute value inequalities of the form $|x| > a$.** Let us now solve an absolute value inequality of the form $|X| > a$, such as $|x| \ge 3$. The solution set contains all numbers whose distance from 0 is 3 or more units. Thus the graph of the solution set contains 3 and all points to the right of 3 on the number line or -3 and all points to the left of -3 on the number line.

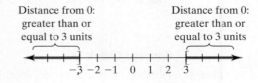

This solution set is written as $\{x \mid x \le -3 \text{ or } x \ge 3\}$. In interval notation, the solution is $(-\infty, -3] \cup [3, \infty)$, since "or" means "union." In general, we have the following.

> **Solving Absolute Value Inequalities of the Form $|X| > a$**
> If a is a positive number, then $|X| > a$ is equivalent to $X < -a$ or $X > a$.

This property also holds true for the inequality symbol $\ge$.

EXAMPLE 5   Solve for y: $|y - 3| > 7$.

Solution   Since 7 is positive, we apply the property for $|X| > a$.

$$|y - 3| > 7 \text{ is equivalent to } y - 3 < -7 \text{ or } y - 3 > 7$$

Next, solve the compound inequality.

$y - 3 < -7$	or	$y - 3 > 7$
$y - 3 + 3 < -7 + 3$	or	$y - 3 + 3 > 7 + 3$ Add 3 to both sides.
$y < -4$	or	$y > 10$ Simplify.

The solution set is $(-\infty, -4) \cup (10, \infty)$, and its graph is shown.

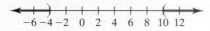

PRACTICE
5   Solve for y: $|y + 4| \ge 6$.

Examples 6 and 8 illustrate special cases of absolute value inequalities. These special cases occur when an isolated absolute value expression is less than, less than or equal to, greater than, or greater than or equal to a negative number or 0.

EXAMPLE 6   Solve: $|2x + 9| + 5 > 3$.

Solution   First isolate the absolute value expression by subtracting 5 from both sides.

$$|2x + 9| + 5 > 3$$
$$|2x + 9| + 5 - 5 > 3 - 5 \quad \text{Subtract 5 from both sides.}$$
$$|2x + 9| > -2 \quad \text{Simplify.}$$

The absolute value of any number is always nonnegative and thus is always greater than -2. This inequality and the original inequality are true for all values of x. The solution set is $\{x \mid x \text{ is a real number}\}$ or $(-\infty, \infty)$ and its graph is shown.

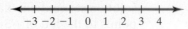

PRACTICE
6   Solve: $|4x + 3| + 5 > 3$. Graph the solution set.

Answer to Concept Check:
$(-\infty, \infty)$ since the absolute value is always nonnegative

Concept Check ☑
Without taking any solution steps, how do you know that the absolute value inequality $|3x - 2| > -9$ has a solution? What is its solution?

EXAMPLE 7   Solve: $\left|\dfrac{x}{3} - 1\right| - 7 \geq -5$.

Solution   First, isolate the absolute value expression by adding 7 to both sides.

$$\left|\frac{x}{3} - 1\right| - 7 \geq -5$$

$$\left|\frac{x}{3} - 1\right| - 7 + 7 \geq -5 - 7 \quad \text{Add 7 to both sides.}$$

$$\left|\frac{x}{3} - 1\right| \geq 2 \qquad\qquad \text{Simplify.}$$

Next, write the absolute value inequality as an equivalent compound inequality and solve.

$$\frac{x}{3} - 1 \leq -2 \qquad \text{or} \qquad \frac{x}{3} - 1 \geq 2$$

$$3\left(\frac{x}{3} - 1\right) \leq 3(-2) \quad \text{or} \quad 3\left(\frac{x}{3} - 1\right) \geq 3(2) \quad \text{Clear the inequalities of fractions.}$$

$$x - 3 \leq -6 \qquad \text{or} \qquad x - 3 \geq 6 \qquad \text{Apply the distributive property.}$$

$$x \leq -3 \qquad \text{or} \qquad x \geq 9 \qquad \text{Add 3 to both sides.}$$

The solution set is $(-\infty, -3] \cup [9, \infty)$, and its graph is shown.

PRACTICE
7   Solve: $\left|\dfrac{x}{2} - 3\right| - 5 > -2$. Graph the solution set.

EXAMPLE 8   Solve for x: $\left|\dfrac{2(x + 1)}{3}\right| \leq 0$.

Solution   Recall that "$\leq$" means "less than or equal to." The absolute value of any expression will never be less than 0, but it may be equal to 0. Thus, to solve $\left|\dfrac{2(x + 1)}{3}\right| \leq 0$ we solve $\left|\dfrac{2(x + 1)}{3}\right| = 0$

$$\frac{2(x + 1)}{3} = 0$$

$$3\left[\frac{2(x + 1)}{3}\right] = 3(0) \quad \text{Clear the equation of fractions.}$$

$$2x + 2 = 0 \qquad \text{Apply the distributive property.}$$

$$2x = -2 \qquad \text{Subtract 2 from both sides.}$$

$$x = -1 \qquad \text{Divide both sides by 2.}$$

The solution set is $\{-1\}$.

PRACTICE
8   Solve for x: $\left|\dfrac{3(x - 2)}{5}\right| \leq 0$.

The following box summarizes the types of absolute value equations and inequalities.

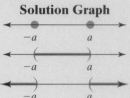

Solving Absolute Value Equations and Inequalities with $a > 0$

Algebraic Solution	Solution Graph
$|X| = a$ is equivalent to $X = a$ or $X = -a$.	
$|X| < a$ is equivalent to $-a < X < a$.	
$|X| > a$ is equivalent to $X < -a$ or $X > a$.	

VOCABULARY & READINESS CHECK

Match each absolute value statement with an equivalent statement.

1. $|2x + 1| = 3$
2. $|2x + 1| \leq 3$
3. $|2x + 1| < 3$
4. $|2x + 1| \geq 3$
5. $|2x + 1| > 3$

A. $2x + 1 > 3$ or $2x + 1 < -3$
B. $2x + 1 \geq 3$ or $2x + 1 \leq -3$
C. $-3 < 2x + 1 < 3$
D. $2x + 1 = 3$ or $2x + 1 = -3$
E. $-3 \leq 2x + 1 \leq 3$

2.7 EXERCISE SET

MyMathLab® PRACTICE WATCH DOWNLOAD READ REVIEW

Solve each inequality. Then graph the solution set and write it in interval notation. See Examples 1 through 4.

1. $|x| \leq 4$
2. $|x| < 6$
3. $|x - 3| < 2$
4. $|y - 7| \leq 5$
5. $|x + 3| < 2$
6. $|x + 4| < 6$
7. $|2x + 7| \leq 13$
8. $|5x - 3| \leq 18$
9. $|x| + 7 \leq 12$
10. $|x| + 6 \leq 7$
11. $|3x - 1| < -5$
12. $|8x - 3| < -2$
13. $|x - 6| - 7 \leq -1$
14. $|z + 2| - 7 < -3$

Solve each inequality. Graph the solution set and write it in interval notation. See Examples 5 through 7.

15. $|x| > 3$
16. $|y| \geq 4$
17. $|x + 10| \geq 14$
18. $|x - 9| \geq 2$
19. $|x| + 2 > 6$
20. $|x| - 1 > 3$
21. $|5x| > -4$
22. $|4x - 11| > -1$
23. $|6x - 8| + 3 > 7$
24. $|10 + 3x| + 1 > 2$

Solve each inequality. Graph the solution set and write it in interval notation. See Example 8.

25. $|x| \leq 0$
26. $|x| \geq 0$
27. $|8x + 3| > 0$
28. $|5x - 6| < 0$

MIXED PRACTICE

Solve each inequality. Graph the solution set and write it in interval notation. See Examples 1 through 8.

29. $|x| \leq 2$
30. $|z| < 8$
31. $|y| > 1$
32. $|x| \geq 10$
33. $|x - 3| < 8$
34. $|-3 + x| \leq 10$
35. $|0.6x - 3| > 0.6$
36. $|1 + 0.3x| \geq 0.1$
37. $5 + |x| \leq 2$
38. $8 + |x| < 1$
39. $|x| > -4$
40. $|x| \leq -7$
41. $|2x - 7| \leq 11$
42. $|5x + 2| < 8$
43. $|x + 5| + 2 \geq 8$
44. $|-1 + x| - 6 > 2$
45. $|x| > 0$
46. $|x| < 0$
47. $9 + |x| > 7$
48. $5 + |x| \geq 4$
49. $6 + |4x - 1| \leq 9$
50. $-3 + |5x - 2| \leq 4$
51. $\left|\dfrac{2}{3}x + 1\right| > 1$
52. $\left|\dfrac{3}{4}x - 1\right| \geq 2$
53. $|5x + 3| < -6$
54. $|4 + 9x| \geq -6$
55. $\left|\dfrac{8x - 3}{4}\right| \leq 0$
56. $\left|\dfrac{5x + 6}{2}\right| \leq 0$
57. $|1 + 3x| + 4 < 5$
58. $|7x - 3| - 1 \leq 10$
59. $\left|\dfrac{x + 6}{3}\right| > 2$
60. $\left|\dfrac{7 + x}{2}\right| \geq 4$
61. $-15 + |2x - 7| \leq -6$

62. $-9 + |3 + 4x| < -4$

63. $\left|2x + \dfrac{3}{4}\right| - 7 \le -2$

64. $\left|\dfrac{3}{5} + 4x\right| - 6 < -1$

MIXED PRACTICE

Solve each equation or inequality for x. (Sections 2.6, 2.7)

65. $|2x - 3| < 7$

66. $|2x - 3| > 7$

67. $|2x - 3| = 7$

68. $|5 - 6x| = 29$

69. $|x - 5| \ge 12$

70. $|x + 4| \ge 20$

71. $|9 + 4x| = 0$

72. $|9 + 4x| \ge 0$

73. $|2x + 1| + 4 < 7$

74. $8 + |5x - 3| \ge 11$

75. $|3x - 5| + 4 = 5$

76. $|5x - 3| + 2 = 4$

77. $|x + 11| = -1$

78. $|4x - 4| = -3$

79. $\left|\dfrac{2x - 1}{3}\right| = 6$

80. $\left|\dfrac{6 - x}{4}\right| = 5$

81. $\left|\dfrac{3x - 5}{6}\right| > 5$

82. $\left|\dfrac{4x - 7}{5}\right| < 2$

REVIEW AND PREVIEW

Recall the formula:

$$\text{Probability of an event} = \frac{\text{number of ways that the event can occur}}{\text{number of possible outcomes}}$$

Find the probability of rolling each number on a single toss of a die. (Recall that a die is a cube with each of its six sides containing 1, 2, 3, 4, 5, and 6 black dots, respectively.) See Section 2.3.

83. $P(\text{rolling a 2})$ **84.** $P(\text{rolling a 5})$

85. $P(\text{rolling a 7})$ **86.** $P(\text{rolling a 0})$

87. $P(\text{rolling a 1 or 3})$

88. $P(\text{rolling a 1, 2, 3, 4, 5, or 6})$

Consider the equation $3x - 4y = 12$. For each value of x or y given, find the corresponding value of the other variable that makes the statement true. See Section 2.3.

89. If $x = 2$, find y **90.** If $y = -1$, find x

91. If $y = -3$, find x **92.** If $x = 4$, find y

CONCEPT EXTENSIONS

93. Write an absolute value inequality representing all numbers x whose distance from 0 is less than 7 units.

94. Write an absolute value inequality representing all numbers x whose distance from 0 is greater than 4 units.

95. Write $-5 \le x \le 5$ as an equivalent inequality containing an absolute value.

96. Write $x > 1$ or $x < -1$ as an equivalent inequality containing an absolute value.

97. Describe how solving $|x - 3| = 5$ is different from solving $|x - 3| < 5$.

98. Describe how solving $|x + 4| = 0$ is similar to solving $|x + 4| \le 0$.

The expression $|x_T - x|$ is defined to be the absolute error in x, where x_T is the true value of a quantity and x is the measured value or value as stored in a computer.

99. If the true value of a quantity is 3.5 and the absolute error must be less than 0.05, find the acceptable measured values.

100. If the true value of a quantity is 0.2 and the approximate value stored in a computer is $\dfrac{51}{256}$, find the absolute error.

THE BIGGER PICTURE   SOLVING EQUATIONS AND INEQUALITIES

We now continue the outline from Sections 2.4 and 2.5. Although suggestions will be given, this outline should be in your own words and you should include at least "how to recognize" and "how to begin to solve" under each letter heading.

    For example:

Solving Equations and Inequalities

I. Equations

    A. Linear equations (Section 2.1)

    B. Absolute Value Equations: Equation contains the absolute value of a variable expression. (Section 2.6)

$$|3x - 1| - 12 = -4 \quad \text{Absolute value equation.}$$

$$|3x - 1| = 8 \quad \text{Isolate absolute value.}$$

$$3x - 1 = 8 \quad \text{or} \quad 3x - 1 = -8$$

$$3x = 9 \quad \text{or} \quad 3x = -7$$

$$x = 3 \quad \text{or} \quad x = -\frac{7}{3}$$

$|x - 5| = |x + 1|$ Absolute value equation.

$x - 5 = x + 1$ or $x - 5 = -(x + 1)$

$\underbrace{-5 = 1}_{\text{No solution}}$ or $x - 5 = -x - 1$

or $2x = 4$

$x = 2$

II. **Inequalities**

   A. **Linear Inequalities** (Section 2.4)

   B. **Compound Inequalities** (Section 2.5)

   C. **Absolute Value Inequalities:** Inequality with absolute value bars about variable expression. (Section 2.7)

$\|x - 5\| - 8 < -2$	$\|2x + 1\| \geq 17$
$\|x - 5\| < 6$	$2x + 1 \geq 17$ or $2x + 1 \leq -17$
$-6 < x - 5 < 6$	$2x \geq 16$ or $2x \leq -18$
$-1 < x < 11$	$x \geq 8$ or $x \leq -9$
$(-1, 11)$	$(-\infty, -9] \cup [8, \infty)$

Solve. If an inequality, write your solutions in interval notation.

1. $9x - 14 = 11x + 2$
2. $|x - 4| = 17$
3. $x - 1 \leq 5$ or $3x - 2 \leq 10$
4. $-x < 7$ and $4x \leq 20$
5. $|x - 2| = |x + 15|$
6. $9y - 6y + 1 = 4y + 10 - y + 3$
7. $1.5x - 3 = 1.2x - 18$
8. $\dfrac{7x + 1}{8} - 3 = x + \dfrac{2x + 1}{4}$
9. $|5x + 2| - 10 \leq -3$
10. $|x + 11| > 2$
11. $|9x + 2| - 1 = 24$
12. $\left|\dfrac{3x - 1}{2}\right| = |2x + 5|$

CHAPTER 2 GROUP ACTIVITY

Analyzing Municipal Budgets

Nearly all cities, towns, and villages operate with an annual budget. Budget items might include expenses for fire and police protection as well as for street maintenance and parks. No matter how big or small the budget, city officials need to know if municipal spending is over or under budget. In this project, you will have the opportunity to analyze a municipal budget and make budgetary recommendations. This project may be completed by working in groups or individually.

   Suppose that each year your town creates a municipal budget. The next year's annual municipal budget is submitted for approval by the town's citizens at the annual town meeting. This year's budget was printed in the town newspaper earlier in the year.

   You have joined a group of citizens who are concerned about your town's budgeting and spending processes. Your group plans to analyze this year's budget along with what was actually spent by the town this year. You hope to present your findings at the annual town meeting and make some budgetary recommendations for next year's budget. The municipal budget contains many different areas of spending. To help focus your group's analysis, you have decided to research spending habits only for categories in which the actual expenses differ from the budgeted amount by more than 12% of the budgeted amount.

1. For each category in the budget, write a specific absolute value inequality that describes the condition that must be met

before your group will research spending habits for that category. In each case, let the variable x represent the actual expense for a budget category.

2. For each category in the budget, write an equivalent compound inequality for the condition described in Question 1. Again, let the variable x represent the actual expense for a budget category.

3. On the next page is a listing of the actual expenditures made this year for each budget category. Use the inequalities from either Question 1 or Question 2 to complete the Budget Worksheet given at the end of this project. (The first category has been filled in.) From the Budget Worksheet, decide which categories must be researched.

4. Can you think of possible reasons why spending in the categories that must be researched were over or under budget?

5. Based on this year's municipal budget and actual expenses, what recommendations would you make for next year's budget? Explain your reasoning.

6. (Optional) Research the annual budget used by your own town or your college or university. Conduct a similar analysis of the budget with respect to actual expenses. What can you conclude?

	Department/Program	Actual Expenditure
I.	**Board of Health**	
	Immunization Programs	$14,800
	Inspections	$41,900
II.	**Fire Department**	
	Equipment	$375,000
	Salaries	$268,500
III.	**Libraries**	
	Book/Periodical Purchases	$107,300
	Equipment	$29,000
	Salaries	$118,400
IV.	**Parks and Recreation**	
	Maintenance	$82,500
	Playground Equipment	$45,000
	Salaries	$118,000
	Summer Programs	$96,200
V.	**Police Department**	
	Equipment	$328,000
	Salaries	$405,000
VI.	**Public Works**	
	Recycling	$48,100
	Sewage	$92,500
	Snow Removal & Road Salt	$268,300
	Street Maintenance	$284,000
	Water Treatment	$94,100
	TOTAL	$2,816,600

THE TOWN CRIER
Annual Budget Set at Town Meeting
ANYTOWN, USA (MG)—This year's annual budget is as follows:

	Amount Budgeted
BOARD OF HEALTH	
Immunization Programs	$15,000
Inspections	$50,000
FIRE DEPARTMENT	
Equipment	$450,000
Salaries	$275,000
LIBRARIES	
Book/Periodical Purchases	$90,000
Equipment	$30,000
Salaries	$120,000
PARKS AND RECREATION	
Maintenance	$70,000
Playground Equipment	$50,000
Salaries	$140,000
Summer Programs	$80,000
POLICE DEPARTMENT	
Equipment	$300,000
Salaries	$400,000
PUBLIC WORKS	
Recycling	$50,000
Sewage	$100,000
Snow Removal & Road Salt	$200,000
Street Maintenance	$250,000
Water Treatment	$100,000
TOTAL	**$2,770,000**

BUDGET WORKSHEET

Budget category	Budgeted amount	Minimum allowed	Actual expense	Maximum allowed	Within budget?	Amt over/ under budget
Immunization Programs	$15,000	$13,200	$14,800	$16,800	Yes	Under $200

CHAPTER 2 VOCABULARY CHECK

Fill in each blank with one of the words or phrases listed below.

contradiction   linear inequality in one variable   compound inequality   solution
absolute value   consecutive integers   identity   union
formula   linear equation in one variable   intersection

1. The statement "$x < 5$ or $x > 7$" is called a(n) _____.

2. An equation in one variable that has no solution is called a(n) _____.

3. The _____ of two sets is the set of all elements common to both sets.

4. The _____ of two sets is the set of all elements that belong to either of the sets.

5. An equation in one variable that has every number (for which the equation is defined) as a solution
is called a(n) _____.

6. The equation $d = rt$ is also called a(n) _____.

7. A number's distance from 0 is called its _____.

8. When a variable in an equation is replaced by a number and the resulting equation is true, then that number is called a(n) _____ of the equation.

9. The integers 17, 18, 19 are examples of _____.

10. The statement $5x - 0.2 < 7$ is an example of a(n) _____.

11. The statement $5x - 0.2 = 7$ is an example of a(n) _____.

> ▶ **Helpful Hint**
>
> Are you preparing for your test? Don't forget to take the Chapter 2 Test on page 115. Then check your answers at the back of the text and use the Chapter Test Prep Video CD to see the fully worked-out solutions to any of the exercises you want to review.

CHAPTER 2 HIGHLIGHTS

DEFINITIONS AND CONCEPTS	EXAMPLES

SECTION 2.1 LINEAR EQUATIONS IN ONE VARIABLE

An **equation** is a statement that two expressions are equal.

Equations:

$$5 = 5 \qquad 7x + 2 = -14 \qquad 3(x - 1)^2 = 9x^2 - 6$$

A **linear equation in one variable** is an equation that can be written in the form $ax + b = c$, where a, b, and c are real numbers and a is not 0.

Linear equations:

$$7x + 2 = -14 \qquad x = -3$$
$$5(2y - 7) = -2(8y - 1)$$

A **solution** of an equation is a value for the variable that makes the equation a true statement.

Check to see that -1 is a solution of

$3(x - 1) = 4x - 2$.

$$3(-1 - 1) = 4(-1) - 2$$
$$3(-2) = -4 - 2$$
$$-6 = -6 \qquad \text{True}$$

Equivalent equations have the same solution.

Thus, -1 is a solution.

$x - 12 = 14$ and $x = 26$ are equivalent equations.

The **addition property of equality** guarantees that the same number may be added to (or subtracted from) both sides of an equation, and the result is an equivalent equation.

Solve for x: $-3x - 2 = 10$.

$$-3x - 2 + 2 = 10 + 2 \quad \text{Add 2 to both sides.}$$
$$-3x = 12$$
$$\frac{-3x}{-3} = \frac{12}{-3} \qquad \text{Divide both sides by } -3.$$
$$x = -4$$

The **multiplication property of equality** guarantees that both sides of an equation may be multiplied by (or divided by) the same nonzero number, and the result is an equivalent equation.

Solve for x:

$$x - \frac{x - 2}{6} = \frac{x - 7}{3} + \frac{2}{3}$$

To solve linear equations in one variable:

1. Clear the equation of fractions.

1.
$$6\left(x - \frac{x - 2}{6}\right) = 6\left(\frac{x - 7}{3} + \frac{2}{3}\right) \quad \text{Multiply both sides by 6.}$$
$$6x - (x - 2) = 2(x - 7) + 2(2)$$

2. Remove grouping symbols such as parentheses.

2. $6x - x + 2 = 2x - 14 + 4 \quad \text{Remove grouping symbols.}$

3. Simplify by combining like terms.

3. $5x + 2 = 2x - 10$

4. Write variable terms on one side and numbers on the other side using the addition property of equality.

4.
$$5x + 2 - 2 = 2x - 10 - 2 \quad \text{Subtract 2.}$$
$$5x = 2x - 12$$
$$5x - 2x = 2x - 12 - 2x \quad \text{Subtract } 2x.$$
$$3x = -12$$

DEFINITIONS AND CONCEPTS	EXAMPLES

SECTION 2.1 LINEAR EQUATIONS IN ONE VARIABLE

5. Isolate the variable using the multiplication property of equality.

6. Check the proposed solution in the original equation.

5.
$$\frac{3x}{3} = \frac{-12}{3}$$ Divide by 3.
$$x = -4$$

6. $-4 - \dfrac{-4 - 2}{6} \stackrel{?}{=} \dfrac{-4 - 7}{3} + \dfrac{2}{3}$ Replace x with -4 in the original equation.

$$-4 - \frac{-6}{6} \stackrel{?}{=} \frac{-11}{3} + \frac{2}{3}$$

$$-4 - (-1) \stackrel{?}{=} \frac{-9}{3}$$

$$-3 = -3$$ True

SECTION 2.2 AN INTRODUCTION TO PROBLEM SOLVING

Problem-Solving Strategy

1. UNDERSTAND the problem.

Colorado is shaped like a rectangle whose length is about 1.3 times its width. If the perimeter of Colorado is 2070 kilometers, find its dimensions.

1. Read and reread the problem. Guess a solution and check your guess.
Let x = width of Colorado in kilometers. Then $1.3x$ = length of Colorado in kilometers

$1.3x$

2. TRANSLATE the problem.

2. In words:

twice the length	+	twice the width	=	perimeter
↘		↓		↓

Translate: $2(1.3x)$ + $2x$ = 2070

3. SOLVE the equation.

3. $2.6x + 2x = 2070$
$$4.6x = 2070$$
$$x = 450$$

4. INTERPRET the results.

4. If $x = 450$ kilometers, then $1.3x = 1.3(450) = 585$ kilometers. *Check:* The perimeter of a rectangle whose width is 450 kilometers and length is 585 kilometers is $2(450) + 2(585) = 2070$ kilometers, the required perimeter. *State:* The dimensions of Colorado are 450 kilometers by 585 kilometers

SECTION 2.3 FORMULAS AND PROBLEM SOLVING

An equation that describes a known relationship among quantities is called a **formula.**

Formulas:

$$A = \pi r^2 \text{ (area of a circle)}$$

$$I = PRT \quad (\text{interest} = \text{principal} \cdot \text{rate} \cdot \text{time})$$

(continued)

DEFINITIONS AND CONCEPTS	EXAMPLES

SECTION 2.3 FORMULAS AND PROBLEM SOLVING (continued)

To solve a formula for a specified variable, use the steps for solving an equation. Treat the specified variable as the only variable of the equation.	Solve $A = 2HW + 2LW + 2LH$ for H

$A - 2LW = 2HW + 2LH$ Subtract $2LW$.

$A - 2LW = H(2W + 2L)$ Factor out H.

$$\dfrac{A - 2LW}{2W + 2L} = \dfrac{H(2W + 2L)}{2W + 2L}$$ Divide by $2W + 2L$.

$$\dfrac{A - 2LW}{2W + 2L} = H$$ Simplify.

SECTION 2.4 LINEAR INEQUALITIES AND PROBLEM SOLVING

A **linear inequality in one variable** is an inequality that can be written in the form $ax + b < c$, where a, b, and c are real numbers and $a \neq 0$. (The inequality symbols $\leq$, $>$, and $\geq$ also apply here.)

Linear inequalities:

$$5x - 2 \leq -7 \qquad 3y > 1 \qquad \dfrac{z}{7} < -9(z - 3)$$

The **addition property of inequality** guarantees that the same number may be added to (or subtracted from) both sides of an inequality, and the resulting inequality will have the same solution set.

$x - 9 \leq -16$

$x - 9 + 9 \leq -16 + 9$ Add 9.

$x \leq -7$

Solve.

$6x < -66$

$\dfrac{6x}{6} < \dfrac{-66}{6}$ Divide by 6. Do not reverse direction of inequality symbol.

$x < -11$

The **multiplication property of inequality** guarantees that both sides of an inequality may be multiplied by (or divided by) the same **positive** number, and the resulting inequality will have the same solution set. We may also multiply (or divide) both sides of an inequality by the same **negative** number and **reverse the direction of the inequality symbol,** and the result is an inequality with the same solution set.

Solve.

$-6x < -66$

$\dfrac{-6x}{-6} > \dfrac{-66}{-6}$ Divide by -6. Reverse direction of inequality symbol.

$x > 11$

To solve a linear inequality in one variable:

Solve for x:

$$\dfrac{3}{7}(x - 4) \geq x + 2$$

1. Clear the equation of fractions.

1. $7\left[\dfrac{3}{7}(x - 4)\right] \geq 7(x + 2)$ Multiply by 7.

$3(x - 4) \geq 7(x + 2)$

2. Remove grouping symbols such as parentheses.

2. $3x - 12 \geq 7x + 14$ Apply the distributive property.

3. Simplify by combining like terms.

4. Write variable terms on one side and numbers on the other side using the addition property of inequality.

4. $-4x - 12 \geq 14$ Subtract $7x$.

$-4x \geq 26$ Add 12.

$\dfrac{-4x}{-4} \leq \dfrac{26}{-4}$ Divide by -4. Reverse direction of inequality symbol.

5. Isolate the variable using the multiplication property of inequality.

$x \leq -\dfrac{13}{2}$

DEFINITIONS AND CONCEPTS	**EXAMPLES**

Two inequalities joined by the words **and** or **or** are called **compound inequalities.**

Compound inequalities:

$$x - 7 \le 4 \qquad \text{and} \qquad x \ge -21$$
$$2x + 7 > x - 3 \qquad \text{or} \qquad 5x + 2 > -3$$

The solution set of a compound inequality formed by the word **and** is the **intersection** $\cap$ of the solution sets of the two inequalities.

Solve for x:

$$x < 5 \text{ and } x < 3$$

$\{x \mid x < 5\}$ $(-\infty, 5)$

$\{x \mid x < 3\}$ $(-\infty, 3)$

$\{x \mid x < 3$ and $x < 5\}$ $(-\infty, 3)$

The solution set of a compound inequality formed by the word **or** is the **union**, $\cup$, of the solution sets of the two inequalities.

Solve for x:

$$x - 2 \ge -3 \qquad \text{or} \qquad 2x \le -4$$
$$x \ge -1 \qquad \text{or} \qquad x \le -2$$

$\{x \mid x \ge -1\}$ $[-1, \infty)$

$\{x \mid x \le -2\}$ $(-\infty, -2]$

$\{x \mid x \le -2$ or $x \ge -1\}$ $(-\infty, -2] \cup [-1, \infty)$

If a is a positive number, then $|x| = a$ is equivalent to $x = a$ or $x = -a$.

Solve for y:

$$|5y - 1| - 7 = 4$$
$$|5y - 1| = 11$$

$$5y - 1 = 11 \quad \text{or} \quad 5y - 1 = -11 \quad \text{Add 7.}$$
$$5y = 12 \quad \text{or} \qquad 5y = -10 \quad \text{Add 1.}$$
$$y = \frac{12}{5} \qquad \text{or} \quad y = -2 \quad \text{Divide by 5.}$$

The solutions are -2 and $\frac{12}{5}$.

If a is negative, then $|x| = a$ has no solution.

Solve for x:

$$\left| \frac{x}{2} - 7 \right| = -1$$

The solution set is $\{ \ \}$ or $\varnothing$.

If an absolute value equation is of the form $|x| = |y|$, solve $x = y$ or $x = -y$.

Solve for x:

$$|x - 7| = |2x + 1|$$

$$x - 7 = 2x + 1 \qquad \text{or} \qquad x - 7 = -(2x + 1)$$
$$x = 2x + 8 \qquad\qquad\qquad x - 7 = -2x - 1$$
$$-x = 8 \qquad\qquad\qquad\qquad x = -2x + 6$$
$$x = -8 \qquad \text{or} \qquad\qquad 3x = 6$$
$$x = 2$$

The solutions are -8 and 2.

DEFINITIONS AND CONCEPTS	EXAMPLES

SECTION 2.7   ABSOLUTE VALUE INEQUALITIES

If a is a positive number, then $|x| < a$ is equivalent to $-a < x < a$.

Solve for y:

$$|y - 5| \leq 3$$
$$-3 \leq y - 5 \leq 3$$
$$-3 + 5 \leq y - 5 + 5 \leq 3 + 5 \quad \text{Add 5.}$$
$$2 \leq y \leq 8$$

The solution set is $[2, 8]$.

If a is a positive number, then $|x| > a$ is equivalent to $x < -a$ or $x > a$.

Solve for x:

$$\left| \frac{x}{2} - 3 \right| > 7$$

$$\frac{x}{2} - 3 < -7 \quad \text{or} \quad \frac{x}{2} - 3 > 7$$
$$x - 6 < -14 \quad \text{or} \quad x - 6 > 14 \quad \text{Multiply by 2.}$$
$$x < -8 \quad \text{or} \quad x > 20 \quad \text{Add 6.}$$

The solution set is $(-\infty, -8) \cup (20, \infty)$.

 STUDY SKILLS BUILDER

Are You Prepared for a Test on Chapter 2?

Below I have listed some common trouble areas for students in Chapter 2. After studying for your test—but before taking your test—read these.

- Remember to reverse the direction of the inequality symbol when multiplying or dividing both sides of an inequality by a negative number.

$$-11x < 33$$
$$\frac{-11x}{-11} > \frac{33}{-11} \quad \text{Direction of arrow is reversed.}$$
$$x > -3$$

- Remember the differences when solving absolute value equations and inequalities.

$\|x + 1\| = 3$	$\|x + 1\| < 3$	$\|x + 1\| > 3$
$x + 1 = 3$ or $x + 1 = -3$	$-3 < x + 1 < 3$	$x + 1 < -3$ or $x + 1 > 3$
$x = 2$ or $x = -4$	$-3 - 1 < x < 3 - 1$	$x < -4$ or $x > 2$
$\{2, -4\}$	$-4 < x < 2$	$(-\infty, -4) \cup (2, \infty)$
	$(-4, 2)$	

- Remember that an equation is not solved for a specified variable unless the variable is alone on one side of an equation *and* the other side contains *no* specified variables.

$$y = 10x + 6 - y \quad \text{Equation is } not \text{ solved for } y.$$
$$2y = 10x + 6 \quad \text{Add } y \text{ to both sides.}$$
$$y = 5x + 3 \quad \text{Divide both sides by 2.}$$

Remember: This is simply a checklist of common trouble areas. For a review of Chapter 2, see the Highlights and Chapter Review at the end of this chapter.

CHAPTER 2 REVIEW

(2.1) *Solve each linear equation.*

1. $4(x - 5) = 2x - 14$

2. $x + 7 = -2(x + 8)$

3. $3(2y - 1) = -8(6 + y)$

4. $-(z + 12) = 5(2z - 1)$

5. $n - (8 + 4n) = 2(3n - 4)$

6. $4(9v + 2) = 6(1 + 6v) - 10$

7. $0.3(x - 2) = 1.2$

8. $1.5 = 0.2(c - 0.3)$

9. $-4(2 - 3x) = 2(3x - 4) + 6x$

10. $6(m - 1) + 3(2 - m) = 0$

11. $6 - 3(2g + 4) - 4g = 5(1 - 2g)$

12. $20 - 5(p + 1) + 3p = -(2p - 15)$

13. $\dfrac{x}{3} - 4 = x - 2$

14. $\dfrac{9}{4}y = \dfrac{2}{3}y$

15. $\dfrac{3n}{8} - 1 = 3 + \dfrac{n}{6}$

16. $\dfrac{z}{6} + 1 = \dfrac{z}{2} + 2$

17. $\dfrac{y}{4} - \dfrac{y}{2} = -8$

18. $\dfrac{2x}{3} - \dfrac{8}{3} = x$

19. $\dfrac{b - 2}{3} = \dfrac{b + 2}{5}$

20. $\dfrac{2t - 1}{3} = \dfrac{3t + 2}{15}$

21. $\dfrac{2(t + 1)}{3} = \dfrac{2(t - 1)}{3}$

22. $\dfrac{3a - 3}{6} = \dfrac{4a + 1}{15} + 2$

(2.2) *Solve.*

23. Twice the difference of a number and 3 is the same as 1 added to three times the number. Find the number.

24. One number is 5 more than another number. If the sum of the numbers is 285, find the numbers.

25. Find 40% of 130.

26. Find 1.5% of 8.

27. In 2000, a record number of music CDs were sold by manufacturers in the United States. By 2005, this number had decreased to 705.4 million music CDs. If this represented a decrease of 25%, find the number of music CDs sold by U.S. manufacturers in 2000. (*Source:* Recording Industry Association of America)

28. Find four consecutive integers such that twice the first subtracted from the sum of the other three integers is 16.

29. Determine whether there are two consecutive odd integers such that 5 times the first exceeds 3 times the second by 54.

30. The length of a rectangular playing field is 5 meters less than twice its width. If 230 meters of fencing goes around the field, find the dimensions of the field.

31. A car rental company charges $19.95 per day for a compact car plus 12 cents per mile for every mile over 100 miles driven per day. If Mr. Woo's bill for 2 days use is $46.86, find how many miles he drove.

32. The cost C of producing x number of scientific calculators is given by $C = 4.50x + 3000$ and the revenue R from selling them is given by $R = 16.50x$. Find the number of calculators that must be sold to break even. (Recall that to break even, revenue = cost.)

(2.3) *Solve each equation for the specified variable.*

△ 33. $V = LWH$ for W

△ 34. $C = 2\pi r$ for r

35. $5x - 4y = -12$ for y

36. $5x - 4y = -12$ for x

37. $y - y_1 = m(x - x_1)$ for m

38. $y - y_1 = m(x - x_1)$ for x

39. $E = I(R + r)$ for r

40. $S = vt + gt^2$ for g

41. $T = gr - gvt$ for g

42. $I = Prt + P$ for P

43. A principal of $3000 is invested in an account paying an annual percentage rate of 3%. Find the amount (to the nearest cent) in the account after 7 years if the amount is compounded
   a. semiannually.
   b. weekly.

44. The high temperature in Slidell, Louisiana, one day was 90° Fahrenheit. Convert this temperature to degrees Celsius.

△ 45. Angie Applegate has a photograph for which the length is 2 inches longer than the width. If she increases each dimension by 4 inches, the area is increased by 88 square inches. Find the original dimensions.

△ 46. One-square-foot floor tiles come 24 to a package. Find how many packages are needed to cover a rectangular floor 18 feet by 21 feet.

(2.4) *Solve each linear inequality. Write your answers in interval notation.*

47. $3(x - 5) > -(x + 3)$

48. $-2(x + 7) \geq 3(x + 2)$

49. $4x - (5 + 2x) < 3x - 1$

50. $3(x - 8) < 7x + 2(5 - x)$

51. $24 \geq 6x - 2(3x - 5) + 2x$

52. $\dfrac{x}{3} + \dfrac{1}{2} > \dfrac{2}{3}$

53. $x + \dfrac{3}{4} < -\dfrac{x}{2} + \dfrac{9}{4}$

54. $\dfrac{x - 5}{2} \leq \dfrac{3}{8}(2x + 6)$

Solve.

55. George Boros can pay his housekeeper $15 per week to do his laundry, or he can have the laundromat do it at a cost of 50 cents per pound for the first 10 pounds and 40 cents for each additional pound. Use an inequality to find the weight at which it is more economical to use the housekeeper than the laundromat.

56. Ceramic firing temperatures usually range from 500° to 1000° Fahrenheit. Use a compound inequality to convert this range to the Celsius scale. Round to the nearest degree.

57. In the Olympic gymnastics competition, Nana must average a score of 9.65 to win the silver medal. Seven of the eight judges have reported scores of 9.5, 9.7, 9.9, 9.7, 9.7, 9.6, and 9.5. Use an inequality to find the minimum score that Nana must receive from the last judge to win the silver medal.

58. Carol would like to pay cash for a car when she graduates from college and estimates that she can afford a car that costs between $4000 and $8000. She has saved $500 so far and plans to earn the rest of the money by working the next two summers. If Carol plans to save the same amount each summer, use a compound inequality to find the range of money she must save each summer to buy the car.

(2.5) *Solve each inequality. Write your answers in interval notation.*

59. $1 \le 4x - 7 \le 3$

60. $-2 \le 8 + 5x < -1$

61. $-3 < 4(2x - 1) < 12$

62. $-6 < x - (3 - 4x) < -3$

63. $\dfrac{1}{6} < \dfrac{4x - 3}{3} \le \dfrac{4}{5}$

64. $x \le 2$ and $x > -5$

65. $3x - 5 > 6$ or $-x < -5$

(2.6) *Solve each absolute value equation.*

66. $|x - 7| = 9$

67. $|8 - x| = 3$

68. $|2x + 9| = 9$

69. $|-3x + 4| = 7$

70. $|3x - 2| + 6 = 10$

71. $5 + |6x + 1| = 5$

72. $-5 = |4x - 3|$

73. $|5 - 6x| + 8 = 3$

74. $-8 = |x - 3| - 10$

75. $\left|\dfrac{3x - 7}{4}\right| = 2$

76. $|6x + 1| = |15 + 4x|$

(2.7) *Solve each absolute value inequality. Graph the solution set and write it in interval notation.*

77. $|5x - 1| < 9$

78. $|6 + 4x| \ge 10$

79. $|3x| - 8 > 1$

80. $9 + |5x| < 24$

81. $|6x - 5| \le -1$

82. $\left|3x + \dfrac{2}{5}\right| \ge 4$

83. $\left|\dfrac{x}{3} + 6\right| - 8 > -5$

84. $\left|\dfrac{4(x - 1)}{7}\right| + 10 < 2$

MIXED REVIEW

Solve.

85. $\dfrac{x - 2}{5} + \dfrac{x + 2}{2} = \dfrac{x + 4}{3}$

86. $\dfrac{2z - 3}{4} - \dfrac{4 - z}{2} = \dfrac{z + 1}{3}$

87. China, the United States, and France are predicted to be the top tourist destinations by 2020. In this year, the United States is predicted to have 9 million more tourists than France, and China is predicted to have 44 million more tourists than France. If the total number of tourists predicted for these three countries is 332 million, find the number predicted for each country in 2020.

△ **88.** $A = \dfrac{h}{2}(B + b)$ for B

△ **89.** $V = \dfrac{1}{3}\pi r^2 h$ for h

△ **90.** Determine which container holds more ice cream, an 8 inch × 5 inch × 3 inch box or a cylinder with radius of 3 inches and height of 6 inches.

91. Erasmos Gonzalez left Los Angeles at 11 a.m. and drove nonstop to San Diego, 130 miles away. If he arrived at 1:15 p.m., find his average speed, rounded to the nearest mile per hour.

Solve. If an inequality, write your solutions in interval notation.

92. $48 + x \ge 5(2x + 4) - 2x$

93. $\dfrac{3(x - 2)}{5} > \dfrac{-5(x - 2)}{3}$

94. $0 \le \dfrac{2(3x + 4)}{5} \le 3$

95. $x \le 2$ or $x > -5$

96. $-2x \le 6$ and $-2x + 3 < -7$

97. $|7x| - 26 = -5$

98. $\left|\dfrac{9 - 2x}{5}\right| = -3$

99. $|x - 3| = |7 + 2x|$

100. $|6x - 5| \ge -1$

101. $\left|\dfrac{4x - 3}{5}\right| < 1$

CHAPTER 2 TEST

TEST PREP [VIDEO] Remember to use the Chapter Test Prep Video CD to see the fully worked-out solutions to any of the exercises you want to review.

Solve each equation.

1. $8x + 14 = 5x + 44$
2. $9(x + 2) = 5[11 - 2(2 - x) + 3]$
3. $3(y - 4) + y = 2(6 + 2y)$
4. $7n - 6 + n = 2(4n - 3)$
5. $\dfrac{7w}{4} + 5 = \dfrac{3w}{10} + 1$
6. $\dfrac{z + 7}{9} + 1 = \dfrac{2z + 1}{6}$
7. $|6x - 5| - 3 = -2$
8. $|8 - 2t| = -6$
9. $|2x - 3| = |4x + 5|$
10. $|x - 5| = |x + 2|$

Solve each equation for the specified variable.

11. $3x - 4y = 8$ for y
12. $S = gt^2 + gvt$ for g
13. $F = \dfrac{9}{5}C + 32$ for C

Solve each inequality. Write your solutions in interval notation.

14. $3(2x - 7) - 4x > -(x + 6)$
15. $\dfrac{3x - 2}{3} - \dfrac{5x + 1}{4} \geq 0$
16. $-3 < 2(x - 3) \leq 4$
17. $|3x + 1| > 5$
18. $|x - 5| - 4 < -2$
19. $x \geq 5$ and $x \geq 4$
20. $x \geq 5$ or $x \geq 4$
21. $-1 \leq \dfrac{2x - 5}{3} < 2$
22. $6x + 1 > 5x + 4$ or $1 - x > -4$
23. Find 12% of 80.
24. In 2014, the number of people employed as network systems and data communications analysts is expected to be 357,000 in the United States. This represents a 55% increase over the number of people employed in these fields in 2004. Find the number of network systems and data communications analysts employed in 2004. (*Source:* Bureau of Labor Statistics)

△ 25. A circular dog pen has a circumference of 78.5 feet. Approximate π by 3.14 and estimate how many hunting dogs could be safely kept in the pen if each dog needs at least 60 square feet of room.

26. The company that makes Photoray sunglasses figures that the cost C to make x number of sunglasses weekly is given by $C = 3910 + 2.8x$, and the weekly revenue R is given by $R = 7.4x$. Use an inequality to find the number of sunglasses that must be made and sold to make a profit. (Revenue must exceed cost in order to make a profit.)

27. Find the amount of money in an account after 10 years if a principal of \$2500 is invested at 3.5% interest compounded quarterly. (Round to the nearest cent.)

28. The most populous city in the United States is New York, although it is only the third most populous city in the world. Tokyo is the most populous city in the world. Second place is held by Seoul, Korea. Seoul's population is 1.3 million more than New York's, and Tokyo's is 10.2 million less than twice the population of New York. If the sum of the populations of these three cities is 78.3 million, find the population of each city.

CHAPTER 2 CUMULATIVE REVIEW

List the elements in each set.

1. **a.** $\{x \mid x$ is a natural number greater than 100$\}$
   b. $\{x \mid x$ is a whole number between 1 and 6$\}$

2. **a.** $\{x \mid x$ is an integer between -3 and 5$\}$
   b. $\{x \mid x$ is a whole number between 3 and 5$\}$

3. Find each value.
   a. $|3|$ **b.** $\left|-\dfrac{1}{7}\right|$
   c. $-|2.7|$ **d.** $-|-8|$
   e. $|0|$

4. Find the opposite of each number.
   a. $\dfrac{2}{3}$ **b.** -9 **c.** 1.5

5. Add.
   a. $-3 + (-11)$ **b.** $3 + (-7)$
   c. $-10 + 15$ **d.** $-8.3 + (-1.9)$
   e. $-\dfrac{2}{3} + \dfrac{3}{7}$

6. Subtract.
   a. $-2 - (-10)$ **b.** $1.7 - 8.9$
   c. $-\dfrac{1}{2} - \dfrac{1}{4}$

7. Find the square roots.

   a. $\sqrt{9}$ **b.** $\sqrt{25}$

   c. $\sqrt{\dfrac{1}{4}}$ **d.** $-\sqrt{36}$

   e. $\sqrt{-36}$

8. Multiply or divide.

   a. $-3(-2)$ **b.** $-\dfrac{3}{4}\left(-\dfrac{4}{7}\right)$

   c. $\dfrac{0}{-2}$ **d.** $\dfrac{-20}{-2}$

9. Evaluate each algebraic expression when $x = 4$ and $y = -3$.

   a. $3x - 7y$

   b. $-2y^2$

   c. $\dfrac{\sqrt{x}}{y} - \dfrac{y}{x}$

10. Find the roots.

   a. $\sqrt[4]{1}$

   b. $\sqrt[3]{8}$

   c. $\sqrt[4]{81}$

11. Write each sentence using mathematical symbols.

   a. The sum of x and 5 is 20.

   b. Two times the sum of 3 and y amounts to 4.

   c. Subtract 8 from x, and the difference is the same as the product of 2 and x.

   d. The quotient of z and 9 amounts to 9 plus z.

12. Insert $<$, $>$, or $=$ between each pair of numbers to form a true statement.

   a. $-3 \quad -5$

   b. $\dfrac{-12}{-4} \quad 3$

   c. $0 \quad -2$

13. Use the commutative property of addition to write an expression equivalent to $7x + 5$.

14. Use the associative property of multiplication to write an expression equivalent to $5 \cdot (7x)$. Then simplify the expression.

Solve for x.

15. $2x + 5 = 9$

16. $11.2 = 1.2 - 5x$

17. $6x - 4 = 2 + 6(x - 1)$

18. $2x + 1.5 = -0.2 + 1.6x$

19. Write the following as algebraic expressions. Then simplify.

   a. The sum of three consecutive integers, if x is the first consecutive integer.

   b. The perimeter of the triangle with sides of length x, $5x$, and $6x - 3$.

20. Write the following as algebraic expressions. Then simplify.

   a. The sum of three consecutive integers if x is the first consecutive integers.

   b. The perimeter of a square with side length $3x + 1$.

21. Find two numbers such that the second number is 3 more than twice the first number and the third number is four times the first number. The sum of the three numbers is 164.

22. Find two numbers such that the second number is 2 more than three times the first number and the difference of the two numbers is 24.

23. Solve $3y - 2x = 7$ for y.

24. Solve $7x - 4y = 10$ for x.

25. Solve $A = \dfrac{1}{2}(B + b)h$ for b.

26. Solve $P = 2l + 2w$ for l.

27. Graph each set on a number line and then write in interval notation.

   a. $\{x \mid x \geq 2\}$

   b. $\{x \mid x < -1\}$

   c. $\{x \mid 0.5 < x \leq 3\}$

28. Graph each set on a number line and then write in interval notation.

   a. $\{x \mid x \leq -3\}$

   b. $\{x \mid -2 \leq x < 0.1\}$

Solve.

29. $-(x - 3) + 2 \leq 3(2x - 5) + x$

30. $2(7x - 1) - 5x > -(-7x) + 4$

31. $2(x + 3) > 2x + 1$

32. $4(x + 1) - 3 < 4x + 1$

33. If $A = \{x \mid x$ is an even number greater than 0 and less than 10$\}$ and $B = \{3, 4, 5, 6\}$, find $A \cap B$.

34. Find the union: $\{-2, 0, 2, 4\} \cup \{-1, 1, 3, 5\}$

35. Solve: $x - 7 < 2$ and $2x + 1 < 9$

36. Solve: $x + 3 \leq 1$ or $3x - 1 < 8$

37. If $A = \{x \mid x$ is an even number greater than 0 and less than 10$\}$ and $B = \{3, 4, 5, 6\}$, find $A \cup B$.

38. Find the intersection: $\{-2, 0, 2, 4\} \cap \{-1, 1, 3, 5\}$

39. Solve: $-2x - 5 < -3$ or $6x < 0$

40. Solve: $-2x - 5 < -3$ and $6x < 0$

Solve.

41. $|p| = 2$

42. $|x| = 5$

43. $\left|\dfrac{x}{2} - 1\right| = 11$

44. $\left|\dfrac{y}{3} + 2\right| = 10$

45. $|x - 3| = |5 - x|$

46. $|x + 3| = |7 - x|$

47. $|x| \leq 3$

48. $|x| > 1$

49. $|2x + 9| + 5 > 3$

50. $|3x + 1| + 9 < 1$

3

Graphs and Functions

Over the past few years, diamonds have gained much higher visibility by increased media advertising. Strong consumer demand has caused the industry to increase production and is the basis for the bar graph below. By a method called least squares (Section 3.2), the function $f(x) = 0.42x + 10.5$ approximates the data below where $f(x)$ is world diamond production value (in billions of dollars) and where x is the number of years past 2000. In Section 3.2, Exercises 87 and 88, page 144, we will use this linear equation to predict diamond production.

The linear equations and inequalities we explored in Chapter 2 are statements about a single variable. This chapter examines statements about two variables: linear equations and inequalities in two variables. We focus particularly on graphs of those equations and inequalities which lead to the notion of relation and to the notion of function, perhaps the single most important and useful concept in all of mathematics.

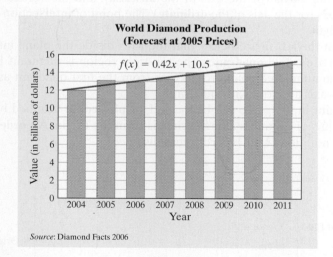

World Diamond Production
(Forecast at 2005 Prices)

$f(x) = 0.42x + 10.5$

Value (in billions of dollars)

Year

Source: Diamond Facts 2006

3.1 GRAPHING EQUATIONS

OBJECTIVES

1 Plot ordered pairs.

2 Determine whether an ordered pair of numbers is a solution to an equation in two variables.

3 Graph linear equations.

4 Graph nonlinear equations.

OBJECTIVE 1 ▶ Plotting ordered pairs. Graphs are widely used today in newspapers, magazines, and all forms of newsletters. A few examples of graphs are shown here.

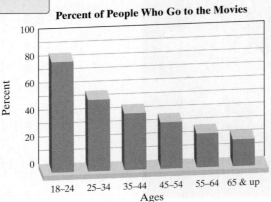

Percent of People Who Go to the Movies

Source: TELENATION/Market Facts, Inc.

Percent of Sales Completed Using Cards*

Source: The Nilson Report

*These include credit or debit cards, prepaid cards and EBT (electronic benefits transfer) cards.

To review how to read these graphs, we review their origin—the rectangular coordinate system. One way to locate points on a plane is by using a **rectangular coordinate system,** which is also called a **Cartesian coordinate system** after its inventor, René Descartes (1596–1650).

A rectangular coordinate system consists of two number lines that intersect at right angles at their 0 coordinates. We position these axes on paper such that one number line is horizontal and the other number line is then vertical. The horizontal number line is called the **x-axis** (or the axis of the **abscissa**), and the vertical number line is called the **y-axis** (or the axis of the **ordinate**). The point of intersection of these axes is named the **origin.**

Notice in the left figure below that the axes divide the plane into four regions. These regions are called **quadrants.** The top-right region is quadrant I. Quadrants II, III, and IV are numbered counterclockwise from the first quadrant as shown. The x-axis and the y-axis are not in any quadrant.

Each point in the plane can be located, or **plotted,** or graphed by describing its position in terms of distances along each axis from the origin. An **ordered pair,** represented by the notation (x, y), records these distances.

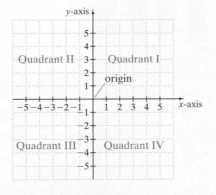

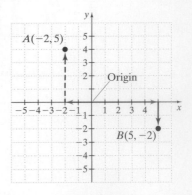

For example, the location of point A in the figure on the right on the previous page is described as 2 units to the left of the origin along the x-axis and 5 units upward parallel to the y-axis. Thus, we identify point A with the ordered pair $(-2, 5)$. Notice that the order of these numbers is *critical*. The x-value -2 is called the **x-coordinate** and is associated with the x-axis. The y-value 5 is called the **y-coordinate** and is associated with the y-axis.

Compare the location of point A with the location of point B, which corresponds to the ordered pair $(5, -2)$. Can you see that the order of the coordinates of an ordered pair matters? Also, two ordered pairs are considered equal and correspond to the same point if and only if their x-coordinates are equal and their y-coordinates are equal.

Keep in mind that **each ordered pair corresponds to exactly one point in the real plane and that each point in the plane corresponds to exactly one ordered pair.** Thus, we may refer to the ordered pair (x, y) as the point (x, y).

EXAMPLE 1 Plot each ordered pair on a Cartesian coordinate system and name the quadrant or axis in which the point is located.

a. $(2, -1)$ **b.** $(0, 5)$ **c.** $(-3, 5)$ **d.** $(-2, 0)$ **e.** $\left(-\dfrac{1}{2}, -4\right)$ **f.** $(1.5, 1.5)$

Solution The six points are graphed as shown.

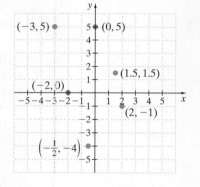

a. $(2, -1)$ lies in quadrant IV.

b. $(0, 5)$ is on the y-axis.

c. $(-3, 5)$ lies in quadrant II.

d. $(-2, 0)$ is on the x-axis.

e. $\left(-\dfrac{1}{2}, -4\right)$ is in quadrant III.

f. $(1.5, 1.5)$ is in quadrant I.

PRACTICE

1 Plot each ordered pair on a Cartesian coordinate system and name the quadrant or axis in which the point is located.

a. $(3, -4)$ **b.** $(0, -2)$ **c.** $(-2, 4)$ **d.** $(4, 0)$ **e.** $\left(-1\dfrac{1}{2}, -2\right)$ **f.** $(2.5, 3.5)$

Notice that the y-coordinate of any point on the x-axis is 0. For example, the point with coordinates $(-2, 0)$ lies on the x-axis. Also, the x-coordinate of any point on the y-axis is 0. For example, the point with coordinates $(0, 5)$ lies on the y-axis. These points that lie on the axes do not lie in any quadrants.

Concept Check ☑

Which of the following correctly describes the location of the point $(3, -6)$ in a rectangular coordinate system?

a. 3 units to the left of the y-axis and 6 units above the x-axis

b. 3 units above the x-axis and 6 units to the left of the y-axis

c. 3 units to the right of the y-axis and 6 units below the x-axis

d. 3 units below the x-axis and 6 units to the right of the y-axis

Answer to Concept Check: c

Many types of real-world data occur in pairs. The graph below was shown at the beginning of this section. Notice the paired data (2013, 57) and the corresponding plotted point, both in blue.

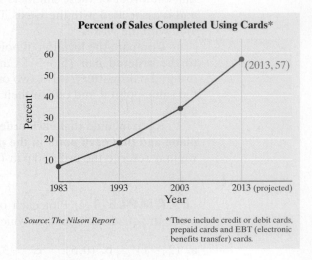

Percent of Sales Completed Using Cards*

Source: The Nilson Report

*These include credit or debit cards, prepaid cards and EBT (electronic benefits transfer) cards.

This paired data point, (2013, 57), means that in the year 2013, it is predicted that 57% of sales will be completed using some type of card (credit, debit, etc.).

OBJECTIVE 2 ▶ Determining whether an ordered pair is a solution. Solutions of equations in two variables consist of two numbers that form a true statement when substituted into the equation. A convenient notation for writing these numbers is as ordered pairs. A solution of an equation containing the variables x and y is written as a pair of numbers in the order (x, y). If the equation contains other variables, we will write ordered pair solutions in alphabetical order.

EXAMPLE 2   Determine whether $(0, -12)$, $(1, 9)$, and $(2, -6)$ are solutions of the equation $3x - y = 12$.

Solution   To check each ordered pair, replace x with the x-coordinate and y with the y-coordinate and see whether a true statement results.

Let $x = 0$ and $y = -12$.   Let $x = 1$ and $y = 9$.   Let $x = 2$ and $y = -6$.

$3x - y = 12$	$3x - y = 12$	$3x - y = 12$
$3(0) - (-12) \stackrel{?}{=} 12$	$3(1) - 9 \stackrel{?}{=} 12$	$3(2) - (-6) \stackrel{?}{=} 12$
$0 + 12 \stackrel{?}{=} 12$	$3 - 9 \stackrel{?}{=} 12$	$6 + 6 \stackrel{?}{=} 12$
$12 = 12$ True	$-6 = 12$ False	$12 = 12$ True

Thus, $(1, 9)$ is not a solution of $3x - y = 12$, but both $(0, -12)$ and $(2, -6)$ are solutions.   □

PRACTICE
2   Determine whether $(1, 4)$, $(0, 6)$, and $(3, -4)$ are solutions of the equation $4x + y = 8$.

OBJECTIVE 3 ▶ Graphing linear equations. The equation $3x - y = 12$, from Example 2, actually has an infinite number of ordered pair solutions. Since it is impossible to list all solutions, we visualize them by graphing.

A few more ordered pairs that satisfy $3x - y = 12$ are $(4, 0)$, $(3, -3)$, $(5, 3)$, and $(1, -9)$. These ordered pair solutions along with the ordered pair solutions from Example 2 are plotted on the following graph. The graph of $3x - y = 12$ is the single line containing these points. Every ordered pair solution of the equation corresponds to a point on this line, and every point on this line corresponds to an ordered pair solution.

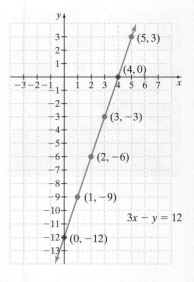

x	y	$3x - y = 12$
5	3	$3 \cdot 5 - 3 = 12$
4	0	$3 \cdot 4 - 0 = 12$
3	-3	$3 \cdot 3 - (-3) = 12$
2	-6	$3 \cdot 2 - (-6) = 12$
1	-9	$3 \cdot 1 - (-9) = 12$
0	-12	$3 \cdot 0 - (-12) = 12$

The equation $3x - y = 12$ is called a linear equation in two variables, and **the graph of every linear equation in two variables is a line.**

Linear Equation in Two Variables

A linear equation in two variables is an equation that can be written in the form

$$Ax + By = C$$

where A and B are not both 0. This form is called **standard form.**

Some examples of equations in standard form:

$$3x - y = 12$$
$$-2.1x + 5.6y = 0$$

▶ **Helpful Hint**

Remember: A linear equation is written in standard form when all of the variable terms are on one side of the equation and the constant is on the other side.

Many real-life applications are modeled by linear equations. Suppose you have a part-time job at a store that sells office products.

Your pay is \$3000 plus 20% or $\frac{1}{5}$ of the price of the products you sell. If we let x represent products sold and y represent monthly salary, the linear equation that models your salary is

$$y = 3000 + \frac{1}{5}x$$

(Although this equation is not written in standard form, it is a linear equation. To see this, subtract $\frac{1}{5}x$ from both sides.)

Some ordered pair solutions of this equation are below.

Products Sold	x	0	1000	2000	3000	4000	10,000
Monthly Salary	y	3000	3200	3400	3600	3800	5000

For example, we say that the ordered pair $(1000, 3200)$ is a solution of the equation $y = 3000 + \frac{1}{5}x$ because when x is replaced with 1000 and y is replaced with 3200, a true statement results.

$$y = 3000 + \frac{1}{5}x$$

$$3200 \stackrel{?}{=} 3000 + \frac{1}{5}(1000) \quad \text{Let } x = 1000 \text{ and } y = 3200.$$

$$3200 \stackrel{?}{=} 3000 + 200$$

$$3200 = 3200 \qquad\qquad \text{True}$$

A portion of the graph of $y = 3000 + \frac{1}{5}x$ is shown in the next example.

Since we assume that the smallest amount of product sold is none, or 0, then x must be greater than or equal to 0. Therefore, only the part of the graph that lies in Quadrant I is shown. Notice that the graph gives a visual picture of the correspondence between products sold and salary.

> ▶ **Helpful Hint**
>
> A line contains an infinite number of points and each point corresponds to an ordered pair that is a solution of its corresponding equation.

EXAMPLE 3 Use the graph of $y = 3000 + \frac{1}{5}x$ to answer the following questions.

a. If the salesperson has $8000 of products sold for a particular month, what is the salary for that month?

b. If the salesperson wants to make more than $5000 per month, what must be the total amount of products sold?

Solution

a. Since x is products sold, find 8000 along the x-axis and move vertically up until you reach a point on the line. From this point on the line, move horizontally to the left until you reach the y-axis. Its value on the y-axis is 4600, which means if $8000 worth of products is sold, the salary for the month is $4600.

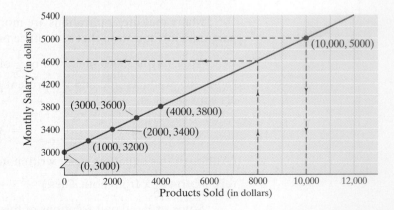

b. Since y is monthly salary, find 5000 along the y-axis and move horizontally to the right until you reach a point on the line. Either read the corresponding x-value from the labeled ordered pair, or move vertically downward until you reach the x-axis. The corresponding x-value is 10,000. This means that $10,000 worth of products sold gives a salary of $5000 for the month. For the salary to be greater than $5000, products sold must be greater that $10,000.

PRACTICE
3   Use the graph in Example 3 to answer the following questions.

a. If the salesperson has $6000 of products sold for a particular month, what is the salary for that month?

b. If the salesperson wants to make more than $4800 per month, what must be the total amount of products sold?

Recall from geometry that a line is determined by two points. This means that to graph a linear equation in two variables, just two solutions are needed. We will find a third solution, just to check our work. To find ordered pair solutions of linear equations in two variables, we can choose an x-value and find its corresponding y-value, or we can choose a y-value and find its corresponding x-value. The number 0 is often a convenient value to choose for x and also for y.

EXAMPLE 4   Graph the equation $y = -2x + 3$.

Solution   This is a linear equation. (In standard form it is $2x + y = 3$.) Find three ordered pair solutions, and plot the ordered pairs. The line through the plotted points is the graph. Since the equation is solved for y, let's choose three x-values. We'll choose 0, 2, and then -1 for x to find our three ordered pair solutions.

Let $x = 0$	Let $x = 2$	Let $x = -1$
$y = -2x + 3$	$y = -2x + 3$	$y = -2x + 3$
$y = -2 \cdot 0 + 3$	$y = -2 \cdot 2 + 3$	$y = -2(-1) + 3$
$y = 3$ Simplify.	$y = -1$ Simplify.	$y = 5$ Simplify.

The three ordered pairs $(0, 3)$, $(2, -1)$ and $(-1, 5)$ are listed in the table and the graph is shown.

x	y
0	3
2	-1
-1	5

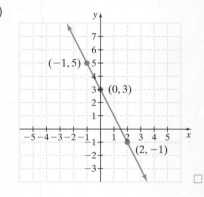

PRACTICE
4   Graph the equation $y = -3x - 2$.

Notice that the graph crosses the y-axis at the point $(0, 3)$. This point is called the **y-intercept.** (You may sometimes see just the number 3 called the y-intercept.) This graph also crosses the x-axis at the point $\left(\frac{3}{2}, 0\right)$. This point is called the **x-intercept.** (You may also see just the number $\frac{3}{2}$ called the x-intercept.)

Since every point on the y-axis has an x-value of 0, we can find the y-intercept of a graph by letting $x = 0$ and solving for y. Also, every point on the x-axis has a y-value of 0. To find the x-intercept, we let $y = 0$ and solve for x.

> **Finding x- and y-Intercepts**
> To find an x-intercept, let $y = 0$ and solve for x.
> To find a y-intercept, let $x = 0$ and solve for y.

We will study intercepts further in Section 3.3.

EXAMPLE 5 Graph the linear equation $y = \frac{1}{3}x$.

Solution   To graph, we find ordered pair solutions, plot the ordered pairs, and draw a line through the plotted points. We will choose x-values and substitute in the equation. To avoid fractions, we choose x-values that are multiples of 3. To find the y-intercept, we let $x = 0$.

> ▶ **Helpful Hint**
> Notice that by using multiples of 3 for x, we avoid fractions.

> ▶ **Helpful Hint**
> Since the equation $y = \frac{1}{3}x$ is solved for y, we choose x-values for finding points. This way, we simply need to evaluate an expression to find the x-value, as shown.

$$y = \frac{1}{3}x$$

If $x = 0$, then $y = \frac{1}{3}(0)$, or 0.

If $x = 6$, then $y = \frac{1}{3}(6)$, or 2.

If $x = -3$, then $y = \frac{1}{3}(-3)$, or -1.

x	y
0	0
6	2
-3	-1

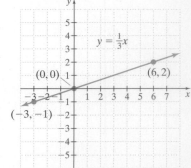

This graph crosses the x-axis at $(0, 0)$ and the y-axis at $(0, 0)$. This means that the x-intercept is $(0, 0)$ and that the y-intercept is $(0, 0)$.   □

PRACTICE
5   Graph the linear equation $y = -\frac{1}{2}x$.

OBJECTIVE 4 ▶ Graphing nonlinear equations. Not all equations in two variables are linear equations, and not all graphs of equations in two variables are lines.

EXAMPLE 6   Graph $y = x^2$.

Solution   This equation is not linear because the x^2 term does not allow us to write it in the form $Ax + By = C$. Its graph is not a line. We begin by finding ordered pair solutions. Because this graph is solved for y, we choose x-values and find corresponding y-values.

If $x = -3$, then $y = (-3)^2$, or 9.

If $x = -2$, then $y = (-2)^2$, or 4.

If $x = -1$, then $y = (-1)^2$, or 1.

If $x = 0$, then $y = 0^2$, or 0.

If $x = 1$, then $y = 1^2$, or 1.

If $x = 2$, then $y = 2^2$, or 4.

If $x = 3$, then $y = 3^2$, or 9.

x	y
-3	9
-2	4
-1	1
0	0
1	1
2	4
3	9

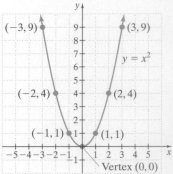

Study the table a moment and look for patterns. Notice that the ordered pair solution $(0, 0)$ contains the smallest y-value because any other x-value squared will give a positive result. This means that the point $(0, 0)$ will be the lowest point on the graph. Also notice that all other y-values correspond to two different x-values. For example, $3^2 = 9$ and also $(-3)^2 = 9$. This means that the graph will be a mirror image of itself across the y-axis. Connect the plotted points with a smooth curve to sketch the graph.

This curve is given a special name, a parabola. We will study more about parabolas in later chapters.   □

PRACTICE
6   Graph $y = 2x^2$.

EXAMPLE 7   Graph the equation $y = |x|$.

Solution   This is not a linear equation since it cannot be written in the form $Ax + By = C$. Its graph is not a line. Because we do not know the shape of this graph, we find many ordered pair solutions. We will choose x-values and substitute to find corresponding y-values.

If $x = -3$, then $y = |-3|$, or 3.

If $x = -2$, then $y = |-2|$, or 2.

If $x = -1$, then $y = |-1|$, or 1.

If $x = 0$, then $y = |0|$, or 0.

If $x = 1$, then $y = |1|$, or 1.

If $x = 2$, then $y = |2|$, or 2.

If $x = 3$, then $y = |3|$, or 3.

x	y
-3	3
-2	2
-1	1
0	0
1	1
2	2
3	3

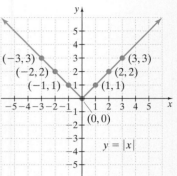

Again, study the table of values for a moment and notice any patterns.

From the plotted ordered pairs, we see that the graph of this absolute value equation is V-shaped.

PRACTICE
7   Graph $y = -|x|$.

Graphing Calculator Explorations

In this section, we begin a study of graphing calculators and graphing software packages for computers. These graphers use the same point plotting technique that we introduced in this section. The advantage of this graphing technology is, of course, that graphing calculators and computers can find and plot ordered pair solutions much faster than we can. Note, however, that the features described in these boxes may not be available on all graphing calculators.

The rectangular screen where a portion of the rectangular coordinate system is displayed is called a **window**. We call it a **standard window** for graphing when both the x- and y-axes display coordinates between -10 and 10. This information is often displayed in the window menu on a graphing calculator as

$$\text{Xmin} = -10$$
$$\text{Xmax} = 10$$
$$\text{Xscl} = 1 \quad \text{The scale on the } x\text{-axis is one unit per tick mark.}$$
$$\text{Ymin} = -10$$
$$\text{Ymax} = 10$$
$$\text{Yscl} = 1 \quad \text{The scale on the } y\text{-axis is one unit per tick mark.}$$

To use a graphing calculator to graph the equation $y = -5x + 4$, press the $\boxed{Y =}$ key and enter the keystrokes

$\boxed{(-)}$ $\boxed{5}$ $\boxed{x}$ $\boxed{+}$ $\boxed{4}$.

↑

(Check your owner's manual to make sure the "negative" key is pressed here and not the "subtraction" key.)

The top row should now read $Y_1 = -5x + 4$. Next press the $\boxed{\text{GRAPH}}$ key, and the display should look like this:

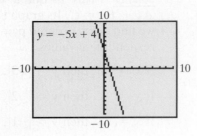

Use a standard window and graph the following equations. (Unless otherwise stated, we will use a standard window when graphing.)

1. $y = -3.2x + 7.9$
2. $y = -x + 5.85$

3. $y = \frac{1}{4}x - \frac{2}{3}$
4. $y = \frac{2}{3}x - \frac{1}{5}$

5. $y = |x - 3| + 2$
6. $y = |x + 1| - 1$

7. $y = x^2 + 3$
8. $y = (x + 3)^2$

VOCABULARY & READINESS CHECK

Determine the coordinates of each point on the graph.

1. Point A
2. Point B
3. Point C
4. Point D
5. Point E
6. Point F
7. Point G
8. Point H

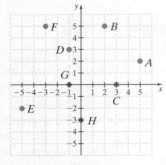

Without graphing, visualize the location of each point. Then give its location by quadrant or x- or y-axis.

9. $(2, 3)$
10. $(0, 5)$
11. $(-2, 7)$
12. $(-3, 0)$
13. $(-1, -4)$
14. $(4, -2)$
15. $(0, -100)$
16. $(10, 30)$
17. $(-10, -30)$
18. $(0, 0)$
19. $(-87, 0)$
20. $(-42, 17)$

Plot each point and name the quadrant or axis in which the point lies. See Example 1.

1. $(3, 2)$
2. $(2, -1)$
3. $(-5, 3)$
4. $(-3, -1)$
5. $\left(5\frac{1}{2}, -4\right)$
6. $\left(-2, 6\frac{1}{3}\right)$
7. $(0, 3.5)$
8. $(-5.2, 0)$

9. $(-2, -4)$
10. $(-4.2, 0)$

Given that x is a positive number and that y is a positive number, determine the quadrant or axis in which each point lies. See Example 1.

11. $(x, -y)$
12. $(-x, y)$
13. $(x, 0)$
14. $(0, -y)$
15. $(-x, -y)$
16. $(0, 0)$

Determine whether each ordered pair is a solution of the given equation. See Example 2.

17. $y = 3x - 5;\ (0, 5),\ (-1, -8)$

18. $y = -2x + 7;\ (1, 5),\ (-2, 3)$

19. $-6x + 5y = -6;\ (1, 0),\ \left(2, \dfrac{6}{5}\right)$

20. $5x - 3y = 9;\ (0, 3),\ \left(\dfrac{12}{5}, -1\right)$

21. $y = 2x^2;\ (1, 2),\ (3, 18)$

22. $y = 2|x|;\ (-1, 2),\ (0, 2)$

23. $y = x^3;\ (2, 8),\ (3, 9)$

24. $y = x^4;\ (-1, 1),\ (2, 16)$

25. $y = \sqrt{x} + 2;\ (1, 3),\ (4, 4)$

26. $y = \sqrt[3]{x} - 4;\ (1, -3),\ (8, 6)$

MIXED PRACTICE
Determine whether each equation is linear or not. Then graph the equation by finding and plotting ordered-pair solutions. See Examples 3 through 7.

27. $x + y = 3$

28. $y - x = 8$

29. $y = 4x$

30. $y = 6x$

31. $y = 4x - 2$

32. $y = 6x - 5$

33. $y = |x| + 3$

34. $y = |x| + 2$

35. $2x - y = 5$

36. $4x - y = 7$

37. $y = 2x^2$

38. $y = 3x^2$

39. $y = x^2 - 3$

40. $y = x^2 + 3$

41. $y = -2x$

42. $y = -3x$

43. $y = -2x + 3$

44. $y = -3x + 2$

45. $y = |x + 2|$

46. $y = |x - 1|$

47. $y = x^3$
   (*Hint:* Let $x = -3, -2, -1, 0, 1, 2.$)

48. $y = x^3 - 2$
   (*Hint:* Let $x = -3, -2, -1, 0, 1, 2.$)

49. $y = -|x|$

50. $y = -x^2$

51. $y = \dfrac{1}{3}x - 1$

52. $y = \dfrac{1}{2}x - 3$

53. $y = -\dfrac{3}{2}x + 1$

54. $y = -\dfrac{2}{3}x + 1$

REVIEW AND PREVIEW

Solve the following equations. See Section 2.1.

55. $3(x - 2) + 5x = 6x - 16$

56. $5 + 7(x + 1) = 12 + 10x$

57. $3x + \dfrac{2}{5} = \dfrac{1}{10}$

58. $\dfrac{1}{6} + 2x = \dfrac{2}{3}$

Solve the following inequalities. See Section 2.4.

59. $3x \le -15$

60. $-3x > 18$

61. $2x - 5 > 4x + 3$

62. $9x + 8 \le 6x - 4$

CONCEPT EXTENSIONS

Solve. See the Concept Check in this section.

63. Which correctly describes the location of the point $(-1, 5.3)$ in a rectangular coordinate system?

   a. 1 unit to the right of the y-axis and 5.3 units above the x-axis

   b. 1 unit to the left of the y-axis and 5.3 units above the x-axis

   c. 1 unit to the left of the y-axis and 5.3 units below the x-axis

   d. 1 unit to the right of the y-axis and 5.3 units below the x-axis

64. Which correctly describes the location of the point $\left(0, -\dfrac{3}{4}\right)$ in a rectangular coordinate system?

   a. on the x-axis and $\dfrac{3}{4}$ unit to the left of the y-axis

   b. on the x-axis and $\dfrac{3}{4}$ unit to the right of the y-axis

   c. on the y-axis and $\dfrac{3}{4}$ unit above the x-axis

   d. on the y-axis and $\dfrac{3}{4}$ unit below the x-axis

For Exercises 65 through 68, match each description with the graph that best illustrates it.

65. Moe worked 40 hours per week until the fall semester started. He quit and didn't work again until he worked 60 hours a week during the holiday season starting mid-December.

66. Kawana worked 40 hours a week for her father during the summer. She slowly cut back her hours to not working at all during the fall semester. During the holiday season in December, she started working again and increased her hours to 60 hours per week.

67. Wendy worked from July through February, never quitting. She worked between 10 and 30 hours per week.

68. Bartholomew worked from July through February. The rest of the time, he worked between 10 and 40 hours per week. During the holiday season between mid-November and the beginning of January, he worked 40 hours per week.

a.

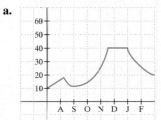

b.

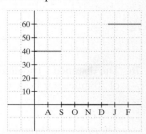

c.

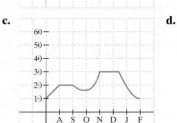

d.

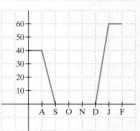

The graph below shows first-class postal rates and the years it increased. Use this graph for Exercises 69 through 72.

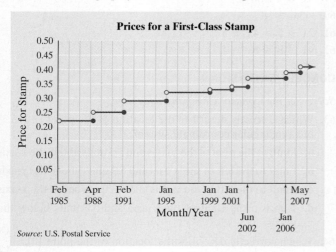

Source: U.S. Postal Service

69. What was the first year that the price for a first-class stamp rose above $0.25?

70. What was the first year that the price for a first-class stamp rose above $0.30?

71. Why do you think that this graph is shaped the way it is?

72. The U.S. Postal Service issued first-class stamps as far back as 1885. The cost for a first-class stamp then was $0.02. By how much had it increased by 2007?

73. Graph $y = x^2 - 4x + 7$. Let $x = 0, 1, 2, 3, 4$ to generate ordered pair solutions.

74. Graph $y = x^2 + 2x + 3$. Let $x = -3, -2, -1, 0, 1$ to generate ordered pair solutions.

△ **75.** The perimeter y of a rectangle whose width is a constant 3 inches and whose length is x inches is given by the equation

$$y = 2x + 6$$

   a. Draw a graph of this equation.
   b. Read from the graph the perimeter y of a rectangle whose length x is 4 inches.

76. The distance y traveled in a train moving at a constant speed of 50 miles per hour is given by the equation

$$y = 50x$$

where x is the time in hours traveled.

   a. Draw a graph of this equation.
   b. Read from the graph the distance y traveled after 6 hours.

*For income tax purposes, Jason Verges, owner of Copy Services, uses a method called **straight-line depreciation** to show the loss in value of a copy machine he recently purchased. Jason assumes that he can use the machine for 7 years. The following graph shows the value of the machine over the years. Use this graph to answer Exercises 77 through 82.*

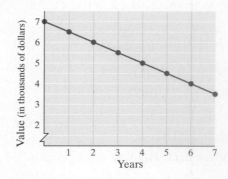

77. What was the purchase price of the copy machine?

78. What is the depreciated value of the machine in 7 years?

79. What loss in value occurred during the first year?

80. What loss in value occurred during the second year?

81. Why do you think that this method of depreciating is called straight-line depreciation?

82. Why is the line tilted downward?

83. On the same set of axes, graph $y = 2x$, $y = 2x - 5$, and $y = 2x + 5$. What patterns do you see in these graphs?

84. On the same set of axes, graph $y = 2x$, $y = x$, and $y = -2x$. Describe the differences and similarities in these graphs.

85. Explain why we generally use three points to graph a line, when only two points are needed.

Write each statement as an equation in two variables. Then graph each equation.

86. The y-value is 5 more than three times the x-value.

87. The y-value is -3 decreased by twice the x-value.

88. The y-value is 2 more than the square of the x-value.

89. The y-value is 5 decreased by the square of the x-value.

Use a graphing calculator to verify the graphs of the following exercises.

90. Exercise 39

91. Exercise 40

92. Exercise 47

93. Exercise 48

How Well Do You Know Your Textbook?

The questions below will determine whether you are familiar with your textbook. For help, see Section 1.1 in this text.

1. What does the 🕸 icon mean?
2. What does the ❭ icon mean?
3. What does the △ icon mean?
4. Which exercise set answers are given in the back of your text?
5. Where can you find a review for each chapter? What answers to this review can be found in the back of your text?
6. Each chapter contains an overview of the chapter along with examples. What is this feature called?

7. Each chapter contains a review of vocabulary. What is this feature called?
8. There is a CD in your text. What content is contained on this CD?
9. What is the location of the section that is entirely devoted to study skills?
10. There is a Practice exercise located after each worked example in the text. What are they and how can they be used?
11. There is a Practice Final Exam in your text. Where is it located?

3.2 INTRODUCTION TO FUNCTIONS

OBJECTIVES

1. Define relation, domain, and range.
2. Identify functions.
3. Use the vertical line test for functions.
4. Find the domain and range of a function.
5. Use function notation.

OBJECTIVE 1 ▶ Defining relation, domain, and range. Recall our example from the last section about products sold and monthly salary. We modeled the data given by the equation $y = 3000 + \frac{1}{5}x$. This equation describes a relationship between x-values and y-values. For example, if $x = 1000$, then this equation describes how to find the y-value related to $x = 1000$. In words, the equation $y = 3000 + \frac{1}{5}x$ says that 3000 plus $\frac{1}{5}$ of the x-value gives the corresponding y-value. The x-value of 1000 corresponds to the y-value of $3000 + \frac{1}{5} \cdot 1000 = 3200$ for this equation, and we have the ordered pair $(1000, 3200)$.

There are other ways of describing relations or correspondences between two numbers or, in general, a first set (sometimes called the set of *inputs*) and a second set (sometimes called the set of *outputs*). For example,

First Set: Input	— *Correspondence*	→ *Second Set: Output*
People in a certain city	— Each person's age	→ The set of nonnegative integers

A few examples of ordered pairs from this relation might be (Ana, 4); (Bob, 36); (Trey, 21); and so on.

Below are just a few other ways of describing relations between two sets and the ordered pairs that they generate.

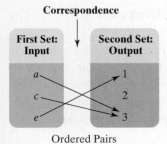

Ordered Pairs
$(a, 3), (c, 3), (e, 1)$

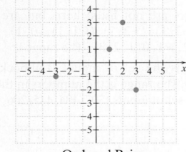

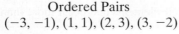

Ordered Pairs
$(-3, -1), (1, 1), (2, 3), (3, -2)$

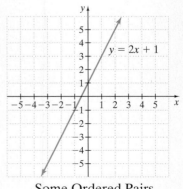

Some Ordered Pairs
$(1, 3), (0, 1),$ and so on

> **Relation, Domain, and Range**
>
> A **relation** is a set of ordered pairs.
> The **domain** of the relation is the set of all first components of the ordered pairs.
> The **range** of the relation is the set of all second components of the ordered pairs.

For example, the domain for our relation in the bottom left of the previous page is $\{a, c, e\}$ and the range is $\{1, 3\}$. Notice that the range does not include the element 2 of the second set. This is because no element of the first set is assigned to this element. If a relation is defined in terms of x- and y-values, we will agree that the domain corresponds to x-values and that the range corresponds to y-values that have x-values assigned to them.

> ▶ **Helpful Hint**
> Remember that the range only includes elements that are paired with domain values. For the correspondence below, the range is $\{a\}$.
>
> **Correspondence**
>
>

EXAMPLE 1 Determine the domain and range of each relation.

a. $\{(2, 3), (2, 4), (0, -1), (3, -1)\}$

b.

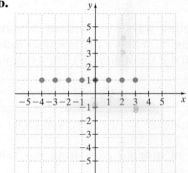

c.

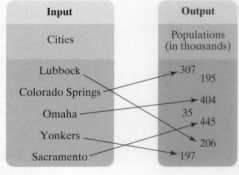

Solution

a. The domain is the set of all first coordinates of the ordered pairs, $\{2, 0, 3\}$. The range is the set of all second coordinates, $\{3, 4, -1\}$.

b. Ordered pairs are not listed here, but are given in graph form. The relation is $\{(-4, 1), (-3, 1), (-2, 1), (-1, 1), (0, 1), (1, 1), (2, 1), (3, 1)\}$. The domain is $\{-4, -3, -2, -1, 0, 1, 2, 3\}$. The range is $\{1\}$.

c. The domain is the set of inputs, {Lubbock, Colorado Springs, Omaha, Yonkers, Sacramento}. The range is the numbers in the set of outputs that correspond to elements in the set of inputs {307, 404, 445, 206, 197}.

> ▶ **Helpful Hint**
> Domain or range elements that occur more than once need only to be listed once.

PRACTICE
1   Determine the domain and range of each relation.

a. {(4, 1)(4, −3)(5, −2)(5, 6)}

b.

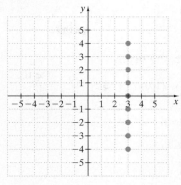

c.

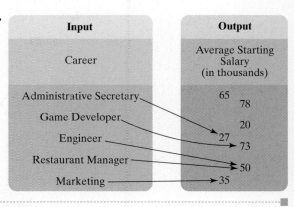

Input	Output
Career	Average Starting Salary (in thousands)
Administrative Secretary	65
Game Developer	78
Engineer	20
Restaurant Manager	27
Marketing	73
	50
	35

OBJECTIVE 2 ▶ Identifying functions. Now we consider a special kind of relation called a function.

Function

A **function** is a relation in which each first component in the ordered pairs corresponds to *exactly* one second component.

▶ Helpful Hint

A function is a special type of relation, so all functions are relations, but not all relations are functions.

EXAMPLE 2   Which of the following relations are also functions?

a. {(−2, 5), (2, 7), (−3, 5), (9, 9)}

b.

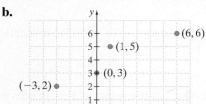

c.

Input	Correspondence	Output
People in a certain city	Each person's age	The set of nonnegative integers

Solution

a. Although the ordered pairs (−2, 5) and (−3, 5) have the same *y*-value, each *x*-value is assigned to only one *y*-value, so this set of ordered pairs is a function.

b. The *x*-value 0 is assigned to two *y*-values, −2 and 3, in this graph so this relation does not define a function.

c. This relation is a function because although two different people may have the same age, each person has only one age. This means that each element in the first set is assigned to only one element in the second set.

PRACTICE
2 Which of the following relations are also functions?

a. $\{(3, 1), (-3, -4), (8, 5), (9, 1)\}$

b.
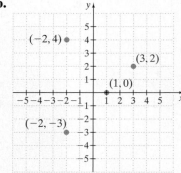

c.

Input	Correspondence	Output
People in a certain city	Birth date (day of month)	Set of nonnegative integers

Concept Check ☑

Explain why a function can contain both the ordered pairs $(1, 3)$ and $(2, 3)$ but not both $(3, 1)$ and $(3, 2)$.

We will call an equation such as $y = 2x + 1$ a **relation** since this equation defines a set of ordered pair solutions.

EXAMPLE 3 Is the relation $y = 2x + 1$ also a function?*

Solution The relation $y = 2x + 1$ is a function if each x-value corresponds to just one y-value. For each x-value substituted in the equation $y = 2x + 1$, the multiplication and addition performed on each gives a single result, so only one y-value will be associated with each x-value. Thus, $y = 2x + 1$ is a function.

*For further discussion including the graph, see Objective 3. □

PRACTICE
3 Is the relation $y = -3x + 5$ also a function?

EXAMPLE 4 Is the relation $x = y^2$ also a function?*

Solution In $x = y^2$, if $y = 3$, then $x = 9$. Also, if $y = -3$, then $x = 9$. In other words, we have the ordered pairs $(9, 3)$ and $(9, -3)$. Since the x-value 9 corresponds to two y-values, 3 and -3, $x = y^2$ is not a function.

*For further discussion including the graph, see Objective 3. □

PRACTICE
4 Is the relation $y = -x^2$ also a function?

Answer to Concept Check:
Two different ordered pairs can have the same y-value, but not the same x-value in a function.

OBJECTIVE 3 ▶ **Using the vertical line test.** As we have seen so far, not all relations are functions. Consider the graphs of $y = 2x + 1$ and $x = y^2$ shown next. For the graph of $y = 2x + 1$, notice that each x-value corresponds to only one y-value. Recall from Example 3 that $y = 2x + 1$ is a function.

Graph of Example 3:
$$y = 2x + 1$$

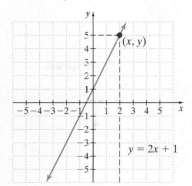

Graph of Example 4:
$$x = y^2$$

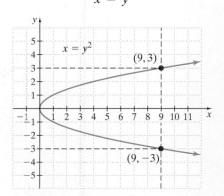

For the graph of $x = y^2$ the x-value 9, for example, corresponds to two y-values, 3 and -3, as shown by the vertical line. Recall from Example 4 that $x = y^2$ is not a function.

Graphs can be used to help determine whether a relation is also a function by the following vertical line test.

> **Vertical Line Test**
>
> If no vertical line can be drawn so that it intersects a graph more than once, the graph is the graph of a function.

EXAMPLE 5 Which of the following graphs are graphs of functions?

a.

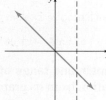

b.

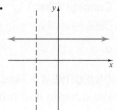

c.

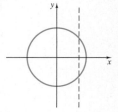

Solution

Yes, this is the graph of a function since no vertical line will intersect this graph more than once.

Yes, this is the graph of a function.

No, this is not the graph of a function. Note that vertical lines can be drawn that intersect the graph in two points.

d.

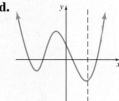

e.

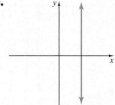

Solution

Yes, this is the graph of a function.

No, this is not the graph of a function. A vertical line can be drawn that intersects this line at every point.

PRACTICE
5 Which of the following graphs are graphs of functions?

a. *no*

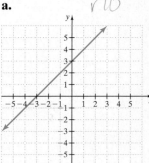

b. *yes*

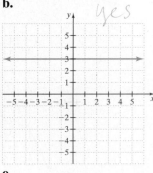

c. *no*

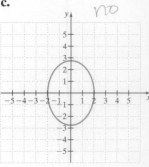

d.

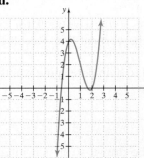

e.

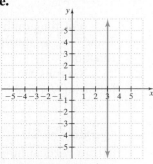

Recall that the graph of a linear equation in two variables is a line, and a line that is not vertical will pass the vertical line test. Thus, **all linear equations are functions except those whose graph is a vertical line.**

Concept Check ☑

Determine which equations represent functions. Explain your answer.

a. $y = |x|$ **b.** $y = x^2$ **c.** $x + y = 6$

OBJECTIVE 4 ▶ Finding the domain and range of a function. Next, we practice finding the domain and range of a relation from its graph.

EXAMPLE 6 Find the domain and range of each relation. Determine whether the relation is also a function.

a.

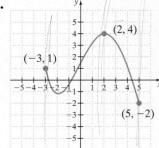

b.

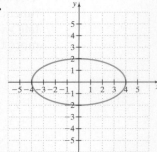

c.

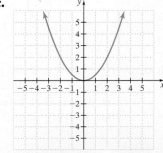

d.

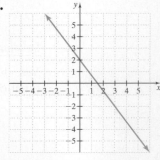

Solution   By the vertical line test, graphs **a**, **c**, and **d** are graphs of functions. The domain is the set of values of x and the range is the set of values of y. We read these values from each graph.

> ▶ **Helpful Hint**
>
> In Example 6, Part **a**, notice that the graph contains the endpoints $(-3, 1)$ and $(5, -2)$ whereas the graphs in Parts **c** and **d** contain arrows that indicate that they continue forever.

a.

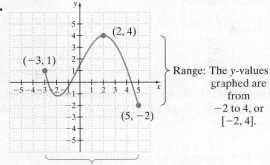

Range: The y-values graphed are from -2 to 4, or $[-2, 4]$.

Domain: The x-values graphed are from -3 to 5, or $[-3, 5]$.

b.

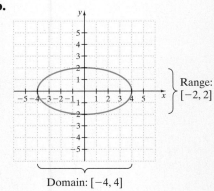

Range: $[-2, 2]$

Domain: $[-4, 4]$

c.

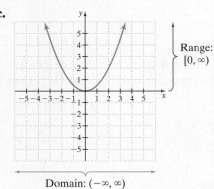

Range: $[0, \infty)$

Domain: $(-\infty, \infty)$

d.

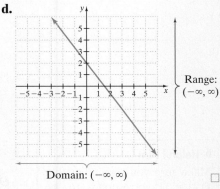

Range: $(-\infty, \infty)$

Domain: $(-\infty, \infty)$

PRACTICE

6   Find the domain and range of each relation. Determine whether each relation is also a function.

a.

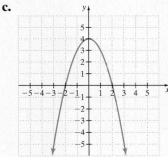

b.

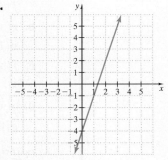

c.

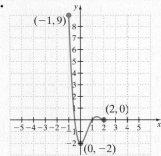

d.

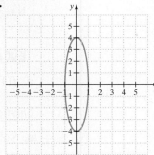

OBJECTIVE 5 ▶ **Using function notation.** Many times letters such as $f, g,$ and h are used to name functions.

> **Function Notation**
>
> To denote that y is a function of x, we can write
>
> $$y = \underbrace{f(x)} \quad \text{(Read "}f\text{ of }x\text{.")}$$
> **Function Notation**
>
> This notation means that **y is a function of x** or that y *depends on x.* For this reason, y is called the **dependent variable** and x the **independent variable.**

For example, to use function notation with the function $y = 4x + 3$, we write $f(x) = 4x + 3$. The notation $f(1)$ means to replace x with 1 and find the resulting y or function value. Since

$$f(x) = 4x + 3$$

then

$$f(1) = 4(1) + 3 = 7$$

This means that when $x = 1$, y or $f(x) = 7$. The corresponding ordered pair is $(1, 7)$. Here, the input is 1 and the output is $f(1)$ or 7. Now let's find $f(2), f(0),$ and $f(-1)$.

$$f(x) = 4x + 3 \qquad\qquad f(x) = 4x + 3 \qquad\qquad f(x) = 4(x) + 3$$
$$f(2) = 4(2) + 3 \qquad\qquad f(0) = 4(0) + 3 \qquad\qquad f(-1) = 4(-1) + 3$$
$$= 8 + 3 \qquad\qquad\qquad = 0 + 3 \qquad\qquad\qquad = -4 + 3$$
$$= 11 \qquad\qquad\qquad\quad = 3 \qquad\qquad\qquad\quad = -1$$

> ▶ **Helpful Hint**
> Make sure you remember that $f(2) = 11$ corresponds to the ordered pair $(2, 11)$.

Ordered Pairs:

$(2, 11)$ \qquad\qquad\qquad $(0, 3)$ \qquad\qquad\qquad $(-1, -1)$

> ▶ **Helpful Hint**
> Note that $f(x)$ is a special symbol in mathematics used to denote a function. The symbol $f(x)$ is read "f of x." It does *not* mean $f \cdot x$ (f times x).

EXAMPLE 7 If $f(x) = 7x^2 - 3x + 1$ and $g(x) = 3x - 2$, find the following.

a. $f(1)$ \qquad **b.** $g(1)$ \qquad **c.** $f(-2)$ \qquad **d.** $g(0)$

Solution

a. Substitute 1 for x in $f(x) = 7x^2 - 3x + 1$ and simplify.
$$f(x) = 7x^2 - 3x + 1$$
$$f(1) = 7(1)^2 - 3(1) + 1 = 5$$

b. $g(x) = 3x - 2$
$$g(1) = 3(1) - 2 = 1$$

c. $f(x) = 7x^2 - 3x + 1$
$$f(-2) = 7(-2)^2 - 3(-2) + 1 = 35$$

d. $g(x) = 3x - 2$
$$g(0) = 3(0) - 2 = -2$$

PRACTICE
7 If $f(x) = 3x - 2$ and $g(x) = 5x^2 + 2x - 1$, find the following.

a. $f(1)$ \qquad **b.** $g(1)$ \qquad **c.** $f(0)$ \qquad **d.** $g(-2)$

Concept Check ☑

Suppose $y = f(x)$ and we are told that $f(3) = 9$. Which is not true?

a. When $x = 3$, $y = 9$.

b. A possible function is $f(x) = x^2$.

c. A point on the graph of the function is $(3, 9)$.

d. A possible function is $f(x) = 2x + 4$.

If it helps, think of a function, f, as a machine that has been programmed with a certain correspondence or rule. An input value (a member of the domain) is then fed into the machine, the machine does the correspondence or rule and the result is the output (a member of the range).

EXAMPLE 8   Given the graphs of the functions f and g, find each function value by inspecting the graphs.

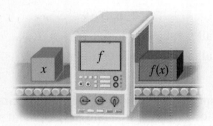   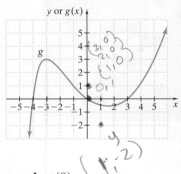

a. $f(4)$ **b.** $f(-2)$ **c.** $g(5)$ **d.** $g(0)$

e. Find all x-values such that $f(x) = 1$.

f. Find all x-values such that $g(x) = 0$.

Solution

a. To find $f(4)$, find the y-value when $x = 4$. We see from the graph that when $x = 4$, y or $f(x) = 2$. Thus, $f(4) = 2$.

b. $f(-2) = 1$ from the ordered pair $(-2, 1)$.

c. $g(5) = 3$ from the ordered pair $(5, 3)$.

d. $g(0) = 0$ from the ordered pair $(0, 0)$.

e. To find x-values such that $f(x) = 1$, we are looking for any ordered pairs on the graph of f whose $f(x)$ or y-value is 1. They are $(2, 1)$ and $(-2, 1)$. Thus $f(2) = 1$ and $f(-2) = 1$. The x-values are 2 and -2.

f. Find ordered pairs on the graph of g whose $g(x)$ or y-value is 0. They are $(3, 0)$ $(0, 0)$ and $(-4, 0)$. Thus $g(3) = 0$, $g(0) = 0$, and $g(-4) = 0$. The x-values are 3, 0, and -4. ☐

PRACTICE
8 Given the graphs of the functions *f* and *g*, find each function value by inspecting the graphs.

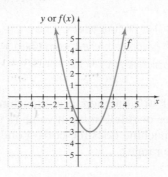

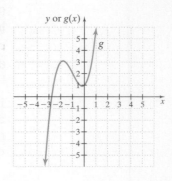

a. $f(1)$ **b.** $f(0)$ **c.** $g(-2)$ **d.** $g(0)$

e. Find all *x*-values such that $f(x) = 1$.

f. Find all *x*-values such that $g(x) = -2$.

Many types of real-world paired data form functions. The broken-line graph below shows the research and development spending by the Pharmaceutical Manufacturers Association.

EXAMPLE 9 The following graph shows the research and development expenditures by the Pharmaceutical Manufacturers Association as a function of time.

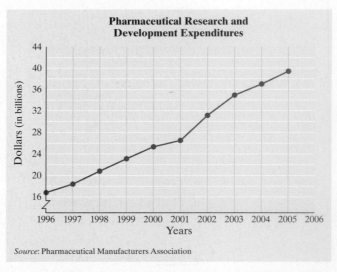

Pharmaceutical Research and Development Expenditures

Source: Pharmaceutical Manufacturers Association

a. Approximate the money spent on research and development in 2002.

b. In 1958, research and development expenditures were $200 million. Find the increase in expenditures from 1958 to 2004.

Solution

a. Find the year 2002 and move upward until you reach the graph. From the point on the graph move horizontally, to the left, until the other axis is reached. In 2002, approximately $31 billion was spent.

b. In 2004, approximately $37 billion, or $37,000 million was spent. The increase in spending from 1958 to 2004 is $37,000 − $200 = $36,800 million or $36.8 billion. ☐

PRACTICE
9 Use the graph in Example 9 and approximate the money spent in 2003.

Notice that the graph in Example 9 is the graph of a function since for each year there is only one total amount of money spent by the Pharmaceutical Manufacturers Association on research and development. Also notice that the graph resembles the graph of a line. Often, businesses depend on equations that "closely fit" data-defined functions like this one in order to model the data and predict future trends. For example, by a method called **least squares,** the function $f(x) = 2.602x - 5178$ approximates the data shown. For this function, x is the year and $f(x)$ is total money spent. Its graph and the actual data function are shown next.

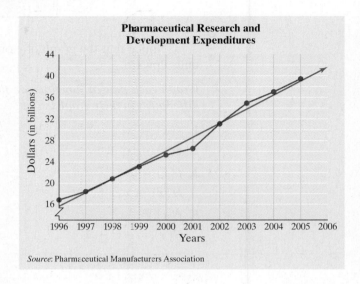

Pharmaceutical Research and Development Expenditures

Source: Pharmaceutical Manufacturers Association

EXAMPLE 10   Use the function $f(x) = 2.602x - 5178$ to predict the amount of money that will be spent by the Pharmaceutical Manufacturers Association on research and development in 2014.

Solution   To predict the amount of money that will be spent in the year 2014 we use $f(x) = 2.602x - 5178$ and find $f(2014)$.

$$f(x) = 2.602x - 5178$$
$$f(2014) = 2.602(2014) - 5178$$
$$= 62.428$$

We predict that in the year 2014, $62.428 billion dollars will be spent on research and development by the Pharmaceutical Manufacturers Association.   □

PRACTICE
10   Use $f(x) = 2.602x - 5178$ to approximate the money spent in 2012.

Graphing Calculator Explorations

It is possible to use a graphing calculator to sketch the graph of more than one equation on the same set of axes. For example, graph the functions $f(x) = x^2$ and $g(x) = x^2 + 4$ on the same set of axes.

To graph on the same set of axes, press the $\boxed{Y =}$ key and enter the equations on the first two lines.

$$Y_1 = x^2$$
$$Y_2 = x^2 + 4$$

Then press the ⬛ GRAPH ⬛ key as usual. The screen should look like this.

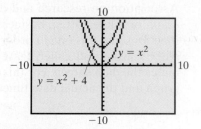

Notice that the graph of y or $g(x) = x^2 + 4$ is the graph of $y = x^2$ moved 4 units upward.

Graph each pair of functions on the same set of axes. Describe the similarities and differences in their graphs.

1. $f(x) = |x|$
$g(x) = |x| + 1$

2. $f(x) = x^2$
$h(x) = x^2 - 5$

3. $f(x) = x$
$H(x) = x - 6$

4. $f(x) = |x|$
$G(x) = |x| + 3$

5. $f(x) = -x^2$
$F(x) = -x^2 + 7$

6. $f(x) = x$
$F(x) = x + 2$

VOCABULARY & READINESS CHECK

Use the choices below to fill in each blank. Some choices may not be used. These exercises have to do with functions and the rectangular coordinate system (Sections 3.1 and 3.2).

x	domain	vertical	relation	$(1.7, -2)$	line	parabola
y	range	horizontal	function	$(-2, 1.7)$	origin	V-shaped

1. The intersection of the x-axis and y-axis is a point, called the _____.

2. To find an x-intercept, let _____ = 0 and solve for _____.

3. To find a y-intercept, let _____ = 0 and solve for _____.

4. The graph of $Ax + By = C$, where A and B are not both 0 is a _____.

5. The graph of $y = |x|$ looks _____.

6. The graph of $y = x^2$ is a _____.

7. A _____ is a set of ordered pairs.

8. The _____ of a relation is the set of all second components of the ordered pairs.

9. The _____ of a relation is the set of all first components of the ordered pairs.

10. A _____ is a relation in which each first component in the ordered pairs corresponds to *exactly* one second component.

11. By the vertical line test, all linear equations are functions except those whose graphs are _____ lines.

12. If $f(-2) = 1.7$, the corresponding ordered pair is _____.

3.2 | EXERCISE SET

 MyMathLab Powered by CourseCompass™ and MathXL™

 Math XL
PRACTICE

WATCH

DOWNLOAD

READ

REVIEW

Find the domain and the range of each relation. Also determine whether the relation is a function. See Examples 1 and 2.

1. $\{(-1, 7), (0, 6), (-2, 2), (5, 6)\}$

2. $\{(4, 9), (-4, 9), (2, 3), (10, -5)\}$

3. $\{(-2, 4), (6, 4), (-2, -3), (-7, -8)\}$

4. $\{(6, 6), (5, 6), (5, -2), (7, 6)\}$

5. $\{(1, 1), (1, 2), (1, 3), (1, 4)\}$

6. $\{(1, 1), (2, 1), (3, 1), (4, 1)\}$

7. $\left\{ \left(\frac{3}{2}, \frac{1}{2}\right), \left(1\frac{1}{2}, -7\right), \left(0, \frac{4}{5}\right) \right\}$

8. $\{(\pi, 0), (0, \pi), (-2, 4), (4, -2)\}$

9. $\{(-3, -3), (0, 0), (3, 3)\}$

10. $\left\{ \left(\frac{1}{2}, \frac{1}{4}\right), \left(0, \frac{7}{8}\right), (0.5, \pi) \right\}$

11.

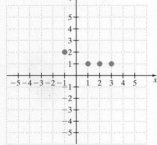

12.

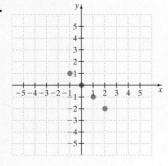

13.

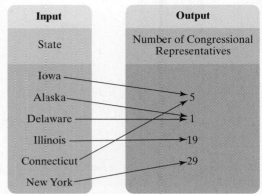

14.

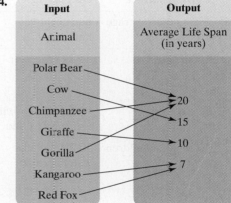

15.

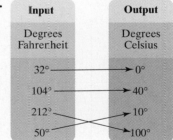

16.

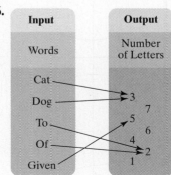

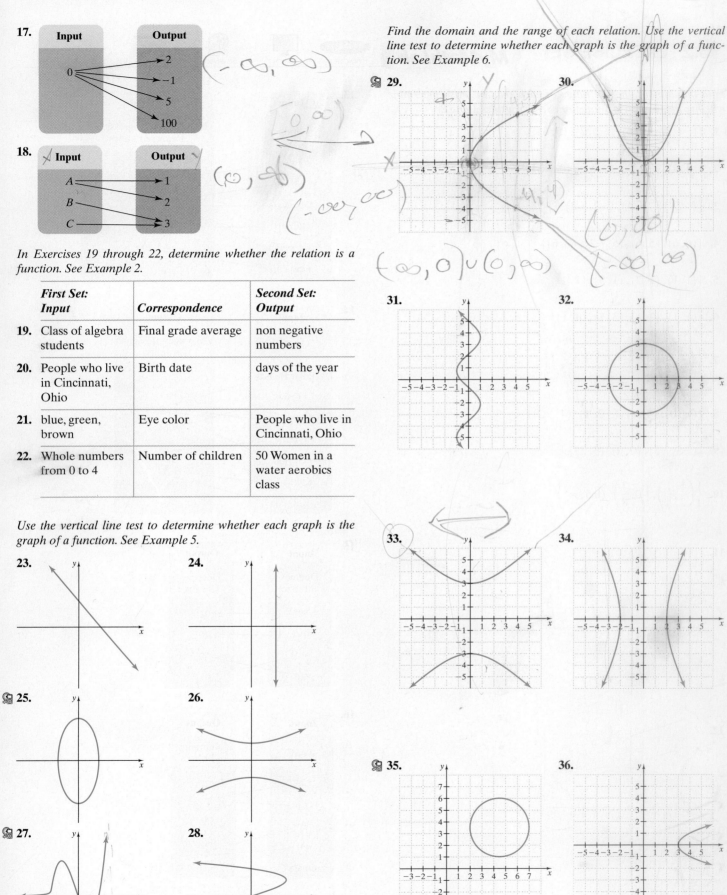

17.

Input	Output
0	2
	−1
	5
	100

18.

Input	Output
A	1
B	2
C	3

In Exercises 19 through 22, determine whether the relation is a function. See Example 2.

First Set: Input	Correspondence	Second Set: Output
19. Class of algebra students	Final grade average	non negative numbers
20. People who live in Cincinnati, Ohio	Birth date	days of the year
21. blue, green, brown	Eye color	People who live in Cincinnati, Ohio
22. Whole numbers from 0 to 4	Number of children	50 Women in a water aerobics class

Use the vertical line test to determine whether each graph is the graph of a function. See Example 5.

23.

24.

25.

26.

27.

28.

Find the domain and the range of each relation. Use the vertical line test to determine whether each graph is the graph of a function. See Example 6.

29.

30.

31.

32.

33.

34.

35.

36.

37.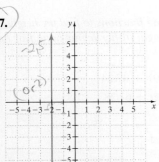

38.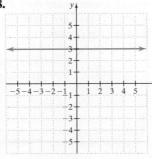

39.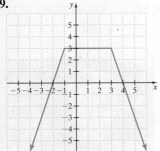

40.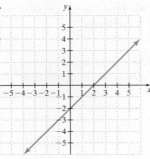

41. In your own words define **(a)** function; **(b)** domain; **(c)** range.

42. Explain the vertical line test and how it is used.

MIXED PRACTICE

Decide whether each is a function. See Examples 3 through 6.

43. $y = x + 1$

44. $y = x - 1$

45. $x = 2y^2$

46. $y = x^2$

47. $y - x = 7$

48. $2x - 3y = 9$

49. $y = \dfrac{1}{x}$

50. $y = \dfrac{1}{x - 3}$

51. $y = 5x - 12$

52. $y = \dfrac{1}{2}x + 4$

53. $x = y^2$

54. $x = |y|$

If $f(x) = 3x + 3$, $g(x) = 4x^2 - 6x + 3$, and $h(x) = 5x^2 - 7$, find the following. See Example 7.

55. $f(4)$

56. $f(-1)$

57. $h(-3)$

58. $h(0)$

59. $g(2)$

60. $g(1)$

61. $g(0)$

62. $h(-2)$

Given the following functions, find the indicated values. See Example 7.

63. $f(x) = \dfrac{1}{2}x;$

  a. $f(0)$ **b.** $f(2)$ **c.** $f(-2)$

64. $g(x) = -\dfrac{1}{3}x;$

  a. $g(0)$ **b.** $g(-1)$ **c.** $g(3)$

65. $g(x) = 2x^2 + 4;$

  a. $g(-11)$ **b.** $g(-1)$ **c.** $g\left(\dfrac{1}{2}\right)$

66. $h(x) = -x^2;$

  a. $h(-5)$ **b.** $h\left(-\dfrac{1}{3}\right)$ **c.** $h\left(\dfrac{1}{3}\right)$

67. $f(x) = -5;$

  a. $f(2)$ **b.** $f(0)$ **c.** $f(606)$

68. $h(x) = 7;$

  a. $h(7)$ **b.** $h(542)$ **c.** $h\left(-\dfrac{3}{4}\right)$

69. $f(x) = 1.3x^2 - 2.6x + 5.1$

  a. $f(2)$ **b.** $f(-2)$ **c.** $f(3.1)$

70. $g(x) = 2.7x^2 + 6.8x - 10.2$

  a. $g(1)$ **b.** $g(-5)$ **c.** $g(7.2)$

Use the graph of the functions below to answer Exercises 71 through 82. See Example 8.

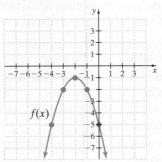

71. If $f(1) = -10$, write the corresponding ordered pair.

72. If $f(-5) = -10$, write the corresponding ordered pair.

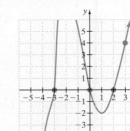

73. If $g(4) = 56$, write the corresponding ordered pair.

74. If $g(-2) = 8$, write the corresponding ordered pair.

75. Find $f(-1)$.

76. Find $f(-2)$.

77. Find $g(2)$.

78. Find $g(-4)$.

79. Find all values of x such that $f(x) = -5$.

80. Find all values of x such that $f(x) = -2$.

81. Find all positive values of x such that $g(x) = 4$.

82. Find all values of x such that $g(x) = 0$.

83. What is the greatest number of x-intercepts that a function may have? Explain your answer.

84. What is the greatest number of y-intercepts that a function may have? Explain your answer.

Use the graph in Example 9 to answer the following. Also see Example 10.

85. **a.** Use the graph to approximate the money spent on research and development in 1996.

    b. Recall that the function $f(x) = 2.602x - 5178$ approximates the graph in Example 9. Use this equation to approximate the money spent on research and development in 1996.

86. **a.** Use the graph to approximate the money spent on research and development in 1999.

    b. Use the function $f(x) = 2.602x - 5178$ to approximate the money spent on research and development in 1999.

The function $f(x) = 0.42x + 10.5$, can be used to predict diamond production. For this function, x is the number of years after 2000, and $f(x)$ is the value (in billions of dollars) of the years diamond production. (See the Chapter 3 opener.)

87. Use the function in the directions above to predict diamond production in 2012.

88. Use the function in the directions above to predict diamond production in 2015.

89. Since $y = x + 7$ describes a function, rewrite the equation using function notation.

90. In your own words, explain how to find the domain of a function given its graph.

The function $A(r) = \pi r^2$ may be used to find the area of a circle if we are given its radius.

91. Find the area of a circle whose radius is 5 centimeters. (Do not approximate π.)

92. Find the area of a circular garden whose radius is 8 feet. (Do not approximate π.)

The function $V(x) = x^3$ may be used to find the volume of a cube if we are given the length x of a side.

93. Find the volume of a cube whose side is 14 inches.

94. Find the volume of a die whose side is 1.7 centimeters.

Forensic scientists use the following functions to find the height of a woman if they are given the height of her femur bone f or her tibia bone t in centimeters.

$$H(f) = 2.59f + 47.24$$
$$H(t) = 2.72t + 61.28$$

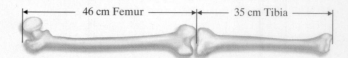

46 cm Femur   35 cm Tibia

95. Find the height of a woman whose femur measures 46 centimeters.

96. Find the height of a woman whose tibia measures 35 centimeters.

The dosage in milligrams D of Ivermectin, a heartworm preventive, for a dog who weighs x pounds is given by

$$D(x) = \frac{136}{25}x$$

97. Find the proper dosage for a dog that weighs 30 pounds.

98. Find the proper dosage for a dog that weighs 50 pounds.

99. The per capita consumption (in pounds) of all poultry in the United States is approximated by the function $C(x) = 2.28x + 94.86$, where x is the number of years since 2001. (*Source*: Based on actual and estimated data from the Economic Research Service, U.S. Department of Agriculture)

    a. Find and interpret $C(5)$.

    b. Estimate the per capita consumption of all poultry in the United States in 2007.

100. The average length of U.S. hospital stays has been decreasing, following the equation $y = -0.09x + 8.02$ where x is the number of years since 1970. (*Source:* National Center for Health Statistics)

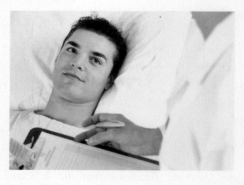

    a. What was the length of the average hospital stay in 1995?

    b. If this trend continues, what will the average length be in 2011?

REVIEW AND PREVIEW

Complete the given table and use the table to graph the linear equation. See Section 3.1.

101. $x - y = -5$

x	0		1
y		0	

102. $2x + 3y = 10$

x	0		
y		0	2

103. $7x + 4y = 8$

x	0		
y		0	-1

104. $5y - x = -15$

x	0		-2
y		0	

105. $y = 6x$

x	0		-1
y		0	

106. $y = -2x$

x	0		-2
y		0	

△ **107.** Is it possible to find the perimeter of the following geometric figure? If so, find the perimeter.

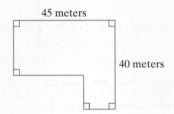

45 meters

40 meters

CONCEPT EXTENSIONS

For Exercises 108 through 111, suppose that $y = f(x)$ and it is true that $f(7) = 50$. Determine whether each is true or false. See the second Concept Check in this section.

108. An ordered-pair solution of the function is $(7, 50)$.

109. When x is 50, y is 7.

110. A possible function is $f(x) = x^2 + 1$.

111. A possible function is $f(x) = 10x - 20$.

Given the following functions, find the indicated values.

112. $f(x) = 2x + 7$;
   a. $f(2)$ **b.** $f(a)$

113. $g(x) = -3x + 12$;
   a. $g(s)$ **b.** $g(r)$

114. $h(x) = x^2 + 7$;
   a. $h(3)$ **b.** $h(a)$

115. $f(x) = x^2 - 12$;
   a. $f(12)$ **b.** $f(a)$

116. Describe a function whose domain is the set of people in your hometown.

117. Describe a function whose domain is the set of people in your algebra class.

3.3 GRAPHING LINEAR FUNCTIONS

OBJECTIVES

1 Graph linear functions.

2 Graph linear functions by finding intercepts.

3 Graph vertical and horizontal lines.

OBJECTIVE 1 ▶ Graphing linear functions. In this section, we identify and graph linear functions. By the vertical line test, we know that all linear equations except those whose graphs are vertical lines are functions. For example, we know from Section 3.1 that $y = 2x$ is a linear equation in two variables. Its graph is shown.

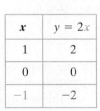

x	y = 2x
1	2
0	0
-1	-2

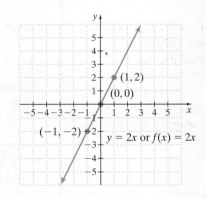

$y = 2x$ or $f(x) = 2x$

Because this graph passes the vertical line test, we know that $y = 2x$ is a function. If we want to emphasize that this equation describes a function, we may write $y = 2x$ as $f(x) = 2x$.

EXAMPLE 1 Graph $g(x) = 2x + 1$. Compare this graph with the graph of $f(x) = 2x$.

Solution To graph $g(x) = 2x + 1$, find three ordered pair solutions.

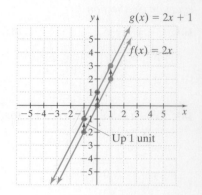

x	$f(x) = 2x$	$g(x) = 2x + 1$
		⌐add 1⌐
0	0	1
−1	−2	−1
1	2	3

Notice that y-values for the graph of $g(x) = 2x + 1$ are obtained by adding 1 to each y-value of each corresponding point of the graph of $f(x) = 2x$. The graph of $g(x) = 2x + 1$ is the same as the graph of $f(x) = 2x$ shifted upward 1 unit. □

PRACTICE
1 Graph $g(x) = 4x - 3$ and $f(x) = 4x$ on the same axes.

In general, a **linear function** is a function that can be written in the form $f(x) = mx + b$. For example, $g(x) = 2x + 1$ is in this form, with $m = 2$ and $b = 1$.

EXAMPLE 2 Graph the linear functions $f(x) = -3x$ and $g(x) = -3x - 6$ on the same set of axes.

Solution To graph $f(x)$ and $g(x)$, find ordered pair solutions.

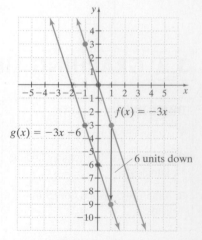

x	$f(x) = -3x$	$g(x) = -3x - 6$
		⌐subtract 6⌐
0	0	−6
1	−3	−9
−1	3	−3
−2	6	0
	⌐subtract 6⌐	

Each y-value for the graph of $g(x) = -3x - 6$ is obtained by subtracting 6 from the y-value of the corresponding point of the graph of $f(x) = -3x$. The graph of $g(x) = -3x - 6$ is the same as the graph of $f(x) = -3x$ shifted down 6 units. □

PRACTICE
2 Graph the linear functions $f(x) = -2x$ and $g(x) = -2x + 5$ on the same set of axes.

OBJECTIVE 2 ▶ Graphing linear functions using intercepts. Notice that the y-intercept of the graph of $g(x) = -3x - 6$ in the preceding figure is $(0, -6)$. In general, if *a linear function is written in the form* $f(x) = mx + b$ *or* $y = mx + b$, *the y-intercept is* $(0, b)$. This is because if x is 0, then $f(x) = mx + b$ becomes $f(0) = m \cdot 0 + b = b$, and we have the ordered pair solution $(0, b)$. We will study this form more in the next section.

EXAMPLE 3   Find the y-intercept of the graph of each equation.

a. $f(x) = \dfrac{1}{2}x + \dfrac{3}{7}$ **b.** $y = -2.5x - 3.2$

Solution

a. The y-intercept of $f(x) = \dfrac{1}{2}x + \dfrac{3}{7}$ is $\left(0, \dfrac{3}{7}\right)$.

b. The y-intercept of $y = -2.5x - 3.2$ is $(0, -3.2)$.   ☐

PRACTICE

3   Find the y-intercept of the graph of each equation.

a. $f(x) = \dfrac{3}{4}x - \dfrac{2}{5}$ **b.** $y = 2.6x + 4.1$

In general, to find the y-intercept of the graph of an equation not in the form $y = mx + b$, let $x = 0$ since any point on the y-axis has an x-coordinate of 0. To find the x-intercept of a line, let $y = 0$ or $f(x) = 0$ since any point on the x-axis has a y-coordinate of 0.

> **Finding x- and y-Intercepts**
> To find an x-intercept, let $y = 0$ or $f(x) = 0$ and solve for x.
> To find a y-intercept, let $x = 0$ and solve for y.

Intercepts are usually easy to find and plot since one coordinate is 0.

EXAMPLE 4   Find the intercepts and graph: $3x + 4y = -12$.

Solution   To find the y-intercept, we let $x = 0$ and solve for y. To find the x-intercept, we let $y = 0$ and solve for x. Let's let $x = 0$, $y = 0$, and then let $x = 2$ to find a third point as a check.

Let $x = 0$.	Let $y = 0$.	Let $x = 2$.
$3x + 4y = -12$	$3x + 4y = -12$	$3x + 4y = -12$
$3 \cdot 0 + 4y = -12$	$3x + 4 \cdot 0 = -12$	$3 \cdot 2 + 4y = -12$
$4y = -12$	$3x = -12$	$6 + 4y = -12$
$y = -3$	$x = -4$	$4y = -18$
		$y = -\dfrac{18}{4} = -4\dfrac{1}{2}$
$(0, -3)$	$(-4, 0)$	$\left(2, -4\dfrac{1}{2}\right)$

The ordered pairs are on the table below. The graph of $3x + 4y = -12$ is the line drawn through these points, as shown.

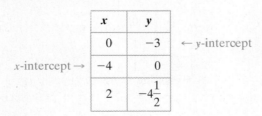

x	y	
0	-3	← y-intercept
-4	0	
2	$-4\dfrac{1}{2}$	

x-intercept →

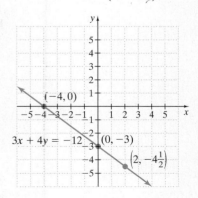

PRACTICE

4   Find the intercepts and graph: $4x - 5y = -20$.

Notice that the equation $3x + 4y = -12$ describes a linear function—"linear" because its graph is a line and "function" because the graph passes the vertical line test.

If we want to emphasize that the equation $3x + 4y = -12$ from Example 4 describes a function, first solve the equation for y.

$$3x + 4y = -12$$

$$4y = -3x - 12 \quad \text{Subtract } x \text{ from both sides.}$$

$$\frac{4y}{4} = \frac{-3x}{4} - \frac{12}{4} \quad \text{Divide both sides by } -3.$$

$$y = -\frac{3}{4}x - 3 \quad \text{Simplify.}$$

Next, let

$$y = f(x).$$

$$f(x) = -\frac{3}{4}x - 3$$

> ▶ **Helpful Hint**
>
> Any linear equation that describes a function can be written using function notation. To do so,
>
> 1. solve the equation for y and then
> 2. replace y with $f(x)$, as we did above.

EXAMPLE 5 Graph $x = -2y$ by plotting intercepts.

Solution Let $y = 0$ to find the x-intercept and $x = 0$ to find the y-intercept.

If $y = 0$	then	If $x = 0$	then
$x = -2(0)$	or	$0 = -2y$	or
$x = 0$		$0 = y$	
$(0, 0)$		$(0, 0)$	

Ordered pairs Both the x-intercept and y-intercept are $(0, 0)$. This happens when the graph passes through the origin. Since two points are needed to determine a line, we must find at least one more ordered pair that satisfies $x = -2y$. Let $y = -1$ to find a second ordered pair solution and let $y = 1$ as a check point.

If $y = -1$	then	If $y = 1$	then
$x = -2(-1)$	or	$x = -2(1)$	or
$x = 2$		$x = -2$	

The ordered pairs are $(0, 0)$, $(2, -1)$, and $(-2, 1)$. Plot these points to graph $x = -2y$.

x	y
0	0
2	−1
−2	1

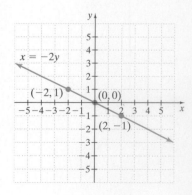

PRACTICE
5 Graph $y = -3x$ by plotting intercepts.

OBJECTIVE 3 ▶ Graphing vertical and horizontal lines. The equations $x = c$ and $y = c$, where c is a real number constant, are both linear equations in two variables. Why? Because $x = c$ can be written as $x + 0y = c$ and $y = c$ can be written as $0x + y = c$. We graph these two special linear equations below.

EXAMPLE 6   Graph $x = 2$.

Solution   The equation $x = 2$ can be written as $x + 0y = 2$. For any y-value chosen, notice that x is 2. No other value for x satisfies $x + 0y = 2$. Any ordered pair whose x-coordinate is 2 is a solution to $x + 0y = 2$ because 2 added to 0 times any value of y is $2 + 0$, or 2. We will use the ordered pairs $(2, 3), (2, 0)$ and $(2, -3)$ to graph $x = 2$.

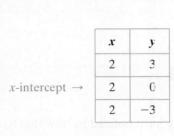

	x	y
	2	3
x-intercept →	2	0
	2	-3

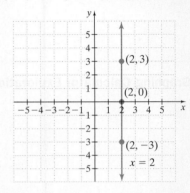

The graph is a vertical line with x-intercept $(2, 0)$. Notice that this graph is not the graph of a function, and it has no y-intercept because x is never 0.   ☐

PRACTICE
6   Graph $x = -4$.

EXAMPLE 7   Graph $y = -3$.

Solution   The equation $y = -3$ can be written as $0x + y = -3$. For any x-value chosen, y is -3. If we choose 4, 0, and -2 as x-values, the ordered pair solutions are $(4, -3), (0, -3)$, and $(-2, -3)$. We will use these ordered pairs to graph $y = -3$.

x	y
4	-3
0	-3	← y-intercept
-2	-3

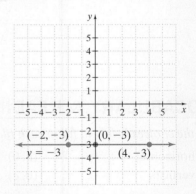

The graph is a horizontal line with y-intercept $(0, -3)$ and no x-intercept. Notice that this graph is the graph of a function.   ☐

PRACTICE
7   Graph $y = 4$.

From Examples 6 and 7, we have the following generalization.

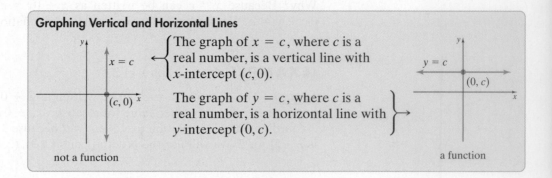

Graphing Vertical and Horizontal Lines

The graph of $x = c$, where c is a real number, is a vertical line with x-intercept $(c, 0)$.

The graph of $y = c$, where c is a real number, is a horizontal line with y-intercept $(0, c)$.

not a function

a function

Graphing Calculator Explorations

You may have noticed by now that to use the $\boxed{Y =}$ key on a graphing calculator to graph an equation, the equation must be solved for y.

Graph each function by first solving the function for y.

1. $x = 3.5y$

2. $-2.7y = x$

3. $5.78x + 2.31y = 10.98$

4. $-7.22x + 3.89y = 12.57$

5. $y - |x| = 3.78$

6. $3y - 5x^2 = 6x - 4$

7. $y - 5.6x^2 = 7.7x + 1.5$

8. $y + 2.6|x| = -3.2$

VOCABULARY & READINESS CHECK

Use the choices below to fill in each blank. Some choices may be used more than once and some not at all.

| horizontal | y | $(c, 0)$ | $(b, 0)$ | $(m, 0)$ | linear |
| vertical | x | $(0, c)$ | $(0, b)$ | $(0, m)$ | $f(x)$ |

1. A _____ function can be written in the form $f(x) = mx + b$.

2. In the form $f(x) = mx + b$, the y-intercept is _____.

3. The graph of $x = c$ is a _____ line with x-intercept _____.

4. The graph of $y = c$ is a _____ line with y-intercept _____.

5. To find an x-intercept, let _____ = 0 or _____ = 0 and solve for _____.

6. To find a y-intercept, let _____ = 0 and solve for _____.

3.3 | EXERCISE SET

  MyMathLab

Powered by CourseCompass™ and MathXL®

Math XL
PRACTICE   WATCH   DOWNLOAD   READ   REVIEW

Graph each linear function. See Examples 1 and 2.

1. $f(x) = -2x$

2. $f(x) = 2x$

3. $f(x) = -2x + 3$

4. $f(x) = 2x + 6$

5. $f(x) = \frac{1}{2}x$

6. $f(x) = \frac{1}{3}x$

7. $f(x) = \frac{1}{2}x - 4$

8. $f(x) = \frac{1}{3}x - 2$

The graph of $f(x) = 5x$ follows. Use this graph to match each linear function with its graph. See Examples 1 through 3.

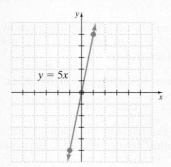

$y = 5x$

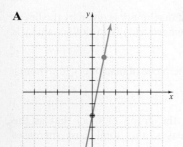

A

B

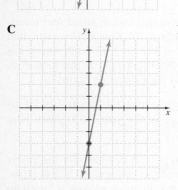

C

D

9. $f(x) = 5x - 3$

10. $f(x) = 5x - 2$

11. $f(x) = 5x + 1$

12. $f(x) = 5x + 3$

Graph each linear function by finding x- and y-intercepts. Then write each equation using function notation. See Examples 4 and 5.

13. $x - y = 3$

14. $x - y = -4$

15. $x = 5y$

16. $2x = y$

17. $-x + 2y = 6$

18. $x - 2y = -8$

19. $2x - 4y = 8$

20. $2x + 3y = 6$

21. In your own words, explain how to find x- and y-intercepts.

22. Explain why it is a good idea to use three points to graph a linear equation.

Graph each linear equation. See Examples 6 and 7.

23. $x = -1$

24. $y = 5$

25. $y = 0$

26. $x = 0$

27. $y + 7 = 0$

28. $x - 3 = 0$

Match each equation below with its graph.

A

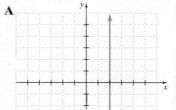

B

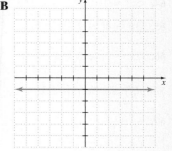

C

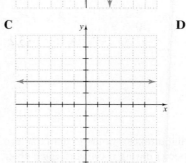

D

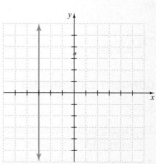

29. $y = 2$

30. $x = -3$

31. $x - 2 = 0$

32. $y + 1 = 0$

33. Discuss whether a vertical line ever has a y-intercept.

34. Discuss whether a horizontal line ever has an x-intercept.

MIXED PRACTICE

Graph each linear equation. See Examples 1 through 7.

35. $x + 2y = 8$

36. $x - 3y = 3$

37. $3x + 5y = 7$

38. $3x - 2y = 5$

39. $x + 8y = 8$

40. $x - 3y = 9$

41. $5 = 6x - y$

42. $4 = x - 3y$

43. $-x + 10y = 11$

44. $-x + 9 = -y$

45. $y = \dfrac{3}{2}$

46. $x = \dfrac{3}{2}$

47. $2x + 3y = 6$

48. $4x + y = 5$

49. $x + 3 = 0$

50. $y - 6 = 0$

51. $f(x) = \dfrac{3}{4}x + 2$

52. $f(x) = \dfrac{4}{3}x + 2$

53. $f(x) = x$

54. $f(x) = -x$

55. $f(x) = \dfrac{1}{2}x$

56. $f(x) = -2x$

57. $f(x) = 4x - \dfrac{1}{3}$

58. $f(x) = -3x + \dfrac{3}{4}$

59. $x = -3$

60. $f(x) = 3$

REVIEW AND PREVIEW

Solve the following. See Sections 2.6 and 2.7.

61. $|x - 3| = 6$

62. $|x + 2| < 4$

63. $|2x + 5| > 3$

64. $|5x| = 10$

65. $|3x - 4| \le 2$

66. $|7x - 2| \ge 5$

Simplify. See Section 1.3.

67. $\dfrac{-6 - 3}{2 - 8}$

68. $\dfrac{4 - 5}{-1 - 0}$

69. $\dfrac{-8 - (-2)}{-3 - (-2)}$

70. $\dfrac{12 - 3}{10 - 9}$

71. $\dfrac{0 - 6}{5 - 0}$

72. $\dfrac{2 - 2}{3 - 5}$

CONCEPT EXTENSIONS

Solve.

73. Broyhill Furniture found that it takes 2 hours to manufacture each table for one of its special dining room sets. Each chair takes 3 hours to manufacture. A total of 1500 hours is available to produce tables and chairs of this style. The linear equation that models this situation is $2x + 3y = 1500$, where x represents the number of tables produced and y the number of chairs produced.

  a. Complete the ordered pair solution $(0, \ )$ of this equation. Describe the manufacturing situation this solution corresponds to.

  b. Complete the ordered pair solution $(\ , 0)$ for this equation. Describe the manufacturing situation this solution corresponds to.

  c. If 50 tables are produced, find the greatest number of chairs the company can make.

74. While manufacturing two different camera models, Kodak found that the basic model costs \$55 to produce, whereas the deluxe model costs \$75. The weekly budget for these two models is limited to \$33,000 in production costs. The linear equation that models this situation is $55x + 75y = 33,000$, where x represents the number of basic models and y the number of deluxe models.

  a. Complete the ordered pair solution $(0, \ )$ of this equation. Describe the manufacturing situation this solution corresponds to.

  b. Complete the ordered pair solution $(\ , 0)$ of this equation. Describe the manufacturing situation this solution corresponds to.

  c. If 350 deluxe models are produced, find the greatest number of basic models that can be made in one week.

75. The cost of renting a car for a day is given by the linear function $C(x) = 0.2x + 24$, where $C(x)$ is in dollars and x is the number of miles driven.

  a. Find the cost of driving the car 200 miles.

  b. Graph $C(x) = 0.2x + 24$.

  c. How can you tell from the graph of $C(x)$ that as the number of miles driven increases, the total cost increases also?

76. The cost of renting a piece of machinery is given by the linear function $C(x) = 4x + 10$, where $C(x)$ is in dollars and x is given in hours.

  a. Find the cost of renting the piece of machinery for 8 hours.

  b. Graph $C(x) = 4x + 10$.

  c. How can you tell from the graph of $C(x)$ that as the number of hours increases, the total cost increases also?

77. The yearly cost of tuition (in-state) and required fees for attending a public two-year college full time can be estimated by the linear function $f(x) = 107.3x + 1245.62$, where x is the number of years after 2000 and $f(x)$ is the total cost. (*Source:* U.S. National Center for Education Statistics)

  a. Use this function to approximate the yearly cost of attending a two-year college in the year 2015. [*Hint:* Find $f(15)$.]

  b. Use the given function to predict in what year the yearly cost of tuition and required fees will exceed \$2500. [*Hint:* Let $f(x) = 2500$, solve for x, then round your solution up to the next whole year.

  c. Use this function to approximate the yearly cost of attending a two-year college in the present year. If you attend a two-year college, is this amount greater than or less than the amount that is currently charged by the college you attend?

78. The yearly cost of tuition (in-state) and required fees for attending a public four-year college full time can be estimated by the linear function $f(x) = 291.5x + 2944.05$, where x is the number of years after 2000 and $f(x)$ is the total cost in dollars. (*Source:* U.S. National Center for Education Statistics)

  a. Use this function to approximate the yearly cost of attending a four-year college in the year 2015. [*Hint:* Find $f(15)$.]

  b. Use the given function to predict in what year the yearly cost of tuition and required fees will exceed $6000. [*Hint:* Let $f(x) = 6000$, solve for x, then round your solution up to the next whole year.]

  c. Use this function to approximate the yearly cost of attending a four-year college in the present year. If you attend a four-year college, is this amount greater than or less than the amount that is currently charged by the college you attend?

Use a graphing calculator to verify the results of each exercise.

79. Exercise 9   **80.** Exercise 10

81. Exercise 17   **82.** Exercise 18

83. The graph of $f(x)$ or $y = -4x$ is given below. Without actually graphing, describe the shape and location of

  a. $y = -4x + 2$ **b.** $y = -4x - 5$

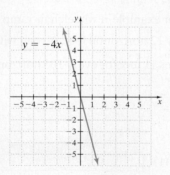

It is true that for any function $f(x)$, the graph of $f(x) + K$ is the same as the graph of $f(x)$ shifted K units up if K is positive and $|K|$ units down if K is negative. (We study this further in Section 3.7.)

The graph of $y = |x|$ is

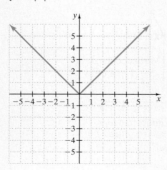

Without actually graphing, match each equation with its graph.

  a. $y = |x| - 1$

  b. $y = |x| + 1$

  c. $y = |x| - 3$

  d. $y = |x| + 3$

84.

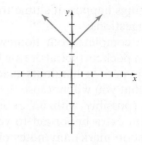

85.

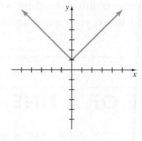

86.

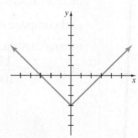

87.

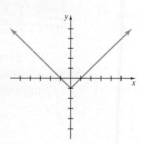

STUDY SKILLS BUILDER

Are You Organized?

When it's time to study for a test, are your notes neat and organized? Have you ever had trouble reading your own mathematics handwriting? (Be honest—I have.)

When any of these things happen, it's time to get organized. Here are a few suggestions:

Write your notes and complete your homework assignment in a notebook with pockets (spiral or ring binder.) When you receive graded papers or handouts, place them in the notebook pocket so that you will not lose them.

Remember to mark (possibly with an exclamation point) any note(s) that seem extra important to you. Also mark (possibly with a question mark) any notes or homework that you are having trouble with.

Also, if you are having trouble reading your own handwriting, *slow down* and write your mathematics work clearly!

Exercises

1. Have you been completing your assignments on time?
2. Have you been correcting any exercises you may be having difficulty with?
3. If you are having trouble with a mathematical concept or correcting any homework exercises, have you visited your instructor, a tutor, or your campus math lab?
4. Are you taking lecture notes in your mathematics course? (By the way, these notes should include all worked-out examples solved by your instructor.)
5. Is your mathematics course material (handouts, graded papers, lecture notes) organized?
6. If your answer to Exercise 5 is no, take a moment and review your course material. List at least two ways that you might better organize it. Then read the Study Skills Builder on organizing a notebook in Chapter 2.

3.4 THE SLOPE OF A LINE

OBJECTIVES

1 Find the slope of a line given two points on the line.

2 Find the slope of a line given the equation of a line.

3 Interpret the slope-intercept form in an application.

4 Find the slopes of horizontal and vertical lines.

5 Compare the slopes of parallel and perpendicular lines.

OBJECTIVE 1 ▶ Finding slope given two points. You may have noticed by now that different lines often tilt differently. It is very important in many fields to be able to measure and compare the tilt, or **slope,** of lines. For example, a wheelchair ramp with a slope of $\frac{1}{12}$ means that the ramp rises 1 foot for every 12 horizontal feet. A road with a slope or grade of 11% $\left(\text{or } \frac{11}{100}\right)$ means that the road rises 11 feet for every 100 horizontal feet.

We measure the slope of a line as a ratio of **vertical change** to **horizontal change.** Slope is usually designated by the letter m.

Suppose that we want to measure the slope of the following line.

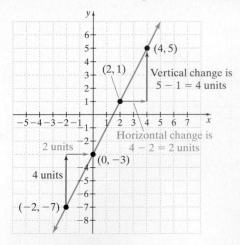

The vertical change between *both* pairs of points on the line is 4 units per horizontal change of 2 units. Then

$$\text{slope } m = \frac{\text{change in } y \text{ (vertical change)}}{\text{change in } x \text{ (horizontal change)}} = \frac{4}{2} = 2$$

We can also think of slope as a **rate of change** between points. A slope of 2 or $\frac{2}{1}$ means that between pairs of points on the line, the rate of change is a vertical change of 2 units per horizontal change of 1 unit.

Consider the line in the box below, which passes through the points (x_1, y_1) and (x_2, y_2). (The notation x_1 is read "x-sub-one.") The vertical change, or *rise*, between these points is the difference of the y-coordinates: $y_2 - y_1$. The horizontal change, or *run*, between the points is the difference of the x-coordinates: $x_2 - x_1$.

Slope of a Line

Given a line passing through points (x_1, y_1) and (x_2, y_2) the **slope** m of the line is

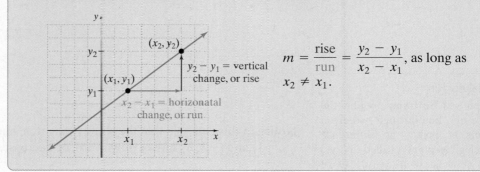

$$m = \frac{\text{rise}}{\text{run}} = \frac{y_2 - y_1}{x_2 - x_1}, \text{ as long as } x_2 \neq x_1.$$

Concept Check ✓

In the definition of slope, we state that $x_2 \neq x_1$. Explain why.

EXAMPLE 1   Find the slope of the line containing the points $(0, 3)$ and $(2, 5)$. Graph the line.

Solution   We use the slope formula. It does not matter which point we call (x_1, y_1) and which point we call (x_2, y_2). We'll let $(x_1, y_1) = (0, 3)$ and $(x_2, y_2) = (2, 5)$.

$$m = \frac{y_2 - y_1}{x_2 - x_1}$$

$$= \frac{5 - 3}{2 - 0} = \frac{2}{2} = 1$$

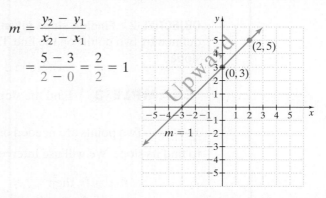

Notice in this example that the slope is *positive* and that the graph of the line containing $(0, 3)$ and $(2, 5)$ moves *upward*, or increases, as we go from left to right.   □

PRACTICE

1   Find the slope of the line containing the points $(4, 0)$ and $(-2, 3)$. Graph the line.

Answer to Concept Check:
So that the denominator is not 0

> ▶ **Helpful Hint**
> The slope of a line is the same no matter which 2 points of a line you choose to calculate slope. The line in Example 1 also contains the point $(-3, 0)$. Below, we calculate the slope of the line using $(0, 3)$ as (x_1, y_1) and $(-3, 0)$ as (x_2, y_2).
>
> $$m = \frac{y_2 - y_1}{x_2 - x_1} = \frac{0 - 3}{-3 - 0} = \frac{-3}{-3} = 1 \quad \text{Same slope as found in Example 1.}$$

EXAMPLE 2 Find the slope of the line containing the points $(5, -4)$ and $(-3, 3)$. Graph the line.

Solution We use the slope formula, and let $(x_1, y_1) = (5, -4)$ and $(x_2, y_2) = (-3, 3)$.

$$m = \frac{y_2 - y_1}{x_2 - x_1}$$

$$= \frac{3 - (-4)}{-3 - 5} = \frac{7}{-8} = -\frac{7}{8}$$

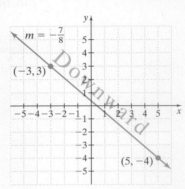

Notice in this example that the slope is negative and that the graph of the line through $(5, -4)$ and $(-3, 3)$ moves downward, or decreases, as we go from left to right. □

PRACTICE
2 Find the slope of the line containing the points $(-5, -4)$ and $(5, 2)$. Graph the line.

> ▶ **Helpful Hint**
> When we are trying to find the slope of a line through two given points, it makes no difference which given point is called (x_1, y_1) and which is called (x_2, y_2). Once an x-coordinate is called x_1, however, make sure its corresponding y-coordinate is called y_1.

Concept Check ☑

Find and correct the error in the following calculation of slope of the line containing the points $(12, 2)$ and $(4, 7)$.

$$m = \frac{12 - 4}{2 - 7} = \cancel{\frac{8}{-5}} = -\frac{8}{5}$$

OBJECTIVE 2 ▶ Finding slope given an equation. As we have seen, the slope of a line is defined by two points on the line. Thus, if we know the equation of a line, we can find its slope.

EXAMPLE 3 Find the slope of the line whose equation is $f(x) = \frac{2}{3}x + 4$.

Solution Two points are needed on the line defined by $f(x) = \frac{2}{3}x + 4$ or $y = \frac{2}{3}x + 4$ to find its slope. We will use intercepts as our two points.

If $x = 0$, then

$$y = \frac{2}{3} \cdot 0 + 4$$

$$y = 4$$

If $y = 0$, then

$$0 = \frac{2}{3}x + 4$$

$$-4 = \frac{2}{3}x \quad \text{Subtract 4.}$$

$$\frac{3}{2}(-4) = \frac{3}{2} \cdot \frac{2}{3}x \quad \text{Multiply by } \frac{3}{2}.$$

$$-6 = x$$

Answer to Concept Check:
$m = \dfrac{2 - 7}{12 - 4} = \dfrac{-5}{8} = -\dfrac{5}{8}$

Use the points $(0, 4)$ and $(-6, 0)$ to find the slope. Let (x_1, y_1) be $(0, 4)$ and (x_2, y_2) be $(-6, 0)$. Then

$$m = \frac{y_2 - y_1}{x_2 - x_1} = \frac{0 - 4}{-6 - 0} = \frac{-4}{-6} = \frac{2}{3}$$

□

PRACTICE
3 Find the slope of the line whose equation is $f(x) = -4x + 6$.

Analyzing the results of Example 3, you may notice a striking pattern:
The slope of $y = \frac{2}{3}x + 4$ is $\frac{2}{3}$, the same as the coefficient of x.
Also, the y-intercept is $(0, 4)$, as expected.

When a linear equation is written in the form $f(x) = mx + b$ or $y = mx + b$, m is the slope of the line and $(0, b)$ is its y-intercept. The form $y = mx + b$ is appropriately called the **slope–intercept form.**

> **Slope–Intercept Form**
> When a linear equation in two variables is written in slope–intercept form,
>
> slope y-intercept is $(0, b)$
> ↓   ↓
> $$y = mx + b$$
>
> then m is the slope of the line and $(0, b)$ is the y-intercept of the line.

EXAMPLE 4 Find the slope and the y-intercept of the line $3x - 4y = 4$.

Solution We write the equation in slope–intercept form by solving for y.

$$3x - 4y = 4$$
$$-4y = -3x + 4 \qquad \text{Subtract } 3x \text{ from both sides.}$$
$$\frac{-4y}{-4} = \frac{-3x}{-4} + \frac{4}{-4} \qquad \text{Divide both sides by } -4.$$
$$y = \frac{3}{4}x - 1 \qquad \text{Simplify.}$$

The coefficient of x, $\frac{3}{4}$, is the slope, and the y-intercept is $(0, -1)$.   □

PRACTICE
4 Find the slope and the y-intercept of the line $2x - 3y = 9$.

OBJECTIVE 3 ▶ Interpreting slope-intercept form. On the following page is the graph of one-day ticket prices at Disney World for the years shown.

Notice that the graph resembles the graph of a line. Recall that businesses often depend on equations that "closely fit" graphs like this one to model the data and to predict future trends. By the **least squares** method, the linear function $f(x) = 2.7x + 33.64$ approximates the data shown, where x is the number of years since 1996 and y is the ticket price for that year.

> ▶ **Helpful Hint**
> The notation $0 \leftrightarrow 1996$ below the graph on the next page means that the number 0 corresponds to the year 1996, 1 corresponds to the year 1997, and so on.

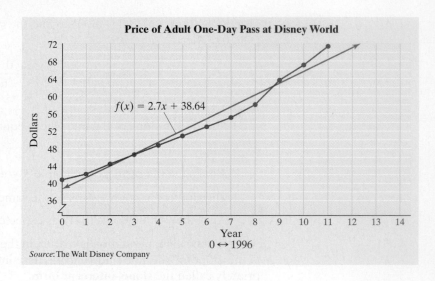

Price of Adult One-Day Pass at Disney World

$f(x) = 2.7x + 38.64$

Dollars

Year
0 ↔ 1996

Source: The Walt Disney Company

EXAMPLE 5   **Predicting Future Prices**

The adult one-day pass price $f(x)$ for Disney World is given by

$$f(x) = 2.7x + 38.64$$

where x is the number of years since 1996

a. Use this equation to predict the ticket price for the year 2010.

b. What does the slope of this equation mean?

c. What does the y-intercept of this equation mean?

Solution

a. To predict the price of a pass in 2010, we need to find $f(14)$. (Since year 1996 corresponds to $x = 0$, year 2010 corresponds to $x = 14$.)

$$f(x) = 2.7x + 38.64$$
$$f(14) = 2.7(14) + 38.64 \quad \text{Let } x = 14.$$
$$= 76.44$$

We predict that in the year 2010 the price of an adult one-day pass to Disney World will be about \$76.44.

b. The slope of $f(x) = 2.7x + 38.64$ is 2.7. We can think of this number as $\dfrac{\text{rise}}{\text{run}}$ or $\dfrac{2.7}{1}$. This means that the ticket price increases on the average by \$2.70 every 1 year.

c. The y-intercept of $f(x) = 2.7x + 38.64$ is $(0, \ 38.64)$.
      ↑   ↑
  year price

This means that at year 0, or 1996, the ticket price was about \$38.64.   □

PRACTICE

5   Use the equation from Example 5 to predict the ticket price for the year 2012.

OBJECTIVE 4 ▶ Finding slopes of horizontal and vertical lines. Next we find the slopes of two special types of lines: vertical lines and horizontal lines.

EXAMPLE 6   Find the slope of the line $x = -5$.

Solution   Recall that the graph of $x = -5$ is a vertical line with x-intercept $(-5, 0)$. To find the slope, we find two ordered pair solutions of $x = -5$. Of course, solutions of $x = -5$ must have an x-value of -5. We will let $(x_1, y_1) = (-5, 0)$ and $(x_2, y_2) = (-5, 4)$.

Then

$$m = \frac{y_2 - y_1}{x_2 - x_1}$$

$$= \frac{4 - 0}{-5 - (-5)}$$

$$= \frac{4}{0}$$

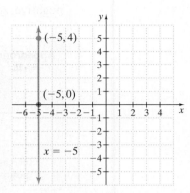

Since $\frac{4}{0}$ is undefined, we say that the slope of the vertical line $x = -5$ is undefined.   □

PRACTICE
6   Find the slope of the line $x = 4$.

EXAMPLE 7   Find the slope of the line $y = 2$.

Solution   Recall that the graph of $y = 2$ is a horizontal line with y-intercept $(0, 2)$. To find the slope, we find two points on the line, such as $(0, 2)$ and $(1, 2)$, and use these points to find the slope.

$$m = \frac{2 - 2}{1 - 0}$$

$$= \frac{0}{1}$$

$$= 0$$

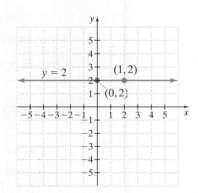

The slope of the horizontal line $y = 2$ is 0.   □

PRACTICE
7   Find the slope of the line $y = -3$.

From the previous two examples, we have the following generalization.

The slope of any vertical line is undefined.
The slope of any horizontal line is 0.

▶ **Helpful Hint**
Slope of 0 and undefined slope are not the same. Vertical lines have undefined slope, whereas horizontal lines have slope of 0.

The following four graphs summarize the overall appearance of lines with positive, negative, zero, or undefined slopes.

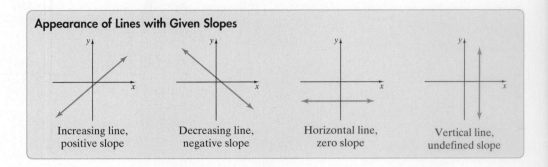

Appearance of Lines with Given Slopes

Increasing line, positive slope

Decreasing line, negative slope

Horizontal line, zero slope

Vertical line, undefined slope

The appearance of a line can give us further information about its slope.

The graphs of $y = \frac{1}{2}x + 1$ and $y = 5x + 1$ are shown to the right. Recall that the graph of $y = \frac{1}{2}x + 1$ has a slope of $\frac{1}{2}$ and that the graph of $y = 5x + 1$ has a slope of 5.

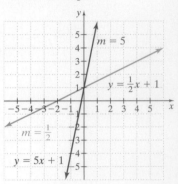

Notice that the line with the slope of 5 is steeper than the line with the slope of $\frac{1}{2}$. This is true in general for positive slopes.

> For a line with positive slope m, as m increases, the line becomes steeper.

To see why this is so, compare the slopes from above.

$\frac{1}{2}$ means a vertical change of 1 unit per horizontal change of 2 units

5 or $\frac{10}{2}$ means a vertical change of 10 units per horizontal change of 2 units

For larger positive slopes, the vertical change is greater for the same horizontal change. Thus, larger positive slopes mean steeper lines.

OBJECTIVE 5 ▶ Comparing slopes of parallel and perpendicular lines. Slopes of lines can help us determine whether lines are parallel. Parallel lines are distinct lines with the same steepness, so it follows that they have the same slope.

Parallel Lines

Two nonvertical lines are parallel if they have the same slope and different y-intercepts.

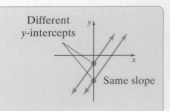

Different y-intercepts

Same slope

How do the slopes of perpendicular lines compare? (Two lines intersecting at right angles are called **perpendicular lines.**) Suppose that a line has a slope of $\frac{a}{b}$. If the line is rotated 90°, the rise and run are now switched, except that the run is now negative. This means that the new slope is $-\dfrac{b}{a}$. Notice that

$$\left(\dfrac{a}{b}\right) \cdot \left(-\dfrac{b}{a}\right) = -1$$

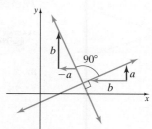

This is how we tell whether two lines are perpendicular.

Perpendicular Lines

Two nonvertical lines are perpendicular if the product of their slopes is −1.

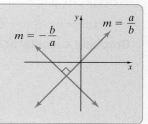

In other words, two nonvertical lines are perpendicular if the slope of one is the negative reciprocal of the slope of the other.

EXAMPLE 8   Are the following pairs of lines parallel, perpendicular, or neither?

a. $3x + 7y = 4$ **b.** $-x + 3y = 2$
    $6x + 14y = 7$ $2x + 6y = 5$

Solution   Find the slope of each line by solving each equation for y.

a.
$$3x + 7y = 4 \qquad\qquad 6x + 14y = 7$$
$$7y = -3x + 4 \qquad\qquad 14y = -6x + 7$$
$$\dfrac{7y}{7} = \dfrac{-3x}{7} + \dfrac{4}{7} \qquad\qquad \dfrac{14y}{14} = \dfrac{-6x}{14} + \dfrac{7}{14}$$
$$y = -\dfrac{3}{7}x + \dfrac{4}{7} \qquad\qquad y = -\dfrac{3}{7}x + \dfrac{1}{2}$$

slope   y-intercept   slope   y-intercept

$$\left(0, \dfrac{4}{7}\right) \qquad\qquad\qquad \left(0, \dfrac{1}{2}\right)$$

The slopes of both lines are $-\dfrac{3}{7}$.

The y-intercepts are different, so the lines are not the same.

Therefore, the lines are parallel.

$6x + 14y = 7$ $3x + 7y = 4$

b.
$$-x + 3y = 2 \qquad\qquad 2x + 6y = 5$$
$$3y = x + 2 \qquad\qquad 6y = -2x + 5$$
$$\dfrac{3y}{3} = \dfrac{x}{3} + \dfrac{2}{3} \qquad\qquad \dfrac{6y}{6} = \dfrac{-2x}{6} + \dfrac{5}{6}$$
$$y = \dfrac{1}{3}x + \dfrac{2}{3} \qquad\qquad y = -\dfrac{1}{3}x + \dfrac{5}{6}$$

slope   y-intercept   slope   y-intercept

$$\left(0, \dfrac{2}{3}\right) \qquad\qquad\qquad \left(0, \dfrac{5}{6}\right)$$

2x + 6y = 5

−x + 3y = 2

The slopes are not the same and their product is not −1. $\left[\left(\frac{1}{3}\right)\cdot\left(-\frac{1}{3}\right)=-\frac{1}{9}\right]$

Therefore, the lines are neither parallel nor perpendicular.

PRACTICE

8   Are the following pairs of lines parallel, perpendicular, or neither?

a. $x - 2y = 3$

$2x + y = 3$

b. $4x - 3y = 2$

$-8x + 6y = -6$

Concept Check ☑

What is *different* about the equations of two parallel lines?

Answer to Concept Check:

y-intercepts are different

Graphing Calculator Explorations

Many graphing calculators have a TRACE feature. This feature allows you to trace along a graph and see the corresponding *x*- and *y*-coordinates appear on the screen. Use this feature for the following exercises.

Graph each function and then use the TRACE feature to complete each ordered pair solution. (Many times the tracer will not show an exact *x*- or *y*-value asked for. In each case, trace as closely as you can to the given *x*- or *y*-coordinate and approximate the other, unknown coordinate to one decimal place.)

1. $y = 2.3x + 6.7$

$x = 5.1, y = ?$

2. $y = -4.8x + 2.9$

$x = -1.8, y = ?$

3. $y = -5.9x - 1.6$

$x = ?, y = 7.2$

4. $y = 0.4x - 8.6$

$x = ?, y = -4.4$

5. $y = x^2 + 5.2x - 3.3$

$x = 2.3, y = ?$

$x = ?, y = 36$

(There will be two answers here.)

6. $y = 5x^2 - 6.2x - 8.3$

$x = 3.2, y = ?$

$x = ?, y = 12$

(There will be two answers here.)

VOCABULARY & READINESS CHECK

Use the choices below to fill in each blank. Some choices may be used more than once and some not at all.

horizontal	the same	−1	*y*-intercepts	$(0, b)$	slope
vertical	different	*m*	*x*-intercepts	$(b, 0)$	slope-intercept

1. The measure of the steepness or tilt of a line is called _____.

2. The slope of a line through two points is measured by the ratio of _____ change to _____ change.

3. If a linear equation is in the form $y = mx + b$, or $f(x) = mx + b$, the slope of the line is _____ and the *y*-intercept is _____.

4. The form $y = mx + b$ or $f(x) = mx + b$ is the _____ form.

5. The slope of a _____ line is 0.

6. The slope of a _____ line is undefined.

7. Two non-vertical perpendicular lines have slopes whose product is _____.

8. Two non-vertical lines are parallel if they have _____ slope and different _____.

Decide whether a line with the given slope slants upward or downward from left to right, or is horizontal or vertical.

9. $m = \dfrac{7}{6}$

10. $m = -3$

11. $m = 0$

12. *m* is undefined

3.4 EXERCISE SET

Find the slope of the line that goes through the given points. See Examples 1 and 2.

1. $(3, 2), (8, 11)$
2. $(1, 6), (7, 11)$

3. $(3, 1), (1, 8)$
4. $(2, 9), (6, 4)$

5. $(-2, 8), (4, 3)$
6. $(3, 7), (-2, 11)$

7. $(-2, -6), (4, -4)$
8. $(-3, -4), (-1, 6)$

9. $(-3, -1), (-12, 11)$
10. $(3, -1), (-6, 5)$

11. $(-2, 5), (3, 5)$
12. $(4, 2), (4, 0)$

13. $(-1, 1), (-1, -5)$
14. $(-2, -5), (3, -5)$

15. $(0, 6), (-3, 0)$
16. $(5, 2), (0, 5)$

17. $(-1, 2), (-3, 4)$
18. $(3, -2), (-1, -6)$

Two lines are graphed on each set of axes. Decide whether l_1 or l_2 has the greater slope. See the boxed material on page 160.

19.
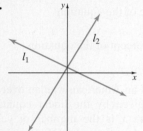

20.
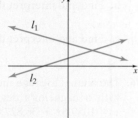

21.
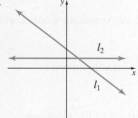

22.
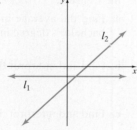

23.
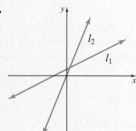

24.
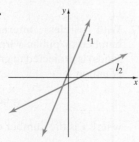

Find the slope and the y-intercept of each line. See Examples 3 and 4.

25. $f(x) = 5x - 2$

26. $f(x) = -2x + 6$

27. $2x + y = 7$

28. $-5x + y = 10$

29. $2x - 3y = 10$

30. $-3x - 4y = 6$

31. $f(x) = \dfrac{1}{2}x$

32. $f(x) = -\dfrac{1}{4}x$

Match each graph with its equation. See Examples 1 and 2.

A
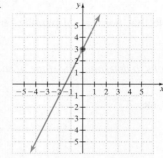

B
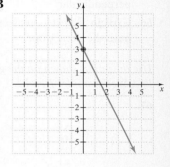

C
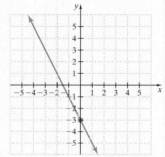

D
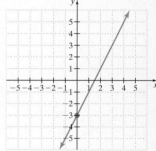

33. $f(x) = 2x + 3$
34. $f(x) = 2x - 3$

35. $f(x) = -2x + 3$
36. $f(x) = -2x - 3$

Find the slope of each line. See Examples 6 and 7.

37. $x = 1$
38. $y = -2$

39. $y = -3$
40. $x = 4$

41. $x + 2 = 0$
42. $y - 7 = 0$

43. Explain how merely looking at a line can tell us whether its slope is negative, positive, undefined, or zero.

44. Explain why the graph of $y = b$ is a horizontal line.

MIXED PRACTICE

Find the slope and the y-intercept of each line. See Examples 3 through 7.

45. $f(x) = -x + 5$
46. $f(x) = x + 2$

47. $-6x + 5y = 30$
48. $4x - 7y = 28$

49. $3x + 9 = y$
50. $2y - 7 = x$

51. $y = 4$
52. $x = 7$

53. $f(x) = 7x$
54. $f(x) = \dfrac{1}{7}x$

55. $6 + y = 0$
56. $x - 7 = 0$

57. $2 - x = 3$
58. $2y + 4 = -7$

Determine whether the lines are parallel, perpendicular, or neither. See Example 8.

△ 🔧 **59.** $f(x) = -3x + 6$
$g(x) = 3x + 5$

△ **60.** $f(x) = 5x - 6$
$g(x) = 5x + 2$

△ **61.** $-4x + 2y = 5$
$2x - y = 7$

△ **62.** $2x - y = -10$
$2x + 4y = 2$

△ **63.** $-2x + 3y = 1$
$3x + 2y = 12$

△ **64.** $x + 4y = 7$
$2x - 5y = 0$

✏ △ **65.** Explain whether two lines, both with positive slopes, can be perpendicular.

✏ △ **66.** Explain why it is reasonable that nonvertical parallel lines have the same slope.

Use the points shown on the graphs to determine the slope of each line. See Examples 1 and 2.

67.
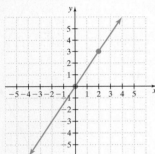

68.
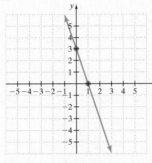

69.
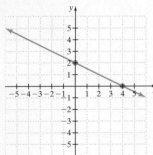

70.
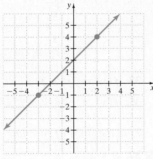

Find each slope. See Examples 1 and 2.

71. Find the pitch, or slope, of the roof shown.

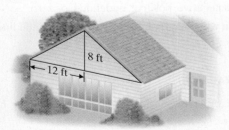

8 ft
12 ft

72. Upon takeoff, a Delta Airlines jet climbs to 3 miles as it passes over 25 miles of land below it. Find the slope of its climb.

3 mi
25 mi

73. Driving down Bald Mountain in Wyoming, Bob Dean finds that he descends 1600 feet in elevation by the time he is 2.5 miles (horizontally) away from the high point on the mountain road. Find the slope of his descent rounded to two decimal places (1 mile = 5280 feet).

74. Find the grade, or slope, of the road shown.

15 ft
100 ft

Solve. See Example 5.

✏ **75.** The annual average income y of an American man over 25 with an associate's degree is approximated by the linear equation $y = 694.9x + 43,884.9$, where x is the number of years after 2000. (*Source:* Based on data from the U.S. Bureau of the Census).

a. Predict the average income of an American man with an associate's degree in 2009.

b. Find and interpret the slope of the equation.

c. Find and interpret the y-intercept of the equation.

✏ **76.** The annual average income of an American woman over 25 with a bachelor's degree is given by the linear equation $y = 1059.6x + 36,827.4$, where x is the number of years after 2000. (*Source:* Based on data from the U.S. Bureau of the Census).

a. Find the average income of an American woman with a bachelor's degree in 2009.

b. Find and interpret the slope of the equation.

c. Find and interpret the y-intercept of the equation.

🔧 ✏ **77.** With wireless Internet (WiFi) gaining popularity, the number of public wireless Internet access points (in thousands) is projected to grow from 2003 to 2008 according to the equation

$$-66x + 2y = 84$$

where x is the number of years after 2003.

a. Find the slope and *y*-intercept of the linear equation.

b. What does the slope mean in this context?

c. What does the *y*-intercept mean in this context?

78. One of the faster growing occupations over the next few years is expected to be nursing. The number of people *y* in thousands employed in nursing in the United States can be estimated by the linear equation $-266x + 10y = 27{,}409$, where *x* is the number of years after 2000. (*Source:* Based on data from American Nurses Association)

a. Find the slope and *y*-intercept of the linear equation.

b. What does the slope mean in this context?

c. What does the *y*-intercept mean in this context?

79. In an earlier section, it was given that the yearly cost of tuition and required fees for attending a public four-year college full-time can be estimated by the linear function

$$f(x) = 291.5x + 2944.05$$

where *x* is the number of years after 2000 and $f(x)$ is the total cost. (*Source:* U.S. National Center for Education Statistics)

a. Find and interpret the slope of this equation.

b. Find and interpret the *y*-intercept of this equation.

80. In an earlier section, it was given that the yearly cost of tuition and required fees for attending a public two-year college full-time can be estimated by the linear function

$$f(x) = 107.3x + 1245.62$$

where *x* is the number of years after 2000 and $f(x)$ is the total cost. (*Source:* U.S. National Center for Education Statistics)

a. Find and interpret the slope of this equation.

b. Find and interpret the *y*-intercept of this equation.

REVIEW AND PREVIEW

Simplify and solve for y. See Section 2.3.

81. $y - 2 = 5(x + 6)$

82. $y - 0 = -3[x - (-10)]$

83. $y - (-1) = 2(x - 0)$

84. $y - 9 = -8[x - (-4)]$

CONCEPT EXTENSIONS

Each slope calculation is incorrect. Find the error and correct the calculation. See the Concept Check in this section.

85. $(-2, 6)$ and $(7, -14)$

$$m = \frac{\cancel{-14 - 6}}{7 - 2} = \frac{-20}{5} = -4$$

86. $(-1, 4)$ and $(-3, 9)$

$$m = \frac{\cancel{9 - 4}}{-3 - 1} = \frac{5}{-4} \text{ or } -\frac{5}{4}$$

87. $(-8, -10)$ and $(-11, -5)$

$$m = \frac{\cancel{-10 - 5}}{-8 - 11} = \frac{-15}{-19} = \frac{15}{19}$$

88. $(0, -4)$ and $(-6, -6)$

$$m = \frac{\cancel{0 - (-6)}}{-4 - (-6)} = \frac{6}{2} = 3$$

89. Find the slope of a line parallel to the line $f(x) = -\frac{7}{2}x - 6$.

△ **90.** Find the slope of a line parallel to the line $f(x) = x$.

△ **91.** Find the slope of a line perpendicular to the line

$$f(x) = -\frac{7}{2}x - 6.$$

△ **92.** Find the slope of a line perpendicular to the line $f(x) = x$.

△ **93.** Find the slope of a line parallel to the line $5x - 2y = 6$.

△ **94.** Find the slope of a line parallel to the line $-3x + 4y = 10$.

△ **95.** Find the slope of a line perpendicular to the line $5x - 2y = 6$.

96. Each line below has negative slope.

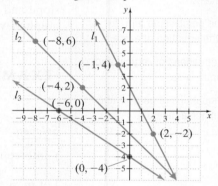

a. Find the slope of each line.

b. Use the result of Part **a** to fill in the blank. For lines with negative slopes, the steeper line has the _____ (greater/lesser) slope.

97. The following graph shows the altitude of a seagull in flight over a time period of 30 seconds.

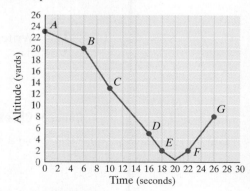

a. Find the coordinates of point *B*.

b. Find the coordinates of point *C*.

c. Find the rate of change of altitude between points *B* and *C*. (Recall that the rate of change between points is the slope between points. This rate of change will be in yards per second.)

d. Find the rate of change of altitude (in yards per second) between points F and G.

98. Professional plumbers suggest that a sewer pipe should be sloped 0.25 inch for every foot. Find the recommended slope for a sewer pipe. (*Source: Rules of Thumb* by Tom Parker, 1983, Houghton Mifflin Company)

99. Support the result of Exercise 61 by graphing the pair of equations on a graphing calculator.

100. Support the result of Exercise 62 by graphing the pair of equations on a graphing calculator. (*Hint:* Use the window showing $[-15, 15]$ on the x-axis and $[-10, 10]$ on the y-axis.)

101. a. On a single screen, graph $y = \frac{1}{2}x + 1$, $y = x + 1$ and $y = 2x + 1$. Notice the change in slope for each graph.

b. On a single screen, graph $y = -\frac{1}{2}x + 1$, $y = -x + 1$ and $y = -2x + 1$. Notice the change in slope for each graph.

c. Determine whether the following statement is true or false for slope m of a given line. As $|m|$ becomes greater, the line becomes steeper.

3.5 EQUATIONS OF LINES

OBJECTIVES

1 Use the slope–intercept form to write the equation of a line.

2 Graph a line using its slope and y-intercept.

3 Use the point–slope form to write the equation of a line.

4 Write equations of vertical and horizontal lines.

5 Find equations of parallel and perpendicular lines.

OBJECTIVE 1 ▶ Using slope-intercept form to write equations of lines. In the last section, we learned that the slope–intercept form of a linear equation is $y = mx + b$. When a linear equation is written in this form, the slope of the line is the same as the coefficient m of x. Also, the y-intercept of the line is $(0, b)$. For example, the slope of the line defined by $y = 2x + 3$ is, 2, and its y-intercept is $(0, 3)$.

We may also use the slope–intercept form to write the equation of a line given its slope and y-intercept. The equation of a line is a linear equation in 2 variables that, if graphed, would produce the line described.

EXAMPLE 1 Write an equation of the line with y-intercept $(0, -3)$ and slope of $\frac{1}{4}$.

Solution We want to write a linear equation in 2 variables that describes the line with y-intercept $(0, -3)$ and has a slope of $\frac{1}{4}$. We are given the slope and the y-intercept.

Let $m = \frac{1}{4}$ and $b = -3$, and write the equation in slope–intercept form, $y = mx + b$.

$$y = mx + b$$
$$y = \frac{1}{4}x + (-3) \quad \text{Let } m = \frac{1}{4} \text{ and } b = -3.$$
$$y = \frac{1}{4}x - 3 \quad \text{Simplify.}$$

PRACTICE 1 Write an equation of the line with y-intercept $(0, 4)$ and slope of $-\frac{3}{4}$.

Concept Check ✓

What is wrong with the following equation of a line with y-intercept $(0, 4)$ and slope 2?

$$y = 4x + 2$$

Answer to Concept Check:
y-intercept and slope were switched, should be $y = 2x + 4$

OBJECTIVE 2 ▶ Graph a line using slope and y-intercept. Given the slope and y-intercept of a line, we may graph the line as well as write its equation. Let's graph the line from Example 1.

EXAMPLE 2   Graph $y = \frac{1}{4}x - 3$.

Solution   Recall that the slope of the graph of $y = \frac{1}{4}x - 3$ is $\frac{1}{4}$ and the y-intercept is $(0, -3)$. To graph the line, we first plot the y-intercept $(0, -3)$. To find another point on the line, we recall that slope is $\frac{\text{rise}}{\text{run}} = \frac{1}{4}$. Another point may then be plotted by starting at $(0, -3)$, rising 1 unit up, and then running 4 units to the right. We are now at the point $(4, -2)$. The graph is the line through these two points.

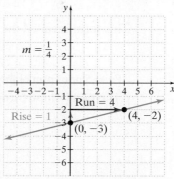

Notice that the line does have a y-intercept of $(0, -3)$ and a slope of $\frac{1}{4}$.

PRACTICE
2   Graph $y = \frac{3}{4}x + 2$.

EXAMPLE 3   Graph $2x + 3y = 12$.

Solution   First, we solve the equation for y to write it in slope–intercept form. In slope–intercept form, the equation is $y = -\frac{2}{3}x + 4$. Next we plot the y-intercept $(0, 4)$. To find another point on the line, we use the slope $-\frac{2}{3}$, which can be written as $\frac{\text{rise}}{\text{run}} = \frac{-2}{3}$. We start at $(0, 4)$ and move down 2 units since the numerator of the slope is -2; then we move 3 units to the right since the denominator of the slope is 3. We arrive at the point $(3, 2)$. The line through these points is the graph, shown below to the left.

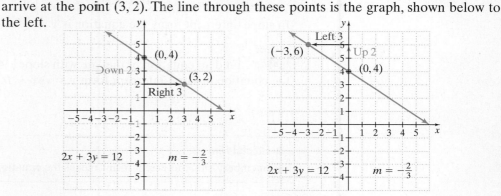
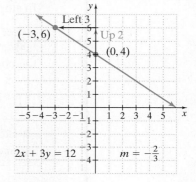

The slope $\frac{-2}{3}$ can also be written as $\frac{2}{-3}$, so to find another point in Example 3 we could start at $(0, 4)$ and move up 2 units and then 3 units to the left. We would arrive at the point $(-3, 6)$. The line through $(-3, 6)$ and $(0, 4)$ is the same line as shown previously through $(3, 2)$ and $(0, 4)$. See the graph above to the right.

PRACTICE
3   Graph $x - 2y = 6$.

OBJECTIVE 3 ▶ Using point-slope form to write equations of lines. When the slope of a line and a point on the line are known, the equation of the line can also be found. To do this, use the slope formula to write the slope of a line that passes through points (x_1, y_1) and (x, y). We have

$$m = \frac{y - y_1}{x - x_1}$$

Multiply both sides of this equation by $x - x_1$ to obtain

$$y - y_1 = m(x - x_1)$$

This form is called the **point–slope form** of the equation of a line.

Point-Slope Form of the Equation of a Line

The **point-slope form** of the equation of a line is

$$\overset{\text{slope}}{\underset{\text{point}}{y - y_1 = m(x - x_1)}}$$

where m is the slope of the line and (x_1, y_1) is a point on the line.

EXAMPLE 4 Find an equation of the line with slope -3 containing the point $(1, -5)$. Write the equation in slope–intercept form $y = mx + b$.

Solution Because we know the slope and a point of the line, we use the point–slope form with $m = -3$ and $(x_1, y_1) = (1, -5)$.

$$y - y_1 = m(x - x_1) \quad \text{Point-slope form}$$
$$y - (-5) = -3(x - 1) \quad \text{Let } m = -3 \text{ and } (x_1, y_1) = (1, -5).$$
$$y + 5 = -3x + 3 \quad \text{Apply the distributive property.}$$
$$y = -3x - 2 \quad \text{Write in slope-intercept form.}$$

In slope–intercept form, the equation is $y = -3x - 2$. □

PRACTICE
4 Find an equation of the line with slope -4 containing the point $(-2, 5)$. Write the equation in slope-intercept form $y = mx + b$.

▶ **Helpful Hint**
Remember, "slope-intercept form" means the equation is "solved for y."

EXAMPLE 5 Find an equation of the line through points $(4, 0)$ and $(-4, -5)$. Write the equation using function notation.

Solution First, find the slope of the line.

$$m = \frac{-5 - 0}{-4 - 4} = \frac{-5}{-8} = \frac{5}{8}$$

Next, make use of the point–slope form. Replace (x_1, y_1) by either $(4, 0)$ or $(-4, -5)$ in the point–slope equation. We will choose the point $(4, 0)$. The line through $(4, 0)$ with slope $\dfrac{5}{8}$ is

$$y - y_1 = m(x - x_1) \qquad \text{Point–slope form.}$$

$$y - 0 = \frac{5}{8}(x - 4) \qquad \text{Let } m = \frac{5}{8} \text{ and } (x_1, y_1) = (4, 0).$$

$$8y = 5(x - 4) \qquad \text{Multiply both sides by 8.}$$

$$8y = 5x - 20 \qquad \text{Apply the distributive property.}$$

To write the equation using function notation, we solve for y, then replace y with $f(x)$.

$$8y = 5x - 20$$

$$y = \frac{5}{8}x - \frac{20}{8} \qquad \text{Divide both sides by 8.}$$

$$f(x) = \frac{5}{8}x - \frac{5}{2} \qquad \text{Write using function notation.} \qquad \square$$

PRACTICE
5   Find an equation of the line through points $(-1, 2)$ and $(2, 0)$. Write the equation using function notation.

> **▶ Helpful Hint**
>
> If two points of a line are given, either one may be used with the point-slope form to write an equation of the line.

EXAMPLE 6   Find an equation of the line graphed. Write the equation in standard form.

Solution   First, find the slope of the line by identifying the coordinates of the noted points on the graph.

The points have coordinates $(-1, 2)$ and $(3, 5)$.

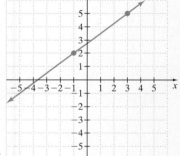

$$m = \frac{5 - 2}{3 - (-1)} = \frac{3}{4}$$

Next, use the point-slope form. We will choose $(3, 5)$ for (x_1, y_1), although it makes no difference which point we choose. The line through $(3, 5)$ with slope $\dfrac{3}{4}$ is

$$y - y_1 = m(x - x_1) \qquad \text{Point-slope form}$$

$$y - 5 = \frac{3}{4}(x - 3) \qquad \text{Let } m = \frac{3}{4} \text{ and } (x_1, y_1) = (3, 5).$$

$$4(y - 5) = 3(x - 3) \qquad \text{Multiply both sides by 4.}$$

$$4y - 20 = 3x - 9 \qquad \text{Apply the distributive property.}$$

To write the equation in standard form, move x- and y-terms to one side of the equation and any numbers (constants) to the other side.

$$4y - 20 = 3x - 9$$

$$-3x + 4y = 11 \qquad \text{Subtract } 3x \text{ from both sides and add 20 to both sides.}$$

The equation of the graphed line is $-3x + 4y = 11$. $\qquad \square$

PRACTICE
6   Find an equation of the line graphed. Write the equation in standard form.

The point–slope form of an equation is very useful for solving real-world problems.

EXAMPLE 7 **Predicting Sales**

Southern Star Realty is an established real estate company that has enjoyed constant growth in sales since 2000. In 2002 the company sold 200 houses, and in 2007 the company sold 275 houses. Use these figures to predict the number of houses this company will sell in the year 2016.

Solution

1. UNDERSTAND. Read and reread the problem. Then let

   x = the number of years after 2000 and

   y = the number of houses sold in the year corresponding to x.

   The information provided then gives the ordered pairs $(2, 200)$ and $(7, 275)$. To better visualize the sales of Southern Star Realty, we graph the linear equation that passes through the points $(2, 200)$ and $(7, 275)$.

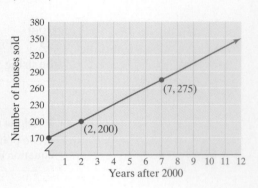

2. TRANSLATE. We write a linear equation that passes through the points $(2, 200)$ and $(7, 275)$. To do so, we first find the slope of the line.

$$m = \frac{275 - 200}{7 - 2} = \frac{75}{5} = 15$$

Then, using the point–slope form and the point $(2, 200)$ to write the equation, we have

$$y - y_1 = m(x - x_1)$$
$$y - 200 = 15(x - 2) \quad \text{Let } m = 15 \text{ and } (x_1, y_1) = (2, 200).$$
$$y - 200 = 15x - 30 \quad \text{Multiply.}$$
$$y = 15x + 170 \quad \text{Add 200 to both sides.}$$

3. SOLVE. To predict the number of houses sold in the year 2016, we use $y = 15x + 170$ and complete the ordered pair $(16, \quad)$, since $2016 - 2000 = 16$.

$$y = 15(16) + 170 \quad \text{Let } x = 16.$$
$$y = 410$$

4. INTERPRET.

Check: Verify that the point $(16, 410)$ is a point on the line graphed in step 1.

State: Southern Star Realty should expect to sell 410 houses in the year 2016. □

PRACTICE

7 Southwest Florida, including Fort Myers and Cape Coral, has been a growing real estate market in past years. In 2002, there were 7513 house sales in the area, and in 2006, there were 9198 house sales. Use these figures to predict the number of house sales there will be in 2014.

OBJECTIVE 4 ▶ Writing equations of vertical and horizontal lines. A few special types of linear equations are linear equations whose graphs are vertical and horizontal lines.

EXAMPLE 8   Find an equation of the horizontal line containing the point (2, 3).

Solution   Recall that a horizontal line has an equation of the form $y = b$. Since the line contains the point (2, 3), the equation is $y = 3$, as shown to the right.

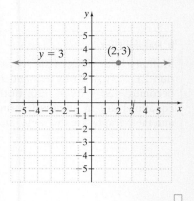

PRACTICE
8   Find the equation of the horizontal line containing the point (6, −2).

EXAMPLE 9   Find an equation of the line containing the point (2, 3) with undefined slope

Solution   Since the line has undefined slope, the line must be vertical. A vertical line has an equation of the form $x = c$. Since the line contains the point (2, 3), the equation is $x = 2$, as shown to the right.

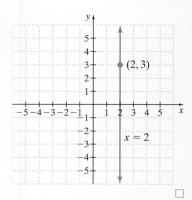

PRACTICE
9   Find an equation of the line containing the point (6, −2) with undefined slope.

OBJECTIVE 5 ▶ Finding equations of parallel and perpendicular lines. Next, we find equations of parallel and perpendicular lines.

EXAMPLE 10   Find an equation of the line containing the point (4, 4) and parallel to the line $2x + 3y = -6$. Write the equation in standard form.

Solution   Because the line we want to find is *parallel* to the line $2x + 3y = -6$, the two lines must have equal slopes. Find the slope of $2x + 3y = -6$ by writing it in the form $y = mx + b$. In other words, solve the equation for y.

$$2x + 3y = -6$$

$$3y = -2x - 6 \qquad \text{Subtract } 2x \text{ from both sides.}$$

$$y = \frac{-2x}{3} - \frac{6}{3} \qquad \text{Divide by 3.}$$

$$y = -\frac{2}{3}x - 2 \qquad \text{Write in slope-intercept form.}$$

The slope of this line is $-\frac{2}{3}$. Thus, a line parallel to this line will also have a slope of $-\frac{2}{3}$. The equation we are asked to find describes a line containing the point $(4, 4)$ with a slope of $-\frac{2}{3}$. We use the point-slope form.

$$y - y_1 = m(x - x_1)$$

$$y - 4 = -\frac{2}{3}(x - 4) \quad \text{Let } m = -\frac{2}{3}, x_1 = 4, \text{ and } y_1 = 4.$$

$$3(y - 4) = -2(x - 4) \quad \text{Multiply both sides by 3.}$$

$$3y - 12 = -2x + 8 \quad \text{Apply the distributive property.}$$

$$2x + 3y = 20 \quad \text{Write in standard form.} \quad \square$$

> **▶ Helpful Hint**
>
> Multiply both sides of the equation $2x + 3y = 20$ by -1 and it becomes $-2x - 3y = -20$. Both equations are in standard form, and their graphs are the same line.

PRACTICE

10 Find an equation of the line containing the point $(8, -3)$ and parallel to the line $3x + 4y = 1$. Write the equation in standard form.

EXAMPLE 11 Write a function that describes the line containing the point $(4, 4)$ and is perpendicular to the line $2x + 3y = -6$.

Solution In the previous example, we found that the slope of the line $2x + 3y = -6$ is $-\frac{2}{3}$. A line perpendicular to this line will have a slope that is the negative reciprocal of $-\frac{2}{3}$, or $\frac{3}{2}$. From the point-slope equation, we have

$$y - y_1 = m(x - x_1)$$

$$y - 4 = \frac{3}{2}(x - 4) \quad \text{Let } x_1 = 4, y_1 = 4 \text{ and } m = \frac{3}{2}.$$

$$2(y - 4) = 3(x - 4) \quad \text{Multiply both sides by 2.}$$

$$2y - 8 = 3x - 12 \quad \text{Apply the distributive property.}$$

$$2y = 3x - 4 \quad \text{Add 8 to both sides.}$$

$$y = \frac{3}{2}x - 2 \quad \text{Divide both sides by 2.}$$

$$f(x) = \frac{3}{2}x - 2 \quad \text{Write using function notation.} \quad \square$$

PRACTICE

11 Write a function that describes the line containing the point $(8, -3)$ and is perpendicular to the line $3x + 4y = 1$.

Forms of Linear Equations

$Ax + By = C$	**Standard form** of a linear equation A and B are not both 0.
$y = mx + b$	**Slope–intercept form** of a linear equation The slope is m, and the y-intercept is $(0, b)$.
$y - y_1 = m(x - x_1)$	**Point–slope form** of a linear equation The slope is m, and (x_1, y_1) is a point on the line.
$y = c$	**Horizontal line** The slope is 0, and the y-intercept is $(0, c)$.
$x = c$	**Vertical line** The slope is undefined and the x-intercept is $(c, 0)$.

Parallel and Perpendicular Lines

Nonvertical parallel lines have the same slope. The product of the slopes of two nonvertical perpendicular lines is -1.

VOCABULARY & READINESS CHECK

State the slope and the y-intercept of each line with the given equation.

1. $y = -4x + 12$

2. $y = \dfrac{2}{3}x - \dfrac{7}{2}$

3. $y = 5x$

4. $y = -x$

5. $y = \dfrac{1}{2}x + 6$

6. $y = -\dfrac{2}{3}x + 5$

Decide whether the lines are parallel, perpendicular, or neither.

7. $y = 12x + 6$
   $y = 12x - 2$

8. $y = -5x + 8$
   $y = -5x - 8$

9. $y = -9x + 3$
   $y = \dfrac{3}{2}x - 7$

10. $y = 2x - 12$
   $y = \dfrac{1}{2}x - 6$

3.5 | EXERCISE SET

MyMathLab   PRACTICE   WATCH   DOWNLOAD   READ   REVIEW

Use the slope-intercept form of the linear equation to write the equation of each line with the given slope and y-intercept. See Example 1.

1. Slope -1; y-intercept $(0, 1)$

2. Slope $\dfrac{1}{2}$; y-intercept $(0, -6)$

3. Slope 2; y-intercept $\left(0, \dfrac{3}{4}\right)$

4. Slope -3; y-intercept $\left(0, -\dfrac{1}{5}\right)$

5. Slope $\dfrac{2}{7}$; y-intercept $(0, 0)$

6. Slope $-\dfrac{4}{5}$; y-intercept $(0, 0)$

Graph each linear equation. See Examples 2 and 3.

7. $y = 5x - 2$

8. $y = 2x + 1$

9. $4x + y = 7$

10. $3x + y = 9$

11. $-3x + 2y = 3$

12. $-2x + 5y = -16$

Find an equation of the line with the given slope and containing the given point. Write the equation in slope-intercept form. See Example 4.

13. Slope 3; through $(1, 2)$

14. Slope 4; through $(5, 1)$

15. Slope -2; through $(1, -3)$

16. Slope -4; through $(2, -4)$

17. Slope $\dfrac{1}{2}$; through $(-6, 2)$

18. Slope $\dfrac{2}{3}$; through $(-9, 4)$

19. Slope $-\dfrac{9}{10}$; through $(-3, 0)$

20. Slope $-\dfrac{1}{5}$; through $(4, -6)$

Find an equation of the line passing through the given points. Use function notation to write the equation. See Example 5.

21. $(2, 0), (4, 6)$

22. $(3, 0), (7, 8)$

23. $(-2, 5), (-6, 13)$

24. $(7, -4), (2, 6)$

25. $(-2, -4), (-4, -3)$

26. $(-9, -2), (-3, 10)$

27. $(-3, -8), (-6, -9)$

28. $(8, -3), (4, -8)$

29. $\left(\dfrac{3}{5}, \dfrac{4}{10}\right)$ and $\left(-\dfrac{1}{5}, \dfrac{7}{10}\right)$

30. $\left(\dfrac{1}{2}, -\dfrac{1}{4}\right)$ and $\left(\dfrac{3}{2}, \dfrac{3}{4}\right)$

Find an equation of each line graphed. Write the equation in standard form. See Example 6.

31.

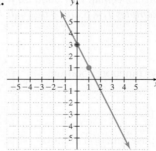

32.

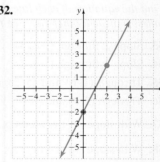

33.

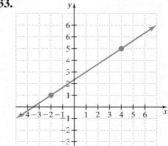

34.

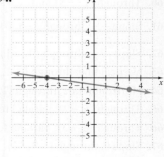

Use the graph of the following function f(x) to find each value.

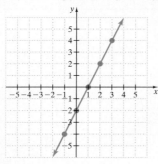

35. $f(0)$

36. $f(-1)$

37. $f(2)$

38. $f(1)$

39. Find x such that $f(x) = -6$.

40. Find x such that $f(x) = 4$.

Write an equation of each line. See Examples 8 and 9.

41. Slope 0; through $(-2, -4)$

42. Horizontal; through $(-3, 1)$

43. Vertical; through $(4, 7)$

44. Vertical; through $(2, 6)$

45. Horizontal; through $(0, 5)$

46. Undefined slope; through $(0, 5)$

Find an equation of each line. Write the equation using function notation. See Examples 10 and 11.

47. Through $(3, 8)$; parallel to $f(x) = 4x - 2$

48. Through $(1, 5)$; parallel to $f(x) = 3x - 4$

49. Through $(2, -5)$; perpendicular to $3y = x - 6$

50. Through $(-4, 8)$; perpendicular to $2x - 3y = 1$

51. Through $(-2, -3)$; parallel to $3x + 2y = 5$

52. Through $(-2, -3)$; perpendicular to $3x + 2y = 5$

MIXED PRACTICE

Find the equation of each line. Write the equation in standard form unless indicated otherwise. See Examples 1, 4, 5 and 8 through 11.

53. Slope 2; through $(-2, 3)$

54. Slope 3; through $(-4, 2)$

55. Through $(1, 6)$ and $(5, 2)$; use function notation.

56. Through $(2, 9)$ and $(8, 6)$

57. With slope $-\dfrac{1}{2}$; y-intercept 11

58. With slope -4; y-intercept $\dfrac{2}{9}$; use function notation.

59. Through $(-7, -4)$ and $(0, -6)$

60. Through $(2, -8)$ and $(-4, -3)$

61. Slope $-\dfrac{4}{3}$; through $(-5, 0)$

62. Slope $-\dfrac{3}{5}$; through $(4, -1)$

63. Vertical line; through $(-2, -10)$

64. Horizontal line; through $(1, 0)$

65. Through $(6, -2)$; parallel to the line $2x + 4y = 9$

66. Through $(8, -3)$; parallel to the line $6x + 2y = 5$

67. Slope 0; through $(-9, 12)$

68. Undefined slope; through $(10, -8)$

69. Through $(6, 1)$; parallel to the line $8x - y = 9$

70. Through $(3, 5)$; perpendicular to the line $2x - y = 8$

71. Through $(5, -6)$; perpendicular to $y = 9$

72. Through $(-3, -5)$; parallel to $y = 9$

73. Through $(2, -8)$ and $(-6, -5)$; use function notation.

74. Through $(-4, -2)$ and $(-6, 5)$; use function notation.

Solve. See Example 7.

75. Del Monte Fruit Company recently released a new apple-sauce. By the end of its first year, profits on this product amounted to $30,000. The anticipated profit for the end of the fourth year is $66,000. The ratio of change in time to change in profit is constant. Let x be years and P be profit.

  a. Write a linear function $P(x)$ that expresses profit as a function of time.

  b. Use this function to predict the company's profit at the end of the seventh year.

  c. Predict when the profit should reach $126,000.

76. The value of a computer bought in 2003 depreciates, or decreases, as time passes. Two years after the computer was bought, it was worth $2000; 4 years after it was bought, it was worth $800.

  a. If this relationship between number of years past 2003 and value of computer is linear, write an equation describing this relationship. [Use ordered pairs of the form (years past 2003, value of computer).]

  b. Use this equation to estimate the value of the computer in the year 2008.

77. The Pool Fun Company has learned that, by pricing a newly released Fun Noodle at $3, sales will reach 10,000 Fun Noodles per day during the summer. Raising the price to $5 will cause the sales to fall to 8000 Fun Noodles per day.

  a. Assume that the relationship between sales price and number of Fun Noodles sold is linear and write an equation describing this relationship.

  b. Predict the daily sales of Fun Noodles if the price is $3.50.

78. The value of a building bought in 1990 appreciates, or increases, as time passes. Seven years after the building was bought, it was worth $165,000; 12 years after it was bought, it was worth $180,000.

  a. If this relationship between number of years past 1990 and value of building is linear, write an equation describing this relationship. [Use ordered pairs of the form (years past 1990, value of building).]

  b. Use this equation to estimate the value of the building in the year 2010.

79. In 2006, the median price of an existing home in the United States was approximately $222,000. In 2001, the median price of an existing home was $150,900. Let y be the median price of an existing home in the year x, where $x = 0$ represents 2001. (*Source:* National Association of REALTORS®)

  a. Write a linear equation that models the median existing home price in terms of the year x. [*Hint:* The line must pass through the points $(0, 150{,}900)$ and $(5, 222{,}000)$.]

b. Use this equation to predict the median existing home price for the year 2010.

c. Interpret the slope of the equation found in part **a.**

80. The number of births (in thousands) in the United States in 2000 was 4060. The number of births (in thousands) in the United States in 2004 was 4116. Let y be the number of births (in thousands) in the year x, where $x = 0$ represents 2000. (*Source:* National Center for Health Statistics)

a. Write a linear equation that models the number of births (in thousands) in terms of the year x. (See hint for Exercise 79a.)

b. Use this equation to predict the number of births in the United States for the year 2013.

c. Interpret the slope of the equation in part a.

81. The number of people employed in the United States as medical assistants was 387 thousand in 2004. By the year 2014, this number is expected to rise to 589 thousand. Let y be the number of medical assistants (in thousands) employed in the United States in the year x, where $x = 0$ represents 2004. (*Source:* Bureau of Labor Statistics)

a. Write a linear equation that models the number of people (in thousands) employed as medical assistants in the year x. (See hint for Exercise 79a.)

b. Use this equation to estimate the number of people who will be employed as medical assistants in the year 2013.

82. The number of people employed in the United States as systems analysts was 487 thousand in 2004. By the year 2014, this number is expected to rise to 640 thousand. Let y be the number of systems analysts (in thousands) employed in the United States in the year x, where $x = 0$ represents 2004. (*Source:* Bureau of Labor Statistics)

a. Write a linear equation that models the number of people (in thousands) employed as systems analysts in the year x. (See hint for Exercise 79a.)

b. Use this equation to estimate the number of people who will be employed as systems analysts in the year 2012.

REVIEW AND PREVIEW

Solve. Write the solution in interval notation. See Section 2.4.

83. $2x - 7 \leq 21$

84. $-3x + 1 > 0$

85. $5(x - 2) \geq 3(x - 1)$

86. $-2(x + 1) \leq -x + 10$

87. $\dfrac{x}{2} + \dfrac{1}{4} < \dfrac{1}{8}$

88. $\dfrac{x}{5} - \dfrac{3}{10} \geq \dfrac{x}{2} - 1$

CONCEPT EXTENSIONS

Answer true or false.

89. A vertical line is always perpendicular to a horizontal line.

90. A vertical line is always parallel to a vertical line.

Example:

Find an equation of the perpendicular bisector of the line segment whose endpoints are $(2, 6)$ and $(0, -2)$.

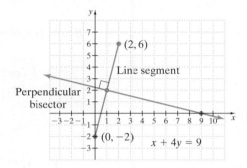

Solution:

A perpendicular bisector is a line that contains the midpoint of the given segment and is perpendicular to the segment.

Step 1: The midpoint of the segment with endpoints $(2, 6)$ and $(0, -2)$ is $(1, 2)$.

Step 2: The slope of the segment containing points $(2, 6)$ and $(0, -2)$ is 4.

Step 3: A line perpendicular to this line segment will have slope of $-\dfrac{1}{4}$.

Step 4: The equation of the line through the midpoint $(1, 2)$ with a slope of $-\dfrac{1}{4}$ will be the equation of the perpendicular bisector. This equation in standard form is $x + 4y = 9$.

Find an equation of the perpendicular bisector of the line segment whose endpoints are given. See the previous example.

△ **91.** $(3, -1); (-5, 1)$

△ **92.** $(-6, -3); (-8, -1)$

△ **93.** $(-2, 6); (-22, -4)$

△ **94.** $(5, 8); (7, 2)$

△ **95.** $(2, 3); (-4, 7)$

△ **96.** $(-6, 8); (-4, -2)$

97. Describe how to check to see if the graph of $2x - 4y = 7$ passes through the points $(1.4, -1.05)$ and $(0, -1.75)$. Then follow your directions and check these points.

Use a graphing calculator with a TRACE feature to see the results of each exercise.

98. Exercise 56: graph the equation and verify that it passes through $(2, 9)$ and $(8, 6)$.

99. Exercise 55; graph the function and verify that it passes through $(1, 6)$ and $(5, 2)$.

100. Exercise 62; graph the equation. See that it has a negative slope and passes through $(4, -1)$.

101. Exercise 61; graph the equation. See that it has a negative slope and passes through $(-5, 0)$.

102. Exercise 48: Graph the equation and verify that it passes through $(1, 5)$ and is parallel to $y = 3x - 4$.

103. Exercise 47: Graph the equation and verify that it passes through $(3, 8)$ and is parallel to $y = 4x - 2$.

INTEGRATED REVIEW LINEAR EQUATIONS IN TWO VARIABLES

Sections 3.1–3.5

Below is a review of equations of lines.

Forms of Linear Equations

$Ax + By = C$	**Standard form** of a linear equation A and B are not both 0.
$y = mx + b$	**Slope-intercept form** of a linear equation. The slope is m, and the y-intercept is $(0, b)$.
$y - y_1 = m(x - x_1)$	**Point-slope form** of a linear equation. The slope is m, and (x_1, y_1) is a point on the line.
$y = c$	**Horizontal line** The slope is 0, and the y-intercept is $(0, c)$.
$x = c$	**Vertical line** The slope is undefined and the x-intercept is $(c, 0)$.

Parallel and Perpendicular Lines

Nonvertical parallel lines have the same slope. The product of the slopes of two nonvertical perpendicular lines is -1.

Graph each linear equation.

1. $y = -2x$ **2.** $3x - 2y = 6$ **3.** $x = -3$ **4.** $y = 1.5$

Find the slope of the line containing each pair of points.

5. $(-2, -5), (3, -5)$ **6.** $(5, 2), (0, 5)$

Find the slope and y-intercept of each line.

7. $y = 3x - 5$ **8.** $5x - 2y = 7$

Determine whether each pair of lines is parallel, perpendicular, or neither.

9. $y = 8x - 6$
$y = 8x + 6$

10. $y = \dfrac{2}{3}x + 1$
$2y + 3x = 1$

Find the equation of each line. Write the equation in the form $x = a$, $y = b$, or $y = mx + b$. For Exercises 14 through 17, write the equation in the form $f(x) = mx + b$.

11. Through $(1, 6)$ and $(5, 2)$

12. Vertical line; through $(-2, -10)$

13. Horizontal line; through $(1, 0)$

14. Through $(2, -9)$ and $(-6, -5)$

Next, **let's graph the nonlinear function** $f(x) = x^2$ **or** $y = x^2$.

This equation is not linear because the x^2 term does not allow us to write it in the form $Ax + By = C$. Its graph is not a line. We begin by finding ordered pair solutions. Because this graph is solved for $f(x)$, or y, we choose x-values and find corresponding $f(x)$, or y-values.

If $x = -3$, then $y = (-3)^2$, or 9.

If $x = -2$, then $y = (-2)^2$, or 4.

If $x = -1$, then $y = (-1)^2$, or 1.

If $x = 0$, then $y = 0^2$, or 0.

If $x = 1$, then $y = 1^2$, or 1.

If $x = 2$, then $y = 2^2$, or 4.

If $x = 3$, then $y = 3^2$, or 9.

x	$f(x)$ or y
-3	9
-2	4
-1	1
0	0
1	1
2	4
3	9

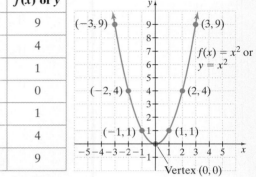

Study the table for a moment and look for patterns. Notice that the ordered pair solution $(0, 0)$ contains the smallest y-value because any other x-value squared will give a positive result. This means that the point $(0, 0)$ will be the lowest point on the graph. Also notice that all other y-values correspond to two different x-values. For example, $3^2 = 9$ and also $(-3)^2 = 9$. This means that the graph will be a mirror image of itself across the y-axis. Connect the plotted points with a smooth curve to sketch its graph.

This curve is given a special name, a **parabola.** We will study more about parabolas in later chapters.

Next, **let's graph another nonlinear function** $f(x) = |x|$ **or** $y = |x|$.

This is not a linear equation since it cannot be written in the form $Ax + By = C$. Its graph is not a line. Because we do not know the shape of this graph, we find many ordered pair solutions. We will choose x-values and substitute to find corresponding y-values.

If $x = -3$, then $y = |-3|$, or 3.

If $x = -2$, then $y = |-2|$, or 2.

If $x = -1$, then $y = |-1|$, or 1.

If $x = 0$, then $y = |0|$, or 0.

If $x = 1$, then $y = |1|$, or 1.

If $x = 2$, then $y = |2|$, or 2.

If $x = 3$, then $y = |3|$, or 3.

x	y
-3	3
-2	2
-1	1
0	0
1	1
2	2
3	3

Again, study the table of values for a moment and notice any patterns.

From the plotted ordered pairs, we see that the graph of this absolute value equation is V-shaped.

Finally, a fourth common function, $f(x) = \sqrt{x}$ or $y = \sqrt{x}$. For this graph, you need to recall basic facts about square roots and use your calculator to approximate some square roots to help locate points. Recall also that the square root of a negative number is not a real number, so be careful when finding your domain.

Now **let's graph the square root function** $f(x) = \sqrt{x}$, **or** $y = \sqrt{x}$.

To graph, we identify the domain, evaluate the function for several values of x, plot the resulting points, and connect the points with a smooth curve. Since $\sqrt{x}$ represents the nonnegative square root of x, the domain of this function is the set of all nonnegative numbers, $\{x \mid x \geq 0\}$, or $[0, \infty)$. We have approximated $\sqrt{3}$ below to help us locate the point corresponding to $(3, \sqrt{3})$.

If $x = 0$, then $y = \sqrt{0}$, or 0.

If $x = 1$, then $y = \sqrt{1}$, or 1.

If $x = 3$, then $y = \sqrt{3}$, or 1.7.

If $x = 4$, then $y = \sqrt{4}$, or 2.

If $x = 9$, then $y = \sqrt{9}$, or 3.

x	$f(x) = \sqrt{x}$
0	0
1	1
3	$\sqrt{3} \approx 1.7$
4	2
9	3

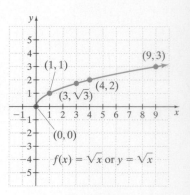

Notice that the graph of this function passes the vertical line test, as expected.

Below is a summary of our four common graphs. Take a moment and study these graphs. Your success in the rest of this section depends on your knowledge of these graphs.

Common Graphs

$f(x) = x$

$f(x) = x^2$

$f(x) = \sqrt{x}$

$f(x) = |x|$

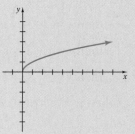

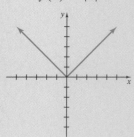

Your knowledge of the slope-intercept form, $f(x) = mx + b$, will help you understand simple shifting of transformations such as vertical shifts. For example, what is the difference between the graphs of $f(x) = x$ and $g(x) = x + 3$?

$f(x) = x$

slope, $m = 1$

y-intercept is $(0, 0)$

$g(x) = x + 3$

slope, $m = 1$

y-intercept is $(0, 3)$

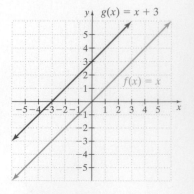

Notice that the graph of $g(x) = x + 3$ is the same as the graph of $f(x) = x$, but moved upward 3 units. This is an example of a **vertical shift** and is true for graphs in general.

Vertical Shifts (Upward and Downward)
Let k be a Positive Number

Graph of	Same As	Moved
$g(x) = f(x) + k$	$f(x)$	k units upward
$g(x) = f(x) - k$	$f(x)$	k units downward

EXAMPLES   Without plotting points, sketch the graph of each pair of functions on the same set of axes.

3. $f(x) = x^2$ and $g(x) = x^2 + 2$ **4.** $f(x) = \sqrt{x}$ and $g(x) = \sqrt{x} - 3$

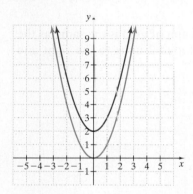   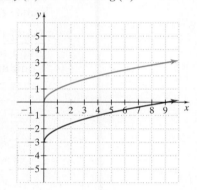

PRACTICES

3–4   Without plotting points, sketch the graphs of each pair of functions on the same set of axes.

3. $f(x) = x^2$ and $g(x) = x^2 - 3$ **4.** $f(x) = \sqrt{x}$ and $g(x) = \sqrt{x} + 1$

A horizontal shift to the left or right may be slightly more difficult to understand. Let's graph $g(x) = |x - 2|$ and compare it with $f(x) = |x|$.

EXAMPLE 5   Sketch the graphs of $f(x) = |x|$ and $g(x) = |x - 2|$ on the same set of axes.

Solution   Study the table to the left to understand the placement of both graphs.

x	$f(x) = |x|$	$g(x) = |x - 2|$
−3	3	5
−2	2	4
−1	1	3
0	0	2
1	1	1
2	2	0
3	3	1

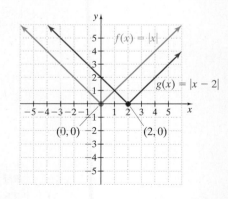

PRACTICE

5   Sketch the graphs of $f(x) = |x|$ and $g(x) = |x - 3|$ on the same set of axes.

The graph of $g(x) = |x - 2|$ is the same as the graph of $f(x) = |x|$, but moved 2 units to the right. This is an example of a **horizontal shift** and is true for graphs in general.

Horizontal Shift (To the Left or Right)
Let h be a Positive Number

Graph of	Same as	Moved
$g(x) = f(x - h)$	$f(x)$	h units to the right
$g(x) = f(x + h)$	$f(x)$	h units to the left

> ▶ **Helpful Hint**
> Notice that $f(x - h)$ corresponds to a shift to the right and $f(x + h)$ corresponds to a shift to the left.

Vertical and horizontal shifts can be combined.

EXAMPLE 6   Sketch the graphs of $f(x) = x^2$ and $g(x) = (x - 2)^2 + 1$ on the same set of axes.

<u>**Solution**</u>   The graph of $g(x)$ is the same as the graph of $f(x)$ shifted 2 units to the right and 1 unit up.

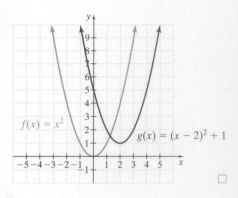

PRACTICE
6   Sketch the graphs of $f(x) = |x|$ and $g(x) = |x - 2| + 3$ on the same set of axes.

OBJECTIVE 3 ▶ **Reflecting graphs.**   Another type of transformation is called a **reflection.** In this section, we will study reflections (mirror images) about the x-axis only. For example, take a moment and study these two graphs. The graph of $g(x) = -x^2$ can be verified, as usual, by plotting points.

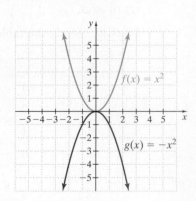

Reflection about the x-axis
The graph of $g(x) = -f(x)$ is the graph of $f(x)$ reflected about the x-axis.

EXAMPLE 7 Sketch the graph of $h(x) = -|x - 3| + 2$.

Solution The graph of $h(x) = -|x - 3| + 2$ is the same as the graph of $f(x) = |x|$ reflected about the x-axis, then moved three units to the right and two units upward.

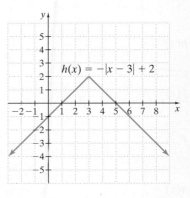

PRACTICE
7 Sketch the graph of $h(x) = -(x + 2)^2 - 1$.

There are other transformations, such as stretching that won't be covered in this section. For a review of this transformation, see the Appendix.

VOCABULARY & READINESS CHECK

Match each equation with its graph.

1. $y = \sqrt{x}$
A

2. $y = x^2$
B

3. $y = x$
C

4. $y = |x|$
D

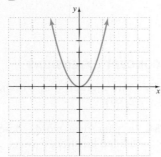

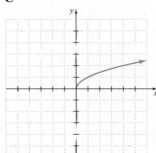

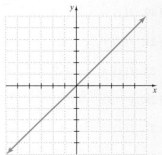

3.6 | EXERCISE SET

Graph each piecewise-defined function. See Examples 1 and 2.

1. $f(x) = \begin{cases} 2x & \text{if } x < 0 \\ x + 1 & \text{if } x \geq 0 \end{cases}$

2. $f(x) = \begin{cases} 3x & \text{if } x < 0 \\ x + 2 & \text{if } x \geq 0 \end{cases}$

3. $f(x) = \begin{cases} 4x + 5 & \text{if } x \leq 0 \\ \dfrac{1}{4}x + 2 & \text{if } x > 0 \end{cases}$

4. $f(x) = \begin{cases} 5x + 4 & \text{if } x \leq 0 \\ \dfrac{1}{3}x - 1 & \text{if } x > 0 \end{cases}$

5. $g(x) = \begin{cases} -x & \text{if } x \leq 1 \\ 2x + 1 & \text{if } x > 1 \end{cases}$

6. $g(x) = \begin{cases} 3x - 1 & \text{if } x \leq 2 \\ -x & \text{if } x > 2 \end{cases}$

7. $f(x) = \begin{cases} 5 & \text{if } x < -2 \\ 3 & \text{if } x \geq -2 \end{cases}$

8. $f(x) = \begin{cases} 4 & \text{if } x < -3 \\ -2 & \text{if } x \geq -3 \end{cases}$

MIXED PRACTICE

(Sections 3.2, 3.6) Graph each piecewise-defined function. Use the graph to determine the domain and range of the function. See Examples 1 and 2.

9. $f(x) = \begin{cases} -2x & \text{if } x \leq 0 \\ 2x + 1 & \text{if } x > 0 \end{cases}$

10. $g(x) = \begin{cases} -3x & \text{if } x \leq 0 \\ 3x + 2 & \text{if } x > 0 \end{cases}$

11. $h(x) = \begin{cases} 5x - 5 & \text{if } x < 2 \\ -x + 3 & \text{if } x \geq 2 \end{cases}$

12. $f(x) = \begin{cases} 4x - 4 & \text{if } x < 2 \\ -x + 1 & \text{if } x \geq 2 \end{cases}$

13. $f(x) = \begin{cases} x + 3 & \text{if } x < -1 \\ -2x + 4 & \text{if } x \geq -1 \end{cases}$

14. $h(x) = \begin{cases} x + 2 & \text{if } x < 1 \\ 2x + 1 & \text{if } x \geq 1 \end{cases}$

15. $g(x) = \begin{cases} -2 & \text{if } x \leq 0 \\ -4 & \text{if } x \geq 1 \end{cases}$

16. $f(x) = \begin{cases} -1 & \text{if } x \leq 0 \\ -3 & \text{if } x \geq 2 \end{cases}$

MIXED PRACTICE

Sketch the graph of function. See Examples 3 through 6.

17. $f(x) = |x| + 3$

18. $f(x) = |x| - 2$

19. $f(x) = \sqrt{x} - 2$

20. $f(x) = \sqrt{x} + 3$

21. $f(x) = |x - 4|$

22. $f(x) = |x + 3|$

23. $f(x) = \sqrt{x + 2}$

24. $f(x) = \sqrt{x - 2}$

25. $y = (x - 4)^2$

26. $y = (x + 4)^2$

27. $f(x) = x^2 + 4$

28. $f(x) = x^2 - 4$

29. $f(x) = \sqrt{x - 2} + 3$

30. $f(x) = \sqrt{x - 1} + 3$

31. $f(x) = |x - 1| + 5$

32. $f(x) = |x - 3| + 2$

33. $f(x) = \sqrt{x + 1} + 1$

34. $f(x) = \sqrt{x + 3} + 2$

35. $f(x) = |x + 3| - 1$

36. $f(x) = |x + 1| - 4$

37. $g(x) = (x - 1)^2 - 1$

38. $h(x) = (x + 2)^2 + 2$

39. $f(x) = (x + 3)^2 - 2$

40. $f(x) = (x + 2)^2 + 4$

Sketch the graph of each function. See Examples 3 through 7.

41. $f(x) = -(x - 1)^2$

42. $g(x) = -(x + 2)^2$

43. $h(x) = -\sqrt{x} + 3$

44. $f(x) = -\sqrt{x + 3}$

45. $h(x) = -|x + 2| + 3$

46. $g(x) = -|x + 1| + 1$

47. $f(x) = (x - 3) + 2$

48. $f(x) = (x - 1) + 4$

REVIEW AND PREVIEW

Match each equation with its graph. See Section 3.3.

49. $y = -1$

50. $x = -1$

51. $x = 3$

52. $y = 3$

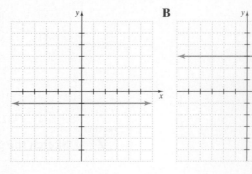

A   B

C   D

CONCEPT EXTENSIONS

53. Draw a graph whose domain is $(-\infty, 5]$ and whose range is $[2, \infty)$.

54. In your own words, describe how to graph a piecewise-defined function.

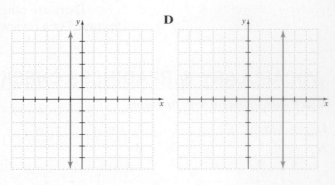

55. Graph: $f(x) = \begin{cases} -\dfrac{1}{2}x & \text{if } x \leq 0 \\ x + 1 & \text{if } 0 < x \leq 2 \\ 2x - 1 & \text{if } x > 2 \end{cases}$

56. Graph: $f(x) = \begin{cases} -\dfrac{1}{3}x & \text{if } x \leq 0 \\ x + 2 & \text{if } 0 < x \leq 4 \\ 3x - 4 & \text{if } x > 4 \end{cases}$

Write the domain and range of the following exercises.

57. Exercise 29

58. Exercise 30

59. Exercise 45

60. Exercise 46

Without graphing, find the domain of each function.

61. $f(x) = 5\sqrt{x - 20} + 1$

62. $g(x) = -3\sqrt{x + 5}$

63. $h(x) = 5|x - 20| + 1$

64. $f(x) = -3|x + 5.7|$

65. $g(x) = 9 - \sqrt{x + 103}$

66. $h(x) = \sqrt{x - 17} - 3$

Sketch the graph of each piecewise-defined function. Write the domain and range of each function.

67. $f(x) = \begin{cases} |x| & \text{if } x \le 0 \\ x^2 & \text{if } x > 0 \end{cases}$

68. $f(x) = \begin{cases} x^2 & \text{if } x < 0 \\ \sqrt{x} & \text{if } x \ge 0 \end{cases}$

69. $g(x) = \begin{cases} |x - 2| & \text{if } x < 0 \\ -x^2 & \text{if } x \ge 0 \end{cases}$

70. $g(x) = \begin{cases} -|x + 1| - 1 & \text{if } x < -2 \\ \sqrt{x + 2} - 4 & \text{if } x \ge -2 \end{cases}$

📖 STUDY SKILLS BUILDER

Tips for Studying for an Exam

To prepare for an exam, try the following study techniques:

- Start the study process days before your exam.
- Make sure that you are up-to-date on your assignments.
- If there is a topic that you are unsure of, use one of the many resources that are available to you. For example,

  See your instructor.

  Visit a learning resource center on campus.

  Read the textbook material and examples on the topic.

  View a video on the topic.

- Reread your notes and carefully review the Chapter Highlights at the end of any chapter.
- Work the review exercises at the end of the chapter. Check your answers and correct any mistakes. If you have trouble, use a resource listed above.
- Find a quiet place to take the Chapter Test found at the end of the chapter. Do not use any resources when taking this sample test. This way, you will have a clear

indication of how prepared you are for your exam. Check your answers and make sure that you correct any missed exercises.

- Get lots of rest the night before the exam. It's hard to show how well you know the material if your brain is foggy from lack of sleep.

Good luck and keep a positive attitude.

Let's see how you did on your last exam.

1. How many days before your last exam did you start studying for that exam?

2. Were you up-to-date on your assignments at that time or did you need to catch up on assignments?

3. List the most helpful text supplement (if you used one).

4. List the most helpful campus supplement (if you used one).

5. List your process for preparing for a mathematics test.

6. Was this process helpful? In other words, were you satisfied with your performance on your exam?

7. If not, what changes can you make in your process that will make it more helpful to you?

3.7 GRAPHING LINEAR INEQUALITIES

OBJECTIVES

1 Graph linear inequalities.

2 Graph the intersection or union of two linear inequalities.

OBJECTIVE 1 ▶ Graphing linear inequalities. Recall that the graph of a linear equation in two variables is the graph of all ordered pairs that satisfy the equation, and we determined that the graph is a line. Here we graph **linear inequalities** in two variables; that is, we graph all the ordered pairs that satisfy the inequality.

If the equal sign in a linear equation in two variables is replaced with an inequality symbol, the result is a linear inequality in two variables.

Examples of Linear Inequalities in Two Variables

$$3x + 5y \geq 6 \qquad 2x - 4y < -3$$
$$4x > 2 \qquad\qquad y \leq 5$$

To graph the linear inequality $x + y < 3$, for example, we first graph the related **boundary** equation $x + y = 3$. The resulting boundary line contains all ordered pairs the sum of whose coordinates is 3. This line separates the plane into two **half-planes.** All points "above" the boundary line $x + y = 3$ have coordinates that satisfy the inequality $x + y > 3$, and all points "below" the line have coordinates that satisfy the inequality $x + y < 3$.

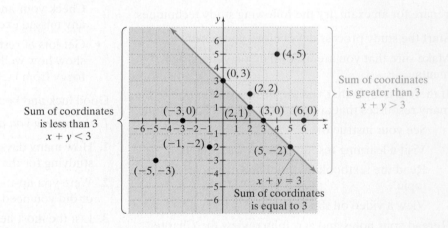

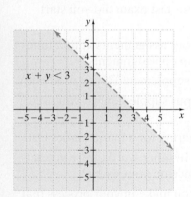

The graph, or **solution region,** for $x + y < 3$, then, is the half-plane below the boundary line and is shown shaded in the graph on the left. The boundary line is shown dashed since it is not a part of the solution region. These ordered pairs on this line satisfy $x + y = 3$ and not $x + y < 3$.

The following steps may be used to graph linear inequalities in two variables.

Graphing a Linear Inequality in Two Variables

STEP 1. Graph the boundary line found by replacing the inequality sign with an equal sign. If the inequality sign is $<$ or $>$, graph a dashed line indicating that points on the line are not solutions of the inequality. If the inequality sign is $\leq$ or $\geq$, graph a solid line indicating that points on the line are solutions of the inequality.

STEP 2. Choose a **test point not on the boundary line** and substitute the coordinates of this test point into the **original inequality.**

STEP 3. If a true statement is obtained in Step 2, shade the half-plane that contains the test point. If a false statement is obtained, shade the half-plane that does not contain the test point.

EXAMPLE 1   Graph $2x - y < 6$.

Solution   First, the boundary line for this inequality is the graph of $2x - y = 6$. Graph a dashed boundary line because the inequality symbol is $<$. Next, choose a test point on either side of the boundary line. The point $(0, 0)$ is not on the boundary line, so we use this point. Replacing x with 0 and y with 0 in the _original inequality_ $2x - y < 6$ leads to the following:

$$2x - y < 6$$
$$2(0) - 0 < 6 \quad \text{Let } x = 0 \text{ and } y = 0.$$
$$0 < 6 \quad \text{True}$$

Because $(0, 0)$ satisfies the inequality, so does every point on the same side of the boundary line as $(0, 0)$. Shade the half-plane that contains $(0, 0)$. The half-plane graph of the inequality is shown at the right.

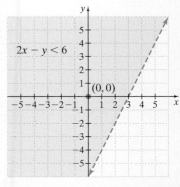

Every point in the shaded half-plane satisfies the original inequality. Notice that the inequality $2x - y < 6$ does not describe a function since its graph does not pass the vertical line test.   □

PRACTICE
1   Graph $3x + y < 8$.

In general, linear inequalities of the form $Ax + By \leq C$, where A and B are not both 0, do not describe functions.

EXAMPLE 2   Graph $3x \geq y$.

Solution   First, graph the boundary line $3x = y$. Graph a solid boundary line because the inequality symbol is $\geq$. Test a point not on the boundary line to determine which half-plane contains points that satisfy the inequality. We choose $(0, 1)$ as our test point.

$$3x \geq y$$
$$3(0) \geq 1 \quad \text{Let } x = 0 \text{ and } y = 1.$$
$$0 \geq 1 \quad \text{False}$$

This point does not satisfy the inequality, so the correct half-plane is on the opposite side of the boundary line from $(0, 1)$. The graph of $3x \geq y$ is the boundary line together with the shaded region shown.

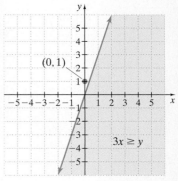

                                                                      □

PRACTICE
2   Graph $x \geq 3y$.

Concept Check ☑

If a point on the boundary line is included in the solution of an inequality in two variables, should the graph of the boundary line be solid or dashed?

OBJECTIVE 2 ▶ Graphing intersections or unions of linear inequalities. The intersection and the union of linear inequalities can also be graphed, as shown in the next two examples.

EXAMPLE 3 Graph the intersection of $x \geq 1$ and $y \geq 2x - 1$.

Solution Graph each inequality. The intersection of the two graphs is all points common to both regions, as shown by the dark pink shading in the third graph.

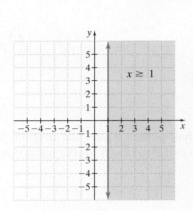 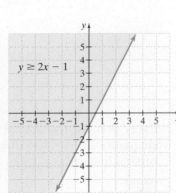 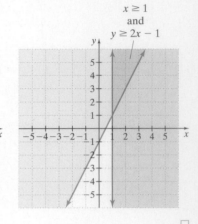

PRACTICE
3 Graph the intersection of $x \leq 3$ and $y \leq x - 2$.

EXAMPLE 4 Graph the union of $x + \frac{1}{2}y \geq -4$ or $y \leq -2$.

Solution Graph each inequality. The union of the two inequalities is both shaded regions, including the solid boundary lines shown in the third graph.

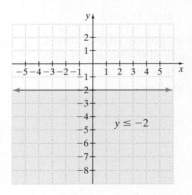 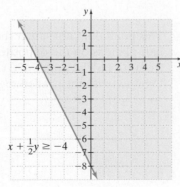 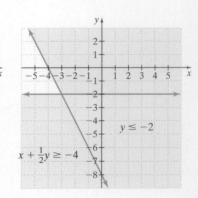

PRACTICE
4 Graph the union of $2x - 3y \leq -2$ or $y \geq 1$.

Answer to Concept Check:

Solid

3.7 | EXERCISE SET

Graph each inequality. See Examples 1 and 2.

1. $x < 2$ **2.** $x > -3$

3. $x - y \geq 7$ **4.** $3x + y \leq 1$

5. $3x + y > 6$ **6.** $2x + y > 2$

7. $y \leq -2x$ **8.** $y \leq 3x$

9. $2x + 4y \geq 8$ **10.** $2x + 6y \leq 12$

11. $5x + 3y > -15$ **12.** $2x + 5y < -20$

13. Explain when a dashed boundary line should be used in the graph of an inequality.

14. Explain why, after the boundary line is sketched, we test a point on either side of this boundary in the original inequality.

Graph each union or intersection. See Examples 3 and 4.

15. The intersection of $x \geq 3$ and $y \leq -2$

16. The union of $x \geq 3$ or $y \leq -2$

17. The union of $x \leq -2$ or $y \geq 4$

18. The intersection of $x \leq -2$ and $y \geq 4$

19. The intersection of $x - y < 3$ and $x > 4$

20. The intersection of $2x > y$ and $y > x + 2$

21. The union of $x + y \leq 3$ or $x - y \geq 5$

22. The union of $x - y \leq 3$ or $x + y > -1$

MIXED PRACTICE

Graph each inequality.

23. $y \geq -2$ **24.** $y \leq 4$

25. $x - 6y < 12$ **26.** $x - 4y < 8$

27. $x > 5$ **28.** $y \geq -2$

29. $-2x + y \leq 4$ **30.** $-3x + y \leq 9$

31. $x - 3y < 0$ **32.** $x + 2y > 0$

33. $3x - 2y \leq 12$ **34.** $2x - 3y \leq 9$

35. The union of $x - y > 2$ or $y < 5$

36. The union of $x - y < 3$ or $x > 4$

37. The intersection of $x + y \leq 1$ and $y \leq -1$

38. The intersection of $y \geq x$ and $2x - 4y \geq 6$

39. The union of $2x + y > 4$ or $x \geq 1$

40. The union of $3x + y < 9$ or $y \leq 2$

41. The intersection of $x \geq -2$ and $x \leq 1$

42. The intersection of $x \geq -4$ and $x \leq 3$

43. The union of $x + y \leq 0$ or $3x - 6y \geq 12$

44. The intersection of $x + y \leq 0$ and $3x - 6y \geq 12$

45. The intersection of $2x - y > 3$ and $x > 0$

46. The union of $2x - y > 3$ or $x > 0$

Match each inequality with its graph.

47. $y \leq 2x + 3$ **48.** $y < 2x + 3$

49. $y > 2x + 3$ **50.** $y \geq 2x + 3$

A 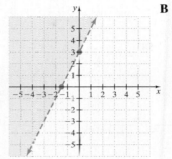   **B**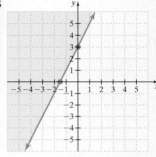

C 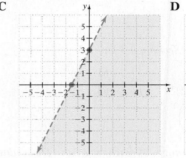   **D**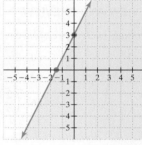

Write the inequality whose graph is given.

51. 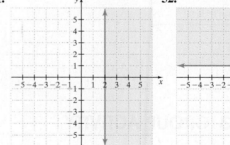   **52.**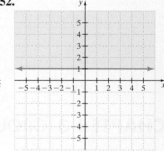

53. 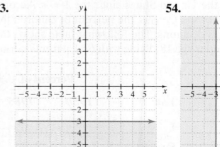   **54.**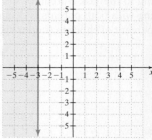

55.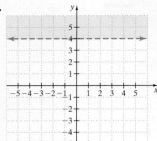

56.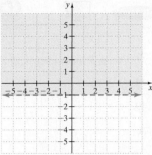

68.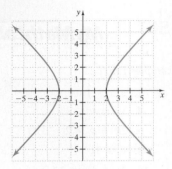

57.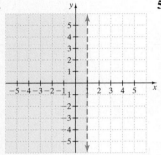

58.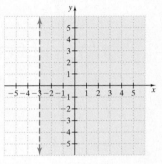

CONCEPT EXTENSIONS

Solve.

69. Rheem Abo-Zahrah decides that she will study at most 20 hours every week and that she must work at least 10 hours every week. Let x represent the hours studying and y represent the hours working. Write two inequalities that model this situation and graph their intersection.

70. The movie and TV critic for the *New York Times* spends between 2 and 6 hours daily reviewing movies and fewer than 5 hours reviewing TV shows. Let x represent the hours watching movies and y represent the time spent watching TV. Write two inequalities that model this situation and graph their intersection.

REVIEW AND PREVIEW

Evaluate each expression. See Sections 1.3 and 1.4.

59. 2^3 **60.** 3^2 **61.** -5^2

62. $(-5)^2$ **63.** $(-2)^4$ **64.** -2^4

65. $\left(\dfrac{3}{5}\right)^3$ **66.** $\left(\dfrac{2}{7}\right)^2$

Find the domain and the range of each relation. Determine whether the relation is also a function. See Section 3.2.

71. Chris-Craft manufactures boats out of Fiberglas and wood. Fiberglas hulls require 2 hours work, whereas wood hulls require 4 hours work. Employees work at most 40 hours a week. The following inequalities model these restrictions, where x represents the number of Fiberglas hulls produced and y represents the number of wood hulls produced.

$$\begin{cases} x \geq 0 \\ y \geq 0 \\ 2x + 4y \leq 40 \end{cases}$$

Graph the intersection of these inequalities.

67.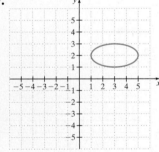

CHAPTER 3 GROUP ACTIVITY

Modeling Real Data

The number of children who live with only one parent has been steadily increasing in the United States since the 1960s. According to the U.S. Bureau of the Census, the percent of children living with both parents is declining. The following table shows the percent of children (under age 18) living with *both* parents during

selected years from 1980 to 2005. In this project, you will have the opportunity to use the data in the table to find a linear function $f(x)$ that represents the data, reflecting the change in living arrangements for children. This project may be completed by working in groups or individually.

Percent of U.S. Children Who Live with Both Parents

Year	*1980*	*1985*	*1990*	*1995*	*2000*	*2005*
x	0	5	10	15	20	25
Percent, y	77	74	73	69	67	68

Source: U.S. Bureau of the Census

1. Plot the data given in the table as ordered pairs.

2. Use a straight edge to draw on your graph what appears to be the line that "best fits" the data you plotted.

3. Estimate the coordinates of two points that fall on your best-fitting line. Use these points to find a linear function $f(x)$ for the line.

4. What is the slope of your line? Interpret its meaning. Does it make sense in the context of this situation?

5. Find the value of $f(50)$. Write a sentence interpreting its meaning in context.

6. Compare your linear function with that of another student or group. Are they different? If so, explain why.

(Optional) Enter the data from the table into a graphing calculator. Use the linear regression feature of the calculator to find a linear function for the data. Compare this function to the one you found in Question 3. How are they alike or different? Find the value of $f(50)$ using the model you found with the graphing calculator. Compare it to the value of $f(50)$ you found in Question 5.

CHAPTER 3 VOCABULARY CHECK

Fill in each blank with one of the words or phrases listed below.

relation   standard   slope–intercept   range   point–slope
line   slope x parallel   perpendicular
function   domain y linear function   linear inequality

1. A _____ is a set of ordered pairs.
2. The graph of every linear equation in two variables is a _____ .
3. The statement $-x + 2y > 0$ is called a _____ in two variables.
4. _____ form of linear equation in two variables is $Ax + By = C$.
5. The _____ of a relation is the set of all second components of the ordered pairs of the relation.
6. _____ lines have the same slope and different y-intercepts.
7. _____ form of a linear equation in two variables is $y = mx + b$.
8. A _____ is a relation in which each first component in the ordered pairs corresponds to exactly one second component.
9. In the equation $y = 4x - 2$, the coefficient of x is the _____ of its corresponding graph.
10. Two lines are _____ if the product of their slopes is -1.
11. To find the x-intercept of a linear equation, let _____ = 0 and solve for the other variable.
12. The _____ of a relation is the set of all first components of the ordered pairs of the relation.
13. A _____ is a function that can be written in the form $f(x) = mx + b$.
14. To find the y-intercept of a linear equation, let _____ = 0 and solve for the other variable.
15. The equation $y - 8 = -5(x + 1)$ is written in _____ form.

> ▶ **Helpful Hint**
>
> Are you preparing for your test? Don't forget to take the Chapter 3 Test on page 200. Then check your answers at the back of the text and use the Chapter Test Prep Video CD to see the fully worked-out solutions to any of the exercises you want to review.

CHAPTER 3 HIGHLIGHTS

DEFINITIONS AND CONCEPTS	**EXAMPLES**

SECTION 3.1   GRAPHING EQUATIONS

The **rectangular coordinate system,** or **Cartesian coordinate system,** consists of a vertical and a horizontal number line intersecting at their 0 coordinate. The vertical number line is called the **y-axis,** and the horizontal number line is called the **x-axis.** The point of intersection of the axes is called the **origin.** The axes divide the plane into four regions called **quadrants.**

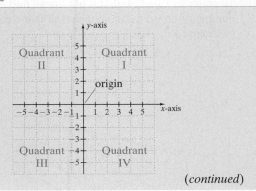

(continued)

DEFINITIONS AND CONCEPTS	EXAMPLES

To **plot** or **graph** an ordered pair means to find its corresponding point on a rectangular coordinate system.

To plot or graph the ordered pair $(-2, 5)$, start at the origin. Move 2 units to the left along the x-axis, then 5 units upward parallel to the y-axis.

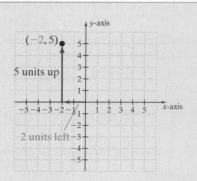

An ordered pair is a **solution** of an equation in two variables if replacing the variables by the corresponding coordinates results in a true statement.

Determine whether $(-2, 3)$ is a solution of

$$3x + 2y = 0$$
$$3(-2) + 2(3) = 0$$
$$-6 + 6 = 0$$
$$0 = 0 \quad \text{True}$$

$(-2, 3)$ is a solution.

A **linear equation in two variables** is an equation that can be written in the form $Ax + By = C$, where A, B, and C are real numbers and A and B are not both 0. The form $Ax + By = C$ is called **standard form.**

Linear Equations in Two Variables

$$y = -2x + 5, \quad x = 7$$
$$y - 3 = 0, \quad 6x - 4y = 10$$

$6x - 4y = 10$ is in standard form.

The graph of a linear equation in two variables is a line. To graph a linear equation in two variables, find three ordered pair solutions. (Use the third ordered-pair to check.) Plot the solution points, and draw the line connecting the points.

Graph $3x + y = -6$.

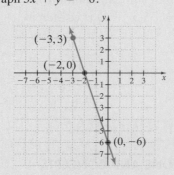

x	y
0	−6
−2	0
−3	3

To graph an equation that is not linear, find a sufficient number of ordered pair solutions so that a pattern may be discovered.

Graph $y = x^3 + 2$.

x	y
−2	−6
−1	1
0	2
1	3
2	10

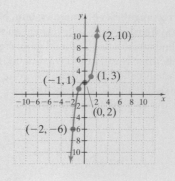

DEFINITIONS AND CONCEPTS	EXAMPLES

A **relation** is a set of ordered pairs. The **domain** of the relation is the set of all first components of the ordered pairs. The **range** of the relation is the set of all second components of the ordered pairs.

Relation

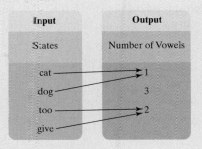

Domain: {cat, dog, too, give}
Range: {1, 2}

A **function** is a relation in which each element of the first set corresponds to exactly one element of the second set.

The previous relation is a function. Each word contains exactly one number of vowels.

Vertical Line Test

If no vertical line can be drawn so that it intersects a graph more than once, the graph is the graph of a function.

Find the domain and the range of the relation. Also determine whether the relation is a function.

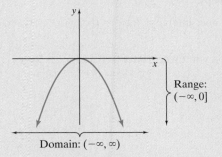

By the vertical line test, this graph is the graph of a function.

The symbol $f(x)$ means **function of x** and is called **function notation.**

If $f(x) = 2x^2 - 5$, find $f(-3)$.

$$f(-3) = 2(-3)^2 - 5 = 2(9) - 5 = 13$$

A **linear function** is a function that can be written in the form $f(x) = mx + b$.

To graph a linear function, find three ordered pair solutions. (Use the third ordered-pair to check.) Graph the solutions and draw a line through the plotted points.

Linear Functions

$$f(x) = -3, g(x) = 5x, h(x) = -\frac{1}{3}x - 7$$

Graph $f(x) = -2x$.

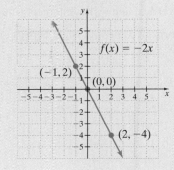

x	y or $f(x)$
-1	2
0	0
2	-4

(continued)

DEFINITIONS AND CONCEPTS	EXAMPLES

The graph of $y = mx + b$ is the same as the graph of $y = mx$, but shifted b units up if b is positive and b units down if b is negative.

Graph $g(x) = -2x + 3$.

This is the same as the graph of $f(x) = -2x$ shifted 3 units up.

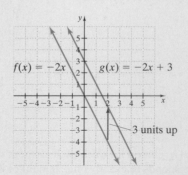

The x-coordinate of a point where a graph crosses the x-axis is called an **x-intercept.** The y-coordinate of a point where a graph crosses the y-axis is called a **y-intercept.**

To find an x-intercept, let $y = 0$ or $f(x) = 0$ and solve for x.

To find a y-intercept, let $x = 0$ and solve for y.

Graph $5x - y = -5$ by finding intercepts.

$$\text{If } x = 0, \text{ then} \qquad \text{If } y = 0, \text{ then}$$
$$5x - y = -5 \qquad\quad 5x - y = -5$$
$$5 \cdot 0 - y = -5 \qquad\quad 5x - 0 = -5$$
$$-y = -5 \qquad\qquad 5x = -5$$
$$y = 5 \qquad\qquad\quad x = -1$$
$$(0, 5) \qquad\qquad (-1, 0)$$

Ordered pairs are $(0, 5)$ and $(-1, 0)$.

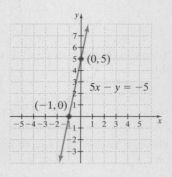

The graph of $x = c$ is a vertical line with x-intercept $(c, 0)$.

The graph of $y = c$ is a horizontal line with y-intercept $(0, c)$.

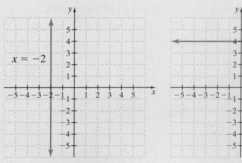
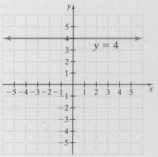

DEFINITIONS AND CONCEPTS	**EXAMPLES**

SECTION 3.4   THE SLOPE OF A LINE

The **slope** m of the line through (x_1, y_1) and (x_2, y_2) is given by

$$m = \frac{y_2 - y_1}{x_2 - x_1} \text{ as long } x_2 \neq x_1$$

The **slope-intercept form** of a linear equation is $y = mx + b$, where m is the slope of the line and b is the y-intercept.

Find the slope of the line through $(-1, 7)$ and $(-2, -3)$.

$$m = \frac{y_2 - y_1}{x_2 - x_1} = \frac{-3 - 7}{-2 - (-1)} = \frac{-10}{-1} = 10$$

Find the slope and y-intercept of $-3x + 2y = -8$.

$$2y = 3x - 8$$
$$\frac{2y}{2} = \frac{3x}{2} - \frac{8}{2}$$
$$y = \frac{3}{2}x - 4$$

The slope the line is $\frac{3}{2}$, and the y-intercept is $(0, -4)$.

Nonvertical parallel lines have the same slope.

If the product of the slopes of two lines is -1, then the lines are perpendicular.

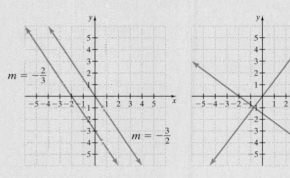

The slope of a horizontal line is 0.

The slope of a vertical line is undefined.

The slope of $y = -2$ is 0.

The slope of $x = 5$ is undefined.

SECTION 3.5   EQUATIONS OF LINES

We can use the slope–intercept form to write an equation of a line given its slope and y-intercept.

Write an equation of the line with y-intercept $(0, -1)$ and slope $\frac{2}{3}$.

$$y = mx + b$$
$$y = \frac{2}{3}x - 1$$

The point–slope form of the equation of a line is $y - y_1 = m(x - x_1)$, where m is the slope of the line and (x_1, y_1) is a point on the line.

Find an equation of the line with slope 2 containing the point $(1, -4)$. Write the equation in standard form: $Ax + By = C$.

$$y - y_1 = m(x - x_1)$$
$$y - (-4) = 2(x - 1)$$
$$y + 4 = 2x - 2$$
$$-2x + y = -6 \qquad \text{Standard form}$$

| DEFINITIONS AND CONCEPTS | EXAMPLES |

Vertical shifts (upward and downward) let k be a positive number.

Graph of	Same as	Moved
$g(x) = f(x) + k$	$f(x)$	k units upward
$g(x) = f(x) + (-k)$	$f(x)$	k units downward

Horizontal shift (to the left or right) let h be a positive number.

Graph of	Same as	Moved
$g(x) = f(x - h)$	$f(x)$	h units to the right
$g(x) = f(x + h)$	$f(x)$	h units to the left

Reflection about the x-axis

The graph of $g(x) = -f(x)$ is the graph of $f(x)$ reflected about the x-axis.

The graph of $h(x) = -|x - 3| + 1$ is the same as the graph of $f(x) = |x|$, reflected about the x-axis, shifted 3 units right, then 1 unit up.

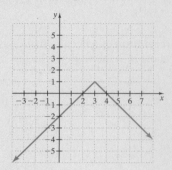

If the equal sign in a linear equation in two variables is replaced with an inequality symbol, the result is a **linear inequality in two variables.**

To graph a linear inequality

1. Graph the boundary line by graphing the related equation. Draw the line solid if the inequality symbol is $\leq$ or $\geq$. Draw the line dashed if the inequality symbol is $<$ or $>$.

2. Choose a test point not on the line. Substitute its coordinates into the original inequality.

3. If the resulting inequality is true, shade the **half-plane** that contains the test point. If the inequality is not true, shade the half-plane that does not contain the test point.

Linear Inequalities in Two Variables

$$x \leq -5 \qquad y \geq 2$$
$$3x - 2y > 7 \qquad x < -5$$

Graph $2x - 4y > 4$.

1. Graph $2x - 4y = 4$. Draw a dashed line because the inequality symbol is $>$.

2. Check the test point $(0, 0)$ in the inequality $2x - 4y > 4$.

$$2 \cdot 0 - 4 \cdot 0 > 4 \quad \text{Let } x = 0 \text{ and } y = 0.$$
$$0 > 4 \quad \text{False}$$

3. The inequality is false, so we shade the half-plane that does not contain $(0, 0)$.

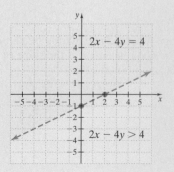

STUDY SKILLS BUILDER

Are You Prepared for a Test on Chapter 3?

Below I have listed some common trouble areas for students in Chapter 3. After studying for your test—but before taking your test—read these.

- Don't forget that the graph of an ordered pair is a *single* point in the rectangular coordinate plane.
- Remember that the slope of a horizontal line is 0 while a vertical line has undefined slope or no slope.
- For a linear equation such as $2y = 3x - 6$, the slope is not the coefficient of x unless the equation is solved for y. Solving this equation for y, we have $y = \frac{3}{2}x - 3$.

  The slope is $\frac{3}{2}$ and the y-intercept is $(0, -3)$.

Slope	Parallel line	Perpendicular line
$m = 6$	$m = 6$	$m = -\frac{1}{6}$
$m = -\frac{2}{3}$	$m = -\frac{2}{3}$	$m = \frac{3}{2}$

- Parallel lines have the same slope while perpendicular lines have negative reciprocal slopes.
- Don't forget that the statement $f(2) = 3$ corresponds to the ordered pair $(2, 3)$.

Remember: this is simply a checklist of common trouble areas. For a review of Chapter 3, see the Highlights and Chapter Review at the end of this chapter.

CHAPTER 3 REVIEW

(3.1) Plot the points and name the quadrant or axis in which each point lies.

1. $A(2, -1), B(-2, 1), C(0, 3), D(-3, -5)$

2. $A(-3, 4), B(4, -3), C(-2, 0), D(-4, 1)$

Determine whether each ordered pair is a solution to the given equation.

3. $7x - 8y = 56; (0, 56), (8, 0)$

4. $-2x + 5y = 10; (-5, 0), (1, 1)$

5. $x = 13; (13, 5), (13, 13)$

6. $y = 2; (7, 2), (2, 7)$

Determine whether each equation is linear or not. Then graph the equation.

7. $y = 3x$

8. $y = 5x$

9. $3x - y = 4$

10. $x - 3y = 2$

11. $y = |x| + 4$

12. $y = x^2 + 4$

13. $y = -\frac{1}{2}x + 2$

14. $y = -x + 5$

15. $y = 2x - 1$

16. $y = \frac{1}{3}x + 1$

17. $y = -1.36x$

18. $y = 2.1x + 5.9$

(3.2) Find the domain and range of each relation. Also determine whether the relation is a function.

19. $\left\{ \left(-\frac{1}{2}, \frac{3}{4}\right), (6, 0.75), (0, -12), (25, 25) \right\}$

20. $\left\{ \left(\frac{3}{4}, -\frac{1}{2}\right), (0.75, 6), (-12, 0), (25, 25) \right\}$

21.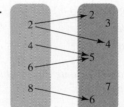

22.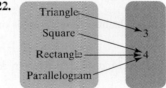

23.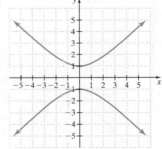

24.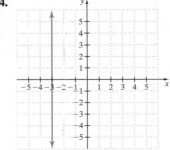

25.

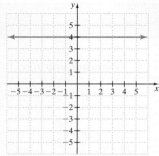

26.

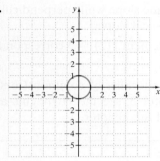

If $f(x) = x - 5$, $g(x) = -3x$, and $h(x) = 2x^2 - 6x + 1$, find the following.

27. $f(2)$ **28.** $g(0)$

29. $g(-6)$ **30.** $h(-1)$

31. $h(1)$ **32.** $f(5)$

The function $J(x) = 2.54x$ may be used to calculate the weight of an object on Jupiter J given its weight on Earth x.

33. If a person weighs 150 pounds on Earth, find the equivalent weight on Jupiter.

34. A 2000-pound probe on Earth weighs how many pounds on Jupiter?

Use the graph of the function below to answer Exercises 35 through 38.

35. Find $f(-1)$.   **36.** Find $f(1)$.

37. Find all values of x such that $f(x) = 1$.

38. Find all values of x such that $f(x) = -1$.

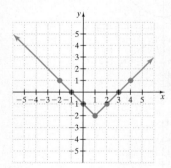

(3.3) Graph each linear function.

39. $f(x) = x$

40. $f(x) = -\dfrac{1}{3}x$

41. $g(x) = 4x - 1$

The graph of $f(x) = 3x$ is sketched below. Use this graph to match each linear function with its graph.

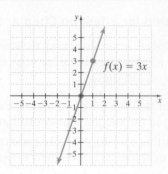

A

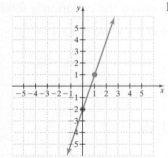

B

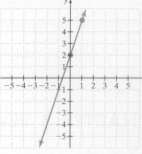

C

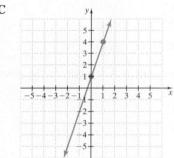

D

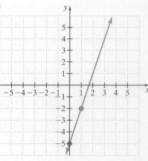

42. $f(x) = 3x + 1$ **43.** $f(x) = 3x - 2$

44. $f(x) = 3x + 2$ **45.** $f(x) = 3x - 5$

Graph each linear equation by finding intercepts if possible.

46. $4x + 5y = 20$ **47.** $3x - 2y = -9$

48. $4x - y = 3$ **49.** $2x + 6y = 9$

50. $y = 5$ **51.** $x = -2$

Graph each linear equation.

52. $x - 2 = 0$ **53.** $y + 3 = 0$

54. The cost C, in dollars, of renting a minivan for a day is given by the linear function $C(x) = 0.3x + 42$, where x is number of miles driven.

     a. Find the cost of renting the minivan for a day and driving it 150 miles.

     b. Graph $C(x) = 0.3x + 42$.

(3.4) Find the slope of the line through each pair of points.

55. $(2, 8)$ and $(6, -4)$ **56.** $(-3, 9)$ and $(5, 13)$

57. $(-7, -4)$ and $(-3, 6)$ **58.** $(7, -2)$ and $(-5, 7)$

Find the slope and y-intercept of each line.

59. $6x - 15y = 20$

60. $4x + 14y = 21$

Find the slope of each line.

61. $y - 3 = 0$ **62.** $x = -5$

Two lines are graphed on each set of axes. Decide whether l_1 or l_2 has the greater slope.

63. 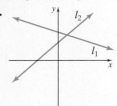   **64.**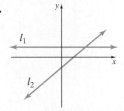

65. 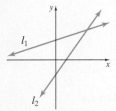   **66.**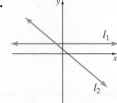

67. Recall from Exercise 54, that the cost C, in dollars, of renting a minivan for a day is given by the linear equation $y = 0.3x + 42$, where x is number of miles driven.

   a. Find and interpret the slope of this equation.

   b. Find and interpret the y-intercept of this equation.

Decide whether the lines are parallel, perpendicular, or neither.

△ **68.** $f(x) = -2x + 6$ △ **69.** $-x + 3y = 2$
      $g(x) = 2x - 1$ $6x - 18y = 3$

(3.5) Graph each linear equation using the slope and y-intercept.

70. $y = -x + 1$ **71.** $y = 4x - 3$
72. $3x - y = 6$ **73.** $y = -5x$

Find an equation of the line satisfying the given conditions.

74. Horizontal; through $(3, -1)$

75. Vertical; through $(-2, -4)$

△ **76.** Parallel to the line $x = 6$; through $(-4, -3)$

77. Slope 0; through $(2, 5)$

Find the standard form equation of each line satisfying the given conditions.

78. Through $(-3, 5)$; slope 3

79. Slope 2; through $(5, -2)$

80. Through $(-6, -1)$ and $(-4, -2)$

81. Through $(-5, 3)$ and $(-4, -8)$

△ **82.** Through $(-2, 3)$; perpendicular to $x = 4$

△ **83.** Through $(-2, -5)$; parallel to $y = 8$

Find the equation of each line satisfying the given conditions. Write each equation using function notation.

84. Slope $-\dfrac{2}{3}$; y-intercept $(0, 4)$

85. Slope -1; y-intercept $(0, -2)$

△ **86.** Through $(2, -5)$; parallel to $6x + 3y = 5$

△ **87.** Through $(-4, -2)$; parallel to $3x + 2y = 8$

△ **88.** Through $(-6, -1)$; perpendicular to $4x + 3y = 5$

△ **89.** Through $(-4, 5)$; perpendicular to $2x - 3y = 6$

90. In 2005, the percent of U.S. drivers wearing seat belts was 82%. The number of drivers wearing seat belts in 2000 was 71%. Let y be the number of drivers wearing seat belts in the year x, where $x = 0$ represents 2000. (*Source:* Strategis Group for Personal Communications Asso.)

   a. Write a linear equation that models the percent of U.S. drivers wearing seat belts in terms of the year x. [*Hint:* Write 2 ordered pairs of the form (years past 2000, percent of drivers).]

   b. Use this equation to predict the number of U.S. drivers wearing seat belts in the year 2009. (Round to the nearest percent.)

91. In 1998, the number of people (in millions) reporting arthritis was 43. The number of people (in millions) predicted to be reporting arthritis in 2020 is 60. Let y be the number of people (in millions) reporting arthritis in the year x, where $x = 0$ represents 1998. (*Source:* Arthritis Foundation)

   a. Write a linear equation that models the number of people (in millions) reporting arthritis in terms of the year x (See the hint for Exercise 90.)

   b. Use this equation to predict the number of people reporting arthritis in 2010. (Round to the nearest million.)

(3.6) Graph each function.

92. $f(x) = \begin{cases} -3x & \text{if } x < 0 \\ x - 3 & \text{if } x \geq 0 \end{cases}$

93. $g(x) = \begin{cases} -\dfrac{1}{5}x & \text{if } x \leq -1 \\ -4x + 2 & \text{if } x > -1 \end{cases}$

Graph each function.

94. $y = \sqrt{x} - 4$ **95.** $f(x) = \sqrt{x - 4}$
96. $g(x) = |x - 2| - 2$ **97.** $h(x) = -(x + 3)^2 - 1$

(3.7) *Graph each linear inequality.*

98. $3x + y > 4$ **99.** $\frac{1}{2}x - y < 2$

100. $5x - 2y \le 9$ **101.** $3y \ge x$

102. $y < 1$ **103.** $x > -2$

104. Graph the union of $y > 2x + 3$ or $x \le -3$.

105. Graph the intersection of $2x < 3y + 8$ and $y \ge -2$.

MIXED REVIEW

Graph each linear equation or inequality.

106. $3x - 2y = -9$ **107.** $x = -4y$

108. $3y \ge x$

Write an equation of the line satisfying each set of conditions. If possible, write the equation in the form $y = mx + b$.

109. Vertical; through $\left(-7, -\frac{1}{2}\right)$

110. Slope 0; through $\left(-4, \frac{9}{2}\right)$

111. Slope $\frac{3}{4}$; through $(-8, -4)$

112. Through $(-3, 8)$ and $(-2, 3)$

113. Through $(-6, 1)$; parallel to $y = -\frac{3}{2}x + 11$

114. Through $(-5, 7)$; perpendicular to $5x - 4y = 10$

Graph each piecewise-defined function.

115. $f(x) = \begin{cases} x - 2 & \text{if } x \le 0 \\ -\dfrac{x}{3} & \text{if } x \ge 3 \end{cases}$

116. $g(x) = \begin{cases} 4x - 3 & \text{if } x \le 1 \\ 2x & \text{if } x > 1 \end{cases}$

Graph each function.

117. $f(x) = \sqrt{x - 2}$

118. $f(x) = |x + 1| - 3$

CHAPTER 3 TEST

TEST PREP VIDEO Remember to use the Chapter Test Prep Video CD to see the fully worked-out solutions to any of the exercises you want to review.

1. Plot the points, and name the quadrant or axis in which each is located: $A(6, -2), B(4, 0), C(-1, 6)$.

Graph each line.

2. $2x - 3y = -6$ **3.** $4x + 6y = 7$

4. $f(x) = \frac{2}{3}x$ **5.** $y = -3$

6. Find the slope of the line that passes through $(5, -8)$ and $(-7, 10)$.

7. Find the slope and the y-intercept of the line $3x + 12y = 8$.

Graph each nonlinear function. Suggested x-values have been given for ordered pair solutions.

8. $f(x) = (x - 1)^2$ Let $x = -2, -1, 0, 1, 2, 3, 4$

9. $g(x) = |x| + 2$ Let $x = -3, -2, -1, 0, 1, 2, 3$

Find an equation of each line satisfying the given conditions. Write Exercises 10–14 in standard form. Write Exercises 15–17 using function notation.

10. Horizontal; through $(2, -8)$

11. Vertical; through $(-4, -3)$

△ **12.** Perpendicular to $x = 5$; through $(3, -2)$

13. Through $(4, -1)$; slope -3

14. Through $(0, -2)$; slope 5

15. Through $(4, -2)$ and $(6, -3)$

△ **16.** Through $(-1, 2)$; perpendicular to $3x - y = 4$

△ **17.** Parallel to $2y + x = 3$; through $(3, -2)$

△ **18.** Line L_1 has the equation $2x - 5y = 8$. Line L_2 passes through the points $(1, 4)$ and $(-1, -1)$. Determine whether these lines are parallel lines, perpendicular lines, or neither.

Graph each inequality.

19. $x \le -4$ **20.** $2x - y > 5$

21. The intersection of $2x + 4y < 6$ and $y \le -4$

Find the domain and range of each relation. Also determine whether the relation is a function.

22.

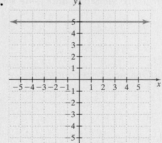

23.

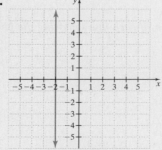

24.

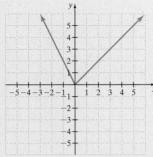

25.

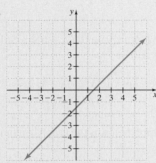

26. The average yearly earnings for high school graduates age 18 and older is given by the linear function

$$f(x) = 1031x + 25{,}193$$

where x is the number of years since 2000 that a person graduated. (*Source:* U.S. Census Bureau)

  a. Find the average earnings in 2000 for high school graduates.

  b. Find the average earnings for high school graduates in the year 2007.

  c. Predict the first whole year that the average earnings for high school graduates will be greater than $40,000.

  d. Find and interpret the slope of this equation.

  e. Find and interpret the y-intercept of this equation.

Graph each function. For Exercises 27 and 29, state the domain and the range of the function.

27. $f(x) = \begin{cases} -\dfrac{1}{2}x & \text{if } x \le 0 \\ 2x - 3 & \text{if } x > 0 \end{cases}$

28. $f(x) = (x - 4)^2$

29. $g(x) = -|x + 2| - 1$

30. $h(x) = \sqrt{x} - 1$

CHAPTER 3   CUMULATIVE REVIEW

1. Evaluate: $3x - y$ when $x = 15$ and $y = 4$.

2. Add.

  a. $-4 + (-3)$

  b. $\dfrac{1}{2} - \left(-\dfrac{1}{3}\right)$

  c. $7 - 20$

3. Determine whether the following statements are true or false.

  a. 3 is a real number.

  b. $\frac{1}{5}$ is an irrational number.

  c. Every rational number is an integer.

  d. $\{1, 5\} \subseteq \{2, 3, 4, 5\}$

4. Write the opposite of each.

  a. -7

  b. 0

  c. $\dfrac{1}{4}$

5. Subtract.

  a. $2 - 8$

  b. $-8 - (-1)$

  c. $-11 - 5$

  d. $10.7 - (-9.8)$

  e. $\dfrac{2}{3} - \dfrac{1}{2}$

  f. $1 - 0.06$

  g. Subtract 7 from 4.

6. Multiply or divide.

  a. $\dfrac{-42}{-6}$

  b. $\dfrac{0}{14}$

  c. $-1(-5)(-2)$

7. Simplify each expression.

  a. 3^2

  b. $\left(\dfrac{1}{2}\right)^4$

  c. -5^2

  d. $(-5)^2$

  e. -5^3

  f. $(-5)^3$

8. Which property is illustrated?

  a. $5(x + 7) = 5 \cdot x + 5 \cdot 7$

  b. $5(x + 7) = 5(7 + x)$

9. Insert $<$, $>$, or $=$ between each pair of numbers to form a true statement.

  a. $-1 \quad\quad -2$

  b. $\dfrac{12}{4} \quad\quad 3$

  c. $-5 \quad\quad 0$

  d. $-3.5 \quad\quad -3.05$

10. Evaluate $2x^2$ for

  a. $x = 7$

  b. $x = -7$

11. Write the multiplicative inverse, or reciprocal, of each.

  a. 11

  b. -9

  c. $\dfrac{7}{4}$

12. Simplify $-2 + 3[5 - (7 - 10)]$.

13. Solve: $0.6 = 2 - 3.5c$

14. Solve: $2(x - 3) = -40$.

15. Solve for x: $3x + 5 = 3(x + 2)$

16. Solve: $5(x - 7) = 4x - 35 + x$.

17. Write the following as algebraic expressions. Then simplify.

  a. The sum of three consecutive integers, if x is the first consecutive integer.

  b. The perimeter of a triangle with sides of length x, $5x$, and $6x - 3$.

18. Find 25% of 16.

19. Kelsey Ohleger was helping her friend Benji Burnstine study for an algebra exam. Kelsey told Benji that her three latest art history quiz scores are three consecutive even integers whose sum is 264. Help Benji find the scores.

20. Find 3 consecutive odd integers whose sum is 213.

21. Solve $V = lwh$ for h.

22. Solve $7x + 3y = 21$ for y

23. Solve: $x - 2 < 5$.

24. Solve: $-x - 17 \geq 9$.

25. Solve: $\dfrac{2}{5}(x - 6) \geq x - 1$

26. $3x + 10 > \dfrac{5}{2}(x - 1)$.

27. Solve: $2x \geq 0$ and $4x - 1 \leq -9$

28. Solve: $x - 2 < 6$ and $3x + 1 > 1$.

29. Solve: $5x - 3 \leq 10$ or $x + 1 \geq 5$

30. Solve: $x - 2 < 6$ or $3x + 1 > 1$.

31. Solve: $|5w + 3| = 7$

32. Solve: $|5x - 2| = 3$.

33. Solve: $|3x + 2| = |5x - 8|$

34. Solve: $|7x - 2| = |7x + 4|$

35. Solve: $|5x + 1| + 1 \leq 10$

36. Solve: $|-x + 8| - 2 \leq 8$

37. Solve for y: $|y - 3| > 7$

38. Solve for x: $|x + 3| > 1$.

39. Determine whether $(0, -12), (1, 9),$ and $(2, -6)$ are solutions of the equation $3x - y = 12$.

40. Find the slope and y-intercept of $7x + 2y = 10$.

41. Is the relation $y = 2x + 1$ also a function?

42. Determine whether the graph below is the graph of a function.

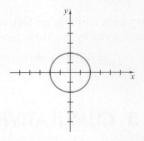

43. Find the y-intercept of the graph of each equation.

  a. $f(x) = \dfrac{1}{2}x + \dfrac{3}{7}$

  b. $y = -2.5x - 3.2$

44. Find the slope of the line through $(-1, 6)$ and $(0, 9)$.

45. Find the slope of the line whose equation is $f(x) = \dfrac{2}{3}x + 4$.

46. Find an equation of the vertical line through $\left(-2, -\dfrac{3}{4}\right)$.

47. Write an equation of the line with y-intercept $(0, -3)$ and slope of $\dfrac{1}{4}$.

48. Find an equation of the horizontal line through $\left(-2, -\dfrac{3}{4}\right)$.

49. Graph: $2x - y < 6$.

50. Write an equation of the line through $(-2, 5)$ and $(-4, 7)$.

4 Systems of Equations

M y Space and Facebook are both popular social networking Web sites offering interactive, user-submitted network of friends, personal profiles, blogs, groups, music, videos, and photos.

My Space is currently the world's sixth most popular Web site in any language and the third most popular Web site in the United States. Facebook was launched in early 2004 and is currently the 7th most visited Web site.

In Section 4.3, Exercise 53, page 234, we will form and use the functions graphed below to solve the system of equations.

In this chapter, two or more equations in two or more variables are solved simultaneously. Such a collection of equations is called a **system of equations.** Systems of equations are good mathematical models for many real-world problems because these problems may involve several related patterns.

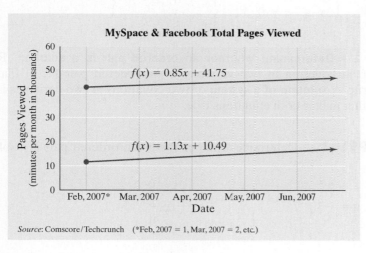

MySpace & Facebook Total Pages Viewed

$f(x) = 0.85x + 41.75$

$f(x) = 1.13x + 10.49$

Pages Viewed (minutes per month in thousands)

Feb, 2007* Mar, 2007 Apr, 2007 May, 2007 Jun, 2007

Date

Source: Comscore/Techcrunch (*Feb, 2007 = 1, Mar, 2007 = 2, etc.)

4.1 SOLVING SYSTEMS OF LINEAR EQUATIONS IN TWO VARIABLES

OBJECTIVES

1 Determine whether an ordered pair is a solution of a system of two linear equations.

2 Solve a system by graphing.

3 Solve a system by substitution.

4 Solve a system by elimination.

An important problem that often occurs in the fields of business and economics concerns the concepts of revenue and cost. For example, suppose that a small manufacturing company begins to manufacture and sell compact disc storage units. The revenue of a company is the company's income from selling these units, and the cost is the amount of money that a company spends to manufacture these units. The following coordinate system shows the graphs of revenue and cost for the storage units.

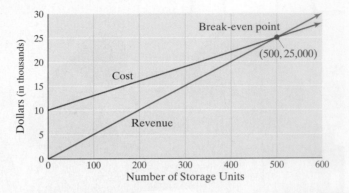

These lines intersect at the point (500, 25,000). This means that when 500 storage units are manufactured and sold, both cost and revenue are $25,000. In business, this point of intersection is called the **break-even point.** Notice that for *x*-values (units sold) less than 500, the cost graph is above the revenue graph, meaning that cost of manufacturing is greater than revenue, and so the company is losing money. For *x*-values (units sold) greater than 500, the revenue graph is above the cost graph, meaning that revenue is greater than cost, and so the company is making money.

Recall from Chapter 3 that each line is a graph of some linear equation in two variables. Both equations together form a **system of equations.** The common point of intersection is called the **solution of the system.** Some examples of systems of linear equations in two variables are

Systems of Linear Equations in Two Variables

$$\begin{cases} x - 2y = -7 \\ 3x + y = 0 \end{cases} \qquad \begin{cases} x = 5 \\ x + \dfrac{y}{2} = 9 \end{cases} \qquad \begin{cases} x - 3 = 2y + 6 \\ y = 1 \end{cases}$$

OBJECTIVE 1 ▶ Determining whether an ordered pair is a solution. Recall that a solution of an equation in two variables is an ordered pair (x, y) that makes the equation true. A **solution of a system** of two equations in two variables is an ordered pair (x, y) that makes both equations true.

EXAMPLE 1 Determine whether the given ordered pair is a solution of the system.

a. $\begin{cases} -x + y = 2 \\ 2x - y = -3 \end{cases}$ $(-1, 1)$ **b.** $\begin{cases} 5x + 3y = -1 \\ x - y = 1 \end{cases}$ $(-2, 3)$

Solution

a. We replace *x* with -1 and *y* with 1 in each equation.

$-x + y = 2$ First equation $2x - y = -3$ Second equation

$-(-1) + (1) \overset{?}{=} 2$ Let $x = -1$ and $y = 1$. $2(-1) - (1) \overset{?}{=} -3$ Let $x = -1$ and $y = 1$.

$1 + 1 \overset{?}{=} 2$ $-2 - 1 \overset{?}{=} -3$

$2 = 2$ True $-3 = -3$ True

Since $(-1, 1)$ makes *both* equations true, it is a solution. Using set notation, the solution set is $\{(-1, 1)\}$.

b. We replace x with -2 and y with 3 in each equation.

$$5x + 3y = -1 \quad \text{First equation} \qquad\qquad\qquad x - y = 1 \quad \text{Second equation}$$
$$5(-2) + 3(3) \stackrel{?}{=} -1 \quad \text{Let } x = -2 \text{ and } y = 3. \qquad (-2) - (3) \stackrel{?}{=} 1 \quad \text{Let } x = -2 \text{ and } y = 3.$$
$$-10 + 9 \stackrel{?}{=} -1 \qquad\qquad\qquad\qquad\qquad -5 = 1 \quad \text{False}$$
$$-1 = -1 \quad \text{True}$$

Since the ordered pair $(-2, 3)$ does not make *both* equations true, it is not a solution of the system. $\qquad\square$

PRACTICE

1   Determine whether the given ordered pair is a solution of the system.

a. $\begin{cases} -x - 4y = 1 \\ 2x + y = 5 \end{cases}$ $(3, -1)$ **b.** $\begin{cases} 4x + y = -4 \\ -x + 3y = 8 \end{cases}$ $(-2, 4)$

> **Helpful Hint**
>
> Reading values from graphs may not be accurate. Until a proposed solution is checked in both equations of the system, we can only assume that we have *estimated* a solution.

OBJECTIVE 2 ▶ Solving a system by graphing. We can *estimate* the solutions of a system by graphing each equation on the same coordinate system and estimating the coordinates of any point of intersection.

EXAMPLE 2   Solve each system by graphing. If the system has just one solution, estimate the solution.

a. $\begin{cases} x + y = 2 \\ 3x - y = -2 \end{cases}$ **b.** $\begin{cases} x - 2y = 4 \\ x = 2y \end{cases}$ **c.** $\begin{cases} 2x + 4y = 10 \\ x + 2y = 5 \end{cases}$

Solution   Since the graph of a linear equation in two variables is a line, graphing two such equations yields two lines in a plane.

a. $\begin{cases} x + y = 2 \\ 3x - y = -2 \end{cases}$

These lines intersect at one point as shown in the figure to the right. The coordinates of the point of intersection appear to be $(0, 2)$. Check this estimated solution by replacing x with 0 and y with 2 in **both** equations.

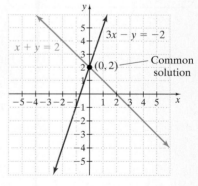

$$x + y = 2 \quad \text{First equation} \qquad\qquad 3x - y = -2 \quad \text{Second equation}$$
$$0 + 2 \stackrel{?}{=} 2 \quad \text{Let } x = 0 \text{ and } y = 2. \qquad 3 \cdot 0 - 2 \stackrel{?}{=} -2 \quad \text{Let } x = 0 \text{ and } y = 2.$$
$$2 = 2 \quad \text{True} \qquad\qquad\qquad\qquad -2 = -2 \quad \text{True}$$

The ordered pair $(0, 2)$ does satisfy both equations. We conclude therefore that $(0, 2)$ is the solution of the system. A system that has at least one solution, such as this one, is said to be **consistent.**

b. $\begin{cases} x - 2y = 4 \\ x \quad\quad = 2y \end{cases}$

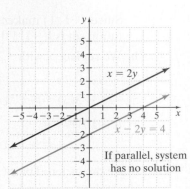

If parallel, system
has no solution

The lines appear to be parallel. To be sure, write each equation in point–slope form, $y = mx + b$.

$x - 2y = 4$ First equation

$-2y = -x + 4$ Subtract x from both sides.

$y = \dfrac{1}{2}x - 2$ Divide both sides by -2.

$x = 2y$ Second equation

$\dfrac{1}{2}x = y$ Divide both sides by 2.

$y = \dfrac{1}{2}x$

The graphs of these equations have the same slope, $\dfrac{1}{2}$, but different y-intercepts, so we have confirmed that these lines are parallel. Therefore, the system has no solution since the equations have no common solution (there are no intersection points). A system that has no solution is said to be **inconsistent.**

c. $\begin{cases} 2x + 4y = 10 \\ x + 2y = 5 \end{cases}$

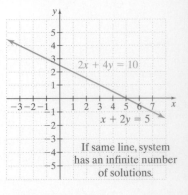

2x + 4y = 10

x + 2y = 5

If same line, system
has an infinite number
of solutions.

The graph of each equation appears to be in the same line. To confirm this, notice that if both sides of the second equation are multiplied by 2, the result is the first equation. This means that the equations have identical solutions. Any ordered pair solution of one equation satisfies the other equation also. Thus, these equations are said to be **dependent equations.** The solution set of the system is $\{(x, y)\,|\,x + 2y = 5\}$ or, equivalently, $\{(x, y)\,|\,2x + 4y = 10\}$ since the lines describe identical ordered pairs. Written this way, the solution set is read "the set of all ordered pairs (x, y), such that $2x + 4y = 10$." There are therefore an infinite number of solutions to this system. □

PRACTICE

2   Solve each system by graphing. If the system has just one solution, estimate the solution.

a. $\begin{cases} 3x - 2y = 4 \\ -9x + 6y = -12 \end{cases}$ **b.** $\begin{cases} y = 5x \\ 2x + y = 7 \end{cases}$ **c.** $\begin{cases} y = \dfrac{3}{4}x + 1 \\ 3x - 4y = 12 \end{cases}$

Concept Check ☑

The equations in the system are dependent and the system has an infinite number of solutions. Which ordered pairs below are solutions?

$$\begin{cases} -x + 3y = 4 \\ 2x + 8 = 6y \end{cases}$$

a. $(4, 0)$ **b.** $(-4, 0)$ **c.** $(-1, 1)$

We can summarize the information discovered in Example 2 as follows.

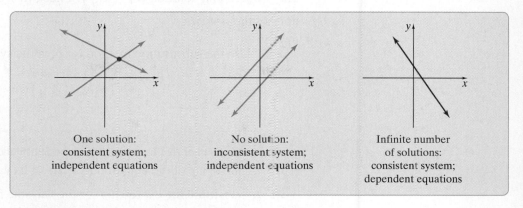

One solution:
consistent system;
independent equations

No solution:
inconsistent system;
independent equations

Infinite number
of solutions:
consistent system;
dependent equations

Concept Check ✓

How can you tell just by looking at the following system that it has no solution?

$$\begin{cases} y = 3x + 5 \\ y = 3x - 7 \end{cases}$$

How can you tell just by looking at the following system that it has infinitely many solutions?

$$\begin{cases} x + y = 5 \\ 2x + 2y = 10 \end{cases}$$

OBJECTIVE 3 ▶ Solving a system by substitution. Graphing the equations of a system by hand is often a good method of finding approximate solutions of a system, but it is not a reliable method of finding exact solutions of a system. We turn instead to two algebraic methods of solving systems. We use the first method, the **substitution method,** to solve the system

$$\begin{cases} 2x + 4y = -6 & \text{First equation} \\ x = 2y - 5 & \text{Second equation} \end{cases}$$

EXAMPLE 3 Use the substitution method to solve the system.

$$\begin{cases} 2x + 4y = -6 & \text{First equation} \\ x = 2y - 5 & \text{Second equation} \end{cases}$$

Solution In the second equation, we are told that x is equal to $2y - 5$. Since they are equal, we can *substitute* $2y - 5$ for x in the first equation. This will give us an equation in one variable, which we can solve for y.

$$2x + 4y = -6 \qquad \text{First equation}$$

$$2\overbrace{(2y - 5)} + 4y = -6 \qquad \text{Substitute } 2y - 5 \text{ for } x.$$

$$4y - 10 + 4y = -6$$

$$8y = 4$$

$$y = \frac{4}{8} = \frac{1}{2} \qquad \text{Solve for } y.$$

The y-coordinate of the solution is $\frac{1}{2}$. To find the x-coordinate, we replace y with $\frac{1}{2}$ in the second equation,

$$x = 2y - 5.$$

$$x = 2y - 5$$

$$x = 2\left(\frac{1}{2}\right) - 5 = 1 - 5 = -4$$

The ordered pair solution is $\left(-4, \dfrac{1}{2}\right)$. Check to see that $\left(-4, \dfrac{1}{2}\right)$ satisfies both equations of the system.

□

PRACTICE
3 Use the substitution method to solve the system.

$$\begin{cases} y = 4x + 7 \\ 2x + y = 4 \end{cases}$$

Solving a System of Two Equations Using the Substitution Method

STEP 1. Solve one of the equations for one of its variables.

STEP 2. Substitute the expression for the variable found in Step 1 into the other equation.

STEP 3. Find the value of one variable by solving the equation from Step 2.

STEP 4. Find the value of the other variable by substituting the value found in Step 3 into the equation from Step 1.

STEP 5. Check the ordered pair solution in *both* original equations.

EXAMPLE 4   Use the substitution method to solve the system.

$$\begin{cases} -\dfrac{x}{6} + \dfrac{y}{2} = \dfrac{1}{2} \\ \dfrac{x}{3} - \dfrac{y}{6} = -\dfrac{3}{4} \end{cases}$$

Solution   First we multiply each equation by its least common denominator to clear the system of fractions. We multiply the first equation by 6 and the second equation by 12.

$$\begin{cases} 6\left(-\dfrac{x}{6} + \dfrac{y}{2}\right) = 6\left(\dfrac{1}{2}\right) \\ 12\left(\dfrac{x}{3} - \dfrac{y}{6}\right) = 12\left(-\dfrac{3}{4}\right) \end{cases} \quad \text{simplifies to} \quad \begin{cases} -x + 3y = 3 & \text{First equation} \\ 4x - 2y = -9 & \text{Second equation} \end{cases}$$

> ▶ **Helpful Hint**
> To avoid tedious fractions, solve for a variable whose coefficient is 1 or −1, if possible.

To use the substitution method, we now solve the first equation for x.

$$-x + 3y = 3 \quad \text{First equation}$$
$$3y - 3 = x \quad \text{Solve for } x.$$

Next we replace x with $3y - 3$ in the second equation.

$$4x - 2y = -9 \quad \text{Second equation}$$
$$4\overbrace{(3y - 3)} - 2y = -9$$
$$12y - 12 - 2y = -9$$
$$10y = 3$$
$$y = \dfrac{3}{10} \quad \text{Solve for } y.$$

To find the corresponding x-coordinate, we replace y with $\dfrac{3}{10}$ in the equation $x = 3y - 3$. Then

$$x = 3\left(\dfrac{3}{10}\right) - 3 = \dfrac{9}{10} - 3 = \dfrac{9}{10} - \dfrac{30}{10} = -\dfrac{21}{10}$$

The ordered pair solution is $\left(-\dfrac{21}{10}, \dfrac{3}{10}\right)$. Check to see that this solution satisfies both original equations.

□

PRACTICE

4 Use the substitution method to solve the system.

$$\begin{cases} \dfrac{x}{3} + \dfrac{y}{4} = \dfrac{1}{2} \\ \dfrac{x}{4} - \dfrac{y}{2} = -\dfrac{1}{4} \end{cases}$$

> ▶ **Helpful Hint**
> If a system of equations contains equations with fractions, first clear the equations of fractions.

OBJECTIVE 4 ▶ **Solving a system by elimination.** The **elimination method,** or **addition method,** is a second algebraic technique for solving systems of equations. For this method, we rely on a version of the addition property of equality, which states that "equals added to equals are equal."

$$\text{If } A = B \text{ and } C = D \quad \text{then} \quad A + C = B + D.$$

EXAMPLE 5 Use the elimination method to solve the system.

$$\begin{cases} x - 5y = -12 & \text{First equation} \\ -x + y = 4 & \text{Second equation} \end{cases}$$

Solution Since the left side of each equation is equal to the right side, we add equal quantities by adding the left sides of the equations and the right sides of the equations. This sum gives us an equation in one variable, y, which we can solve for y.

$$\begin{array}{ll} x - 5y = -12 & \text{First equation} \\ \underline{-x + y = 4} & \text{Second equation} \\ -4y = -8 & \text{Add.} \\ y = 2 & \text{Solve for } y. \end{array}$$

The y-coordinate of the solution is 2. To find the corresponding x-coordinate, we replace y with 2 in either original equation of the system. Let's use the second equation.

$$\begin{array}{ll} -x + y = 4 & \text{Second equation} \\ -x + 2 = 4 & \text{Let } y = 2. \\ -x = 2 & \\ x = -2 & \end{array}$$

The ordered pair solution is $(-2, 2)$. Check to see that $(-2, 2)$ satisfies both equations of the system.

□

PRACTICE

5 Use the elimination method to solve the system.

$$\begin{cases} 3x - y = 5 \\ 5x + y = 11 \end{cases}$$

The steps below summarize the elimination method.

Solving a System of Two Linear Equations Using the Elimination Method

STEP 1. Rewrite each equation in standard form, $Ax + By = C$.

STEP 2. If necessary, multiply one or both equations by some nonzero number so that the coefficients of a variable are opposites of each other.

STEP 3. Add the equations.

STEP 4. Find the value of one variable by solving the equation from Step 3.

STEP 5. Find the value of the second variable by substituting the value found in Step 4 into either original equation.

STEP 6. Check the proposed ordered pair solution in *both* original equations.

EXAMPLE 6   Use the elimination method to solve the system.

$$\begin{cases} 3x - 2y = 10 \\ 4x - 3y = 15 \end{cases}$$

Solution   If we add the two equations, the sum will still be an equation in two variables. Notice, however, that we can eliminate y when the equations are added if we multiply both sides of the first equation by 3 and both sides of the second equation by -2. Then

$$\begin{cases} 3(3x - 2y) = 3(10) \\ -2(4x - 3y) = -2(15) \end{cases} \quad \text{simplifies to} \quad \begin{cases} 9x - 6y = 30 \\ -8x + 6y = -30 \end{cases}$$

Next we add the left sides and add the right sides.

$$\begin{array}{r} 9x - 6y = 30 \\ -8x + 6y = -30 \\ \hline x \qquad\quad = 0 \end{array}$$

To find y, we let $x = 0$ in either equation of the system.

$$3x - 2y = 10 \qquad \text{First equation}$$
$$3(0) - 2y = 10 \qquad \text{Let } x = 0.$$
$$-2y = 10$$
$$y = -5$$

The ordered pair solution is $(0, -5)$. Check to see that $(0, -5)$ satisfies both equations of the system.   □

PRACTICE
6   Use the elimination method to solve the system.

$$\begin{cases} 3x - 2y = -6 \\ 4x + 5y = -8 \end{cases}$$

EXAMPLE 7 Use the elimination method to solve the system.

$$\begin{cases} 3x + \dfrac{y}{2} = 2 \\ 6x + y = 5 \end{cases}$$

Solution If we multiply both sides of the first equation by -2, the coefficients of x in the two equations will be opposites. Then

$$\begin{cases} -2\left(3x + \dfrac{y}{2}\right) = -2(2) \\ 6x + y = 5 \end{cases} \quad \text{simplifies to} \quad \begin{cases} -6x - y = -4 \\ 6x + y = 5 \end{cases}$$

Now we can add the left sides and add the right sides.

$$\begin{array}{r} -6x - y = -4 \\ 6x + y = 5 \\ \hline 0 = 1 \quad \text{False} \end{array}$$

The resulting equation, $0 = 1$, is false for all values of y or x. Thus, the system has no solution. The solution set is $\{\ \}$ or $\varnothing$. This system is inconsistent, and the graphs of the equations are parallel lines. ☐

PRACTICE
7 Use the elimination method to solve the system.

$$\begin{cases} 8x + y = 6 \\ 2x + \dfrac{y}{4} = -2 \end{cases}$$

EXAMPLE 8 Use the elimination method to solve the system.

$$\begin{cases} -5x - 3y = 9 \\ 10x + 6y = -18 \end{cases}$$

Solution To eliminate x when the equations are added, we multiply both sides of the first equation by 2. Then

$$\begin{cases} 2(-5x - 3y) = 2(9) \\ 10x + 6y = -18 \end{cases} \quad \text{simplifies to} \quad \begin{cases} -10x - 6y = 18 \\ 10x + 6y = -18 \end{cases}$$

Next we add the equations.

$$\begin{array}{r} -10x - 6y = 18 \\ 10x + 6y = -18 \\ \hline 0 = 0 \end{array}$$

The resulting equation, $0 = 0$, is true for all possible values of y or x. Notice in the original system that if both sides of the first equation are multiplied by -2, the result is the second equation. This means that the two equations are equivalent. They have the same solution set and there are an infinite number of solutions. Thus, the equations of this system are dependent, and the solution set of the system is

$$\{(x, y)\,|\,-5x - 3y = 9\} \quad \text{or, equivalently,} \quad \{(x, y)\,|\,10x + 6y = -18\}. \quad ☐$$

PRACTICE
8 Use the elimination method to solve the system.

$$\begin{cases} -3x + 2y = -1 \\ 9x - 6y = 3 \end{cases}$$

▶ **Helpful Hint**

Remember that not all ordered pairs are solutions of the system in Example 8. Only the infinite number of ordered pairs that satisfy $-5x - 3y = 9$ or equivalently $10x + 6y = -18$.

Graphing Calculator Explorations

A graphing calculator may be used to approximate solutions of systems of equations by graphing each equation on the same set of axes and approximating any points of intersection. For example, approximate the solution of the system

$$\begin{cases} y = -2.6x + 5.6 \\ y = 4.3x - 4.9 \end{cases}$$

First use a standard window and graph both equations on a single screen.

The two lines intersect. To approximate the point of intersection, trace to the point of intersection and use an Intersect feature of the graphing calculator or a Zoom In feature.

Using either method, we find that the approximate point of intersection is $(1.52, 1.64)$.

Solve each system of equations. Approximate the solutions to two decimal places.

1. $y = -1.65x + 3.65$
$y = 4.56x - 9.44$

2. $y = 7.61x + 3.48$
$y = -1.26x - 6.43$

3. $2.33x - 4.72y = 10.61$
$5.86x + 6.22y = -8.89$

4. $-7.89x - 5.68y = 3.26$
$-3.65x + 4.98y = 11.77$

VOCABULARY & READINESS CHECK

Match each graph with the solution of the corresponding system.

A

B

C

D

1. no solution

2. Infinite number of solutions

3. $(1, -2)$

4. $(-3, 0)$

4.1 | EXERCISE SET

Determine whether each given ordered pair is a solution of each system. See Example 1.

1. $\begin{cases} x - y = 3 \\ 2x - 4y = 8 \end{cases}$ $(2, -1)$

2. $\begin{cases} x - y = -4 \\ 2x + 10y = 4 \end{cases}$ $(-3, 1)$

3. $\begin{cases} 2x - 3y = -9 \\ 4x + 2y = -2 \end{cases}$ $(3, 5)$

4. $\begin{cases} 2x - 5y = -2 \\ 3x + 4y = 4 \end{cases}$ $(4, 2)$

5. $\begin{cases} 3x + 7y = -19 \\ -6x = 5y + 8 \end{cases}$ $\left(\dfrac{2}{3}, -3\right)$

6. $\begin{cases} 4x + 5y = -7 \\ -8x = 3y - 1 \end{cases}$ $\left(\dfrac{3}{4}, -2\right)$

Solve each system by graphing. See Example 2.

7. $\begin{cases} x + y = 1 \\ x - 2y = 4 \end{cases}$

8. $\begin{cases} 2x - y = 8 \\ x + 3y = 11 \end{cases}$

9. $\begin{cases} 2y - 4x = 0 \\ x + 2y = 5 \end{cases}$ **10.** $\begin{cases} 4x - y = 6 \\ x - y = 0 \end{cases}$

11. $\begin{cases} 3x - y = 4 \\ 6x - 2y = 4 \end{cases}$ **12.** $\begin{cases} -x + 3y = 6 \\ 3x - 9y = 9 \end{cases}$

13. Can a system consisting of two linear equations have exactly two solutions? Explain why or why not.

14. Suppose the graph of the equations in a system of two equations in two variables consists of a circle and a line. Discuss the possible number of solutions for this system.

Solve each system of equations by the substitution method. See Examples 3 and 4.

15. $\begin{cases} x + y = 10 \\ y = 4x \end{cases}$ **16.** $\begin{cases} 5x + 2y = -17 \\ x = 3y \end{cases}$

17. $\begin{cases} 4x - y = 9 \\ 2x + 3y = -27 \end{cases}$ **18.** $\begin{cases} 3x - y = 6 \\ -4x + 2y = -8 \end{cases}$

19. $\begin{cases} \dfrac{1}{2}x + \dfrac{3}{4}y = -\dfrac{1}{4} \\ \dfrac{3}{4}x - \dfrac{1}{4}y = 1 \end{cases}$ **20.** $\begin{cases} \dfrac{2}{5}x + \dfrac{1}{5}y = -1 \\ x + \dfrac{2}{5}y = -\dfrac{8}{5} \end{cases}$

21. $\begin{cases} \dfrac{x}{3} + y = \dfrac{4}{3} \\ -x + 2y = 11 \end{cases}$ **22.** $\begin{cases} \dfrac{x}{8} - \dfrac{y}{2} = 1 \\ \dfrac{x}{3} - y = 2 \end{cases}$

Solve each system of equations by the elimination method. See Examples 5 through 8.

23. $\begin{cases} -x + 2y = 0 \\ x + 2y = 5 \end{cases}$ **24.** $\begin{cases} -2x + 3y = 0 \\ 2x + 6y = 3 \end{cases}$

25. $\begin{cases} 5x + 2y = 1 \\ x - 3y = 7 \end{cases}$ **26.** $\begin{cases} 6x - y = -5 \\ 4x - 2y = 6 \end{cases}$

27. $\begin{cases} \dfrac{3}{4}x + \dfrac{5}{2}y = 11 \\ \dfrac{1}{16}x - \dfrac{3}{4}y = -1 \end{cases}$ **28.** $\begin{cases} \dfrac{2}{3}x + \dfrac{1}{4}y = -\dfrac{3}{2} \\ \dfrac{1}{2}x - \dfrac{1}{4}y = -2 \end{cases}$

29. $\begin{cases} 3x - 5y = 11 \\ 2x - 6y = 2 \end{cases}$ **30.** $\begin{cases} 6x - 3y = -3 \\ 4x + 5y = -9 \end{cases}$

31. $\begin{cases} x - 2y = 4 \\ 2x - 4y = 4 \end{cases}$ **32.** $\begin{cases} -x + 3y = 6 \\ 3x - 9y = 9 \end{cases}$

33. $\begin{cases} 3x + y = 1 \\ 2y = 2 - 6x \end{cases}$ **34.** $\begin{cases} y = 2x - 5 \\ 8x - 4y = 20 \end{cases}$

MIXED PRACTICE

Solve each system of equations.

35. $\begin{cases} 2x + 5y = 8 \\ 6x + y = 10 \end{cases}$ **36.** $\begin{cases} x - 4y = -5 \\ -3x - 8y = 0 \end{cases}$

37. $\begin{cases} x + y = 1 \\ x - 2y = 4 \end{cases}$ **38.** $\begin{cases} 2x - y = 8 \\ x + 3y = 11 \end{cases}$

39. $\begin{cases} \dfrac{1}{3}x + y = \dfrac{4}{3} \\ -\dfrac{1}{4}x - \dfrac{1}{2}y = -\dfrac{1}{4} \end{cases}$ **40.** $\begin{cases} \dfrac{3}{4}x - \dfrac{1}{2}y = -\dfrac{1}{2} \\ x + y = -\dfrac{3}{2} \end{cases}$

41. $\begin{cases} 2x + 6y = 8 \\ 3x + 9y = 12 \end{cases}$ **42.** $\begin{cases} x = 3y - 1 \\ 2x - 6y = -2 \end{cases}$

43. $\begin{cases} 4x + 2y = 5 \\ 2x + y = -1 \end{cases}$ **44.** $\begin{cases} 3x + 6y = 15 \\ 2x + 4y = 3 \end{cases}$

45. $\begin{cases} 10y - 2x = 1 \\ 5y = 4 - 6x \end{cases}$ **46.** $\begin{cases} 3x + 4y = 0 \\ 7x = 3y \end{cases}$

47. $\begin{cases} 5x - 2y = 27 \\ -3x + 5y = 18 \end{cases}$ **48.** $\begin{cases} 3x + 4y = 2 \\ 2x + 5y = -1 \end{cases}$

49. $\begin{cases} x = 3y + 2 \\ 5x - 15y = 10 \end{cases}$ **50.** $\begin{cases} y = \dfrac{1}{7}x + 3 \\ x - 7y = -21 \end{cases}$

51. $\begin{cases} 2x - y = -1 \\ y = -2x \end{cases}$ **52.** $\begin{cases} x = \dfrac{1}{5}y \\ x - y = -4 \end{cases}$

53. $\begin{cases} 2x = 6 \\ y = 5 - x \end{cases}$ **54.** $\begin{cases} x = 3y + 4 \\ -y = 5 \end{cases}$

55. $\begin{cases} \dfrac{x + 5}{2} = \dfrac{6 - 4y}{3} \\ \dfrac{3x}{5} = \dfrac{21 - 7y}{10} \end{cases}$ **56.** $\begin{cases} \dfrac{y}{5} = \dfrac{8 - x}{2} \\ x = \dfrac{2y - 8}{3} \end{cases}$

57. $\begin{cases} 4x - 7y = 7 \\ 12x - 21y = 24 \end{cases}$ **58.** $\begin{cases} 2x - 5y = 12 \\ -4x + 10y = 20 \end{cases}$

59. $\begin{cases} \dfrac{2}{3}x - \dfrac{3}{4}y = -1 \\ -\dfrac{1}{6}x + \dfrac{3}{8}y = 1 \end{cases}$ **60.** $\begin{cases} \dfrac{1}{2}x - \dfrac{1}{3}y = -3 \\ \dfrac{1}{8}x + \dfrac{1}{6}y = 0 \end{cases}$

61. $\begin{cases} 0.7x - 0.2y = -1.6 \\ 0.2x - y = -1.4 \end{cases}$ **62.** $\begin{cases} -0.7x + 0.6y = 1.3 \\ 0.5x - 0.3y = -0.8 \end{cases}$

63. $\begin{cases} 4x - 1.5y = 10.2 \\ 2x + 7.8y = -25.68 \end{cases}$ **64.** $\begin{cases} x - 3y = -5.3 \\ 6.3x + 6y = 3.96 \end{cases}$

REVIEW AND PREVIEW

Determine whether the given replacement values make each equation true or false. See Section 1.3.

65. $3x - 4y + 2z = 5$; $x = 1$, $y = 2$, and $z = 5$

66. $x + 2y - z = 7$; $x = 2$, $y = -3$, and $z = 3$

67. $-x - 5y + 3z = 15$; $x = 0$, $y = -1$, and $z = 5$

68. $-4x + y - 8z = 4$; $x = 1$, $y = 0$, and $z = -1$

Add the equations. See Section 4.1.

69. $\begin{aligned} 3x + 2y - 5z &= 10 \\ -3x + 4y + z &= 15 \end{aligned}$ **70.** $\begin{aligned} x + 4y - 5z &= 20 \\ 2x - 4y - 2z &= -17 \end{aligned}$

71. $10x + 5y + 6z = 14$
$-9x + 5y - 6z = -12$

72. $-9x - 8y - z = 31$
$9x + 4y - z = 12$

CONCEPT EXTENSIONS

The concept of supply and demand is used often in business. In general, as the unit price of a commodity increases, the demand for that commodity decreases. Also, as a commodity's unit price increases, the manufacturer normally increases the supply. The point where supply is equal to demand is called the equilibrium point. The following shows the graph of a demand equation and the graph of a supply equation for previously rented DVDs. The x-axis represents the number of DVDs in thousands, and the y-axis represents the cost of a DVD. Use this graph to answer Exercises 73 through 76.

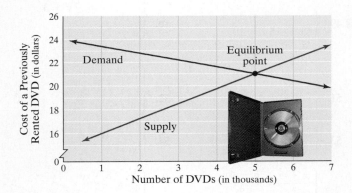

73. Find the number of DVDs and the price per DVD when supply equals demand.

74. When x is between 3 and 4, is supply greater than demand or is demand greater than supply?

75. When x is greater than 7, is supply greater than demand or is demand greater than supply?

76. For what x-values are the y-values corresponding to the supply equation greater than the y-values corresponding to the demand equation?

The revenue equation for a certain brand of toothpaste is $y = 2.5x$, where x is the number of tubes of toothpaste sold and y is the total income for selling x tubes. The cost equation is $y = 0.9x + 3000$, where x is the number of tubes of toothpaste manufactured and y is the cost of producing x tubes. The following set of axes shows the graph of the cost and revenue equations. Use this graph for Exercises 77 through 82.

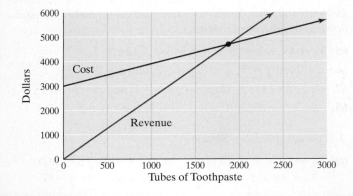

77. Find the coordinates of the point of intersection, or break-even point, by solving the system
$$\begin{cases} y = 2.5x \\ y = 0.9x + 3000 \end{cases}$$

78. Explain the meaning of the ordered pair point of intersection.

79. If the company sells 2000 tubes of toothpaste, does the company make money or lose money?

80. If the company sells 1000 tubes of toothpaste, does the company make money or lose money?

81. For what x-values will the company make a profit? (*Hint:* For what x-values is the revenue graph "higher" than the cost graph?)

82. For what x-values will the company lose money? (*Hint:* For what x-values is the revenue graph "lower" than the cost graph?)

83. Write a system of two linear equations in x and y that has the ordered pair solution $(2, 5)$.

84. Which method would you use to solve the system?
$$\begin{cases} 5x - 2y = 6 \\ 2x + 3y = 5 \end{cases}$$

Explain your choice.

85. The amount y of red meat consumed per person in the United States (in pounds) in the year x can be modeled by the linear equation $y = -0.3x + 113$. The amount y of all poultry consumed per person in the United States (in pounds) in the year x can be modeled by the linear equation $y = x + 68$. In both models, $x = 0$ represents the year 2000. (*Source:* Based on data and forecasts from the Economic Research Service, U.S. Department of Agriculture)

    a. What does the slope of each equation tell you about the patterns of red meat and poultry consumption in the United States?

    b. Solve this system of equations. (Round your final results to the nearest whole numbers.)

    c. Explain the meaning of your answer to part (b).

86. The number of books (in thousands) in the University of Texas libraries y for the years 2002 through 2005 can be modeled by the linear equation $y = 230x + 8146$. For the same time period, the number of books (in thousands) in the Columbia University libraries can be modeled by $y = 611x + 7378$, where x is the number of years since 2002. (*Source:* Association of Research Libraries)

    a. What does the slope of each equation tell you about the pattern of books in these two university libraries?

    b. Solve this system of equations. (Round your results to the nearest whole number.)

    c. Explain the meaning of your answer to part (b).

Solve each system. To do so you may want to let $a = \dfrac{1}{x}$ (if x is in the denominator) and let $b = \dfrac{1}{y}$ (if y is in the denominator.)

87. $\begin{cases} \dfrac{1}{x} + y = 12 \\ \dfrac{3}{x} - y = 4 \end{cases}$

88. $\begin{cases} x + \dfrac{2}{y} = 7 \\ 3x + \dfrac{3}{y} = 6 \end{cases}$

89. $\begin{cases} \dfrac{1}{x} + \dfrac{1}{y} = 5 \\ \dfrac{1}{x} - \dfrac{1}{y} = 1 \end{cases}$

90. $\begin{cases} \dfrac{2}{x} + \dfrac{3}{y} = 5 \\ \dfrac{5}{x} - \dfrac{3}{y} = 2 \end{cases}$

93. $\begin{cases} \dfrac{2}{x} - \dfrac{4}{y} = 5 \\ \dfrac{1}{x} - \dfrac{2}{y} = \dfrac{3}{2} \end{cases}$

91. $\begin{cases} \dfrac{2}{x} + \dfrac{3}{y} = -1 \\ \dfrac{3}{x} - \dfrac{2}{y} = 18 \end{cases}$

92. $\begin{cases} \dfrac{3}{x} - \dfrac{2}{y} = -18 \\ \dfrac{2}{x} + \dfrac{3}{y} = 1 \end{cases}$

94. $\begin{cases} \dfrac{5}{x} + \dfrac{7}{y} = 1 \\ -\dfrac{10}{x} - \dfrac{14}{y} = 0 \end{cases}$

📖 STUDY SKILLS BUILDER

Are You Familiar with Your Textbook Supplements?

There are many student supplements available for additional study. Below, I have listed some of these. See the preface of this text or your instructor for further information.

- *Chapter Test Prep Video CD.* This material is found in your textbook and is fully explained. The CD contains video clip solutions to the Chapter Test exercises in this text and are excellent help when studying for chapter tests.

- *Lecture Video CDs.* These video segments are keyed to each section of the text. The material is presented by me, Elayn Martin-Gay, and I have placed a video icon by each exercise in the text that I have worked on the video.

- *The Student Solutions Manual.* This contains worked out solutions to odd-numbered exercises as well as every exercise in the Integrated Reviews, Chapter Reviews, Chapter Tests, and Cumulative Reviews.

- *Prentice Hall Tutor Center.* Mathematics questions may be phoned, faxed, or emailed to this center.
- *MyMathLab, MathXL, and Interact Math.* These are computer and Internet tutorials. This supplement may already be available to you somewhere on campus, for example at your local learning resource lab. Take a moment and find the name and location of any such lab on campus.

As usual, your instructor is your best source of information.

Let's see how you are doing with textbook supplements:

1. Name one way the Chapter Test Prep Video can help you prepare for a chapter test.
2. List any textbook supplements that you have found useful.
3. Have you located and visited a learning resource lab located on your campus?
4. List the textbook supplements that are currently housed in your campus' learning resource lab.

4.2 SOLVING SYSTEMS OF LINEAR EQUATIONS IN THREE VARIABLES

OBJECTIVE

1 Solve a system of three linear equations in three variables.

In this section, the algebraic methods of solving systems of two linear equations in two variables are extended to systems of three linear equations in three variables. We call the equation $3x - y + z = -15$, for example, a **linear equation in three variables** since there are three variables and each variable is raised only to the power 1. A solution of this equation is an **ordered triple (x, y, z)** that makes the equation a true statement. For example, the ordered triple $(2, 0, -21)$ is a solution of $3x - y + z = -15$ since replacing x with 2, y with 0, and z with -21 yields the true statement $3(2) - 0 + (-21) = -15$. The graph of this equation is a plane in three-dimensional space, just as the graph of a linear equation in two variables is a line in two-dimensional space.

Although we will not discuss the techniques for graphing equations in three variables, visualizing the possible patterns of intersecting planes gives us insight into the possible patterns of solutions of a system of three three-variable linear equations. There are four possible patterns.

1. Three planes have a single point in common. This point represents the single solution of the system. This system is **consistent.**

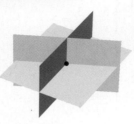

2. Three planes intersect at no point common to all three. This system has no solution. A few ways that this can occur are shown. This system is **inconsistent.**

3. Three planes intersect at all the points of a single line. The system has infinitely many solutions. This system is **consistent.**

4. Three planes coincide at all points on the plane. The system is consistent, and the equations are **dependent.**

OBJECTIVE 1 ▶ Solving a system of three linear equations in three variables. Just as with systems of two equations in two variables, we can use the elimination or substitution method to solve a system of three equations in three variables. To use the elimination method, we eliminate a variable and obtain a system of two equations in two variables. Then we use the methods we learned in the previous section to solve the system of two equations.

EXAMPLE 1   Solve the system.

$$\begin{cases} 3x - y + z = -15 & \text{Equation (1)} \\ x + 2y - z = 1 & \text{Equation (2)} \\ 2x + 3y - 2z = 0 & \text{Equation (3)} \end{cases}$$

**Solution**   Add equations (1) and (2) to eliminate z.

$$\begin{array}{r} 3x - y + z = -15 \\ \underline{x + 2y - z = 1} \\ 4x + y = -14 \quad \text{Equation (4)} \end{array}$$

> ▶ **Helpful Hint**
>
> Don't forget to add two other equations besides equations (1) and (2) *and* to **eliminate the same variable.**

Next, add two *other* equations and *eliminate z again*. To do so, multiply both sides of equation (1) by 2 and add this resulting equation to equation (3). Then

$$\begin{cases} 2(3x - y + z) = 2(-15) \\ 2x + 3y - 2z = 0 \end{cases} \quad \text{simplifies to} \quad \begin{cases} 6x - 2y + 2z = -30 \\ \underline{2x + 3y - 2z = 0} \\ 8x + y \qquad = -30 \end{cases} \text{Equation (5)}$$

Now solve equations (4) and (5) for x and y. To solve by elimination, multiply both sides of equation (4) by -1 and add this resulting equation to equation (5). Then

$$\begin{cases} -1(4x + y) = -1(-14) \\ 8x + y = -30 \end{cases} \quad \text{simplifies to} \quad \begin{cases} -4x - y = 14 \\ \underline{8x + y = -30} \\ 4x \qquad = -16 \quad \text{Add the equations.} \\ x = -4 \quad \text{Solve for } x. \end{cases}$$

Replace x with -4 in equation (4) or (5).

$$4x + y = -14 \quad \text{Equation (4)}$$
$$4(-4) + y = -14 \quad \text{Let } x = -4.$$
$$y = 2 \quad \text{Solve for } y.$$

Finally, replace x with -4 and y with 2 in equation (1), (2), or (3).

$$x + 2y - z = 1 \quad \text{Equation (2)}$$
$$-4 + 2(2) - z = 1 \quad \text{Let } x = -4 \text{ and } y = 2.$$
$$-4 + 4 - z = 1$$
$$-z = 1$$
$$z = -1$$

The solution is $(-4, 2, -1)$. To check, let $x = -4$, $y = 2$, and $z = -1$ in all three original equations of the system.

Equation (1)	*Equation (2)*	*Equation (3)*
$3x - y + z = -15$	$x + 2y - z = 1$	$2x + 3y - 2z = 0$
$3(-4) - 2 + (-1) \overset{?}{=} -15$	$-4 + 2(2) - (-1) \overset{?}{=} 1$	$2(-4) + 3(2) - 2(-1) \overset{?}{=} 0$
$-12 - 2 - 1 \overset{?}{=} -15$	$-4 + 4 + 1 \overset{?}{=} 1$	$-8 + 6 + 2 \overset{?}{=} 0$
$-15 = -15$	$1 = 1$	$0 = 0$
True	True	True

All three statements are true, so the solution is $(-4, 2, -1)$.   □

PRACTICE
1   Solve the system. $\begin{cases} 3x + 2y - z = 0 \\ x - y + 5z = 2 \\ 2x + 3y + 3z = 7 \end{cases}$

EXAMPLE 2   Solve the system.

$$\begin{cases} 2x - 4y + 8z = 2 & (1) \\ -x - 3y + z = 11 & (2) \\ x - 2y + 4z = 0 & (3) \end{cases}$$

Solution Add equations (2) and (3) to eliminate x, and the new equation is

$$-5y + 5z = 11 \quad (4)$$

To eliminate x again, multiply both sides of equation (2) by 2, and add the resulting equation to equation (1). Then

$$\begin{cases} 2x - 4y + 8z = 2 \\ 2(-x - 3y + z) = 2(11) \end{cases} \quad \begin{array}{l} \text{simplifies} \\ \text{to} \end{array} \quad \begin{cases} 2x - 4y + 8z = 2 \\ \underline{-2x - 6y + 2z = 22} \\ -10y + 10z = 24 \quad (5) \end{cases}$$

Next, solve for y and z using equations (4) and (5). Multiply both sides of equation (4) by -2, and add the resulting equation to equation (5).

$$\begin{cases} -2(-5y + 5z) = -2(11) \\ -10y + 10z = 24 \end{cases} \quad \begin{array}{l} \text{simplifies} \\ \text{to} \end{array} \quad \begin{cases} 10y - 10z = -22 \\ \underline{-10y + 10z = 24} \\ 0 = 2 \quad \text{False} \end{cases}$$

Since the statement is false, this system is inconsistent and has no solution. The solution set is the empty set $\{\ \}$ or $\varnothing$. □

PRACTICE
2   Solve the system. $\begin{cases} 6x - 3y + 12z = 4 \\ -6x + 4y - 2z = 7 \\ -2x + y - 4z = 3 \end{cases}$

The elimination method is summarized next.

Solving a System of Three Linear Equations by the Elimination Method

STEP 1. Write each equation in standard form $Ax + By + Cz = D$.

STEP 2. Choose a pair of equations and use the equations to eliminate a variable.

STEP 3. Choose any **other** pair of equations and eliminate the **same variable** as in Step 2.

STEP 4. Two equations in two variables should be obtained from Step 2 and Step 3. Use methods from Section 4.1 to solve this system for both variables.

STEP 5. To solve for the third variable, substitute the values of the variables found in Step 4 into any of the original equations containing the third variable.

STEP 6. Check the ordered triple solution in *all three* original equations.

▶ **Helpful Hint**
Make sure you read closely and follow Step 3.

Concept Check ✓

In the system

$$\begin{cases} x + y + z = 6 & \text{Equation (1)} \\ 2x - y + z = 3 & \text{Equation (2)} \\ x + 2y + 3z = 14 & \text{Equation (3)} \end{cases}$$

equations (1) and (2) are used to eliminate y. Which action could be used to best finish solving? Why?

a. Use (1) and (2) to eliminate z.   **b.** Use (2) and (3) to eliminate y.

c. Use (1) and (3) to eliminate x.

Answer to Concept Check: b

EXAMPLE 3   Solve the system.

$$\begin{cases} 2x + 4y = 1 & (1) \\ 4x - 4z = -1 & (2) \\ y - 4z = -3 & (3) \end{cases}$$

**Solution**   Notice that equation (2) has no term containing the variable y. Let us eliminate y using equations (1) and (3). Multiply both sides of equation (3) by -4, and add the resulting equation to equation (1). Then

$$\begin{cases} 2x + 4y = 1 \\ -4(y - 4z) = -4(-3) \end{cases} \text{ simplifies to } \begin{cases} 2x + 4y = 1 \\ - 4y + 16z = 12 \\ \hline 2x + 16z = 13 (4) \end{cases}$$

Next, solve for z using equations (4) and (2). Multiply both sides of equation (4) by -2 and add the resulting equation to equation (2).

$$\begin{cases} -2(2x + 16z) = -2(13) \\ 4x - 4z = -1 \end{cases} \text{ simplifies to } \begin{cases} -4x - 32z = -26 \\ 4x - 4z = -1 \\ \hline -36z = -27 \\ z = \dfrac{3}{4} \end{cases}$$

Replace z with $\dfrac{3}{4}$ in equation (3) and solve for y.

$$y - 4\left(\frac{3}{4}\right) = -3 \quad \text{Let } z = \frac{3}{4} \text{ in equation (3).}$$
$$y - 3 = -3$$
$$y = 0$$

Replace y with 0 in equation (1) and solve for x.

$$2x + 4(0) = 1$$
$$2x = 1$$
$$x = \frac{1}{2}$$

The solution is $\left(\dfrac{1}{2}, 0, \dfrac{3}{4}\right)$. Check to see that this solution satisfies all three equations of the system. □

PRACTICE
3   Solve the system. $\begin{cases} 3x + 4y = 0 \\ 9x - 4z = 6 \\ -2y + 7z = 1 \end{cases}$

EXAMPLE 4   Solve the system.

$$\begin{cases} x - 5y - 2z = 6 & (1) \\ -2x + 10y + 4z = -12 & (2) \\ \dfrac{1}{2}x - \dfrac{5}{2}y - z = 3 & (3) \end{cases}$$

**Solution**   Multiply both sides of equation (3) by 2 to eliminate fractions, and multiply both sides of equation (2) by $-\dfrac{1}{2}$ so that the coefficient of x is 1. The resulting system is then

$$\begin{cases} x - 5y - 2z = 6 & (1) \\ x - 5y - 2z = 6 & \text{Multiply (2) by } -\dfrac{1}{2}. \\ x - 5y - 2z = 6 & \text{Multiply (3) by 2.} \end{cases}$$

All three equations are identical, and therefore equations (1), (2), and (3) are all equivalent. There are infinitely many solutions of this system. The equations are dependent. The solution set can be written as $\{(x, y, z)|x - 5y - 2z = 6\}$. □

PRACTICE 4 Solve the system.
$$\begin{cases} 2x + y - 3z = 6 \\ x + \dfrac{1}{2}y - \dfrac{3}{2}z = 3 \\ -4x - 2y + 6z = -12 \end{cases}$$

As mentioned earlier, we can also use the substitution method to solve a system of linear equations in three variables.

EXAMPLE 5 Solve the system:
$$\begin{cases} x - 4y - 5z = 35 & (1) \\ x - 3y \quad\;\; = 0 & (2) \\ -y + z = -55 & (3) \end{cases}$$

Solution Notice in equations (2) and (3) that a variable is missing. Also notice that both equations contain the variable y. Let's use the substitution method by solving equation (2) for x and equation (3) for z and substituting the results in equation (1).

$$x - 3y = 0 \qquad (2)$$
$$x = 3y \qquad \text{Solve equation (2) for } x.$$
$$-y + z = -55 \qquad (3)$$
$$z = y - 55 \qquad \text{Solve equation (3) for } z.$$

Now substitute $3y$ for x and $y - 55$ for z in equation (1).

$$x - 4y - 5z = 35 \qquad (1)$$

▶ **Helpful Hint**
Do not forget to distribute.

$$3y - 4y - 5(y - 55) = 35 \qquad \text{Let } x = 3y \text{ and } z = y - 55.$$
$$3y - 4y - 5y + 275 = 35 \qquad \text{Use the distributive law and multiply.}$$
$$-6y + 275 = 35 \qquad \text{Combine like terms.}$$
$$-6y = -240 \qquad \text{Subtract 275 from both sides.}$$
$$y = 40 \qquad \text{Solve.}$$

To find x, recall that $x = 3y$ and substitute 40 for y. Then $x = 3y$ becomes $x = 3 \cdot 40 = 120$. To find z, recall that $z = y - 55$ and substitute 40 for y, also. Then $z = y - 55$ becomes $z = 40 - 55 = -15$. The solution is $(120, 40, -15)$. □

PRACTICE 5 Solve the system.
$$\begin{cases} x + 2y + 4z = 16 \\ x \quad\quad + 2z = -4 \\ y - 3z = 30 \end{cases}$$

4.2 | EXERCISE SET

PRACTICE   WATCH   DOWNLOAD   READ   REVIEW

Solve.

1. Choose the equation(s) that has $(-1, 3, 1)$ as a solution.

  a. $x + y + z = 3$ **b.** $-x + y + z = 5$

  c. $-x + y + 2z = 0$ **d.** $x + 2y - 3z = 2$

2. Choose the equation(s) that has $(2, 1, -4)$ as a solution.

  a. $x + y + z = -1$ **b.** $x - y - z = -3$

  c. $2x - y + z = -1$ **d.** $-x - 3y - z = -1$

3. Use the result of Exercise 1 to determine whether $(-1, 3, 1)$ is a solution of the system below. Explain your answer.

$$\begin{cases} x + y + z = 3 \\ -x + y + z = 5 \\ x + 2y - 3z = 2 \end{cases}$$

4. Use the result of Exercise 2 to determine whether $(2, 1, -4)$ is a solution of the system below. Explain your answer.

$$\begin{cases} x + y + z = -1 \\ x - y - z = -3 \\ 2x - y + z = -1 \end{cases}$$

MIXED PRACTICE

Solve each system. See Examples 1 through 5.

5. $\begin{cases} x - y + z = -4 \\ 3x + 2y - z = 5 \\ -2x + 3y - z = 15 \end{cases}$

6. $\begin{cases} x + y - z = -1 \\ -4x - y + 2z = -7 \\ 2x - 2y - 5z = 7 \end{cases}$

7. $\begin{cases} x + y = 3 \\ 2y = 10 \\ 3x + 2y - 3z = 1 \end{cases}$

8. $\begin{cases} 5x = 5 \\ 2x + y = 4 \\ 3x + y - 4z = -15 \end{cases}$

9. $\begin{cases} 2x + 2y + z = 1 \\ -x + y + 2z = 3 \\ x + 2y + 4z = 0 \end{cases}$

10. $\begin{cases} 2x - 3y + z = 5 \\ x + y + z = 0 \\ 4x + 2y + 4z = 4 \end{cases}$

11. $\begin{cases} x - 2y + z = -5 \\ -3x + 6y - 3z = 15 \\ 2x - 4y + 2z = -10 \end{cases}$

12. $\begin{cases} 3x + y - 2z = 2 \\ -6x - 2y + 4z = -2 \\ 9x + 3y - 6z = 6 \end{cases}$

13. $\begin{cases} 4x - y + 2z = 5 \\ 2y + z = 4 \\ 4x + y + 3z = 10 \end{cases}$

14. $\begin{cases} 5y - 7z = 14 \\ 2x + y + 4z = 10 \\ 2x + 6y - 3z = 30 \end{cases}$

15. $\begin{cases} x + 5z = 0 \\ 5x + y = 0 \\ y - 3z = 0 \end{cases}$

16. $\begin{cases} x - 5y = 0 \\ x - z = 0 \\ -x + 5z = 0 \end{cases}$

17. $\begin{cases} 6x - 5z = 17 \\ 5x - y + 3z = -1 \\ 2x + y = -41 \end{cases}$

18. $\begin{cases} x + 2y = 6 \\ 7x + 3y + z = -33 \\ x - z = 16 \end{cases}$

19. $\begin{cases} x + y + z = 8 \\ 2x - y - z = 10 \\ x - 2y - 3z = 22 \end{cases}$

20. $\begin{cases} 5x + y + 3z = 1 \\ x - y + 3z = -7 \\ -x + y = 1 \end{cases}$

21. $\begin{cases} x + 2y - z = 5 \\ 6x + y + z = 7 \\ 2x + 4y - 2z = 5 \end{cases}$

22. $\begin{cases} 4x - y + 3z = 10 \\ x + y - z = 5 \\ 8x - 2y + 6z = 10 \end{cases}$

23. $\begin{cases} 2x - 3y + z = 2 \\ x - 5y + 5z = 3 \\ 3x + y - 3z = 5 \end{cases}$

24. $\begin{cases} 4x + y - z = 8 \\ x - y + 2z = 3 \\ 3x - y + z = 6 \end{cases}$

25. $\begin{cases} -2x - 4y + 6z = -8 \\ x + 2y - 3z = 4 \\ 4x + 8y - 12z = 16 \end{cases}$

26. $\begin{cases} -6x + 12y + 3z = -6 \\ 2x - 4y - z = 2 \\ -x + 2y + \dfrac{z}{2} = -1 \end{cases}$

27. $\begin{cases} 2x + 2y - 3z = 1 \\ y + 2z = -14 \\ 3x - 2y = -1 \end{cases}$

28. $\begin{cases} 7x + 4y = 10 \\ x - 4y + 2z = 6 \\ y - 2z = -1 \end{cases}$

29. $\begin{cases} x + 2y - z = 5 \\ -3x - 2y - 3z = 11 \\ 4x + 4y + 5z = -18 \end{cases}$

30. $\begin{cases} 3x - 3y + z = -1 \\ 3x - y - z = 3 \\ -6x + 2y + 2z = -6 \end{cases}$

31. $\begin{cases} \dfrac{3}{4}x - \dfrac{1}{3}y + \dfrac{1}{2}z = 9 \\ \dfrac{1}{6}x + \dfrac{1}{3}y - \dfrac{1}{2}z = 2 \\ \dfrac{1}{2}x - y + \dfrac{1}{2}z = 2 \end{cases}$

32. $\begin{cases} \dfrac{1}{3}x - \dfrac{1}{4}y + z = -9 \\ \dfrac{1}{2}x - \dfrac{1}{3}y - \dfrac{1}{4}z = -6 \\ x - \dfrac{1}{2}y - z = -8 \end{cases}$

REVIEW AND PREVIEW

Solve. See Section 2.2.

33. The sum of two numbers is 45 and one number is twice the other. Find the numbers.

34. The difference between two numbers is 5. Twice the smaller number added to five times the larger number is 53. Find the numbers.

Solve. See Section 2.1.

35. $2(x - 1) - 3x = x - 12$

36. $7(2x - 1) + 4 = 11(3x - 2)$

37. $-y - 5(y + 5) = 3y - 10$

38. $z - 3(z + 7) = 6(2z + 1)$

CONCEPT EXTENSIONS

39. Write a single linear equation in three variables that has $(-1, 2, -4)$ as a solution. (There are many possibilities.) Explain the process you used to write an equation.

40. Write a system of three linear equations in three variables that has $(2, 1, 5)$ as a solution. (There are many possibilities.) Explain the process you used to write an equation.

41. Write a system of linear equations in three variables that has the solution $(-1, 2, -4)$. Explain the process you used to write your system.

42. When solving a system of three equation in three unknowns, explain how to determine that a system has no solution.

43. The fraction $\frac{1}{24}$ can be written as the following sum:

$$\frac{1}{24} = \frac{x}{8} + \frac{y}{4} + \frac{z}{3}$$

where the numbers $x, y,$ and z are solutions of

$$\begin{cases} x + y + z = 1 \\ 2x - y + z = 0 \\ -x + 2y + 2z = -1 \end{cases}$$

Solve the system and see that the sum of the fractions is $\frac{1}{24}$.

44. The fraction $\frac{1}{18}$ can be written as the following sum:

$$\frac{1}{18} = \frac{x}{2} + \frac{y}{3} + \frac{z}{9}$$

where the numbers $x, y,$ and z are solutions of

$$\begin{cases} x + 3y + z = -3 \\ -x + y + 2z = -14 \\ 3x + 2y - z = 12 \end{cases}$$

Solve the system and see that the sum of the fractions is $\frac{1}{18}$.

Solving systems involving more than three variables can be accomplished with methods similar to those encountered in this section. Apply what you already know to solve each system of equations in four variables.

45. $\begin{cases} x + y \quad\quad - w = 0 \\ \quad y + 2z + w = 3 \\ x \quad\quad - z \quad\quad = 1 \\ 2x - y \quad\quad - w = -1 \end{cases}$

46. $\begin{cases} 5x + 4y \quad\quad\quad = 29 \\ \quad y + z - w = -2 \\ 5x \quad\quad + z \quad\quad = 23 \\ \quad y - z + w = 4 \end{cases}$

47. $\begin{cases} x + y + z + w = 5 \\ 2x + y + z + w = 6 \\ x + y + z \quad\quad = 2 \\ x + y \quad\quad\quad = 0 \end{cases}$

48. $\begin{cases} 2x \quad\quad - z \quad\quad = -1 \\ \quad y + z + w = 9 \\ \quad y \quad\quad - 2w = -6 \\ x + y \quad\quad\quad = 3 \end{cases}$

49. Write a system of three linear equations in three variables that are dependent equations.

50. What is the solution to the system in Exercise 49?

4.3 SYSTEMS OF LINEAR EQUATIONS AND PROBLEM SOLVING

OBJECTIVES

1 Solve problems that can be modeled by a system of two linear equations.

2 Solve problems with cost and revenue functions.

3 Solve problems that can be modeled by a system of three linear equations.

OBJECTIVE 1 ▶ Solving problem modeled by systems of two equations. Thus far, we have solved problems by writing one-variable equations and solving for the variable. Some of these problems can be solved, perhaps more easily, by writing a system of equations, as illustrated in this section.

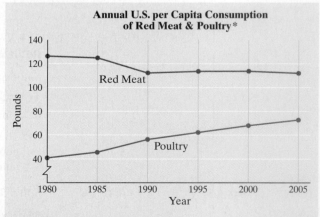

Annual U.S. per Capita Consumption of Red Meat & Poultry*

Source: USDA Economic Research Service
* Excludes shipments to Puerto Rico and other U.S. possessions

EXAMPLE 1 **Predicting Equal Consumption of Red Meat and Poultry**

America's consumption of red meat has decreased most years since 1980 while consumption of poultry has increased. The function $y = -0.59x + 124.6$ approximates the annual pounds of red meat consumed per capita, where x is the number of years since 1980. The function $y = 1.34x + 40.9$ approximates the annual pounds of poultry consumed per capita, where x is also the number of years since 1980. If this trend continues, determine the year in which the annual consumption of red meat and poultry is equal. (*Source:* Based on data from Economic Research Service, U.S. Dept. of Agriculture)

Solution

1. **UNDERSTAND.** Read and reread the problem and guess a year. Let's guess the year 2020. This year is 40 years since 1980, so $x = 40$. Now let $x = 40$ in each given function.

Red meat : $y = -0.59x + 124.6 = -0.59(40) + 124.6 = 101$ pounds

Poultry : $y = 1.34x + 40.9 \quad = 1.34(40) + 40.9 \quad = 94.5$ pounds

Since the projected pounds in 2020 for red meat and poultry are not the same, we guessed incorrectly, but we do have a better understanding of the problem. We also know that the year will be later than 2020 since projected consumption of red meat is still greater than poultry that year.

2. **TRANSLATE.** We are already given the system of equations.

3. **SOLVE.** We want to know the year x in which pounds y are the same, so we solve the system:

$$\begin{cases} y = -0.59x + 124.6 \\ y = 1.34x - 40.9 \end{cases}.$$

Since both equations are solved for y, one way to solve is to use the substitution method.

$$y = -0.59x + 124.6 \quad \text{First equation}$$

$$1.34x + 40.9 = -0.59x + 124.6 \quad \text{Let } y = 1.34x + 40.9.$$

$$1.93x = 83.7$$

$$x = \frac{83.7}{1.93} \approx 43.37$$

4. **INTERPRET.** Since we are only asked to give the year, we need only solve for x.

Check: To check, see whether $x \approx 43.37$ gives approximately the same number of pounds of red meat and poultry.

Red meat: $-0.59x + 124.6 = -0.59(43.37) + 124.6 = 99.01$ pounds

Poultry: $1.34x + 40.9 = 1.34(43.37) + 40.9 = 99.02$ pounds

Since we rounded the number of years, the number of pounds do differ slightly. They differ only by 0.0041, so we can assume that we solved correctly.

State: The consumption of red meat and poultry will be the same about 43.37 years after 1980, or 2023.37. Thus, in the year 2023, we predict the consumption will be the same. □

PRACTICE

1 Read Example 1. If we use the years 1995, 2000, and 2005 only to write functions approximating the consumption of red meat and poultry, we have the following:

Red meat: $y = -0.16x + 113.9$

Poultry: $y = \quad 1.06x + 62.3$

where x is the years since 1995 and y is pounds per year consumed.

a. Assuming this trend continues, predict the year in which the consumption of red meat and poultry will be the same.

b. Does your answer differ from the example? Why or why not?

Note: A similar exercise is found in Section 4.1, Exercise 85. In the example above, the data years used to generate the equations are 1980–2005. In Section 4.1, the data years used are 2000–2005. Note the differing equations and answers.

EXAMPLE 2 **Finding Unknown Numbers**

A first number is 4 less than a second number. Four times the first number is 6 more than twice the second. Find the numbers.

Solution

1. UNDERSTAND. Read and reread the problem and guess a solution. If a first number is 10 and this is 4 less than a second number, the second number is 14. Four times the first number is $4(10)$, or 40. This is not equal to 6 more than twice the second number, which is $2(14) + 6$ or 34. Although we guessed incorrectly, we now have a better understanding of the problem.

Since we are looking for two numbers, we will let

$$x = \text{first number}$$
$$y = \text{second number}$$

2. TRANSLATE. Since we have assigned two variables to this problem, we will translate the given facts into two equations. For the first statement we have

In words:	the first number	is	4 less than the second number
	↓	↓	↓
Translate:	x	$=$	$y - 4$

Next we translate the second statement into an equation.

In words:	four times the first number	is	6 more than twice the second number
	↓	↓	↓
Translate:	$4x$	$=$	$2y + 6$

3. SOLVE. Here we solve the system

$$\begin{cases} x = y - 4 \\ 4x = 2y + 6 \end{cases}$$

Since the first equation expresses x in terms of y, we will use substitution. We substitute $y - 4$ for x in the second equation and solve for y.

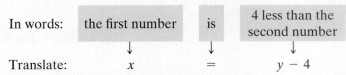

$$4x = 2y + 6 \quad \text{Second equation}$$
$$4\overbrace{(y - 4)} = 2y + 6$$
$$4y - 16 = 2y + 6 \quad \text{Let } x = y - 4.$$
$$2y = 22$$
$$y = 11$$

Now we replace y with 11 in the equation $x = y - 4$ and solve for x. Then $x = y - 4$ becomes $x = 11 - 4 = 7$. The ordered pair solution of the system is $(7, 11)$.

4. INTERPRET. Since the solution of the system is (7, 11), then the first number we are looking for is 7 and the second number is 11.

Check: Notice that 7 *is* 4 less than 11, and 4 times 7 *is* 6 more than twice 11. The proposed numbers, 7 and 11, are correct.

State: The numbers are 7 and 11.   □

PRACTICE
2   A first number is 5 more than a second number. Twice the first number is 2 less than 3 times the second number. Find the numbers.

EXAMPLE 3   Finding the Rate of Speed

Two cars leave Indianapolis, one traveling east and the other west. After 3 hours they are 297 miles apart. If one car is traveling 5 mph faster than the other, what is the speed of each?

Solution

1. UNDERSTAND. Read and reread the problem. Let's guess a solution and use the formula $d = rt$ (distance = rate · time) to check. Suppose that one car is traveling at a rate of 55 miles per hour. This means that the other car is traveling at a rate of 50 miles per hour since we are told that one car is traveling 5 mph faster than the other. To find the distance apart after 3 hours, we will first find the distance traveled by each car. One car's distance is rate · time = 55(3) = 165 miles. The other car's distance is rate · time = 50(3) = 150 miles. Since one car is traveling east and the other west, their distance apart is the sum of their distances, or 165 miles + 150 miles = 315 miles. Although this distance apart is not the required distance of 297 miles, we now have a better understanding of the problem.

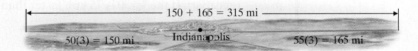

150 + 165 = 315 mi

50(3) = 150 mi   Indianapolis   55(3) = 165 mi

Let's model the problem with a system of equations. We will let

$$x = \text{speed of one car}$$
$$y = \text{speed of the other car}$$

We summarize the information on the following chart. Both cars have traveled 3 hours. Since distance = rate · time, their distances are $3x$ and $3y$ miles, respectively.

	Rate •	Time =	Distance
One Car	x	3	$3x$
Other Car	y	3	$3y$

2. TRANSLATE. We can now translate the stated conditions into two equations.

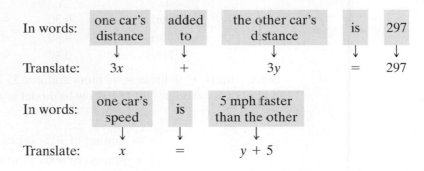

In words:	one car's distance	added to	the other car's distance	is	297
	↓	↓	↓	↓	↓
Translate:	$3x$	$+$	$3y$	$=$	297

In words:	one car's speed	is	5 mph faster than the other
	↓	↓	↓
Translate:	x	$=$	$y + 5$

3. SOLVE. Here we solve the system

$$\begin{cases} 3x + 3y = 297 \\ x = y + 5 \end{cases}$$

Again, the substitution method is appropriate. We replace x with $y + 5$ in the first equation and solve for y.

$$3x + 3y = 297 \quad \text{First equation}$$

$$3(y + 5) + 3y = 297 \quad \text{Let } x = y + 5.$$
$$3y + 15 + 3y = 297$$
$$6y = 282$$
$$y = 47$$

To find x, we replace y with 47 in the equation $x = y + 5$. Then $x = 47 + 5 = 52$. The ordered pair solution of the system is (52, 47).

4. INTERPRET. The solution (52, 47) means that the cars are traveling at 52 mph and 47 mph, respectively.

Check: Notice that one car is traveling 5 mph faster than the other. Also, if one car travels 52 mph for 3 hours, the distance is $3(52) = 156$ miles. The other car traveling for 3 hours at 47 mph travels a distance of $3(47) = 141$ miles. The sum of the distances $156 + 141$ is 297 miles, the required distance.

State: The cars are traveling at 52 mph and 47 mph. ☐

> ▶ **Helpful Hint**
> Don't forget to attach units, if appropriate.

PRACTICE
3 In 2007, the French train TGV V150 became the fastest conventional rail train in the world. It broke the 1990 record of the next fastest conventional rail train, the French TGV Atlantique. Assume the V150 and the Atlantique left the same station in Paris, with one heading west and one heading east. After 2 hours, they were 2150 kilometers apart. If the V150 is 75 kph faster than the Atlantique, what is the speed of each?

EXAMPLE 4 **Mixing Solutions**

Lynn Pike, a pharmacist, needs 70 liters of a 50% alcohol solution. She has available a 30% alcohol solution and an 80% alcohol solution. How many liters of each solution should she mix to obtain 70 liters of a 50% alcohol solution?

Solution

1. UNDERSTAND. Read and reread the problem. Next, guess the solution. Suppose that we need 20 liters of the 30% solution. Then we need $70 - 20 = 50$ liters of the 80% solution. To see if this gives us 70 liters of a 50% alcohol solution, let's find the amount of pure alcohol in each solution.

number of liters	×	alcohol strength	=	amount of pure alcohol
↓		↓		↓
20 liters	×	0.30	=	6 liters
50 liters	×	0.80	=	40 liters
70 liters	×	0.50	=	35 liters

Since 6 liters + 40 liters = 46 liters and not 35 liters, our guess is incorrect, but we have gained some insight as to how to model and check this problem.

We will let

$$x = \text{amount of 30\% solution, in liters}$$

$$y = \text{amount of 80\% solution, in liters}$$

and use a table to organize the given data.

	Number of Liters	Alcohol Strength	Amount of Pure Alcohol
30% Solution	x	30%	$0.30x$
80% Solution	y	80%	$0.80y$
50% Solution Needed	70	50%	$(0.50)(70)$

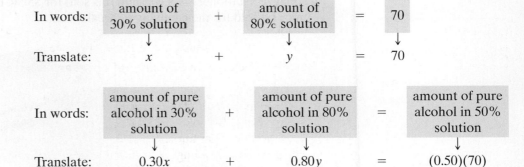

2. TRANSLATE. We translate the stated conditions into two equations.

In words: amount of 30% solution + amount of 80% solution = 70

Translate: x + y = 70

In words: amount of pure alcohol in 30% solution + amount of pure alcohol in 80% solution = amount of pure alcohol in 50% solution

Translate: $0.30x$ + $0.80y$ = $(0.50)(70)$

3. SOLVE. Here we solve the system

$$\begin{cases} x + \quad y = 70 \\ 0.30x + 0.80y = (0.50)(70) \end{cases}$$

To solve this system, we use the elimination method. We multiply both sides of the first equation by -3 and both sides of the second equation by 10. Then

$$\begin{cases} -3(x + y) = -3(70) \\ 10(0.30x + 0.80y) = 10(0.50)(70) \end{cases}$$
simplifies to
$$\begin{cases} -3x - 3y = -210 \\ \underline{3x + 8y = 350} \\ \qquad\quad 5y = 140 \\ \qquad\qquad y = 28 \end{cases}$$

Now we replace y with 28 in the equation $x + y = 70$ and find that $x + 28 = 70$, or $x = 42$.

The ordered pair solution of the system is $(42, 28)$.

4. INTERPRET.

Check: Check the solution in the same way that we checked our guess.

State: The pharmacist needs to mix 42 liters of 30% solution and 28 liters of 80% solution to obtain 70 liters of 50% solution.   □

PRACTICE

4   Keith Robinson is a chemistry teacher who needs 1 liter of a solution of 5% hydrochloric acid to carry out an experiment. If he only has a stock solution of 99% hydrochloric acid, how much water (0% acid) and how much stock solution (99%) of HCL must he mix to get 1 liter of 5% solution? Round answers to the nearest hundredth of a liter.

Concept Check ☑

Suppose you mix an amount of 25% acid solution with an amount of 60% acid solution. You then calculate the acid strength of the resulting acid mixture. For which of the following results should you suspect an error in your calculation? Why?

a. 14%   **b.** 32%   **c.** 55%

OBJECTIVE 2 ▶ Solving problems with cost and revenue functions. Recall that businesses are often computing cost and revenue functions or equations to predict sales, to determine whether prices need to be adjusted, and to see whether the company is making or losing money. Recall also that the value at which revenue equals cost is called the break-even point. When revenue is less than cost, the company is losing money; when revenue is greater than cost, the company is making money.

EXAMPLE 5   **Finding a Break-Even Point**

A manufacturing company recently purchased $3000 worth of new equipment to offer new personalized stationery to its customers. The cost of producing a package of personalized stationery is $3.00, and it is sold for $5.50. Find the number of packages that must be sold for the company to break even.

Solution

1. **UNDERSTAND.** Read and reread the problem. Notice that the cost to the company will include a one-time cost of $3000 for the equipment and then $3.00 per package produced. The revenue will be $5.50 per package sold.

   To model this problem, we will let

   $$x = \text{number of packages of personalized stationery}$$
   $$C(x) = \text{total cost for producing } x \text{ packages of stationery}$$
   $$R(x) = \text{total revenue for selling } x \text{ packages of stationery}$$

2. **TRANSLATE.** The revenue equation is

In words:	revenue for selling x packages of stationery	=	price per package	·	number of packages
	↓		↓		↓
Translate:	$R(x)$	=	5.5	·	x

The cost equation is

In words:	cost for producing x packages of stationery	=	cost per package	·	number of packages	+	cost for equipment
	↓		↓		↓		↓
Translate:	$C(x)$	=	3	·	x	+	3000

Since the break-even point is when $R(x) = C(x)$, we solve the equation

$$5.5x = 3x + 3000$$

3. SOLVE.

$$5.5x = 3x + 3000$$
$$2.5x = 3000 \qquad \text{Subtract } 3x \text{ from both sides.}$$
$$x = 1200 \qquad \text{Divide both sides by 2.5.}$$

4. INTERPRET.

Check: To see whether the break-even point occurs when 1200 packages are produced and sold, see if revenue equals cost when $x = 1200$. When $x = 1200$, $R(x) = 5.5x = 5.5(1200) = 6600$ and $C(x) = 3x + 3000 = 3(1200) + 3000 = 6600$. Since $R(1200) = C(1200) = 6600$, the break-even point is 1200.

State: The company must sell 1200 packages of stationery to break even. The graph of this system is shown.

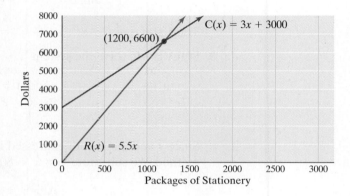

PRACTICE

5 An online-only electronics firm recently purchased $3000 worth of new equipment to create shock-proof packaging for its products. The cost of producing one shock-proof package is $2.50, and the firm charges the customer $4.50 for the packaging. Find the number of packages that must be sold for the company to break even.

OBJECTIVE 3 ▶ Solving problems modeled by systems of three equations. To introduce problem solving by writing a system of three linear equations in three variables, we solve a problem about triangles.

EXAMPLE 6   **Finding Angle Measures**

The measure of the largest angle of a triangle is 80° more than the measure of the smallest angle, and the measure of the remaining angle is 10° more than the measure of the smallest angle. Find the measure of each angle.

Solution

1. UNDERSTAND. Read and reread the problem. Recall that the sum of the measures of the angles of a triangle is 180°. Then guess a solution. If the smallest angle measures 20°, the measure of the largest angle is 80° more, or $20° + 80° = 100°$. The measure of the remaining angle is 10° more than the measure of the smallest angle, or $20° + 10° = 30°$. The sum of these three angles is $20° + 100° + 30° = 150°$, not the required 180°. We now know that the measure of the smallest angle is greater than 20°.

To model this problem we will let

$x =$ degree measure of the smallest angle
$y =$ degree measure of the largest angle
$z =$ degree measure of the remaining angle

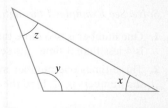

2. TRANSLATE. We translate the given information into three equations.

In words:
the sum of the measures = 180

Translate: $x + y + z = 180$

In words:
the largest angle | is | 80 more than the smallest angle

Translate: $y = x + 80$

In words:
the remaining angle | is | 10 more than the smallest angle

Translate: $z = x + 10$

3. SOLVE. We solve the system

$$\begin{cases} x + y + z = 180 \\ y = x + 80 \\ z = x + 10 \end{cases}$$

Since y and z are both expressed in terms of x, we will solve using the substitution method. We substitute $y = x + 80$ and $z = x + 10$ in the first equation. Then

$$x + y + z = 180 \quad \text{First equation}$$

$$x + (x + 80) + (x + 10) = 180 \quad \text{Let } y = x + 80 \text{ and } z = x + 10.$$

$$3x + 90 = 180$$

$$3x = 90$$

$$x = 30$$

Then $y = x + 80 = 30 + 80 = 110$, and $z = x + 10 = 30 + 10 = 40$. The ordered triple solution is $(30, 110, 40)$.

4. INTERPRET.

Check: Notice that $30° + 40° + 110° = 180°$. Also, the measure of the largest angle, $110°$, is $80°$ more than the measure of the smallest angle, $30°$. The measure of the remaining angle, $40°$, is $10°$ more than the measure of the smallest angle, $30°$. □

PRACTICE

6 The measure of the largest angle of a triangle is $40°$ more than the measure of the smallest angle, and the measure of the remaining angle is $20°$ more than the measure of the smallest angle. Find the measure of each angle.

4.3 | EXERCISE SET

MathXL   PRACTICE   WATCH   DOWNLOAD   READ   REVIEW

MIXED PRACTICE

Solve. See Examples 1 through 4.

1. One number is two more than a second number. Twice the first is 4 less than 3 times the second. Find the numbers.

2. Three times one number minus a second is 8, and the sum of the numbers is 12. Find the numbers.

3. The United States has the world's only "large deck" aircraft carriers which can hold up to 72 aircraft. The Enterprise class carrier is longest in length while the Nimitz class carrier is the second longest. The total length of these two carriers is 2193 feet while the difference of their lengths is only 9 feet. (*Source: U.S.A. Today*)

a. Find the length of each class carrier.

b. If a football field has a length of 100 yards, determine the length of the Enterprise class carrier in terms of number of football fields.

4. The rate of growth of participation (age 7 and older) in sports featured in the X-Games has slowed in recent years, but still surpasses that for some older sports such as football. The most popular X-Game sport is inline roller skating, followed by skateboarding. In 2005, the total number of participants in both sports was 25.1 million. If the number of participants in skateboarding was 14.2 million less than twice the number of participants in inline skating, find the number of participants in each sport. (*Source:* National Sporting Goods Association)

5. A B747 aircraft flew 6 hours with the wind. The return trip took 7 hours against the wind. If the speed of the plane in still air is 13 times the speed of the wind, find the wind speed and the speed of the plane in still air.

6. During a multi-day camping trip, Terry Watkins rowed 17 hours downstream. It took 26.5 hours rowing upstream to travel the same distance. If the speed of the current is 6.8 kilometers per hour less than his rowing speed in still water, find his rowing speed and the speed of the current.

7. Find how many quarts of 4% butterfat milk and 1% butterfat milk should be mixed to yield 60 quarts of 2% butterfat milk.

8. A pharmacist needs 500 milliliters of a 20% phenobarbital solution but has only 5% and 25% phenobarbital solutions available. Find how many milliliters of each he should mix to get the desired solution.

9. In 2005, the United Kingdom was the most popular host country in which U.S. students traveling abroad studied. Italy was the second most popular destination. A total of 56,929 students visited one of the two countries. If 7213 more U.S. students studied in the United Kingdom than in Italy, find how many students studied abroad in each country. (*Source:* Institute of International Education, *Open Doors 2006*)

10. Harvard University and Cornell University are each known for their excellent libraries, and each is participating with Google to put their collections into Google's searchable database. In 2005, Harvard libraries contained 266,791 more printed volumes than twice the number of printed volumes in the libraries of Cornell. Together, these two great libraries house 23,199,904 printed volumes. Find the number of printed volumes in each library. (*Source:* Association of Research Libraries)

11. Karen Karlin bought some large frames for $15 each and some small frames for $8 each at a closeout sale. If she bought 22 frames for $239, find how many of each type she bought.

12. Hilton University Drama Club sold 311 tickets for a play. Student tickets cost 50 cents each; nonstudent tickets cost $1.50. If total receipts were $385.50, find how many tickets of each type were sold.

13. One number is two less than a second number. Twice the first is 4 more than 3 times the second. Find the numbers.

14. Twice a first number plus a second number is 42, and the first number minus the second number is −6. Find the numbers.

15. In the United States, the percent of women using the Internet is increasing faster than the percent of men. For the years 2000–2005, the function $y = 5.3x + 39.5$ can be used to estimate the percent of females using the Internet, while the function $y = 4.5x + 45.5$ can be used to estimate the percent of males. For both functions, x is the number of years since 2000. If this trend continues, predict the year in which the percent of females using the Internet equals the percent of males. (*Source:* Pew Internet & American Life Project)

16. The percent of car vehicle sales has been decreasing over a ten-year period while the percent of light truck (pickups, sport-utility vans, and minivans) vehicles has been increasing. For the years 2000–2006, the function $y = -x + 54.2$ can be used to estimate the percent of new car vehicle sales in the United States, while the function $y = x + 45.8$ can be used to estimate the percent of light truck vehicle sales. For both functions, x is the number of years since 2000. (*Source: USA Today*, Environmental Protection Agency, "Light-Duty Automotive Technology and fuel Economy Trends: 1975–2006")

a. Calculate the year in which the percent of new car sales equaled the percent of light truck sales.

b. Before the actual 2001 vehicle sales data was published, *USA Today* predicted that light truck sales would likely be greater than car sales in the year 2001. Does your finding in part (a) agree with this statement?

17. An office supply store in San Diego sells 7 writing tablets and 4 pens for $6.40. Also, 2 tablets and 19 pens cost $5.40. Find the price of each.

18. A Candy Barrel shop manager mixes M&M's worth $2.00 per pound with trail mix worth $1.50 per pound. Find how many pounds of each she should use to get 50 pounds of a party mix worth $1.80 per pound.

19. A Piper airplane and a B737 aircraft cross each other (at different altitudes) traveling in opposite directions. The B737 travels 5 times the speed of the Piper. If in 4 hours, they are 2160 miles apart, find the speed of each aircraft.

20. Two cyclists start at the same point and travel in opposite directions. One travels 4 mph faster than the other. In 4 hours they are 112 miles apart. Find how fast each is traveling.

21. While it is said that trains opened up the American West to settlement, U.S. railroad miles have been on the decline for decades. On the other hand, the miles of roads in the U.S. highway system have been increasing. The function $y = -1379.4x + 150,604$ represents the U.S. railroad miles, while the function $y = 478.4x + 157,838$ models the number of U.S. highway miles, where x is the number of years after 1995. For each function, x is the number of years after 1995. (*Source:* Association of American Railroads, Federal Highway Administration)

a. Explain how the decrease in railroad miles can be verified by their given function while the increase in highway miles can be verified by their given function.

b. Find the year in which it is estimated that the number of U.S. railroad miles and the number of U.S. highway miles were the same.

22. The annual U.S. per capita consumption of whole milk has decreased since 1980, while the per capita consumption of lower fat milk has increased. For the years 1980–2005, the function $y = -0.40x + 15.9$ approximates the annual U.S. per capita consumption of whole milk in gallons, and the function $y = 0.14x + 11.9$ approximates the annual U.S. per capita consumption of lower fat milk in gallons. Determine the year in which the per capita consumption of whole milk equaled the per capita consumption of lower fat milk. (*Source:* Economic Research Service: U.S.D.A.)

△ **23.** The perimeter of a triangle is 93 centimeters. If two sides are equally long and the third side is 9 centimeters longer than the others, find the lengths of the three sides.

24. Jack Reinholt, a car salesman, has a choice of two pay arrangements: a weekly salary of $200 plus 5% commission on sales, or a straight 15% commission. Find the amount of weekly sales for which Jack's earnings are the same regardless of the pay arrangement.

25. Hertz car rental agency charges $25 daily plus 10 cents per mile. Budget charges $20 daily plus 25 cents per mile. Find the daily mileage for which the Budget charge for the day is twice that of the Hertz charge for the day.

26. Carroll Blakemore, a drafting student, bought three templates and a pencil one day for $6.45. Another day he bought two pads of paper and four pencils for $7.50. If the price of a

pad of paper is three times the price of a pencil, find the price of each type of item.

△ **27.** In the figure, line l and line m are parallel lines cut by transversal t. Find the values of x and y.

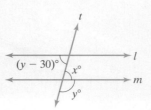

△ **28.** Find the values of x and y in the following isosceles triangle.

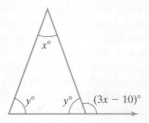

Given the cost function $C(x)$ and the revenue function $R(x)$, find the number of units x that must be sold to break even. See Example 5.

29. $C(x) = 30x + 10,000 \quad R(x) = 46x$

30. $C(x) = 12x + 15,000 \quad R(x) = 32x$

31. $C(x) = 1.2x + 1500 \quad R(x) = 1.7x$

32. $C(x) = 0.8x + 900 \quad R(x) = 2x$

33. $C(x) = 75x + 160,000 \quad R(x) = 200x$

34. $C(x) = 105x + 70,000 \quad R(x) = 245x$

35. The planning department of Abstract Office Supplies has been asked to determine whether the company should introduce a new computer desk next year. The department estimates that $6000 of new manufacturing equipment will need to be purchased and that the cost of constructing each desk will be $200. The department also estimates that the revenue from each desk will be $450.

a. Determine the revenue function $R(x)$ from the sale of x desks.

b. Determine the cost function $C(x)$ for manufacturing x desks.

c. Find the break-even point.

36. Baskets, Inc., is planning to introduce a new woven basket. The company estimates that $500 worth of new equipment will be needed to manufacture this new type of basket and that it will cost $15 per basket to manufacture. The company also estimates that the revenue from each basket will be $31.

a. Determine the revenue function $R(x)$ from the sale of x baskets.

b. Determine the cost function $C(x)$ for manufacturing x baskets.

c. Find the break-even point.

Solve. See Example 6.

37. Rabbits in a lab are to be kept on a strict daily diet that includes 30 grams of protein, 16 grams of fat, and 24 grams of carbohydrates. The scientist has only three food mixes available with the following grams of nutrients per unit.

	Protein	*Fat*	*Carbohydrate*
Mix A	4	6	3
Mix B	6	1	2
Mix C	4	1	12

Find how many units of each mix are needed daily to meet each rabbit's dietary need.

38. Gerry Gundersen mixes different solutions with concentrations of 25%, 40%, and 50% to get 200 liters of a 32% solution. If he uses twice as much of the 25% solution as of the 40% solution, find how many liters of each kind he uses.

△ **39.** The perimeter of a quadrilateral (four-sided polygon) is 29 inches. The longest side is twice as long as the shortest side. The other two sides are equally long and are 2 inches longer than the shortest side. Find the length of all four sides.

△ **40.** The measure of the largest angle of a triangle is 90° more than the measure of the smallest angle, and the measure of the remaining angle is 30° more than the measure of the smallest angle. Find the measure of each angle.

41. The sum of three numbers is 40. One number is five more than a second number. It is also twice the third. Find the numbers.

42. The sum of the digits of a three-digit number is 15. The tens-place digit is twice the hundreds-place digit, and the ones-place digit is 1 less than the hundreds-place digit. Find the three-digit number.

43. Diana Taurasi, of the Phoenix Mercury, was the WNBA's top scorer for the 2006 regular season, with a total of 860 points. The number of two-point field goals that Taurasi made was 65 less than double the number of three-point field goals she made. The number of free throws (each worth one point) she made was 34 less than the number of two-point field goals she made. Find how many free throws, two-point field goals, and three-point field goals Diana Taurasi made during the 2006 regular season. (*Source:* Women's National Basketball Association)

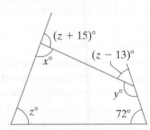

44. During the 2006 NBA playoffs, the top scoring player was Dwayne Wade of the Miami Heat. Wade scored a total of 654 points during the playoffs. The number of free throws (each worth one point) he made was three less than the number of two-point field goals he made. He also made 27 fewer three-point field goals than one-fifth the number of two-point

field goals. How many free throws, two-point field goals, and three-point field goals did Dwayne Wade make during the 2006 playoffs? (*Source:* National Basketball Association)

△ **45.** Find the values of x, y, and z in the following triangle.

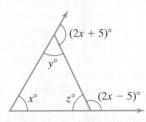

△ **46.** The sum of the measures of the angles of a quadrilateral is 360°. Find the value of x, y, and z in the following quadrilateral.

REVIEW AND PREVIEW

Multiply both sides of equation (1) by 2, and add the resulting equation to equation (2). See Section 4.2.

47. $3x - y + z = 2$ (1)
$\quad -x + 2y + 3z = 6$ (2)

48. $2x + y + 3z = 7$ (1)
$\quad -4x + y + 2z = 4$ (2)

Multiply both sides of equation (1) by -3, and add the resulting equation to equation (2). See Section 4.2.

49. $x + 2y - z = 0$ (1)
$\quad 3x + y - z = 2$ (2)

50. $2x - 3y + 2z = 5$ (1)
$\quad z - 9y + z = -1$ (2)

CONCEPT EXTENSIONS

51. The number of personal bankruptcy petitions filed in the United States was constantly increasing from the early 1980s until the bankruptcy laws were changed in 2006. In 2006, the number of petitions filed was only 25,765 more than the number of petitions filed in 1996. The total number of personal bankruptcies filed in these two years was 2,144,653. Find the number of personal bankruptcies filed in each year. (*Source:* Based on data from the Administrative Office of the United States Courts)

52. In 2006, the median weekly earnings for male postal service mail carriers in the United States was $126 more than the median weekly earnings for female mail postal service carriers. The median weekly earnings for female postal service mail carriers was 0.86 time that of their male counterparts. Also in 2006, the median weekly earnings for female lawyers in the United States was $540 less than the median weekly earnings for male lawyers. The median weekly earnings of male lawyers was 1.4 times that of their female counterparts. (*Source:* Based on data from the Bureau of Labor Statistics)

a. Find the median weekly earnings for female postal service mail carriers in the United States in 2006.

b. Find the median weekly earnings for female lawyers in the United States in 2006.

c. Of the four groups of workers described in the problem, which group makes the greatest weekly earnings? Which group makes the least weekly earnings?

53. My Space and Facebook are both popular social networking Web sites. The function $f(x) = 0.85x + 41.75$ represents the My Space minutes (in thousands)/month while the function $f(x) = 1.13x + 10.49$ represents the Facebook minutes (in thousands)/month. In both of these functions $x = 1$ represents Feb. 2007, $x = 2$ represents March 2007 and so on.

a. Solve the system formed by these functions. Round each coordinate to the nearest whole number.

b. Use your answer to part **a** to predict the month and year in which the total pages viewed for My Space and Facebook are the same.

54. Find the values of a, b, and c such that the equation $y = ax^2 + bx + c$ has ordered pair solutions $(1, 6)$, $(-1, -2)$, and $(0, -1)$. To do so, substitute each ordered pair solution into the equation. Each time, the result is an equation in three unknowns: a, b, and c. Then solve the resulting system of three linear equations in three unknowns, a, b, and c.

55. Find the values of a, b, and c such that the equation $y = ax^2 + bx + c$ has ordered pair solutions $(1, 2), (2, 3)$ and $(-1, 6)$. (*Hint:* See Exercise 53.)

56. Data (x, y) for the total number y (in thousands) of college-bound students who took the ACT assessment in the year x are $(0, 1065)$, $(1, 1070)$ and $(3, 1175)$, where $x = 0$ represents 2000 and $x = 1$ represents 2001. Find the values of a, b, and c such that the equation $y = ax^2 + bx + c$ models this data. According to your model, how many students will take the ACT in 2009? (*Source:* ACT, Inc.)

57. Monthly normal rainfall data (x, y) for Portland, Oregon, are $(4, 2.47)$, $(7, 0.6)$, $(8, 1.1)$, where x represents time in months (with $x = 1$ representing January) and y represents rainfall in inches. Find the values of a, b, and c rounded to 2 decimal places such that the equation $y = ax^2 + bx + c$ models this data. According to your model, how much rain should Portland expect during September? (*Source:* National Climatic Data Center)

INTEGRATED REVIEW SYSTEMS OF LINEAR EQUATIONS

Sections 4.1–4.3

The graphs of various systems of equations are shown. Match each graph with the solution of its corresponding system.

A

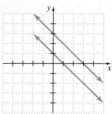

B

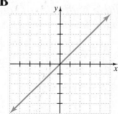

C

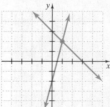

D

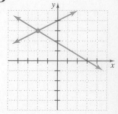

1. Solution: $(1, 2)$

2. Solution: $(-2, 3)$

3. No solution

4. Infinite number of solutions

Solve each system by elimination or substitution.

5. $\begin{cases} x + y = 4 \\ y = 3x \end{cases}$

6. $\begin{cases} x - y = -4 \\ y = 4x \end{cases}$

7. $\begin{cases} x + y = 1 \\ x - 2y = 4 \end{cases}$

8. $\begin{cases} 2x - y = 8 \\ x + 3y = 11 \end{cases}$

9. $\begin{cases} 2x + 5y = 8 \\ 6x + y = 10 \end{cases}$

10. $\begin{cases} \dfrac{1}{8}x - \dfrac{1}{2}y = -\dfrac{5}{8} \\ -3x - 8y = 0 \end{cases}$

11. $\begin{cases} 4x - 7y = 7 \\ 12x - 21y = 24 \end{cases}$

12. $\begin{cases} 2x - 5y = 3 \\ -4x + 10y = -6 \end{cases}$

13. $\begin{cases} y = \dfrac{1}{3}x \\ 5x - 3y = 4 \end{cases}$

14. $\begin{cases} y = \dfrac{1}{4}x \\ 2x - 4y = 3 \end{cases}$

15. $\begin{cases} x + y = 2 \\ -3y + z = -7 \\ 2x + y - z = -1 \end{cases}$

16. $\begin{cases} y + 2z = -3 \\ x - 2y = 7 \\ 2x - y + z = 5 \end{cases}$

17. $\begin{cases} 2x + 4y - 6z = 3 \\ -x + y - z = 6 \\ x + 2y - 3z = 1 \end{cases}$

18. $\begin{cases} x - y + 3z = 2 \\ -2x + 2y - 6z = -4 \\ 3x - 3y + 9z = 6 \end{cases}$

19. $\begin{cases} x + y - 4z = 5 \\ x - y + 2z = -2 \\ 3x + 2y + 4z = 18 \end{cases}$

20. $\begin{cases} 2x - y + 3z = 2 \\ x + y - 6z = 0 \\ 3x + 4y - 3z = 6 \end{cases}$

21. A first number is 8 less than a second number. Twice the first number is 11 more than the second number. Find the numbers.

△ **22.** The sum of the measures of the angles of a quadrilateral is 360°. The two smallest angles of the quadrilateral have the same measure. The third angle measures 30° more than the measure of one of the smallest angles and the fourth angle measures 50° more than the measure of one of the smallest angles. Find the measure of each angle.

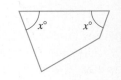

4.4 SOLVING SYSTEMS OF EQUATIONS BY MATRICES

OBJECTIVES

1 Use matrices to solve a system of two equations.

2 Use matrices to solve a system of three equations.

By now, you may have noticed that the solution of a system of equations depends on the coefficients of the equations in the system and not on the variables. In this section, we introduce solving a system of equations by a **matrix.**

OBJECTIVE 1 ▶ Using matrices to solve a system of two equations. A matrix (plural: **matrices**) is a rectangular array of numbers. The following are examples of matrices.

$$\begin{bmatrix} 1 & 0 \\ 0 & 1 \end{bmatrix} \qquad \begin{bmatrix} 2 & 1 & 3 & -1 \\ 0 & -1 & 4 & 5 \\ -6 & 2 & 1 & 0 \end{bmatrix} \qquad \begin{bmatrix} a & b & c \\ d & e & f \end{bmatrix}$$

The numbers aligned horizontally in a matrix are in the same **row.** The numbers aligned vertically are in the same **column.**

$$\begin{matrix} \text{row 1} \rightarrow \\ \text{row 2} \rightarrow \end{matrix} \begin{bmatrix} 2 & 1 & 0 \\ -1 & 6 & 2 \end{bmatrix}$$

This matrix has 2 rows and 3 columns. It is called a 2×3 (read "two by three") matrix.

column 1
column 2
column 3

To see the relationship between systems of equations and matrices, study the example below.

▶ **Helpful Hint**

Before writing the corresponding matrix associated with a system of equations, make sure that the equations are written in standard form.

System of Equations
(in standard form)   ***Corresponding Matrix***

$\begin{cases} 2x - 3y = 6 & \text{Equation 1} \\ x + y = 0 & \text{Equation 2} \end{cases}$ $\begin{bmatrix} 2 & -3 & \vdots & 6 \\ 1 & 1 & \vdots & 0 \end{bmatrix}$ Row 1
Row 2

Notice that the rows of the matrix correspond to the equations in the system. The coefficients of each variable are placed to the left of a vertical dashed line. The constants are placed to the right. Each of these numbers in the matrix is called an **element**.

The method of solving systems by matrices is to write this matrix as an equivalent matrix from which we easily identify the solution. Two matrices are equivalent if they represent systems that have the same solution set. The following **row operations** can be performed on matrices, and the result is an equivalent matrix.

Elementary Row Operations

1. Any two rows in a matrix may be interchanged.
2. The elements of any row may be multiplied (or divided) by the same nonzero number.
3. The elements of any row may be multiplied (or divided) by a nonzero number and added to their corresponding elements in any other row.

▶ **Helpful Hint**

Notice that these *row* operations are the same operations that we can perform on *equations* in a system.

To solve a system of two equations in x and y by matrices, write the corresponding matrix associated with the system. Then use elementary row operations to write equivalent matrices until you have a matrix of the form

$$\begin{bmatrix} 1 & a & b \\ 0 & 1 & c \end{bmatrix},$$

where a, b, and c are constants. Why? If a matrix associated with a system of equations is in this form, we can easily solve for x and y. For example,

Matrix		**System of Equations**
$\begin{bmatrix} 1 & 2 & -3 \\ 0 & 1 & 5 \end{bmatrix}$	corresponds to	$\begin{cases} 1x + 2y = -3 \\ 0x + 1y = 5 \end{cases}$ or $\begin{cases} x + 2y = -3 \\ y = 5 \end{cases}$

In the second equation, we have $y = 5$. Substituting this in the first equation, we have $x + 2(5) = -3$ or $x = -13$. The solution of the system is the ordered pair $(-13, 5)$.

EXAMPLE 1 Use matrices to solve the system.

$$\begin{cases} x + 3y = 5 \\ 2x - y = -4 \end{cases}$$

Solution The corresponding matrix is $\begin{bmatrix} 1 & 3 & 5 \\ 2 & -1 & -4 \end{bmatrix}$. We use elementary row operations to write an equivalent matrix that looks like $\begin{bmatrix} 1 & a & b \\ 0 & 1 & c \end{bmatrix}$.

For the matrix given, the element in the first row, first column is already 1, as desired. Next we write an equivalent matrix with a 0 below the 1. To do this, we multiply row 1 by -2 and add to row 2. *We will change only row 2.*

$$\begin{bmatrix} 1 & 3 & 5 \\ -2(1) + 2 & -2(3) + (-1) & -2(5) + (-4) \end{bmatrix} \text{ simplifies to } \begin{bmatrix} 1 & 3 & 5 \\ 0 & -7 & -14 \end{bmatrix}$$

↑ ↑ ↑ ↑ ↑ ↑
row 1   row 2   row 1   row 2   row 1   row 2
element element element element element element

Now we change the -7 to a 1 by use of an elementary row operation. We divide row 2 by -7, then

$$\begin{bmatrix} 1 & 3 & | & 5 \\ \dfrac{0}{-7} & \dfrac{-7}{-7} & | & \dfrac{-14}{-7} \end{bmatrix} \quad \text{simplifies to} \quad \begin{bmatrix} 1 & 3 & | & 5 \\ 0 & 1 & | & 2 \end{bmatrix}$$

This last matrix corresponds to the system

$$\begin{cases} x + 3y = 5 \\ \quad\;\; y = 2 \end{cases}$$

To find x, we let $y = 2$ in the first equation, $x + 3y = 5$.

$$x + 3y = 5 \qquad \text{First equation}$$
$$x + 3(2) = 5 \qquad \text{Let } y = 2.$$
$$x = -1$$

The ordered pair solution is $(-1, 2)$. Check to see that this ordered pair satisfies both equations. □

PRACTICE

1 Use matrices to solve the system.

$$\begin{cases} x + 4y = -2 \\ 3x - y = 7 \end{cases}$$

EXAMPLE 2 Use matrices to solve the system.

$$\begin{cases} 2x - y = 3 \\ 4x - 2y = 5 \end{cases}$$

Solution The corresponding matrix is $\begin{bmatrix} 2 & -1 & | & 3 \\ 4 & -2 & | & 5 \end{bmatrix}$. To get 1 in the row 1, column 1 position, we divide the elements of row 1 by 2.

$$\begin{bmatrix} \dfrac{2}{2} & -\dfrac{1}{2} & | & \dfrac{3}{2} \\ 4 & -2 & | & 5 \end{bmatrix} \quad \text{simplifies to} \quad \begin{bmatrix} 1 & -\dfrac{1}{2} & | & \dfrac{3}{2} \\ 4 & -2 & | & 5 \end{bmatrix}$$

To get 0 under the 1, we multiply the elements of row 1 by -4 and add the new elements to the elements of row 2.

$$\begin{bmatrix} 1 & -\dfrac{1}{2} & | & \dfrac{3}{2} \\ -4(1) + 4 & -4\left(-\dfrac{1}{2}\right) - 2 & | & -4\left(\dfrac{3}{2}\right) + 5 \end{bmatrix} \quad \text{simplifies to} \quad \begin{bmatrix} 1 & -\dfrac{1}{2} & | & \dfrac{3}{2} \\ 0 & 0 & | & -1 \end{bmatrix}$$

The corresponding system is $\begin{cases} x - \dfrac{1}{2}y = \dfrac{3}{2} \\ \qquad 0 = -1 \end{cases}$. The equation $0 = -1$ is false for all y or

x values; hence the system is inconsistent and has no solution. □

PRACTICE

2 Use matrices to solve the system.

$$\begin{cases} x - 3y = 3 \\ -2x + 6y = 4 \end{cases}$$

Concept Check ☑️

Consider the system

$$\begin{cases} 2x - 3y = 8 \\ x + 5y = -3 \end{cases}$$

What is wrong with its corresponding matrix shown below?

$$\begin{bmatrix} 2 & -3 & | & 8 \\ 0 & 5 & | & -3 \end{bmatrix}$$

OBJECTIVE 2 ▶ Using matrices to solve a system of three equations. To solve a system of three equations in three variables using matrices, we will write the corresponding matrix in the form

$$\begin{bmatrix} 1 & a & b & | & d \\ 0 & 1 & c & | & e \\ 0 & 0 & 1 & | & f \end{bmatrix}$$

EXAMPLE 3 Use matrices to solve the system.

$$\begin{cases} x + 2y + z = 2 \\ -2x - y + 2z = 5 \\ x + 3y - 2z = -8 \end{cases}$$

Solution The corresponding matrix is $\begin{bmatrix} 1 & 2 & 1 & | & 2 \\ -2 & -1 & 2 & | & 5 \\ 1 & 3 & -2 & | & -8 \end{bmatrix}$. Our goal is to

write an equivalent matrix with 1's along the diagonal (see the numbers in red) and 0's below the 1's. The element in row 1, column 1 is already 1. Next we get 0's for each element in the rest of column 1. To do this, first we multiply the elements of row 1 by 2 and add the new elements to row 2. Also, we multiply the elements of row 1 by −1 and add the new elements to the elements of row 3. We *do not change row 1*. Then

$$\begin{bmatrix} 1 & 2 & 1 & | & 2 \\ 2(1)-2 & 2(2)-1 & 2(1)+2 & | & 2(2)+5 \\ -1(1)+1 & -1(2)+3 & -1(1)-2 & | & -1(2)-8 \end{bmatrix} \text{ simplifies to } \begin{bmatrix} 1 & 2 & 1 & | & 2 \\ 0 & 3 & 4 & | & 9 \\ 0 & 1 & -3 & | & -10 \end{bmatrix}$$

We continue down the diagonal and use elementary row operations to get 1 where the element 3 is now. To do this, we interchange rows 2 and 3.

$$\begin{bmatrix} 1 & 2 & 1 & | & 2 \\ 0 & 3 & 4 & | & 9 \\ 0 & 1 & -3 & | & -10 \end{bmatrix} \text{ is equivalent to } \begin{bmatrix} 1 & 2 & 1 & | & 2 \\ 0 & 1 & -3 & | & -10 \\ 0 & 3 & 4 & | & 9 \end{bmatrix}$$

Next we want the new row 3, column 2 element to be 0. We multiply the elements of row 2 by −3 and add the result to the elements of row 3.

$$\begin{bmatrix} 1 & 2 & 1 & | & 2 \\ 0 & 1 & -3 & | & -10 \\ -3(0)+0 & -3(1)+3 & -3(-3)+4 & | & -3(-10)+9 \end{bmatrix} \text{ simplifies to}$$

$$\begin{bmatrix} 1 & 2 & 1 & | & 2 \\ 0 & 1 & -3 & | & -10 \\ 0 & 0 & 13 & | & 39 \end{bmatrix}$$

Answer to Concept Check:

matrix should be $\begin{bmatrix} 2 & -3 & | & 8 \\ 1 & 5 & | & -3 \end{bmatrix}$

Finally, we divide the elements of row 3 by 13 so that the final diagonal element is 1.

$$\begin{bmatrix} 1 & 2 & 1 & | & 2 \\ 0 & 1 & -3 & | & -10 \\ \frac{0}{13} & \frac{0}{13} & \frac{13}{13} & | & \frac{39}{13} \end{bmatrix} \text{ simplifies to } \begin{bmatrix} 1 & 2 & 1 & | & 2 \\ 0 & 1 & -3 & | & -10 \\ 0 & 0 & 1 & | & 3 \end{bmatrix}$$

This matrix corresponds to the system

$$\begin{cases} x + 2y + z = 2 \\ y - 3z = -10 \\ z = 3 \end{cases}$$

We identify the z-coordinate of the solution as 3. Next we replace z with 3 in the second equation and solve for y.

$$y - 3z = -10 \quad \text{Second equation}$$
$$y - 3(3) = -10 \quad \text{Let } z = 3.$$
$$y = -1$$

To find x, we let $z = 3$ and $y = -1$ in the first equation.

$$x + 2y + z = 2 \quad \text{First equation}$$
$$x + 2(-1) + 3 = 2 \quad \text{Let } z = 3 \text{ and } y = -1.$$
$$x = 1$$

The ordered triple solution is $(1, -1, 3)$. Check to see that it satisfies all three equations in the original system.   □

PRACTICE

3   Use matrices to solve the system.

$$\begin{cases} x + 3y - z = 0 \\ 2x + y + 3z = 5 \\ -x - 2y + 4z = 7 \end{cases}$$

VOCABULARY & READINESS CHECK

Use the choices below to fill in each blank.

column   element   row   matrix

1. A _____ is a rectangular array of numbers.

2. Each of the numbers in a matrix is called an _____.

3. The numbers aligned horizontally in a matrix are in the same _____.

4. The numbers aligned vertically in a matrix are in the same _____.

Answer true or false for each statement about operations within a matrix forming an equivalent matrix.

5. Any two columns may be interchanged. _____

6. Any two rows may be interchanged. _____

7. The elements in a row may be added to their corresponding elements in another row. _____

8. The elements of a column may be multiplied by any nonzero number. _____

4.4 EXERCISE SET

MathXP
PRACTICE   WATCH   DOWNLOAD   READ   REVIEW

Solve each system of linear equations using matrices. See Example 1.

1. $\begin{cases} x + y = 1 \\ x - 2y = 4 \end{cases}$

2. $\begin{cases} 2x - y = 8 \\ x + 3y = 11 \end{cases}$

3. $\begin{cases} x + 3y = 2 \\ x + 2y = 0 \end{cases}$

4. $\begin{cases} 4x - y = 5 \\ 3x + 3y = 0 \end{cases}$

Solve each system of linear equations using matrices. See Example 2.

5. $\begin{cases} x - 2y = 4 \\ 2x - 4y = 4 \end{cases}$

6. $\begin{cases} -x + 3y = 6 \\ 3x - 9y = 9 \end{cases}$

7. $\begin{cases} 3x - 3y = 9 \\ 2x - 2y = 6 \end{cases}$

8. $\begin{cases} 9x - 3y = 6 \\ -18x + 6y = -12 \end{cases}$

Solve each system of linear equations using matrices. See Example 3.

9. $\begin{cases} x + y = 3 \\ 2y = 10 \\ 3x + 2y - 4z = 12 \end{cases}$

10. $\begin{cases} 5x = 5 \\ 2x + y = 4 \\ 3x + y - 5z = -15 \end{cases}$

11. $\begin{cases} 2y - z = -7 \\ x + 4y + z = -4 \\ 5x - y + 2z = 13 \end{cases}$

12. $\begin{cases} 4y + 3z = -2 \\ 5x - 4y = 1 \\ -5x + 4y + z = -3 \end{cases}$

MIXED PRACTICE

Solve each system of linear equations using matrices. See Examples 1 through 3.

13. $\begin{cases} x - 4 = 0 \\ x + y = 1 \end{cases}$

14. $\begin{cases} 3y = 6 \\ x + y = 7 \end{cases}$

15. $\begin{cases} x + y + z = 2 \\ 2x - z = 5 \\ 3y + z = 2 \end{cases}$

16. $\begin{cases} x + 2y + z = 5 \\ x - y - z = 3 \\ y + z = 2 \end{cases}$

17. $\begin{cases} 5x - 2y = 27 \\ -3x + 5y = 18 \end{cases}$

18. $\begin{cases} 4x - y = 9 \\ 2x + 3y = -27 \end{cases}$

19. $\begin{cases} 4x - 7y = 7 \\ 12x - 21y = 24 \end{cases}$

20. $\begin{cases} 2x - 5y = 12 \\ -4x + 10y = 20 \end{cases}$

21. $\begin{cases} 4x - y + 2z = 5 \\ 2y + z = 4 \\ 4x + y + 3z = 10 \end{cases}$

22. $\begin{cases} 5y - 7z = 14 \\ 2x + y + 4z = 10 \\ 2x + 6y - 3z = 30 \end{cases}$

23. $\begin{cases} 4x + y + z = 3 \\ -x + y - 2z = -11 \\ x + 2y + 2z = -1 \end{cases}$

24. $\begin{cases} x + y + z = 9 \\ 3x - y + z = -1 \\ -2x + 2y - 3z = -2 \end{cases}$

REVIEW AND PREVIEW

Determine whether each graph is the graph of a function. See Section 3.2.

25.
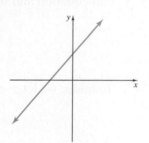

26.
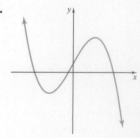

27.
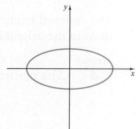

28.
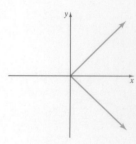

Evaluate. See Section 1.3.

29. $(-1)(-5) - (6)(3)$

30. $(2)(-8) - (-4)(1)$

31. $(4)(-10) - (2)(-2)$

32. $(-7)(3) - (-2)(-6)$

33. $(-3)(-3) - (-1)(-9)$

34. $(5)(6) - (10)(10)$

CONCEPT EXTENSIONS

Solve. See the Concept Check in the section.

35. For the system $\begin{cases} x + z = 7 \\ y + 2z = -6 \\ 3x - y = 0 \end{cases}$, which is the correct corresponding matrix?

a. $\begin{bmatrix} 1 & 1 & | & 7 \\ 1 & 2 & | & -6 \\ 3 & -1 & | & 0 \end{bmatrix}$

b. $\begin{bmatrix} 1 & 0 & 1 & | & 7 \\ 1 & 2 & 0 & | & -6 \\ 3 & -1 & 0 & | & 0 \end{bmatrix}$

c. $\begin{bmatrix} 1 & 0 & 1 & | & 7 \\ 0 & 1 & 2 & | & -6 \\ 3 & -1 & 0 & | & 0 \end{bmatrix}$

36. For the system $\begin{cases} x - 6 = 0 \\ 2x - 3y = 1 \end{cases}$, which is the correct corresponding matrix?

a. $\left[\begin{array}{cc|c} 1 & -6 & 0 \\ 2 & -3 & 1 \end{array}\right]$ **b.** $\left[\begin{array}{cc|c} 1 & 0 & 6 \\ 2 & -3 & 1 \end{array}\right]$ **c.** $\left[\begin{array}{cc|c} 1 & 0 & -6 \\ 2 & -3 & 1 \end{array}\right]$

37. The percent y of U.S. households that owned a black-and-white television set between the years 1980 and 1993 can be modeled by the linear equation $2.3x + y = 52$, where x represents the number of years after 1980. Similarly, the percent y of U.S. households that owned a microwave oven during this same period can be modeled by the linear equation $-5.4x + y = 14$. (*Source:* Based on data from the Energy Information Administration, U.S. Department of Energy)

a. The data used to form these two models was incomplete. It is impossible to tell from the data the year in which the percent of households owning black-and-white television sets was the same as the percent of households owning microwave ovens. Use matrix methods to estimate the year in which this occurred.

b. Did more households own black-and-white television sets or microwave ovens in 1980? In 1993? What trends do these models show? Does this seem to make sense? Why or why not?

c. According to the models, when will the percent of households owning black-and-white television sets reach 0%?

d. Do you think your answer to part c is accurate? Why or why not?

38. The most popular amusement park in the world currently (according to annual attendance) is Disney World's Magic Kingdom, whose annual attendance in thousands can be approximated by the equation $y = 455x + 14123$, where x is the number of years after 2001. This theme park stole the title from Tokyo Disneyland, which had been in first place for many years. The yearly attendance for Tokyo Disneyland, in thousands, can be represented by the equation $y = -776x + 15985$. Find the last year when attendance at Tokyo Disneyland was greater then attendance at Magic Kingdom. (*Source:* Amusement Business, and TEA Park World)

39. For the system $\begin{cases} 2x - 3y = 8 \\ x + 5y = -3 \end{cases}$, explain what is wrong with writing the corresponding matrix as $\left[\begin{array}{cc|c} 2 & 3 & 8 \\ 0 & 5 & -3 \end{array}\right]$.

 STUDY SKILLS BUILDER

Are You Satisfied with Your Performance on a Particular Quiz or Exam?

If not, don't forget to analyze your quiz or exam and look for common errors. Were most of your errors a result of:

- *Carelessness?* Did you turn in your quiz or exam before the allotted time expired? If so, resolve next time to use the entire time allotted. Any extra time can be spent checking your work.

- *Running out of time?* If so, make a point to better manage your time on your next quiz or exam. Try completing any questions that you are unsure of last and delay checking your work until all questions have been answered.

- *Not understanding a concept?* If so, review that concept and correct your work. Try to understand how this happened so that you make sure it doesn't happen before the next quiz or exam.

- *Test conditions?* When studying for a quiz or exam, make sure you place yourself in conditions similar to test conditions. For example, before your next quiz or exam, use a few sheets of blank paper and take a sample test without the aid of your notes or text.

(See your instructor or use the Chapter Test at the end of each chapter.)

Exercises

1. Have you corrected all your previous quizzes and exams?

2. List any errors you have found common to two or more of your graded papers.

3. Is one of your common errors not understanding a concept? If so, are you making sure you understand all the concepts for the next quiz or exam?

4. Is one of your common errors making careless mistakes? If so, are you now taking all the time allotted to check over your work so that you can minimize the number of careless mistakes?

5. Are you satisfied with your grades thus far on quizzes and tests?

6. If your answer to Exercise 5 is no, are there any more suggestions you can make to your instructor or yourself to help? If so, list them here and share these with your instructor.

4.5 SYSTEMS OF LINEAR INEQUALITIES

OBJECTIVE 1 ▶ Graphing systems of linear inequalities. In Section 3.7 we solved linear inequalities in two variables as well as their union and intersection. Just as two or more linear equations make a system of linear equations, two or more linear inequalities make a **system of linear inequalities.** Systems of inequalities are very important in a process called linear programming. Many businesses use linear programming to find the most profitable way to use limited resources such as employees, machines, or buildings.

A **solution of a system of linear inequalities** is an ordered pair that satisfies each inequality in the system. The set of all such ordered pairs is the solution set of the system. Graphing this set gives us a picture of the solution set. We can graph a system of inequalities by graphing each inequality in the system and identifying the region of overlap.

Graphing the Solutions of a System of Linear Inequalities

STEP 1. Graph each inequality in the system on the same set of axes.

STEP 2. The solutions of the system are the points common to the graphs of all the inequalities in the system.

EXAMPLE 1 Graph the solutions of the system: $\begin{cases} 3x \geq y \\ x + 2y \leq 8 \end{cases}$

Solution We begin by graphing each inequality on the *same* set of axes. The graph of the solutions of the system is the region contained in the graphs of both inequalities. In other words, it is their intersection.

First let's graph $3x \geq y$. The boundary line is the graph of $3x = y$. We sketch a solid boundary line since the inequality $3x \geq y$ means $3x > y$ or $3x = y$. The test point $(1, 0)$ satisfies the inequality, so we shade the half-plane that includes $(1, 0)$.

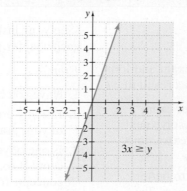
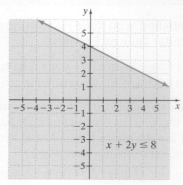

Next we sketch a solid boundary line $x + 2y = 8$ on the same set of axes. The test point $(0, 0)$ satisfies the inequality $x + 2y \leq 8$, so we shade the half-plane that includes $(0, 0)$. (For clarity, the graph of $x + 2y \leq 8$ is shown here on a separate set of axes.) An ordered pair solution of the system must satisfy both inequalities. These solutions are points that lie in both shaded regions. The solution of the system is the darkest shaded region. This solution includes parts of both boundary lines.

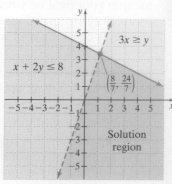

1 Graph the solutions of the system: $\begin{cases} 4x \geq y \\ x + 3y \geq 6 \end{cases}$.

In linear programming, it is sometimes necessary to find the coordinates of the **corner point:** the point at which the two boundary lines intersect. To find the corner point for the system of Example 1, we solve the related linear system

$$\begin{cases} 3x = y \\ x + 2y = 8 \end{cases}$$

using either the substitution or the elimination method. The lines intersect at $\left(\dfrac{8}{7}, \dfrac{24}{7}\right)$, the corner point of the graph.

EXAMPLE 2   Graph the solutions of the system: $\begin{cases} x - y < 2 \\ x + 2y > -1 \\ y < 2 \end{cases}$

Solution   First we graph all three inequalities on the same set of axes. All boundary lines are dashed lines since the inequality symbols are $<$ and $>$. The solution of the system is the region shown by the darkest shading. In this example, the boundary lines are *not* a part of the solution.

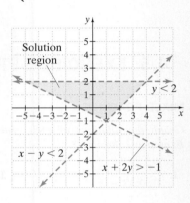

PRACTICE 2   Graph the solutions of the system: $\begin{cases} x - y < 1 \\ y < 4 \\ 3x + y > -3 \end{cases}$.

Concept Check ☑️

Describe the solution of the system of inequalities:

$$\begin{cases} x \le 2 \\ x \ge 2 \end{cases}$$

EXAMPLE 3   Graph the solutions of the system: $\begin{cases} -3x + 4y \le 12 \\ x \le 3 \\ x \ge 0 \\ y \ge 0 \end{cases}$

Solution   We graph the inequalities on the same set of axes. The intersection of the inequalities is the solution region. It is the only region shaded in this graph and includes the portions of all four boundary lines that border the shaded region.

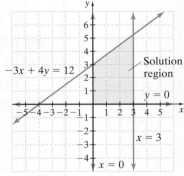

PRACTICE 3   Graph the solutions of the system: $\begin{cases} -2x + 5y \le 10 \\ x \le 4 \\ x \ge 0 \\ y \ge 0 \end{cases}$.

Answer to Concept Check:
the line $x = 2$

VOCABULARY & READINESS CHECK

Use the choices below to fill in each blank. Not all choices will be used.

solution   union   system
corner   intersection

1. Two or more linear inequalities form a _____ of linear inequalities.
2. An ordered pair that satisfies each inequality in a system is a _____ of the system.
3. The point where two boundary lines intersect is a _____ point.
4. The solution region of a system of inequalities consists of the _____ of the solution regions of the inequalities in the system.

4.5 | EXERCISE SET

MyMathLab

PRACTICE   WATCH   DOWNLOAD   READ   REVIEW

MIXED PRACTICE

Graph the solutions of each system of linear inequalities. See Examples 1 through 3.

1. $\begin{cases} y \geq x + 1 \\ y \geq 3 - x \end{cases}$

2. $\begin{cases} y \geq x - 3 \\ y \geq -1 - x \end{cases}$

3. $\begin{cases} y < 3x - 4 \\ y \leq x + 2 \end{cases}$

4. $\begin{cases} y \leq 2x + 1 \\ y > x + 2 \end{cases}$

5. $\begin{cases} y < -2x - 2 \\ y > x + 4 \end{cases}$

6. $\begin{cases} y \leq 2x + 4 \\ y \geq -x - 5 \end{cases}$

7. $\begin{cases} y \geq -x + 2 \\ y \leq 2x + 5 \end{cases}$

8. $\begin{cases} y \geq x - 5 \\ y \leq -3x + 3 \end{cases}$

9. $\begin{cases} x \geq 3y \\ x + 3y \leq 6 \end{cases}$

10. $\begin{cases} -2x < y \\ x + 2y < 3 \end{cases}$

11. $\begin{cases} x \leq 2 \\ y \geq -3 \end{cases}$

12. $\begin{cases} x \geq -3 \\ y \geq -2 \end{cases}$

13. $\begin{cases} y \geq 1 \\ x < -3 \end{cases}$

14. $\begin{cases} y > 2 \\ x \geq -1 \end{cases}$

15. $\begin{cases} y + 2x \geq 0 \\ 5x - 3y \leq 12 \\ y \leq 2 \end{cases}$

16. $\begin{cases} y + 2x \leq 0 \\ 5x + 3y \geq -2 \\ y \leq 4 \end{cases}$

17. $\begin{cases} 3x - 4y \geq -6 \\ 2x + y \leq 7 \\ y \geq -3 \end{cases}$

18. $\begin{cases} 4x - y \geq -2 \\ 2x + 3y \leq -8 \\ y \geq -5 \end{cases}$

19. $\begin{cases} 2x + y \leq 5 \\ x \leq 3 \\ x \geq 0 \\ y \geq 0 \end{cases}$

20. $\begin{cases} 3x + y \leq 4 \\ x \leq 4 \\ x \geq 0 \\ y \geq 0 \end{cases}$

Match each system of inequalities to the corresponding graph.

A
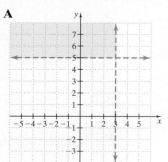

B
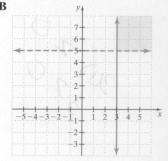

C
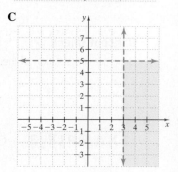

D
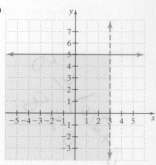

21. $\begin{cases} y < 5 \\ x > 3 \end{cases}$

22. $\begin{cases} y > 5 \\ x < 3 \end{cases}$

23. $\begin{cases} y \leq 5 \\ x < 3 \end{cases}$

24. $\begin{cases} y > 5 \\ x \geq 3 \end{cases}$

REVIEW

Evaluate each expression. See Section 1.3.

25. $(-3)^2$ **26.** $(-5)^3$ **27.** $\left(\dfrac{2}{3}\right)^2$ **28.** $\left(\dfrac{3}{4}\right)^3$

Perform each indicated operation. See Section 1.3.

29. $(-2)^2 - (-3) + 2(-1)$ **30.** $5^2 - 11 + 3(-5)$

31. $8^2 + (-13) - 4(-2)$ **32.** $(-12)^2 + (-1)(2) - 6$

CONCEPT EXTENSIONS

Solve. See the Concept Check in this section.

33. Describe the solution of the system: $\begin{cases} y \leq 3 \\ y \geq 3 \end{cases}$.

34. Describe the solution of the system: $\begin{cases} x \leq 5 \\ x \leq 3 \end{cases}$.

35. Explain how to decide which region to shade to show the solution region of the following system.

    $\begin{cases} x \geq 3 \\ y \geq -2 \end{cases}$

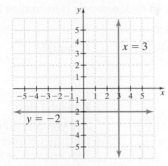

36. Tony Noellert budgets his time at work today. Part of the day he can write bills; the rest of the day he can use to write purchase orders. The total time available is at most 8 hours. Less than 3 hours is to be spent writing bills.

    a. Write a system of inequalities to describe the situation. (Let x = hours available for writing bills and y = hours available for writing purchase orders.)

    b. Graph the solutions of the system.

CHAPTER 4 GROUP ACTIVITY

Another Mathematical Model

Sometimes mathematical models other than linear models are appropriate for data. Suppose that an equation of the form $y = ax^2 + bx + c$ is an appropriate model for the ordered pairs $(x_1, y_1), (x_2, y_2)$, and (x_3, y_3). Then it is necessary to find the values of a, b, and c such that the given ordered pairs are solutions of the equation $y = ax^2 + bx + c$. To do so, substitute each ordered pair into the equation. Each time, the result is an equation in three unknowns: a, b, and c. Solving the resulting system of three linear equations in three unknowns will give the required values of a, b, and c.

1. The table gives the total beef supply (in billions of pounds) in the United States in each of the years listed.

   a. Write the data as ordered pairs of the form (x, y), where y is the beef supply (in billions of pounds) in the year x ($x = 0$ represents 2000).

   b. Find the values of a, b, and c such that the equation $y = ax^2 + bx + c$ models this data.

   c. Verify that the model you found in part (b) gives each of the ordered pair solutions from part (a).

   d. According to the model, what was the U.S. beef supply in 2005?

Total U.S. Beef Supply	
Year	Beef Supply (Billions of Pounds)
2002	27
2004	24.6
2006	25

(*Source:* Economic Research Service, U.S. Department of Agriculture)

2. The table gives Toyota Hybrid sales figures for each of the years listed.

   a. Write the data as ordered pairs of the form (x, y), where y is sales in the year x ($x = 0$ represents 2000).

   b. Find the values of a, b, and c such that the equation $y = ax^2 + bx + c$ models this data.

   c. According to the model, what were the total sales in 2005?

Total Toyota Hybrid Sales	
Year	Sales in Thousands
2002	41
2004	135
2006	313

(*Source:* Toyota Motor Corporation)

3. a. Make up an equation of the form $y = ax^2 + bx + c$.

   b. Find three ordered pair solutions of the equation.

   c. Without revealing your equation from part (a), exchange lists of ordered pair solutions with another group.

   d. Use the method described above to find the values of a, b, and c such that the equation $y = ax^2 + bx + c$ has the ordered pair solutions you received from the other group.

   e. Check with the other group to see if your equation from part (d) is the correct one.

CHAPTER 4 VOCABULARY CHECK

Fill in each blank with one of the words or phrases listed below.

matrix   consistent   system of equations
solution   inconsistent   square

1. Two or more linear equations in two variables form a _____ .
2. A _____ of a system of two equations in two variables is an ordered pair that makes both equations true.
3. A(n) _____ system of equations has at least one solution.
4. If a matrix has the same number of rows and columns, it is called a _____ matrix.
5. A(n) _____ system of equations has no solution.
6. A _____ is a rectangular array of numbers.

> ▶ **Helpful Hint**
>
> Are you preparing for your test? Don't forget to take the Chapter 4 Test on page 253. Then check your answers at the back of the text and use the Chapter Test Prep Video CD to see the fully worked-out solutions to any of the exercises you want to review.

CHAPTER 4 HIGHLIGHTS

DEFINITIONS AND CONCEPTS	EXAMPLES

SECTION 4.1 SOLVING SYSTEMS OF LINEAR EQUATIONS IN TWO VARIABLES

A **system of linear equations** consists of two or more linear equations.

$$\begin{cases} x - 3y = 6 \\ y = \dfrac{1}{2}x \end{cases} \qquad \begin{cases} x + 2y - z = 1 \\ 3x - y + 4z = 0 \\ 5y + z = 6 \end{cases}$$

A **solution** of a system of two equations in two variables is an ordered pair (x, y) that makes both equations true.

Determine whether $(2, -5)$ is a solution of the system.

$$\begin{cases} x + y = -3 \\ 2x - 3y = 19 \end{cases}$$

Replace x with 2 and y with -5 in both equations.

$$x + y = -3 \qquad\qquad 2x - 3y = 19$$
$$2 + (-5) \stackrel{?}{=} -3 \qquad 2(2) - 3(-5) \stackrel{?}{=} 19$$
$$-3 = -3 \quad \text{True} \qquad 4 + 15 \stackrel{?}{=} 19$$
$$19 = 19 \quad \text{True}$$

$(2, -5)$ is a solution of the system.

Geometrically, a solution of a system in two variables is a point of intersection of the graphs of the equations.

Solve by graphing: $\begin{cases} y = 2x - 1 \\ x + 2y = 13 \end{cases}$

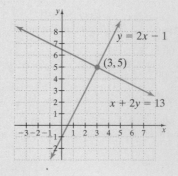

DEFINITIONS AND CONCEPTS	EXAMPLES

A system of equations with at least one solution is a **consistent system.** A system that has no solution is an **inconsistent system.**

If the graphs of two linear equations are identical, the equations are **dependent.**

If their graphs are different, the equations are **independent.**

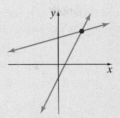

One solution:
Independent equations
Consistent system

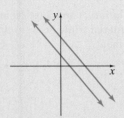

No solution:
Independent equations
Inconsistent system

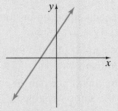

Infinite number of solutions:
Dependent equations
Consistent system

Solving a System of Linear Equations by the Substitution Method

Step 1. Solve one equation for a variable.

Step 2. Substitute the expression for the variable into the other equation.

Step 3. Solve the equation from Step 2 to find the value of one variable.

Step 4. Substitute the value from Step 3 in either original equation to find the value of the other variable.

Step 5. Check the solution in both equations.

Solve by substitution:

$$\begin{cases} y = x + 2 \\ 3x - 2y = -5 \end{cases}$$

Since the first equation is solved for y, substitute $x + 2$ for y in the second equation.

$$
\begin{aligned}
3x - 2y &= -5 \quad &\text{Second equation} \\
3x - 2(x + 2) &= -5 \quad &\text{Let } y = x + 2. \\
3x - 2x - 4 &= -5 \\
x - 4 &= -5 \quad &\text{Simplify.} \\
x &= -1 \quad &\text{Add 4.}
\end{aligned}
$$

To find y, let $x = -1$ in $y = x + 2$, so $y = -1 + 2 = 1$. The solution $(-1, 1)$ checks.

Solving a System of Linear Equations by the Elimination Method

Step 1. Rewrite each equation in standard form, $Ax + By = C$.

Step 2. Multiply one or both equations by a nonzero number so that the coefficients of a variable are opposites.

Step 3. Add the equations.

Step 4. Find the value of the remaining variable by solving the resulting equation.

Step 5. Substitute the value from Step 4 into either original equation to find the value of the other variable.

Step 6. Check the solution in both equations.

Solve by elimination:

$$\begin{cases} x - 3y = -3 \\ -2x + y = 6 \end{cases}$$

Multiply both sides of the first equation by 2.

$$
\begin{aligned}
2x - 6y &= -6 \\
\underline{-2x + y = 6} \\
-5y &= 0 \quad &\text{Add.} \\
y &= 0 \quad &\text{Divide by } -5.
\end{aligned}
$$

To find x, let $y = 0$ in an original equation.

$$
\begin{aligned}
x - 3y &= -3 \\
x - 3 \cdot 0 &= -3 \\
x &= -3
\end{aligned}
$$

The solution $(-3, 0)$ checks.

DEFINITIONS AND CONCEPTS	**EXAMPLES**

A **solution** of an equation in three variables x, y, and z is an **ordered triple** (x, y, z) that makes the equation a true statement.

Verify that $(-2, 1, 3)$ is a solution of $2x + 3y - 2z = -7$. Replace x with -2, y with 1, and z with 3.

$$2(-2) + 3(1) - 2(3) \stackrel{?}{=} -7$$

$$-4 + 3 - 6 \stackrel{?}{=} -7$$

$$-7 = -7 \quad \text{True}$$

$(-2, 1, 3)$ is a solution.

Solving a System of Three Linear Equations by the Elimination Method

Step 1. Write each equation in standard form, $Ax + By + Cz = D$.

Step 2. Choose a pair of equations and use them to eliminate a variable.

Step 3. Choose any other pair of equations and eliminate the same variable.

Step 4. Solve the system of two equations in two variables from Steps 2 and 3.

Step 5. Solve for the third variable by substituting the values of the variables from Step 4 into any of the original equations.

Step 6. Check the solution in all three original equations.

Solve:

$$\begin{cases} 2x + y - z = 0 & (1) \\ x - y - 2z = -6 & (2) \\ -3x - 2y + 3z = -22 & (3) \end{cases}$$

1. Each equation is written in standard form.

2.
$$\begin{array}{l} 2x + y - z = 0 \quad (1) \\ \underline{x - y - 2z = -6} \quad (2) \\ 3x \qquad - 3z = -6 \quad (4) \quad \text{Add.} \end{array}$$

3. Eliminate y from equations (1) and (3) also.

$$\begin{array}{l} 4x + 2y - 2z = 0 \qquad \text{Multiply equation} \\ \underline{-3x - 2y + 3z = -22} \quad (3) \quad (1) \text{ by 2.} \\ x \qquad\quad + z = -22 \quad (5) \quad \text{Add.} \end{array}$$

4. Solve.

$$\begin{cases} 3x - 3z = -6 & (4) \\ x + z = -22 & (5) \end{cases}$$

$$\begin{array}{l} x - z = -2 \qquad \text{Divide equation (4) by 3.} \\ \underline{x + z = -22} \quad (5) \\ 2x \qquad = -24 \\ x \qquad = -12 \end{array}$$

To find z, use equation (5).

$$x + z = -22$$
$$-12 + z = -22$$
$$z = -10$$

5. To find y, use equation (1).

$$2x + y - z = 0$$
$$2(-12) + y - (-10) = 0$$
$$-24 + y + 10 = 0$$
$$y = 14$$

6. The solution $(-12, 14, -10)$ checks.

DEFINITIONS AND CONCEPTS	EXAMPLES

	Two numbers have a sum of 11. Twice one number is 3 less than 3 times the other. Find the numbers.
1. UNDERSTAND the problem.	**1.** Read and reread. x = one number y = other number

2. TRANSLATE.

2. In words:

	sum of numbers	is	11
	↓	↓	↓
Translate:	$x + y$	$=$	11

In words:	twice one number	is	3 less than 3 times the other number
	↓	↓	↓
Translate:	$2x$	$=$	$3y - 3$

3. SOLVE.

3. Solve the system: $\begin{cases} x + y = 11 \\ 2x = 3y - 3 \end{cases}$

In the first equation, $x = 11 - y$. Substitute into the other equation.

$$2x = 3y - 3$$
$$2(11 - y) = 3y - 3$$
$$22 - 2y = 3y - 3$$
$$-5y = -25$$
$$y = 5$$

Replace y with 5 in the equation $x = 11 - y$. Then $x = 11 - 5 = 6$. The solution is $(6, 5)$.

4. INTERPRET.

4. *Check:* See that $6 + 5 = 11$ is the required sum and that twice 6 is 3 times 5 less 3. *State:* The numbers are 6 and 5.

A **matrix** is a rectangular array of numbers.

$$\begin{bmatrix} -7 & 0 & 3 \\ 1 & 2 & 4 \end{bmatrix} \qquad \begin{bmatrix} a & b & c \\ d & e & f \\ g & h & i \end{bmatrix}$$

The **matrix** corresponding to a system is composed of the coefficients of the variables and the constants of the system.

The matrix corresponding to the system

$$\begin{cases} x - y = 1 \\ 2x + y = 11 \end{cases} \quad \text{is} \quad \begin{bmatrix} 1 & -1 & | & 1 \\ 2 & 1 & | & 11 \end{bmatrix}$$

(*continued*)

DEFINITIONS AND CONCEPTS	EXAMPLES

SECTION 4.4 SOLVING SYSTEMS OF EQUATIONS BY MATRICES (continued)

The following **row operations** can be performed on matrices, and the result is an equivalent matrix.

Elementary row operations:

1. Interchange any two rows.
2. Multiply (or divide) the elements of one row by the same nonzero number.
3. Multiply (or divide) the elements of one row by the same nonzero number and add them to their corresponding elements in any other row.

Use matrices to solve: $\begin{cases} x - y = 1 \\ 2x + y = 11 \end{cases}$.

The corresponding matrix is

$$\left[\begin{array}{cc|c} 1 & -1 & 1 \\ 2 & 1 & 11 \end{array}\right]$$

Use row operations to write an equivalent matrix with 1s along the diagonal and 0s below each 1 in the diagonal. Multiply row 1 by -2 and add to row 2. Change row 2 only.

$$\left[\begin{array}{cc|c} 1 & -1 & 1 \\ -2(1) + 2 & -2(-1) + 1 & -2(1) + 11 \end{array}\right]$$

simplifies to $\left[\begin{array}{cc|c} 1 & -1 & 1 \\ 0 & 3 & 9 \end{array}\right]$

Divide row 2 by 3.

$$\left[\begin{array}{cc|c} 1 & -1 & 1 \\ \frac{0}{3} & \frac{3}{3} & \frac{9}{3} \end{array}\right] \text{ simplifies to } \left[\begin{array}{cc|c} 1 & -1 & 1 \\ 0 & 1 & 3 \end{array}\right]$$

This matrix corresponds to the system

$$\begin{cases} x - y = 1 \\ y = 3 \end{cases}$$

Let $y = 3$ in the first equation.

$$x - 3 = 1$$
$$x = 4$$

The ordered pair solution is $(4, 3)$.

SECTION 4.5 SYSTEMS OF LINEAR INEQUALITIES

A **system of linear inequalities** consists of two or more linear inequalities.

To graph a system of inequalities, graph each inequality in the system. The overlapping region is the solution of the system.

$$\begin{cases} x - y \geq 3 \\ y \leq -2x \end{cases}$$

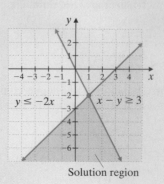

Solution region

CHAPTER 4 REVIEW

(4.1) *Solve each system of equations in two variables by each method: (a) graphing, (b) substitution, and (c) elimination.*

1. $\begin{cases} 3x + 10y = 1 \\ x + 2y = -1 \end{cases}$

2. $\begin{cases} y = \dfrac{1}{2}x + \dfrac{2}{3} \\ 4x + 6y = 4 \end{cases}$

3. $\begin{cases} 2x - 4y = 22 \\ 5x - 10y = 15 \end{cases}$

4. $\begin{cases} 3x - 6y = 12 \\ 2y = x - 4 \end{cases}$

5. $\begin{cases} \dfrac{1}{2}x - \dfrac{3}{4}y = -\dfrac{1}{2} \\ \dfrac{1}{8}x + \dfrac{3}{4}y = \dfrac{19}{8} \end{cases}$

6. The revenue equation for a certain style of backpack is $y = 32x$, where x is the number of backpacks sold and y is the income in dollars for selling x backpacks. The cost equation for these units is $y = 15x + 25{,}500$, where x is the number of backpacks manufactured and y is the cost in dollars for manufacturing x backpacks. Find the number of units to be sold for the company to break even. (*Hint:* Solve the system of equations formed by the two given equations.)

(4.2) *Solve each system of equations in three variables.*

7. $\begin{cases} x + z = 4 \\ 2x - y = 4 \\ x + y - z = 0 \end{cases}$

8. $\begin{cases} 2x + 5y = 4 \\ x - 5y + z = -1 \\ 4x - z = 11 \end{cases}$

9. $\begin{cases} 4y + 2z = 5 \\ 2x + 8y = 5 \\ 6x + 4z = 1 \end{cases}$

10. $\begin{cases} 5x + 7y = 9 \\ 14y - z = 28 \\ 4x + 2z = -4 \end{cases}$

11. $\begin{cases} 3x - 2y + 2z = 5 \\ -x + 6y + z = 4 \\ 3x + 14y + 7z = 20 \end{cases}$

12. $\begin{cases} x + 2y + 3z = 11 \\ y + 2z = 3 \\ 2x + 2z = 10 \end{cases}$

13. $\begin{cases} 7x - 3y + 2z = 0 \\ 4x - 4y - z = 2 \\ 5x + 2y + 3z = 1 \end{cases}$

14. $\begin{cases} x - 3y - 5z = -5 \\ 4x - 2y + 3z = 13 \\ 5x + 3y + 4z = 22 \end{cases}$

(4.3) *Use systems of equations to solve.*

15. The sum of three numbers is 98. The sum of the first and second is two more than the third number, and the second is four times the first. Find the numbers.

16. One number is three times a second number, and twice the sum of the numbers is 168. Find the numbers.

17. Two cars leave Chicago, one traveling east and the other west. After 4 hours they are 492 miles apart. If one car is traveling 7 mph faster than the other, find the speed of each.

18. The foundation for a rectangular Hardware Warehouse has a length three times the width and is 296 feet around. Find the dimensions of the building.

19. James Callahan has available a 10% alcohol solution and a 60% alcohol solution. Find how many liters of each solution he should mix to make 50 liters of a 40% alcohol solution.

20. An employee at See's Candy Store needs a special mixture of candy. She has creme-filled chocolates that sell for $3.00 per pound, chocolate-covered nuts that sell for $2.70 per pound, and chocolate-covered raisins that sell for $2.25 per pound. She wants to have twice as many raisins as nuts in the mixture. Find how many pounds of each she should use to make 45 pounds worth $2.80 per pound.

21. Chris Kringler has $2.77 in her coin jar—all in pennies, nickels, and dimes. If she has 53 coins in all and four more nickels than dimes, find how many of each type of coin she has.

22. If $10,000 and $4000 are invested such that $1250 in interest is earned in one year, and if the rate of interest on the larger investment is 2% more than that on the smaller investment, find the rates of interest.

23. The perimeter of an isosceles (two sides equal) triangle is 73 centimeters. If the unequal side is 7 centimeters longer than the two equal sides, find the lengths of the three sides.

24. The sum of three numbers is 295. One number is five more than a second and twice the third. Find the numbers.

(4.4) *Use matrices to solve each system.*

25. $\begin{cases} 3x + 10y = 1 \\ x + 2y = -1 \end{cases}$

26. $\begin{cases} 3x - 6y = 12 \\ 2y = x - 4 \end{cases}$

27. $\begin{cases} 3x - 2y = -8 \\ 6x + 5y = 11 \end{cases}$

28. $\begin{cases} 6x - 6y = -5 \\ 10x - 2y = 1 \end{cases}$

29. $\begin{cases} 3x - 6y = 0 \\ 2x + 4y = 5 \end{cases}$

30. $\begin{cases} 5x - 3y = 10 \\ -2x + y = -1 \end{cases}$

31. $\begin{cases} 0.2x - 0.3y = -0.7 \\ 0.5x + 0.3y = 1.4 \end{cases}$

32. $\begin{cases} 3x + 2y = 8 \\ 3x - y = 5 \end{cases}$

33. $\begin{cases} x \quad\quad + z = 4 \\ 2x - y \quad\quad = 0 \\ x + y - z = 0 \end{cases}$

34. $\begin{cases} 2x + 5y \quad\quad = 4 \\ x - 5y + z = -1 \\ 4x \quad\quad - z = 11 \end{cases}$

35. $\begin{cases} 3x - y \quad\quad = 11 \\ x \quad\quad + 2z = 13 \\ y - z = -7 \end{cases}$

36. $\begin{cases} 5x + 7y + 3z = 9 \\ 14y - z = 28 \\ 4x \quad\quad + 2z = -4 \end{cases}$

37. $\begin{cases} 7x - 3y + 2z = 0 \\ 4x - 4y - z = 2 \\ 5x + 2y + 3z = 1 \end{cases}$

38. $\begin{cases} x + 2y + 3z = 14 \\ y + 2z = 3 \\ 2x \quad\quad - 2z = 10 \end{cases}$

(4.5) *Graph the solution of each system of linear inequalities.*

39. $\begin{cases} y \ge 2x - 3 \\ y \le -2x + 1 \end{cases}$

40. $\begin{cases} y \le -3x - 3 \\ y \le 2x + 7 \end{cases}$

41. $\begin{cases} x + 2y > 0 \\ x - y \le 6 \end{cases}$

42. $\begin{cases} x - 2y \ge 7 \\ x + y \le -5 \end{cases}$

43. $\begin{cases} 3x - 2y \le 4 \\ 2x + y \ge 5 \\ y \le 4 \end{cases}$

44. $\begin{cases} 4x - y \le 0 \\ 3x - 2y \ge -5 \\ y \ge -4 \end{cases}$

45. $\begin{cases} x + 2y \le 5 \\ x \le 2 \\ x \ge 0 \\ y \ge 0 \end{cases}$

46. $\begin{cases} x + 3y \le 7 \\ y \le 5 \\ x \ge 0 \\ y \ge 0 \end{cases}$

MIXED REVIEW

Solve each system.

47. $\begin{cases} y = x - 5 \\ y = -2x + 2 \end{cases}$

48. $\begin{cases} \dfrac{2}{5}x + \dfrac{3}{4}y = 1 \\ x + 3y = -2 \end{cases}$

49. $\begin{cases} 5x - 2y = 10 \\ x = \dfrac{2}{5}y + 2 \end{cases}$

50. $\begin{cases} x - 4y = 4 \\ \dfrac{1}{8}x - \dfrac{1}{2}y = 3 \end{cases}$

51. $\begin{cases} x - 3y + 2z = 0 \\ 9y - z = 22 \\ 5x \quad\quad + 3z = 10 \end{cases}$

52. One number is five less than three times a second number. If the sum of the numbers is 127, find the numbers.

53. The perimeter of a triangle is 126 units. The length of one side is twice the length of the shortest side. The length of the third side is fourteen more than the length of the shortest side. Find the lengths of the sides of the triangles.

54. Graph the solution of the system: $\begin{cases} y \le 3x - \dfrac{1}{2} \\ 3x + 4y \ge 6 \end{cases}$.

55. In the United States, the consumer spending on VCR decks is decreasing while the spending on DVD players is increasing. For the years 1998–2003, the function $y = -443x + 2584$ estimates the millions of dollars spent on purchasing VCR decks while the function $y = 500x + 551$ estimates the millions of dollars spent on purchasing DVD players. For both functions, x is the number of years since 1998. Use these equations to determine the year in which the amount of money spent on VCR decks equals the amount of money spent on DVD players. (*Source:* Consumer Electronics Association)

CHAPTER 4 TEST TEST PREP VIDEO

Remember to use the Chapter Test Prep Video CD to see the fully worked-out solutions to any of the exercises you want to review.

Solve each system of equations graphically and then solve by the elimination method or the substitution method.

1. $\begin{cases} 2x - y = -1 \\ 5x + 4y = 17 \end{cases}$ **2.** $\begin{cases} 7x - 14y = 5 \\ x = 2y \end{cases}$

Solve each system.

3. $\begin{cases} 4x - 7y = 29 \\ 2x + 5y = -11 \end{cases}$

4. $\begin{cases} 15x + 6y = 15 \\ 10x + 4y = 10 \end{cases}$

5. $\begin{cases} 2x - 3y = 4 \\ 3y + 2z = 2 \\ x - z = -5 \end{cases}$

6. $\begin{cases} 3x - 2y - z = -1 \\ 2x - 2y = 4 \\ 2x - 2z = -12 \end{cases}$

7. $\begin{cases} \dfrac{x}{2} + \dfrac{y}{4} = -\dfrac{3}{4} \\ x + \dfrac{3}{4}y = -4 \end{cases}$

Use matrices to solve each system.

8. $\begin{cases} x - y = -2 \\ 3x - 3y = -6 \end{cases}$

9. $\begin{cases} x + 2y = -1 \\ 2x + 5y = -5 \end{cases}$

10. $\begin{cases} x - y - z = 0 \\ 3x - y - 5z = -2 \\ 2x + 3y = -5 \end{cases}$

11. A motel in New Orleans charges $90 per day for double occupancy and $80 per day for single occupancy. If 80 rooms are occupied for a total of $6930, how many rooms of each kind are occupied?

12. The research department of a company that manufactures children's fruit drinks is experimenting with a new flavor. A 17.5% fructose solution is needed, but only 10% and 20% solutions are available. How many gallons of a 10% fructose solution should be mixed with a 20% fructose solution to obtain 20 gallons of a 17.5% fructose solution?

13. A company that manufactures boxes recently purchased $2000 worth of new equipment to offer gift boxes to its customers. The cost of producing a package of gift boxes is $1.50 and it is sold for $4.00. Find the number of packages that must be sold for the company to break even.

14. The measure of the largest angle of a triangle is 3 less than five times the measure of the smallest angle. The measure of the remaining angle is 1 less than twice the measure of the smallest angle. Find the measure of each angle.

Graph the solutions of each system of linear inequalities.

15. $\begin{cases} 2y - x \geq 1 \\ x + y \geq -4 \\ y \leq 2 \end{cases}$

CHAPTER 4 CUMULATIVE REVIEW

1. Determine whether each statement is true or false.
  a. $3 \in \{x \mid x \text{ is a natural number}\}$
  b. $7 \notin \{1, 2, 3\}$

2. Determine whether each statement is true or false.
  a. $\{0, 7\} \subseteq \{0, 2, 4, 6, 8\}$
  b. $\{1, 3, 5\} \subseteq \{1, 3, 5, 7\}$

3. Simplify the following expressions.
  a. $11 + 2 - 7$
  b. $-5 - 4 + 2$

4. Subtract.
  a. $-7 - (-2)$
  b. $14 - 38$

5. Write the additive inverse, or opposite, of each.
  a. 4
  b. $\dfrac{3}{7}$
  c. -11.2

6. Write the reciprocal of each.
  a. 5
  b. $-\dfrac{2}{3}$

7. Use the distributive property to multiply.
  a. $3(2x + y)$
  b. $-(3x - 1)$
  c. $0.7a(b - 2)$

8. Multiply.
  a. $7(3x - 2y + 4)$
  b. $-(-2s - 3t)$

9. Use the distributive property to simplify each expression.
  a. $3x - 5x + 4$
  b. $7yz + yz$
  c. $4z + 6.1$

10. Simplify.
  a. $5y^2 - 1 + 2(y^2 + 2)$
  b. $(7.8x - 1.2) - (5.6x - 2.4)$

Solve.

11. $-4x - 1 + 5x = 9x + 3 - 7x$

12. $8y - 14 = 6y - 14$

13. $0.3x + 0.1 = 0.27x - 0.02$

14. $2(m - 6) - m = 4(m - 3) - 3m$

15. A pennant in the shape of an isosceles triangle is to be constructed for the Slidell High School Athletic Club and sold at a fund-raiser. The company manufacturing the pennant charges according to perimeter, and the athletic club has determined that a perimeter of 149 centimeters should make a nice profit. If each equal side of the triangle is twice the length of the third side, increased by 12 centimeters, find the lengths of the sides of the triangular pennant.

16. A quadrilateral has 4 angles whose sum is $360°$. In a particular quadrilateral, two angles have the same measure. A third angle is $10°$ more than the measure of one of the equal angles, and the fourth angle is half the measure of one of the equal angles. Find the measures of the angles.

17. Solve: $3x + 4 \geq 2x - 6$. Graph the solution set.

18. Solve: $5(2x - 1) > -5$

19. Solve: $2 < 4 - x < 7$

20. Solve: $-1 < \dfrac{-2x - 1}{3} < 1$

21. Solve: $|2x| + 5 = 7$

22. Solve: $|x - 5| = 4$

23. Solve for m: $|m - 6| < 2$

24. $|2x + 1| > 5$

25. Plot each ordered pair on a Cartesian coordinate system and name the quadrant or axis in which the point is located.

    a. $(2, -1)$ **b.** $(0, 5)$ **c.** $(-3, 5)$

    d. $(-2, 0)$ **e.** $\left(-\dfrac{1}{2}, -4\right)$ **f.** $(1.5, 1.5)$

26. Name the quadrant or axis each point is located.

    a. $(-1, -5)$

    b. $(4, -2)$

    c. $(0, 2)$

27. Is the relation $x = y^2$ also a function?

28. Graph: $-2x + \dfrac{1}{2}y = -2$

29. If $f(x) = 7x^2 - 3x + 1$ and $g(x) = 3x - 2$, find the following.

    a. $f(1)$ **b.** $g(1)$

    c. $f(-2)$ **d.** $g(0)$

30. If $f(x) = 3x^2$, find the following.

    a. $f(5)$ **b.** $f(-2)$

31. Graph $g(x) = 2x + 1$. Compare this graph with the graph of $f(x) = 2x$.

32. Find the slope of the line containing $(-2, 6)$ and $(0, 9)$.

33. Find the slope and the y-intercept of the line $3x - 4y = 4$.

34. Find the slope and y-intercept of the line defined by $y = 2$.

35. Are the following pairs of lines parallel, perpendicular, or neither?

    a. $3x + 7y = 4$
         $6x + 14y = 7$

    b. $-x + 3y = 2$
         $2x + 6y = 5$

36. Find an equation of the line through $(0, -9)$ with slope $\dfrac{1}{5}$.

37. Find an equation of the line through points $(4, 0)$ and $(-4, -5)$. Write the equation using function notation.

38. Find an equation of the line through $(-2, 6)$ perpendicular to $f(x) = \dfrac{1}{2}x - \dfrac{1}{3}$.

39. Graph $3x \geq y$.

40. Graph: $x \geq 1$.

41. Determine whether the given ordered pair is a solution of the system.

    a. $\begin{cases} -x + y = 2 \\ 2x - y = -3 \end{cases}$ $(-1, 1)$

    b. $\begin{cases} 5x + 3y = -1 \\ x - y = 1 \end{cases}$ $(-2, 3)$

42. Solve the system:
$$\begin{cases} 5x + y = -2 \\ 4x - 2y = -10 \end{cases}$$

43. Solve the system.
$$\begin{cases} 3x - y + z = -15 \\ x + 2y - z = 1 \\ 2x + 3y - 2z = 0 \end{cases}$$

44. Solve the system:
$$\begin{cases} x - 2y + z = 0 \\ 3x - y - 2z = -15 \\ 2x - 3y + 3z = 7 \end{cases}$$

45. Use matrices to solve the system.
$$\begin{cases} x + 3y = 5 \\ 2x - y = -4 \end{cases}$$

46. Solve the system:
$$\begin{cases} -6x + 8y = 0 \\ 9x - 12y = 2 \end{cases}$$

5

Exponents, Polynomials, and Polynomial Functions

To remember the Great Lakes, remember the word "**HOMES.**"

H = Huron
O = Ontario
M = Michigan
E = Erie
S = Superior

The Great Lakes are a group of five lakes in North America on or near the United States-Canada border. They were formed at the end of the last ice age, about 10,000 years ago.

The Great Lakes are the largest freshwater lake group on this Earth. They contain about 84% of North America's surface fresh water and 21% of the world's supply. The total surface area of the Great Lakes is about the size of Texas. Lake Superior alone is larger than the state of South Carolina. In Section 5.2, Exercise 99, page 270, we will explore the mass of the water in Lake Superior.

Linear equations are important for solving problems. They are not sufficient, however, to solve all problems. Many real-world phenomena are modeled by polynomials. We begin this chapter by reviewing exponents. We will then study operations on polynomials and how polynomials can be used in problem solving.

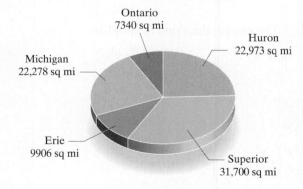

Ontario
7340 sq mi

Huron
22,973 sq mi

Michigan
22,278 sq mi

Erie
9906 sq mi

Superior
31,700 sq mi

Surface Areas of Great Lakes

5.1 EXPONENTS AND SCIENTIFIC NOTATION

OBJECTIVES

1 Use the product rule for exponents.

2 Evaluate expressions raised to the 0 power.

3 Use the quotient rule for exponents.

4 Evaluate expressions raised to the negative nth power.

5 Convert between scientific notation and standard notation.

OBJECTIVE 1 ▶ Using the product rule. Recall that exponents may be used to write repeated factors in a more compact form. As we have seen in the previous chapters, exponents can be used when the repeated factor is a number or a variable. For example,

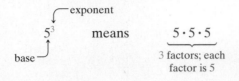

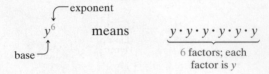

Expressions such as 5^3 and y^6 that contain exponents are called **exponential expressions.**

Exponential expressions can be multiplied, divided, added, subtracted, and themselves raised to powers. In this section, we review operations on exponential expressions.

We review multiplication first. To multiply x^2 by x^3, use the definition of an exponent.

$$x^2 \cdot x^3 = \underbrace{(x \cdot x)(x \cdot x \cdot x)}_{x \text{ is a factor 5 times}}$$
$$= x^5$$

Notice that the result is exactly the same if we add the exponents.

$$x^2 \cdot x^3 = x^{2+3} = x^5$$

This suggests the following.

Product Rule for Exponents

If m and n are positive integers and a is a real number, then

$$a^m \cdot a^n = a^{m+n}$$

In other words, the *product* of exponential expressions with a common base is the common base raised to a power equal to the *sum* of the exponents of the factors.

EXAMPLE 1   Use the product rule to simplify.

a. $2^2 \cdot 2^5$ **b.** $x^7 x^3$ **c.** $y \cdot y^2 \cdot y^4$

Solution

a. $2^2 \cdot 2^5 = 2^{2+5} = 2^7$

b. $x^7 x^3 = x^{7+3} = x^{10}$

c. $y \cdot y^2 \cdot y^4 = (y^1 \cdot y^2) \cdot y^4$
$= y^3 \cdot y^4$
$= y^7$

PRACTICE

1   Use the product rule to simplify.

a. $3^4 \cdot 3^2$ **b.** $x^5 \cdot x^2$ **c.** $y \cdot y^3 \cdot y^5$

EXAMPLE 2 Use the product rule to simplify.

a. $(3x^6)(5x)$ **b.** $(-2.4x^3p^2)(4xp^{10})$

Solution Here, we use properties of multiplication to group together like bases.

a. $(3x^6)(5x) = 3(5)x^6x^1 = 15x^7$

b. $(-2.4x^3p^2)(4xp^{10}) = -2.4(4)x^3x^1p^2p^{10} = -9.6x^4p^{12}$

PRACTICE
2 Use the product rule to simplify.

a. $(5z^3)(7z)$ **b.** $(-4.1t^5q^3)(5tq^5)$

OBJECTIVE 2 ▶ Evaluating expressions raised to the 0 power. The definition of a^n does not include the possibility that n might be 0. But if it did, then, by the product rule,

$$\underbrace{a^0 \cdot a^n}_{} = a^{0+n} = a^n = \underbrace{1 \cdot a^n}_{}$$

From this, we reasonably define that $a^0 = 1$, as long as a does not equal 0.

Zero Exponent

If a does not equal 0, then $a^0 = 1$.

EXAMPLE 3 Evaluate the following.

a. 7^0 **b.** -7^0 **c.** $(2x + 5)^0$ **d.** $2x^0$

Solution

a. $7^0 = 1$

b. Without parentheses, only 7 is raised to the 0 power.

$$-7^0 = -(7^0) = -(1) = -1$$

c. $(2x + 5)^0 = 1$

d. $2x^0 = 2(1) = 2$

PRACTICE
3 Evaluate the following.

a. 5^0 **b.** -5^0 **c.** $(3x - 8)^0$ **d.** $3x^0$

OBJECTIVE 3 ▶ Using the quotient rule. To find quotients of exponential expressions, we again begin with the definition of a^n to simplify $\dfrac{x^9}{x^2}$. For example,

$$\frac{x^9}{x^2} = \frac{x \cdot x \cdot x \cdot x \cdot x \cdot x \cdot x \cdot x \cdot x}{x \cdot x} = x^7$$

(Assume for the next two sections that denominators containing variables are not 0.)
    Notice that the result is exactly the same if we subtract the exponents.

$$\frac{x^9}{x^2} = x^{9-2} = x^7$$

This suggests the following.

Quotient Rule for Exponents

If a is a nonzero real number and n and m are integers, then

$$\frac{a^m}{a^n} = a^{m-n}$$

In other words, the *quotient* of exponential expressions with a common base is the common base raised to a power equal to the *difference* of the exponents.

EXAMPLE 4   Use the quotient rule to simplify.

a. $\dfrac{x^7}{x^4}$ b. $\dfrac{5^8}{5^2}$ c. $\dfrac{20x^6}{4x^5}$ d. $\dfrac{12y^{10}z^7}{14y^8z^7}$

Solution

a. $\dfrac{x^7}{x^4} = x^{7-4} = x^3$

b. $\dfrac{5^8}{5^2} = 5^{8-2} = 5^6$

c. $\dfrac{20x^6}{4x^5} = 5x^{6-5} = 5x^1,$ or $5x$

d. $\dfrac{12y^{10}z^7}{14y^8z^7} = \dfrac{6}{7}y^{10-8} \cdot z^{7-7} = \dfrac{6}{7}y^2z^0 = \dfrac{6}{7}y^2,$ or $\dfrac{6y^2}{7}$

PRACTICE
4   Use the quotient rule to simplify.

a. $\dfrac{z^8}{z^3}$ b. $\dfrac{3^9}{3^3}$ c. $\dfrac{45x^7}{5x^3}$ d. $\dfrac{24a^{14}b^6}{18a^7b^6}$

OBJECTIVE 4 ▶ Evaluating exponents raised to the negative *n*th power. When the exponent of the denominator is larger than the exponent of the numerator, applying the quotient rule yields a negative exponent. For example,

$$\frac{x^3}{x^5} = x^{3-5} = x^{-2}$$

Using the definition of a^n, though, gives us

$$\frac{x^3}{x^5} = \frac{x \cdot x \cdot x}{x \cdot x \cdot x \cdot x \cdot x} = \frac{1}{x^2}$$

From this, we reasonably define $x^{-2} = \dfrac{1}{x^2}$ or, in general, $a^{-n} = \dfrac{1}{a^n}$.

Negative Exponents

If a is a real number other than 0 and n is a positive integer, then

$$a^{-n} = \frac{1}{a^n}$$

EXAMPLE 5   Simplify and write with positive exponents only.

a. 5^{-2} **b.** $(-4)^{-4}$ **c.** $2x^{-3}$ **d.** $(3x)^{-1}$

e. $\dfrac{m^5}{m^{15}}$ **f.** $\dfrac{3^3}{3^6}$ **g.** $2^{-1} + 3^{-2}$ **h.** $\dfrac{1}{t^{-5}}$

Solution

a. $5^{-2} = \dfrac{1}{5^2} = \dfrac{1}{25}$

b. $(-4)^{-4} = \dfrac{1}{(-4)^4} = \dfrac{1}{256}$

c. $2x^{-3} = 2 \cdot \dfrac{1}{x^3} = \dfrac{2}{x^3}$ Without parentheses, only x is raised to the -3 power.

d. $(3x)^{-1} = \dfrac{1}{(3x)^1} = \dfrac{1}{3x}$ With parentheses, both 3 and x are raised to the -1 power.

e. $\dfrac{m^5}{m^{15}} = m^{5-15} = m^{-10} = \dfrac{1}{m^{10}}$

f. $\dfrac{3^3}{3^6} = 3^{3-6} = 3^{-3} = \dfrac{1}{3^3} = \dfrac{1}{27}$

g. $2^{-1} + 3^{-2} = \dfrac{1}{2^1} + \dfrac{1}{3^2} = \dfrac{1}{2} + \dfrac{1}{9} = \dfrac{9}{18} + \dfrac{2}{18} = \dfrac{11}{18}$

h. $\dfrac{1}{t^{-5}} = \dfrac{1}{\dfrac{1}{t^5}} = 1 \div \dfrac{1}{t^5} = 1 \cdot \dfrac{t^5}{1} = t^5$

PRACTICE
5   Simplify and write with positive exponents only.

a. 6^{-2} **b.** $(-2)^{-6}$ **c.** $3x^{-5}$ **d.** $(5y)^{-1}$ **e.** $\dfrac{k^4}{k^{11}}$

f. $\dfrac{5^3}{5^5}$ **g.** $5^{-1} + 2^{-2}$ **h.** $\dfrac{1}{z^{-8}}$

> ▶ **Helpful Hint**
>
> Notice that when a factor containing an exponent is moved from the numerator to the denominator or from the denominator to the numerator, the sign of its exponent changes.
>
> $$x^{-3} = \frac{1}{x^3}, \qquad 5^{-2} = \frac{1}{5^2} = \frac{1}{25}$$
>
> $$\frac{1}{y^{-4}} = y^4, \qquad \frac{1}{2^{-3}} = 2^3 = 8$$

EXAMPLE 6   Simplify and write with positive exponents only.

a. $\dfrac{x^{-9}}{x^2}$ **b.** $\dfrac{5p^4}{p^{-3}}$ **c.** $\dfrac{2^{-3}}{2^{-1}}$ **d.** $\dfrac{2x^{-7}y^2}{10xy^{-5}}$ **e.** $\dfrac{(3x^{-3})(x^2)}{x^6}$

Solution

a. $\dfrac{x^{-9}}{x^2} = x^{-9-2} = x^{-11} = \dfrac{1}{x^{11}}$

b. $\dfrac{5p^4}{p^{-3}} = 5 \cdot p^{4-(-3)} = 5p^7$

c. $\dfrac{2^{-3}}{2^{-1}} = 2^{-3-(-1)} = 2^{-2} = \dfrac{1}{2^2} = \dfrac{1}{4}$

d. $\dfrac{2x^{-7}y^2}{10xy^{-5}} = \dfrac{x^{-7-1} \cdot y^{2-(-5)}}{5} = \dfrac{x^{-8}y^7}{5} = \dfrac{y^7}{5x^8}$

e. Simplify the numerator first.

$$\dfrac{(3x^{-3})(x^2)}{x^6} = \dfrac{3x^{-3+2}}{x^6} = \dfrac{3x^{-1}}{x^6} = 3x^{-1-6} = 3x^{-7} = \dfrac{3}{x^7}$$

PRACTICE
6 Simplify and write with positive exponents only.

a. $\dfrac{z^{-8}}{z^3}$ **b.** $\dfrac{7t^3}{t^{-5}}$ **c.** $\dfrac{3^{-2}}{3^{-4}}$ **d.** $\dfrac{5a^{-5}b^3}{15a^2b^{-4}}$ **e.** $\dfrac{(2x^{-5})(x^6)}{x^5}$

Concept Check ☑

Find and correct the error in the following:

$$\dfrac{y^{-6}}{y^{-2}} = y^{-6-2} = y^{-8} = \dfrac{1}{y^8}$$

EXAMPLE 7 Simplify. Assume that a and t are nonzero integers and that x is not 0.

a. $x^{2a} \cdot x^3$ **b.** $\dfrac{x^{2t-1}}{x^{t-5}}$

Solution

a. $x^{2a} \cdot x^3 = x^{2a+3}$ Use the product rule.

b. $\dfrac{x^{2t-1}}{x^{t-5}} = x^{(2t-1)-(t-5)}$ Use the quotient rule.

$\quad = x^{2t-1-t+5} = x^{t+4}$

PRACTICE
7 Simplify. Assume that a and t are nonzero integers and that x is not 0.

a. $x^{3a} \cdot x^4$ **b.** $\dfrac{x^{3t-2}}{x^{t-3}}$

OBJECTIVE 5 ▶ Converting between scientific notation and standard notation. Very large and very small numbers occur frequently in nature. For example, the distance between the Earth and the Sun is approximately 150,000,000 kilometers. A helium atom has a diameter of 0.000 000 022 centimeters. It can be tedious to write these very large and very small numbers in standard notation like this. **Scientific notation** is a convenient shorthand notation for writing very large and very small numbers.

Helium atom

0.000 000 022
centimeters

150,000,000 km

Answer to Concept Check:

$\dfrac{y^{-6}}{y^{-2}} = y^{-6-(-2)} = y^{-4} = \dfrac{1}{y^4}$

> **Scientific Notation**
>
> A positive number is written in **scientific notation** if it is written as the product of a number a, where $1 \leq a < 10$ and an integer power r of 10:
>
> $$a \times 10^r$$

The following are examples of numbers written in scientific notation.

diameter of helium atom : 2.2×10^{-8} cm; 1.5×10^8 km   ← approximate distance between Earth and Sun

> **Writing a Number in Scientific Notation**
>
> **STEP 1.** Move the decimal point in the original number until the new number has a value between 1 and 10.
>
> **STEP 2.** Count the number of decimal places the decimal point was moved in Step 1. If the original number is 10 or greater, the count is positive. If the original number is less than 1, the count is negative.
>
> **STEP 3.** Write the product of the new number in Step 1 by 10 raised to an exponent equal to the count found in Step 2.

EXAMPLE 8   Write each number in scientific notation.

a. 730,000   **b.** 0.00000104

Solution

a. STEP 1. Move the decimal point until the number is between 1 and 10.

$$730,000.$$

STEP 2. The decimal point is moved 5 places and the original number is 10 or greater, so the count is positive 5.

STEP 3. $730,000 = 7.3 \times 10^5$.

b. STEP 1. Move the decimal point until the number is between 1 and 10.

$$0.00000104$$

STEP 2. The decimal point is moved 6 places and the original number is less then 1, so the count is -6.

STEP 3. $0.00000104 = 1.04 \times 10^{-6}$.   □

PRACTICE
8   Write each number in scientific notation.

a. 65,000   **b.** 0.000038

To write a scientific notation number in standard form, we reverse the preceding steps.

> **Writing a Scientific Notation Number in Standard Notation**
>
> Move the decimal point in the number the same number of places as the exponent on 10. If the exponent is positive, move the decimal point to the right. If the exponent is negative, move the decimal point to the left.

EXAMPLE 9 Write each number in standard notation.

a. 7.7×10^8 **b.** 1.025×10^{-3}

Solution

a. $7.7 \times 10^8 = 770{,}000{,}000$ Since the exponent is positive, move the decimal point 8 places to the right. Add zeros as needed.

b. $1.025 \times 10^{-3} = 0.001025$ Since the exponent is negative, move the decimal point 3 places to the left. Add zeros as needed.

PRACTICE
9 Write each number in standard notation.

a. 6.2×10^5 **b.** 3.109×10^{-2}

Concept Check ✓

Which of the following numbers have values that are less than 1?

Answers to Concept Check:
a, c, d

a. 3.5×10^{-5} **b.** 3.5×10^5 **c.** -3.5×10^5 **d.** -3.5×10^{-5}

Scientific Calculator Explorations

Multiply 5,000,000 by 700,000 on your calculator. The display should read
| 3.5　12 | or | 3.5 E 12 |, which is the product written in scientific notation. Both these notations mean 3.5×10^{12}.

To enter a number written in scientific notation on a calculator, find the key marked | EE |. (On some calculators, this key may be marked | EXP |.)
To enter 7.26×10^{13}, press the keys

| 7.26 |　| EE |　| 13 |

The display will read | 7.26　13 | or | 7.26 E 13 |.

Use your calculator to perform each operation indicated.

1. Multiply 3×10^{11} and 2×10^{32}.

2. Divide 6×10^{14} by 3×10^9.

3. Multiply 5.2×10^{23} and 7.3×10^4.

4. Divide 4.38×10^{41} by 3×10^{17}.

VOCABULARY & READINESS CHECK

State the base of the exponent 5 in each expression.

1. $9x^5$ **2.** yz^5 **3.** -3^5 **4.** $(-3)^5$ **5.** $(y^7)^5$ **6.** $9 \cdot 2^5$

Write each expression with positive exponents.

7. $5x^{-1}y^{-2}$ **8.** $7xy^{-4}$ **9.** $a^2b^{-1}c^{-5}$ **10.** $a^{-4}b^2c^{-6}$ **11.** $\dfrac{y^{-2}}{x^{-4}}$ **12.** $\dfrac{x^{-7}}{z^{-3}}$

5.1 | EXERCISE SET

Use the product rule to simplify each expression. See Examples 1 and 2.

1. $4^2 \cdot 4^3$
2. $3^3 \cdot 3^5$
3. $x^5 \cdot x^3$
4. $a^2 \cdot a^9$
5. $m \cdot m^7 \cdot m^6$
6. $n \cdot n^{10} \cdot n^{12}$
7. $(4xy)(-5x)$
8. $(-7xy)(7y)$
9. $(-4x^3p^2)(4y^3x^3)$
10. $(-6a^2b^3)(-3ab^3)$

Evaluate each expression. See Example 3.

11. -8^0
12. $(-9)^0$
13. $(4x + 5)^0$
14. $(3x - 1)^0$
15. $-x^0$
16. $-5x^0$
17. $4x^0 + 5$
18. $8x^0 + 1$

Use the quotient rule to simplify. See Example 4.

19. $\dfrac{a^5}{a^2}$
20. $\dfrac{x^9}{x^4}$
21. $-\dfrac{26z^{11}}{2z^7}$
22. $-\dfrac{16x^5}{8x}$
23. $\dfrac{x^9y^6}{x^8y^6}$
24. $\dfrac{a^{12}b^2}{a^9b}$
25. $\dfrac{12x^4y^7}{9xy^5}$
26. $\dfrac{24a^{10}b^{11}}{10ab^3}$
27. $\dfrac{-36a^5b^7c^{10}}{6ab^3c^4}$
28. $\dfrac{49a^3bc^{14}}{-7abc^8}$

Simplify and write using positive exponents only. See Examples 5 and 6.

29. 4^{-2}
30. 2^{-3}
31. $(-3)^{-3}$
32. $(-6)^{-2}$
33. $\dfrac{x^7}{x^{15}}$
34. $\dfrac{z}{z^3}$
35. $5a^{-4}$
36. $10b^{-1}$
37. $\dfrac{x^{-7}}{y^{-2}}$
38. $\dfrac{p^{-13}}{q^{-3}}$
39. $\dfrac{x^{-2}}{x^5}$
40. $\dfrac{z^{-12}}{z^{10}}$
41. $\dfrac{8r^4}{2r^{-4}}$
42. $\dfrac{3s^3}{15s^{-3}}$
43. $\dfrac{x^{-9}x^4}{x^{-5}}$
44. $\dfrac{y^{-7}y}{y^8}$
45. $\dfrac{2a^{-6}b^2}{18ab^{-5}}$
46. $\dfrac{18ab^{-6}}{3a^{-3}b^6}$
47. $\dfrac{(24x^8)(x)}{20x^{-7}}$
48. $\dfrac{(30z^2)(z^5)}{55z^{-4}}$

MIXED PRACTICE

Simplify and write using positive exponents only. See Examples 1 through 6.

49. $-7x^3 \cdot 20x^9$
50. $-3y \cdot -9y^4$
51. $x^7 \cdot x^8 \cdot x$
52. $y^6 \cdot y \cdot y^9$
53. $2x^2 \cdot 5x^7$
54. $-3z^4 \cdot 10z^7$
55. $(5x)^0 + 5x^0$
56. $4y^0 - (4y)^0$
57. $\dfrac{z^{12}}{z^{15}}$
58. $\dfrac{x^{11}}{x^{20}}$
59. $3^0 - 3t^0$
60. $4^0 + 4x^0$
61. $\dfrac{y^{-3}}{y^{-7}}$
62. $\dfrac{y^{-6}}{y^{-9}}$
63. $4^{-1} - 3^{-2}$
64. $1^{-3} - 4^{-2}$
65. $3x^{-1}$
66. $(4x)^{-1}$
67. $\dfrac{r^2}{r^{-4}}$
68. $\dfrac{x^{-5}}{x^3}$
69. $\dfrac{x^{-7}y^{-2}}{z^2y^2}$
70. $\dfrac{a^{-5}b^7}{a^{-2}b^{-3}}$
71. $(-4x^2y)(3x^4)(-2xy^5)$
72. $(-6a^4b)(2b^3)(-3ab^6)$
73. $2^{-4} \cdot x$
74. $5^{-2} \cdot y$
75. $\dfrac{5^{17}}{5^{13}}$
76. $\dfrac{10^{25}}{10^{23}}$
77. $\dfrac{8^{-7}}{8^{-6}}$
78. $\dfrac{13^{-10}}{13^{-9}}$
79. $\dfrac{9^{-5}a^4}{9^{-3}a^{-1}}$
80. $\dfrac{11^{-9}b^3}{11^{-7}b^{-4}}$
81. $\dfrac{14x^{-2}yz^{-4}}{2xyz}$
82. $\dfrac{30x^{-7}yz^{-14}}{3xyz}$

Simplify. Assume that variables in the exponents represent nonzero integers and that x, y, and z are not 0. See Example 7.

83. $x^5 \cdot x^{7a}$
84. $y^{2p} \cdot y^{9p}$
85. $\dfrac{x^{3t-1}}{x^t}$
86. $\dfrac{y^{4p-2}}{y^{3p}}$
87. $x^{4a} \cdot x^7$
88. $x^{9y} \cdot x^{-7y}$
89. $\dfrac{z^{6x}}{z^{-7}}$
90. $\dfrac{y^6}{y^{4z}}$
91. $\dfrac{x^{3t} \cdot x^{4t-1}}{x^t}$
92. $\dfrac{z^{5x} \cdot z^{x-7}}{z^x}$

Write each number in scientific notation. See Example 8.

93. $31,250,000$
94. $678,000$
95. 0.016
96. 0.007613
97. $67,413$
98. $36,800,000$

99. 0.0125   **100.** 0.00084
101. 0.000053   **102.** 98,700,000,000

Write each number in scientific notation.

103. Total revenues for Wal-Mart in fiscal year ending January 2007 were $344,992,000,000. (*Source:* Wal-Mart Stores, Inc.)

104. The University of Texas system has more than 170,000 students statewide. (*Source:* University of Texas)

105. On a recent day, the Apple iTunes Store featured more than 3,500,000 songs to buy for $0.99 each.

106. In 2006, approximately 61,049,000 passengers passed through the Los Angeles International Airport. (*Source:* Los Angeles International Airport)

107. Lake Mead, created from the Colorado River by the Hoover Dam, has a capacity of 124,000,000,000 cubic feet of water. (*Source:* U.S. Bureau of Reclamation)

108. The temperature of the core of the sun is about 27,000,000°F.

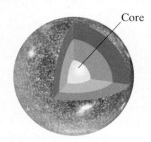

Core

109. A pulsar is a rotating neutron star that gives off sharp, regular pulses of radio waves. For one particular pulsar, the rate of pulses is every 0.001 second.

△ **110.** To convert from cubic inches to cubic meters, multiply by 0.0000164.

Write each number in standard notation, without exponents. See Example 9.

111. 3.6×10^{-9} **112.** 2.7×10^{-5}
113. 9.3×10^{7} **114.** 6.378×10^{8}
115. 1.278×10^{6} **116.** 7.6×10^{4}
117. 7.35×10^{12} **118.** 1.66×10^{-5}
119. 4.03×10^{-7} **120.** 8.007×10^{8}

Write each number in standard notation.

121. The estimated world population in 1 A.D. was 3.0×10^{8}. (*Source:* World Almanac and Book of Facts)

122. There are 3.949×10^{6} miles of highways, roads, and streets in the United States. (*Source:* Bureau of Transportation Statistics)

123. In 2006, teenagers had an estimated spending power of 1.53×10^{11} dollars. (*Source:* A. C. Neilson Research)

124. Each day, an estimated 1.2×10^{9} beverages consumed throughout the world are Coca Cola products. (*Source:* Coca-Cola)

REVIEW AND PREVIEW

Evaluate. See Sections 1.3 and 5.1.

125. $(5 \cdot 2)^{2}$ **126.** $5^{2} \cdot 2^{2}$
127. $\left(\dfrac{3}{4}\right)^{3}$ **128.** $\dfrac{3^{3}}{4^{3}}$
129. $(2^{3})^{2}$ **130.** $(2^{2})^{3}$

CONCEPT EXTENSIONS

131. Explain how to convert a number from standard notation to scientific notation.

132. Explain how to convert a number from scientific notation to standard notation.

133. Explain why $(-5)^{0}$ simplifies to 1 but -5^{0} simplifies to -1.

134. Explain why both $4x^{0} - 3y^{0}$ and $(4x - 3y)^{0}$ simplify to 1.

135. Simplify where possible.

a. $x^{a} \cdot x^{a}$ **b.** $x^{a} + x^{a}$
c. $\dfrac{x^{a}}{x^{b}}$ **d.** $x^{a} \cdot x^{b}$
e. $x^{a} + x^{b}$

136. Which numbers are equal to 36,000? Of these, which is written in scientific notation?

a. 36×10^{3} **b.** 360×10^{2}
c. 0.36×10^{5} **d.** 3.6×10^{4}

Without calculating, determine which number is larger.

137. 7^{11} or 7^{13} **138.** 5^{10} or 5^{9}
139. 7^{-11} or 7^{-13} **140.** 5^{-10} or 5^{-9}

STUDY SKILLS BUILDER

What to Do the Day of an Exam?

Your first exam may be soon. On the day of an exam, don't forget to try the following:

- Allow yourself plenty of time to arrive.
- Read the directions on the test carefully.
- Read each problem carefully as you take your test. Make sure that you answer the question asked.
- Watch your time and pace yourself so that you may attempt each problem on your test.
- Check your work and answers.
- **Do not turn your test in early.** If you have extra time, spend it double-checking your work.

Good luck!

Answer the following questions based on your most recent mathematics exam, whenever that was.

1. How soon before class did you arrive?
2. Did you read the directions on the test carefully?
3. Did you make sure you answered the question asked for each problem on the exam?
4. Were you able to attempt each problem on your exam?
5. If your answer to question 4 is no, list reasons why.
6. Did you have extra time on your exam?
7. If your answer to question 6 is yes, describe how you spent that extra time.

5.2 MORE WORK WITH EXPONENTS AND SCIENTIFIC NOTATION

OBJECTIVES

1 Use the power rules for exponents.

2 Use exponent rules and definitions to simplify exponential expressions.

3 Compute, using scientific notation.

OBJECTIVE 1 ▶ Using the power rules. The volume of the cube shown whose side measures x^2 units is $(x^2)^3$ cubic units. To simplify an expression such as $(x^2)^3$, we use the definition of a^n. Then

$$(x^2)^3 = \underbrace{(x^2)(x^2)(x^2)}_{x^2 \text{ is a factor 3 times}} = x^{2+2+2} = x^6$$

Notice that the result is exactly the same if the exponents are multiplied.

$$(x^2)^3 = x^{2\cdot3} = x^6$$

This suggests that the power of an exponential expression raised to a power is the product of the exponents. Two additional rules for exponents are given in the following box.

x^2 units

The Power Rule and Power of a Product or Quotient Rules for Exponents

If a and b are real numbers and m and n are integers, then

$$(a^m)^n = a^{m\cdot n} \qquad \text{Power rule}$$
$$(ab)^m = a^m b^m \qquad \text{Power of a product}$$
$$\left(\frac{a}{b}\right)^n = \frac{a^n}{b^n}(b \neq 0) \quad \text{Power of a quotient}$$

EXAMPLE 1   Use the power rule to simplify the following expressions. Use positive exponents to write all results.

a. $(x^5)^7$ **b.** $(2^2)^3$ **c.** $(5^{-1})^2$ **d.** $(y^{-3})^{-4}$

Solution

a. $(x^5)^7 = x^{5\cdot7} = x^{35}$ **b.** $(2^2)^3 = 2^{2\cdot3} = 2^6 = 64$

c. $(5^{-1})^2 = 5^{-1\cdot2} = 5^{-2} = \dfrac{1}{5^2} = \dfrac{1}{25}$ **d.** $(y^{-3})^{-4} = y^{-3(-4)} = y^{12}$

PRACTICE
1   Use the power rule to simplify the following expressions. Use positive exponents to write all results.

a. $(z^3)^5$ **b.** $(5^2)^2$ **c.** $(3^{-1})^3$ **d.** $(x^{-4})^{-6}$

EXAMPLE 2   Use the power rules to simplify the following. Use positive exponents to write all results.

a. $(5x^2)^3$ **b.** $\left(\dfrac{2}{3}\right)^3$ **c.** $\left(\dfrac{3p^4}{q^5}\right)^2$ **d.** $\left(\dfrac{2^{-3}}{y}\right)^{-2}$ **e.** $(x^{-5}y^2z^{-1})^7$

Solution

a. $(5x^2)^3 = 5^3 \cdot (x^2)^3 = 5^3 \cdot x^{2\cdot3} = 125x^6$

b. $\left(\dfrac{2}{3}\right)^3 = \dfrac{2^3}{3^3} = \dfrac{8}{27}$

c. $\left(\dfrac{3p^4}{q^5}\right)^2 = \dfrac{(3p^4)^2}{(q^5)^2} = \dfrac{3^2 \cdot (p^4)^2}{(q^5)^2} = \dfrac{9p^8}{q^{10}}$

d. $\left(\dfrac{2^{-3}}{y}\right)^{-2} = \dfrac{(2^{-3})^{-2}}{y^{-2}}$

$= \dfrac{2^6}{y^{-2}} = 64y^2$ Use the negative exponent rule.

e. $(x^{-5}y^2z^{-1})^7 = (x^{-5})^7 \cdot (y^2)^7 \cdot (z^{-1})^7$

$= x^{-35}y^{14}z^{-7} = \dfrac{y^{14}}{x^{35}z^7}$

PRACTICE
2   Use the power rules to simplify the following. Use positive exponents to write all results.

a. $(2x^3)^5$ **b.** $\left(\dfrac{3}{5}\right)^2$ **c.** $\left(\dfrac{2a^5}{b^7}\right)^4$ **d.** $\left(\dfrac{3^{-2}}{x}\right)^{-1}$ **e.** $(a^{-2}b^{-5}c^4)^{-2}$

OBJECTIVE 2 ▶ Using exponent rules and definitions to simplify. In the next few examples, we practice the use of several of the rules and definitions for exponents. The following is a summary of these rules and definitions.

Summary of Rules for Exponents

If a and b are real numbers and m and n are integers, then

Product rule	$a^m \cdot a^n = a^{m+n}$	
Zero exponent	$a^0 = 1$	$(a \neq 0)$
Negative exponent	$a^{-n} = \dfrac{1}{a^n}$	$(a \neq 0)$
Quotient rule	$\dfrac{a^m}{a^n} = a^{m-n}$	$(a \neq 0)$
Power rule	$(a^m)^n = a^{m\cdot n}$	
Power of a product	$(ab)^m = a^m \cdot b^m$	
Power of a quotient	$\left(\dfrac{a}{b}\right)^m = \dfrac{a^m}{b^m}$	$(b \neq 0)$

EXAMPLE 3   Simplify each expression. Use positive exponents to write the answers.

a. $(2x^0y^{-3})^{-2}$ **b.** $\left(\dfrac{x^{-5}}{x^{-2}}\right)^{-3}$ **c.** $\left(\dfrac{2}{7}\right)^{-2}$ **d.** $\dfrac{5^{-2}x^{-3}y^{11}}{x^2y^{-5}}$

Solution

a. $(2x^0y^{-3})^{-2} = 2^{-2}(x^0)^{-2}(y^{-3})^{-2}$

$\qquad\qquad = 2^{-2}x^0y^6$

$\qquad\qquad = \dfrac{1(y^6)}{2^2}$ Write x^0 as 1.

$\qquad\qquad = \dfrac{y^6}{4}$

b. $\left(\dfrac{x^{-5}}{x^{-2}}\right)^{-3} = \dfrac{(x^{-5})^{-3}}{(x^{-2})^{-3}} = \dfrac{x^{15}}{x^6} = x^{15-6} = x^9$

c. $\left(\dfrac{2}{7}\right)^{-2} = \dfrac{2^{-2}}{7^{-2}} = \dfrac{7^2}{2^2} = \dfrac{49}{4}$

d. $\dfrac{5^{-2}x^{-3}y^{11}}{x^2y^{-5}} = (5^{-2})\left(\dfrac{x^{-3}}{x^2}\right)\left(\dfrac{y^{11}}{y^{-5}}\right) = 5^{-2}x^{-3-2}y^{11-(-5)} = 5^{-2}x^{-5}y^{16}$

$\qquad\qquad = \dfrac{y^{16}}{5^2x^5} = \dfrac{y^{16}}{25x^5}$

PRACTICE
3   Simplify each expression. Use positive exponents to write the answer.

a. $(3ab^{-5})^{-3}$ **b.** $\left(\dfrac{y^{-7}}{y^{-4}}\right)^{-5}$ **c.** $\left(\dfrac{3}{8}\right)^{-2}$ **d.** $\dfrac{9^{-2}a^{-4}b^3}{a^2b^{-5}}$

EXAMPLE 4   Simplify each expression. Use positive exponents to write the answers.

a. $\left(\dfrac{3x^2y}{y^{-9}z}\right)^{-2}$ **b.** $\left(\dfrac{3a^2}{2x^{-1}}\right)^3\left(\dfrac{x^{-3}}{4a^{-2}}\right)^{-1}$

Solution   There is often more than one way to simplify exponential expressions. Here, we will simplify inside the parentheses if possible before we apply the power rules for exponents.

a. $\left(\dfrac{3x^2y}{y^{-9}z}\right)^{-2} = \left(\dfrac{3x^2y^{10}}{z}\right)^{-2} = \dfrac{3^{-2}x^{-4}y^{-20}}{z^{-2}} = \dfrac{z^2}{3^2x^4y^{20}} = \dfrac{z^2}{9x^4y^{20}}$

b. $\left(\dfrac{3a^2}{2x^{-1}}\right)^3\left(\dfrac{x^{-3}}{4a^{-2}}\right)^{-1} = \dfrac{27a^6}{8x^{-3}} \cdot \dfrac{x^3}{4^{-1}a^2}$

$\qquad\qquad = \dfrac{27 \cdot 4 \cdot a^6x^3x^3}{8 \cdot c^2} = \dfrac{27a^4x^6}{2}$

PRACTICE
4   Simplify each expression. Use positive exponents to write the answers.

a. $\left(\dfrac{5a^4b}{a^{-8}c}\right)^{-3}$ **b.** $\left(\dfrac{2x^4}{5y^{-2}}\right)^3\left(\dfrac{x^{-4}}{10y^{-2}}\right)^{-1}$

EXAMPLE 5 Simplify each expression. Assume that a and b are integers and that x and y are not 0.

a. $x^{-b}(2x^b)^2$ **b.** $\dfrac{(y^{3a})^2}{y^{a-6}}$

Solution

a. $x^{-b}(2x^b)^2 = x^{-b}2^2x^{2b} = 4x^{-b+2b} = 4x^b$

b. $\dfrac{(y^{3a})^2}{y^{a-6}} = \dfrac{y^{6a}}{y^{a-6}} = y^{6a-(a-6)} = y^{6a-a+6} = y^{5a+6}$ □

PRACTICE
5 Simplify each expression. Assume that a and b are integers and that x and y are not 0.

a. $x^{-2a}(3x^a)^3$ **b.** $\dfrac{(y^{3b})^3}{y^{4b-3}}$

OBJECTIVE 3 ▶ Computing, using scientific notation. To perform operations on numbers written in scientific notation, we use properties of exponents.

EXAMPLE 6 Perform the indicated operations. Write each result in scientific notation.

a. $(8.1 \times 10^5)(5 \times 10^{-7})$ **b.** $\dfrac{1.2 \times 10^4}{3 \times 10^{-2}}$

Solution

a. $(8.1 \times 10^5)(5 \times 10^{-7}) = 8.1 \times 5 \times 10^5 \times 10^{-7}$

$= 40.5 \times 10^{-2}$ Not in scientific notation because 40.5 is not between 1 and 10.

$= (4.05 \times 10^1) \times 10^{-2}$

$= 4.05 \times 10^{-1}$

b. $\dfrac{1.2 \times 10^4}{3 \times 10^{-2}} = \left(\dfrac{1.2}{3}\right)\left(\dfrac{10^4}{10^{-2}}\right) = 0.4 \times 10^{4-(-2)}$

$= 0.4 \times 10^6 = (4 \times 10^{-1}) \times 10^6 = 4 \times 10^5$ □

PRACTICE
6 Perform the indicated operations. Write each result in scientific notation.

a. $(3.4 \times 10^4)(5 \times 10^{-7})$ **b.** $\dfrac{5.6 \times 10^8}{4 \times 10^{-2}}$

EXAMPLE 7 Use scientific notation to simplify $\dfrac{2000 \times 0.000021}{700}$. Write the result in scientific notation.

Solution $\dfrac{2000 \times 0.000021}{700} = \dfrac{(2 \times 10^3)(2.1 \times 10^{-5})}{7 \times 10^2} = \dfrac{2(2.1)}{7} \cdot \dfrac{10^3 \cdot 10^{-5}}{10^2}$

$= 0.6 \times 10^{-4}$

$= (6 \times 10^{-1}) \times 10^{-4}$

$= 6 \times 10^{-5}$ □

PRACTICE
7 Use scientific notation to simplify $\dfrac{2400 \times 0.0000014}{800}$. Write the result in scientific notation.

VOCABULARY & READINESS CHECK

Simplify. See Examples 1 through 4.

1. $(x^4)^5$

2. $(5^6)^2$

3. $x^4 \cdot x^5$

4. $x^7 \cdot x^8$

5. $(y^6)^7$

6. $(x^3)^4$

7. $(z^4)^9$

8. $(z^3)^7$

9. $(z^{-6})^{-3}$

10. $(y^{-4})^{-2}$

5.2 | EXERCISE SET

MyMathLab   PRACTICE   WATCH   DOWNLOAD   READ   REVIEW

Simplify. Write each answer using positive exponents only. See Examples 1 and 2.

1. $(3^{-1})^2$

2. $(2^{-2})^2$

3. $(x^4)^{-9}$

4. $(y^7)^{-3}$

5. $(y)^{-5}$

6. $(z^{-1})^{10}$

7. $(3x^2y^3)^2$

8. $(4x^3yz)^2$

9. $\left(\dfrac{2x^5}{y^{-3}}\right)^4$

10. $\left(\dfrac{3a^{-4}}{b^7}\right)^3$

11. $(a^2bc^{-3})^{-6}$

12. $(6x^{-6}y^7z^0)^{-2}$

13. $\left(\dfrac{x^7y^{-3}}{z^{-4}}\right)^{-5}$

14. $\left(\dfrac{a^{-2}b^{-5}}{c^{-11}}\right)^{-6}$

15. $(5^{-1})^3$

Simplify. Write each answer using positive exponents only. See Examples 3 and 4.

16. $\left(\dfrac{a^{-4}}{a^{-5}}\right)^{-2}$

17. $\left(\dfrac{x^{-9}}{x^{-4}}\right)^{-3}$

18. $\left(\dfrac{2a^{-2}b^5}{4a^2b^7}\right)^{-2}$

19. $\left(\dfrac{5x^7y^4}{10x^3y^{-2}}\right)^{-3}$

20. $\dfrac{4^{-1}x^2yz}{x^{-2}yz^3}$

21. $\dfrac{8^{-2}x^{-3}y^{11}}{x^2y^{-5}}$

22. $\left(\dfrac{6p^6}{p^{12}}\right)^2$

23. $\left(\dfrac{4p^6}{p^9}\right)^3$

24. $(-8y^3xa^{-2})^{-3}$

25. $(-xy^0x^2a^3)^{-3}$

26. $\left(\dfrac{x^{-2}y^{-2}}{a^{-3}}\right)^{-7}$

27. $\left(\dfrac{x^{-1}y^{-2}}{5^{-3}}\right)^{-5}$

MIXED PRACTICE

Simplify. Write each answer using positive exponents.

28. $(8^2)^{-1}$

29. $(x^7)^{-9}$

30. $(y^{-4})^5$

31. $\left(\dfrac{7}{8}\right)^3$

32. $\left(\dfrac{4}{3}\right)^2$

33. $(4x^2)^2$

34. $(-8x^3)^2$

35. $(-2^{-2}y)^3$

36. $(-4^{-6}y^{-6})^{-4}$

37. $\left(\dfrac{4^{-4}}{y^3x}\right)^{-2}$

38. $\left(\dfrac{7^{-3}}{ab^2}\right)^{-2}$

39. $\left(\dfrac{1}{4}\right)^{-3}$

40. $\left(\dfrac{1}{8}\right)^{-2}$

41. $\left(\dfrac{3x^5}{6x^4}\right)^4$

42. $\left(\dfrac{8^{-3}}{y^2}\right)^{-2}$

43. $\dfrac{(y^3)^{-4}}{y^3}$

44. $\dfrac{2(y^3)^{-3}}{y^{-3}}$

45. $\left(\dfrac{zx^{-3}}{y^{-1}}\right)^{-3}$

46. $\left(\dfrac{n^5}{2m^{-2}}\right)^{-4}$

47. $\dfrac{3^{-2}a^{-5}b^6}{4^{-2}a^{-7}b^{-3}}$

48. $\dfrac{2^{-3}m^{-4}n^{-5}}{5^{-2}m^{-5}n}$

49. $(4x^6y^5)^{-2}(6x^4y^3)$

50. $(5xy)^3(z^{-2})^{-3}$

51. $x^6(x^6bc)^{-6}$

52. $2(y^2b)^{-4}$

53. $\dfrac{2^{-3}x^2y^{-5}}{5^{-2}x^7y^{-1}}$

54. $\dfrac{7^{-1}a^{-3}b^5}{a^2b^{-2}}$

55. $\left(\dfrac{2x^2}{y^4}\right)^3\left(\dfrac{2x^5}{y}\right)^{-2}$

56. $\left(\dfrac{3z^{-2}}{y}\right)^2\left(\dfrac{9y^{-4}}{z^{-3}}\right)^{-1}$

Simplify the following. Assume that variables in the exponents represent integers and that all other variables are not 0. See Example 5.

57. $(x^{3a+6})^3$

58. $(x^{2b+7})^2$

59. $\dfrac{x^{4a}(x^{4a})^3}{x^{4a-2}}$

60. $\dfrac{x^{-5y+2}x^{2y}}{x}$

61. $(b^{5x-2})^2$

62. $(c^{2a+3})^3$

63. $\dfrac{(y^{2a})^8}{y^{a-3}}$

64. $\dfrac{(y^{4a})^7}{y^{2a-1}}$

65. $\left(\dfrac{2x^{3t}}{x^{2t-1}}\right)^4$

66. $\left(\dfrac{3y^{5a}}{y^{-a+1}}\right)^2$

67. $\dfrac{25x^{2a+1}y^{a-1}}{5x^{3a+1}y^{2a-3}}$

68. $\dfrac{16x^{-5-3a}y^{-2a-b}}{2x^{-5+3b}y^{-2b-a}}$

Perform each indicated operation. Write each answer in scientific notation. See Examples 6 and 7.

69. $(5 \times 10^{11})(2.9 \times 10^{-3})$

70. $(3.6 \times 10^{-12})(6 \times 10^9)$

71. $(2 \times 10^5)^3$

72. $(3 \times 10^{-7})^3$

73. $\dfrac{3.6 \times 10^{-4}}{9 \times 10^2}$

74. $\dfrac{1.2 \times 10^9}{2 \times 10^{-5}}$

75. $\dfrac{0.0069}{0.023}$

76. $\dfrac{0.00048}{0.0016}$

77. $\dfrac{18,200 \times 100}{91,000}$

78. $\dfrac{0.0003 \times 0.0024}{0.0006 \times 20}$

79. $\dfrac{6000 \times 0.006}{0.009 \times 400}$

80. $\dfrac{0.00016 \times 300}{0.064 \times 100}$

81. $\dfrac{0.00064 \times 2000}{16,000}$

82. $\dfrac{0.00072 \times 0.003}{0.00024}$

83. $\dfrac{66,000 \times 0.001}{0.002 \times 0.003}$

84. $\dfrac{0.0007 \times 11,000}{0.001 \times 0.0001}$

85. $\dfrac{9.24 \times 10^{15}}{(2.2 \times 10^{-2})(1.2 \times 10^{-5})}$

86. $\dfrac{(2.6 \times 10^{-3})(4.8 \times 10^{-4})}{1.3 \times 10^{-12}}$

Solve.

87. A computer can add two numbers in about 10^{-8} second. Express in scientific notation how long it would take this computer to do this task 200,000 times.

88. To convert from square inches to square meters, multiply by 6.452×10^{-4}. The area of the following square is 4×10^{-2} square inches. Convert this area to square meters.

4×10^{-2} sq in.

89. To convert from cubic inches to cubic meters, multiply by 1.64×10^{-5}. A grain of salt is in the shape of a cube. If an average size of a grain of salt is 3.8×10^{-6} cubic inches, convert this volume to cubic meters.

REVIEW AND PREVIEW

Simplify each expression. See Section 1.4.

90. $-5y + 4y - 18 - y$

91. $12m - 14 - 15m - 1$

92. $-3x - (4x - 2)$

93. $-9y - (5 - 6y)$

94. $3(z - 4) - 2(3z + 1)$

95. $5(x - 3) - 4(2x - 5)$

CONCEPT EXTENSIONS

96. Each side of the cube shown is $\dfrac{2x^{-2}}{y}$ meters. Find its volume.

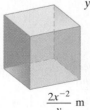

$\dfrac{2x^{-2}}{y}$ m

97. The lot shown is in the shape of a parallelogram with base $\dfrac{3x^{-1}}{y^{-3}}$ feet and height $5x^{-7}$ feet. Find its area.

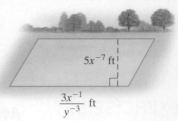

$5x^{-7}$ ft

$\dfrac{3x^{-1}}{y^{-3}}$ ft

98. The density D of an object is equivalent to the quotient of its mass M and volume V. Thus $D = \dfrac{M}{V}$. Express in scientific notation the density of an object whose mass is 500,000 pounds and whose volume is 250 cubic feet.

99. The density of ordinary water is 3.12×10^{-2} tons per cubic foot. The volume of water in the largest of the Great Lakes, Lake Superior, is 4.269×10^{14} cubic feet. Use the formula $D = \dfrac{M}{V}$ (see Exercise 98) to find the mass (in tons) of the water in Lake Superior. Express your answer in scientific notation. (*Source:* National Ocean Service)

100. Is there a number a such that $a^{-1} = a^{1}$? If so, give the value of a.

101. Is there a number a such that a^{-2} is a negative number? If so, give the value of a.

102. Explain whether 0.4×10^{-5} is written in scientific notation.

103. The estimated population of the United States in 2007 was 3.016×10^8. The land area of the United States is 3.536×10^6 square miles. Find the population density (number of people per square mile) for the United States in 2007. Round to the nearest whole number. (*Source:* U.S. Census Bureau)

104. In 2006, the value of goods imported into the United States was $\$1.855 \times 10^{12}$. The estimated population of the United States in 2006 was 2.98×10^8. Find the average value of imports per person in the United States for 2006. Round to the nearest dollar. (*Sources:* U.S. Census Bureau, Bureau of Economic Analysis)

105. The largest subway system in the world (based on passenger volume) is in Tokyo, Japan, with an estimated 2.82×10^9 riders per year. The subway system in Toronto boasts an estimated 4.44×10^8 riders per year. How many times greater is the Tokyo subway volume than the Toronto subway volume? Round to the nearest tenth. (*Source:* Tokyo and Toronto Transit Authorities)

106. Explain whether 0.4×10^{-5} is written in scientific notation.

107. In 2006, the population of Beijing was approximately 15.38×10^6. To prepare for the 2008 Summer Olympic Games, the Chinese put forth a massive effort to increase the numbers of their population who speak a foreign language. By the end of 2006, about 4.87×10^6 people in Beijing could boast that they speak a foreign language. What percent of the residents of Beijing could speak a foreign language at the end of 2006? Round to the nearest tenth of a percent. (*Source: China Daily*)

108. In 2006, downtown office space in downtown New York City was estimated to be 4.21×10^8 sq ft, while office space in downtown Dallas was 4.8×10^7 sq feet. How many times greater is the square footage of office space in New York City than Dallas? Round to the nearest tenth. (*Source: National Center for Real Estate Research*)

5.3 | POLYNOMIALS AND POLYNOMIAL FUNCTIONS

OBJECTIVES

1 Identify term, constant, polynomial, monomial, binomial, trinomial, and the degree of a term and of a polynomial.

2 Define polynomial functions.

3 Review combining like terms.

4 Add polynomials.

5 Subtract polynomials.

6 Recognize the graph of a polynomial function from the degree of the polynomial.

OBJECTIVE 1 ▶ Identifing polynomial terms and degrees of terms and polynomials. A **term** is a number or the product of a number and one or more variables raised to powers. The **numerical coefficient,** or simply the **coefficient,** is the numerical factor of a term.

Term	Numerical Coefficient of Term
$-1.2x^5$	-1.2
$x^3 y$	1
$-z$	-1
2	2
$\dfrac{x^9}{7} \left(\text{or } \dfrac{1}{7}x^9 \right)$	$\dfrac{1}{7}$

If a term contains only a number, it is called a **constant term,** or simply a **constant.** A **polynomial** is a finite sum of terms in which all variables are raised to nonnegative integer powers and no variables appear in any denominator.

Polynomials	Not Polynomials	
$4x^5 y + 7xz$	$5x^{-3} + 2x$	Negative integer exponent
$-5x^2 + 2x + \dfrac{2}{3}$	$\dfrac{6}{x^2} - 5x + 1$	Variable in denominator

A polynomial that contains only one variable is called a **polynomial in one variable.** For example, $3x^2 - 2x + 7$ is a **polynomial in x.** This polynomial in x is written in *descending order* since the terms are listed in descending order of the variable's exponents. (The term 7 can be thought of as $7x^0$.) The following examples are polynomials in one variable written in **descending order.**

$$4x^3 - 7x^2 + 5 \qquad y^2 - 4 \qquad 8a^4 - 7a^2 + 4a$$

A **monomial** is a polynomial consisting of one term. A **binomial** is a polynomial consisting of two terms. A **trinomial** is a polynomial consisting of three terms.

Monomials	Binomials	Trinomials
ax^2	$x + y$	$x^2 + 4xy + y^2$
$-3x$	$6y^2 - 2$	$-x^4 + 3x^3 + 1$
4	$\dfrac{5}{7}z^3 - 2z$	$8y^2 - 2y - 10$

By definition, all monomials, binomials, and trinomials are also polynomials.
Each term of a polynomial has a **degree.**

Degree of a Term
The **degree of a term** is the sum of the exponents on the *variables* contained in the term.

EXAMPLE 1   Find the degree of each term.

a. $3x^2$ **b.** -2^3x^5 **c.** y **d.** $12x^2yz^3$ **e.** 5.27

Solution

a. The exponent on x is 2, so the degree of the term is 2.

b. The exponent on x is 5, so the degree of the term is 5. (Recall that the degree is the sum of the exponents on only the *variables*.)

c. The degree of y, or y^1, is 1.

d. The degree is the sum of the exponents on the variables, or $2 + 1 + 3 = 6$.

e. The degree of 5.27, which can be written as $5.27x^0$, is 0.

PRACTICE

1   Find the degree of each term.

a. $4x^5$ **b.** -4^3y^3 **c.** z **d.** $65a^3b^7c$ **e.** 36

From the preceding example, we can say that the degree of a constant is 0. Also, the term 0 has no degree.
Each polynomial also has a degree.

Degree of a Polynomial
The **degree of a polynomial** is the largest degree of all its terms.

EXAMPLE 2   Find the degree of each polynomial and indicate whether the polynomial is also a monomial, binomial, or trinomial.

	Polynomial	Degree	Classification
a.	$7x^3 - \dfrac{3}{4}x + 2$	3	Trinomial
b.	$-xyz$	$1 + 1 + 1 = 3$	Monomial
c.	$x^4 - 16.5$	4	Binomial

PRACTICE
2   Find the degree of each polynomial and indicate whether the polynomial is also a monomial, binomial, or trinomial.

	Polynomial	Degree	Classification
a.	$3x^4 + 2x^2 - 3$		
b.	$9abc^3$		
c.	$8x^5 + 5x^3$		

EXAMPLE 3   Find the degree of the polynomial
$$3xy + x^2y^2 - 5x^2 - 6.7$$

Solution   The degree of each term is

$$3xy + x^2y^2 - 5x^2 - 6.7$$
$$\downarrow \qquad \downarrow \qquad \downarrow \qquad \downarrow$$
Degree: 2   4   2   0

The largest degree of any term is 4, so the degree of this polynomial is 4.

PRACTICE
3   Find the degree of the polynomial $2x^3y - 3x^3y^2 - 9y^5 + 9.6$.

OBJECTIVE 2 ▶ **Defining polynomial functions.**   At times, it is convenient to use function notation to represent polynomials. For example, we may write $P(x)$ to represent the polynomial $3x^2 - 2x - 5$. In symbols, this is

$$P(x) = 3x^2 - 2x - 5$$

This function is called a **polynomial function** because the expression $3x^2 - 2x - 5$ is a polynomial.

▶ **Helpful Hint**
Recall that the symbol $P(x)$ **does not mean** P times x. It is a special symbol used to denote a function.

EXAMPLE 4   If $P(x) = 3x^2 - 2x - 5$, find the following.

a. $P(1)$ **b.** $P(-2)$

Solution

a. Substitute 1 for x in $P(x) = 3x^2 - 2x - 5$ and simplify.

$$P(x) = 3x^2 - 2x - 5$$
$$P(1) = 3(1)^2 - 2(1) - 5 = -4$$

b. Substitute -2 for x in $P(x) = 3x^2 - 2x - 5$ and simplify.

$$P(x) = 3x^2 - 2x - 5$$
$$P(-2) = 3(-2)^2 - 2(-2) - 5 = 11$$

PRACTICE
4   If $P(x) = -5x^2 + 2x - 8$, find the following.

a. $P(-1)$ **b.** $P(3)$

Many real-world phenomena are modeled by polynomial functions. If the polynomial function model is given, we can often find the solution of a problem by evaluating the function at a certain value.

EXAMPLE 5 Finding the Height of an Object

The world's highest bridge, the Millau Viaduct in France, is 1125 feet above the River Tarn. An object is dropped from the top of this bridge. Neglecting air resistance, the height of the object at time t seconds is given by the polynomial function $P(t) = -16t^2 + 1125$. Find the height of the object when $t = 1$ second and when $t = 8$ seconds.

Solution To find the height of the object at 1 second, we find $P(1)$.

$$P(t) = -16t^2 + 1125$$
$$P(1) = -16(1)^2 + 1125$$
$$P(1) = 1109$$

When $t = 1$ second, the height of the object is 1109 feet.
To find the height of the object at 8 seconds, we find $P(8)$.

$$P(t) = -16t^2 + 1125$$
$$P(8) = -16(8)^2 + 1125$$
$$P(8) = 101$$

When $t = 8$ seconds, the height of the object is 101 feet. Notice that as time t increases, the height of the object decreases. ☐

PRACTICE
5 The largest natural bridge is in the canyons at the base of Navajo Mountain, Utah. From the base to the top of the arch, it measures 290 feet. Neglecting air resistance, the height of an object dropped off the bridge is given by the polynomial function $P(t) = -16t^2 + 290$ at time t seconds. Find the height of the object at time $t = 0$ second and $t = 2$ seconds.

OBJECTIVE 3 ▶ Combining like terms review. Before we add polynomials, recall that terms are considered to be **like terms** if they contain exactly the same variables raised to exactly the same powers.

Like Terms	Unlike Terms
$-5x^2, -x^2$	$4x^2, 3x$
$7xy^3z, -2xzy^3$	$12x^2y^3, -2xy^3$

To simplify a polynomial, **combine like terms** by using the distributive property. For example, by the distributive property,

$$5x + 7x = (5 + 7)x = 12x$$

EXAMPLE 6 Simplify by combining like terms.

a. $-12x^2 + 7x^2 - 6x$ **b.** $3xy - 2x + 5xy - x$

Solution By the distributive property,

a. $-12x^2 + 7x^2 - 6x = (-12 + 7)x^2 - 6x = -5x^2 - 6x$

b. Use the associative and commutative properties to group together like terms; then combine.

$$3xy - 2x + 5xy - x = 3xy + 5xy - 2x - x$$
$$= (3 + 5)xy + (-2 - 1)x$$
$$= \underbrace{8xy} - \underbrace{3x} \qquad \square$$

> ▶ **Helpful Hint**
> These two terms are unlike terms. They cannot be combined.

PRACTICE
6 Simplify by combining like terms.

a. $8x^4 - 5x^4 - 5x$ **b.** $4ab - 5b + 3ab + 2b$

OBJECTIVE 4 ▶ Adding polynomials. Now we have reviewed the necessary skills to add polynomials.

> **Adding Polynomials**
> To add polynomials, combine all like terms.

EXAMPLE 7 Add.

a. $(7x^3y - xy^3 + 11) + (6x^3y - 4)$ **b.** $(3a^3 - b + 2a - 5) + (a + b + 5)$

Solution

a. To add, remove the parentheses and group like terms.

$$(7x^3y - xy^3 + 11) + (6x^3y - 4)$$
$$= 7x^3y - xy^3 + 11 + 6x^3y - 4$$
$$= 7x^3y + 6x^3y - xy^3 + 11 - 4 \quad \text{Group like terms.}$$
$$= 13x^3y - xy^3 + 7 \quad \text{Combine like terms.}$$

b.
$$(3a^3 - b + 2a - 5) + (a + b + 5)$$
$$= 3a^3 - b + 2a - 5 + a + b + 5$$
$$= 3a^3 - b + b + 2a + a - 5 + 5 \quad \text{Group like terms.}$$
$$= 3a^3 + 3a \quad \text{Combine like terms.} \qquad \square$$

PRACTICE
7 Add.

a. $(3a^4b - 5ab^2 + 7) + (9ab^2 - 12)$ **b.** $(2x^5 - 3y + x - 6) + (4y - 2x - 3)$

EXAMPLE 8 Add $11x^3 - 12x^2 + x - 3$ and $x^3 - 10x + 5$.

Solution $(11x^3 - 12x^2 + x - 3) + (x^3 - 10x + 5)$
$$= 11x^3 + x^3 - 12x^2 + x - 10x - 3 + 5 \quad \text{Group like terms.}$$
$$= 12x^3 - 12x^2 - 9x + 2 \quad \text{Combine like terms.} \qquad \square$$

PRACTICE
8 Add $5x^3 - 3x^2 - 9x - 8$ and $x^3 + 9x^2 + 2x$.

Sometimes it is more convenient to add polynomials vertically. To do this, line up like terms beneath one another and add like terms.

OBJECTIVE 5 ▶ Subtracting polynomials. The definition of subtraction of real numbers can be extended to apply to polynomials. To subtract a number, we add its opposite.

$$a - b = a + (-b)$$

Likewise, to subtract a polynomial, we add its opposite. In other words, if P and Q are polynomials, then

$$P - Q = P + (-Q)$$

The polynomial $-Q$ is the **opposite,** or **additive inverse,** of the polynomial Q. We can find $-Q$ by writing the opposite of each term of Q.

Subtracting Polynomials
To subtract a polynomial, add its opposite.

For example,

To subtract, change the signs; then add.

$$(3x^2 + 4x - 7) - (3x^2 - 2x - 5) = (3x^2 + 4x - 7) + (-3x^2 + 2x + 5)$$
$$= 3x^2 + 4x - 7 - 3x^2 + 2x + 5$$
$$= 6x - 2 \qquad \text{Combine like terms.}$$

Concept Check ✓
Which polynomial is the opposite of $16x^3 - 5x + 7$?

a. $-16x^3 - 5x + 7$ **b.** $-16x^3 + 5x - 7$
c. $16x^3 + 5x + 7$ **d.** $-16x^3 + 5x + 7$

EXAMPLE 9 Subtract: $(12z^5 - 12z^3 + z) - (-3z^4 + z^3 + 12z)$

Solution To subtract, add the opposite of the second polynomial to the first polynomial.

$$(12z^5 - 12z^3 + z) - (-3z^4 + z^3 + 12z)$$
$$= 12z^5 - 12z^3 + z + 3z^4 - z^3 - 12z) \qquad \begin{array}{l}\text{Add the opposite of the}\\ \text{polynomial being subtracted.}\end{array}$$
$$= 12z^5 + 3z^4 - 12z^3 - z^3 + z - 12z \qquad \text{Group like terms.}$$
$$= 12z^5 + 3z^4 - 13z^3 - 11z \qquad \text{Combine like terms.} \qquad \square$$

PRACTICE
9 Subtract: $(13a^4 - 7a^3 - 9) - (-2a^4 + 8a^3 - 12)$.

Concept Check ✓
Why is the following subtraction incorrect?

$$(7z - 5) - (3z - 4)$$
$$= 7z - 5 - 3z - 4$$
$$= 4z - 9$$

Answers to Concept Check:
b;
With parentheses removed, the expression should be
$7z - 5 - 3z + 4 = 4z - 1$

EXAMPLE 10   Subtract $4x^3y^2 - 3x^2y^2 + 2y^2$ from $10x^3y^2 - 7x^2y^2$.

Solution   If we subtract 2 from 8, the difference is $8 - 2 = 6$. Notice the order of the numbers, and then write "Subtract $4x^3y^2 - 3x^2y^2 + 2y^2$ from $10x^3y^2 - 7x^2y^2$" as a mathematical expression.

$$(10x^3y^2 - 7x^2y^2) - (4x^3y^2 - 3x^2y^2 + 2y^2)$$
$$= 10x^3y^2 - 7x^2y^2 - 4x^3y^2 - 3x^2y^2 - 2y^2 \quad \text{Remove parentheses.}$$
$$= 6x^3y^2 - 4x^2y^2 - 2y^2 \qquad\qquad \text{Combine like terms.} \quad \square$$

PRACTICE
10   Subtract $5x^2y^2 - 3xy^2 + 5y^3$ from $11x^2y^2 - 7xy^2$.

- ∎

To add or subtract polynomials vertically, just remember to line up like terms. For example, perform the subtraction $(10x^3y^2 - 7x^2y^2) - (4x^3y^2 - 3x^2y^2 + 2y^2)$ vertically.

Add the opposite of the second polynomial.

$$
\begin{array}{l}
10x^3y^2 - 7x^2y^2 \\
\underline{-(4x^3y^2 - 3x^2y^2 + 2y^2)}
\end{array}
\quad \text{is equivalent to} \quad
\begin{array}{l}
10x^3y^2 - 7x^2y^2 \\
\underline{-4x^3y^2 + 3x^2y^2 - 2y^2} \\
6x^3y^2 - 4x^2y^2 - 2y^2
\end{array}
$$

Polynomial functions, like polynomials, can be added, subtracted, multiplied, and divided. For example, if

$$P(x) = x^2 + x + 1$$

then

$$2P(x) = 2(x^2 + x + 1) = 2x^2 + 2x + 2 \quad \text{Use the distributive property.}$$

Also, if $Q(x) = 5x^2 - 1$, then $P(x) + Q(x) = (x^2 + x + 1) + (5x^2 - 1) = 6x^2 + x$.

A useful business and economics application of subtracting polynomial functions is finding the profit function $P(x)$ when given a revenue function $R(x)$ and a cost function $C(x)$. In business, it is true that

$$\text{profit} = \text{revenue} - \text{cost, or}$$
$$P(x) = R(x) - C(x)$$

For example, if the revenue function is $R(x) = 7x$ and the cost function is $C(x) = 2x + 5000$, then the profit function is

$$P(x) = R(x) - C(x)$$

or

$$P(x) = 7x - (2x + 5000) \quad \text{Substitute } R(x) = 7x$$
$$P(x) = 5x - 5000 \qquad\qquad \text{and } C(x) = 2x + 5000.$$

Problem-solving exercises involving profit are in the exercise set.

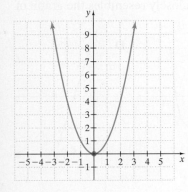

OBJECTIVE 6 ▶ Recognizing graphs of polynomial functions from their degree. In this section, we reviewed how to find the degree of a polynomial. Knowing the degree of a polynomial can help us recognize the graph of the related polynomial function. For example, we know from Section 3.1 that the graph of the polynomial function $f(x) = x^2$ is a parabola as shown to the left.

The polynomial x^2 has degree 2. The graphs of all polynomial functions of degree 2 will have this same general shape—opening upward, as shown, or downward. Graphs of polynomial functions of degree 2 or 3 will, in general, resemble one of the graphs shown next.

General Shapes of Graphs of Polynomial Functions

Degree 2

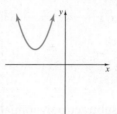

Coefficient of x^2
is a positive number.

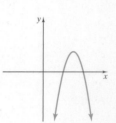

Coefficient of x^2
is a negative number.

Degree 3

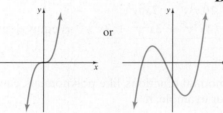

or

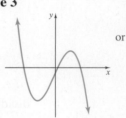

or

Coefficient of x^3
is a positive number.

Coefficient of x^3
is a negative number.

EXAMPLE 11 Determine which of the following graphs most closely resembles the graph of $f(x) = 5x^3 - 6x^2 + 2x + 3$

A 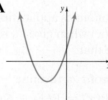 B 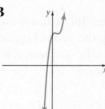 C 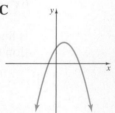 D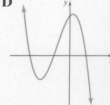

Solution The degree of $f(x)$ is 3, which means that its graph has the shape of B or D. The coefficient of x^3 is 5, a positive number, so the graph has the shape of B. □

PRACTICE
11 Determine which of the following graphs most closely resembles the graph of $f(x) = x^3 - 3$.

A 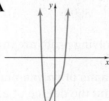 B 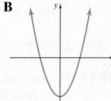 C 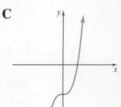 D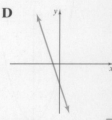

Graphing Calculator Explorations

A graphing calculator may be used to visualize addition and subtraction of polynomials in one variable. For example, to visualize the following polynomial subtraction statement

$$(3x^2 - 6x + 9) - (x^2 - 5x + 6) = 2x^2 - x + 3$$

graph both

$$Y_1 = (3x^2 - 6x + 9) - (x^2 - 5x + 6) \quad \text{Left side of equation}$$

and

$$Y_2 = 2x^2 - x + 3 \quad \text{Right side of equation}$$

on the same screen and see that their graphs coincide. (*Note:* If the graphs do not coincide, we can be sure that a mistake has been made in combining polynomials or in calculator keystrokes. If the graphs appear to coincide, we cannot be sure that our work is correct. This is because it is possible for the graphs to differ so slightly that we do not notice it.)

The graphs of Y_1 and Y_2 are shown. The graphs appear to coincide, so the subtraction statement

$$(3x^2 - 6x + 9) - (x^2 - 5x + 6) = 2x^2 - x + 3$$

appears to be correct.

Perform the indicated operations. Then visualize by using the procedure described above.

1. $(2x^2 + 7x + 6) + (x^3 - 6x^2 - 14)$
2. $(-14x^3 - x + 2) + (-x^3 + 3x^2 + 4x)$
3. $(1.8x^2 - 6.8x - 1.7) - (3.9x^2 - 3.6x)$
4. $(-4.8x^2 + 12.5x - 7.8) - (3.1x^2 - 7.8x)$
5. $(1.29x - 5.68) + (7.69x^2 - 2.55x + 10.98)$
6. $(-0.98x^2 - 1.56x + 5.57) + (4.36x - 3.71)$

VOCABULARY & READINESS CHECK

Use the choices below to fill in each blank. Not all choices will be used.

monomial	trinomial	like	degree	coefficient
binomial	polynomial	unlike	variables	term

1. The numerical factor of a term is the _____.
2. A _____ is a finite sum of terms in which all variables are raised to nonnegative integer powers and no variables appear in any denominator.
3. A _____ is a polynomial with 2 terms.
4. A _____ is a polynomial with 1 term.
5. A _____ is a polynomial with 3 terms.
6. The degree of a term is the sum of the exponents on the _____ in the term.
7. The _____ of a polynomial is the largest degree of all its terms.
8. _____ terms contain the same variables raised to the same powers.

Add or subtract, if possible.

9. $5x + x$ 10. $5x - x$ 11. $y + y$ 12. $z^2 + z^2$ 13. $7xy^2 - y^2$ 14. $x^3 - 9x^3$

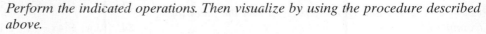

5.3 | EXERCISE SET

PRACTICE   WATCH   DOWNLOAD   READ   REVIEW

Find the degree of each term. See Example 1.

1. 4

2. 7

3. $5x^2$

4. $-z^3$

5. $-3xy^2$

6. $12x^3z$

7. -8^7y^3

8. $-9^{11}y^5$

9. $3.78ab^3c^5$

10. $9.11r^2st^{12}$

Find the degree of each polynomial and indicate whether the polynomial is a monomial, binomial, trinomial, or none of these. See Examples 2 and 3.

11. $6x + 0.3$

12. $7x - 0.8$

13. $3x^2 - 2x + 5$

14. $5x^2 - 3x - 2$

15. -3^4xy^2

16. -7^5abc

17. $x^2y - 4xy^2 + 5x + y^4$

18. $-2x^2y - 3y^2 + 4x + y^5$

If $P(x) = x^2 + x + 1$ and $Q(x) = 5x^2 - 1$, find the following. See Example 4.

19. $P(7)$

20. $Q(4)$

21. $Q(-10)$

22. $P(-4)$

23. $Q\left(\dfrac{1}{4}\right)$

24. $P\left(\dfrac{1}{2}\right)$

Refer to Example 5 for Exercises 25 through 28.

25. Find the height of the object at $t = 2$ seconds.

26. Find the height of the object at $t = 4$ seconds.

27. Find the height of the object at $t = 6$ seconds.

28. Approximate (to the nearest second) how long it takes before the object hits the ground. (*Hint:* The object hits the ground when $P(x) = 0$.)

Simplify by combining like terms. See Example 6.

29. $5y + y$

30. $-x + 3x$

31. $4x + 7x - 3$

32. $-8y + 9y + 4y^2$

33. $4xy + 2x - 3xy - 1$

34. $-8xy^2 + 4x - x + 2xy^2$

35. $7x^2 - 2xy + 5y^2 - x^2 + xy + 11y^2$

36. $-a^2 + 18ab - 2b^2 + 14a^2 - 12ab - b^2$

MIXED PRACTICE

Perform the indicated operations. See Examples 7 through 10.

37. $(9y^2 - 8) + (9y^2 - 9)$

38. $(x^2 + 4x - 7) + (8x^2 + 9x - 7)$

39. Add $(x^2 + xy - y^2)$ and $(2x^2 - 4xy + 7y^2)$.

40. Add $(4x^3 - 6x^2 + 5x + 7)$ and $(2x^2 + 6x - 3)$.

41.
$$\begin{array}{r} x^2 - 6x + 3 \\ + \quad (2x + 5) \\ \hline \end{array}$$

42.
$$\begin{array}{r} -2x^2 + 3x - 9 \\ + \quad (2x - 3) \\ \hline \end{array}$$

43. $(9y^2 - 7y + 5) - (8y^2 - 7y + 2)$

44. $(2x^2 + 3x + 12) - (5x - 7)$

45. Subtract $(6x^2 - 3x)$ from $(4x^2 + 2x)$.

46. Subtract $(xy + x - y)$ from $(xy + x - 3)$.

47.
$$\begin{array}{r} 3x^2 - 4x + 8 \\ - \quad (5x^2 - 7) \\ \hline \end{array}$$

48.
$$\begin{array}{r} -3x^2 - 4x + 8 \\ - \quad (5x + 12) \\ \hline \end{array}$$

49. $(5x - 11) + (-x - 2)$

50. $(3x^2 - 2x) + (5x^2 - 9x)$

51. $(7x^2 + x + 1) - (6x^2 + x - 1)$

52. $(4x - 4) - (-x - 4)$

53. $(7x^3 - 4x + 8) + (5x^3 + 4x + 8x)$

54. $(9xyz + 4x - y) + (-9xyz - 3x + y + 2)$

55. $(9x^3 - 2x^2 + 4x - 7) - (2x^3 - 6x^2 - 4x + 3)$

56. $(3x^2 + 6xy + 3y^2) - (8x^2 - 6xy - y^2)$

57. Add $(y^2 + 4yx + 7)$ and $(-19y^2 + 7yx + 7)$.

58. Subtract $(x - 4)$ from $(3x^2 - 4x + 5)$.

59. $(3x^3 - b + 2a - 6) + (-4x^3 + b + 6a - 6)$

60. $(5x^2 - 6) + (2x^2 - 4x + 8)$

61. $(4x^2 - 6x + 2) - (-x^2 + 3x + 5)$

62. $(5x^2 + x + 9) - (2x^2 - 9)$

63. $(-3x + 8) + (-3x^2 + 3x - 5)$

64. $(5y^2 - 2y + 4) + (3y + 7)$

65. $(-3 + 4x^2 + 7xy^2) + (2x^3 - x^2 + xy^2)$

66. $(-3x^2y + 4) - (-7x^2y - 8y)$

67.
$$\begin{array}{r} 6y^2 - 6y + 4 \\ -(-y^2 - 6y + 7) \\ \hline \end{array}$$

68.
$$\begin{array}{r} -4x^3 + 4x^2 - 4x \\ -(2x^3 - 2x^2 + 3x) \\ \hline \end{array}$$

69.
$$\begin{array}{r} 3x^2 + 15x + 8 \\ +(2x^2 + 7x + 8) \\ \hline \end{array}$$

70.
$$\begin{array}{r} 9x^2 + 9x - 4 \\ +(7x^2 - 3x - 4) \\ \hline \end{array}$$

71. $\left(\dfrac{1}{2}x^2 - \dfrac{1}{3}x^2y + 2y^3\right) + \left(\dfrac{1}{4}x^2 - \dfrac{8}{3}x^2y^2 - \dfrac{1}{2}y^3\right)$

72. $\left(\dfrac{2}{5}a^2 - ab + \dfrac{4}{3}b^2\right) + \left(\dfrac{1}{5}a^2b - ab + \dfrac{5}{6}b^2\right)$

73. Find the sum of $(5q^4 - 2q^2 - 3q)$ and $(-6q^4 + 3q^2 + 5)$.

74. Find the sum of $(5y^4 - 7y^2 + x^2 - 3)$ and $(-3y^4 + 2y^2 - 4)$.

75. Subtract $(3x + 7)$ from the sum of $(7x^2 + 4x + 9)$ and $(8x^2 + 7x - 8)$.

76. Subtract $(9x + 8)$ from the sum of $(3x^2 - 2x - x^3 + 2)$ and $(5x^2 - 8x - x^3 + 4)$.

77. Find the sum of $(4x^4 - 7x^2 + 3)$ and $(2 - 3x^4)$.

78. Find the sum of $(8x^4 - 14x^2 + 6)$ and $(-12x^6 - 21x^4 - 9x^2)$.

79. $\left(\dfrac{2}{3}x^2 - \dfrac{1}{6}x + \dfrac{5}{6}\right) - \left(\dfrac{1}{3}x^2 + \dfrac{5}{6}x - \dfrac{1}{6}\right)$

80. $\left(\dfrac{3}{16}x^2 + \dfrac{5}{8}x - \dfrac{1}{4}\right) - \left(\dfrac{5}{16}x^2 - \dfrac{3}{8}x + \dfrac{3}{4}\right)$

Solve. See Example 5.

The surface area of a rectangular box is given by the polynomial function

$$f(x) = 2HL + 2LW + 2HW$$

and is measured in square units. In business, surface area is often calculated to help determine cost of materials.

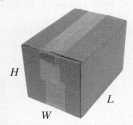

△ **81.** A rectangular box is to be constructed to hold a new camcorder. The box is to have dimensions 5 inches by 4 inches by 9 inches. Find the surface area of the box.

△ **82.** Suppose it has been determined that a box of dimensions 4 inches by 4 inches by 8.5 inches can be used to contain the camcorder in Exercise 81. Find the surface area of this box and calculate the square inches of material saved by using this box instead of the box in Exercise 81.

83. A projectile is fired upward from the ground with an initial velocity of 300 feet per second. Neglecting air resistance, the height of the projectile at any time t can be described by the polynomial function $P(t) = -16t^2 + 300t$. Find the height of the projectile at each given time.

  a. $t = 1$ second   **b.** $t = 2$ seconds

  c. $t = 3$ seconds   **d.** $t = 4$ seconds

  e. Explain why the height increases and then decreases as time passes.

  f. Approximate (to the nearest second) how long before the object hits the ground.

84. An object is thrown upward with an initial velocity of 25 feet per second from the top of the 984-foot-high Eiffel Tower in Paris, France. The height of the object at any time t can be described by the polynomial function $P(t) = -16t^2 + 25t + 984$. Find the height of the projectile at each given time. (*Source:* Council on Tall Buildings and Urban Habitat, Lehigh University)

  a. $t = 1$ second

  b. $t = 3$ seconds

  c. $t = 5$ seconds

  d. Approximate (to the nearest second) how long before the object hits the ground.

85. The polynomial function $P(x) = 45x - 100,000$ models the relationship between the number of computer briefcases x that a company sells and the profit the company makes, $P(x)$. Find $P(4000)$, the profit from selling 4000 computer briefcases.

86. The total cost (in dollars) for MCD, Inc., Manufacturing Company to produce x blank audiocassette tapes per week is given by the polynomial function $C(x) = 0.8x + 10,000$. Find the total cost of producing 20,000 tapes per week.

87. The total revenues (in dollars) for MCD, Inc., Manufacturing Company to sell x blank audiocasette tapes per week is given by the polynomial function $R(x) = 2x$. Find the total revenue from selling 20,000 tapes per week.

88. In business, profit equals revenue minus cost, or $P(x) = R(x) - C(x)$. Find the profit function for MCD, Inc. by subtracting the given functions in Exercises 86 and 87.

Match each equation with its graph. See Example 11.

89. $f(x) = 3x^2 - 2$

90. $h(x) = 5x^3 - 6x + 2$

91. $g(x) = -2x^3 - 3x^2 + 3x - 2$

92. $F(x) = -2x^2 - 6x + 2$

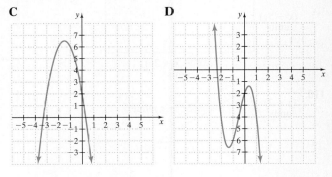
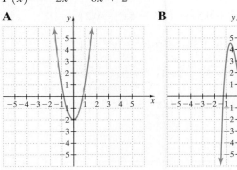

REVIEW AND PREVIEW

Multiply. See Section 1.4.

93. $5(3x - 2)$ **94.** $-7(2z - 6y)$

95. $-2(x^2 - 5x + 6)$ **96.** $5(-3y^2 - 2y + 7)$

CONCEPT EXTENSIONS

Solve. See the Concept Checks in this section.

97. Which polynomial(s) is the opposite of $8x - 6$?

   a. $-(8x - 6)$ **b.** $8x + 6$

   c. $-8x + 6$ **d.** $-8x - 6$

98. Which polynomial(s) is the opposite of $-y^5 + 10y^3 - 2.3$?

   a. $y^5 + 10y^3 + 2.3$ **b.** $-y^5 - 10y^3 - 2.3$

   c. $y^5 + 10y^3 - 2.3$ **d.** $y^5 - 10y^3 + 2.3$

99. Correct the subtraction.
$$(12x - 1.7) - (15x + 6.2) = 12x - 1.7 - 15x + 6.2$$
$$= -3x + 4.5$$

100. Correct the addition.
$$(12x - 1.7) + (15x + 6.2) = 12x - 1.7 + 15x + 6.2$$
$$= 27x + 7.9$$

101. Write a function, $P(x)$, so that $P(0) = 7$.

102. Write a function, $R(x)$, so that $R(1) = 2$.

103. In your own words, describe how to find the degree of a term.

104. In your own words, describe how to find the degree of a polynomial.

Perform the indicated operations.

105. $(4x^{2a} - 3x^a + 0.5) - (x^{2a} - 5x^a - 0.2)$

106. $(9y^{5a} - 4y^{3a} + 1.5y) - (6y^{5a} - y^{3a} + 4.7y)$

107. $(8x^{2y} - 7x^y + 3) + (-4x^{2y} + 9x^y - 14)$

108. $(14z^{5x} + 3z^{2x} + z) - (2z^{5x} - 10z^{2x} + 3z)$

Find each perimeter.

△ **109.**

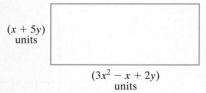

$(x + 5y)$ units

$(3x^2 - x + 2y)$ units

△ **110.**

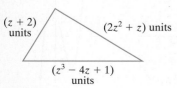

$(z + 2)$ units $(2z^2 + z)$ units

$(z^3 - 4z + 1)$ units

If $P(x) = 3x + 3$, $Q(x) = 4x^2 - 6x + 3$, and $R(x) = 5x^2 - 7$, find the following.

111. $P(x) + Q(x)$

112. $R(x) + P(x)$

113. $Q(x) - R(x)$

114. $P(x) - Q(x)$

115. $2[Q(x)] - R(x)$

116. $-5[P(x)] - Q(x)$

117. $3[R(x)] + 4[P(x)]$

118. $2[Q(x)] + 7[R(x)]$

*If $P(x)$ is the polynomial given, find **a.** $P(a)$, **b.** $P(-x)$, and **c.** $P(x + h)$.*

119. $P(x) = 2x - 3$

120. $P(x) = 8x + 3$

121. $P(x) = 4x$

122. $P(x) = -4x$

123. $P(x) = 4x - 1$

124. $P(x) = 3x - 2$

125. The function $f(x) = 0.07x^2 - 0.8x + 3.6$ can be used to approximate the amazing growth of the number of Web logs (Blogs) appearing on the Internet from January 2004 to October 2006, where January, 2004 = 1 for x, February 2004 = 2 for x, and so on, and y is the number of blogs (in millions). Round answers to the nearest tenth of a million. (Note: This is one company's tracking of the cumulative number of blogs. These numbers vary greatly according to source and activity of blog.) (*Source:* Technorati)

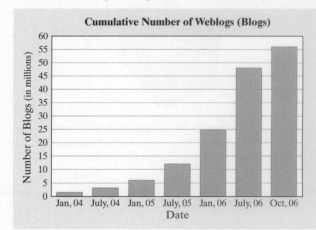

Cumulative Number of Weblogs (Blogs)

   a. Approximate the number of Web logs on the Internet in January 2004.

   b. Approximate the number of Web logs on the Internet in October 2006.

   c. Use this function to approximate the number of Web logs on the Internet in May 2009. (65 months)

   d. From parts (a), (b), and (c), determine whether the number of Web logs on the Internet is increasing at a steady rate. Explain why or why not.

126. The function $f(x) = -61x^2 - 5530x + 585,753$ can be used to approximate the number of international students studying in the United States during the academic years 2002 through 2006, where x is the number of years after 2002 and $f(x)$ is the number of international students.

(*Source:* Institute of International Education: *Open Doors 2006*)

a. Approximate the number of international students studying in the United States in 2003.

b. Approximate the number of international students studying in the United States in 2005.

c. Use the function to predict the number of international students studying in the United States in 2008.

127. The function $f(x) = -0.39x^2 + 2.49x + 38.7$ can be used to approximate the number of Americans under age 65 without health insurance during the period 1999–2005, where x is the number of years after 1999 and $f(x)$ is the number in millions of Americans. Round answers to the nearest tenth of a million. (*Source:* National Center for Health Statistics)

a. Approximate the number of Americans under 65 without health insurance in 2003.

b. Use the function to predict the number of Americans under 65 without health insurance in 2008.

128. University libraries need to continue to grow to meet the educational needs of their students. The function $f(x) = -14x^2 + 269.2x + 7414.2$ approximates the number of written volumes (in thousands) to be found in the University of California, Los Angeles, libraries for the years from 2002 to 2005, where x is the number of years after 2002. (*Source:* Association of Research Libraries)

a. Approximate the number of volumes in 2004.

b. Use the function to estimate the number of volumes at UCLA libraries in 2008.

129. Sport utility vehicle (SUV) sales in the United States have increased since 1995. The function $f(x) = -0.005x^2 + 0.377x + 1.71$ can be used to approximate the number of SUV sales during the years 1995–2004, where x is the number of years after 1995 and $f(x)$ is the SUV sales (in millions). Round answers to the nearest tenth of a million. (*Source:* Bureau of Transportation Statistics)

a. Approximate the number of SUVs sold in 2003.

b. Use the function to predict the number of SUVs sold in 2010.

130. The function $f(x) = 873x^2 - 4104x + 40,263$ can be used to approximate the number of AIDS cases diagnosed in the United States from 2001 to 2005, where x is the number of years since 2001. (*Source:* Based on data from the U.S. Centers for Disease Control and Prevention)

a. Approximate the number of AIDS cases diagnosed in the United States in 2001.

b. Approximate the number of AIDS cases diagnosed in the United States in 2003.

c. Approximate the number of AIDS cases diagnosed in the United States in 2005.

d. Describe the trend in the number of AIDS cases diagnosed during the period covered by this model.

5.4   MULTIPLYING POLYNOMIALS

OBJECTIVES

1 Multiply two polynomials.

2 Multiply binomials.

3 Square binomials.

4 Multiply the sum and difference of two terms.

5 Multiply three or more polynomials.

6 Evaluate polynomial functions.

OBJECTIVE 1 ▶ Multiplying two polynomials. Properties of real numbers and exponents are used continually in the process of multiplying polynomials. To multiply monomials, for example, we apply the commutative and associative properties of real numbers and the product rule for *exponents*.

EXAMPLE 1   Multiply.

a. $(2x^3)(5x^6)$ **b.** $(7y^4z^4)(-xy^{11}z^5)$

Solution   Group like bases and apply the product rule for exponents.

a. $(2x^3)(5x^6) = 2(5)(x^3)(x^6) = 10x^9$

b. $(7y^4z^4)(-xy^{11}z^5) = 7(-1)x(y^4y^{11})(z^4z^5) = -7xy^{15}z^9$ □

PRACTICE

1   Multiply.

a. $(3x^4)(2x^2)$ **b.** $(-5m^4np^3)(-8mnp^5)$

To multiply a monomial by a polynomial other than a monomial, we use an expanded form of the distributive property.

$$a(b + c + d + \cdots + z) = ab + ac + ad + \cdots + az$$

Notice that the monomial a is multiplied by each term of the polynomial.

▶ **Helpful Hint**

See Sections 5.1 and 5.2 to review exponential expressions further.

EXAMPLE 2 Multiply.

a. $2x(5x - 4)$ **b.** $-3x^2(4x^2 - 6x + 1)$ **c.** $-xy(7x^2y + 3xy - 11)$

<u>Solution</u> Apply the distributive property.

a. $2x(5x - 4) = 2x(5x) + 2x(-4)$ Use the distributive property.

$= 10x^2 - 8x$ Multiply.

b. $-3x^2(4x^2 - 6x + 1) = -3x^2(4x^2) + (-3x^2)(-6x) + (-3x^2)(1)$

$= -12x^4 + 18x^3 - 3x^2$

c. $-xy(7x^2y + 3xy - 11) = -xy(7x^2y) + (-xy)(3xy) + (-xy)(-11)$

$= -7x^3y^2 - 3x^2y^2 + 11xy$

PRACTICE

2 Multiply.

a. $3x(7x - 1)$ **b.** $-5a^2(3a^2 - 6a + 5)$ **c.** $-mn^3(5m^2n^2 + 2mn - 5m)$

To multiply any two polynomials, we can use the following.

> **Multiplying Two Polynomials**
>
> To multiply any two polynomials, use the distributive property and multiply each term of one polynomial by each term of the other polynomial. Then combine any like terms.

Concept Check ☑

Find the error:

$$4x(x - 5) + 2x$$
$$= 4x(x) + 4x(-5) + 4x(2x)$$
$$= 4x^2 - 20x + 8x^2$$
$$= 12x^2 - 20x$$

EXAMPLE 3 Multiply and simplify the product if possible.

a. $(x + 3)(2x + 5)$ **b.** $(2x - 3)(5x^2 - 6x + 7)$

<u>Solution</u>

a. Multiply each term of $(x + 3)$ by $(2x + 5)$.

$(x + 3)(2x + 5) = x(2x + 5) + 3(2x + 5)$ Apply the distributive property.

$= 2x^2 + 5x + 6x + 15$ Apply the distributive property again.

$= 2x^2 + 11x + 15$ Combine like terms.

b. Multiply each term of $(2x - 3)$ by each term of $(5x^2 - 6x + 7)$.

$(2x - 3)(5x^2 - 6x + 7) = 2x(5x^2 - 6x + 7) + (-3)(5x^2 - 6x + 7)$

$= 10x^3 - 12x^2 + 14x - 15x^2 + 18x - 21$

$= 10x^3 - 27x^2 + 32x - 21$ Combine like terms.

Answer to Concept Check:

$4x(x - 5) + 2x$
$= 4x(x) + 4x(-5) + 2x$
$= 4x^2 - 20x + 2x$
$= 4x^2 - 18x$

PRACTICE

3 Multiply and simplify the product if possible.

a. $(x + 5)(2x + 3)$ **b.** $(3x - 1)(x^2 - 6x + 2)$

Sometimes polynomials are easier to multiply vertically, in the same way we multiply real numbers. When multiplying vertically, we line up like terms in the **partial products** vertically. This makes combining like terms easier.

EXAMPLE 4   Multiply vertically $(4x^2 + 7)(x^2 + 2x + 8)$.

Solution

$$
\begin{array}{r}
x^2 + 2x + 8 \\
4x^2 + 7 \\
\hline
7x^2 + 14x + 56 \\
4x^4 + 8x^3 + 32x^2 \\
\hline
4x^4 + 8x^3 + 39x^2 + 14x + 56
\end{array}
$$

$7(x^2 + 2x + 8)$
$4x^2(x^2 + 2x + 8)$
Combine like terms.   □

PRACTICE
4   Multiply vertically: $(3x^2 + 2)(x^2 - 4x - 5)$.

OBJECTIVE 2 ▶ **Multiplying binomials.**   When multiplying a binomial by a binomial, we can use a special order of multiplying terms, called the **FOIL** order. The letters of FOIL stand for "First-Outer-Inner-Last." To illustrate this method, let's multiply $(2x - 3)$ by $(3x + 1)$.

Multiply the **F**irst terms of each binomial. $(2x - 3)(3x + 1)$ **F** $2x(3x) = 6x^2$

Multiply the **O**uter terms of each binomial. $(2x - 3)(3x + 1)$ **O** $2x(1) = 2x$

Multiply the **I**nner terms of each binomial. $(2x - 3)(3x + 1)$ **I** $-3(3x) = -9x$

Multiply the **L**ast terms of each binomial. $(2x - 3)(3x + 1)$ **L** $-3(1) = -3$
Combine like terms.

$$6x^2 + 2x - 9x - 3 = 6x^2 - 7x - 3$$

EXAMPLE 5   Use the FOIL order to multiply $(x - 1)(x + 2)$.

Solution

$$
\begin{aligned}
(x - 1)(x + 2) &= \overset{\text{First}}{x \cdot x} + \overset{\text{Outer}}{2 \cdot x} + \overset{\text{Inner}}{(-1)x} + \overset{\text{Last}}{(-1)(2)} \\
&= x^2 + 2x - x - 2 \\
&= x^2 + x - 2 \quad \text{Combine like terms.} \quad \square
\end{aligned}
$$

PRACTICE
5   Use the FOIL order to multiply $(x - 5)(x + 3)$.

EXAMPLE 6   Multiply.

a. $(2x - 7)(3x - 4)$ **b.** $(3x^2 + y)(5x^2 - 2y)$

Solution

$$
\begin{aligned}
\text{\textbf{a.} } (2x - 7)(3x - 4) &= \overset{\text{First}}{2x(3x)} + \overset{\text{Outer}}{2x(-4)} + \overset{\text{Inner}}{(-7)(3x)} + \overset{\text{Last}}{(-7)(-4)} \\
&= 6x^2 - 8x - 21x + 28 \\
&= 6x^2 - 29x + 28
\end{aligned}
$$

F   O   I   L

b. $(3x^2 + y)(5x^2 - 2y) = 15x^4 - 6x^2y + 5x^2y - 2y^2$
$$= 15x^4 - x^2y - 2y^2$$

PRACTICE
6 Multiply.

a. $(3x - 5)(2x - 7)$ **b.** $(2x^2 - 3y)(4x^2 + y)$

OBJECTIVE 3 ▶ Squaring binomials. The **square of a binomial** is a special case of the product of two binomials. By the FOIL order for multiplying two binomials, we have

$$(a + b)^2 = (a + b)(a + b)$$

F   O   I   L

$$= a^2 + ab + ba + b^2$$
$$= a^2 + 2ab + b^2$$

This product can be visualized geometrically by analyzing areas.

Area of larger square: $(a + b)^2$

Sum of areas of smaller rectangles: $a^2 + 2ab + b^2$

Thus, $(a + b)^2 = a^2 + 2ab + b^2$

The same pattern occurs for the square of a difference. In general,

Square of a Binomial
$$(a + b)^2 = a^2 + 2ab + b^2 \qquad (a - b)^2 = a^2 - 2ab + b^2$$

In other words, a binomial squared is the sum of the first term squared, twice the product of both terms, and the second term squared.

EXAMPLE 7 Multiply.

a. $(x + 5)^2$ **b.** $(x - 9)^2$ **c.** $(3x + 2z)^2$ **d.** $(4m^2 - 3n)^2$

Solution

$$(a + b)^2 = a^2 + 2 \cdot a \cdot b + b^2$$

a. $(x + 5)^2 = x^2 + 2 \cdot x \cdot 5 + 5^2 = x^2 + 10x + 25$

b. $(x - 9)^2 = x^2 - 2 \cdot x \cdot 9 + 9^2 = x^2 - 18x + 81$

c. $(3x + 2z)^2 = (3x)^2 + 2(3x)(2z) + (2z)^2 = 9x^2 + 12xz + 4z^2$

d. $(4m^2 - 3n)^2 = (4m^2)^2 - 2(4m^2)(3n) + (3n)^2 = 16m^4 - 24m^2n + 9n^2$

PRACTICE
7 Multiply.

a. $(x + 6)^2$ **b.** $(x - 2)^2$ **c.** $(3x + 5y)^2$ **d.** $(3x^2 - 8b)^2$

▶ **Helpful Hint**
Note that $(a + b)^2 = a^2 + 2ab + b^2$, **not** $a^2 + b^2$. Also,
$$(a - b)^2 = a^2 - 2ab + b^2, \quad \textbf{not} \quad a^2 - b^2.$$

OBJECTIVE 4 ▶ Multiplying the sum and difference of two terms. Another special product applies to the sum and difference of the same two terms. Multiply $(a + b)(a - b)$ to see a pattern.

$$(a + b)(a - b) = a^2 - ab + ba - b^2$$
$$= a^2 - b^2$$

Product of the Sum and Difference of Two Terms

$$(a + b)(a - b) = a^2 - b^2$$

The product of the sum and difference of the same two terms is the difference of the first term squared and the second term squared.

EXAMPLE 8   Multiply.

a. $(x - 3)(x + 3)$

b. $(4y + 1)(4y - 1)$

c. $(x^2 + 2y)(x^2 - 2y)$

d. $\left(3m^2 - \dfrac{1}{2}\right)\left(3m^2 + \dfrac{1}{2}\right)$

Solution

$$(a + b)(a - b) = a^2 - b^2$$

a.
$$(x + 3)(x - 3) = x^2 - 3^2 = x^2 - 9$$

b. $(4y + 1)(4y - 1) = (4y)^2 - 1^2 = 16y^2 - 1$

c. $(x^2 + 2y)(x^2 - 2y) = (x^2)^2 - (2y)^2 = x^4 - 4y^2$

d. $\left(3m^2 - \dfrac{1}{2}\right)\left(3m^2 + \dfrac{1}{2}\right) = (3m^2)^2 - \left(\dfrac{1}{2}\right)^2 = 9m^4 - \dfrac{1}{4}$

PRACTICE
8   Multiply.

a. $(x - 7)(x + 7)$

b. $(2a + 5)(2a - 5)$

c. $\left(5x^2 + \dfrac{1}{4}\right)\left(5x^2 - \dfrac{1}{4}\right)$

d. $(a^3 - 4b^2)(a^3 + 4b^2)$

EXAMPLE 9   Multiply $[3 + (2a + b)]^2$.

Solution   Think of 3 as the first term and $(2a + b)$ as the second term, and apply the method for squaring a binomial.

$$[a + b]^2 = a^2 + 2(a) \cdot b + b^2$$
$$[3 + (2a + b)]^2 = 3^2 + 2(3)(2a + b) + (2a + b)^2$$
$$= 9 + 6(2a + b) + (2a + b)^2$$
$$= 9 + 12a + 6b + (2a)^2 + 2(2a)(b) + b^2 \quad \text{Square } (2a + b).$$
$$= 9 + 12a + 6b + 4a^2 + 4ab + b^2$$

PRACTICE
9   Multiply $[2 + (3x - y)]^2$.

EXAMPLE 10 Multiply $[(5x - 2y) - 1][(5x - 2y) + 1]$.

Solution Think of $(5x - 2y)$ as the first term and 1 as the second term, and apply the method for the product of the sum and difference of two terms.

$$(a \quad - b) \quad (a \quad + b) = \quad a^2 \quad - b^2$$

$$[(5x - 2y) - 1][(5x - 2y) + 1] = (5x - 2y)^2 - 1^2$$
$$= (5x)^2 - 2(5x)(2y) + (2y)^2 - 1 \quad \text{Square}$$
$$\qquad\qquad\qquad\qquad\qquad\qquad (5x - 2y).$$
$$= 25x^2 - 20xy + 4y^2 - 1$$

PRACTICE
10 Multiply $[(3x - y) - 5][(3x - y) + 5]$.

OBJECTIVE 5 ▶ Multiplying three or more polynomials. To multiply three or more polynomials, more than one method may be needed.

EXAMPLE 11 Multiply: $(x - 3)(x + 3)(x^2 - 9)$

Solution We multiply the first two binomials, the sum and difference of two terms. Then we multiply the resulting two binomials, the square of a binomial.

$$(x - 3)(x + 3)(x^2 - 9) = (x^2 - 9)(x^2 - 9) \quad \text{Multiply } (x - 3)(x + 3).$$
$$= (x^2 - 9)^2$$
$$= x^4 - 18x^2 + 81 \quad \text{Square } (x^2 - 9).$$

PRACTICE
11 Multiply $(x + 4)(x - 4)(x^2 - 16)$.

OBJECTIVE 6 ▶ Evaluating polynomial functions. Our work in multiplying polynomials is often useful in evaluating polynomial functions.

EXAMPLE 12 If $f(x) = x^2 + 5x - 2$, find $f(a + 1)$.

Solution To find $f(a + 1)$, replace x with the expression $a + 1$ in the polynomial function $f(x)$.

$$f(x) = x^2 + 5x - 2$$
$$f(a + 1) = (a + 1)^2 + 5(a + 1) - 2$$
$$= a^2 + 2a + 1 + 5a + 5 - 2$$
$$= a^2 + 7a + 4$$

PRACTICE
12 If $f(x) = x^2 - 3x + 5$, find $f(h + 1)$.

Graphing Calculator Explorations

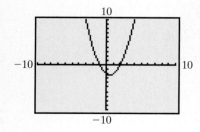

In the previous section, we used a graphing calculator to visualize addition and subtraction of polynomials in one variable. In this section, the same method is used to visualize multiplication of polynomials in one variable. For example, to see that

$$(x - 2)(x + 1) = x^2 - x - 2,$$

graph both $Y_1 = (x - 2)(x + 1)$ and $Y_2 = x^2 - x - 2$ on the same screen and see whether their graphs coincide.

By tracing along both graphs, we see that the graphs of Y_1 and Y_2 appear to coincide, and thus $(x - 2)(x + 1) = x^2 - x - 2$ appears to be correct.

Multiply. Then use a graphing calculator to visualize the results.

1. $(x + 4)(x - 4)$

2. $(x + 3)(x + 3)$

3. $(3x - 7)^2$

4. $(5x - 2)^2$

5. $(5x + 1)(x^2 - 3x - 2)$

6. $(7x + 4)(2x^2 + 3x - 5)$

VOCABULARY & READINESS CHECK

Use the choices to fill in each blank.

1. $(6x^3)\left(\dfrac{1}{2}x^3\right) =$ _____

    a. $3x^3$ **b.** $3x^6$ **c.** $10x^6$ **d.** $\dfrac{13}{2}x^6$

2. $(x + 7)^2 =$ _____

    a. $x^2 + 49$ **b.** $x^2 - 49$ **c.** $x^2 + 14x + 49$ **d.** $x^2 + 7x + 49$

3. $(x + 7)(x - 7) =$ _____

    a. $x^2 + 49$ **b.** $x^2 - 49$ **c.** $x^2 + 14x - 49$ **d.** $x^2 + 7x - 49$

4. The product of $(3x - 1)(4x^2 - 2x + 1)$ is a polynomial of degree _____.

    a. 3   **b.** 12   **c.** $12x^3$ **d.** 2

5. If $f(x) = x^2 + 1$ then $f(a + 1) =$ _____

    a. $(a + 1)^2$ **b.** $a + 1$ **c.** $(a + 1)^2 + (a + 1)$ **d.** $(a + 1)^2 + 1$

6. $[x + (2y + 1)]^2 =$ _____

    a. $[x + (2y + 1)][x - (2y + 1)]$ **b.** $[x + (2y + 1)][x + (2y + 1)]$ **c.** $[x + (2y + 1)][x + (2y - 1)]$

5.4 | EXERCISE SET

Multiply. See Examples 1 through 4.

1. $(-4x^3)(3x^2)$

2. $(-6a)(4a)$

3. $3x(4x + 7)$

4. $5x(6x - 4)$

5. $-6xy(4x + y)$

6. $-8y(6xy + 4x)$

7. $-4ab(xa^2 + ya^2 - 3)$

8. $-6b^2z(z^2a + baz - 3b)$

9. $(x - 3)(2x + 4)$

10. $(y + 5)(3y - 2)$

11. $(2x + 3)(x^3 - x + 2)$

12. $(a + 2)(3a^2 - a + 5)$

13. $\begin{array}{r} 3x - 2 \\ \times\ 5x + 1 \end{array}$

14. $\begin{array}{r} 2z - 4 \\ \times\ 6z - 2 \end{array}$

15. $\begin{array}{r} 3m^2 + 2m - 1 \\ \times\ \quad\ 5m + 2 \end{array}$

16. $\begin{array}{r} 2x^2 - 3x - 4 \\ \times\ \quad\ x + 5 \end{array}$

Multiply the binomials. See Examples 5 and 6.

17. $(x - 3)(x + 4)$

18. $(c - 3)(c + 1)$

19. $(5x + 8y)(2x - y)$

20. $(2n - 9m)(n - 7m)$

21. $(3x - 1)(x - 3)$

22. $(5d - 3)(d + 6)$

23. $\left(3x + \dfrac{1}{2}\right)\left(3x - \dfrac{1}{2}\right)$

24. $\left(2x - \dfrac{1}{3}\right)\left(2x + \dfrac{1}{3}\right)$

25. $(5x^2 - 2y^2)(x^2 - 3y^2)$

26. $(4x^2 - 5y^2)(x^2 - 2y^2)$

Multiply, using special product methods. See Examples 7 and 8.

27. $(x + 4)^2$

28. $(x - 5)^2$

29. $(6y - 1)(6y + 1)$

30. $(7x - 9)(7x + 9)$

31. $(3x - y)^2$

32. $(4x - z)^2$

33. $(5b - 6y)(5b + 6y)$

34. $(2x - 4y)(2x + 4y)$

Multiply, using special product methods. See Examples 9 and 10.

35. $[3 + (4b + 1)]^2$

36. $[5 - (3b - 3)]^2$

37. $[(2s - 3) - 1][(2s - 3) + 1]$

38. $[(2y + 5) + 6][(2y + 5) - 6]$

39. $[(xy + 4) - 6]^2$

40. $[(2a^2 + 4a) + 1]^2$

41. Explain when the FOIL method can be used to multiply polynomials.

42. Explain why the product of $(a + b)$ and $(a - b)$ is not a trinomial.

Multiply. See Example 11.

43. $(x + y)(x - y)(x^2 - y^2)$

44. $(z - y)(z + y)(z^2 - y^2)$

45. $(x - 2)^4$

46. $(x - 1)^4$

47. $(x - 5)(x + 5)(x^2 + 25)$

48. $(x + 3)(x - 3)(x^2 + 9)$

MIXED PRACTICE

Multiply.

49. $(3x + 1)(3x + 5)$

50. $(4x - 5)(5x + 6)$

51. $(2x^3 + 5)(5x^2 + 4x + 1)$

52. $(3y^3 - 1)(3y^3 - 6y + 1)$

53. $(7x - 3)(7x + 3)$

54. $(4x + 1)(4x - 1)$

55. $3x^2 + 4x - 4$
  $\underline{\times \qquad 3x + 6}$

56. $6x^2 + 2x - 1$
  $\underline{\times \qquad 3x - 6}$

57. $\left(4x + \dfrac{1}{3}\right)\left(4x - \dfrac{1}{2}\right)$

58. $\left(4y - \dfrac{1}{3}\right)\left(3y - \dfrac{1}{8}\right)$

59. $(6x + 1)^2$

60. $(4x + 7)^2$

61. $(x^2 + 2y)(x^2 - 2y)$

62. $(3x + 2y)(3x - 2y)$

63. $-6a^2b^2[5a^2b^2 - 6a - 6b]$

64. $7x^2y^3(-3ax - 4xy + z)$

65. $(a - 4)(2a - 4)$

66. $(2x - 3)(x + 1)$

67. $(7ab + 3c)(7ab - 3c)$

68. $(3xy - 2b)(3xy + 2b)$

69. $(m - 4)^2$

70. $(x + 2)^2$

71. $(3x + 1)^2$

72. $(4x + 6)^2$

73. $(y - 4)(y - 3)$

74. $(c - 8)(c + 2)$

75. $(x + y)(2x - 1)(x + 1)$

76. $(z + 2)(z - 3)(2z + 1)$

77. $(3x^2 + 2x - 1)^2$

78. $(4x^2 + 4x - 4)^2$

79. $(3x + 1)(4x^2 - 2x + 5)$

80. $(2x - 1)(5x^2 - x - 2)$

If $f(x) = x^2 - 3x$, find the following. See Example 12.

81. $f(a)$

82. $f(c)$

83. $f(a + h)$

84. $f(a + 5)$

85. $f(b - 2)$

86. $f(a - b)$

REVIEW AND PREVIEW

Use the slope-intercept form of a line, $y = mx + b$, to find the slope of each line. See Section 3.4.

87. $y = -2x + 7$

88. $y = \dfrac{3}{2}x - 1$

89. $3x - 5y = 14$

90. $x + 7y = 2$

Use the vertical line test to determine which of the following are graphs of functions. See Section 3.2.

91. **92.**

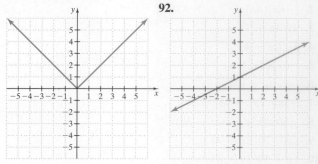

CONCEPT EXTENSIONS

Solve. See the Concept Check in this section.

93. Find the error: $7y(3z - 2) + 1$
$$= 21yz - 14y + 7y$$
$$= 21yz - 7y$$

94. Find the error: $2x + 3x(12 - x)$
$$= 5x(2 - x)$$
$$= 60x - 5x^2$$

95. Explain how to multiply a polynomial by a polynomial.

96. Explain why $(3x + 2)^2$ does not equal $9x^2 + 4$.

97. If $F(x) = x^2 + 3x + 2$, find
 a. $F(a + h)$
 b. $F(a)$
 c. $F(a + h) - F(a)$

98. If $g(x) = x^2 + 2x + 1$, find
 a. $g(a + h)$
 b. $g(a)$
 c. $g(a + h) - g(a)$

Multiply. Assume that variables represent positive integers.

99. $5x^2y^n(6y^{n+1} - 2)$
100. $-3yz^n(2y^3z^{2n} - 1)$
101. $(x^a + 5)(x^{2a} - 3)$
102. $(x^a + y^{2b})(x^a - y^{2b})$

For Exercises 103 through 106, write the result as a simplified polynomial.

△ **103.** Find the area of the circle. Do not approximate π.

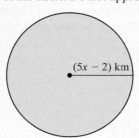

$(5x - 2)$ km

△ **104.** Find the volume of the cylinder. Do not approximate π.

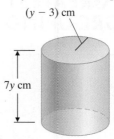

$(y - 3)$ cm

$7y$ cm

Find the area of each shaded region.

△ **105.**

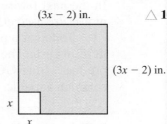

$(3x - 2)$ in.

$(3x - 2)$ in.

x

x

△ **106.**

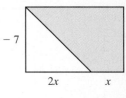

$x - 7$

$2x$ x

107. Perform each indicated operation. Explain the difference between the two problems.
 a. $(3x + 5) + (3x + 7)$
 b. $(3x + 5)(3x + 7)$

108. Explain when the FOIL method can be used to multiply polynomials.

If $R(x) = x + 5$, $Q(x) = x^2 - 2$, and $P(x) = 5x$, find the following.

109. $P(x) \cdot R(x)$
110. $P(x) \cdot Q(x)$
111. $[Q(x)]^2$
112. $[R(x)]^2$
113. $R(x) \cdot Q(x)$
114. $P(x) \cdot R(x) \cdot Q(x)$

📖 STUDY SKILLS BUILDER

Are You Getting All the Mathematics Help That You Need?

Remember that, in addition to your instructor, there are many places to get help with your mathematics course. For example,

- This text has an accompanying video lesson for every section and worked out solutions to every Chapter Test exercise on video.

- The back of the book contains answers to odd-numbered exercises and selected solutions.

- A *student Solutions Manual* is available that contains worked-out solutions to odd-numbered exercises as well as solutions to every exercise in the Integrated Reviews, Chapter Reviews, Chapter Tests, and Cumulative Reviews.

- Don't forget to check with your instructor for other local resources available to you, such as a tutor center.

Exercises

1. List items you find helpful in the text and all student supplements to this text.

2. List all the campus help that is available to you for this course.

3. List any help (besides the textbook) from Exercises 1 and 2 above that you are using.

4. List any help (besides the textbook) that you feel you should try.

5. Write a goal for yourself that includes trying anything you listed in Exercise 4 during the next week.

5.5 THE GREATEST COMMON FACTOR AND FACTORING BY GROUPING

OBJECTIVES

1 Identify the GCF.

2 Factor out the GCF of a polynomial's terms.

3 Factor polynomials by grouping.

OBJECTIVE 1 ▶ Identifying the GCF. Factoring is the reverse process of multiplying. It is the process of writing a polynomial as a product.

$$\overset{\text{factoring}}{6x^2 + 13x - 5 = (3x - 1)(2x + 5)}\\ \underset{\text{multiplying}}{}$$

In the next few sections, we review techniques for factoring polynomials. These techniques are used at the end of this chapter to solve polynomial equations.

To factor a polynomial, we first factor out the greatest common factor (GCF) of its terms, using the distributive property. The GCF of a list of terms or monomials is the product of the GCF of the numerical coefficients and each GCF of the powers of a common variable.

Finding the GCF of a List of Monomials

STEP 1. Find the GCF of the numerical coefficients.

STEP 2. Find the GCF of the variable factors.

STEP 3. The product of the factors found in Steps 1 and 2 is the GCF of the monomials.

EXAMPLE 1 Find the GCF of $20x^3y$, $10x^2y^2$, and $35x^3$.

Solution The GCF of the numerical coefficients 20, 10, and 35 is 5, the largest integer that is a factor of each integer. The GCF of the variable factors x^3, x^2, and x^3 is x^2 because x^2 is the largest factor common to all three powers of x. The variable y is not a common factor because it does not appear in all three monomials. The GCF is thus

$$5 \cdot x^2, \quad \text{or} \quad 5x^2$$

To see this in factored form,

$$20x^3y = 2 \cdot 2 \cdot 5 \cdot x^2 \cdot x \cdot y$$
$$10x^2y^2 = 2 \cdot 5 \cdot x^2 \cdot y$$
$$35x^3 = 3 \cdot 5 \cdot x^2 \cdot x$$
$$\text{GCF} = 5 \cdot x^2$$

PRACTICE
1 Find the GCF of $32x^4y^2$, $48x^3y$, $24y^2$.

OBJECTIVE 2 ▶ Factoring out the GCF of a polynomial's terms. A first step in factoring polynomials is to use the distributive property and write the polynomial as a product of the GCF of its monomial terms and a simpler polynomial. This is called **factoring out** the GCF.

EXAMPLE 2 Factor.

a. $8x^2 + 4$ **b.** $5y - 2z^4$ **c.** $6x^2 - 3x^3 + 12x^4$

Solution

a. The GCF of terms $8x^2$ and 4 is 4.

$$8x^2 + 4 = 4 \cdot 2x^2 + 4 \cdot 1 \quad \text{Factor out 4 from each term.}$$
$$= 4(2x^2 + 1) \quad \text{Apply the distributive property.}$$

The factored form of $8x^2 + 4$ is $4(2x^2 + 1)$. To check, multiply $4(2x^2 + 1)$ to see that the product is $8x^2 + 4$.

b. There is no common factor of the terms $5y$ and $-2z^4$ other than 1 (or -1).

c. The greatest common factor of $6x^2$, $-3x^3$, and $12x^4$ is $3x^2$. Thus,

$$6x^2 - 3x^3 + 12x^4 = 3x^2 \cdot 2 - 3x^2 \cdot x + 3x^2 \cdot 4x^2$$
$$= 3x^2(2 - x + 4x^2)$$ □

PRACTICE

2   Factor.

a. $6x^2 + 9 + 15x$ **b.** $3x - 8y^3$ **c.** $8a^4 - 2a^3$

▶ **Helpful Hint**

To verify that the GCF has been factored out correctly, multiply the factors together and see that their product is the original polynomial.

EXAMPLE 3   Factor $17x^3y^2 - 34x^4y^2$.

Solution   The GCF of the two terms is $17x^3y^2$, which we factor out of each term.

$$17x^3y^2 - 34x^4y^2 = 17x^3y^2 \cdot 1 - 17x^3y^2 \cdot 2x$$
$$= 17x^3y^2(1 - 2x)$$ □

PRACTICE

3   Factor $64x^5y^2 - 8x^3y^2$.

▶ **Helpful Hint**

If the GCF happens to be one of the terms in the polynomial, a factor of 1 will remain for this term when the GCF is factored out. For example, in the polynomial $21x^2 + 7x$, the GCF of $21x^2$ and $7x$ is $7x$, so

$$21x^2 + 7x = 7x \cdot 3x + 7x \cdot 1 = 7x(3x + 1)$$

Concept Check ☑

Which factorization of $12x^2 + 9x - 3$ is correct?

a. $3(4x^2 + 3x + 1)$ **b.** $3(4x^2 + 3x - 1)$ **c.** $3(4x^2 + 3x - 3)$ **d.** $3(4x^2 + 3x)$

EXAMPLE 4   Factor $-3x^3y + 2x^2y - 5xy$.

Solution   Two possibilities are shown for factoring this polynomial. First, the common factor xy is factored out.

$$-3x^3y + 2x^2y - 5xy = xy(-3x^2 + 2x - 5)$$

Also, the common factor $-xy$ can be factored out as shown.

$$-3x^3y + 2x^2y - 5xy = -xy(3x^2) + (-xy)(-2x) + (-xy)(5)$$
$$= -xy(3x^2 - 2x + 5)$$

Both of these alternatives are correct. □

PRACTICE

4   Factor $-9x^4y^2 + 5x^2y^2 + 7xy^2$.

EXAMPLE 5 Factor $2(x - 5) + 3a(x - 5)$.

Solution The greatest common factor is the binomial factor $(x - 5)$.

$$2(x - 5) + 3a(x - 5) = (x - 5)(2 + 3a)$$ □

PRACTICE
5 Factor $3(x + 4) + 5b(x + 4)$.

EXAMPLE 6 Factor $7x(x^2 + 5y) - (x^2 + 5y)$.

Solution $7x(x^2 + 5y) - (x^2 + 5y) = 7x(x^2 + 5y) - 1(x^2 + 5y)$

$$= (x^2 + 5y)(7x - 1)$$ □

> ▶ **Helpful Hint**
>
> Notice that we wrote $-(x^2 + 5y)$ as $-1(x^2 + 5y)$ to aid in factoring.

PRACTICE
6 Factor $8b(a^3 + 2y) - (a^3 + 2y)$.

OBJECTIVE 3 ▶ Factoring polynomials by grouping. Sometimes it is possible to factor a polynomial by grouping the terms of the polynomial and looking for common factors in each group. This method of factoring is called **factoring by grouping.**

EXAMPLE 7 Factor $ab - 6a + 2b - 12$.

Solution First look for the GCF of all four terms. The GCF of all four terms is 1. Next group the first two terms and the last two terms and factor out common factors from each group.

$$ab - 6a + 2b - 12 = (ab - 6a) + (2b - 12)$$

Factor a from the first group and 2 from the second group.

$$= a(b - 6) + 2(b - 6)$$

Now we see a GCF of $(b - 6)$. Factor out $(b - 6)$ to get

$$a(b - 6) + 2(b - 6) = (b - 6)(a + 2)$$

Check: To check, multiply $(b - 6)$ and $(a + 2)$ to see that the product is $ab - 6a + 2b - 12$. □

PRACTICE
7 Factor $xy + 2y - 10 - 5x$.

> ▶ **Helpful Hint**
>
> Notice that the polynomial $a(b - 6) + 2(b - 6)$ is _not_ in factored form. It is a _sum_, not a _product_. The factored form is $(b - 6)(a + 2)$.

EXAMPLE 8 Factor $x^3 + 5x^2 + 3x + 15$.

Solution $x^3 + 5x^2 + 3x + 15 = (x^3 + 5x^2) + (3x + 15)$ Group pairs of terms.

$$= x^2(x + 5) + 3(x + 5)$$ Factor each binomial.

$$= (x + 5)(x^2 + 3)$$ Factor out the common factor, $(x + 5)$. □

PRACTICE
8 Factor $a^3 + 2a^2 + 5a + 10$.

EXAMPLE 9   Factor $m^2n^2 + m^2 - 2n^2 - 2$.

Solution $m^2n^2 + m^2 - 2n^2 - 2 = (m^2n^2 + m^2) + (-2n^2 - 2)$ Group pairs of terms.

$$= m^2(n^2 + 1) - 2(n^2 + 1)$$ Factor each binomial.

$$= (n^2 + 1)(m^2 - 2)$$ Factor out the common factor, $(n^2 + 1)$.   □

PRACTICE
9   Factor $x^2y^2 + 3y^2 - 5x^2 - 15$.

EXAMPLE 10   Factor $xy + 2x - y - 2$.

Solution $xy + 2x - y - 2 = (xy + 2x) + (-y - 2)$ Group pairs of terms.

$$= x(y + 2) - 1(y + 2)$$ Factor each binomial.

$$= (y + 2)(x - 1)$$ Factor out the common factor $(y + 2)$.   □

PRACTICE
10   Factor $pq + 3p - q - 3$.

VOCABULARY & READINESS CHECK

Use the choices below to fill in each blank. Some choices will be used more than once and some not at all.

| least | greatest | sum | product | factoring | x^3 | x^7 | true | false |

1. The reverse process of multiplying is _____.

2. The greatest common factor (GCF) of x^7, x^3, x^5 is _____.

3. In general, the GCF of a list of common variables raised to powers is the _____ exponent in the list.

4. Factoring means writing as a _____.

5. True or false: A factored form of $2xy^3 + 10xy$ is $2xy \cdot y^2 + 2xy \cdot 5$. _____

6. True or false: A factored form of $x^3 - 6x^2 + x$ is $x(x^2 - 6x)$. _____

7. True or false: A factored form of $5x - 5y + x^3 - x^2y$ is $5(x - y) + x^2(x - y)$. _____

8. True or false: A factored form of $5x - 5y + x^3 - x^2y$ is $(x - y)(5 + x^2)$. _____

Find the GCF of each list of monomials.

9. $6, 12$ **10.** $9, 27$ **11.** $15x, 10$ **12.** $9x, 12$

13. $13x, 2x$ **14.** $4y, 5y$ **15.** $7x, 14x$ **16.** $8z, 4z$

5.5 | EXERCISE SET

Find the GCF of each list of monomials. See Example 1.

1. a^8, a^5, a^3 **2.** b^9, b^2, b^5

3. $x^2y^3z^3, y^2z^3, xy^2z^2$ **4.** $xy^2z^3, x^2y^2z^2, x^2y^3$

5. $6x^3y, 9x^2y^2, 12x^2y$ **6.** $4xy^2, 16xy^3, 8x^2y^2$

7. $10x^3yz^3, 20x^2z^5, 45xz^3$ **8.** $12y^2z^4, 9xy^3z^4, 15x^2y^2z^3$

Factor out the GCF in each polynomial. See Examples 2 through 6.

9. $18x - 12$

10. $21x + 14$

11. $4y^2 - 16xy^3$

12. $3z - 21xz^4$

13. $6x^5 - 8x^4 + 2x^3$

14. $9x + 3x^2 - 6x^3$

15. $8a^3b^3 - 4a^2b^2 + 4ab + 16ab^2$

16. $12a^3b - 6ab + 18ab^2 - 18a^2b$

17. $6(x + 3) + 5a(x + 3)$

18. $2(x - 4) + 3y(x - 4)$

19. $2x(z + 7) + (z + 7)$

20. $x(y - 2) + (y - 2)$

21. $3x(x^2 + 5) - 2(x^2 + 5)$

22. $4x(2y + 3) - 5(2y + 3)$

23. When $3x^2 - 9x + 3$ is factored, the result is $3(x^2 - 3x + 1)$. Explain why it is necessary to include the term 1 in this factored form.

24. Construct a trinomial whose GCF is $5x^2y^3$.

Factor each polynomial by grouping. See Examples 7 through 10.

25. $ab + 3a + 2b + 6$

26. $ab + 2a + 5b + 10$

27. $ac + 4a - 2c - 8$

28. $bc + 8b - 3c - 24$

29. $2xy - 3x - 4y + 6$

30. $12xy - 18x - 10y + 15$

31. $12xy - 8x - 3y + 2$

32. $20xy - 15x - 4y + 3$

MIXED PRACTICE

Factor each polynomial

33. $6x^3 + 9$

34. $6x^2 - 8$

35. $x^3 + 3x^2$

36. $x^4 - 4x^3$

37. $8a^3 - 4a$

38. $12b^4 + 3b^2$

39. $-20x^2y + 16xy^3$

40. $-18xy^3 + 27x^4y$

41. $10a^2b^3 + 5ab^2 - 15ab^3$

42. $10ef - 20e^2f^3 + 30e^3f$

43. $9abc^2 + 6a^2bc - 6ab + 3bc$

44. $4a^2b^2c - 6ab^2c - 4ac + 8a$

45. $4x(y - 2) - 3(y - 2)$

46. $8y(z + 8) - 3(z + 8)$

47. $6xy + 10x + 9y + 15$

48. $15xy + 20x + 6y + 8$

49. $xy + 3y - 5x - 15$

50. $xy + 4y - 3x - 12$

51. $6ab - 2a - 9b + 3$

52. $16ab - 8a - 6b + 3$

53. $12xy + 18x + 2y + 3$

54. $20xy + 8x + 5y + 2$

55. $2m(n - 8) - (n - 8)$

56. $3a(b - 4) - (b - 4)$

57. $15x^3y^2 - 18x^2y^2$

58. $12x^4y^2 - 16x^3y^3$

59. $2x^2 + 3xy + 4x + 6y$

60. $3x^2 + 12x + 4xy + 16y$

61. $5x^2 + 5xy - 3x - 3y$

62. $4x^2 + 2xy - 10x - 5y$

63. $x^3 + 3x^2 + 4x + 12$

64. $x^3 + 4x^2 + 3x + 12$

65. $x^3 - x^2 - 2x + 2$

66. $x^3 - 2x^2 - 3x + 6$

REVIEW AND PREVIEW

Simplify the following. See Section 5.1.

67. $(5x^2)(11x^5)$

68. $(7y)(-2y^3)$

69. $(5x^2)^3$

70. $(-2y^3)^4$

Find each product by using the FOIL order of multiplying binomials. See Section 5.4.

71. $(x + 2)(x - 5)$

72. $(x - 7)(x - 1)$

73. $(x + 3)(x + 2)$

74. $(x - 4)(x + 2)$

75. $(y - 3)(y - 1)$

76. $(s + 8)(s + 10)$

CONCEPT EXTENSIONS

Solve. See the Concept Check in this section.

77. Which factorization of $10x^2 - 2x - 2$ is correct?

 a. $2(5x^2 - x + 1)$ **b.** $2(5x^2 - x)$

 c. $2(5x^2 - x - 2)$ **d.** $2(5x^2 - x - 1)$

78. Which factorization of $x^4 + 5x^3 - x^2$ is correct?

 a. $-1(x^4 + 5x^3 + x^2)$ **b.** $x^2(x^2 + 5x^3 - x^2)$

 c. $x^2(x^2 + 5x - 1)$ **d.** $5x^2(x^2 + 5x - 5)$

Solve.

△ **79.** The area of the material needed to manufacture a tin can is given by the polynomial $2\pi r^2 + 2\pi rh$, where the radius is r and height is h. Factor this expression.

80. To estimate the cost of a new product, one expression used by the production department is $4\pi r^2 + \frac{4}{3}\pi r^3$. Write an equivalent expression by factoring $4\pi r^2$ from both terms.

81. At the end of T years, the amount of money A in a savings account earning simple interest from an initial investment of $5600 at rate r is given by the formula $A = 5600 + 5600rt$. Write an equivalent equation by factoring the expression $5600 + 5600rt$.

△ **82.** An open-topped box has a square base and a height of 10 inches. If each of the bottom edges of the box has length x inches, find the amount of material needed to construct the box. Write the answer in factored form.

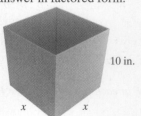

83. Explain why $9(5 - x) + y(5 - x)$ is not a factored form of $45 - 9x + 5y - xy$.

84. Construct a 4-term polynomial whose greatest common factor is $2a^3b^4$.

85. A factored polynomial can be in many forms. For example, a factored form of $xy - 3x - 2y + 6$ is $(x - 2)(y - 3)$. Which of the following is not a factored form of $xy - 3x - 2y + 6$?

  a. $(2 - x)(3 - y)$ **b.** $(-2 + x)(-3 + y)$

  c. $(y - 3)(x - 2)$ **d.** $(-x + 2)(-y + 3)$

86. Consider the following sequence of algebraic steps:

$$x^3 - 6x^2 + 2x - 10 = (x^3 - 6x^2) + (2x - 10)$$
$$= x^2(x - 6) + 2(x - 5)$$

Explain whether the final result is the factored form of the original polynomial.

87. Which factorization of $12x^2 + 9x + 3$ is correct?

  a. $3(4x^2 + 3x + 1)$ **b.** $3(4x^2 + 3x - 1)$

  c. $3(4x^2 + 3x - 3)$ **d.** $3(4x^2 + 3x)$

88. The amount E of voltage in an electrical circuit is given by the formula

$$IR_1 + IR_2 = E$$

Write an equivalent equation by factoring the expression $IR_1 + IR_2$.

89. At the end of T years, the amount of money A in a savings account earning simple interest from an initial investment of P dollars at rate R is given by the formula

$$A = P + PRT$$

Write an equivalent equation by factoring the expression $P + PRT$.

Factor out the greatest common factor. Assume that variables used as exponents represent positive integers.

90. $x^{3n} - 2x^{2n} + 5x^n$

91. $3y^n + 3y^{2n} + 5y^{8n}$

92. $6x^{8a} - 2x^{5a} - 4x^{3a}$

93. $3x^{5a} - 6x^{3a} + 9x^{2a}$

94. An object is thrown upward from the ground with an initial velocity of 64 feet per second. The height $h(t)$ in feet of the object after t seconds is given by the polynomial function

$$h(t) = -16t^2 + 64t$$

  a. Write an equivalent factored expression for the function $h(t)$ by factoring $-16t^2 + 64t$.

  b. Find $h(1)$ by using

$$h(t) = -16t^2 + 64t$$

and then by using the factored form of $h(t)$.

  c. Explain why the values found in part (b) are the same.

95. An object is dropped from the gondola of a hot-air balloon at a height of 224 feet. The height $h(t)$ of the object after t seconds is given by the polynomial function

$$h(t) = -16t^2 + 224$$

224 ft

  a. Write an equivalent factored expression for the function $h(t)$ by factoring $-16t^2 + 224$.

  b. Find $h(2)$ by using $h(t) = -16t^2 + 224$ and then by using the factored form of the function.

  c. Explain why the values found in part **b** are the same.

5.6 FACTORING TRINOMIALS

OBJECTIVES

1 Factor trinomials of the form $x^2 + bx + c$.

2 Factor trinomials of the form $ax^2 + bx + c$.
  a. Method 1—Trial and Check
  b. Method 2—Grouping

3 Factor by substitution.

OBJECTIVE 1 ▶ Factoring trinomials of the form $x^2 + bx + c$. In the previous section, we used factoring by grouping to factor four-term polynomials. In this section, we present techniques for factoring trinomials. Since $(x - 2)(x + 5) = x^2 + 3x - 10$, we say that $(x - 2)(x + 5)$ is a factored form of $x^2 + 3x - 10$. Taking a close look at how $(x - 2)$ and $(x + 5)$ are multiplied suggests a pattern for factoring trinomials of the form

$$x^2 + bx + c$$

$$(x - 2)(x + 5) = x^2 + 3x - 10$$

$$-2 + 5$$
$$-2 \cdot 5$$

The pattern for factoring is summarized next.

> **Factoring a Trinomial of the Form $x^2 + bx + c$**
>
> Find two numbers whose product is c and whose sum is b. The factored form of $x^2 + bx + c$ is
>
> $$(x + \text{one number})(x + \text{other number})$$

EXAMPLE 1   Factor $x^2 + 10x + 16$.

Solution   We look for two integers whose product is 16 and whose sum is 10. Since our integers must have a positive product and a positive sum, we look at only positive factors of 16.

Positive Factors of 16	*Sum of Factors*	
1, 16	$1 + 16 = 17$	
4, 4	$4 + 4 = 8$	
2, 8	$2 + 8 = 10$	Correct pair

The correct pair of numbers is 2 and 8 because their product is 16 and their sum is 10. Thus,

$$x^2 + 10x + 16 = (x + 2)(x + 8)$$

Check: To check, see that $(x + 2)(x + 8) = x^2 + 10x + 16$.   □

PRACTICE
1   Factor $x^2 + 5x + 6$.

EXAMPLE 2   Factor $x^2 - 12x + 35$.

Solution   We need to find two integers whose product is 35 and whose sum is -12. Since our integers must have a positive product and a negative sum, we consider only negative factors of 35.

Negative Factors of 35	*Sum of Factors*	
$-1, -35$	$-1 + (-35) = -36$	
$-5, -7$	$-5 + (-7) = -12$	Correct pair

The numbers are -5 and -7.

$$x^2 - 12x + 35 = [x + (-5)][x + (-7)]$$
$$= (x - 5)(x - 7)$$

Check: To check, see that $(x - 5)(x - 7) = x^2 - 12x + 35$.   □

PRACTICE
2   Factor $x^2 - 11x + 24$.

EXAMPLE 3   Factor $5x^3 - 30x^2 - 35x$.

Solution   First we factor out the greatest common factor, $5x$.

$$5x^3 - 30x^2 - 35x = 5x(x^2 - 6x - 7)$$

Next we try to factor $x^2 - 6x - 7$ by finding two numbers whose product is -7 and whose sum is -6. The numbers are 1 and -7.

$$5x^3 - 30x^2 - 35x = 5x(x^2 - 6x - 7)$$
$$= 5x(x + 1)(x - 7)$$ □

PRACTICE
3   Factor $3x^3 - 9x^2 - 30x$.

> ▶ Helpful Hint
>
> If the polynomial to be factored contains a common factor that is factored out, don't forget to include that common factor in the final factored form of the original polynomial.

EXAMPLE 4 Factor $2n^2 - 38n + 80$.

Solution The terms of this polynomial have a greatest common factor of 2, which we factor out first.

$$2n^2 - 38n + 80 = 2(n^2 - 19n + 40)$$

Next we factor $n^2 - 19n + 40$ by finding two numbers whose product is 40 and whose sum is -19. Both numbers must be negative since their sum is -19. Possibilities are

$$-1 \text{ and } -40, \quad -2 \text{ and } -20, \quad -4 \text{ and } -10, \quad -5 \text{ and } -8$$

None of the pairs has a sum of -19, so no further factoring with integers is possible. The factored form of $2n^2 - 38n + 80$ is

$$2n^2 - 38n + 80 = 2(n^2 - 19n + 40)$$ ☐

PRACTICE
4 Factor $2b^2 - 18b - 22$.

We call a polynomial such as $n^2 - 19n + 40$ that cannot be factored further, a **prime polynomial.**

OBJECTIVE 2 ▶ **Factoring trinomials of the form $ax^2 + bx + c$.** Next, we factor trinomials of the form $ax^2 + bx + c$, where the coefficient a of x^2 is not 1. Don't forget that the first step in factoring any polynomial is to factor out the greatest common factor of its terms. We will review two methods here. The first method we'll call trial and check.

EXAMPLE 5 **Method 1—Trial and Check**

Factor $2x^2 + 11x + 15$.

Solution Factors of $2x^2$ are $2x$ and x. Let's try these factors as first terms of the binomials.

$$2x^2 + 11x + 15 = (2x + \quad)(x + \quad)$$

Next we try combinations of factors of 15 until the correct middle term, $11x$, is obtained. We will try only positive factors of 15 since the coefficient of the middle term, 11, is positive. Positive factors of 15 are 1 and 15 and 3 and 5.

Thus, the factored form of $2x^2 + 11x + 15$ is $(2x + 5)(x + 3)$. ☐

PRACTICE
5 Factor $2x^2 + 13x + 6$.

> **Factoring a Trinomial of the Form** $ax^2 + bx + c$
>
> **STEP 1.** Write all pairs of factors of ax^2.
>
> **STEP 2.** Write all pairs of factors of c, the constant term.
>
> **STEP 3.** Try various combinations of these factors until the correct middle term bx is found.
>
> **STEP 4.** If no combination exists, the polynomial is **prime.**

EXAMPLE 6   Factor $3x^2 - x - 4$.

Solution   Factors of $3x^2$: $3x \cdot x$

Factors of -4: $-1 \cdot 4$, $1 \cdot -4$, $-2 \cdot 2$, $2 \cdot -2$

Let's try possible combinations of these factors.

$$(3x - 1)(x + 4)$$
$$-1x$$
$$\frac{12x}{11x} \quad \text{Incorrect middle term}$$

$$(3x + 4)(x - 1)$$
$$4x$$
$$\frac{-3x}{1x} \quad \text{Incorrect middle term}$$

$$(3x - 4)(x + 1)$$
$$-4x$$
$$\frac{3x}{-1x} \quad \text{Correct middle term}$$

Thus, $3x^2 - x - 4 = (3x - 4)(x + 1)$.   □

PRACTICE
6   Factor $4x^2 + 5x - 6$.

> ▶ **Helpful Hint—Sign Patterns**
>
> A positive constant in a trinomial tells us to look for two numbers with the same sign. The sign of the coefficient of the middle term tells us whether the signs are both positive or both negative.
>
>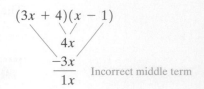
>
> $$2x^2 + 7x + 3 = (2x + 1)(x + 3) \qquad 2x^2 - 7x + 3 = (2x - 1)(x - 3)$$
>
> A negative constant in a trinomial tells us to look for two numbers with opposite signs.
>
> opposite signs ↓   opposite signs ↓
>
> $$2x^2 - 5x - 3 = (2x + 1)(x - 3) \qquad 2x^2 + 5x - 3 = (2x - 1)(x + 3)$$

EXAMPLE 7   Factor $12x^3y - 22x^2y + 8xy$.

Solution   First we factor out the greatest common factor of the terms of this trinomial, $2xy$.

$$12x^3y - 22x^2y + 8xy = 2xy(6x^2 - 11x + 4)$$

Now we try to factor the trinomial $6x^2 - 11x + 4$.

Factors of $6x^2$: $2x \cdot 3x$, $6x \cdot x$

Let's try $2x$ and $3x$.

$$2xy(6x^2 - 11x + 4) = 2xy(2x + \quad)(3x + \quad)$$

The constant term, 4, is positive and the coefficient of the middle term, -11, is negative, so we factor 4 into negative factors only.

Negative factors of 4: $-4(-1)$, $-2(-2)$

Let's try -4 and -1.

$$2xy(2x - 4)(3x - 1)$$

$$\begin{array}{r} -12x \\ -2x \\ \hline -14x \end{array}$$ Incorrect middle term

This combination cannot be correct, because one of the factors, $(2x - 4)$, has a common factor of 2. This cannot happen if the polynomial $6x^2 - 11x + 4$ has no common factors.

Now let's try -1 and -4.

$$2xy(2x - 1)(3x - 4)$$

$$\begin{array}{r} -3x \\ -8x \\ \hline -11x \end{array}$$ Correct middle term

Thus,

$$12x^3y - 22x^2y + 8xy = 2xy(2x - 1)(3x - 4)$$

If this combination had not worked, we would have tried -2 and -2 as factors of 4 and then $6x$ and x as factors of $6x^2$. □

PRACTICE
7   Factor $18b^4 - 57b^3 + 30b^2$.

▶ **Helpful Hint**
If a trinomial has no common factor (other than 1), then none of its binomial factors will contain a common factor (other than 1).

EXAMPLE 8   Factor $16x^2 + 24xy + 9y^2$.

Solution   No greatest common factor can be factored out of this trinomial.

Factors of $16x^2$: $16x \cdot x$, $8x \cdot 2x$, $4x \cdot 4x$

Factors of $9y^2$: $y \cdot 9y$, $3y \cdot 3y$

We try possible combinations until the correct factorization is found.

$$16x^2 + 24xy + 9y^2 = (4x + 3y)(4x + 3y) \quad \text{or} \quad (4x + 3y)^2 \qquad □$$

PRACTICE
8   Factor $25x^2 + 20xy + 4y^2$.

The trinomial $16x^2 + 24xy + 9y^2$ in Example 8 is an example of a **perfect square trinomial** since its factors are two identical binomials. In the next section, we examine a special method for factoring perfect square trinomials.

Method 2—Grouping

There is another method we can use when factoring trinomials of the form $ax^2 + bx + c$: Write the trinomial as a four-term polynomial, and then factor by grouping.

> **Factoring a Trinomial of the Form $ax^2 + bx + c$ by Grouping**
>
> **STEP 1.** Find two numbers whose product is $a \cdot c$ and whose sum is b.
>
> **STEP 2.** Write the term bx as a sum by using the factors found in Step 1.
>
> **STEP 3.** Factor by grouping.

EXAMPLE 9 Factor $6x^2 + 13x + 6$.

Solution In this trinomial, $a = 6$, $b = 13$, and $c = 6$.

STEP 1. Find two numbers whose product is $a \cdot c$, or $6 \cdot 6 = 36$, and whose sum is b, 13. The two numbers are 4 and 9.

STEP 2. Write the middle term, $13x$, as the sum $4x + 9x$.

$$6x^2 + 13x + 6 = 6x^2 + 4x + 9x + 6$$

STEP 3. Factor $6x^2 + 4x + 9x + 6$ by grouping.

$$(6x^2 + 4x) + (9x + 6) = 2x(3x + 2) + 3(3x + 2)$$
$$= (3x + 2)(2x + 3)$$

PRACTICE
9 Factor $20x^2 + 23x + 6$.

Concept Check ☑

Name one way that a factorization can be checked.

EXAMPLE 10 Factor $18x^2 - 9x - 2$.

Solution In this trinomial, $a = 18$, $b = -9$, and $c = -2$.

STEP 1. Find two numbers whose product is $a \cdot c$ or $18(-2) = -36$ and whose sum is b, -9. The two numbers are -12 and 3.

STEP 2. Write the middle term, $-9x$, as the sum $-12x + 3x$.

$$18x^2 - 9x - 2 = 18x^2 - 12x + 3x - 2$$

STEP 3. Factor by grouping.

$$(18x^2 - 12x) + (3x - 2) = 6x(3x - 2) + 1(3x - 2)$$
$$= (3x - 2)(6x + 1).$$

PRACTICE
10 Factor $15x^2 + 4x - 3$.

Answer to Concept Check:
Answers may vary. A sample is: By multiplying the factors to see that the product is the original polynomial.

OBJECTIVE 3 ▶ Factoring by substitution. A complicated looking polynomial may be a simpler trinomial "in disguise." Revealing the simpler trinomial is possible by substitution.

EXAMPLE 11   Factor $2(a + 3)^2 - 5(a + 3) - 7$.

Solution   The quantity $(a + 3)$ is in two of the terms of this polynomial. **_Substitute_** x for $(a + 3)$, and the result is the following simpler trinomial.

$$2(a + 3)^2 - 5(a + 3) - 7 \quad \text{Original trinomial.}$$
$$\downarrow \qquad\qquad \downarrow$$
$$= 2(x)^2 \quad - \quad 5(x) - 7 \quad \text{Substitute } x \text{ for } (a + 3).$$

Now factor $2x^2 - 5x - 7$.

$$2x^2 - 5x - 7 = (2x - 7)(x + 1)$$

But the quantity in the original polynomial was $(a + 3)$, not x. Thus, we need to reverse the substitution and replace x with $(a + 3)$.

$$(2x - 7)(x + 1) \qquad\qquad \text{Factored expression.}$$
$$= [2(a + 3) - 7][(a + 3) + 1] \quad \text{Substitute } (a + 3) \text{ for } x.$$
$$= (2a + 6 - 7)(a + 3 + 1) \qquad \text{Remove inside parentheses.}$$
$$= (2a - 1)(a + 4) \qquad\qquad \text{Simplify.}$$

Thus, $2(a + 3)^2 - 5(a + 3) - 7 = (2a - 1)(a + 4)$. □

PRACTICE
11   Factor $3(x + 1)^2 - 7(x + 1) - 20$.

EXAMPLE 12   Factor $5x^4 + 29x^2 - 42$.

Solution   Again, substitution may help us factor this polynomial more easily. Since this polynomial contains the variable x, we will choose a different substitution variable. Let $y = x^2$, so $y^2 = (x^2)^2$, or x^4. Then

$$5x^4 + 29x^2 - 42$$
$$\downarrow \qquad \downarrow$$

becomes

$$5y^2 + 29y - 42$$

which factors as

$$5y^2 + 29y - 42 = (5y - 6)(y + 7)$$

Next, replace y with x^2 to get

$$(5x^2 - 6)(x^2 + 7)$$ □

PRACTICE
12   Factor $6x^4 - 11x^2 - 10$.

VOCABULARY & READINESS CHECK

1. Find two numbers whose product is 10 and whose sum is 7.

2. Find two numbers whose product is 12 and whose sum is 8.

3. Find two numbers whose product is 24 and whose sum is 11.

4. Find two numbers whose product is 30 and whose sum is 13.

5.6 | EXERCISE SET

MyMathLab

PRACTICE   WATCH   DOWNLOAD   READ   REVIEW

Factor each trinomial. See Examples 1 through 4.

1. $x^2 + 9x + 18$

2. $x^2 + 9x + 20$

3. $x^2 - 12x + 32$

4. $x^2 - 12x + 27$

5. $x^2 + 10x - 24$

6. $x^2 + 3x - 54$

7. $x^2 - 2x - 24$

8. $x^2 - 9x - 36$

9. $3x^2 - 18x + 24$

10. $x^2y^2 + 4xy^2 + 3y^2$

11. $4x^2z + 28xz + 40z$

12. $5x^2 - 45x + 70$

13. $2x^2 - 24x - 64$

14. $3n^2 - 6n - 51$

Factor each trinomial. See Examples 5 through 10.

15. $5x^2 + 16x + 3$

16. $3x^2 + 8x + 4$

17. $2x^2 - 11x + 12$

18. $3x^2 - 19x + 20$

19. $2x^2 + 25x - 20$

20. $6x^2 + 13x + 8$

21. $4x^2 - 12x + 9$

22. $25x^2 - 30x + 9$

23. $12x^2 + 10x - 50$

24. $12y^2 - 48y + 45$

25. $3y^4 - y^3 - 10y^2$

26. $2x^2z + 5xz - 12z$

27. $6x^3 + 8x^2 + 24x$

28. $18y^3 + 12y^2 + 2y$

29. $2x^2 - 5xy - 3y^2$

30. $6x^2 + 11xy + 4y^2$

31. $28y^2 + 22y + 4$

32. $24y^3 - 2y^2 - y$

33. $2x^2 + 15x - 27$

34. $3x^2 + 14x + 15$

Use substitution to factor each polynomial completely. See Examples 11 and 12.

35. $x^4 + x^2 - 6$

36. $x^4 - x^2 - 20$

37. $(5x + 1)^2 + 8(5x + 1) + 7$

38. $(3x - 1)^2 + 5(3x - 1) + 6$

39. $x^6 - 7x^3 + 12$

40. $x^6 - 4x^3 - 12$

41. $(a + 5)^2 - 5(a + 5) - 24$

42. $(3c + 6)^2 + 12(3c + 6) - 28$

MIXED PRACTICE

Factor each polynomial completely. See Examples 1 through 12.

43. $x^2 - 24x - 81$

44. $x^2 - 48x - 100$

45. $x^2 - 15x - 54$

46. $x^2 - 15x + 54$

47. $3x^2 - 6x + 3$

48. $8x^2 - 8x + 2$

49. $3x^2 - 5x - 2$

50. $5x^2 - 14x - 3$

51. $8x^2 - 26x + 15$

52. $12x^2 - 17x + 6$

53. $18x^4 + 21x^3 + 6x^2$

54. $20x^5 + 54x^4 + 10x^3$

55. $x^2 + 8xz + 7z^2$

56. $a^2 - 2ab - 15b^2$

57. $x^2 - x - 12$

58. $x^2 + 4x - 5$

59. $3a^2 + 12ab + 12b^2$

60. $2x^2 + 16xy + 32y^2$

61. $x^2 + 4x + 5$

62. $x^2 + 6x + 8$

63. $2(x + 4)^2 + 3(x + 4) - 5$

64. $3(x + 3)^2 + 2(x + 3) - 5$

65. $6x^2 - 49x + 30$

66. $4x^2 - 39x + 27$

67. $x^4 - 5x^2 - 6$

68. $x^4 - 5x^2 + 6$

69. $6x^3 - x^2 - x$

70. $12x^3 + x^2 - x$

71. $12a^2 - 29ab + 15b^2$

72. $16y^2 + 6yx - 27x^2$

73. $9x^2 + 30x + 25$

74. $4x^2 + 6x + 9$

75. $3x^2y - 11xy + 8y$

76. $5xy^2 - 9xy + 4x$

77. $2x^2 + 2x - 12$

78. $3x^2 + 6x - 45$

79. $(x - 4)^2 + 3(x - 4) - 18$

80. $(x - 3)^2 - 2(x - 3) - 8$

81. $2x^6 + 3x^3 - 9$

82. $3x^6 - 14x^3 + 8$

83. $72xy^4 - 24xy^2z + 2xz^2$

84. $36xy^2 - 48xyz^2 + 16xz^4$

85. $2x^3y + 2x^2y - 12xy$

86. $3x^2y^3 + 6x^2y^2 - 45x^2y$

87. $x^2 + 6xy + 5y^2$

88. $x^2 + 6xy + 8y^2$

REVIEW AND PREVIEW

Multiply. See Section 5.4.

89. $(x - 3)(x + 3)$

90. $(x - 4)(x + 4)$

91. $(2x + 1)^2$

92. $(3x + 5)^2$

93. $(x - 2)(x^2 + 2x + 4)$

94. $(y + 1)(y^2 - y + 1)$

CONCEPT EXTENSIONS

95. Find all positive and negative integers b such that $x^2 + bx + 6$ is factorable.

96. Find all positive and negative integers b such that $x^2 + bx - 10$ is factorable.

97. The volume $V(x)$ of a box in terms of its height x is given by the function $V(x) = x^3 + 2x^2 - 8x$. Factor this expression for $V(x)$.

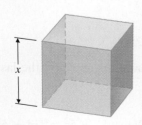

98. Based on your results from Exercise 97, find the length and width of the box if the height is 5 inches and the dimensions of the box are whole numbers.

99. Suppose that a movie is being filmed in New York City. An action shot requires an object to be thrown upward with an initial velocity of 80 feet per second off the top of 1 Madison Square Plaza, a height of 576 feet. The height $h(t)$ in feet of the object after t seconds is given by the function $h(t) = -16t^2 + 80t + 576$. (*Source: The World Almanac*)

a. Find the height of the object at $t = 0$ seconds, $t = 2$ seconds, $t = 4$ seconds, and $t = 6$ seconds.

b. Explain why the height of the object increases and then decreases as time passes.

c. Factor the polynomial $-16t^2 + 80t + 576$.

576 ft

100. Suppose that an object is thrown upward with an initial velocity of 64 feet per second off the edge of a 960-foot cliff. The height $h(t)$ in feet of the object after t seconds is given by the function

$$h(t) = -16t^2 + 64t + 960$$

a. Find the height of the object at $t = 0$ seconds, $t = 3$ seconds, $t = 6$ seconds, and $t = 9$ seconds.

b. Explain why the height of the object increases and then decreases as time passes.

c. Factor the polynomial $-16t^2 + 64t + 960$.

Factor. Assume that variables used as exponents represent positive integers.

101. $x^{2n} + 10x^n + 16$

102. $x^{2n} - 7x^n + 12$

103. $x^{2n} - 3x^n - 18$

104. $x^{2n} + 7x^n - 18$

105. $2x^{2n} + 11x^n + 5$

106. $3x^{2n} - 8x^n + 4$

107. $4x^{2n} - 12x^n + 9$

108. $9x^{2n} + 24x^n + 16$

Recall that a graphing calculator may be used to check addition, subtraction, and multiplication of polynomials. In the same manner, a graphing calculator may be used to check factoring of polynomials in one variable. For example, to see that

$$2x^3 - 9x^2 - 5x = x(2x + 1)(x - 5)$$

graph $Y_1 = 2x^3 - 9x^2 - 5x$ and $Y_2 = x(2x + 1)(x - 5)$. Then trace along both graphs to see that they coincide. Factor the following and use this method to check your results.

109. $x^4 + 6x^3 + 5x^2$

110. $x^3 + 6x^2 + 8x$

111. $30x^3 + 9x^2 - 3x$

112. $-6x^4 + 10x^3 - 4x^2$

STUDY SKILLS BUILDER

Is Your Notebook Still Organized?

It's never too late to organize your material in a course. Let's see how you are doing.

1. Are all your graded papers in one place in your math notebook or binder?

2. Flip through the pages of your notebook. Are your notes neat and readable?

3. Are your notes complete with no sections missing?

4. Are important notes marked in some way (like an exclamation point) so that you will know to review them before a quiz or test?

5. Are your assignments complete?

6. Do exercises that have given you trouble have a mark (like a question mark) so that you will remember to talk to your instructor or a tutor about them?

7. Describe your attitude toward this course.

8. List ways your attitude can improve and make a commitment to work on at least one of these during the next week.

5.7 FACTORING BY SPECIAL PRODUCTS

OBJECTIVES

1. Factor a perfect square trinomial.

2. Factor the difference of two squares.

3. Factor the sum or difference of two cubes.

OBJECTIVE 1 ▶ Factoring a perfect square trinomial. In the previous section, we considered a variety of ways to factor trinomials of the form $ax^2 + bx + c$. In one particular example, we factored $16x^2 + 24xy + 9y^2$ as

$$16x^2 + 24xy + 9y^2 = (4x + 3y)^2$$

Recall that $16x^2 + 24xy + 9y^2$ is a perfect square trinomial because its factors are two identical binomials. A perfect square trinomial can be factored quickly if you recognize the trinomial as a perfect square.

A trinomial is a perfect square trinomial if it can be written so that its first term is the square of some quantity a, its last term is the square of some quantity b, and its middle term is twice the product of the quantities a and b. The following special formulas can be used to factor perfect square trinomials.

Perfect Square Trinomials

$$a^2 + 2ab + b^2 = (a + b)^2$$
$$a^2 - 2ab + b^2 = (a - b)^2$$

Notice that these formulas above are the same special products from Section 5.4 for the square of a binomial.

From

$$a^2 + 2ab + b^2 = (a + b)^2,$$

we see that

$$16x^2 + 24xy + 9y^2 = (4x)^2 + 2(4x)(3y) + (3y)^2 = (4x + 3y)^2$$

EXAMPLE 1 Factor $m^2 + 10m + 25$.

Solution Notice that the first term is a square: $m^2 = (m)^2$, the last term is a square: $25 = 5^2$; and $10m = 2 \cdot 5 \cdot m$.

Thus,

$$m^2 + 10m + 25 = m^2 + 2(m)(5) + 5^2 = (m + 5)^2$$ □

PRACTICE

1 Factor $b^2 + 16b + 64$.

EXAMPLE 2   Factor $3a^2x - 12abx + 12b^2x$.

<u>*Solution*</u>   The terms of this trinomial have a GCF of $3x$, which we factor out first.

$$3a^2x - 12abx + 12b^2x = 3x(a^2 - 4ab + 4b^2)$$

Now, the polynomial $a^2 - 4ab + 4b^2$ is a perfect square trinomial. Notice that the first term is a square: $a^2 = (a)^2$; the last term is a square: $4b^2 = (2b)^2$; and $4ab = 2(a)(2b)$. The factoring can now be completed as

$$3x(a^2 - 4ab + 4b^2) = 3x(a - 2b)^2$$

PRACTICE

2   Factor $45x^2b - 30xb + 5b$.

▶ **Helpful Hint**

If you recognize a trinomial as a perfect square trinomial, use the special formulas to factor. However, methods for factoring trinomials in general from Section 5.6 will also result in the correct factored form.

OBJECTIVE 2 ▶ **Factoring the difference of two squares.** We now factor special types of binomials, beginning with the **difference of two squares.** The special product pattern presented in Section 5.4 for the product of a sum and a difference of two terms is used again here. However, the emphasis is now on factoring rather than on multiplying.

Difference of Two Squares

$$a^2 - b^2 = (a + b)(a - b)$$

Notice that a binomial is a difference of two squares when it is the difference of the square of some quantity a and the square of some quantity b.

EXAMPLE 3   Factor the following.

a. $x^2 - 9$ **b.** $16y^2 - 9$ **c.** $50 - 8y^2$ **d.** $x^2 - \dfrac{1}{4}$

<u>*Solution*</u>

a. $x^2 - 9 = x^2 - 3^2$ **b.** $16y^2 - 9 = (4y)^2 - 3^2$
$ = (x + 3)(x - 3)$ $ = (4y + 3)(4y - 3)$

c. First factor out the common factor of 2.
$50 - 8y^2 = 2(25 - 4y^2)$
$ = 2(5 + 2y)(5 - 2y)$

d. $x^2 - \dfrac{1}{4} = x^2 - \left(\dfrac{1}{2}\right)^2 = \left(x + \dfrac{1}{2}\right)\left(x - \dfrac{1}{2}\right)$

PRACTICE

3   Factor the following.

a. $x^2 - 16$

b. $25b^2 - 49$

c. $45 - 20x^2$

d. $y^2 - \dfrac{1}{81}$

The binomial $x^2 + 9$ is a **sum of two squares** and cannot be factored by using real numbers. **In general, except for factoring out a GCF, the sum of two squares usually cannot be factored by using real numbers.**

> ▶ **Helpful Hint**
> The sum of two squares whose GCF is 1 usually cannot be factored by using real numbers. For example, $x^2 + 9$ is called a prime polynomial.

EXAMPLE 4 Factor the following.

a. $p^4 - 16$ **b.** $(x + 3)^2 - 36$

Solution

a. $p^4 - 16 = (p^2)^2 - 4^2$

$= (p^2 + 4)(p^2 - 4)$

The binomial factor $p^2 + 4$ cannot be factored by using real numbers, but the binomial factor $p^2 - 4$ is a difference of squares.

$$(p^2 + 4)(p^2 - 4) = (p^2 + 4)(p + 2)(p - 2)$$

b. Factor $(x + 3)^2 - 36$ as the difference of squares.

$$(x + 3)^2 - 36 = (x + 3)^2 - 6^2$$

$= [(x + 3) + 6][(x + 3) - 6]$ Factor.

$= [x + 3 + 6][x + 3 - 6]$ Remove parentheses.

$= (x + 9)(x - 3)$ Simplify.   □

PRACTICE
4   Factor the following.

a. $x^4 - 10000$ **b.** $(x + 2)^2 - 49$

Concept Check ☑

Is $(x - 4)(y^2 - 9)$ completely factored? Why or why not?

EXAMPLE 5   Factor $x^2 + 4x + 4 - y^2$.

Solution   Factoring by grouping comes to mind since the sum of the first three terms of this polynomial is a perfect square trinomial.

$$x^2 + 4x + 4 - y^2 = (x^2 + 4x + 4) - y^2$$ Group the first three terms.

$$= (x + 2)^2 - y^2$$ Factor the perfect square trinomial.

This is not factored yet since we have a *difference*, not a *product*. Since $(x + 2)^2 - y^2$ is a difference of squares, we have

$$(x + 2)^2 - y^2 = [(x + 2) + y][(x + 2) - y]$$

$$= (x + 2 + y)(x + 2 - y)$$ □

PRACTICE
5   Factor $m^2 + 6m + 9 - n^2$.

Answer to Concept Check:
no; $(y^2 - 9)$ can be factored

OBJECTIVE 3 ▶ Factoring the sum or difference of two cubes. Although the sum of two squares usually cannot be factored, the sum of two cubes, as well as the difference of two cubes, can be factored as follows.

> **Sum and Difference of Two Cubes**
> $$a^3 + b^3 = (a + b)(a^2 - ab + b^2)$$
> $$a^3 - b^3 = (a - b)(a^2 + ab + b^2)$$

To check the first pattern, let's find the product of $(a - b)$ and $(a^2 - ab + b^2)$.

$$(a + b)(a^2 - ab + b^2) = a(a^2 - ab + b^2) + b(a^2 - ab + b^2)$$
$$= a^3 - a^2b + ab^2 + a^2b - ab^2 + b^3$$
$$= a^3 + b^3$$

EXAMPLE 6   Factor $x^3 + 8$.

Solution   First we write the binomial in the form $a^3 + b^3$. Then we use the formula

$$a^3 + b^3 = (a + b)(a^2 - a \cdot b + b^2), \quad \text{where } a \text{ is } x \text{ and } b \text{ is } 2.$$
$$\downarrow \quad \downarrow \qquad \downarrow \quad \downarrow \quad \downarrow \qquad \downarrow \quad \downarrow \qquad \downarrow$$
$$x^3 + 8 = x^3 + 2^3 = (x + 2)(x^2 - x \cdot 2 + 2^2)$$

Thus, $x^3 + 8 = (x + 2)(x^2 - 2x + 4)$ ☐

PRACTICE
6   Factor $x^3 + 64$.

EXAMPLE 7   Factor $p^3 + 27q^3$.

Solution
$$p^3 + 27q^3 = p^3 + (3q)^3$$
$$= (p + 3q)[p^2 - (p)(3q) + (3q)^2]$$
$$= (p + 3q)(p^2 - 3pq + 9q^2)$$ ☐

PRACTICE
7   Factor $a^3 + 8b^3$.

EXAMPLE 8   Factor $y^3 - 64$.

Solution   This is a difference of cubes since $y^3 - 64 = y^3 - 4^3$.

From
$$a^3 - b^3 = (a - b)(a^2 - a \cdot b + b^2)$$
$$\downarrow \quad \downarrow \qquad \downarrow \quad \downarrow \quad \downarrow \qquad \downarrow \quad \downarrow \qquad \downarrow$$
$$y^3 - 4^3 = (y - 4)(y^2 + y \cdot 4 + 4^2)$$
$$= (y - 4)(y^2 + 4y + 16)$$ ☐

PRACTICE
8   Factor $27 - y^3$.

▶ **Helpful Hint**

When factoring sums or differences of cubes, be sure to notice the sign patterns.

Same sign

$$x^3 + y^3 = (x + y)(x^2 - xy + y^2)$$

Opposite sign

Always positive

Same sign

$$x^3 - y^3 = (x - y)(x^2 + xy + y^2)$$

Opposite sign

EXAMPLE 9   Factor $125q^2 - n^3q^2$.

Solution   First we factor out a common factor of q^2.

$$125q^2 - n^3q^2 = q^2(125 - n^3)$$
$$= q^2(5^3 - n^3)$$

Opposite sign   Positive

$$= q^2(5 - n)[5^2 + (5)(n) + (n^2)]$$
$$= q^2(5 - n)(25 + 5n + n^2)$$

Thus, $125q^2 - n^3q^2 = q^2(5 - n)(25 + 5n + n^2)$. The trinomial $25 + 5n + n^2$ cannot be factored further. □

PRACTICE
9   Factor $b^3x^2 - 8x^2$.

VOCABULARY & READINESS CHECK

Write each term as a square. For example $25x^2$ as a square is $(5x)^2$.

1. $81y^2$ **2.** $4z^2$ **3.** $64x^6$ **4.** $49y^6$

Write each number or term as a cube.

5. 125   **6.** 216   **7.** $8x^3$ **8.** $27y^3$ **9.** $64x^6$ **10.** x^3y^6

5.7 | EXERCISE SET

Factor the following. See Examples 1 and 2.

1. $x^2 + 6x + 9$

2. $x^2 - 10x + 25$

3. $4x^2 - 12x + 9$

4. $25x^2 + 10x + 1$

5. $3x^2 - 24x + 48$

6. $x^3 + 14x^2 + 49x$

7. $9y^2x^2 + 12yx^2 + 4x^2$

8. $32x^2 - 16xy + 2y^2$

Factor the following. See Examples 3 through 5.

9. $x^2 - 25$

10. $y^2 - 100$

11. $9 - 4z^2$

12. $16x^2 - y^2$

13. $(y + 2)^2 - 49$

14. $(x - 1)^2 - z^2$

15. $64x^2 - 100$

16. $4x^2 - 36$

Factor the following. See Examples 6 through 9.

17. $x^3 + 27$

18. $y^3 + 1$

19. $z^3 - 1$

20. $x^3 - 8$

21. $m^3 + n^3$

22. $r^3 + 125$

23. $x^3y^2 - 27y^2$

24. $64 - p^3$

25. $a^3b + 8b^4$

26. $8ab^3 + 27a^4$

27. $125y^3 - 8x^3$

28. $54y^3 - 128$

Factor the following. See Example 5.

29. $x^2 + 6x + 9 - y^2$

30. $x^2 + 12x + 36 - y^2$

31. $x^2 - 10x + 25 - y^2$

32. $x^2 - 18x + 81 - y^2$

33. $4x^2 + 4x + 1 - z^2$

34. $9y^2 + 12y + 4 - x^2$

MIXED PRACTICE

Factor each polynomial completely.

35. $9x^2 - 49$

36. $25x^2 - 4$

37. $x^2 - 12x + 36$

38. $x^2 - 18x + 81$

39. $x^4 - 81$

40. $x^4 - 256$

41. $x^2 + 8x + 16 - 4y^2$

42. $x^2 + 14x + 49 - 9y^2$

43. $(x + 2y)^2 - 9$

44. $(3x + y)^2 - 25$

45. $x^3 - 216$

46. $8 - a^3$

47. $x^3 + 125$

48. $x^3 + 216$

49. $4x^2 + 25$

50. $16x^2 + 25$

51. $4a^2 + 12a + 9$

52. $9a^2 - 30a + 25$

53. $18x^2y - 2y$

54. $12xy^2 - 108x$

55. $8x^3 + y^3$

56. $27x^3 - y^3$

57. $x^6 - y^3$

58. $x^3 - y^6$

59. $x^2 + 16x + 64 - x^4$

60. $x^2 + 20x + 100 - x^4$

61. $3x^6y^2 + 81y^2$

62. $x^2y^9 + x^2y^3$

63. $(x + y)^3 + 125$

64. $(x + y)^3 + 27$

65. $(2x + 3)^3 - 64$

66. $(4x + 2)^3 - 125$

REVIEW AND PREVIEW

Solve the following equations. See Section 2.1.

67. $x - 5 = 0$

68. $x + 7 = 0$

69. $3x + 1 = 0$

70. $5x - 15 = 0$

71. $-2x = 0$

72. $3x = 0$

73. $-5x + 25 = 0$

74. $-4x - 16 = 0$

CONCEPT EXTENSIONS

Determine whether each polynomial is factored completely or not. See the Concept Check in this section.

75. $5x(x^2 - 4)$

76. $x^2y^2(x^3 - y^3)$

77. $7y(a^2 + a + 1)$

78. $9z(x^2 + 4)$

△ **79.** A manufacturer of metal washers needs to determine the cross-sectional area of each washer. If the outer radius of the washer is R and the radius of the hole is r, express the area of the washer as a polynomial. Factor this polynomial completely.

△ **80.** Express the area of the shaded region as a polynomial. Factor the polynomial completely.

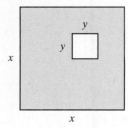

Express the volume of each solid as a polynomial. To do so, subtract the volume of the "hole" from the volume of the larger solid. Then factor the resulting polynomial.

△ **81.**
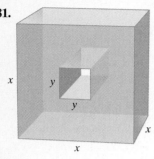

△ **82.**

Find the value of c that makes each trinomial a perfect square trinomial.

83. $x^2 + 6x + c$

84. $y^2 + 10y + c$

85. $m^2 - 14m + c$

86. $n^2 - 2n + c$

87. $x^2 + cx + 16$

88. $x^2 + cx + 36$

89. Factor $x^6 - 1$ completely, using the following methods from this chapter.

   a. Factor the expression by treating it as the difference of two squares, $(x^3)^2 - 1^2$.

   b. Factor the expression treating it as the difference of two cubes, $(x^2)^3 - 1^3$.

   c. Are the answers to parts **a** and **b** the same? Why or why not?

Factor. Assume that variables used as exponents represent positive integers.

90. $x^{2n} - 25$

91. $x^{2n} - 36$

92. $36x^{2n} - 49$

93. $25x^{2n} - 81$

94. $x^{4n} - 16$

95. $x^{4n} - 625$

INTEGRATED REVIEW OPERATIONS ON POLYNOMIALS AND FACTORING STRATEGIES

Sections 5.1–5.7

OPERATIONS ON POLYNOMIALS

Perform each indicated operation.

1. $(-y^2 + 6y - 1) + (3y^2 - 4y - 10)$

2. $(5z^4 - 6z^2 + z + 1) - (7z^4 - 2z + 1)$

3. Subtract $(x - 5)$ from $(x^2 - 6x + 2)$.

4. $(2x^2 + 6x - 5) + (5x^2 - 10x)$

5. $(5x - 3)^2$

6. $(5x^2 - 14x - 3) \div (5x + 1)$

7. $(2x^4 - 3x^2 + 5x - 2) \div (x + 2)$

8. $(4x - 1)(x^2 - 3x - 2)$

FACTORING STRATEGIES

The key to proficiency in factoring polynomials is to practice until you are comfortable with each technique. A strategy for factoring polynomials completely is given next.

Factoring a Polynomial

STEP 1. Are there any common factors? If so, factor out the greatest common factor.

STEP 2. How many terms are in the polynomial?

   a. If there are *two* terms, decide if one of the following formulas may be applied:

   i. Difference of two squares: $a^2 - b^2 = (a - b)(a + b)$

   ii. Difference of two cubes: $a^3 - b^3 = (a - b)(a^2 + ab + b^2)$

   iii. Sum of two cubes: $a^3 + b^3 = (a + b)(a^2 - ab + b^2)$

   b. If there are *three* terms, try one of the following:

   i. Perfect square trinomial: $a^2 + 2ab + b^2 = (a + b)^2$
   $$a^2 - 2ab + b^2 = (a - b)^2$$

   ii. If not a perfect square trinomial, factor by using the methods presented in Section 5.5.

   c. If there are *four* or more terms, try factoring by grouping.

STEP 3. See whether any factors in the factored polynomial can be factored further.

A few examples are worked for you below.

EXAMPLE 1 Factor each polynomial completely.

a. $8a^2b - 4ab$ b. $36x^2 - 9$ c. $2x^2 - 5x - 7$

d. $5p^2 + 5 + qp^2 + q$ e. $9x^2 + 24x + 16$ f. $y^2 + 25$

Solution

a. **STEP 1.** The terms have a common factor of $4ab$, which we factor out.

$$8a^2b - 4ab = 4ab(2a - 1)$$

STEP 2. There are two terms, but the binomial $2a - 1$ is not the difference of two squares or the sum or difference of two cubes.

STEP 3. The factor $2a - 1$ cannot be factored further.

b. **STEP 1.** Factor out a common factor of 9.

$$36x^2 - 9 = 9(4x^2 - 1)$$

STEP 2. The factor $4x^2 - 1$ has two terms, and it is the difference of two squares.

$$9(4x^2 - 1) = 9(2x + 1)(2x - 1)$$

STEP 3. No factor with more than one term can be factored further.

c. **STEP 1.** The terms of $2x^2 - 5x - 7$ contain no common factor other than 1 or -1.

STEP 2. There are three terms. The trinomial is not a perfect square, so we factor by methods from Section 5.6.

$$2x^2 - 5x - 7 = (2x - 7)(x + 1)$$

STEP 3. No factor with more than one term can be factored further.

d. **STEP 1.** There is no common factor of all terms of $5p^2 + 5 + qp^2 + q$.

STEP 2. The polynomial has four terms, so try factoring by grouping.

$$5p^2 + 5 + qp^2 + q = (5p^2 + 5) + (qp^2 + q) \quad \text{Group the terms.}$$
$$= 5(p^2 + 1) + q(p^2 + 1)$$
$$= (p^2 + 1)(5 + q)$$

STEP 3. No factor can be factored further.

e. **STEP 1.** The terms of $9x^2 + 24x + 16$ contain no common factor other than 1 or -1.

STEP 2. The trinomial $9x^2 + 24x + 16$ is a perfect square trinomial, and $9x^2 + 24x + 16 = (3x + 4)^2$.

STEP 3. No factor can be factored further.

f. **STEP 1.** There is no common factor of $y^2 + 25$ other than 1.

STEP 2. This binomial is the sum of two squares and is prime.

STEP 3. The binomial $y^2 + 25$ cannot be factored further. □

PRACTICE

1 Factor each polynomial completely.

a. $12x^2y - 3xy$ b. $49x^2 - 4$

c. $5x^2 + 2x - 3$ d. $3x^2 + 6 + x^3 + 2x$

e. $4x^2 + 20x + 25$ f. $b^2 + 100$

EXAMPLE 2 Factor each completely.

a. $27a^3 - b^3$ **b.** $3n^2m^4 - 48m^6$ **c.** $2x^2 - 12x + 18 - 2z^2$
d. $8x^4y^2 + 125xy^2$ **e.** $(x - 5)^2 - 49y^2$

<u>Solution</u>

a. This binomial is the difference of two cubes.

$$27a^3 - b^3 = (3a)^3 - b^3$$
$$= (3a - b)[(3a)^2 + (3a)(b) + b^2]$$
$$= (3a - b)(9a^2 + 3ab + b^2)$$

b. $3n^2m^4 - 48m^6 = 3m^4(n^2 - 16m^2)$ Factor out the GCF, $3m^4$.

                     $= 3m^4(n + 4m)(n - 4m)$ Factor the difference of squares.

c. $2x^2 - 12x + 18 - 2z^2 = 2(x^2 - 6x + 9 - z^2)$ The GCF is 2.

                           $= 2[(x^2 - 6x + 9) - z^2]$ Group the first three terms together.

                           $= 2[(x - 3)^2 - z^2]$ Factor the perfect square trinomial.

                           $= 2[(x - 3) + z][(x - 3) - z]$ Factor the difference of squares.

                           $= 2(x - 3 + z)(x - 3 - z)$

d. $8x^4y^2 + 125xy^2 = xy^2(8x^3 + 125)$ The GCF is xy^2.

                      $= xy^2[(2x)^3 + 5^3]$

                      $= xy^2(2x + 5)[(2x)^2 - (2x)(5) + 5^2]$ Factor the sum of cubes.

                      $= xy^2(2x + 5)(4x^2 - 10x + 25)$

e. This binomial is the difference of squares.

$$(x - 5)^2 - 49y^2 = (x - 5)^2 - (7y)^2$$
$$= [(x - 5) + 7y][(x - 5) - 7y]$$
$$= (x - 5 + 7y)(x - 5 - 7y)$$

PRACTICE
2 Factor each polynomial completely.

a. $64x^3 + y^3$
b. $7x^2y^2 - 63y^4$
c. $3x^2 + 12x + 12 - 3b^2$
d. $x^5y^4 + 27x^2y$
e. $(x + 7)^2 - 81y^2$

Factor completely.

9. $x^2 - 8x + 16 - y^2$

11. $x^4 - x$

13. $14x^2y - 2xy$

15. $4x^2 - 16$

10. $12x^2 - 22x - 20$

12. $(2x + 1)^2 - 3(2x + 1) + 2$

14. $24ab^2 - 6ab$

16. $9x^2 - 81$

17. $3x^2 - 8x - 11$

18. $5x^2 - 2x - 3$

19. $4x^2 + 8x - 12$

20. $6x^2 - 6x - 12$

21. $4x^2 + 36x + 81$

22. $25x^2 + 40x + 16$

23. $8x^3 + 125y^3$

24. $27x^3 - 64y^3$

25. $64x^2y^3 - 8x^2$

26. $27x^5y^4 - 216x^2y$

27. $(x + 5)^3 + y^3$

28. $(y - 1)^3 + 27x^3$

29. $(5a - 3)^2 - 6(5a - 3) + 9$

30. $(4r + 1)^2 + 8(4r + 1) + 16$

31. $7x^2 - 63x$

32. $20x^2 + 23x + 6$

33. $ab - 6a + 7b - 42$

34. $20x^2 - 220x + 600$

35. $x^4 - 1$

36. $15x^2 - 20x$

37. $10x^2 - 7x - 33$

38. $45m^3n^3 - 27m^2n^2$

39. $5a^3b^3 - 50a^3b$

40. $x^4 + x$

41. $16x^2 + 25$

42. $20x^3 + 20y^3$

43. $10x^3 - 210x^2 + 1100x$

44. $9y^2 - 42y + 49$

45. $64a^3b^4 - 27a^3b$

46. $y^4 - 16$

47. $2x^3 - 54$

48. $2sr + 10s - r - 5$

49. $3y^5 - 5y^4 + 6y - 10$

50. $64a^2 + b^2$

51. $100z^3 + 100$

52. $250x^4 - 16x$

53. $4b^2 - 36b + 81$

54. $2a^5 - a^4 + 6a - 3$

55. $(y - 6)^2 + 3(y - 6) + 2$

56. $(c + 2)^2 - 6(c + 2) + 5$

△ **57.** Express the area of the shaded region as a polynomial. Factor the polynomial completely.

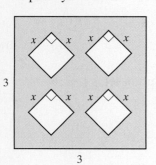

5.8 SOLVING EQUATIONS BY FACTORING AND PROBLEM SOLVING

OBJECTIVES

1 Solve polynomial equations by factoring.

2 Solve problems that can be modeled by polynomial equations.

3 Find the x-intercepts of a polynomial function.

OBJECTIVE 1 ▶ **Solving polynomial equations by factoring.** In this section, your efforts to learn factoring start to pay off. We use factoring to solve polynomial equations, which in turn helps us solve problems that can be modeled by polynomial equations and also helps us sketch the graph of polynomial functions.

A **polynomial equation** is the result of setting two polynomials equal to each other. Examples of polynomial equations are

$$3x^3 - 2x^2 = x^2 + 2x - 1 \qquad 2.6x + 7 = -1.3 \qquad -5x^2 - 5 = -9x^2 - 2x + 1$$

A polynomial equation is in **standard form** if one side of the equation is 0. In standard form the polynomial equations above are

$$3x^3 - 3x^2 - 2x + 1 = 0 \qquad 2.6x + 8.3 = 0 \qquad 4x^2 + 2x - 6 = 0$$

The degree of a simplified polynomial equation in standard form is the same as the highest degree of any of its terms. A polynomial equation of degree 2 is also called a **quadratic equation.**

A solution of a polynomial equation in one variable is a value of the variable that makes the equation true. The method presented in this section for solving polynomial equations is called the **factoring method.** This method is based on the **zero-factor property.**

> **Zero-Factor Property**
>
> If a and b are real numbers and $a \cdot b = 0$, then $a = 0$ or $b = 0$. This property is true for three or more factors also.

In other words, if the product of two or more real numbers is zero, then at least one number must be zero.

EXAMPLE 1 Solve: $(x + 2)(x - 6) = 0$.

Solution By the zero-factor property, $(x + 2)(x - 6) = 0$ only if $x + 2 = 0$ or $x - 6 = 0$.

$$x + 2 = 0 \quad \text{or} \quad x - 6 = 0 \qquad \text{Apply the zero-factor property.}$$
$$x = -2 \quad \text{or} \qquad x = 6 \qquad \text{Solve each linear equation.}$$

To check, let $x = -2$ and then let $x = 6$ in the original equation.

Let $x = -2$.   Let $x = 6$.

Then $(x + 2)(x - 6) = 0$ Then $(x + 2)(x - 6) = 0$

becomes $(-2 + 2)(-2 - 6) \stackrel{?}{=} 0$ becomes $(6 + 2)(6 - 6) \stackrel{?}{=} 0$

$(0)(-8) \stackrel{?}{=} 0$ $(8)(0) \stackrel{?}{=} 0$

$0 = 0$ True $0 = 0$ True

Both -2 and 6 check, so they are both solutions. The solution set is $\{-2, 6\}$. ☐

PRACTICE

1 Solve: $(x + 8)(x - 5) = 0$.

EXAMPLE 2   Solve: $2x^2 + 9x - 5 = 0$.

Solution   To use the zero-factor property, one side of the equation must be 0, and the other side must be in factored form.

$$2x^2 + 9x - 5 = 0$$
$$(2x - 1)(x + 5) = 0 \qquad\qquad \text{Factor.}$$
$$2x - 1 = 0 \quad \text{or} \quad x + 5 = 0 \quad \text{Set each factor equal to zero.}$$
$$2x = 1$$
$$x = \frac{1}{2} \quad \text{or} \quad x = -5 \quad \text{Solve each linear equation.}$$

The solutions are -5 and $\frac{1}{2}$. To check, let $x = \frac{1}{2}$ in the original equation; then let $x = -5$ in the original equation. The solution set is $\left\{ -5, \frac{1}{2} \right\}$.   □

PRACTICE
2   Solve: $3x^2 + 10x - 8 = 0$.

Solving Polynomial Equations by Factoring

STEP 1. Write the equation in standard form so that one side of the equation is 0.

STEP 2. Factor the polynomial completely.

STEP 3. Set each factor containing a variable equal to 0.

STEP 4. Solve the resulting equations.

STEP 5. Check each solution in the original equation.

Since it is not always possible to factor a polynomial, not all polynomial equations can be solved by factoring. Other methods of solving polynomial equations are presented in Chapter 8.

EXAMPLE 3   Solve: $x(2x - 7) = 4$.

Solution   First, write the equation in standard form; then, factor.

$$x(2x - 7) = 4$$
$$2x^2 - 7x = 4 \qquad\qquad \text{Multiply.}$$
$$2x^2 - 7x - 4 = 0 \qquad\qquad \text{Write in standard form.}$$
$$(2x + 1)(x - 4) = 0 \qquad\qquad \text{Factor.}$$
$$2x + 1 = 0 \quad \text{or} \quad x - 4 = 0 \quad \text{Set each factor equal to zero.}$$
$$2x = -1 \qquad\qquad\qquad \text{Solve.}$$
$$x = -\frac{1}{2} \quad \text{or} \quad x = 4$$

The solutions are $-\frac{1}{2}$ and 4. Check both solutions in the original equation.   □

PRACTICE
3   Solve: $x(3x + 14) = -8$.

▶ **Helpful Hint**

To apply the zero-factor property, one side of the equation must be 0, and the other side of the equation must be factored. To solve the equation $x(2x - 7) = 4$, for example, you may **not** set each factor equal to 4.

EXAMPLE 4 Solve: $3(x^2 + 4) + 5 = -6(x^2 + 2x) + 13$.

Solution   Rewrite the equation so that one side is 0.

$$3(x^2 + 4) + 5 = -6(x^2 + 2x) + 13.$$
$$3x^2 + 12 + 5 = -6x^2 - 12x + 13 \qquad \text{Apply the distributive property.}$$
$$9x^2 + 12x + 4 = 0 \qquad \text{Rewrite the equation so that one side is 0.}$$
$$(3x + 2)(3x + 2) = 0 \qquad \text{Factor.}$$
$$3x + 2 = 0 \quad \text{or} \quad 3x + 2 = 0 \qquad \text{Set each factor equal to 0.}$$
$$3x = -2 \quad \text{or} \qquad 3x = -2$$
$$x = -\frac{2}{3} \quad \text{or} \qquad x = -\frac{2}{3} \qquad \text{Solve each equation.}$$

The solution is $-\dfrac{2}{3}$. Check by substituting $-\dfrac{2}{3}$ into the original equation. □

PRACTICE
4   Solve: $8(x^2 + 3) + 4 = -8x(x + 3) + 19$.

If the equation contains fractions, we clear the equation of fractions as a first step.

EXAMPLE 5   Solve: $2x^2 = \dfrac{17}{3}x + 1$.

Solution $$2x^2 = \frac{17}{3}x + 1$$

$$3(2x^2) = 3\left(\frac{17}{3}x + 1\right) \qquad \text{Clear the equation of fractions.}$$
$$6x^2 = 17x + 3 \qquad \text{Apply the distributive property.}$$
$$6x^2 - 17x - 3 = 0 \qquad \text{Rewrite the equation in standard form.}$$
$$(6x + 1)(x - 3) = 0 \qquad \text{Factor.}$$
$$6x + 1 = 0 \quad \text{or} \quad x - 3 = 0 \qquad \text{Set each factor equal to zero.}$$
$$6x = -1$$
$$x = -\frac{1}{6} \quad \text{or} \qquad x = 3 \qquad \text{Solve each equation.}$$

The solutions are $-\dfrac{1}{6}$ and 3. □

PRACTICE
5   Solve: $4x^2 = \dfrac{15}{2}x + 1$.

EXAMPLE 6   Solve: $x^3 = 4x$.

Solution $$x^3 = 4x$$
$$x^3 - 4x = 0 \qquad \text{Rewrite the equation so that one side is 0.}$$
$$x(x^2 - 4) = 0 \qquad \text{Factor out the GCF, } x.$$
$$x(x + 2)(x - 2) = 0 \qquad \text{Factor the difference of squares.}$$
$$x = 0 \quad \text{or} \quad x + 2 = 0 \quad \text{or} \quad x - 2 = 0 \qquad \text{Set each factor equal to 0.}$$
$$x = 0 \quad \text{or} \qquad x = -2 \quad \text{or} \qquad x = 2 \qquad \text{Solve each equation.}$$

The solutions are $-2, 0,$ and 2. Check by substituting into the original equation. □

PRACTICE
6   Solve: $x^3 = 2x^2 + 3x$.

Notice that the _third_-degree equation of Example 6 yielded _three_ solutions.

EXAMPLE 7   Solve: $x^3 + 5x^2 = x + 5$.

Solution   First, write the equation so that one side is 0.

$$x^3 + 5x^2 - x - 5 = 0$$
$$(x^3 - x) + (5x^2 - 5) = 0 \qquad \text{Factor by grouping.}$$
$$x(x^2 - 1) + 5(x^2 - 1) = 0$$
$$(x^2 - 1)(x + 5) = 0$$
$$(x + 1)(x - 1)(x + 5) = 0 \qquad \text{Factor the difference of squares.}$$
$$x + 1 = 0 \quad \text{or} \quad x - 1 = 0 \quad \text{or} \quad x + 5 = 0 \qquad \text{Set each factor equal to 0.}$$
$$x = -1 \quad \text{or} \qquad x = 1 \quad \text{or} \qquad x = -5 \qquad \text{Solve each equation.}$$

The solutions are -5, -1, and 1. Check in the original equation.   □

PRACTICE
7   Solve: $x^3 - 9x = 18 - 2x^2$.

- ■

Concept Check ☑

Which solution strategies are incorrect? Why?

a. Solve $(y - 2)(y + 2) = 4$ by setting each factor equal to 4.
b. Solve $(x + 1)(x + 3) = 0$ by setting each factor equal to 0.
c. Solve $z^2 + 5z + 6 = 0$ by factoring $z^2 + 5z + 6$ and setting each factor equal to 0.
d. Solve $x^2 + 6x + 8 = 10$ by factoring $x^2 + 6x + 8$ and setting each factor equal to 0.

OBJECTIVE 2 ▶ **Solving problems modeled by polynomial equations.** Some problems may be modeled by polynomial equations. To solve these problems, we use the same problem-solving steps that were introduced in Section 2.2. When solving these problems, keep in mind that a solution of an equation that models a problem is not always a solution to the problem. For example, a person's weight or the length of a side of a geometric figure is always a positive number. Discard solutions that do not make sense as solutions of the problem.

EXAMPLE 8   **Finding the Return Time of a Rocket**

An Alpha III model rocket is launched from the ground with an A8–3 engine. Without a parachute, the height of the rocket h at time t seconds is approximated by the equation,

$$h = -16t^2 + 144t$$

Find how long it takes the rocket to return to the ground.

Solution

1. UNDERSTAND. Read and reread the problem. The equation $h = -16t^2 + 144t$ models the height of the rocket. Familiarize yourself with this equation by finding a few values.

When $t = 1$ second, the height of the rocket is

$$h = -16(1)^2 + 144(1) = 128 \text{ feet}$$

When $t = 2$ seconds, the height of the rocket is

$$h = -16(2)^2 + 144(2) = 224 \text{ feet}$$

2. TRANSLATE. To find how long it takes the rocket to return to the ground, we want to know what value of t makes the height h equal to 0. That is, we want to solve $h = 0$.

$$-16t^2 + 144t = 0$$

Answer to Concept Check:
a and d; the zero-factor property
works only if one side of the
equation is 0

3. SOLVE the quadratic equation by factoring.

$$-16t^2 + 144t = 0$$
$$-16t(t - 9) = 0$$
$$-16t = 0 \quad \text{or} \quad t - 9 = 0$$
$$t = 0 \qquad\qquad t = 9$$

4. INTERPRET. The height h is 0 feet at time 0 seconds (when the rocket is launched) and at time 9 seconds.

Check: See that the height of the rocket at 9 seconds equals 0.

$$h = -16(9)^2 + 144(9) = -1296 + 1296 = 0$$

State: The rocket returns to the ground 9 seconds after it is launched. ☐

PRACTICE

8 A model rocket is launched from the ground. Its height h in feet at time t seconds is approximated by the equation $h = -16t^2 + 96t$. Find how long it takes the rocket to return to the ground.

Some of the exercises at the end of this section make use of the **Pythagorean theorem**. Before we review this theorem, recall that a **right triangle** is a triangle that contains a 90° angle, or right angle. The **hypotenuse** of a right triangle is the side opposite the right angle and is the longest side of the triangle. The **legs** of a right triangle are the other sides of the triangle.

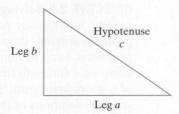

Hypotenuse
c

Leg b

Leg a

Pythagorean Theorem

In a right triangle, the sum of the squares of the lengths of the two legs is equal to the square of the length of the hypotenuse.

$$(\text{leg})^2 + (\text{leg})^2 = (\text{hypotenuse})^2 \quad \text{or} \quad a^2 + b^2 = c^2$$

△ **EXAMPLE 9** **Using the Pythagorean Theorem**

While framing an addition to an existing home, Kim Menzies, a carpenter, used the Pythagorean theorem to determine whether a wall was "square"—that is, whether the wall formed a right angle with the floor. He used a triangle whose sides are three consecutive integers. Find a right triangle whose sides are three consecutive integers.

?

Solution

1. UNDERSTAND. Read and reread the problem.

Let x, $x + 1$, and $x + 2$ be three consecutive integers. Since these integers represent lengths of the sides of a right triangle, we have

$$x = \text{one leg}$$
$$x + 1 = \text{other leg}$$
$$x + 2 = \text{hypotenuse (longest side)}$$

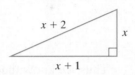

2. TRANSLATE. By the Pythagorean theorem, we have

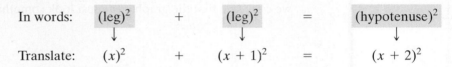

In words: $(\text{leg})^2$ $+$ $(\text{leg})^2$ $=$ $(\text{hypotenuse})^2$

Translate: $(x)^2$ $+$ $(x + 1)^2$ $=$ $(x + 2)^2$

3. SOLVE the equation.

$$x^2 + (x + 1)^2 = (x + 2)^2$$
$$x^2 + x^2 + 2x + 1 = x^2 + 4x + 4 \qquad \text{Multiply.}$$
$$2x^2 + 2x + 1 = x^2 + 4x + 4$$
$$x^2 - 2x - 3 = 0 \qquad\qquad \text{Write in standard form.}$$
$$(x - 3)(x + 1) = 0$$
$$x - 3 = 0 \quad \text{or} \quad x + 1 = 0$$
$$x = 3 \qquad\qquad x = -1$$

4. INTERPRET. Discard $x = -1$ since length cannot be negative. If $x = 3$, then $x + 1 = 4$ and $x + 2 = 5$.

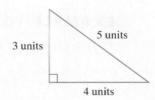

Check: To check, see that $(\text{leg})^2 + (\text{leg})^2 = (\text{hypotenuse})^2$

$$3^2 + 4^2 = 5^2$$
$$9 + 16 = 25 \quad \text{True}$$

State: The lengths of the sides of the right triangle are 3, 4, and 5 units. Kim used this information, for example, by marking off lengths of 3 and 4 feet on the floor and framing respectively. If the diagonal length between these marks was 5 feet, the wall was "square." If not, adjustments were made. ☐

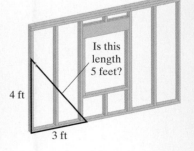

PRACTICE
9 Find a right triangle whose sides are consecutive even integers.

OBJECTIVE 3 ▶ Finding the *x*-intercepts of polynomial functions. Recall that to find the *x*-intercepts of the graph of a function, let   or   and solve for *x*. This fact gives us a visual interpretation of the results of this section.

From Example 1, we know that the solutions of the equation $(x + 2)(x - 6) = 0$ are -2 and 6. These solutions give us important information about the related polynomial function $p(x) = (x + 2)(x - 6)$. We know that when *x* is -2 or when *x* is 6, the value of $p(x)$ is 0.

$$p(x) = (x + 2)(x - 6)$$
$$p(-2) = (-2 + 2)(-2 - 6) = (0)(-8) = 0$$
$$p(6) = (6 + 2)(6 - 6) = (8)(0) = 0$$

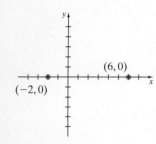

Thus, we know that $(-2, 0)$ and $(6, 0)$ are the *x*-intercepts of the graph of $p(x)$.

We also know that the graph of $p(x)$ does not cross the *x*-axis at any other point. For this reason, and the fact that $p(x) = (x + 2)(x - 6) = x^2 - 4x - 12$ has degree 2, we conclude that the graph of *p* must look something like one of these two graphs:

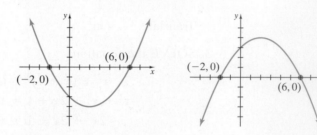

In a later chapter, we explore these graphs more fully. For the moment, know that the solutions of a polynomial equation are the *x*-intercepts of the graph of the related function and that the *x*-intercepts of the graph of a polynomial function are the solutions of the related polynomial equation. These values are also called **roots**, or **zeros**, of a polynomial function.

EXAMPLE 10   **Match Each Function with Its Graph**

$$f(x) = (x - 3)(x + 2) \quad g(x) = x(x + 2)(x - 2) \quad h(x) = (x - 2)(x + 2)(x - 1)$$

A
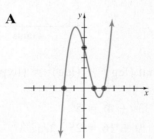

B
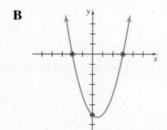

C
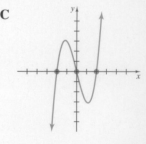

<u>Solution</u>   The graph of the function $f(x) = (x - 3)(x + 2)$ has two *x*-intercepts, $(3, 0)$ and $(-2, 0)$, because the equation $0 = (x - 3)(x + 2)$ has two solutions, 3 and -2.

The graph of $f(x)$ is graph B.

The graph of the function $g(x) = x(x + 2)(x - 2)$ has three *x*-intercepts $(0, 0)$, $(-2, 0)$, and $(2, 0)$, because the equation $0 = x(x + 2)(x - 2)$ has three solutions, $0, -2$, and 2.

The graph of $g(x)$ is graph C.

The graph of the function $h(x) = (x - 2)(x + 2)(x - 1)$ has three x-intercepts, $(-2, 0)$, $(1, 0)$, and $(2, 0)$, because the equation $0 = (x - 2)(x + 2)(x - 1)$ has three solutions, -2, 1, and 2.

The graph of $h(x)$ is graph A. $\quad\square$

PRACTICE
10 Match each function with its graph.

$$f(x) = (x - 1)(x + 3) \qquad g(x) = x(x + 3)(x - 2) \qquad h(x) = (x - 3)(x + 2)(x - 2)$$

A 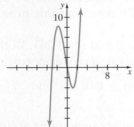 **B** 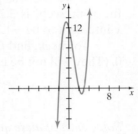 **C**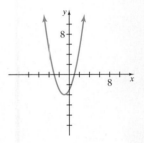

Graphing Calculator Explorations

We can use a graphing calculator to approximate real number solutions of any quadratic equation in standard form, whether the associated polynomial is factorable or not. For example, let's solve the quadratic equation $x^2 - 2x - 4 = 0$. The solutions of this equation will be the x-intercepts of the graph of the function $f(x) = x^2 - 2x - 4$. (Recall that to find x-intercepts, we let $f(x) = 0$, or $y = 0$.) When we use a standard window, the graph of this function looks like this.

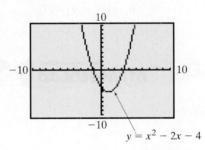

The graph appears to have one x-intercept between -2 and -1 and one between 3 and 4. To find the x-intercept between 3 and 4 to the nearest hundredth, we can use a zero feature, a Zoom feature, which magnifies a portion of the graph around the cursor, or we can redefine our window. If we redefine our window to

$$\text{Xmin} = 2 \qquad\qquad \text{Ymin} = -1$$
$$\text{Xmax} = 5 \qquad\qquad \text{Ymax} = 1$$
$$\text{Xscl} = 1 \qquad\qquad \text{Yscl} = 1$$

the resulting screen is

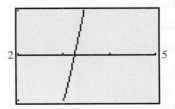

By using the Trace feature, we can now see that one of the intercepts is between 3.21 and 3.25. To approximate to the nearest hundredth, Zoom again or redefine the window to

Xmin = 3.2	Ymin = −0.1
Xmax = 3.3	Ymax = 0.1
Xscl = 1	Yscl = 1

If we use the Trace feature again, we see that, to the nearest hundredth, the x-intercept is 3.24. By repeating this process, we can approximate the other x-intercept to be −1.24.

To check, find $f(3.24)$ and $f(-1.24)$. Both of these values should be close to 0. (They will not be exactly 0 since we approximated these solutions.)

$$f(3.24) = 0.0176 \quad \text{and} \quad f(-1.24) = 0.0176$$

Solve each of these quadratic equations by graphing a related function and approximating the x-intercepts to the nearest thousandth.

1. $x^2 + 3x - 2 = 0$ **2.** $5x^2 - 7x + 1 = 0$

3. $2.3x^2 - 4.4x - 5.6 = 0$ **4.** $0.2x^2 + 6.2x + 2.1 = 0$

5. $0.09x^2 - 0.13x - 0.08 = 0$ **6.** $x^2 + 0.08x - 0.01 = 0$

VOCABULARY & READINESS CHECK

Solve each equation for the variable. See Example 1.

1. $(x - 3)(x + 5) = 0$ **2.** $(y + 5)(y + 3) = 0$ **3.** $(z - 3)(z + 7) = 0$

4. $(c - 2)(c - 4) = 0$ **5.** $x(x - 9) = 0$ **6.** $w(w + 7) = 0$

5.8 EXERCISE SET

PRACTICE   WATCH   DOWNLOAD   READ   REVIEW

Solve each equation. See Example 1.

1. $(x + 3)(3x - 4) = 0$

2. $(5x + 1)(x - 2) = 0$

3. $3(2x - 5)(4x + 3) = 0$

4. $8(3x - 4)(2x - 7) = 0$

Solve each equation. See Examples 2 through 5.

5. $x^2 + 11x + 24 = 0$ **6.** $y^2 - 10y + 24 = 0$

7. $12x^2 + 5x - 2 = 0$ **8.** $3y^2 - y - 14 = 0$

9. $z^2 + 9 = 10z$ **10.** $n^2 + n = 72$

11. $x(5x + 2) = 3$ **12.** $n(2n - 3) = 2$

13. $x^2 - 6x = x(8 + x)$ **14.** $n(3 + n) = n^2 + 4n$

15. $\dfrac{z^2}{6} - \dfrac{z}{2} - 3 = 0$ **16.** $\dfrac{c^2}{20} - \dfrac{c}{4} + \dfrac{1}{5} = 0$

17. $\dfrac{x^2}{2} + \dfrac{x}{20} = \dfrac{1}{10}$ **18.** $\dfrac{y^2}{30} = \dfrac{y}{15} + \dfrac{1}{2}$

19. $\dfrac{4t^2}{5} = \dfrac{t}{5} + \dfrac{3}{10}$ **20.** $\dfrac{5x^2}{6} - \dfrac{7x}{2} + \dfrac{2}{3} = 0$

Solve each equation. See Examples 6 and 7.

21. $(x + 2)(x - 7)(3x - 8) = 0$

22. $(4x + 9)(x - 4)(x + 1) = 0$

23. $y^3 = 9y$ **24.** $n^3 = 16n$

25. $x^3 - x = 2x^2 - 2$ **26.** $m^3 = m^2 + 12m$

27. Explain how solving $2(x - 3)(x - 1) = 0$ differs from solving $2x(x - 3)(x - 1) = 0$.

28. Explain why the zero-factor property works for more than two numbers whose product is 0.

MIXED PRACTICE

Solve each equation.

29. $(2x + 7)(x - 10) = 0$ **30.** $(x + 4)(5x - 1) = 0$

31. $3x(x - 5) = 0$ **32.** $4x(2x + 3) = 0$

33. $x^2 - 2x - 15 = 0$

34. $x^2 + 6x - 7 = 0$

35. $12x^2 + 2x - 2 = 0$

36. $8x^2 + 13x + 5 = 0$

37. $w^2 - 5w = 36$

38. $x^2 + 32 = 12x$

39. $25x^2 - 40x + 16 = 0$

40. $9n^2 + 30n + 25 = 0$

41. $2r^3 + 6r^2 = 20r$

42. $-2t^3 = 108t - 30t^2$

43. $z(5z - 4)(z + 3) = 0$

44. $2r(r + 3)(5r - 4) = 0$

45. $2z(z + 6) = 2z^2 + 12z - 8$

46. $3c^2 - 8c + 2 = c(3c - 8)$

47. $(x - 1)(x + 4) = 24$

48. $(2x - 1)(x + 2) = -3$

49. $\dfrac{x^2}{4} - \dfrac{5}{2}x + 6 = 0$

50. $\dfrac{x^2}{18} + \dfrac{x}{2} + 1 = 0$

51. $y^2 + \dfrac{1}{4} = -y$

52. $\dfrac{x^2}{10} + \dfrac{5}{2} = x$

53. $y^3 + 4y^2 = 9y + 36$

54. $x^3 + 5x^2 = x + 5$

55. $2x^3 = 50x$

56. $m^5 = 36m^3$

57. $x^2 + (x + 1)^2 = 61$

58. $y^2 + (y + 2)^2 = 34$

59. $m^2(3m - 2) = m$

60. $x^2(5x + 3) = 26x$

61. $3x^2 = -x$

62. $y^2 = -5y$

63. $x(x - 3) = x^2 + 5x + 7$

64. $z^2 - 4z + 10 = z(z - 5)$

65. $3(t - 8) + 2t = 7 + t$

66. $7c - 2(3c + 1) = 5(4 - 2c)$

67. $-3(x - 4) + x = 5(3 - x)$

68. $-4(a + 1) - 3a = -7(2a - 3)$

69. Which solution strategies are incorrect? Why?

    a. Solve $(y - 2)(y + 2) = 4$ by setting each factor equal to 4.

    b. Solve $(x + 1)(x + 3) = 0$ by setting each factor equal to 0.

    c. Solve $z^2 + 5z + 6 = 0$ by factoring $z^2 + 5z + 6$ and setting each factor equal to 0.

    d. Solve $x^2 + 6x + 8 = 10$ by factoring $x^2 + 6x + 8$ and setting each factor equal to 0.

70. Describe two ways a linear equation differs from a quadratic equation.

Solve. See Examples 8 and 9.

71. One number exceeds another by five, and their product is 66. Find the numbers.

72. If the sum of two numbers is 4 and their product is $\dfrac{15}{4}$, find the numbers.

73. An electrician needs to run a cable from the top of a 60-foot tower to a transmitter box located 45 feet away from the base of the tower. Find how long he should make the cable.

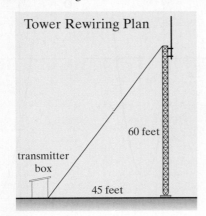

Tower Rewiring Plan

transmitter box

60 feet

45 feet

74. A stereo system installer needs to run speaker wire along the two diagonals of a rectangular room whose dimensions are 40 feet by 75 feet. Find how much speaker wire she needs.

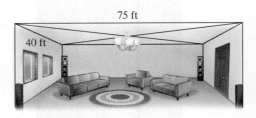

75 ft

40 ft

75. If the cost, $C(x)$, for manufacturing x units of a certain product is given by $C(x) = x^2 - 15x + 50$, find the number of units manufactured at a cost of $9500.

76. Determine whether any three consecutive integers represent the lengths of the sides of a right triangle.

77. The shorter leg of a right triangle is 3 centimeters less than the other leg. Find the length of the two legs if the hypotenuse is 15 centimeters.

78. The longer leg of a right triangle is 4 feet longer than the other leg. Find the length of the two legs if the hypotenuse is 20 feet.

79. Marie Mulroney has a rectangular board 12 inches by 16 inches around which she wants to put a uniform border of shells. If she has enough shells for a border whose area is 128 square inches, determine the width of the border.

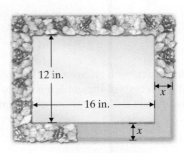

12 in.

16 in.

x

x

80. A gardener has a rose garden that measures 30 feet by 20 feet. He wants to put a uniform border of pine bark around the outside of the garden. Find how wide the border should be if he has enough pine bark to cover 336 square feet.

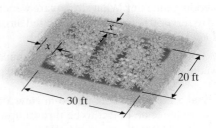

x

x

20 ft

30 ft

81. While hovering near the top of Ribbon Falls in Yosemite National Park at 1600 feet, a helicopter pilot accidentally drops his sunglasses. The height $h(t)$ of the sunglasses after

t seconds is given by the polynomial function

$$h(t) = -16t^2 + 1600$$

When will the sunglasses hit the ground?

82. After t seconds, the height $h(t)$ of a model rocket launched from the ground into the air is given by the function

$$h(t) = -16t^2 + 80t$$

Find how long it takes the rocket to reach a height of 96 feet.

△ **83.** The floor of a shed has an area of 90 square feet. The floor is in the shape of a rectangle whose length is 3 feet less than twice the width. Find the length and the width of the floor of the shed.

△ **84.** A vegetable garden with an area of 200 square feet is to be fertilized. If the length of the garden is 1 foot less than three times the width, find the dimensions of the garden.

85. The function $W(x) = 0.5x^2$ gives the number of servings of wedding cake that can be obtained from a two-layer x-inch square wedding cake tier. What size square wedding cake tier is needed to serve 50 people? (*Source:* Based on data from the *Wilton 2000 Yearbook of Cake Decorating*)

86. Use the function in Exercise 85 to determine what size square wedding cake tier is needed to serve 200 people.

87. Suppose that a movie is being filmed in New York City. An action shot requires an object to be thrown upward with an initial velocity of 80 feet per second off the top of 1 Madison Square Plaza, a height of 576 feet. The height $h(t)$ in feet of the object after t seconds is given by the function

$$h(t) = -16t^2 + 80t + 576.$$

Determine how long before the object strikes the ground. (See Exercise 99, Section 5.6) (*Source: The World Almanac*)

576 ft

88. Suppose that an object is thrown upward with an initial velocity of 64 feet per second off the edge of a 960-foot-cliff. The height $h(t)$ in feet of the object after t seconds is given by the function

$$h(t) = -16t^2 + 64t + 960$$

Determine how long before the object strikes the ground. (See Exercise 100, Section 5.6)

Match each polynomial function with its graph (A–F). See Example 10.

89. $f(x) = (x - 2)(x + 5)$

90. $g(x) = (x + 1)(x - 6)$

91. $h(x) = x(x + 3)(x - 3)$

92. $F(x) = (x + 1)(x - 2)(x + 5)$

93. $G(x) = 2x^2 + 9x + 4$

94. $H(x) = 2x^2 - 7x - 4$

A

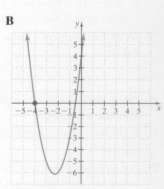

B

C

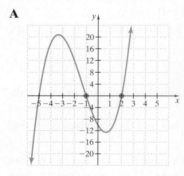

D

E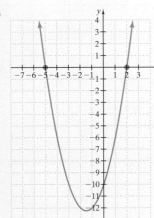

F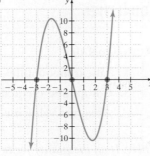

REVIEW AND PREVIEW

Write the x- and y-intercepts for each graph and determine whether the graph is the graph of a function. See Sections 3.1 and 3.2.

95.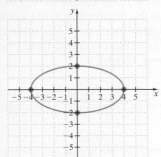

96.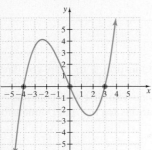

97.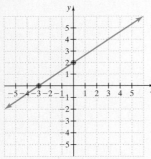

98.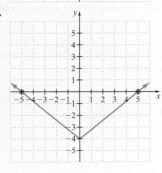

99. Draw a function with intercepts $(-3, 0)$, $(5, 0)$, and $(0, 4)$.

100. Draw a function with intercepts $(-7, 0)$, $\left(-\frac{1}{2}, 0\right)$, $(4, 0)$, and $(0, -1)$.

CONCEPT EXTENSIONS

Each exercise contains an error. Find and correct the error. See the Concept Check in the section.

101. $(x - 5)(x + 2) = 0$
$x - 5 = 0 \quad \text{or} \quad x + 2 = 0$
$x = -5 \quad \text{or} \quad x = -2$

102. $(4x - 5)(x + 7) = 0$
$4x - 5 = 0 \quad \text{or} \quad x + 7 = 0$
$x = \dfrac{4}{5} \quad \text{or} \quad x = -7$

103. $y(y - 5) = -6$
$y = -6 \quad \text{or} \quad y - 5 = -5$
$y = -7 \quad \text{or} \quad y = 0$

104. $3x^2 - 19x = 14$
$-16x = 14$
$x = -\dfrac{14}{16}$
$x = -\dfrac{7}{8}$

Solve.

105. $(x^2 + x - 6)(3x^2 - 14x - 5) = 0$

106. $(x^2 - 9)(x^2 + 8x + 16) = 0$

107. Is the following step correct? Why or why not?
$$x(x - 3) = 5$$
$$x = 5 \quad \text{or} \quad x - 3 = 5$$

Write a quadratic equation that has the given numbers as solutions.

108. $5, 3$

109. $6, 7$

110. $-1, 2$

111. $4, -3$

THE BIGGER PICTURE SOLVING EQUATIONS AND INEQUALITIES

Continue the outline started in Section 2.4 and continued in Sections 2.5 and 2.7. Write how to recognize and how to solve quadratic equations by factoring.

Solving Equations and Inequalities

I. **Equations**

   A. **Linear equations** (Sec. 2.1)

   B. **Absolute value equations** (Sec. 2.6)

   C. **Quadratic equations:** Equation can be written in the standard form $ax^2 + bx + c = 0$, with $a \neq 0$.

   Solve: $2x^2 - 7x = 9$

$2x^2 - 7x - 9 = 0$	Write in standard form so that equation is equal to 0.
$(2x - 9)(x + 1) = 0$	Factor.
$2x - 9 = 0$ or $x + 1 = 0$	Set each factor equal to 0.
$x = \dfrac{9}{2}$ or $x = -1$	Solve.

II. **Inequalities**

   A. **Linear inequalities** (Sec. 2.4)

   B. **Compound inequalities** (Sec. 2.5)

   C. **Absolute value inequalities** (Sec. 2.7)

Solve. If an inequality write your answer in interval notation.

1. $|7x - 3| = |5x + 9|$

2. $\left| \dfrac{x + 2}{5} \right| < 1$

3. $3(x - 6) + 2 = 9 + 5(3x - 1)$

4. $(x - 6)(2x + 3) = 0$

5. $|-3x + 10| \geq -2$

6. $|-2x - 5| = 11$

7. $x(x - 7) = 30$

8. $8x - 4 \geq 15x - 4$

CHAPTER 5 GROUP ACTIVITY

Finding the Largest Area

This activity may be completed by working in groups or individually.

A picture framer has a piece of wood that measures 1 inch wide by 50 inches long. She would like to make a picture frame with the largest possible interior area. Complete the following activity to help her determine the dimensions of the frame that she should use to achieve her goal.

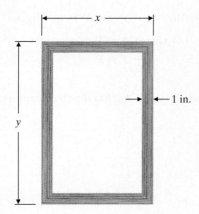

1. Use the situation shown in the figure to write an equation in x and y for the *outer* perimeter of the frame. (Remember that the outer perimeter will equal 50 inches.)

2. Use your equation from Question 1 to help you find the value of y for each value of x given in the table. Complete the y column of the table. (*Note:* The first two columns of the table give possible combinations for the outer dimensions of the frame.)

3. How is the interior width of the frame related to the exterior width of the frame? How is the interior height of the frame related to the exterior height of the frame? Use these relationships to complete the two columns of the table labeled "Interior Width" and "Interior Height."

4. Complete the last column of the table labeled "Interior Area" by using the columns of dimensions for the interior width and height.

5. From the table, what appears to be the largest interior area of the frame? Which exterior dimensions of the frame provide this area?

6. Use the patterns in the table to write an algebraic expression in terms of x for the interior width of the frame.

7. Use the patterns in the table to write an algebraic expression in terms of y for the interior height of the frame.

8. Use the perimeter equation from Question 1 to rewrite the algebraic expression for the interior height of the frame in terms of x.

Frame's Interior Dimensions				
x	y	*Interior Width*	*Interior Height*	*Interior Area*
2.0				
2.5				
3.0				
3.5				
4.0				
4.5				
5.0				
5.5				
6.0				
6.5				
7.0				
7.5				
8.0				
8.5				

Frame's Interior Dimensions				
x	y	*Interior Width*	*Interior Height*	*Interior Area*
9.0				
9.5				
10.0				
10.5				
11.0				
11.5				
12.0				
12.5				
13.0				
13.5				
14.0				
14.5				
15.0				

9. Find a function A that gives the interior area of the frame in terms of its exterior width x. (*Hint:* Study the patterns in the table. How could the expressions from Questions 6 and 8 be used to write this function?)

10. Graph the function A. Locate and label the point from the table that represents the maximum interior area. Describe the location of the point in relation to the rest of the graph.

CHAPTER 5 VOCABULARY CHECK

Fill in each blank with one of the words or phrases listed below.

| quadratic equation | scientific notation | polynomial | exponents | 1 | 0 | monomial |
| binomial | trinomial | degree of a polynomial | degree of a term | | | factoring |

1. A _____ is a finite sum of terms in which all variables are raised to nonnegative integer powers and no variables appear in any denominator.

2. _____ is the process of writing a polynomial as a product.

3. _____ are used to write repeated factors in a more compact form.

4. The _____ is the sum of the exponents on the variables contained in the term.

5. A _____ is a polynomial with one term.

6. If a is not 0, $a^0 = $ _____.

7. A _____ is a polynomial with three terms.

8. A polynomial equation of degree 2 is also called a _____.

9. A positive number is written in _____ if it is written as the product of a number a, such that $1 \le a < 10$ and a power of 10.

10. The _____ is the largest degree of all of its terms.

11. A _____ is a polynomial with two terms.

12. If a and b are real numbers and $a \cdot b = $ _____, then $a = 0$ or $b = 0$.

▶ **Helpful Hint**

Are you preparing for your test? Don't forget to take the Chapter 5 Test on page 335. Then check your answers at the back of the text and use the Chapter Test Prep Video CD to see the fully worked-out solutions to any of the exercises you want to review.

CHAPTER 5 HIGHLIGHTS

DEFINITIONS AND CONCEPTS	EXAMPLES

SECTION 5.1 EXPONENTS AND SCIENTIFIC NOTATION

Product rule: $a^m \cdot a^n = a^{m+n}$

Zero exponent: $a^0 = 1, a \neq 0$

Quotient rule: $\dfrac{a^m}{a^n} = a^{m-n}, a \neq 0$

Negative exponent: $a^{-n} = \dfrac{1}{a^n}, a \neq 0$

A positive number is written in **scientific notation** if it is written as the product of a number a, where $1 \leq a < 10$, and an integer power of 10: $a \times 10^r$.

$x^2 \cdot x^3 = x^5$

$7^0 = 1, (-10)^0 = 1$

$\dfrac{y^{10}}{y^4} = y^{10-4} = y^6$

$3^{-2} = \dfrac{1}{3^2} = \dfrac{1}{9}, \dfrac{x^{-5}}{x^{-7}} = x^{-5-(-7)} = x^2$

Numbers written in scientific notation

$568,000 = 5.68 \times 10^5$

$0.0002117 = 2.117 \times 10^{-4}$

SECTION 5.2 MORE WORK WITH EXPONENTS AND SCIENTIFIC NOTATION

Power rules:

$$(a^m)^n = a^{m \cdot n}$$

$$(ab)^m = a^m b^m$$

$$\left(\frac{a}{b}\right)^n = \frac{a^n}{b^n}, b \neq 0$$

$(7^8)^2 = 7^{16}$

$(2y)^3 = 2^3 y^3 = 8y^3$

$$\left(\frac{5x^{-3}}{x^2}\right)^{-2} = \frac{5^{-2}x^6}{x^{-4}}$$

$$= 5^{-2} \cdot x^{6-(-4)}$$

$$= \frac{x^{10}}{5^2}, \quad \text{or} \quad \frac{x^{10}}{25}$$

SECTION 5.3 POLYNOMIALS AND POLYNOMIAL FUNCTIONS

A **polynomial** is a finite sum of terms in which all variables have exponents raised to nonnegative integer powers and no variables appear in the denominator.

A function P is a **polynomial function** if $P(x)$ is a polynomial.

To add polynomials, combine all like terms.

To subtract polynomials, change the signs of the terms of the polynomial being subtracted, then add.

Polynomials

$1.3x^2$ (monomial)

$-\dfrac{1}{3}y + 5$ (binomial)

$6z^2 - 5z + 7$ (trinomial)

For the polynomial function

$$P(x) = -x^2 + 6x - 12, \text{find } P(-2)$$
$$P(-2) = -(-2)^2 + 6(-2) - 12 = -28.$$

Add

$$(3y^2x - 2yx + 11) + (-5y^2x - 7)$$
$$= -2y^2x - 2yx + 4$$

Subtract

$$(-2z^3 - z + 1) - (3z^3 + z - 6)$$
$$= -2z^3 - z + 1 - 3z^3 - z + 6$$
$$= -5z^3 - 2z + 7$$

DEFINITIONS AND CONCEPTS	**EXAMPLES**

SECTION 5.4   MULTIPLYING POLYNOMIALS

To multiply two polynomials, use the distributive property and multiply each term of one polynomial by each term of the other polynomial; then combine like terms.

Multiply

$$(x^2 - 2x)(3x^2 - 5x + 1)$$
$$= 3x^4 - 5x^3 + x^2 - 6x^3 + 10x^2 - 2x$$
$$= 3x^4 - 11x^3 + 11x^2 - 2x$$
$$(3m + 2n)^2 = 9m^2 + 12mn + 4n^2$$
$$(z^2 - 5)^2 = z^4 - 10z^2 + 25$$
$$(7y + 1)(7y - 1) = 49y^2 - 1$$

Special products

$$(a + b)^2 = a^2 + 2ab + b^2$$
$$(a - b)^2 = a^2 - 2ab + b^2$$
$$(a + b)(a - b) = a^2 - b^2$$

The FOIL method may be used when multiplying two binomials.

Multiply

$$(x^2 + 5)(2x^2 - 9)$$

$$\quad \text{F} \qquad \text{O} \qquad \text{I} \qquad \text{L}$$
$$= x^2(2x^2) + x^2(-9) + 5(2x^2) + 5(-9)$$
$$= 2x^4 - 9x^2 + 10x^2 - 45$$
$$= 2x^4 + x^2 - 45$$

SECTION 5.5   THE GREATEST COMMON FACTOR AND FACTORING BY GROUPING

The greatest common factor (GCF) of the terms of a polynomial is the product of the GCF of the numerical coefficients and the GCF of the variable factors.

Factor: $14xy^3 - 2xy^2 = 2 \cdot 7 \cdot x \cdot y^3 - 2 \cdot x \cdot y^2$.

The GCF is $2 \cdot x \cdot y^2$, or $2xy^2$.

$$14xy^3 - 2xy^2 = 2xy^2(7y - 1)$$

To factor a polynomial by grouping, group the terms so that each group has a common factor. Factor out these common factors. Then see if the new groups have a common factor.

Factor $x^4y - 5x^3 + 2xy - 10$.

$$x^4y - 5x^3 + 2xy - 10 = x^3(xy - 5) + 2(xy - 5)$$
$$= (xy - 5)(x^3 + 2)$$

SECTION 5.6   FACTORING TRINOMIALS

To factor $ax^2 + bx + c$, by trial and check,

Step 1. Write all pairs of factors of ax^2.

Step 2. Write all pairs of factors of c.

Step 3. Try combinations of these factors until the middle term bx is found.

Factor $28x^2 - 27x - 10$.

Factors of $28x^2$: $28x$ and x, $2x$ and $14x$, $4x$ and $7x$.

Factors of -10: -2 and 5, 2 and -5, -10 and 1, 10 and -1.

$$28x^2 - 27x - 10 = (7x + 2)(4x - 5)$$

To factor $ax^2 + bx + c$ by grouping,

Find two numbers whose product is $a \cdot c$ and whose sum is b, write the term bx using the two numbers found, and then factor by grouping.

$$2x^2 - 3x - 5 = 2x^2 - 5x + 2x - 5$$
$$= x(2x - 5) + 1(2x - 5)$$
$$= (2x - 5)(x + 1)$$

DEFINITIONS AND CONCEPTS	EXAMPLES

SECTION 5.7   FACTORING BY SPECIAL PRODUCTS

Perfect square trinomial

$$a^2 + 2ab + b^2 = (a + b)^2$$
$$a^2 - 2ab + b^2 = (a - b)^2$$

Factor

$$25x^2 + 30x + 9 = (5x + 3)^2$$
$$49z^2 - 28z + 4 = (7z - 2)^2$$

Difference of two squares

$$a^2 - b^2 = (a + b)(a - b)$$

Sum and difference of two cubes

$$a^3 + b^3 = (a + b)(a^2 - ab + b^2)$$
$$a^3 - b^3 = (a - b)(a^2 + ab + b^2)$$

$$36x^2 - y^2 = (6x + y)(6x - y)$$
$$8y^3 + 1 = (2y + 1)(4y^2 - 2y + 1)$$
$$27p^3 - 64q^3 = (3p - 4q)(9p^2 + 12pq + 16q^2)$$

Factor $10x^4y + 5x^2y - 15y$.

$$10x^4y + 5x^2y - 15y = 5y(2x^4 + x^2 - 3)$$

To factor a polynomial

Step 1. Factor out the GCF.

Step 2. If the polynomial is a binomial, see if it is a difference of two squares or a sum or difference of two cubes. If it is a trinomial, see if it is a perfect square trinomial. If not, try factoring by methods of Section 5.6. If it is a polynomial with 4 or more terms, try factoring by grouping.

Step 3. See if any factors can be factored further.

$$= 5y(2x^2 + 3)(x^2 - 1)$$
$$= 5y(2x^2 + 3)(x + 1)(x - 1)$$

SECTION 5.8   SOLVING EQUATIONS BY FACTORING AND PROBLEM SOLVING

To solve polynomial equations by factoring:

Step 1. Write the equation so that one side is 0.

Step 2. Factor the polynomial completely.

Step 3. Set each factor equal to 0.

Step 4. Solve the resulting equations.

Step 5. Check each solution.

Solve

$$2x^3 - 5x^2 = 3x$$
$$2x^3 - 5x^2 - 3x = 0$$
$$x(2x + 1)(x - 3) = 0$$
$$x = 0 \quad \text{or} \quad 2x + 1 = 0 \quad \text{or} \quad x - 3 = 0$$
$$x = 0 \quad \text{or} \quad x = -\frac{1}{2} \quad \text{or} \quad x = 3$$

The solutions are $0, -\frac{1}{2}$, and 3.

CHAPTER 5 REVIEW

(5.1) *Evaluate.*

1. $(-2)^2$

2. $(-3)^4$

3. -2^2

4. -3^4

5. 8^0

6. -9^0

7. -4^{-2}

8. $(-4)^{-2}$

Simplify each expression. Use only positive exponents.

9. $-xy^2 \cdot y^3 \cdot xy^2z$

10. $(-4xy)(-3xy^2b)$

11. $a^{-14} \cdot a^5$

12. $\dfrac{a^{16}}{a^{17}}$

13. $\dfrac{x^{-7}}{x^4}$

14. $\dfrac{9a(a^{-3})}{18a^{15}}$

15. $\dfrac{y^{6p-3}}{y^{6p+2}}$

Write in scientific notation.

16. 36,890,000

17. −0.000362

Write each number without exponents.

18. 1.678×10^{-6}

19. 4.1×10^5

(5.2) *Simplify. Use only positive exponents.*

20. $(8^5)^3$

21. $\left(\dfrac{a}{4}\right)^2$

22. $(3x)^3$

23. $(-4x)^{-2}$

24. $\left(\dfrac{6x}{5}\right)^2$

25. $(8^6)^{-3}$

26. $\left(\dfrac{4}{3}\right)^{-2}$

27. $(-2x^3)^{-3}$

28. $\left(\dfrac{8p^6}{4p^4}\right)^{-2}$

29. $(-3x^{-2}y^2)^3$

30. $\left(\dfrac{x^{-5}y^{-3}}{z^3}\right)^{-5}$

31. $\dfrac{4^{-1}x^3yz}{x^{-2}yx^4}$

32. $(5xyz)^{-4}(x^{-2})^{-3}$

33. $\dfrac{2(3yz)^{-3}}{y^{-3}}$

Simplify each expression.

34. $x^{4a}(3x^{5a})^3$

35. $\dfrac{4y^{3x-3}}{2y^{2x+4}}$

Use scientific notation to find the quotient. Express each quotient in scientific notation.

36. $\dfrac{(0.00012)(144,000)}{0.0003}$

37. $\dfrac{(-0.00017)(0.00039)}{3000}$

Simplify. Use only positive exponents.

38. $\dfrac{27x^{-5}y^5}{18x^{-6}y^2}\cdot\dfrac{x^4y^{-2}}{x^{-2}y^3}$

39. $\dfrac{3x^5}{y^{-4}}\cdot\dfrac{(3xy^{-3})^{-2}}{(z^{-3})^{-4}}$

40. $\dfrac{(x^w)^2}{(x^{w-4})^{-2}}$

(5.3) *Find the degree of each polynomial.*

41. $x^2y-3xy^3z+5x+7y$

42. $3x+2$

Simplify by combining like terms.

43. $4x+8x-6x^2-6x^2y$

44. $-8xy^3+4xy^3-3x^3y$

Add or subtract as indicated.

45. $(3x+7y)+(4x^2-3x+7)+(y-1)$

46. $(4x^2-6xy+9y^2)-(8x^2-6xy-y^2)$

47. $(3x^2-4b+28)+(9x^2-30)-(4x^2-6b+20)$

48. Add $(9xy+4x^2+18)$ and $(7xy-4x^3-9x)$.

49. Subtract $(x-7)$ from the sum of $(3x^2y-7xy-4)$ and $(9x^2y+x)$.

50. $\begin{array}{r}x^2-5x+7\\ -(x+4)\\\hline\end{array}$

51. $\begin{array}{r}x^3+2xy^2-y\\ +(x-4xy^2-7)\\\hline\end{array}$

If $P(x)=9x^2-7x+8$, find the following.

52. $P(6)$

53. $P(-2)$

54. $P(-3)$

If $P(x)=2x-1$ and $Q(x)=x^2-2x-5$, find the following.

55. $P(x)+Q(x)$

56. $2[P(x)]-Q(x)$

△ **57.** Find the perimeter of the rectangle.

x^2y+5 cm

$2x^2y-6x+1$ cm

(5.4) *Multiply.*

58. $-6x(4x^2-6x+1)$

59. $-4ab^2(3ab^3+7ab+1)$

60. $(x-4)(2x+9)$

61. $(-3xa+4b)^2$

62. $(9x^2+4x+1)(4x-3)$

63. $(5x-9y)(3x+9y)$

64. $\left(x-\dfrac{1}{3}\right)\left(x+\dfrac{2}{3}\right)$

65. $(x^2+9x+1)^2$

Multiply, using special products.

66. $(3x-y)^2$

67. $(4x+9)^2$

68. $(x+3y)(x-3y)$

69. $[4+(3a-b)][4-(3a-b)]$

70. If $P(x)=2x-1$ and $Q(x)=x^2+2x-5$, find $P(x)\cdot Q(x)$.

△ **71.** Find the area of the rectangle.

$3y-7z$ units

$3y+7z$ units

Multiply. Assume that all variable exponents represent integers.

72. $4a^b(3a^{b+2}-7)$

73. $(4xy^z-b)^2$

74. $(3x^a-4)(3x^a+4)$

(5.5) *Factor out the greatest common factor.*

75. $16x^3 - 24x^2$

76. $36y - 24y^2$

77. $6ab^2 + 8ab - 4a^2b^2$

78. $14a^2b^2 - 21ab^2 + 7ab$

79. $6a(a + 3b) - 5(a + 3b)$

80. $4x(x - 2y) - 5(x - 2y)$

81. $xy - 6y + 3x - 18$

82. $ab - 8b + 4a - 32$

83. $pq - 3p - 5q + 15$

84. $x^3 - x^2 - 2x + 2$

△ **85.** A smaller square is cut from a larger rectangle. Write the area of the shaded region as a factored polynomial.

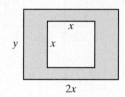

(5.6) *Completely factor each polynomial.*

86. $x^2 - 14x - 72$

87. $x^2 + 16x - 80$

88. $2x^2 - 18x + 28$

89. $3x^2 + 33x + 54$

90. $2x^3 - 7x^2 - 9x$

91. $3x^2 + 2x - 16$

92. $6x^2 + 17x + 10$

93. $15x^2 - 91x + 6$

94. $4x^2 + 2x - 12$

95. $9x^2 - 12x - 12$

96. $y^2(x + 6)^2 - 2y(x + 6)^2 - 3(x + 6)^2$

97. $(x + 5)^2 + 6(x + 5) + 8$

98. $x^4 - 6x^2 - 16$

99. $x^4 + 8x^2 - 20$

(5.7) *Factor each polynomial completely.*

100. $x^2 - 100$

101. $x^2 - 81$

102. $2x^2 - 32$

103. $6x^2 - 54$

104. $81 - x^4$

105. $16 - y^4$

106. $(y + 2)^2 - 25$

107. $(x - 3)^2 - 16$

108. $x^3 + 216$

109. $y^3 + 512$

110. $8 - 27y^3$

111. $1 - 64y^3$

112. $6x^4y + 48xy$

113. $2x^5 + 16x^2y^3$

114. $x^2 - 2x + 1 - y^2$

115. $x^2 - 6x + 9 - 4y^2$

116. $4x^2 + 12x + 9$

117. $16a^2 - 40ab + 25b^2$

△ **118.** The volume of the cylindrical shell is $\pi R^2 h - \pi r^2 h$ cubic units. Write this volume as a factored expression.

(5.8) *Solve each polynomial equation for the variable.*

119. $(3x - 1)(x + 7) = 0$

120. $3(x + 5)(8x - 3) = 0$

121. $5x(x - 4)(2x - 9) = 0$

122. $6(x + 3)(x - 4)(5x + 1) = 0$

123. $2x^2 = 12x$

124. $4x^3 - 36x = 0$

125. $(1 - x)(3x + 2) = -4x$

126. $2x(x - 12) = -40$

127. $3x^2 + 2x = 12 - 7x$

128. $2x^2 + 3x = 35$

129. $x^3 - 18x = 3x^2$

130. $19x^2 - 42x = -x^3$

131. $12x = 6x^3 + 6x^2$

132. $8x^3 + 10x^2 = 3x$

133. The sum of a number and twice its square is 105. Find the number.

△ **134.** The length of a rectangular piece of carpet is 5 meters less than twice its width. Find the dimensions of the carpet if its area is 33 square meters.

135. A scene from an adventure film calls for a stunt dummy to be dropped from above the second-story platform of the

Eiffel Tower, a distance of 400 feet. Its height $h(t)$ at time t seconds is given by

$$h(t) = -16t^2 + 400$$

Determine when the stunt dummy will reach the ground.

400 ft

MIXED REVIEW

136. The Royal Gorge suspension bridge in Colorado is 1053 feet above the Arkansas River. Neglecting air resistance, the height of an object dropped off the bridge is given by the polynomial function $P(t) = -16t^2 + 1053$ after time t seconds. Find the height of the object when $t = 1$ second and when $t = 8$ seconds.

Perform the indicated operation.

137. $(x + 5)(3x^2 - 2x + 1)$

138. $(3x^2 + 4x - 1.2) - (5x^2 - x + 5.7)$

139. $(3x^2 + 4x - 1.2) + (5x^2 - x + 5.7)$

140. $\left(7ab - \dfrac{1}{2}\right)^2$

If $P(x) = -x^2 + x - 4$, find

141. $P(5)$ **142.** $P(-2)$

Factor each polynomial completely.

143. $12y^5 - 6y^4$

144. $x^2y + 4x^2 - 3y - 12$

145. $6x^2 - 34x - 12$

146. $y^2(4x + 3)^2 - 19y(4x + 3)^2 - 20(4x + 3)^2$

147. $4z^7 - 49z^5$

148. $5x^4 - 4x^2 - 9$

Solve each equation.

149. $8x^2 = 24x$ **150.** $x(x - 11) = 26$

CHAPTER 5 TEST TEST PREP   VIDEO

Remember to use the Chapter Test Prep Video CD to see the fully worked-out solutions to any of the exercises you want to review.

Simplify. Use positive exponents to write the answers.

1. $(-9x)^{-2}$

2. $-3xy^{-2}(4xy^2)z$

3. $\dfrac{6^{-1}a^2b^{-3}}{3^{-2}a^{-5}b^2}$

4. $\left(\dfrac{-xy^{-5}z}{xy^3}\right)^{-5}$

Write Exercises 5 and 6 in scientific notation.

5. 630,000,000

6. 0.01200

7. Write 5×10^{-6} without exponents.

8. Use scientific notation to find the quotient.

$$\frac{(0.0024)(0.00012)}{0.00032}$$

Perform the indicated operations.

9. $(4x^3y - 3x - 4) - (9x^3y + 8x + 5)$

10. $-3xy(4x + y)$

11. $(3x + 4)(4x - 7)$

12. $(5a - 2b)(5a + 2b)$

13. $(6m + n)^2$

14. $(2x - 1)(x^2 - 6x + 4)$

Factor each polynomial completely.

15. $16x^3y - 12x^2y^4$

16. $x^2 - 13x - 30$

17. $4y^2 + 20y + 25$

18. $6x^2 - 15x - 9$

19. $4x^2 - 25$

20. $x^3 + 64$

21. $3x^2y - 27y^3$

22. $6x^2 + 24$

23. $16y^3 - 2$

24. $x^2y - 9y - 3x^2 + 27$

Solve the equation for the variable.

25. $3n(7n - 20) = 96$

26. $(x + 2)(x - 2) = 5(x + 4)$

27. $2x^3 + 5x^2 = 8x + 20$

△ **28.** Write the area of the shaded region as a factored polynomial.

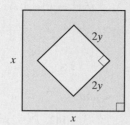

29. A pebble is hurled upward from the top of the Canada Trust Tower, which is 880 feet tall, with an initial velocity of 96 feet per second. Neglecting air resistance, the height $h(t)$ of the pebble after t seconds is given by the polynomial function

$$h(t) = -16t^2 + 96t + 880$$

a. Find the height of the pebble when $t = 1$.

b. Find the height of the pebble when $t = 5.1$.

c. When will the pebble hit the ground?

CHAPTER 5 CUMULATIVE REVIEW

1. Find the roots.

a. $\sqrt[3]{27}$

b. $\sqrt[5]{1}$

c. $\sqrt[4]{16}$

2. Find the roots.

a. $\sqrt[3]{64}$

b. $\sqrt[4]{81}$

c. $\sqrt[5]{32}$

3. Solve: $2(x - 3) = 5x - 9$.

4. Solve: $0.3y + 2.4 = 0.1y + 4$

5. Karen Estes just received an inheritance of $10,000 and plans to place all the money in a savings account that pays 5% compounded quarterly to help her son go to college in 3 years. How much money will be in the account in 3 years?

6. A gallon of latex paint can cover 400 square feet. How many gallon containers of paint should be bought to paint two coats on each wall of a rectangular room whose dimensions are 14 feet by 18 feet? (Assume 8-foot ceilings).

7. Solve and graph the solution set.

a. $\frac{1}{4}x \le \frac{3}{8}$

b. $-2.3x < 6.9$

8. Solve. Graph the solution set and write it in interval notation.

$x + 2 \le \frac{1}{4}(x - 7)$

Solve.

9. $-1 \le \frac{2x}{3} + 5 \le 2$

10. Solve: $-\frac{1}{3} < \frac{3x + 1}{6} \le \frac{1}{3}$

11. $|y| = 0$

12. Solve: $8 + |4c| = 24$

13. $\left|2x - \frac{1}{10}\right| < -13$

14. Solve: $|5x - 1| + 9 > 5$

15. Graph the linear equation $y = \frac{1}{3}x$.

16. Graph the linear equation $y = 3x$.

17. Evaluate $f(2)$, $f(-6)$, and $f(0)$ for the function

$$f(x) = \begin{cases} 2x + 3 & \text{if } x \le 0 \\ -x - 1 & \text{if } x > 0 \end{cases}$$

Write your results in ordered-pair form.

18. If $f(x) = 3x^2 + 2x + 3$, find $f(-3)$.

19. Graph $x = 2$.

20. Graph $y - 5 = 0$

21. Find the slope of the line $y = 2$.

22. Find the slope of the line, $f(x) = -2x - 3$.

23. Find an equation of the horizontal line containing the point $(2, 3)$.

24. Find the equation of the vertical line containing the point $(-3, 2)$.

25. Graph the union of $x + \frac{1}{2}y \ge -4$ or $y \le -2$.

26. Find the equation of the line containing the point $(-2, 3)$ and slope of 0.

27. Use the substitution method to solve the system.
$\begin{cases} 2x + 4y = -6 \\ x = 2y - 5 \end{cases}$

28. Use the substitution method to solve the system.
$\begin{cases} 4x - 2y = 8 \\ y = 3x - 6 \end{cases}$

29. Solve the system. $\begin{cases} 2x + 4y = 1 \\ 4x - 4z = -1 \\ y - 4z = -3 \end{cases}$

30. Solve the system. $\begin{cases} x + y - \frac{3}{2}z = \frac{1}{2} \\ -y - 2z = 14 \\ x - \frac{2}{3}y = -\frac{1}{3} \end{cases}$

31. A first number is 4 less than a second number. Four times the first number is 6 more than twice the second. Find the numbers.

32. One solution contains 20% acid and a second solution contains 60% acid. How many ounces of each solution should be mixed in order to have 50 ounces of a 30% acid solution?

33. Use matrices to solve the system. $\begin{cases} 2x - y = 3 \\ 4x - 2y = 5 \end{cases}$

34. Use matrices to solve the system. $\begin{cases} 4y = 8 \\ x + y = 7 \end{cases}$

35. The measure of the largest angle of a triangle is 80° more than the measure of the smallest angle, and the measure of the remaining angle is 10° more than the measure of the smallest angle. Find the measure of each angle.

36. Find the equation of the line with slope $\frac{1}{2}$, through the point $(0, 5)$. Write the equation using function notation.

37. Write each number in scientific notation.

  a. 730,000

  b. 0.00000104

38. Write each number in scientific notation.

  a. 8,250,000

  b. 0.0000346

39. Simplify each expression. Use positive exponents to write the answers.

  a. $(2x^0 y^{-3})^{-2}$ **b.** $\left(\dfrac{x^{-5}}{x^{-2}} \right)^{-3}$

  c. $\left(\dfrac{2}{7} \right)^{-2}$ **d.** $\dfrac{5^{-2} x^{-3} y^{11}}{x^2 y^{-5}}$

40. Simplify each expression. Use positive exponents to write the answers.

  a. $(4a^{-1}b^0)^{-3}$ **b.** $\left(\dfrac{a^{-6}}{a^{-8}} \right)^{-2}$

  c. $\left(\dfrac{2}{3} \right)^{-3}$ **d.** $\dfrac{3^{-2} a^{-2} b^{12}}{a^4 b^{-5}}$

41. Find the degree of the polynomial $3xy + x^2 y^2 - 5x^2 - 6$.

42. Subtract $(5x^2 + 3x)$ from $(3x^2 - 2x)$.

43. Multiply.

  a. $(2x^3)(5x^6)$

  b. $(7y^4 z^4)(-xy^{11} z^5)$

44. Multiply.

  a. $(3y^6)(4y^2)$

  b. $(6a^3 b^2)(-a^2 bc^4)$

Factor.

45. $17x^3 y^2 - 34x^4 y^2$

46. Factor completely $12x^3 y - 3xy^3$

47. $x^2 + 10x + 16$

48. Factor $5a^2 + 14a - 3$

49. Solve $2x^2 + 9x - 5 = 0$.

50. Solve $3x^2 - 10x - 8 = 0$

6 Rational Expressions

Polynomials are to algebra what integers are to arithmetic. We have added, subtracted, multiplied, and raised polynomials to powers, each operation yielding another polynomial, just as these operations on integers yield another integer. But when we divide one integer by another, the result may or may not be another integer. Likewise, when we divide one polynomial by another, we may or may not get a polynomial in return. The quotient $x \div (x + 1)$ is not a polynomial; it is a *rational expression* that can be written as

$$\frac{x}{x + 1}.$$

In this chapter, we study these new algebraic forms known as rational expressions and the *rational functions* they generate.

Movies still attract more people (1,448 million annually) than either theme parks (341 million) or major professional league sports (137 million) combined. U.S. theater admissions grew 3.3% in 2006 and movie advertising is changing, with advertising on TV or in the newspaper decreasing and online advertising increasing.

The graph below shows yearly rating changes for top grossing films. In Section 6.6, Exercises 60 and 61, page 392, you will have the opportunity to solve applications about movie ratings and costs to make a movie.

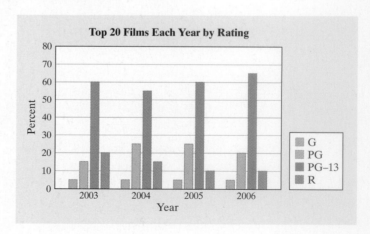

6.1 RATIONAL FUNCTIONS AND MULTIPLYING AND DIVIDING RATIONAL EXPRESSIONS

OBJECTIVES

1 Find the domain of a rational expression.

2 Simplify rational expressions.

3 Multiply rational expressions.

4 Divide rational expressions.

5 Use rational functions in applications.

Recall that a *rational number,* or *fraction,* is a number that can be written as the quotient $\frac{p}{q}$ of two integers p and q as long as q is not 0. A **rational expression** is an expression that can be written as the quotient $\frac{P}{Q}$ of two polynomials P and Q as long as Q is not 0.

Examples of Rational Expressions

$$\frac{3x + 7}{2} \qquad \frac{5x^2 - 3}{x - 1} \qquad \frac{7x - 2}{2x^2 + 7x + 6}$$

Rational expressions are sometimes used to describe functions. For example, we call the function $f(x) = \frac{x^2 + 2}{x - 3}$ a **rational function** since $\frac{x^2 + 2}{x - 3}$ is a rational expression.

OBJECTIVE 1 ▶ Finding the domain of a rational expression. As with fractions, a rational expression is **undefined** if the denominator is 0. If a variable in a rational expression is replaced with a number that makes the denominator 0, we say that the rational expression is **undefined** for this value of the variable. For example, the rational expression $\frac{x^2 + 2}{x - 3}$ is undefined when x is 3, because replacing x with 3 results in a denominator of 0. For this reason, we must exclude 3 from the domain of the function $f(x) = \frac{x^2 + 2}{x - 3}$.

The domain of f is then

$$\{x \mid x \text{ is a real number and } x \neq 3\}$$

"The set of all x such that x is a real number and x is not equal to 3."

In this section, we will use this set builder notations to write domains. Unless told otherwise, we assume that the domain of a function described by an equation is the set of all real numbers for which the equation is defined.

EXAMPLE 1   Find the domain of each rational function.

a. $f(x) = \dfrac{8x^3 + 7x^2 + 20}{2}$ **b.** $g(x) = \dfrac{5x^2 - 3}{x - 1}$ **c.** $f(x) = \dfrac{7x - 2}{x^2 - 2x - 15}$

Solution   The domain of each function will contain all real numbers except those values that make the denominator 0.

a. No matter what the value of x, the denominator of $f(x) = \dfrac{8x^3 + 7x^2 + 20}{2}$ is never 0, so the domain of f is $\{x \mid x \text{ is a real number}\}$.

b. To find the values of x that make the denominator of $g(x)$ equal to 0, we solve the equation "denominator = 0":

$$x - 1 = 0, \quad \text{or} \quad x = 1$$

The domain must exclude 1 since the rational expression is undefined when x is 1. The domain of g is $\{x \mid x \text{ is a real number and } x \neq 1\}$.

c. We find the domain by setting the denominator equal to 0.

$$x^2 - 2x - 15 = 0 \quad \text{Set the denominator equal to 0 and solve.}$$
$$(x - 5)(x + 3) = 0$$
$$x - 5 = 0 \quad \text{or} \quad x + 3 = 0$$
$$x = 5 \quad \text{or} \quad x = -3$$

If x is replaced with 5 or with -3, the rational expression is undefined.

The domain of f is $\{x \mid x \text{ is a real number and } x \neq 5, x \neq -3\}$. ☐

PRACTICE
1 Find the domain of each rational function.

a. $f(x) = \dfrac{4x^5 - 3x^2 + 2}{-6}$ **b.** $g(x) = \dfrac{6x^2 + 1}{x + 3}$ **c.** $h(x) = \dfrac{8x - 3}{x^2 - 5x + 6}$

Concept Check ☑

For which of these values (if any) is the rational expression $\dfrac{x - 3}{x^2 + 2}$ undefined?

a. 2 **b.** 3 **c.** -2 **d.** 0 **e.** None of these

OBJECTIVE 2 ▶ Simplifying rational expressions. Recall that a fraction is in lowest terms or simplest form if the numerator and denominator have no common factors other than 1 (or -1). For example, $\dfrac{3}{13}$ is in lowest terms since 3 and 13 have no common factors other than 1 (or -1).

To **simplify** a rational expression, or to write it in lowest terms, we use a method similar to simplifying a fraction.

Recall that to simplify a fraction, we essentially "remove factors of 1." Our ability to do this comes from these facts:

- If $c \neq 0$, then $\dfrac{c}{c} = 1$. For example, $\dfrac{7}{7} = 1$ and $\dfrac{-8.65}{-8.65} = 1$.

- $n \cdot 1 = n$. For example, $-5 \cdot 1 = -5$, $126.8 \cdot 1 = 126.8$, and $\dfrac{a}{b} \cdot 1 = \dfrac{a}{b}, b \neq 0$.

In other words, we have the following:

$$\frac{a \cdot c}{b \cdot c} = \frac{a}{b} \cdot \underbrace{\frac{c}{c}}_{} = \frac{a}{b}$$

Since $\frac{a}{b} \cdot 1 = \frac{a}{b}$

Let's practice simplifying a fraction by simplifying $\dfrac{15}{65}$.

$$\frac{15}{65} = \frac{3 \cdot 5}{13 \cdot 5} = \frac{3}{13} \cdot \underbrace{\frac{5}{5}}_{} = \frac{3}{13} \cdot 1 = \frac{3}{13}$$

Let's use the same technique and simplify the rational expression $\dfrac{(x + 2)^2}{x^2 - 4}$.

$$\frac{(x + 2)^2}{x^2 - 4} = \frac{(x + 2)(x + 2)}{(x - 2)(x + 2)}$$
$$= \frac{(x + 2)}{(x - 2)} \cdot \frac{x + 2}{x + 2}$$
$$= \frac{x + 2}{x - 2} \cdot 1$$
$$= \frac{x + 2}{x - 2}$$

This means that the rational expression $\dfrac{(x + 2)^2}{x^2 - 4}$ has the same value as the rational expression $\dfrac{x + 2}{x - 2}$ for all values of x except 2 and -2. (Remember that when x is 2, the denominators of both rational expressions are 0 and that when x is -2, the original rational expression has a denominator of 0.)

As we simplify rational expressions, we will assume that the simplified rational expression is equivalent to the original rational expression for all real numbers except those for which either denominator is 0.

Just as for numerical fractions, we can use a shortcut notation. Remember that as long as exact factors in both the numerator and denominator are divided out, we are "removing a factor of 1." We can use the following notation:

$$\frac{(x + 2)^2}{x^2 - 4} = \frac{(x + 2)\,\boxed{(x + 2)}}{(x - 2)\,\boxed{(x + 2)}} \qquad \text{A factor of 1 is identified by the shading.}$$

$$= \frac{x + 2}{x - 2} \qquad \text{"Remove" the factor of 1.}$$

This "removing a factor of 1" is stated in the principle below:

Fundamental Principle of Rational Expressions

For any rational expression $\dfrac{P}{Q}$ and any polynomial R, where $R \neq 0$,

$$\frac{PR}{QR} = \frac{P}{Q} \cdot \frac{R}{R} = \frac{P}{Q} \cdot 1 = \frac{P}{Q}$$

or, simply,

$$\frac{PR}{QR} = \frac{P}{Q}$$

In general, the following steps may be used to simplify rational expressions or to write a rational expression in lowest terms.

Simplifying or Writing a Rational Expression in Lowest Terms

STEP 1. Completely factor the numerator and denominator of the rational expression.

STEP 2. Divide out factors common to the numerator and denominator. (This is the same as "removing a factor of 1.")

For now, we assume that variables in a rational expression do not represent values that make the denominator 0.

EXAMPLE 2 Simplify each rational expression.

a. $\dfrac{2x^2}{10x^3 - 2x^2}$ **b.** $\dfrac{9x^2 + 13x + 4}{8x^2 + x - 7}$

Solution

a. $\dfrac{2x^2}{10x^3 - 2x^2} = \dfrac{2x^2 \cdot 1}{2x^2\,(5x - 1)} = 1 \cdot \dfrac{1}{5x - 1} = \dfrac{1}{5x - 1}$

b. $\dfrac{9x^2 + 13x + 4}{8x^2 + x - 7} = \dfrac{(9x + 4)\,(x + 1)}{(8x - 7)\,(x + 1)}$ Factor the numerator and denominator.

$= \dfrac{9x + 4}{8x - 7} \cdot 1$ Since $\dfrac{x + 1}{x + 1} = 1$

$= \dfrac{9x + 4}{8x - 7}$ Simplest form

PRACTICE
2   Simplify each rational expressions.

a. $\dfrac{5z^4}{10z^5 - 5z^4}$ **b.** $\dfrac{5x^2 + 13x + 6}{6x^2 + 7x - 10}$

EXAMPLE 3   Simplify each rational expression.

a. $\dfrac{2 + x}{x + 2}$ **b.** $\dfrac{2 - x}{x - 2}$

Solution

a. $\dfrac{2 + x}{x + 2} = \dfrac{x + 2}{x + 2} = 1$ By the commutative property of addition, $2 + x = x + 2$.

b. $\dfrac{2 - x}{x - 2}$

The terms in the numerator of $\dfrac{2 - x}{x - 2}$ differ by sign from the terms of the denominator, so the polynomials are opposites of each other and the expression simplifies to -1. To see this, we factor out -1 from the numerator or the denominator. If -1 is factored from the numerator, then

$$\dfrac{2 - x}{x - 2} = \dfrac{-1(-2 + x)}{x - 2} = \dfrac{-1\,(x - 2)}{x - 2} = \dfrac{-1}{1} = -1$$

> **▶ Helpful Hint**
> When the numerator and the denominator of a rational expression are opposites of each other, the expression simplifies to -1.

If -1 is factored from the denominator, the result is the same.

$$\dfrac{2 - x}{x - 2} = \dfrac{2 - x}{-1(-x + 2)} = \dfrac{2 - x}{-1\,(2 - x)} = \dfrac{1}{-1} = -1$$

PRACTICE
3   Simplify each rational expression.

a. $\dfrac{x + 3}{3 + x}$ **b.** $\dfrac{3 - x}{x - 3}$

EXAMPLE 4   Simplify $\dfrac{18 - 2x^2}{x^2 - 2x - 3}$.

Solution $\dfrac{18 - 2x^2}{x^2 - 2x - 3} = \dfrac{2(9 - x^2)}{(x + 1)(x - 3)}$ Factor.

$= \dfrac{2(3 + x)(3 - x)}{(x + 1)(x - 3)}$ Factor completely.

$= \dfrac{2(3 + x) \cdot -1\,(x - 3)}{(x + 1)\,(x - 3)}$ Notice the opposites $3 - x$ and $x - 3$. Write $3 - x$ as $-1(x - 3)$ and simplify.

$= -\dfrac{2(3 + x)}{x + 1}$

PRACTICE
4   Simplify $\dfrac{20 - 5x^2}{x^2 + x - 6}$.

> ▶ **Helpful Hint**
>
> Recall that for a fraction $\dfrac{a}{b}$,
>
> $$\frac{a}{-b} = \frac{-a}{b} = -\frac{a}{b}$$
>
> For example
>
> $$\frac{-(x+1)}{(x+2)} = \frac{(x+1)}{-(x+2)} = -\frac{x+1}{x+2}$$

Concept Check ☑

Which of the following expressions are equivalent to $\dfrac{x}{8-x}$?

a. $\dfrac{-x}{x-8}$ **b.** $\dfrac{-x}{8-x}$ **c.** $\dfrac{x}{x-8}$ **d.** $\dfrac{-x}{-8+x}$

EXAMPLE 5   Simplify each rational expression.

a. $\dfrac{x^3+8}{2+x}$ **b.** $\dfrac{2y^2+2}{y^3-5y^2+y-5}$

Solution

a. $\dfrac{x^3+8}{2+x} = \dfrac{(x+2)(x^2-2x+4)}{x+2}$ Factor the sum of the two cubes.

$= x^2 - 2x + 4$ Divide out common factors.

b. $\dfrac{2y^2+2}{y^3-5y^2+y-5} = \dfrac{2(y^2+1)}{(y^3-5y^2)+(y-5)}$ Factor the numerator.

$= \dfrac{2(y^2+1)}{y^2(y-5)+1(y-5)}$ Factor the denominator by grouping.

$= \dfrac{2(y^2+1)}{(y-5)(y^2+1)}$

$= \dfrac{2}{y-5}$ Divide out common factors.   □

PRACTICE
5   Simplify each rational expression.

a. $\dfrac{x^3+64}{4+x}$ **b.** $\dfrac{5z^2+10}{z^3-3z^2+2z-6}$

Concept Check ☑

Does $\dfrac{n}{n+2}$ simplify to $\dfrac{1}{2}$? Why or why not?

OBJECTIVE 3 ▶ Multiplying rational expressions. Arithmetic operations on rational expressions are performed in the same way as they are on rational numbers.

Answers to Concept Check:
a and d
no; answers may vary.

> **Multiplying Rational Expressions**
>
> The rule for multiplying rational expressions is
>
> $$\frac{P}{Q} \cdot \frac{R}{S} = \frac{PR}{QS} \quad \text{as long as } Q \neq 0 \text{ and } S \neq 0.$$
>
> To multiply rational expressions, you may use these steps:
>
> **STEP 1.** Completely factor each numerator and denominator.
>
> **STEP 2.** Use the rule above and multiply the numerators and the denominators.
>
> **STEP 3.** Simplify the product by dividing the numerator and denominator by their common factors.

When we multiply rational expressions, notice that we factor each numerator and denominator first. This helps when we apply the fundamental principle to write the product in simplest form.

EXAMPLE 6   Multiply.

a. $\dfrac{1 + 3n}{2n} \cdot \dfrac{2n - 4}{3n^2 - 2n - 1}$
    b. $\dfrac{x^3 - 1}{-3x + 3} \cdot \dfrac{15x^2}{x^2 + x + 1}$

Solution

a. $\dfrac{1 + 3n}{2n} \cdot \dfrac{2n - 4}{3n^2 - 2n - 1} = \dfrac{1 + 3n}{2n} \cdot \dfrac{2(n - 2)}{(3n + 1)(n - 1)}$ Factor.

$\qquad\qquad = \dfrac{(1 + 3n) \cdot 2(n - 2)}{2n(3n + 1)(n - 1)}$ Multiply.

$\qquad\qquad = \dfrac{n - 2}{n(n - 1)}$ Divide out common factors.

b. $\dfrac{x^3 - 1}{-3x + 3} \cdot \dfrac{15x^2}{x^2 + x + 1} = \dfrac{(x - 1)(x^2 + x + 1)}{-3(x - 1)} \cdot \dfrac{15x^2}{x^2 + x + 1}$ Factor.

$\qquad\qquad = \dfrac{(x - 1)(x^2 + x + 1) \cdot 3 \cdot 5x^2}{-1 \cdot 3(x - 1)(x^2 + x + 1)}$ Factor.

$\qquad\qquad = \dfrac{5x^2}{-1} = -5x^2$ Simplest form   □

PRACTICE
6   Multiply.

a. $\dfrac{2 + 5n}{3n} \cdot \dfrac{6n + 3}{5n^2 - 3n - 2}$
    b. $\dfrac{x^3 - 8}{-6x + 12} \cdot \dfrac{6x^2}{x^2 + 2x + 4}$

OBJECTIVE 4 ▶ Dividing rational expressions. Recall that two numbers are reciprocals of each other if their product is 1. Similarly, if $\dfrac{P}{Q}$ is a rational expression, then $\dfrac{Q}{P}$ is its **reciprocal,** since

$$\frac{P}{Q} \cdot \frac{Q}{P} = \frac{P \cdot Q}{Q \cdot P} = 1$$

The following are examples of expressions and their reciprocals.

Expression	*Reciprocal*
$\dfrac{3}{x}$	$\dfrac{x}{3}$
$\dfrac{2 + x^2}{4x - 3}$	$\dfrac{4x - 3}{2 + x^2}$
x^3	$\dfrac{1}{x^3}$
0	no reciprocal

Dividing Rational Expressions

The rule for dividing rational expressions is

$$\frac{P}{Q} \div \frac{R}{S} = \frac{P}{Q} \cdot \frac{S}{R} = \frac{PS}{QR} \quad \text{as long as } Q \neq 0, S \neq 0, \text{ and } R \neq 0.$$

To divide by a rational expression, use the rule above and multiply by its reciprocal. Then simplify if possible.

Notice that division of rational expressions is the same as for rational numbers.

EXAMPLE 7   Divide.

a. $\dfrac{8m^2}{3m^2 - 12} \div \dfrac{40}{2 - m}$

b. $\dfrac{18y^2 + 9y - 2}{24y^2 - 10y + 1} \div \dfrac{3y^2 + 17y + 10}{8y^2 + 18y - 5}$

Solution

a. $\dfrac{8m^2}{3m^2 - 12} \div \dfrac{40}{2 - m} = \dfrac{8m^2}{3m^2 - 12} \cdot \dfrac{2 - m}{40}$ Multiply by the reciprocal of the divisor.

$\qquad = \dfrac{8m^2(2 - m)}{3(m + 2)(m - 2) \cdot 40}$ Factor and multiply.

$\qquad = \dfrac{8m^2 \cdot -1\,(m - 2)}{3(m + 2)\,(m - 2)\, \cdot 8 \cdot 5}$ Write $(2 - m)$ as $-1(m - 2)$.

$\qquad = -\dfrac{m^2}{15(m + 2)}$ Simplify.

b. $\dfrac{18y^2 + 9y - 2}{24y^2 - 10y + 1} \div \dfrac{3y^2 + 17y + 10}{8y^2 + 18y - 5}$

$\qquad = \dfrac{18y^2 + 9y - 2}{24y^2 - 10y + 1} \cdot \dfrac{8y^2 + 18y - 5}{3y^2 + 17y + 10}$ Multiply by the reciprocal.

$\qquad = \dfrac{(6y - 1)(3y + 2)}{(6y - 1)(4y - 1)} \cdot \dfrac{(4y - 1)(2y + 5)}{(3y + 2)(y + 5)}$ Factor.

$\qquad = \dfrac{2y + 5}{y + 5}$ Simplest form   □

PRACTICE
7   Divide.

a. $\dfrac{6y^3}{3y^2 - 27} \div \dfrac{42}{3 - y}$

b. $\dfrac{10x^2 + 23x - 5}{5x^2 - 51x + 10} \div \dfrac{2x^2 + 9x + 10}{7x^2 - 68x - 20}$

> ▶ **Helpful Hint**
>
> When dividing rational expressions, do not divide out common factors until the division problem is rewritten as a multiplication problem.

EXAMPLE 8   Perform each indicated operation.

$$\frac{x^2 - 25}{(x + 5)^2} \cdot \frac{3x + 15}{4x} \div \frac{x^2 - 3x - 10}{x}$$

Solution $\dfrac{x^2 - 25}{(x + 5)^2} \cdot \dfrac{3x + 15}{4x} \div \dfrac{x^2 - 3x - 10}{x}$

$$= \frac{x^2 - 25}{(x + 5)^2} \cdot \frac{3x + 15}{4x} \cdot \frac{x}{x^2 - 3x - 10} \qquad \begin{array}{l}\text{To divide, multiply by}\\ \text{the reciprocal}\end{array}$$

$$= \frac{(x + 5)(x - 5)}{(x + 5)(x + 5)} \cdot \frac{3\,(x + 5)}{4\,x} \cdot \frac{x}{(x - 5)\,(x + 2)}$$

$$= \frac{3}{4(x + 2)}$$

PRACTICE
8   Perform each indicated operation.

$$\frac{x^2 - 16}{(x - 4)^2} \cdot \frac{5x - 20}{3x} \div \frac{x^2 + x - 12}{x}$$

OBJECTIVE 5 ▶ Using rational functions in applications. Rational functions occur often in real-life situations.

EXAMPLE 9   **Cost for Pressing Compact Discs**

For the ICL Production Company, the rational function $C(x) = \dfrac{2.6x + 10,000}{x}$ describes the company's cost per disc of pressing x compact discs. Find the cost per disc for pressing:

a. 100 compact discs
b. 1000 compact discs

Solution

a. $C(100) = \dfrac{2.6(100) + 10,000}{100} = \dfrac{10,260}{100} = 102.6$

The cost per disc for pressing 100 compact discs is $102.60.

b. $C(1000) = \dfrac{2.6(1000) + 10,000}{1000} = \dfrac{12,600}{1000} = 12.6$

The cost per disc for pressing 1000 compact discs is $12.60. Notice that as more compact discs are produced, the cost per disc decreases.

PRACTICE
9   A company's cost per tee shirt for silk screening x tee shirts is given by the rational function $C(x) = \dfrac{3.2x + 400}{x}$. Find the cost per tee shirt for printing:

a. 100 tee shirts   **b.** 1000 tee shirts

Graphing Calculator Explorations

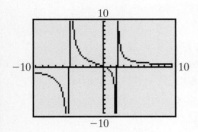

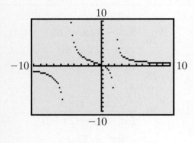

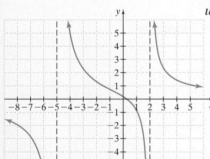

Recall that since the rational expression $\dfrac{7x - 2}{(x - 2)(x + 5)}$ is not defined when $x = 2$ or when $x = -5$, we say that the domain of the rational function $f(x) = \dfrac{7x - 2}{(x - 2)(x + 5)}$ is all real numbers except 2 and -5. This domain can be written as $\{x \mid x \text{ is a real number and } x \neq 2, x \neq -5\}$. This means that the graph of $f(x)$ should not cross the vertical lines $x = 2$ and $x = -5$. The graph of $f(x)$ in *connected* mode is to the left. In connected mode the graphing calculator tries to connect all dots of the graph so that the result is a smooth curve. This is what has happened in the graph. Notice that the graph appears to contain vertical lines at $x = 2$ and at $x = -5$. We know that this cannot happen because the function is not defined at $x = 2$ and at $x = -5$. We also know that this cannot happen because the graph of this function would not pass the vertical line test.

The graph of $f(x)$ in *dot* mode, is to the left. In dot mode the graphing calculator will not connect dots with a smooth curve. Notice that the vertical lines have disappeared, and we have a better picture of the graph. The graph, however, actually appears more like the hand-drawn graph below. By using a Table feature, a Calculate Value feature, or by tracing, we can see that the function is not defined at $x = 2$ and at $x = -5$.

Find the domain of each rational function. Then graph each rational function and use the graph to confirm the domain.

1. $f(x) = \dfrac{x + 1}{x^2 - 4}$

2. $g(x) = \dfrac{5x}{x^2 - 9}$

3. $h(x) = \dfrac{x^2}{2x^2 + 7x - 4}$

4. $f(x) = \dfrac{3x + 2}{4x^2 - 19x - 5}$

VOCABULARY & READINESS CHECK

Use the choices below to fill in each blank. Some choices may not be used.

1	true	rational	simplified	$\dfrac{-a}{-b}$	$\dfrac{-a}{b}$	$\dfrac{a}{-b}$
-1	false	domain	0			

1. A _____ expression is an expression that can be written as the quotient $\dfrac{P}{Q}$ of two polynomials P and Q as long as $Q \neq 0$.

2. A rational expression is undefined if the denominator is _____.

3. The _____ of the rational function $f(x) = \dfrac{2}{x}$ is $\{x \mid x \text{ is a real number and } x \neq 0\}$.

4. A rational expression is _____ if the numerator and denominator have no common factors other than 1 or -1.

5. The expression $\dfrac{x^2 + 2}{2 + x^2}$ simplifies to _____.

6. The expression $\dfrac{y - z}{z - y}$ simplifies to _____.

7. For a rational expression, $-\dfrac{a}{b} = $ _____ $= $ _____ .

8. True or false: $\dfrac{a-6}{a+2} = \dfrac{-(a-6)}{-(a+2)} = \dfrac{-a+6}{-a-2}$. _____

Multiply.

9. $\dfrac{x}{5} \cdot \dfrac{y}{2}$

10. $\dfrac{y}{6} \cdot \dfrac{z}{5}$

11. $\dfrac{2}{x} \cdot \dfrac{y}{3}$

12. $\dfrac{a}{5} \cdot \dfrac{7}{b}$

13. $\dfrac{m}{6} \cdot \dfrac{m}{6}$

14. $\dfrac{9}{x} \cdot \dfrac{8}{x}$

6.1 EXERCISE SET

 MyMathLab PRACTICE   WATCH   DOWNLOAD   READ   REVIEW

Find the domain of each rational expression. See Example 1.

1. $f(x) = \dfrac{5x-7}{4}$

2. $g(x) = \dfrac{4-3x}{2}$

3. $s(t) = \dfrac{t^2+1}{2t}$

4. $v(t) = -\dfrac{5t+t^2}{3t}$

5. $f(x) = \dfrac{3x}{7-x}$

6. $f(x) = \dfrac{-4x}{-2+x}$

7. $f(x) = \dfrac{x}{3x-1}$

8. $g(x) = \dfrac{-2}{2x+5}$

9. $R(x) = \dfrac{3+2x}{x^3+x^2-2x}$

10. $h(x) = \dfrac{5-3x}{2x^2-14x+20}$

11. $C(x) = \dfrac{x+3}{x^2-4}$

12. $R(x) = \dfrac{5}{x^2-7x}$

Simplify each rational expression. See Examples 2 through 5.

13. $\dfrac{8x-16x^2}{8x}$

14. $\dfrac{3x-6x^2}{3x}$

15. $\dfrac{x^2-9}{3+x}$

16. $\dfrac{x^2-25}{5+x}$

17. $\dfrac{9y-18}{7y-14}$

18. $\dfrac{6y-18}{2y-6}$

19. $\dfrac{x^2+6x-40}{x+10}$

20. $\dfrac{x^2-8x+16}{x-4}$

21. $\dfrac{x-9}{9-x}$

22. $\dfrac{x-4}{4-x}$

23. $\dfrac{x^2-49}{7-x}$

24. $\dfrac{x^2-y^2}{y-x}$

25. $\dfrac{2x^2-7x-4}{x^2-5x+4}$

26. $\dfrac{3x^2-11x+10}{x^2-7x+10}$

27. $\dfrac{x^3-125}{2x-10}$

28. $\dfrac{4x+4}{x^3+1}$

29. $\dfrac{3x^2-5x-2}{6x^3+2x^2+3x+1}$

30. $\dfrac{2x^2-x-3}{2x^3-3x^2+2x-3}$

31. $\dfrac{9x^2-15x+25}{27x^3+125}$

32. $\dfrac{8x^3-27}{4x^2+6x+9}$

Multiply and simplify. See Example 6.

33. $\dfrac{2x-4}{15} \cdot \dfrac{6}{2-x}$

34. $\dfrac{10-2x}{7} \cdot \dfrac{14}{5x-25}$

35. $\dfrac{18a-12a^2}{4a^2+4a+1} \cdot \dfrac{4a^2+8a+3}{4a^2-9}$

36. $\dfrac{a-5b}{a^2+ab} \cdot \dfrac{b^2-a^2}{10b-2a}$

37. $\dfrac{9x+9}{4x+8} \cdot \dfrac{2x+4}{3x^2-3}$

38. $\dfrac{2x^2-2}{10x+30} \cdot \dfrac{12x+36}{3x-3}$

39. $\dfrac{2x^3-16}{6x^2+6x-36} \cdot \dfrac{9x+18}{3x^2+6x+12}$

40. $\dfrac{x^2-3x+9}{5x^2-20x-105} \cdot \dfrac{x^2-49}{x^3+27}$

41. $\dfrac{a^3+a^2b+a+b}{5a^3+5a} \cdot \dfrac{6a^2}{2a^2-2b^2}$

42. $\dfrac{4a^2-8a}{ab-2b+3a-6} \cdot \dfrac{8b+24}{3a+6}$

43. $\dfrac{x^2-6x-16}{2x^2-128} \cdot \dfrac{x^2+16x+64}{3x^2+30x+48}$

44. $\dfrac{2x^2+12x-32}{x^2+16x+64} \cdot \dfrac{x^2+10x+16}{x^2-3x-10}$

Divide and simplify. See Example 7.

45. $\dfrac{2x}{5} \div \dfrac{6x+12}{5x+10}$

46. $\dfrac{7}{3x} \div \dfrac{14 - 7x}{18 - 9x}$

47. $\dfrac{a + b}{ab} \div \dfrac{a^2 - b^2}{4a^3b}$

48. $\dfrac{6a^2b^2}{a^2 - 4} \div \dfrac{3ab^2}{a - 2}$

49. $\dfrac{x^2 - 6x + 9}{x^2 - x - 6} \div \dfrac{x^2 - 9}{4}$

50. $\dfrac{x^2 - 4}{3x + 6} \div \dfrac{2x^2 - 8x + 8}{x^2 + 4x + 4}$

51. $\dfrac{x^2 - 6x - 16}{2x^2 - 128} \div \dfrac{x^2 + 10x + 16}{x^2 + 16x + 64}$

52. $\dfrac{a^2 - a - 6}{a^2 - 81} \div \dfrac{a^2 - 7a - 18}{4a + 36}$

53. $\dfrac{3x - x^2}{x^3 - 27} \div \dfrac{x}{x^2 + 3x + 9}$

54. $\dfrac{x^2 - 3x}{x^3 - 27} \div \dfrac{2x}{2x^2 + 6x + 18}$

55. $\dfrac{8b + 24}{3a + 6} \div \dfrac{ab - 2b + 3a - 6}{a^2 - 4a + 4}$

56. $\dfrac{2a^2 - 2b^2}{a^3 + a^2b + a + b} \div \dfrac{6a^2}{a^3 + a}$

MIXED PRACTICE

Perform each indicated operation. See Examples 2 through 8.

57. $\dfrac{x^2 - 9}{4} \cdot \dfrac{x^2 - x - 6}{x^2 - 6x + 9}$

58. $\dfrac{x^2 - 4}{9} \cdot \dfrac{x^2 - 6x + 9}{x^2 - 5x + 6}$

59. $\dfrac{2x^2 - 4x - 30}{5x^2 - 40x - 75} \div \dfrac{x^2 - 8x + 15}{x^2 - 6x + 9}$

60. $\dfrac{4a + 36}{a^2 - 7a - 18} \div \dfrac{a^2 - a - 6}{a^2 - 81}$

61. Simplify: $\dfrac{r^3 + s^3}{r + s}$

62. Simplify: $\dfrac{m^3 - n^3}{m - n}$

63. $\dfrac{4}{x} \div \dfrac{3xy}{x^2} \cdot \dfrac{6x^2}{x^4}$

64. $\dfrac{4}{x} \cdot \dfrac{3xy}{x^2} \div \dfrac{6x^2}{x^4}$

65. $\dfrac{3x^2 - 5x - 2}{y^2 + y - 2} \cdot \dfrac{y^2 + 4y - 5}{12x^2 + 7x + 1} \div \dfrac{5x^2 - 9x - 2}{8x^2 - 2x - 1}$

66. $\dfrac{x^2 + x - 2}{3y^2 - 5y - 2} \cdot \dfrac{12y^2 + y - 1}{x^2 + 4x - 5} \div \dfrac{8y^2 - 6y + 1}{5y^2 - 9y - 2}$

67. $\dfrac{5a^2 - 20}{3a^2 - 12a} \div \dfrac{a^3 + 2a^2}{2a^2 - 8a} \cdot \dfrac{9a^3 + 6a^2}{2a^2 - 4a}$

68. $\dfrac{5a^2 - 20}{3a^2 - 12a} \div \left(\dfrac{a^3 + 2a^2}{2a^2 - 8a} \cdot \dfrac{9a^3 + 6a^2}{2a^2 - 4a} \right)$

69. $\dfrac{5x^4 + 3x^2 - 2}{x - 1} \cdot \dfrac{x + 1}{x^4 - 1}$

70. $\dfrac{3x^4 - 10x^2 - 8}{x - 2} \cdot \dfrac{3x + 6}{15x^2 + 10}$

Find each function value. See Example 9.

71. If $f(x) = \dfrac{x + 8}{2x - 1}$, find $f(2)$, $f(0)$, and $f(-1)$.

72. If $f(x) = \dfrac{x - 2}{-5 + x}$, find $f(-5)$, $f(0)$, and $f(10)$.

73. If $g(x) = \dfrac{x^2 + 8}{x^3 - 25x}$, find $g(3)$, $g(-2)$, and $g(1)$.

74. If $s(t) = \dfrac{t^3 + 1}{t^2 + 1}$, find $s(-1)$, $s(1)$, and $s(2)$.

75. The total revenue from the sale of a popular book is approximated by the rational function $R(x) = \dfrac{1000x^2}{x^2 + 4}$, where x is the number of years since publication and $R(x)$ is the total revenue in millions of dollars.

   a. Find the total revenue at the end of the first year.

   b. Find the total revenue at the end of the second year.

   c. Find the revenue during the second year only.

   d. Find the domain of function R.

76. The function $f(x) = \dfrac{100,000x}{100 - x}$ models the cost in dollars for removing x percent of the pollutants from a bayou in which a nearby company dumped creosol.

   a. Find the cost of removing 20% of the pollutants from the bayou. [*Hint:* Find $f(20)$.]

   b. Find the cost of removing 60% of the pollutants and then 80% of the pollutants.

   c. Find $f(90)$, then $f(95)$, and then $f(99)$. What happens to the cost as x approaches 100%?

   d. Find the domain of function f.

REVIEW AND PREVIEW

Perform each indicated operation. See Section 1.3.

77. $\dfrac{4}{5} + \dfrac{3}{5}$

78. $\dfrac{4}{10} - \dfrac{7}{10}$

79. $\dfrac{5}{28} - \dfrac{2}{21}$

80. $\dfrac{5}{13} + \dfrac{2}{7}$

81. $\dfrac{3}{8} + \dfrac{1}{2} - \dfrac{3}{16}$

82. $\dfrac{2}{9} - \dfrac{1}{6} + \dfrac{2}{3}$

CONCEPT EXTENSIONS

Solve. For Exercises 83 and 84, see the first Concept Check in this section; for Exercises 85 and 86, see the second Concept Check.

83. Which of the expressions are equivalent to $\dfrac{x}{5 - x}$?

   a. $\dfrac{-x}{5 - x}$

   b. $\dfrac{-x}{-5 + x}$

   c. $\dfrac{x}{x - 5}$

   d. $\dfrac{-x}{x - 5}$

84. Which of the expressions are equivalent to $\dfrac{-2 + x}{x}$?

   a. $\dfrac{2 - x}{-x}$

   b. $-\dfrac{2 - x}{x}$

   c. $\dfrac{x - 2}{x}$

   d. $\dfrac{x - 2}{-x}$

85. Does $\dfrac{x}{x+5}$ simplify to $\dfrac{1}{5}$? Why or why not?

86. Does $\dfrac{x+7}{x}$ simplify to 7? Why or why not?

87. Find the area of the rectangle.

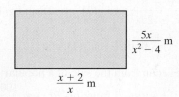

$\dfrac{5x}{x^2-4}$ m

$\dfrac{x+2}{x}$ m

88. Find the area of the triangle.

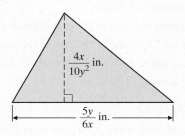

$\dfrac{4x}{10y^2}$ in.

$\dfrac{5y}{6x}$ in.

89. A parallelogram has an area of $\dfrac{x^2+x-2}{x^3}$ square feet and a height of $\dfrac{x^2}{x-1}$ feet. Express the length of its base as a rational expression in x. (*Hint:* Since $A = b \cdot h$, then $b = \dfrac{A}{h}$ or $b = A \div h$.)

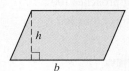

h

b

90. A lottery prize of $\dfrac{15x^3}{y^2}$ dollars is to be divided among $5x$ people. Express the amount of money each person is to receive as a rational expression in x and y.

91. In your own words explain how to simplify a rational expression.

92. In your own words, explain the difference between multiplying rational expressions and dividing rational expressions.

93. Decide whether each rational expression equals 1, −1, or neither.

a. $\dfrac{x+5}{5+x}$

b. $\dfrac{x-5}{5-x}$

c. $\dfrac{x+5}{x-5}$

d. $\dfrac{-x-5}{x+5}$

e. $\dfrac{x-5}{-x+5}$

f. $\dfrac{-5+x}{x-5}$

94. In our definition of division for

$$\frac{P}{Q} \div \frac{R}{S}$$

we stated that $Q \neq 0$, $S \neq 0$, and $R \neq 0$. Explain why R cannot equal 0.

95. Find the polynomial in the second numerator such that the following statement is true.

$$\frac{x^2-4}{x^2-7x+10} \cdot \frac{?}{2x^2+11x+14} = 1$$

96. In your own words, explain how to find the domain of a rational function.

97. Graph a portion of the function $f(x) = \dfrac{20x}{100-x}$. To do so, complete the given table, plot the points, and then connect the plotted points with a smooth curve.

x	0	10	30	50	70	90	95	99
y or $f(x)$								

98. The domain of the function $f(x) = \dfrac{1}{x}$ is all real numbers except 0. This means that the graph of this function will be in two pieces: one piece corresponding to x values less than 0 and one piece corresponding to x values greater than 0. Graph the function by completing the following tables, separately plotting the points, and connecting each set of plotted points with a smooth curve.

x	$\dfrac{1}{4}$	$\dfrac{1}{2}$	1	2	4
y or $f(x)$					

x	−4	−2	−1	$-\dfrac{1}{2}$	$-\dfrac{1}{4}$
y or $f(x)$					

Perform the indicated operation. Write all answers in lowest terms.

99. $\dfrac{x^{2n}-4}{7x} \cdot \dfrac{14x^3}{x^n-2}$

100. $\dfrac{x^{2n}+4x^n+4}{4x-3} \cdot \dfrac{8x^2-6x}{x^n+2}$

101. $\dfrac{y^{2n}+9}{10y} \cdot \dfrac{y^n-3}{y^{4n}-81}$

102. $\dfrac{y^{4n}-16}{y^{2n}+4} \cdot \dfrac{6y}{y^n+2}$

103. $\dfrac{y^{2n}-y^n-2}{2y^n-4} \div \dfrac{y^{2n}-1}{1+y^n}$

104. $\dfrac{y^{2n}+7y^n+10}{10} \div \dfrac{y^{2n}+4y^n+4}{5y^n+25}$

STUDY SKILLS BUILDER

Are You Satisfied with Your Performance in this Course thus Far?

To see if there is room for improvement, answer these questions:

1. Am I attending all classes and arriving on time?

2. Am I working and checking my homework assignments on time?

3. Am I getting help (from my instructor or a campus learning resource lab) when I need it?

4. In addition to my instructor, am I using the text supplements that might help me?

5. Am I satisfied with my performance on quizzes and exams?

If you answered no to any of these questions, read or reread Section 1.1 for suggestions in these areas. Also, you might want to contact your instructor for additional feedback.

6.2 ADDING AND SUBTRACTING RATIONAL EXPRESSIONS

OBJECTIVES

1 Add or subtract rational expressions with common denominators.

2 Identify the least common denominator of two or more rational expressions.

3 Add or subtract rational expressions with unlike denominators.

OBJECTIVE 1 ▶ Adding or subtracting rational expressions with common denominators. Rational expressions, like rational numbers, can be added or subtracted. We add or subtract rational expressions in the same way that we add or subtract rational numbers (fractions).

> **Adding or Subtracting Rational Expressions with Common Denominators**
>
> If $\dfrac{P}{Q}$ and $\dfrac{R}{Q}$ are rational expressions, then
>
> $$\frac{P}{Q} + \frac{R}{Q} = \frac{P+R}{Q} \quad \text{and} \quad \frac{P}{Q} - \frac{R}{Q} = \frac{P-R}{Q}$$

To add or subtract rational expressions with common denominators, add or subtract the numerators and write the sum or difference over the common denominator.

EXAMPLE 1   Add or subtract.

a. $\dfrac{x}{4} + \dfrac{5x}{4}$ **b.** $\dfrac{5}{7z^2} + \dfrac{x}{7z^2}$ **c.** $\dfrac{x^2}{x+7} - \dfrac{49}{x+7}$ **d.** $\dfrac{x}{3y^2} - \dfrac{x+1}{3y^2}$

Solution   The rational expressions have common denominators, so add or subtract their numerators and place the sum or difference over their common denominator.

a. $\dfrac{x}{4} + \dfrac{5x}{4} = \dfrac{x+5x}{4} = \dfrac{6x}{4} = \dfrac{3x}{2}$ Add the numerators and write the result over the common denominator.

b. $\dfrac{5}{7z^2} + \dfrac{x}{7z^2} = \dfrac{5+x}{7z^2}$

c. $\dfrac{x^2}{x+7} - \dfrac{49}{x+7} = \dfrac{x^2-49}{x+7}$ Subtract the numerators and write the result over the common denominator.

$\qquad\qquad\qquad = \dfrac{(x+7)(x-7)}{x+7}$ Factor the numerator.

$\qquad\qquad\qquad = x - 7$ Simplify.

> **Helpful Hint**
>
> **Very Important:** Be sure to insert parentheses here so that the entire numerator is subtracted.

d. $\dfrac{x}{3y^2} - \dfrac{x+1}{3y^2} = \dfrac{x - (x+1)}{3y^2}$ Subtract the numerators.

$= \dfrac{x - x - 1}{3y^2}$ Use the distributive property.

$= -\dfrac{1}{3y^2}$ Simplify.

PRACTICE

1   Add or subtract.

a. $\dfrac{9}{11z^2} + \dfrac{x}{11z^2}$ **b.** $\dfrac{x}{8} + \dfrac{5x}{8}$ **c.** $\dfrac{x^2}{x+4} - \dfrac{16}{x+4}$ **d.** $\dfrac{z}{2a^2} - \dfrac{z+3}{2a^2}$

Concept Check ✓

Find and correct the error.

$$\dfrac{3+2y}{y^2-1} - \dfrac{y+3}{y^2-1} = \dfrac{3+2y-y+3}{y^2-1}$$

$$= \dfrac{y+6}{y^2-1}$$

OBJECTIVE 2 ▶ **Identifying the least common denominator of rational expressions.**
To add or subtract rational expressions with unlike denominators, first write the rational expressions as equivalent rational expressions with common denominators.

The **least common denominator (LCD)** is usually the easiest common denominator to work with. The LCD of a list of rational expressions is a polynomial of least degree whose factors include the denominator factors in the list.

Use the following steps to find the LCD.

Finding the Least Common Denominator (LCD)

STEP 1. Factor each denominator completely.

STEP 2. The LCD is the product of all unique factors each raised to a power equal to the greatest number of times that the factor appears in any factored denominator.

EXAMPLE 2   Find the LCD of the rational expressions in each list.

a. $\dfrac{2}{3x^5y^2}, \dfrac{3z}{5xy^3}$ **b.** $\dfrac{7}{z+1}, \dfrac{z}{z-1}$

c. $\dfrac{m-1}{m^2-25}, \dfrac{2m}{2m^2-9m-5}, \dfrac{7}{m^2-10m+25}$ **d.** $\dfrac{x}{x^2-4}, \dfrac{11}{6-3x}$

Solution

a. First we factor each denominator.

$$3x^5y^2 = 3 \cdot x^5 \cdot y^2$$
$$5xy^3 = 5 \cdot x \cdot y^3$$
$$\text{LCD} = 3 \cdot 5 \cdot x^5 \cdot y^3 = 15x^5y^3$$

> **Helpful Hint**
>
> The greatest power of x is 5, so we have a factor of x^5. The greatest power of y is 3, so we have a factor of y^3.

Answer to Concept Check:

$\dfrac{3+2y}{y^2-1} - \dfrac{y+3}{y^2-1}$

$= \dfrac{3+2y-y-3}{y^2-1} = \dfrac{y}{y^2-1}$

b. The denominators $z + 1$ and $z - 1$ do not factor further. Thus,

$$\text{LCD} = (z + 1)(z - 1)$$

c. We first factor each denominator.

$$m^2 - 25 = (m + 5)(m - 5)$$
$$2m^2 - 9m - 5 = (2m + 1)(m - 5)$$
$$m^2 - 10m + 25 = (m - 5)(m - 5)$$
$$\text{LCD} = (m + 5)(2m + 1)(m - 5)^2$$

d. Factor each denominator.

$$x^2 - 4 = (x + 2)(x - 2)$$
$$6 - 3x = 3(2 - x) = 3(-1)(x - 2)$$
$$\text{LCD} = 3(-1)(x + 2)(x - 2)$$
$$= -3(x + 2)(x - 2)$$

> ▶ **Helpful Hint**
>
> $(x - 2)$ and $(2 - x)$ are opposite factors. Notice that -1 was factored from $(2 - x)$ so that the factors are identical.

> ▶ **Helpful Hint**
>
> If opposite factors occur, do not use both in the LCD. Instead, factor -1 from one of the opposite factors so that the factors are then identical.

PRACTICE
2   Find the LCD of the rational expression in each list.

a. $\dfrac{7}{6x^3y^5}, \dfrac{2}{9x^2y^4}$

b. $\dfrac{11}{x - 2}, \dfrac{x}{x + 3}$

c. $\dfrac{b + 2}{b^2 - 16}, \dfrac{8}{b^2 - 8b + 16}, \dfrac{5b}{2b^2 - 5b - 12}$

d. $\dfrac{y}{y^2 - 9}, \dfrac{3}{12 - 4y}$

OBJECTIVE 3 ▶ **Adding or subtracting rational expressions with unlike denominators.**
To add or subtract rational expressions with unlike denominators, we write each rational expression as an equivalent rational expression so that their denominators are alike.

> **Adding or Subtracting Rational Expressions with Unlike Denominators**
>
> **STEP 1.** Find the LCD of the rational expressions.
>
> **STEP 2.** Write each rational expression as an equivalent rational expression whose denominator is the LCD found in Step 1.
>
> **STEP 3.** Add or subtract numerators, and write the result over the common denominator.
>
> **STEP 4.** Simplify the resulting rational expression.

EXAMPLE 3   Perform the indicated operation.

a. $\dfrac{2}{x^2y} + \dfrac{5}{3x^3y}$

b. $\dfrac{3}{x + 2} + \dfrac{2x}{x - 2}$

c. $\dfrac{2x - 6}{x - 1} - \dfrac{4}{1 - x}$

Solution

a. The LCD is $3x^3y$. Write each fraction as an equivalent fraction with denominator $3x^3y$. To do this, we multiply both the numerator and denominator of each fraction by the factors needed to obtain the LCD as denominator.

The first fraction is multiplied by $\dfrac{3x}{3x}$ so that the new denominator is the LCD.

$$\frac{2}{x^2 y} + \frac{5}{3x^3 y} = \frac{2 \cdot 3x}{x^2 y \cdot 3x} + \frac{5}{3x^3 y} \qquad \text{The second expression already has a denominator of } 3x^3 y.$$

$$= \frac{6x}{3x^3 y} + \frac{5}{3x^3 y}$$

$$= \frac{6x + 5}{3x^3 y} \qquad \text{Add the numerators.}$$

b. The LCD is the product of the two denominators: $(x + 2)(x - 2)$.

$$\frac{3}{x + 2} + \frac{2x}{x - 2} = \frac{3 \cdot (x - 2)}{(x + 2) \cdot (x - 2)} + \frac{2x \cdot (x + 2)}{(x - 2) \cdot (x + 2)} \qquad \text{Write equivalent rational expressions.}$$

$$= \frac{3x - 6}{(x + 2)(x - 2)} + \frac{2x^2 + 4x}{(x + 2)(x - 2)} \qquad \text{Multiply in the numerators.}$$

$$= \frac{3x - 6 + 2x^2 + 4x}{(x + 2)(x - 2)} \qquad \text{Add the numerators.}$$

$$= \frac{2x^2 + 7x - 6}{(x + 2)(x - 2)} \qquad \text{Simplify the numerator.}$$

c. The LCD is either $x - 1$ or $1 - x$. To get a common denominator of $x - 1$, we factor -1 from the denominator of the second rational expression.

$$\frac{2x - 6}{x - 1} - \frac{4}{1 - x} = \frac{2x - 6}{x - 1} - \frac{4}{-1(x - 1)} \qquad \text{Write } 1 - x \text{ as } -1(x - 1).$$

$$= \frac{2x - 6}{x - 1} - \frac{-1 \cdot 4}{x - 1} \qquad \text{Write } \frac{4}{-1(x - 1)} \text{ as } \frac{-1 \cdot 4}{x - 1}.$$

$$= \frac{2x - 6 - (-4)}{x - 1} \qquad \text{Combine the numerators.}$$

$$= \frac{2x - 6 + 4}{x - 1} \qquad \text{Simplify.}$$

$$= \frac{2x - 2}{x - 1}$$

$$= \frac{2(x - 1)}{x - 1} \qquad \text{Factor.}$$

$$= 2 \qquad \text{Simplest form}$$

PRACTICE
3   Perform the indicated operation.

a. $\dfrac{4}{p^3 q} + \dfrac{3}{5p^4 q}$ **b.** $\dfrac{4}{y + 3} + \dfrac{5y}{y - 3}$ **c.** $\dfrac{3z - 18}{z - 5} - \dfrac{3}{5 - z}$

EXAMPLE 4   Subtract $\dfrac{5k}{k^2 - 4} - \dfrac{2}{k^2 + k - 2}$.

Solution $\dfrac{5k}{k^2 - 4} - \dfrac{2}{k^2 + k - 2} = \dfrac{5k}{(k + 2)(k - 2)} - \dfrac{2}{(k + 2)(k - 1)}$ Factor each denominator to find the LCD.

The LCD is $(k + 2)(k - 2)(k - 1)$. We write equivalent rational expressions with the LCD as denominators.

$$\frac{5k}{(k + 2)(k - 2)} - \frac{2}{(k + 2)(k - 1)}$$

$$= \frac{5k \cdot (k - 1)}{(k + 2)(k - 2) \cdot (k - 1)} - \frac{2 \cdot (k - 2)}{(k + 2)(k - 1) \cdot (k - 2)} \qquad \text{Write equivalent rational expressions.}$$

$$= \frac{5k^2 - 5k}{(k + 2)(k - 2)(k - 1)} - \frac{2k - 4}{(k + 2)(k - 2)(k - 1)} \qquad \text{Multiply in the numerators.}$$

$$= \frac{5k^2 - 5k - 2k + 4}{(k + 2)(k - 2)(k - 1)} \qquad \text{Subtract the numerators.}$$

$$= \frac{5k^2 - 7k + 4}{(k + 2)(k - 2)(k - 1)} \qquad \text{Simplify.} \qquad \square$$

> ▶ **Helpful Hint**
> **Very Important:** Because we are subtracting; notice the sign change on 4.

PRACTICE 4 Subtract $\dfrac{t}{t^2 - 25} - \dfrac{3}{t^2 - 3t - 10}$.

EXAMPLE 5 Add $\dfrac{2x - 1}{2x^2 - 9x - 5} + \dfrac{x - 3}{6x^2 - x - 2}$.

Solution

$$\frac{2x - 1}{2x^2 - 9x - 5} + \frac{x + 3}{6x^2 - x - 2} = \frac{2x - 1}{(2x + 1)(x - 5)} + \frac{x + 3}{(2x + 1)(3x - 2)} \qquad \text{Factor the denominators.}$$

The LCD is $(2x + 1)(x - 5)(3x - 2)$.

$$= \frac{(2x - 1) \cdot (3x - 2)}{(2x + 1)(x - 5) \cdot (3x - 2)} + \frac{(x + 3) \cdot (x - 5)}{(2x + 1)(3x - 2) \cdot (x - 5)}$$

$$= \frac{6x^2 - 7x + 2}{(2x + 1)(x - 5)(3x - 2)} + \frac{x^2 - 2x - 15}{(2x + 1)(x - 5)(3x - 2)} \qquad \text{Multiply in the numerators.}$$

$$= \frac{6x^2 - 7x + 2 + x^2 - 2x - 15}{(2x + 1)(x - 5)(3x - 2)} \qquad \text{Add the numerators.}$$

$$= \frac{7x^2 - 9x - 13}{(2x + 1)(x - 5)(3x - 2)} \qquad \text{Simplify.} \qquad \square$$

PRACTICE 5 Add $\dfrac{2x + 3}{3x^2 - 5x - 2} + \dfrac{x - 6}{6x^2 - 13x - 5}$.

EXAMPLE 6 Perform each indicated operation.

$$\frac{7}{x - 1} + \frac{10x}{x^2 - 1} - \frac{5}{x + 1}$$

Solution $\dfrac{7}{x - 1} + \dfrac{10x}{x^2 - 1} - \dfrac{5}{x + 1} = \dfrac{7}{x - 1} + \dfrac{10x}{(x - 1)(x + 1)} - \dfrac{5}{x + 1}$ Factor the denominators.

The LCD is $(x - 1)(x + 1)$.

$$= \frac{7 \cdot (x + 1)}{(x - 1) \cdot (x + 1)} + \frac{10x}{(x - 1)(x + 1)} - \frac{5 \cdot (x - 1)}{(x + 1) \cdot (x - 1)}$$

$$= \frac{7x + 7}{(x - 1)(x + 1)} + \frac{10x}{(x - 1)(x + 1)} - \frac{5x - 5}{(x + 1)(x - 1)} \quad \text{Multiply in the numerators.}$$

$$= \frac{7x + 7 + 10x - 5x + 5}{(x - 1)(x + 1)} \quad \text{Add and subtract the numerators.}$$

$$= \frac{12x + 12}{(x - 1)(x + 1)} \quad \text{Simplify.}$$

$$= \frac{12\,(x + 1)}{(x - 1)\,(x + 1)} \quad \text{Factor the numerator.}$$

$$= \frac{12}{x - 1} \quad \text{Divide out common factors.}$$

PRACTICE
6   Perform each indicated operation.

$$\frac{2}{x - 2} + \frac{3x}{x^2 - x - 2} - \frac{1}{x + 1}$$

Graphing Calculator Explorations

A graphing calculator can be used to support the results of operations on rational expressions. For example, to verify the result of Example 3b, graph

$$Y_1 = \frac{3}{x + 2} + \frac{2x}{x - 2} \quad \text{and} \quad Y_2 = \frac{2x^2 + 7x - 6}{(x + 2)(x - 2)}$$

on the same set of axes. The graphs should be the same. Use a Table feature or a Trace feature to see that this is true.

VOCABULARY & READINESS CHECK

Name the operation(s) below that make each statement true.

   a. Addition   **b.** Subtraction   **c.** Multiplication   **d.** Division

1. The denominators must be the same before performing the operation. _____
2. To perform this operation, you multiply the first rational expression by the reciprocal of the second rational expression. _____
3. Numerator times numerator all over denominator times denominator. _____
4. These operations are commutative (order doesn't matter.) _____

For the rational expressions $\dfrac{5}{y}$ and $\dfrac{7}{y}$, perform each operation mentally.

5. Addition   **6.** Subtraction   **7.** Multiplication   **8.** Division
_____   _____   _____   _____

Be careful when subtracting! For example, $\dfrac{8}{x+1} - \dfrac{x+5}{x+1} = \dfrac{8-(x+5)}{x+1} = \dfrac{3-x}{x+1}$ or $\dfrac{-x+3}{x+1}$.

Use this example to help you perform the subtractions.

9. $\dfrac{5}{2x} - \dfrac{x+1}{2x} =$ _____

10. $\dfrac{9}{5x} - \dfrac{6-x}{5x} =$ _____

11. $\dfrac{y+11}{y-2} - \dfrac{y-5}{y-2} =$ _____

12. $\dfrac{z-1}{z+6} - \dfrac{z+4}{z+6} =$ _____

6.2 EXERCISE SET

MyMathLab Powered by CourseCompass™ and MathXL® MathXL PRACTICE WATCH DOWNLOAD READ REVIEW

Add or subtract as indicated. Simplify each answer. See Example 1.

1. $\dfrac{2}{xz^2} - \dfrac{5}{xz^2}$

2. $\dfrac{4}{x^2 y} - \dfrac{2}{x^2 y}$

3. $\dfrac{2}{x-2} + \dfrac{x}{x-2}$

4. $\dfrac{x}{5-x} + \dfrac{7}{5-x}$

5. $\dfrac{x^2}{x+2} - \dfrac{4}{x+2}$

6. $\dfrac{x^2}{x+6} - \dfrac{36}{x+6}$

7. $\dfrac{2x-6}{x^2+x-6} + \dfrac{3-3x}{x^2+x-6}$

8. $\dfrac{5x+2}{x^2+2x-8} + \dfrac{2-4x}{x^2+2x-8}$

9. $\dfrac{x-5}{2x} - \dfrac{x+5}{2x}$

10. $\dfrac{x+4}{4x} - \dfrac{x-4}{4x}$

Find the LCD of the rational expressions in each list. See Example 2.

11. $\dfrac{2}{7}, \dfrac{3}{5x}$

12. $\dfrac{4}{5y}, \dfrac{3}{4y^2}$

13. $\dfrac{3}{x}, \dfrac{2}{x+1}$

14. $\dfrac{5}{2x}, \dfrac{7}{2+x}$

15. $\dfrac{12}{x+7}, \dfrac{8}{x-7}$

16. $\dfrac{1}{2x-1}, \dfrac{8}{2x+1}$

17. $\dfrac{5}{3x+6}, \dfrac{2x}{2x-4}$

18. $\dfrac{2}{3a+9}, \dfrac{5}{5a-15}$

19. $\dfrac{2a}{a^2-b^2}, \dfrac{1}{a^2-2ab+b^2}$

20. $\dfrac{2a}{a^2+8a+16}, \dfrac{7a}{a^2+a-12}$

21. $\dfrac{x}{x^2-9}, \dfrac{5}{x}, \dfrac{7}{12-4x}$

22. $\dfrac{9}{x^2-25}, \dfrac{1}{50-10x}, \dfrac{6}{x}$

Add or subtract as indicated. Simplify each answer. See Examples 3a and 3b.

23. $\dfrac{4}{3x} + \dfrac{3}{2x}$

24. $\dfrac{10}{7x} + \dfrac{5}{2x}$

25. $\dfrac{5}{2y^2} - \dfrac{2}{7y}$

26. $\dfrac{4}{11x^4} - \dfrac{1}{4x^2}$

27. $\dfrac{x-3}{x+4} - \dfrac{x+2}{x-4}$

28. $\dfrac{x-1}{x-5} - \dfrac{x+2}{x+5}$

29. $\dfrac{1}{x-5} - \dfrac{19-2x}{(x-5)(x+4)}$

30. $\dfrac{4x-2}{(x-5)(x+4)} - \dfrac{2}{x+4}$

Perform the indicated operation. If possible, simplify your answer. See Example 3c.

31. $\dfrac{1}{a-b} + \dfrac{1}{b-a}$

32. $\dfrac{1}{a-3} - \dfrac{1}{3-a}$

33. $\dfrac{x+1}{1-x} + \dfrac{1}{x-1}$

34. $\dfrac{5}{1-x} - \dfrac{1}{x-1}$

35. $\dfrac{5}{x-2} + \dfrac{x+4}{2-x}$

36. $\dfrac{3}{5-x} + \dfrac{x+2}{x-5}$

Perform each indicated operation. If possible, simplify your answer. See Examples 4 through 6.

37. $\dfrac{y+1}{y^2-6y+8} - \dfrac{3}{y^2-16}$

38. $\dfrac{x+2}{x^2-36} - \dfrac{x}{x^2+9x+18}$

39. $\dfrac{x+4}{3x^2+11x+6} + \dfrac{x}{2x^2+x-15}$

40. $\dfrac{x+3}{5x^2+12x+4} + \dfrac{6}{x^2-x-6}$

41. $\dfrac{7}{x^2-x-2} - \dfrac{x-1}{x^2+4x+3}$

42. $\dfrac{a}{a^2+10a+25} - \dfrac{4-a}{a^2+6a+5}$

43. $\dfrac{x}{x^2-8x+7} - \dfrac{x+2}{2x^2-9x-35}$

44. $\dfrac{x}{x^2-7x+6} - \dfrac{x+4}{3x^2-2x-1}$

45. $\dfrac{2}{a^2+2a+1} + \dfrac{3}{a^2-1}$

46. $\dfrac{9x+2}{3x^2-2x-8} + \dfrac{7}{3x^2+x-4}$

MIXED PRACTICE

Add or subtract as indicated. If possible, simplify your answer. See Examples 1 through 6.

47. $\dfrac{4}{3x^2y^3} + \dfrac{5}{3x^2y^3}$

48. $\dfrac{7}{2xy^4} + \dfrac{1}{2xy^4}$

49. $\dfrac{13x - 5}{2x} - \dfrac{13x + 5}{2x}$

50. $\dfrac{17x + 4}{4x} - \dfrac{17x - 4}{4x}$

51. $\dfrac{3}{2x + 10} + \dfrac{8}{3x + 15}$

52. $\dfrac{10}{3x - 3} + \dfrac{1}{7x - 7}$

53. $\dfrac{-2}{x^2 - 3x} - \dfrac{1}{x^3 - 3x^2}$

54. $\dfrac{-3}{2a + 8} - \dfrac{8}{a^2 + 4a}$

55. $\dfrac{ab}{a^2 - b^2} + \dfrac{b}{a + b}$

56. $\dfrac{x}{25 - x^2} + \dfrac{2}{3x - 15}$

57. $\dfrac{5}{x^2 - 4} - \dfrac{3}{x^2 + 4x + 4}$

58. $\dfrac{3z}{z^2 - 9} - \dfrac{2}{3 - z}$

59. $\dfrac{3x}{2x^2 - 11x + 5} + \dfrac{7}{x^2 - 2x - 15}$

60. $\dfrac{2x}{3x^2 - 13x + 4} + \dfrac{5}{x^2 - 2x - 8}$

61. $\dfrac{2}{x + 1} - \dfrac{3x}{3x + 3} + \dfrac{1}{2x + 2}$

62. $\dfrac{5}{3x - 6} - \dfrac{x}{x - 2} + \dfrac{3 + 2x}{5x - 10}$

63. $\dfrac{3}{x + 3} + \dfrac{5}{x^2 + 6x + 9} - \dfrac{x}{x^2 - 9}$

64. $\dfrac{x + 2}{x^2 - 2x - 3} + \dfrac{x}{x - 3} - \dfrac{x}{x + 1}$

65. $\dfrac{x}{x^2 - 9} + \dfrac{3}{x^2 - 6x + 9} - \dfrac{1}{x + 3}$

66. $\dfrac{3}{x^2 - 9} - \dfrac{x}{x^2 - 6x + 9} + \dfrac{1}{x + 3}$

67. $\left(\dfrac{1}{x} + \dfrac{2}{3}\right) - \left(\dfrac{1}{x} - \dfrac{2}{3}\right)$

68. $\left(\dfrac{1}{2} + \dfrac{2}{x}\right) - \left(\dfrac{1}{2} - \dfrac{1}{x}\right)$

MIXED PRACTICE (SECTIONS 6.1, 6.2)

Perform the indicated operation. If possible, simplify your answer.

69. $\left(\dfrac{2}{3} - \dfrac{1}{x}\right) \cdot \left(\dfrac{3}{x} + \dfrac{1}{2}\right)$

70. $\left(\dfrac{2}{3} - \dfrac{1}{x}\right) \div \left(\dfrac{3}{x} + \dfrac{1}{2}\right)$

71. $\left(\dfrac{2a}{3}\right)^2 \div \left(\dfrac{a^2}{a + 1} - \dfrac{1}{a + 1}\right)$

72. $\left(\dfrac{x + 2}{2x} - \dfrac{x - 2}{2x}\right) \cdot \left(\dfrac{5x}{4}\right)^2$

73. $\left(\dfrac{2x}{3}\right)^2 \div \left(\dfrac{x}{3}\right)^2$

74. $\left(\dfrac{2x}{3}\right)^2 \cdot \left(\dfrac{3}{x}\right)^2$

75. $\left(\dfrac{x}{x + 1} - \dfrac{x}{x - 1}\right) \div \dfrac{x}{2x + 2}$

76. $\dfrac{x}{2x + 2} \div \left(\dfrac{x}{x + 1} + \dfrac{x}{x - 1}\right)$

77. $\dfrac{4}{x} \cdot \left(\dfrac{2}{x + 2} - \dfrac{2}{x - 2}\right)$

78. $\dfrac{1}{x + 1} \cdot \left(\dfrac{5}{x} + \dfrac{2}{x - 3}\right)$

REVIEW AND PREVIEW

Use the distributive property to multiply the following. See Section 1.4.

79. $12\left(\dfrac{2}{3} + \dfrac{1}{6}\right)$

80. $14\left(\dfrac{1}{7} + \dfrac{3}{14}\right)$

81. $x^2\left(\dfrac{4}{x^2} + 1\right)$

82. $5y^2\left(\dfrac{1}{y^2} - \dfrac{1}{5}\right)$

Find each root. See Section 1.3.

83. $\sqrt{100}$

84. $\sqrt{25}$

85. $\sqrt[3]{8}$

86. $\sqrt[3]{27}$

87. $\sqrt[4]{81}$

88. $\sqrt[4]{16}$

Use the Pythagorean theorem to find each unknown length of a right triangle. See Section 5.8.

△ **89.**

3 meters

4 meters

△ **90.**

7 feet

24 feet

CONCEPT EXTENSIONS

Find and correct each error. See the Concept Check in this section.

91. $\dfrac{2x - 3}{x^2 + 1} - \dfrac{x - 6}{x^2 + 1} = \dfrac{2x - 3 - x - 6}{x^2 + 1}$

$= \dfrac{x - 9}{x^2 + 1}$

92. $\dfrac{7}{x+7} - \dfrac{x+3}{x+7} = \dfrac{7-x-3}{(x+7)^2}$
$= \dfrac{-x+4}{(x+7)^2}$

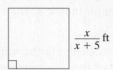

△ **93.** Find the perimeter and the area of the square.

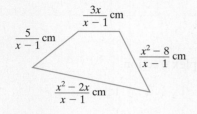

$\dfrac{x}{x+5}$ ft

△ **94.** Find the perimeter of the quadrilateral.

$\dfrac{3x}{x-1}$ cm

$\dfrac{5}{x-1}$ cm

$\dfrac{x^2-8}{x-1}$ cm

$\dfrac{x^2-2x}{x-1}$ cm

95. When is the LCD of two rational expressions equal to the product of their denominators? $\left(\textit{Hint: } \text{What is the LCD of } \dfrac{1}{x} \text{ and } \dfrac{7}{x+5}?\right)$

96. When is the LCD of two rational expressions with different denominators equal to one of the denominators? $\left(\textit{Hint: } \text{What is the LCD of } \dfrac{3x}{x+2} \text{ and } \dfrac{7x+1}{(x+2)^3}?\right)$

97. In your own words, explain how to add rational expressions with different denominators.

98. In your own words, explain how to multiply rational expressions.

99. In your own words, explain how to divide rational expressions.

100. In your own words, explain how to subtract rational expressions with different denominators.

Perform each indicated operation. (Hint: First write each expression with positive exponents.)

101. $x^{-1} + (2x)^{-1}$ **102.** $y^{-1} + (4y)^{-1}$

103. $4x^{-2} - 3x^{-1}$ **104.** $(4x)^{-2} - (3x)^{-1}$

Use a graphing calculator to support the results of each exercise.

105. Exercise 3   **106.** Exercise 4

6.3 SIMPLIFYING COMPLEX FRACTIONS

OBJECTIVES

1 Simplify complex fractions by simplifying the numerator and denominator and then dividing.

2 Simplify complex fractions by multiplying by a common denominator.

3 Simplify expressions with negative exponents.

OBJECTIVE 1 ▶ Simplifying complex fractions: Method 1. A rational expression whose numerator, denominator, or both contain one or more rational expressions is called a **complex rational expression** or a **complex fraction.**

Complex Fractions

$$\dfrac{\frac{1}{a}}{\frac{b}{2}} \qquad \dfrac{\frac{x}{2y^2}}{\frac{6x-2}{9y}} \qquad \dfrac{x+\frac{1}{y}}{y+1}$$

The parts of a complex fraction are

$$\left.\dfrac{\frac{x}{y+2}}{7+\frac{1}{y}}\right\}$$

$\leftarrow$ Numerator of complex fraction
$\leftarrow$ Main fraction bar
$\leftarrow$ Denominator of complex fraction

Our goal in this section is to simplify complex fractions. A complex fraction is simplified when it is in the form $\dfrac{P}{Q}$, where P and Q are polynomials that have no common factors. Two methods of simplifying complex fractions are introduced. The first method evolves from the definition of a fraction as a quotient.

> **Simplifying a Complex Fraction: Method I**
> **STEP 1.** Simplify the numerator and the denominator of the complex fraction so that each is a single fraction.
> **STEP 2.** Perform the indicated division by multiplying the numerator of the complex fraction by the reciprocal of the denominator of the complex fraction.
> **STEP 3.** Simplify if possible.

EXAMPLE 1   Simplify each complex fraction.

a. $\dfrac{\dfrac{2x}{27y^2}}{\dfrac{6x^2}{9}}$
b. $\dfrac{\dfrac{5x}{x+2}}{\dfrac{10}{x-2}}$
c. $\dfrac{\dfrac{x}{y^2}+\dfrac{1}{y}}{\dfrac{y}{x^2}+\dfrac{1}{x}}$

Solution

a. The numerator of the complex fraction is already a single fraction, and so is the denominator. Perform the indicated division by multiplying the numerator, $\dfrac{2x}{27y^2}$, by the reciprocal of the denominator, $\dfrac{6x^2}{9}$. Then simplify.

$$\frac{\dfrac{2x}{27y^2}}{\dfrac{6x^2}{9}} = \frac{2x}{27y^2} \div \frac{6x^2}{9}$$

$$= \frac{2x}{27y^2} \cdot \frac{9}{6x^2} \qquad \text{Multiply by the reciprocal of } \frac{6x^2}{9}.$$

$$= \frac{2x \cdot 9}{27y^2 \cdot 6x^2}$$

$$= \frac{1}{9xy^2}$$

> ▶ **Helpful Hint**
> Both the numerator and denominator are single fractions, so we perform the indicated division.

b. $\dfrac{\left\{\dfrac{5x}{x+2}\right.}{\left\{\dfrac{10}{x-2}\right.} = \dfrac{5x}{x+2} \div \dfrac{10}{x-2} = \dfrac{5x}{x+2} \cdot \dfrac{x-2}{10}$ Multiply by the reciprocal of $\dfrac{10}{x-2}$.

$$= \frac{5x(x-2)}{2 \cdot 5(x+2)}$$

$$= \frac{x(x-2)}{2(x+2)} \qquad \text{Simplify.}$$

c. First simplify the numerator and the denominator of the complex fraction separately so that each is a single fraction. Then perform the indicated division.

$$\frac{\dfrac{x}{y^2}+\dfrac{1}{y}}{\dfrac{y}{x^2}+\dfrac{1}{x}}=\frac{\dfrac{x}{y^2}+\dfrac{1\cdot y}{y\cdot y}}{\dfrac{y}{x^2}+\dfrac{1\cdot x}{x\cdot x}}$$

Simplify the numerator. The LCD is y^2.

Simplify the denominator. The LCD is x^2.

$$=\frac{\dfrac{x+y}{y^2}}{\dfrac{y+x}{x^2}}$$

Add.

$$=\frac{x+y}{y^2}\cdot\frac{x^2}{y+x}$$

Multiply by the reciprocal of $\dfrac{y+x}{x^2}$.

$$=\frac{x^2(x+y)}{y^2(y+x)}$$

$$=\frac{x^2}{y^2}$$

Simplify. □

PRACTICE
1   Simplify each complex fraction.

a. $\dfrac{\dfrac{5k}{36m}}{\dfrac{15k}{9}}$ **b.** $\dfrac{\dfrac{8x}{x-4}}{\dfrac{3}{x+4}}$ **c.** $\dfrac{\dfrac{5}{a}+\dfrac{b}{a^2}}{\dfrac{5a}{b^2}+\dfrac{1}{b}}$

Concept Check ☑

Which of the following are equivalent to $\dfrac{\dfrac{1}{x}}{\dfrac{3}{y}}$?

a. $\dfrac{1}{x}\div\dfrac{3}{y}$ **b.** $\dfrac{1}{x}\cdot\dfrac{y}{3}$ **c.** $\dfrac{1}{x}\div\dfrac{y}{3}$

OBJECTIVE 2 ▶ Simplifying complex fractions: Method 2. Next we look at another method of simplifying complex fractions. With this method we multiply the numerator and the denominator of the complex fraction by the LCD of all fractions in the complex fraction.

Simplifying a Complex Fraction: Method II

STEP 1. Multiply the numerator and the denominator of the complex fraction by the LCD of the fractions in both the numerator and the denominator.

STEP 2. Simplify.

Answer to Concept Check:
a and b

EXAMPLE 2 Simplify each complex fraction.

a. $\dfrac{\dfrac{5x}{x+2}}{\dfrac{10}{x-2}}$

b. $\dfrac{\dfrac{x}{y^2}+\dfrac{1}{y}}{\dfrac{y}{x^2}+\dfrac{1}{x}}$

Solution

a. The least common denominator of $\dfrac{5x}{x+2}$ and $\dfrac{10}{x-2}$ is $(x+2)(x-2)$. Multiply both the numerator, $\dfrac{5x}{x+2}$, and the denominator, $\dfrac{10}{x-2}$, by the LCD.

$$\dfrac{\dfrac{5x}{x+2}}{\dfrac{10}{x-2}} = \dfrac{\left(\dfrac{5x}{x+2}\right)\cdot(x+2)(x-2)}{\left(\dfrac{10}{x-2}\right)\cdot(x+2)(x-2)}$$ Multiply numerator and denominator by the LCD.

$$= \dfrac{5\,x\cdot(x-2)}{2\cdot5\cdot(x+2)}$$ Simplify.

$$= \dfrac{x(x-2)}{2(x+2)}$$ Simplify.

b. The least common denominator of $\dfrac{x}{y^2}, \dfrac{1}{y}, \dfrac{y}{x^2}$, and $\dfrac{1}{x}$ is x^2y^2.

$$\dfrac{\dfrac{x}{y^2}+\dfrac{1}{y}}{\dfrac{y}{x^2}+\dfrac{1}{x}} = \dfrac{\left(\dfrac{x}{y^2}+\dfrac{1}{y}\right)\cdot x^2y^2}{\left(\dfrac{y}{x^2}+\dfrac{1}{x}\right)\cdot x^2y^2}$$ Multiply the numerator and denominator by the LCD.

$$= \dfrac{\dfrac{x}{y^2}\cdot x^2\,y^2 + \dfrac{1}{y}\cdot x^2\,y^2}{\dfrac{y}{x^2}\cdot x^2\,y^2 + \dfrac{1}{x}\cdot x^2\,y^2}$$ Use the distributive property.

$$= \dfrac{x^3 + x^2y}{y^3 + xy^2}$$ Simplify.

$$= \dfrac{x^2(x+y)}{y^2(y+x)}$$ Factor.

$$= \dfrac{x^2}{y^2}$$ Simplify. □

PRACTICE
2 Use Method 2 to simplify:

a. $\dfrac{\dfrac{8x}{x-4}}{\dfrac{3}{x+4}}$

b. $\dfrac{\dfrac{b}{a^2}+\dfrac{1}{a}}{\dfrac{a}{b^2}+\dfrac{1}{b}}$

OBJECTIVE 3 ▶ Simplifying expressions with negative exponents. If an expression contains negative exponents, write the expression as an equivalent expression with positive exponents.

EXAMPLE 3   Simplify.

$$\frac{x^{-1} - 2xy^{-1}}{x^{-2} - x^{-2}y^{-1}}$$

Solution   This fraction does not appear to be a complex fraction. If we write it by using only positive exponents, however, we see that it is a complex fraction.

$$\frac{x^{-1} + 2xy^{-1}}{x^{-2} - x^{-2}y^{-1}} = \frac{\dfrac{1}{x} + \dfrac{2x}{y}}{\dfrac{1}{x^2} - \dfrac{1}{x^2 y}}$$

The LCD of $\dfrac{1}{x}$, $\dfrac{2x}{y}$, $\dfrac{1}{x^2}$, and $\dfrac{1}{x^2 y}$ is $x^2 y$. Multiply both the numerator and denominator by $x^2 y$.

$$= \frac{\left(\dfrac{1}{x} + \dfrac{2x}{y}\right) \cdot x^2 y}{\left(\dfrac{1}{x^2} - \dfrac{1}{x^2 y}\right) \cdot x^2 y}$$

$$= \frac{\dfrac{1}{x} \cdot x^2 y + \dfrac{2x}{y} \cdot x^2 y}{\dfrac{1}{x^2} \cdot x^2 y - \dfrac{1}{x^2 y} \cdot x^2 y} \qquad \text{Apply the distributive property.}$$

$$= \frac{xy + 2x^3}{y - 1} \quad \text{or} \quad \frac{x(y + 2x^2)}{y - 1} \qquad \text{Simplify.} \qquad \square$$

PRACTICE
3   Simplify: $\dfrac{3x^{-1} + x^{-2}y^{-1}}{y^{-2} + xy^{-1}}$.

EXAMPLE 4   Simplify: $\dfrac{(2x)^{-1} + 1}{2x^{-1} - 1}$

Solution $\dfrac{(2x)^{-1} + 1}{2x^{-1} - 1} = \dfrac{\dfrac{1}{2x} + 1}{\dfrac{2}{x} - 1}$ Write using positive exponents.

> **Helpful Hint**
>
> Don't forget that $(2x)^{-1} = \dfrac{1}{2x}$, but $2x^{-1} = 2 \cdot \dfrac{1}{x} = \dfrac{2}{x}$.

$$= \frac{\left(\dfrac{1}{2x} + 1\right) \cdot 2x}{\left(\dfrac{2}{x} - 1\right) \cdot 2x} \qquad \text{The LDC of } \dfrac{1}{2x} \text{ and } \dfrac{2}{x} \text{ is } 2x.$$

$$= \frac{\dfrac{1}{2x} \cdot 2x + 1 \cdot 2x}{\dfrac{2}{x} \cdot 2x - 1 \cdot 2x} \qquad \text{Use distributive property.}$$

$$= \frac{1 + 2x}{4 - 2x} \quad \text{or} \quad \frac{1 + 2x}{2(2 - x)} \qquad \text{Simplify.} \qquad \square$$

PRACTICE
4   Simplify: $\dfrac{(3x)^{-1} - 2}{5x^{-1} + 2}$.

VOCABULARY & READINESS CHECK

Complete the steps by writing the simplified complex fraction.

1. $\dfrac{\dfrac{7}{x}}{\dfrac{1}{x} + \dfrac{z}{x}} = \dfrac{x\left(\dfrac{7}{x}\right)}{x\left(\dfrac{1}{x}\right) + x\left(\dfrac{z}{x}\right)} = $ _____

2. $\dfrac{\dfrac{x}{4}}{\dfrac{x^2}{2} + \dfrac{1}{4}} = \dfrac{4\left(\dfrac{x}{4}\right)}{4\left(\dfrac{x^2}{2}\right) + 4\left(\dfrac{1}{4}\right)} = $ _____

Write each with positive exponents.

3. $x^{-2} = $ _____

4. $y^{-3} = $ _____

5. $2x^{-1} = $ _____

6. $(2x)^{-1} = $ _____

7. $(9y)^{-1} = $ _____

8. $9y^{-2} = $ _____

6.3 | EXERCISE SET

MyMathLab   PRACTICE   WATCH   DOWNLOAD   READ   REVIEW

Simplify each complex fraction. See Examples 1 and 2.

1. $\dfrac{\dfrac{10}{3x}}{\dfrac{5}{6x}}$

2. $\dfrac{\dfrac{15}{2x}}{\dfrac{5}{6x}}$

3. $\dfrac{1 + \dfrac{2}{5}}{2 + \dfrac{3}{5}}$

4. $\dfrac{2 + \dfrac{1}{7}}{3 - \dfrac{4}{7}}$

5. $\dfrac{\dfrac{4}{x-1}}{\dfrac{x}{x-1}}$

6. $\dfrac{\dfrac{x}{x+2}}{\dfrac{2}{x+2}}$

7. $\dfrac{1 - \dfrac{2}{x}}{x + \dfrac{4}{9x}}$

8. $\dfrac{5 - \dfrac{3}{x}}{x + \dfrac{2}{3x}}$

9. $\dfrac{\dfrac{4x^2 - y^2}{xy}}{\dfrac{2}{y} - \dfrac{1}{x}}$

10. $\dfrac{\dfrac{x^2 - 9y^2}{xy}}{\dfrac{1}{y} - \dfrac{3}{x}}$

11. $\dfrac{\dfrac{x+1}{3}}{\dfrac{2x-1}{6}}$

12. $\dfrac{\dfrac{x+3}{12}}{\dfrac{4x-5}{15}}$

13. $\dfrac{\dfrac{2}{x} + \dfrac{3}{x^2}}{\dfrac{4}{x^2} - \dfrac{9}{x}}$

14. $\dfrac{\dfrac{2}{x^2} + \dfrac{1}{x}}{\dfrac{4}{x^2} - \dfrac{1}{x}}$

15. $\dfrac{\dfrac{1}{x} + \dfrac{2}{x^2}}{x + \dfrac{8}{x^2}}$

16. $\dfrac{\dfrac{1}{y} + \dfrac{3}{y^2}}{y + \dfrac{27}{y^2}}$

17. $\dfrac{\dfrac{4}{5-x} + \dfrac{5}{x-5}}{\dfrac{2}{x} + \dfrac{3}{x-5}}$

18. $\dfrac{\dfrac{3}{x-4} - \dfrac{2}{4-x}}{\dfrac{2}{x-4} - \dfrac{2}{x}}$

19. $\dfrac{\dfrac{x+2}{x} - \dfrac{2}{x-1}}{\dfrac{x+1}{x} + \dfrac{x+1}{x-1}}$

20. $\dfrac{\dfrac{5}{a+2} - \dfrac{1}{a-2}}{\dfrac{3}{2+a} + \dfrac{6}{2-a}}$

21. $\dfrac{\dfrac{2}{x} + 3}{\dfrac{4}{x^2} - 9}$

22. $\dfrac{2 + \dfrac{1}{x}}{4x - \dfrac{1}{x}}$

23. $\dfrac{1 - \dfrac{x}{y}}{\dfrac{x^2}{y^2} - 1}$

24. $\dfrac{1 - \dfrac{2}{x}}{x - \dfrac{4}{x}}$

25. $\dfrac{\dfrac{-2x}{x-y}}{\dfrac{y}{x^2}}$

26. $\dfrac{\dfrac{7y}{x^2 + xy}}{\dfrac{y^2}{x^2}}$

27. $\dfrac{\dfrac{2}{x} + \dfrac{1}{x^2}}{\dfrac{y}{x^2}}$

28. $\dfrac{\dfrac{5}{x^2} - \dfrac{2}{x}}{\dfrac{1}{x} + 2}$

29. $\dfrac{\dfrac{x}{9} - \dfrac{1}{x}}{1 + \dfrac{3}{x}}$

30. $\dfrac{\dfrac{x}{4} - \dfrac{4}{x}}{1 - \dfrac{4}{x}}$

31. $\dfrac{\dfrac{x-1}{x^2-4}}{1 + \dfrac{1}{x-2}}$

32. $\dfrac{\dfrac{x+3}{x^2-9}}{1 + \dfrac{1}{x-3}}$

33. $\dfrac{\dfrac{2}{x+5}+\dfrac{4}{x+3}}{\dfrac{3x+13}{x^2+8x+15}}$

34. $\dfrac{\dfrac{2}{x+2}+\dfrac{6}{x+7}}{\dfrac{4x+13}{x^2+9x+14}}$

Simplify. See Examples 3 and 4.

35. $\dfrac{x^{-1}}{x^{-2}+y^{-2}}$

36. $\dfrac{a^{-3}+b^{-1}}{a^{-2}}$

37. $\dfrac{2a^{-1}+3b^{-2}}{a^{-1}-b^{-1}}$

38. $\dfrac{x^{-1}+y^{-1}}{3x^{-2}+5y^{-2}}$

39. $\dfrac{1}{x-x^{-1}}$

40. $\dfrac{x^{-2}}{x+3x^{-1}}$

41. $\dfrac{a^{-1}+1}{a^{-1}-1}$

42. $\dfrac{a^{-1}-4}{4+a^{-1}}$

43. $\dfrac{3x^{-1}+(2y)^{-1}}{x^{-2}}$

44. $\dfrac{5x^{-2}-3y^{-1}}{x^{-1}+y^{-1}}$

45. $\dfrac{2a^{-1}+(2a)^{-1}}{a^{-1}+2a^{-2}}$

46. $\dfrac{a^{-1}+2a^{-2}}{2a^{-1}+(2a)^{-1}}$

47. $\dfrac{5x^{-1}+2y^{-1}}{x^{-2}y^{-2}}$

48. $\dfrac{x^{-2}y^{-2}}{5x^{-1}+2y^{-1}}$

49. $\dfrac{5x^{-1}-2y^{-1}}{25x^{-2}-4y^{-2}}$

50. $\dfrac{3x^{-1}+3y^{-1}}{4x^{-2}-9y^{-2}}$

REVIEW AND PREVIEW

Simplify. See Sections 5.1 and 5.2.

51. $\dfrac{3x^3y^2}{12x}$

52. $\dfrac{-36xb^3}{9xb^2}$

53. $\dfrac{144x^5y^5}{-16x^2y}$

54. $\dfrac{48x^3y^2}{-4xy}$

Solve the following. See Section 2.6.

55. $|x-5|=9$

56. $|2y+1|=1$

CONCEPT EXTENSIONS

Solve. See the Concept Check in the Section.

57. Which of the following are equivalent to $\dfrac{\dfrac{x+1}{9}}{\dfrac{y-2}{5}}$?

a. $\dfrac{x+1}{9}\div\dfrac{y-2}{5}$ **b.** $\dfrac{x+1}{9}\cdot\dfrac{y-2}{5}$ **c.** $\dfrac{x+1}{9}\cdot\dfrac{5}{y-2}$

58. Which of the following are equivalent to $\dfrac{\dfrac{a}{7}}{\dfrac{b}{13}}$?

a. $\dfrac{a}{7}\cdot\dfrac{b}{13}$ **b.** $\dfrac{a}{7}\div\dfrac{b}{13}$ **c.** $\dfrac{a}{7}\div\dfrac{13}{b}$ **d.** $\dfrac{a}{7}\cdot\dfrac{13}{b}$

59. When the source of a sound is traveling toward a listener, the pitch that the listener hears due to the Doppler effect is given by the complex rational compression $\dfrac{a}{1-\dfrac{s}{770}}$, where a is the

actual pitch of the sound and s is the speed of the sound source. Simplify this expression.

60. In baseball, the earned run average (ERA) statistic gives the average number of earned runs scored on a pitcher per game. It is computed with the following expression: $\dfrac{E}{\dfrac{I}{9}}$, where E is the number of earned runs scored on a pitcher and I is the total number of innings pitched by the pitcher. Simplify this expression.

61. Which of the following are equivalent to $\dfrac{\dfrac{1}{x}}{\dfrac{3}{y}}$?

a. $\dfrac{1}{x}\div\dfrac{3}{y}$ **b.** $\dfrac{1}{x}\cdot\dfrac{y}{3}$ **c.** $\dfrac{1}{x}\div\dfrac{y}{3}$

62. In your own words, explain one method for simplifying a complex fraction.

Simplify.

63. $\dfrac{1}{1+(1+x)^{-1}}$

64. $\dfrac{(x+2)^{-1}+(x-2)^{-1}}{(x^2-4)^{-1}}$

65. $\dfrac{x}{1-\dfrac{1}{1+\dfrac{1}{x}}}$

66. $\dfrac{x}{1-\dfrac{1}{1-\dfrac{1}{x}}}$

67. $\dfrac{\dfrac{2}{y^2}-\dfrac{5}{xy}-\dfrac{3}{x^2}}{\dfrac{2}{y^2}+\dfrac{7}{xy}+\dfrac{3}{x^2}}$

68. $\dfrac{\dfrac{2}{x^2}-\dfrac{1}{xy}-\dfrac{1}{y^2}}{\dfrac{1}{x^2}-\dfrac{3}{xy}+\dfrac{2}{y^2}}$

69. $\dfrac{3(a + 1)^{-1} + 4a^{-2}}{(a^3 + a^2)^{-1}}$

70. $\dfrac{9x^{-1} - 5(x - y)^{-1}}{4(x - y)^{-1}}$

In the study of calculus, the difference quotient $\dfrac{f(a + h) - f(a)}{h}$

is often found and simplified. Find and simplify this quotient for each function $f(x)$ by following steps **a** through **d**.

a. Find $(a + h)$.

b. Find $f(a)$.

c. Use steps **a** and **b** to find $\dfrac{f(a + h) - f(a)}{h}$

d. Simplify the result of step **c**.

71. $f(x) = \dfrac{1}{x}$

72. $f(x) = \dfrac{5}{x}$

73. $\dfrac{3}{x + 1}$

74. $\dfrac{2}{x^2}$

 STUDY SKILLS BUILDER

How Are You Doing?

If you haven't done so yet, take a few moments and think about how you are doing in this course. Are you working toward your goal of successfully completing this course? Is your performance on homework, quizzes, and tests satisfactory? If not, you might want to see your instructor to see if he/she has any suggestions on how you can improve your performance. Reread Section 1.1 for ideas on places to get help with your mathematics course.

Answer the following.

1. List any textbook supplements you are using to help you through this course.

2. List any campus resources you are using to help you through this course.

3. Write a short paragraph describing how you are doing in your mathematics course.

4. If improvement is needed, list ways that you can work toward improving your situation as described in Exercise 3.

6.4 DIVIDING POLYNOMIALS: LONG DIVISION AND SYNTHETIC DIVISION

OBJECTIVES

1. Divide a polynomial by a monomial.

2. Divide by a polynomial.

3. Use synthetic division to divide a polynomial by a binomial.

4. Use the remainder theorem to evaluate polynomials.

OBJECTIVE 1 ▶ Dividing a polynomial by a monomial. Recall that a rational expression is a quotient of polynomials. An equivalent form of a rational expression can be obtained by performing the indicated division. For example, the rational expression $\dfrac{10x^3 - 5x^2 + 20x}{5x}$ can be thought of as the polynomial $10x^3 - 5x^2 + 20x$ divided by the monomial $5x$. To perform this division of a polynomial by a monomial (which we do below) recall the following addition fact for fractions with a common denominator.

$$\frac{a}{c} + \frac{b}{c} = \frac{a + b}{c}$$

If a, b, and c are monomials, we might read this equation from right to left and gain insight into dividing a polynomial by a monomial.

> **Dividing a Polynomial by a Monomial**
> Divide each term in the polynomial by the monomial.
>
> $$\frac{a + b}{c} = \frac{a}{c} + \frac{b}{c}, \quad \text{where } c \neq 0$$

EXAMPLE 1   Divide $10x^3 - 5x^2 + 20x$ by $5x$.

Solution   We divide each term of $10x^3 - 5x^2 + 20x$ by $5x$ and simplify.

$$\frac{10x^3 - 5x^2 + 20x}{5x} = \frac{10x^3}{5x} - \frac{5x^2}{5x} + \frac{20x}{5x} = 2x^2 - x + 4$$

Check: To check, see that (quotient) (divisor) = dividend, or

$$(2x^2 - x + 4)(5x) = 10x^3 - 5x^2 + 20x.$$ □

PRACTICE
1   Divide $18a^3 - 12a^2 + 30a$ by $6a$.

EXAMPLE 2   Divide: $\dfrac{3x^5y^2 - 15x^3y - x^2y - 6x}{x^2y}$.

Solution   We divide each term in the numerator by x^2y.

$$\frac{3x^5y^2 - 15x^3y - x^2y - 6x}{x^2y} = \frac{3x^5y^2}{x^2y} - \frac{15x^3y}{x^2y} - \frac{x^2y}{x^2y} - \frac{6x}{x^2y}$$

$$= 3x^3y - 15x - 1 - \frac{6}{xy}$$ □

PRACTICE
2   Divide: $\dfrac{5a^3b^4 - 8a^2b^3 + ab^2 - 8b}{ab^2}$.

OBJECTIVE 2 ▶ Dividing by a polynomial. To divide a polynomial by a polynomial other than a monomial, we use **long division.** Polynomial long division is similar to long division of real numbers. We review long division of real numbers by dividing 7 into 296.

$$\begin{array}{r} 42 \\ \text{Divisor: } 7\overline{)296} \\ \underline{-28} \\ 16 \\ \underline{-14} \\ 2 \end{array}$$

4(7) = 28.

16   Subtract and bring down the next digit in the dividend.

2(7) = 14.

2   Subtract. The remainder is 2.

The quotient is $42\dfrac{2 \text{ (remainder)}}{7 \text{ (divisor)}}$.

Check: To check, notice that

$$42(7) - 2 = 296, \text{ the dividend.}$$

This same division process can be applied to polynomials, as shown next.

EXAMPLE 3   Divide $2x^2 - x - 10$ by $x + 2$.

Solution $2x^2 - x - 10$ is the dividend, and $x + 2$ is the divisor.

STEP 1. Divide $2x^2$ by x.

$$\begin{array}{r} 2x \\ x + 2\overline{)2x^2 - x - 10} \end{array}$$ $\dfrac{2x^2}{x} = 2x$, so $2x$ is the first term of the quotient.

STEP 2. Multiply $2x(x + 2)$.

$$
\begin{array}{r}
2x \\
x + 2 \overline{)2x^2 - x - 10} \\
2x^2 + 4x
\end{array}
$$

$2x(x + 2)$

Like terms are lined up vertically.

STEP 3. Subtract $(2x^2 + 4x)$ from $(2x^2 - x - 10)$ by changing the signs of $(2x^2 + 4x)$ and adding.

$$
\begin{array}{r}
2x \\
x + 2 \overline{)2x^2 - x - 10} \\
\overline{\cancel{+}2x^2 \,\cancel{\mp}\, 4x} \\
-5x
\end{array}
$$

STEP 4. Bring down the next term, -10, and start the process over.

$$
\begin{array}{r}
2x \\
x + 2 \overline{)2x^2 - x - 10} \\
\overline{\cancel{+}2x^2 \,\cancel{\mp}\, 4x} \quad \downarrow \\
-5x - 10
\end{array}
$$

STEP 5. Divide $-5x$ by x.

$$
\begin{array}{r}
2x - 5 \\
x + 2 \overline{)2x^2 - x - 10} \\
\overline{\cancel{+}2x^2 \,\cancel{\mp}\, 4x} \\
-5x - 10
\end{array}
$$

$\dfrac{-5x}{x} = -5$, so -5 is the second term of the quotient.

STEP 6. Multiply $-5(x + 2)$.

$$
\begin{array}{r}
2x - 5 \\
x + 2 \overline{)2x^2 - x - 10} \\
\overline{\cancel{+}2x^2 \,\cancel{\mp}\, 4x} \\
-5x - 10 \\
-5x - 10
\end{array}
$$

Multiply: $-5(x + 2)$. Like terms are lined up vertically.

STEP 7. Subtract by changing signs of $-5x - 10$ and adding.

$$
\begin{array}{r}
2x - 5 \\
x + 2 \overline{)2x^2 - x - 10} \\
\overline{\cancel{+}2x^2 \,\cancel{\mp}\, 4x} \\
-5x - 10 \\
\underline{\cancel{+}5x \,\cancel{\mp}\, 10} \\
0
\end{array}
$$

Subtract.

Remainder

Then $\dfrac{2x^2 - x - 10}{x + 2} = 2x - 5$. There is no remainder.

Check: Check this result by multiplying $2x - 5$ by $x + 2$. Their product is $(2x - 5)(x + 2) = 2x^2 - x - 10$, the dividend. □

PRACTICE

3   Divide $3x^2 + 7x - 6$ by $x + 3$.

EXAMPLE 4   Divide: $(6x^2 - 19x + 12) \div (3x - 5)$

Solution

$$
\begin{array}{r}
2x \\
3x - 5 \overline{)6x^2 - 19x + 12} \\
\underline{{}^{-}6x^2 \overset{+}{\not=} 10x} \qquad \downarrow \\
-9x + 12
\end{array}
$$

Divide $\dfrac{6x^2}{3x} = 2x.$

Multiply $2x(3x - 5)$.
Subtract by adding the opposite.
Bring down the next term, $+12$.

$$
\begin{array}{r}
2x - 3 \\
3x - 5 \overline{)6x^2 - 19x + 12} \\
\underline{{}^{-}6x^2 \not= 10x} \\
-9x + 12 \\
\underline{\overset{+}{\not=}9x \not= 15} \\
-3
\end{array}
$$

Divide $\dfrac{-9x}{3x} = -3.$

Multiply $-3(3x - 5)$.
Subtract by adding the opposite.

Check: divisor   ·   quotient   +   remainder

$$(3x - 5) \qquad (2x - 3) \qquad + 1(-3) = 6x^2 - 19x + 15 - 3$$

$$= 6x^2 - 19x + 12 \qquad \text{The dividend}$$

The division checks, so

$$\frac{6x^2 - 19x + 12}{3x - 5} = 2x - 3 + \frac{-3}{3x - 5}$$

▶ **Helpful Hint**
This fraction is the remainder over the divisor.

$$\text{or} \quad 2x - 3 - \frac{3}{3x - 5}$$

PRACTICE
4   Divide $(6x^2 - 7x + 2)$ by $(2x - 1)$.

EXAMPLE 5   Divide: $(7x^3 + 16x^2 + 2x - 1) \div (x + 4)$.

Solution

$$
\begin{array}{r}
7x^2 - 12x + 50 \\
x + 4 \overline{)7x^3 + 16x^2 + 2x - 1} \\
\underline{{}^{-}7x^3 \not= 28x^2} \\
-12x^2 + 2x \\
\underline{\overset{+}{\not=}12x^2 \not= 48x} \\
50x - 1 \\
\underline{{}^{-}50x \not= 200} \\
-201
\end{array}
$$

Divide $\dfrac{7x^3}{x} = 7x^2.$

$7x^2(x + 4)$

Subtract. Bring down $2x$.

$\dfrac{-12x^2}{x} = -12x$, a term of the quotient.

$-12x(x + 4)$ Subtract. Bring down -1.

$\dfrac{50x}{x} = 50$, a term of the quotient.

$50(x + 4)$.   Subtract.

Thus, $\dfrac{7x^3 + 16x^2 + 2x - 1}{x + 4} = 7x^2 - 12x + 50 + \dfrac{-201}{x + 4}$ or

$$7x^2 - 12x + 50 - \frac{201}{x + 4}.$$

PRACTICE
5   Divide $(5x^3 + 9x^2 - 10x + 30) \div (x + 3)$.

EXAMPLE 6 Divide $3x^4 + 2x^3 - 8x + 6$ by $x^2 - 1$.

Solution Before dividing, we represent any "missing powers" by the product of 0 and the variable raised to the missing power. There is no x^2 term in the dividend, so we include $0x^2$ to represent the missing term. Also, there is no x term in the divisor, so we include $0x$ in the divisor.

$$
\begin{array}{r}
3x^2 + 2x + 3 \\
x^2 + 0x - 1 \overline{)3x^4 + 2x^3 + 0x^2 - 8x + 6} \\
\underline{3x^4 \mp 0x^3 \mp 3x^2} \quad\downarrow \\
2x^3 + 3x^2 - 8x \\
\underline{2x^3 \mp 0x^2 \mp 2x} \quad\downarrow \\
3x^2 - 6x + 6 \\
\underline{3x^2 \mp 0x \mp 3} \\
-6x + 9
\end{array}
$$

$\dfrac{3x^4}{x^2} = 3x^2$

$3x^2(x^2 + 0x - 1)$

Subtract. Bring down $-8x$.

$\dfrac{2x^3}{x^2} = 2x$, a term of the quotient.

$2x(x^2 + 0x - 1)$

Subtract. Bring down 6.

$\dfrac{3x^2}{x^2} = 3$, a term of the quotient.

$3(x^2 + 0x - 1)$

Subtract.

The division process is finished when the degree of the remainder polynomial is less than the degree of the divisor. Thus,

$$
\frac{3x^4 + 2x^3 - 8x + 6}{x^2 - 1} = 3x^2 + 2x + 3 + \frac{-6x + 9}{x^2 - 1} \qquad \square
$$

PRACTICE
6 Divide $2x^4 + 3x^3 - 5x + 2$ by $x^2 + 1$.

EXAMPLE 7 Divide $27x^3 + 8$ by $3x + 2$.

Solution We replace the missing terms in the dividend with $0x^2$ and $0x$.

$$
\begin{array}{r}
9x^2 - 6x + 4 \\
3x + 2 \overline{)27x^3 + 0x^2 + 0x + 8} \\
\underline{27x^3 \mp 18x^2} \quad\downarrow \\
-18x^2 + 0x \\
\underline{\mp 18x^2 \mp 12x} \quad\downarrow \\
12x + 8 \\
\underline{-12x \mp 8}
\end{array}
$$

$9x^2(3x + 2)$

Subtract. Bring down $0x$.

$-6x(3x + 2)$

Subtract. Bring down 8.

$4(3x + 2)$

Thus, $\dfrac{27x^3 + 8}{3x + 2} = 9x^2 - 6x + 4$. $\qquad \square$

PRACTICE
7 Divide $64x^3 - 125$ by $4x - 5$.

Concept Check ☑

In a division problem, the divisor is $4x^3 - 5$. The division process can be stopped when which of these possible remainder polynomials is reached?

a. $2x^4 + x^2 - 3$ **b.** $x^3 - 5^2$ **c.** $4x^2 + 25$

OBJECTIVE 3 ▶ Using synthetic division to divide a polynomial by a binomial. When a polynomial is to be divided by a binomial of the form $x - c$, a shortcut process called **synthetic division** may be used. On the left is an example of long division, and on the right, the same example showing the coefficients of the variables only.

$$
\begin{array}{r}
2x^2 + 5x + 2 \\
x - 3\overline{)2x^3 - x^2 - 13x + 1} \\
\underline{2x^3 - 6x^2} \\
5x^2 - 13x \\
\underline{5x^2 - 15x} \\
2x + 1 \\
\underline{2x - 6} \\
7
\end{array}
\qquad
\begin{array}{r}
2 \quad 5 \quad 2 \\
1 - 3\overline{)2 - 1 - 13 + 1} \\
\underline{2 - 6} \\
5 - 13 \\
\underline{5 - 15} \\
2 + 1 \\
\underline{2 - 6} \\
7
\end{array}
$$

Notice that as long as we keep coefficients of powers of x in the same column, we can perform division of polynomials by performing algebraic operations on the coefficients only. This shortcut process of dividing with coefficients only in a special format is called synthetic division. To find $(2x^3 - x^2 - 13x + 1) \div (x - 3)$ by synthetic division, follow the next example.

EXAMPLE 8   Use synthetic division to divide $2x^3 - x^2 - 13x + 1$ by $x - 3$.

Solution   To use synthetic division, the divisor must be in the form $x - c$. Since we are dividing by $x - 3$, c is 3. Write down 3 and the coefficients of the dividend.

$$
\begin{array}{c|cccc}
c & & & & \\
3 & 2 & -1 & -13 & 1 \\
& & & & \\
\hline
& 2 & & &
\end{array}
$$
Next, draw a line and bring down the first coefficient of the dividend.

$$
\begin{array}{c|cccc}
3 & 2 & -1 & -13 & 1 \\
& & 6 & & \\
\hline
& 2 & & &
\end{array}
$$
Multiply $3 \cdot 2$ and write down the product, 6.

$$
\begin{array}{c|cccc}
3 & 2 & -1 & -13 & 1 \\
& & 6 & & \\
\hline
& 2 & 5 & &
\end{array}
$$
Add $-1 + 6$. Write down the sum, 5.

$$
\begin{array}{c|cccc}
3 & 2 & -1 & -13 & 1 \\
& & 6 & 15 & \\
\hline
& 2 & 5 & 2 &
\end{array}
$$
$3 \cdot 5 = 15$.
$-13 + 15 = 2$.

$$
\begin{array}{c|cccc}
3 & 2 & -1 & -13 & 1 \\
& & 6 & 15 & 6 \\
\hline
& 2 & 5 & 2 & 7
\end{array}
$$
$3 \cdot 2 = 6$.
$1 + 6 = 7$.

The quotient is found in the bottom row. The numbers 2, 5, and 2 are the coefficients of the quotient polynomial, and the number 7 is the remainder. The degree of the quotient polynomial is one less than the degree of the dividend. In our example, the degree of the dividend is 3, so the degree of the quotient polynomial is 2. As we found when we performed the long division, the quotient is

$$2x^2 + 5x + 2, \quad \text{remainder } 7$$

or

$$2x^2 + 5x + 2 + \frac{7}{x - 3}$$

PRACTICE
8   Use synthetic division to divide $4x^3 - 3x^2 + 6x + 5$ by $x - 1$.

EXAMPLE 9 Use synthetic division to divide $x^4 - 2x^3 - 11x^2 + 5x + 34$ by $x + 2$.

Solution The divisor is $x + 2$, which we write in the form $x - c$ as $x - (-2)$. Thus, c is -2. The dividend coefficients are $1, -2, -11, 5,$ and 34.

$$
\begin{array}{r|rrrrr}
-2 & 1 & -2 & -11 & 5 & 34 \\
   &   & -2 & 8 & 6 & -22 \\
\hline
   & 1 & -4 & -3 & 11 & 12 \\
\end{array}
$$

The dividend is a fourth-degree polynomial, so the quotient polynomial is a third-degree polynomial. The quotient is $x^3 - 4x^2 - 3x + 11$ with a remainder of 12. Thus,

$$\frac{x^4 - 2x^3 - 11x^2 + 5x + 34}{x + 2} = x^3 - 4x^2 - 3x + 11 + \frac{12}{x + 2}$$

PRACTICE 9 Use synthetic division to divide $x^4 + 3x^3 - 5x^2 + 6x + 12$ by $x + 3$.

Concept Check ✓

Which division problems are candidates for the synthetic division process?

a. $(3x^2 + 5) \div (x + 4)$ **b.** $(x^3 - x^2 + 2) \div (3x^3 - 2)$
c. $(y^4 + y - 3) \div (x^2 + 1)$ **d.** $x^5 \div (x - 5)$

> **Helpful Hint**
> Before dividing by synthetic division, write the dividend in descending order of variable exponents. Any "missing powers" of the variable should be represented by 0 times the variable raised to the missing power.

EXAMPLE 10 If $P(x) = 2x^3 - 4x^2 + 5$,

a. Find $P(2)$ by substitution.
b. Use synthetic division to find the remainder when $P(x)$ is divided by $x - 2$.

Solution

a. $P(x) = 2x^3 - 4x^2 + 5$
$P(2) = 2(2)^3 - 4(2)^2 + 5$
$= 2(8) - 4(4) + 5 = 16 - 16 + 5 = 5$

Thus, $P(2) = 5$.

b. The coefficients of $P(x)$ are $2, -4, 0,$ and 5. The number 0 is a coefficient of the missing power of x^1. The divisor is $x - 2$, so c is 2.

$$
\begin{array}{r|rrrr}
2 & 2 & -4 & 0 & 5 \\
  &   & 4 & 0 & 0 \\
\hline
  & 2 & 0 & 0 & 5 \\
\end{array}
$$
remainder

The remainder when $P(x)$ is divided by $x - 2$ is 5.

PRACTICE 10 If $P(x) = x^3 - 5x - 2$,

a. Find $P(2)$ by substitution.
b. Use synthetic division to find the remainder when $P(x)$ is divided by $x - 2$.

OBJECTIVE 4 ▶ Using the remainder theorem to evaluate polynomials. Notice in the preceding example that $P(2) = 5$ and that the remainder when $P(x)$ is divided by $x - 2$ is 5. This is no accident. This illustrates the **remainder theorem.**

> **Remainder Theorem**
> If a polynomial $P(x)$ is divided by $x - c$, then the remainder is $P(c)$.

EXAMPLE 11   Use the remainder theorem and synthetic division to find $P(4)$ if

$$P(x) = 4x^6 - 25x^5 + 35x^4 + 17x^2.$$

**Solution**   To find $P(4)$ by the remainder theorem, we divide $P(x)$ by $x - 4$. The coefficients of $P(x)$ are 4, −25, 35, 0, 17, 0, and 0. Also, c is 4.

$$
\begin{array}{r|rrrrrrr}
4 & 4 & -25 & 35 & 0 & 17 & 0 & 0 \\
  &   & 16 & -36 & -4 & -16 & 4 & 16 \\
\hline
  & 4 & -9 & -1 & -4 & 1 & 4 & 16
\end{array}
$$

remainder

Thus, $P(4) = 16$, the remainder.   □

PRACTICE
11   Use the remainder theorem and synthetic division to find $P(3)$ if $P(x) = 2x^5 - 18x^4 + 90x^2 + 59x$.

6.4 | EXERCISE SET

PRACTICE	WATCH	DOWNLOAD	READ	REVIEW

Divide. See Examples 1 and 2.

1. $4a^2 + 8a$ by $2a$

2. $6x^4 - 3x^3$ by $3x^2$

3. $\dfrac{12a^5b^2 + 16a^4b}{4a^4b}$

4. $\dfrac{4x^3y + 12x^2y^2 - 4xy^3}{4xy}$

5. $\dfrac{4x^2y^2 + 6xy^2 - 4y^2}{2x^2y}$

6. $\dfrac{6x^5y + 75x^4y - 24x^3y^2}{3x^4y}$

Divide. See Examples 3 through 7.

7. $(x^2 + 3x + 2) \div (x + 2)$

8. $(y^2 + 7y + 10) \div (y + 5)$

9. $(2x^2 - 6x - 8) \div (x + 1)$

10. $(3x^2 + 19x + 20) \div (x + 5)$

11. $2x^2 + 3x - 2$ by $2x + 4$

12. $6x^2 - 17x - 3$ by $3x - 9$

13. $(4x^3 + 7x^2 + 8x + 20) \div (2x + 4)$

14. $(8x^3 + 18x^2 + 16x + 24) \div (4x + 8)$

15. $(2x^2 + 6x^3 - 18x - 6) \div (3x + 1)$

16. $(4x - 15x^2 + 10x^3 - 6) \div (2x - 3)$

17. $(3x^5 - x^3 + 4x^2 - 12x - 8) \div (x^2 - 2)$

18. $(2x^5 - 6x^4 + x^3 - 4x + 3) \div (x^2 - 3)$

19. $\left(2x^4 + \dfrac{1}{2}x^3 + x^2 + x\right) \div (x - 2)$

20. $\left(x^4 - \dfrac{2}{3}x^3 + x\right) \div (x - 3)$

Use synthetic division to divide. See Examples 8 and 9.

21. $\dfrac{x^2 + 3x - 40}{x - 5}$

22. $\dfrac{x^2 - 14x + 24}{x - 2}$

23. $\dfrac{x^2 + 5x - 6}{x + 6}$

24. $\dfrac{x^2 + 12x + 32}{x + 4}$

25. $\dfrac{x^3 - 7x^2 - 13x + 5}{x - 2}$

26. $\dfrac{x^3 + 6x^2 + 4x - 7}{x + 5}$

27. $\dfrac{4x^2 - 9}{x - 2}$

28. $\dfrac{3x^2 - 4}{x - 1}$

MIXED PRACTICE

Divide. See Examples 1–9.

29. $\dfrac{4x^7y^4 + 8xy^2 + 4xy^3}{4xy^3}$

30. $\dfrac{15x^3y - 5x^2y + 10xy^2}{5x^2y}$

31. $(10x^3 - 5x^2 - 12x + 1) \div (2x - 1)$

32. $(20x^3 - 8x^2 + 5x - 5) \div (5x - 2)$

33. $(2x^3 - 6x^2 - 4) \div (x - 4)$

34. $(3x^3 + 4x - 10) \div (x + 2)$

35. $\dfrac{2x^4 - 13x^3 + 16x^2 - 9x + 20}{x - 5}$

36. $\dfrac{3x^4 + 5x^3 - x^2 + x - 2}{x + 2}$

37. $\dfrac{7x^2 - 4x + 12 + 3x^3}{x + 1}$

38. $\dfrac{4x^3 + x^4 - x^2 - 16x - 4}{x - 2}$

39. $\dfrac{3x^3 + 2x^2 - 4x + 1}{x - \dfrac{1}{3}}$

40. $\dfrac{9y^3 + 9y^2 - y + 2}{y + \dfrac{2}{3}}$

41. $\dfrac{x^3 - 1}{x - 1}$ **42.** $\dfrac{y^3 - 8}{y - 2}$

43. $(25xy^2 + 75xyz + 125x^2yz) \div (-5x^2y)$

44. $(x^6y^6 - x^3y^3z + 7x^3y) \div (-7yz^2)$

45. $(9x^5 + 6x^4 - 6x^2 - 4x) \div (3x + 2)$

46. $(5x^4 - 5x^2 + 10x^3 - 10x) \div (5x + 10)$

For the given polynomial $P(x)$ and the given c, use the remainder theorem to find $P(c)$. See Examples 10 and 11.

47. $P(x) = x^3 + 3x^2 - 7x + 4; 1$

48. $P(x) = x^3 + 5x^2 - 4x - 6; 2$

49. $P(x) = 3x^3 - 7x^2 - 2x + 5; -3$

50. $P(x) = 4x^3 + 5x^2 - 6x - 4; -2$

51. $P(x) = 4x^4 + x^2 - 2; -1$

52. $P(x) = x^4 - 3x^2 - 2x + 5; -2$

53. $P(x) = 2x^4 - 3x^2 - 2; \dfrac{1}{3}$

54. $P(x) = 4x^4 - 2x^3 + x^2 - x - 4; \dfrac{1}{2}$

55. $P(x) = x^5 + x^4 - x^3 + 3; \dfrac{1}{2}$

56. $P(x) = x^5 - 2x^3 + 4x^2 - 5x + 6; \dfrac{2}{3}$

REVIEW AND PREVIEW

Solve each equation for x. See Sections 2.1 and 5.8.

57. $7x + 2 = x - 3$ **58.** $4 - 2x = 17 - 5x$

59. $x^2 = 4x - 4$ **60.** $5x^2 + 10x = 15$

61. $\dfrac{x}{3} - 5 = 13$ **62.** $\dfrac{2x}{9} + 1 = \dfrac{7}{9}$

Factor the following. See Sections 5.5 and 5.7.

63. $x^3 - 1$

64. $8y^3 + 1$

65. $125z^3 + 8$

66. $a^3 - 27$

67. $xy + 2x + 3y + 6$

68. $x^2 - x + xy - y$

69. $x^3 - 9x$

70. $2x^3 - 32x$

CONCEPT EXTENSIONS

Which division problems are candidates for the synthetic division process? See the Concept Checks in this section.

71. $(5x^2 - 3x + 2) \div (x + 2)$

72. $(x^4 - 6) \div (x^3 + 3x - 1)$

73. $(x^7 - 2) \div (x^5 + 1)$

74. $(3x^2 + 7x - 1) \div \left(x - \dfrac{1}{3}\right)$

75. In a long division exercise, if the divisor is $9x^3 - 2x$, then the division process can be stopped when the degree of the remainder is

   a. 1   **b.** 3   **c.** 9   **d.** 2

76. In a division exercise, if the divisor is $x - 3$, then the division process can be stopped when the degree of the remainder is

   a. 1   **b.** 0   **c.** 2   **d.** 3

△ **77.** A board of length $(3x^4 + 6x^2 - 18)$ meters is to be cut into three pieces of the same length. Find the length of each piece.

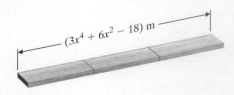

△ **78.** The perimeter of a regular hexagon is given to be $(12x^5 - 48x^3 + 3)$ miles. Find the length of each side.

△ **79.** If the area of the rectangle is $(15x^2 - 29x - 14)$ square inches, and its length is $(5x + 2)$ inches, find its width.

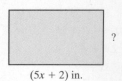

$(5x + 2)$ in.

△ **80.** If the area of a parallelogram is $(2x^2 - 17x + 35)$ square centimeters and its base is $(2x - 7)$ centimeters, find its height.

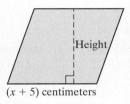

(2x − 7) cm

△ **81.** If the area of a parallelogram is $(x^4 - 23x^2 + 9x - 5)$ square centimeters and its base is $(x + 5)$ centimeters, find its height.

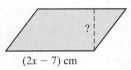

Height

$(x + 5)$ centimeters

△ **82.** If the volume of a box is $(x^4 + 6x^3 - 7x^2)$ cubic meters, its height is x^2 meters, and its length is $(x + 7)$ meters, find its width.

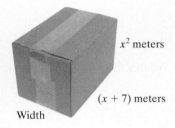

x^2 meters

$(x + 7)$ meters

Width

Divide.

83. $\left(x^4 + \dfrac{2}{3}x^3 + x\right) \div (x - 1)$

84. $\left(2x^3 + \dfrac{9}{2}x^2 - 4x - 10\right) \div (x + 2)$

85. $\left(3x^4 - x - x^3 + \dfrac{1}{2}\right) \div (2x - 1)$

86. $\left(2x^4 + \dfrac{1}{2}x^3 - \dfrac{1}{4}x^2 + x\right) \div (2x + 1)$

87. $(5x^4 - 2x^2 + 10x^3 - 4x) \div (5x + 10)$

88. $(9x^5 + 6x^4 - 6x^2 - 4x) \div (3x + 2)$

For each given f(x) and g(x), find $\dfrac{f(x)}{g(x)}$. Also find any x-values that are not in the domain of $\dfrac{f(x)}{g(x)}$. (Note: Since g(x) is in the denominator, g(x) cannot be 0).

89. $f(x) = 25x^2 - 5x + 30; g(x) = 5x$

90. $f(x) = 12x^4 - 9x^3 + 3x - 1; g(x) = 3x$

91. $f(x) = 7x^4 - 3x^2 + 2; g(x) = x - 2$

92. $f(x) = 2x^3 - 4x^2 + 1; g(x) = x + 3$

93. Try performing the following division without changing the order of the terms. Describe why this makes the process more complicated. Then perform the division again after putting the terms in the dividend in descending order of exponents.

$$\frac{4x^2 - 12x - 12 + 3x^3}{x - 2}$$

94. Explain how to check polynomial long division.

95. Explain an advantage of using the remainder theorem instead of direct substitution.

96. Explain an advantage of using synthetic division instead of long division.

We say that 2 is a factor of 8 because 2 divides 8 evenly, or with a remainder of 0. In the same manner, the polynomial $x - 2$ is a factor of the polynomial $x^3 - 14x^2 + 24x$ because the remainder is 0 when $x^3 - 14x^2 + 24x$ is divided by $x - 2$. Use this information for Exercises 97 through 99.

97. Use synthetic division to show that $x + 3$ is a factor of $x^3 + 3x^2 + 4x + 12$.

98. Use synthetic division to show that $x - 2$ is a factor of $x^3 - 2x^2 - 3x + 6$.

99. From the remainder theorem, the polynomial $x - c$ is a factor of a polynomial function $P(x)$ if $P(c)$ is what value?

100. If a polynomial is divided by $x - 5$, the quotient is $2x^2 + 5x - 6$ and the remainder is 3. Find the original polynomial.

101. If a polynomial is divided by $x + 3$, the quotient is $x^2 - x + 10$ and the remainder is -2. Find the original polynomial.

102. eBay is the leading online auction house. eBay's annual net profit can be modeled by the polynomial function $P(x) = -7x^3 + 94x^2 - 76x + 59$, where $P(x)$ is net profit in millions of dollars and x is the year after 2000. eBay's annual revenue can be modeled by the function $R(x) = 939x - 194$, where $R(x)$ is revenue of millions of dollars and x is years since 2000. (*Source:* eBay, Inc.)

a. Given that

$$\text{Net profit margin} = \frac{\text{net profit}}{\text{revenue}},$$

write a function, $m(x)$, that models eBay's net profit margin.

b. Use part **a** to predict eBay's profit margin in 2010. Round to the nearest hundredth.

6.5 SOLVING EQUATIONS CONTAINING RATIONAL EXPRESSIONS

OBJECTIVE

1 Solve equations containing rational expressions.

▶ **Helpful Hint**

The method described here is for equations only. It may *not* be used for performing operations on expressions.

OBJECTIVE 1 ▶ **Solving equations containing rational expressions.** In this section, we solve equations containing rational expressions. Before beginning this section, make sure that you understand the difference between an *equation* and an *expression*. An **equation** contains an equal sign and an **expression** does not.

$$
\begin{array}{cc}
\textit{Equation} & \textit{Expression} \\
\dfrac{x}{2} + \dfrac{x}{6} = \dfrac{2}{3} & \dfrac{x}{2} + \dfrac{x}{6}
\end{array}
$$

> **Solving Equations Containing Rational Expressions**
>
> To solve *equations* containing rational expressions, first clear the equation of fractions by multiplying both sides of the equation by the LCD of all rational expressions. Then solve as usual.

Concept Check ☑

True or false? Clearing fractions is valid when solving an equation and when simplifying rational expressions. Explain.

EXAMPLE 1 Solve: $\dfrac{4x}{5} + \dfrac{3}{2} = \dfrac{3x}{10}$.

Solution The LCD of $\dfrac{4x}{5}, \dfrac{3}{2}$, and $\dfrac{3x}{10}$ is 10. We multiply both sides of the equation by 10.

$$\frac{4x}{5} + \frac{3}{2} = \frac{3x}{10}$$

$$10\left(\frac{4x}{5} + \frac{3}{2}\right) = 10\left(\frac{3x}{10}\right) \quad \text{Multiply both sides by the LCD.}$$

$$10 \cdot \frac{4x}{5} + 10 \cdot \frac{3}{2} = 10 \cdot \frac{3x}{10} \quad \text{Use the distributive property.}$$

$$8x + 15 = 3x \quad \text{Simplify.}$$

$$15 = -5x \quad \text{Subtract } 8x \text{ from both sides.}$$

$$-3 = x \quad \text{Solve.}$$

Verify this solution by replacing x with -3 in the original equation.

Check:

$$\frac{4x}{5} + \frac{3}{2} = \frac{3x}{10}$$

$$\frac{4(-3)}{5} + \frac{3}{2} \overset{?}{=} \frac{3(-3)}{10}$$

$$\frac{-12}{5} + \frac{3}{2} \overset{?}{=} \frac{-9}{10}$$

$$-\frac{24}{10} + \frac{15}{10} \overset{?}{=} -\frac{9}{10}$$

$$-\frac{9}{10} = -\frac{9}{10} \quad \text{True}$$

The solution is -3 or the solution set is $\{-3\}$.

PRACTICE
1 Solve: $\dfrac{5x}{4} - \dfrac{3}{2} = \dfrac{7x}{8}$.

The important difference of the equations in this section is that the denominator of a rational expression may contain a variable. Recall that a rational expression is undefined for values of the variable that make the denominator 0. If a proposed solution makes the denominator 0, then it must be rejected as a solution of the original equation. Such proposed solutions are called **extraneous solutions.**

EXAMPLE 2 Solve: $\dfrac{3}{x} - \dfrac{x + 21}{3x} = \dfrac{5}{3}$.

Solution The LCD of the denominators x, $3x$, and 3 is $3x$. We multiply both sides by $3x$.

$$\frac{3}{x} - \frac{x + 21}{3x} = \frac{5}{3}$$

$$3x\left(\frac{3}{x} - \frac{x + 21}{3x}\right) = 3x\left(\frac{5}{3}\right) \qquad \text{Multiply both sides by the LCD.}$$

$$3x \cdot \frac{3}{x} - 3x \cdot \frac{x + 21}{3x} = 3x \cdot \frac{5}{3} \qquad \text{Use the distributive property.}$$

$$9 - (x + 21) = 5x \qquad \text{Simplify.}$$

$$9 - x - 21 = 5x$$

$$-12 = 6x$$

$$-2 = x \qquad \text{Solve.}$$

The proposed solution is -2.

Check: Check the proposed solution in the original equation.

$$\frac{3}{x} - \frac{x + 21}{3x} = \frac{5}{3}$$

$$\frac{3}{-2} - \frac{-2 + 21}{3(-2)} \stackrel{?}{=} \frac{5}{3}$$

$$-\frac{9}{6} + \frac{19}{6} \stackrel{?}{=} \frac{5}{3}$$

$$\frac{10}{6} \stackrel{?}{=} \frac{5}{3} \qquad \text{True}$$

The solution is -2 or the solution set is $\{-2\}$. □

PRACTICE
2 Solve: $\dfrac{6}{x} - \dfrac{x - 9}{5x} = \dfrac{2}{5}$.

The following steps may be used to solve equations containing rational expressions.

Solving an Equation Containing Rational Expressions

STEP 1. Multiply both sides of the equation by the LCD of all rational expressions in the equation.

STEP 2. Simplify both sides.

STEP 3. Determine whether the equation is linear, quadratic, or higher degree and solve accordingly.

STEP 4. Check the solution in the original equation.

EXAMPLE 3 Solve: $\dfrac{x+6}{x-2} = \dfrac{2(x+2)}{x-2}$.

Solution First we multiply both sides of the equation by the LCD, $x - 2$. (Remember, we can only do this if $x \neq 2$ so that we are not multiplying by 0.)

$$\frac{x+6}{x-2} = \frac{2(x+2)}{x-2}$$

$$(x-2) \cdot \frac{x+6}{x-2} = (x-2) \cdot \frac{2(x+2)}{x-2} \quad \text{Multiply both sides by } x-2.$$

$$x + 6 = 2(x+2) \qquad \text{Simplify.}$$

$$x + 6 = 2x + 4 \qquad \text{Use the distributive property.}$$

$$2 = x \qquad \text{Solve.}$$

From above, we assumed that $x \neq 2$, so this equation has no solution. This will also show as we attempt to check this proposed solution.

Check: The proposed solution is 2. Notice that 2 makes a denominator 0 in the original equation. This can also be seen in a check. Check the proposed solution 2 in the original equation.

$$\frac{x+6}{x-2} = \frac{2(x+2)}{x-2}$$

$$\frac{2+6}{2-2} = \frac{2(2+2)}{2-2}$$

$$\frac{8}{0} = \frac{2(4)}{0}$$

The denominators are 0, so 2 is not a solution of the original equation. The solution is { } or $\varnothing$. $\qquad\square$

PRACTICE
3 Solve: $\dfrac{x-5}{x+3} = \dfrac{2(x-1)}{x+3}$.

EXAMPLE 4 Solve: $\dfrac{2x}{2x-1} + \dfrac{1}{x} = \dfrac{1}{2x-1}$.

Solution The LCD is $x(2x-1)$. Multiply both sides by $x(2x-1)$. By the distributive property, this is the same as multiplying each term by $x(2x-1)$.

$$x(2x-1) \cdot \frac{2x}{2x-1} + x(2x-1) \cdot \frac{1}{x} = x(2x-1) \cdot \frac{1}{2x-1}$$

$$x(2x) + (2x-1) = x \quad \text{Simplify.}$$

$$2x^2 + 2x - 1 - x = 0$$

$$2x^2 + x - 1 = 0$$

$$(x+1)(2x-1) = 0$$

$$x + 1 = 0 \quad \text{or} \quad 2x - 1 = 0$$

$$x = -1 \qquad\qquad x = \frac{1}{2}$$

The number $\dfrac{1}{2}$ makes the denominator $2x - 1$ equal 0, so it is not a solution. The solution is -1. $\qquad\square$

PRACTICE
4 Solve: $\dfrac{5x}{5x-1} + \dfrac{1}{x} = \dfrac{1}{5x-1}$.

EXAMPLE 5 Solve: $\dfrac{2x}{x-3} + \dfrac{6-2x}{x^2-9} = \dfrac{x}{x+3}$.

Solution We factor the second denominator to find that the LCD is $(x+3)(x-3)$. We multiply both sides of the equation by $(x+3)(x-3)$. By the distributive property, this is the same as multiplying each term by $(x+3)(x-3)$.

$$\frac{2x}{x-3} + \frac{6-2x}{x^2-9} = \frac{x}{x+3}$$

$$(x+3)(x-3)\cdot\frac{2x}{x-3} + (x+3)(x-3)\cdot\frac{6-2x}{(x+3)(x-3)}$$

$$= (x+3)(x-3)\left(\frac{x}{x+3}\right)$$

$$2x(x+3) + (6-2x) = x(x-3) \quad \text{Simplify.}$$

$$2x^2 + 6x + 6 - 2x = x^2 - 3x \quad \text{Use the distributive property.}$$

Next we solve this quadratic equation by the factoring method. To do so, we first write the equation so that one side is 0.

$$x^2 + 7x + 6 = 0$$

$$(x+6)(x+1) = 0 \quad \text{Factor.}$$

$$x = -6 \text{ or } x = -1 \quad \text{Set each factor equal to 0.}$$

Neither -6 nor -1 makes any denominator 0 so they are both solutions. The solutions are -6 and -1. □

PRACTICE
5 Solve: $\dfrac{2}{x-2} - \dfrac{5+2x}{x^2-4} = \dfrac{x}{x+2}$.

EXAMPLE 6 Solve: $\dfrac{z}{2z^2+3z-2} - \dfrac{1}{2z} = \dfrac{3}{z^2+2z}$.

Solution Factor the denominators to find that the LCD is $2z(z+2)(2z-1)$. Multiply both sides by the LCD. Remember, by using the distributive property, this is the same as multiplying each term by $2z(z+2)(2z-1)$.

$$\frac{z}{2z^2+3z-2} - \frac{1}{2z} = \frac{3}{z^2-2z}$$

$$\frac{z}{(2z-1)(z+2)} - \frac{1}{2z} = \frac{3}{z(z+2)}$$

$$2z(z+2)(2z-1)\cdot\frac{z}{(2z-1)(z+2)} - 2z(z+2)(2z-1)\cdot\frac{1}{2z}$$

$$= 2z(z+2)(2z-1)\cdot\frac{3}{z(z+2)} \quad \begin{array}{l}\text{Apply the distributive} \\ \text{property.}\end{array}$$

$$2z(z) - (z+2)(2z-1) = 3\cdot2(2z-1) \quad \text{Simplify.}$$

$$2z^2 - (2z^2+3z-2) = 12z - 6$$

$$2z^2 - 2z^2 - 3z + 2 = 12z - 6$$

$$-3z + 2 = 12z - 6$$

$$-15z = -8$$

$$z = \frac{8}{15} \quad \text{Solve.}$$

The proposed solution $\dfrac{8}{15}$ does not make any denominator 0; the solution is $\dfrac{8}{15}$. □

PRACTICE
6 Solve: $\dfrac{z}{2z^2-z-6} - \dfrac{1}{3z} = \dfrac{2}{z^2-2z}$.

A graph can be helpful in visualizing solutions of equations. For example, to visualize the solution of the equation $\dfrac{3}{x} - \dfrac{x + 21}{3x} = \dfrac{5}{3}$ in Example 2, the graph of the related rational function $f(x) = \dfrac{3}{x} - \dfrac{x + 21}{3x}$ is shown. A solution of the equation is an x-value that corresponds to a y-value of $\dfrac{5}{3}$.

Notice that an x-value of -2 corresponds to a y-value of $\dfrac{5}{3}$. The solution of the equation is indeed -2 as shown in Example 2.

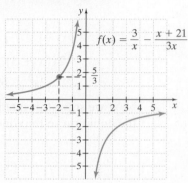

VOCABULARY & READINESS CHECK

Choose the least common denominator (LCD) for the rational expressions in each equation. Do not solve.

1. $\dfrac{x}{7} - \dfrac{x}{2} = \dfrac{1}{2}$; LCD = _____

    a. 7   **b.** 2   **c.** 14   **d.** 28

2. $\dfrac{9}{x + 1} + \dfrac{5}{(x + 1)^2} = \dfrac{x}{x + 1}$; LCD = _____

    a. $x + 1$ **b.** $(x + 1)^2$ **c.** $(x + 1)^3$

3. $\dfrac{7}{x - 4} = \dfrac{x}{x^2 - 16} + \dfrac{1}{x + 4}$; LCD = _____

    a. $(x + 4)(x - 4)$ **b.** $x - 4$ **c.** $x + 4$ **d.** $(x^2 - 16)(x - 4)(x + 4)$

4. $3 = \dfrac{1}{x - 5} - \dfrac{2}{x^2 - 5x}$; LCD = _____

    a. $x - 5$ **b.** $3(x - 5)$ **c.** $3x(x - 5)$ **d.** $x(x - 5)$

6.5 EXERCISE SET

MyMathLab   PRACTICE   WATCH   DOWNLOAD   READ   REVIEW

Solve each equation. See Examples 1 and 2.

1. $\dfrac{x}{2} - \dfrac{x}{3} = 12$

2. $x = \dfrac{x}{2} - 4$

3. $\dfrac{x}{3} = \dfrac{1}{6} + \dfrac{x}{4}$

4. $\dfrac{x}{2} = \dfrac{21}{10} - \dfrac{x}{5}$

5. $\dfrac{2}{x} + \dfrac{1}{2} = \dfrac{5}{x}$

6. $\dfrac{5}{3x} + 1 = \dfrac{7}{6}$

7. $\dfrac{x^2 + 1}{x} = \dfrac{5}{x}$

8. $\dfrac{x^2 - 14}{2x} = -\dfrac{5}{2x}$

Solve each equation. See Examples 3 through 6.

9. $\dfrac{x + 5}{x + 3} = \dfrac{2}{x + 3}$

10. $\dfrac{x - 7}{x - 1} = \dfrac{11}{x - 1}$

11. $\dfrac{5}{x - 2} - \dfrac{2}{x + 4} = -\dfrac{4}{x^2 + 2x - 8}$

12. $\dfrac{1}{x - 1} + \dfrac{1}{x + 1} = \dfrac{2}{x^2 - 1}$

13. $\dfrac{1}{x - 1} = \dfrac{2}{x + 1}$

14. $\dfrac{6}{x+3} = \dfrac{4}{x-3}$

15. $\dfrac{x^2-23}{2x^2-5x-3} + \dfrac{2}{x-3} = \dfrac{-1}{2x+1}$

16. $\dfrac{4x^2-24x}{3x^2-x-2} + \dfrac{3}{3x+2} = \dfrac{-4}{x-1}$

17. $\dfrac{1}{x-4} - \dfrac{3x}{x^2-16} = \dfrac{2}{x+4}$

18. $\dfrac{3}{2x+3} - \dfrac{1}{2x-3} = \dfrac{4}{4x^2-9}$

19. $\dfrac{1}{x-4} = \dfrac{8}{x^2-16}$

20. $\dfrac{2}{x^2-4} = \dfrac{1}{2x-4}$

21. $\dfrac{1}{x-2} - \dfrac{2}{x^2-2x} = 1$

22. $\dfrac{12}{3x^2+12x} = 1 - \dfrac{1}{x+4}$

MIXED PRACTICE

Solve each equation. See Examples 1 through 6.

23. $\dfrac{5}{x} = \dfrac{20}{12}$

24. $\dfrac{2}{x} = \dfrac{10}{5}$

25. $1 - \dfrac{4}{a} = 5$

26. $7 + \dfrac{6}{a} = 5$

27. $\dfrac{x^2+5}{x} - 1 = \dfrac{5(x+1)}{x}$

28. $\dfrac{x^2+6}{x} + 5 = \dfrac{2(x+3)}{x}$

29. $\dfrac{1}{2x} - \dfrac{1}{x+1} = \dfrac{1}{3x^2+3x}$

30. $\dfrac{2}{x-5} + \dfrac{1}{2x} = \dfrac{5}{3x^2-15x}$

31. $\dfrac{1}{x} - \dfrac{x}{25} = 0$

32. $\dfrac{x}{4} + \dfrac{5}{x} = 3$

33. $5 - \dfrac{2}{2y-5} = \dfrac{3}{2y-5}$

34. $1 - \dfrac{5}{y+7} = \dfrac{4}{y+7}$

35. $\dfrac{x-1}{x+2} = \dfrac{2}{3}$

36. $\dfrac{6x+7}{2x+9} = \dfrac{5}{3}$

37. $\dfrac{x+3}{x+2} = \dfrac{1}{x+2}$

38. $\dfrac{2x+1}{4-x} = \dfrac{9}{4-x}$

39. $\dfrac{1}{a-3} + \dfrac{2}{a+3} = \dfrac{1}{a^2-9}$

40. $\dfrac{12}{9-a^2} + \dfrac{3}{3+a} = \dfrac{2}{3-a}$

41. $\dfrac{64}{x^2-16} + 1 = \dfrac{2x}{x-4}$

42. $2 + \dfrac{3}{x} = \dfrac{2x}{x+3}$

43. $\dfrac{-15}{4y+1} + 4 = y$

44. $\dfrac{36}{x^2-9} + 1 = \dfrac{2x}{x+3}$

45. $\dfrac{28}{x^2-9} + \dfrac{2x}{x-3} + \dfrac{6}{x+3} = 0$

46. $\dfrac{x^2-20}{x^2-7x+12} = \dfrac{3}{x-3} + \dfrac{5}{x-4}$

47. $\dfrac{x+2}{x^2+7x+10} = \dfrac{1}{3x+6} - \dfrac{1}{x+5}$

48. $\dfrac{3}{2x-5} + \dfrac{2}{2x+3} = 0$

REVIEW AND PREVIEW

Write each sentence as an equation and solve. See Section 2.2.

49. Four more than 3 times a number is 19.

50. The sum of two consecutive integers is 147.

51. The length of a rectangle is 5 inches more than the width. Its perimeter is 50 inches. Find the length and width.

52. The sum of a number and its reciprocal is $\dfrac{5}{2}$.

The following graph is from statistics gathered for the National Health and Nutrition Examination Survey. Use this histogram to answer Exercises 53 through 57. (Source: Economic Research Service: USDA). See Section 2.2.

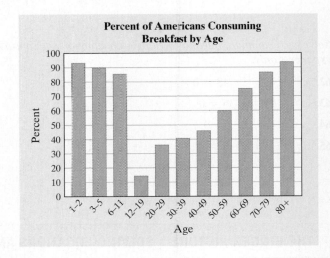

53. What percent of Americans ages 20–29 eat breakfast regularly?

54. What percent of Americans over age 80 eat breakfast regularly?

55. What age category shows the smallest percentage of Americans who eat breakfast regularly?

56. What percent of Americans ages 40–49 eat breakfast regularly?

57. According to the New York City Department of Education, there were about 284,000 high schools students at the end of 2006. Approximately how many of these students would you expect to eat breakfast regularly? Round to the nearest ten thousand.

CONCEPT EXTENSIONS

58. In your own words, explain the differences between equations and expressions.

59. In your own words, explain why it is necessary to check solutions to equations containing rational expressions.

60. The average cost of producing x game disks for a computer is given by the function $f(x) = 3.3 + \dfrac{5400}{x}$. Find the number of game disks that must be produced for the average cost to be $5.10.

61. The average cost of producing x electric pencil sharpeners is given by the function $f(x) = 20 + \dfrac{4000}{x}$. Find the number of electric pencil sharpeners that must be produced for the average cost to be $25.

Solve each equation. Begin by writing each equation with positive exponents only.

62. $x^{-2} - 19x^{-1} + 48 = 0$

63. $x^{-2} - 5x^{-1} - 36 = 0$

64. $p^{-2} + 4p^{-1} - 5 = 0$

65. $6p^{-2} - 5p^{-1} + 1 = 0$

Solve each equation. Round solutions to two decimal places.

66. $\dfrac{1.4}{x - 2.6} = \dfrac{-3.5}{x + 7.1}$

67. $\dfrac{-8.5}{x + 1.9} = \dfrac{5.7}{x - 3.6}$

68. $\dfrac{10.6}{y} - 14.7 = \dfrac{9.92}{3.2} + 7.6$

69. $\dfrac{12.2}{x} + 17.3 = \dfrac{9.6}{x} - 14.7$

Solve each equation by substitution.

For example, to solve Exercise 70, first let $u = x - 1$. After substituting, we have $u^2 + 3u + 2 = 0$. Solve for u and then substitute back to solve for x.

70. $(x - 1)^2 + 3(x - 1) + 2 = 0$

71. $(4 - x)^2 - 5(4 - x) + 6 = 0$

72. $\left(\dfrac{3}{x - 1}\right)^2 + 2\left(\dfrac{3}{x - 1}\right) + 1 = 0$

73. $\left(\dfrac{5}{2 + x}\right)^2 + \left(\dfrac{5}{2 + x}\right) - 20 = 0$

📱 *Use a graphing calculator to verify the solution of each given exercise.*

74. Exercise 23   **75.** Exercise 24

76. Exercise 35   **77.** Exercise 36

THE BIGGER PICTURE   SOLVING EQUATIONS AND INEQUALITIES

Continue the outline from Sections 2.4, 2.5, 2.7, and 5.8. Write how to recognize and how to solve equations with rational expressions in your own words. For example:

Solving Equations and Inequalities

I. Equations

  A. Linear equations (Sec. 2.1)

  B. Absolute value equations (Sec. 2.6)

  C. Quadratic equations (Sec. 5.8)

  D. Equations with rational expressions: Equation contains rational expressions.

$$\frac{7}{x - 1} + \frac{3}{x + 1} = \frac{x + 3}{x^2 - 1} \qquad \text{Equation with rational expressions.}$$

$$(x - 1)(x + 1) \cdot \frac{7}{x - 1} + (x - 1)(x + 1) \cdot \frac{3}{x + 1} = (x - 1)(x + 1) \cdot \frac{x + 3}{(x - 1)(x + 1)} \qquad \text{Multiply by the LCD.}$$

$$7(x + 1) + 3(x - 1) = x + 3 \qquad \text{Simplify.}$$

$$7x + 7 + 3x - 3 = x + 3$$

$$9x = -1$$

$$x = -\frac{1}{9} \qquad \text{Solve.}$$

II. Inequalities

    A. Linear inequalities (Sec. 2.4)

    B. Compound inequalities (Sec. 2.5)

    C. Absolute value inequalities (Sec. 2.7)

Solve. Write solutions to inequalities using interval notation.

1. $|-7x + 1| < 15$

2. $|-7x + 1| = 15$

3. $x^2 - 121 = 0$

4. $\dfrac{8}{x + 2} - \dfrac{3}{x - 1} = \dfrac{x + 6}{x^2 + x - 2}$

5. $9x + 6 = 4x - 2$

6. $3x \le 6$ or $-x \ge 5$

7. $3x \le 6$ and $-x \ge 5$

8. $-9 \le -3x + 21 < 0$

9. $\left|\dfrac{2x - 1}{5}\right| > 7$

10. $15x^3 - 16x^2 = 7x$

INTEGRATED REVIEW   EXPRESSIONS AND EQUATIONS CONTAINING RATIONAL EXPRESSIONS

Sections 6.1–6.5

It is very important that you understand the difference between an expression and an equation containing rational expressions. An equation contains an equal sign; an expression does not.

Expression to be Simplified

$$\frac{x}{2} + \frac{x}{6}$$

Write both rational expressions with the LCD, 6, as the denominator.

$$\frac{x}{2} + \frac{x}{6} = \frac{x \cdot 3}{2 \cdot 3} + \frac{x}{6}$$

$$= \frac{3x}{6} + \frac{x}{6}$$

$$= \frac{4x}{6} = \frac{2x}{3}$$

Equation to be Solved

$$\frac{x}{2} + \frac{x}{6} = \frac{2}{3}$$

Multiply both sides by the LCD, 6.

$$6\left(\frac{1}{2} + \frac{x}{6}\right) = 6\left(\frac{2}{3}\right)$$

$$3 + x = 4$$

$$x = 1$$

Check to see that the solution set is 1.

> ▶ **Helpful Hint**
>
> Remember: Equations can be cleared of fractions; expressions cannot.

Perform each indicated operation and simplify, or solve the equation for the variable.

1. $\dfrac{x}{2} = \dfrac{1}{8} + \dfrac{x}{4}$

2. $\dfrac{x}{4} = \dfrac{3}{2} + \dfrac{x}{10}$

3. $\dfrac{1}{8} + \dfrac{x}{4}$

4. $\dfrac{3}{2} + \dfrac{x}{10}$

5. $\dfrac{4}{x + 2} - \dfrac{2}{x - 1}$

6. $\dfrac{5}{x - 2} - \dfrac{10}{x + 4}$

7. $\dfrac{4}{x + 2} = \dfrac{2}{x - 1}$

8. $\dfrac{5}{x - 2} = \dfrac{10}{x + 4}$

9. $\dfrac{2}{x^2 - 4} = \dfrac{1}{x + 2} - \dfrac{3}{x - 2}$

10. $\dfrac{3}{x^2 - 25} = \dfrac{1}{x + 5} + \dfrac{2}{x - 5}$

11. $\dfrac{5}{x^2 - 3x} + \dfrac{4}{2x - 6}$

12. $\dfrac{5}{x^2 - 3x} \div \dfrac{4}{2x - 6}$

13. $\dfrac{x - 1}{x + 1} + \dfrac{x + 7}{x - 1} = \dfrac{4}{x^2 - 1}$

14. $\left(1 - \dfrac{y}{x}\right) \div \left(1 - \dfrac{x}{y}\right)$

15. $\dfrac{a^2 - 9}{a - 6} \cdot \dfrac{a^2 - 5a - 6}{a^2 - a - 6}$

16. $\dfrac{2}{a-6} + \dfrac{3a}{a^2-5a-6} - \dfrac{a}{5a+5}$

17. $\dfrac{2x+3}{3x-2} = \dfrac{4x+1}{6x+1}$

18. $\dfrac{5x-3}{2x} = \dfrac{10x+3}{4x+1}$

19. $\dfrac{a}{9a^2-1} + \dfrac{2}{6a-2}$

20. $\dfrac{3}{4a-8} - \dfrac{a+2}{a^2-2a}$

21. $-\dfrac{3}{x^2} - \dfrac{1}{x} + 2 = 0$

22. $\dfrac{x}{2x+6} + \dfrac{5}{x^2-9}$

23. $\dfrac{x-8}{x^2-x-2} + \dfrac{2}{x-2}$

24. $\dfrac{x-8}{x^2-x-2} + \dfrac{2}{x-2} = \dfrac{3}{x+1}$

25. $\dfrac{3}{a} - 5 = \dfrac{7}{a} - 1$

26. $\dfrac{7}{3z-9} + \dfrac{5}{z}$

Use $\dfrac{x}{5} - \dfrac{x}{4} = \dfrac{1}{10}$ *and* $\dfrac{x}{5} - \dfrac{x}{4} + \dfrac{1}{10}$ *for Exercises 27 and 28.*

27. a. Which one above is an expression?
   b. Describe the first step to simplify this expression.
   c. Simplify the expression.

28. a. Which one above is an equation?
   b. Describe the first step to solve this equation.
   c. Solve the equation.

For each exercise, choose the correct statement. Each figure represents a real number and no denominators are 0.*

29. a. $\dfrac{\triangle + \square}{\triangle} = \square$ **b.** $\dfrac{\triangle + \square}{\triangle} = 1 + \dfrac{\square}{\triangle}$ **c.** $\dfrac{\triangle + \square}{\triangle} = \dfrac{\square}{\triangle}$ **d.** $\dfrac{\triangle + \square}{\triangle} = 1 + \square$ **e.** $\dfrac{\triangle + \square}{\triangle - \square} = -1$

30. a. $\dfrac{\triangle}{\square} + \dfrac{\square}{\triangle} = \dfrac{\triangle + \square}{\square + \triangle} = 1$ **b.** $\dfrac{\triangle}{\square} + \dfrac{\square}{\triangle} = \dfrac{\triangle + \square}{\triangle\square}$ **c.** $\dfrac{\triangle}{\square} + \dfrac{\square}{\triangle} = \triangle\triangle + \square\square$

   d. $\dfrac{\triangle}{\square} + \dfrac{\square}{\triangle} = \dfrac{\triangle\triangle + \square\square}{\square\triangle}$ **e.** $\dfrac{\triangle}{\square} + \dfrac{\square}{\triangle} = \dfrac{\triangle\square}{\square\triangle} = 1$

31. a. $\dfrac{\triangle}{\square} \cdot \dfrac{\bigcirc}{\square} = \dfrac{\triangle\bigcirc}{\square}$ **b.** $\dfrac{\triangle}{\square} \cdot \dfrac{\bigcirc}{\square} = \triangle\bigcirc$ **c.** $\dfrac{\triangle}{\square} \cdot \dfrac{\bigcirc}{\square} = \dfrac{\triangle + \bigcirc}{\square + \square}$ **d.** $\dfrac{\triangle}{\square} \cdot \dfrac{\bigcirc}{\square} = \dfrac{\triangle\bigcirc}{\square\square}$

32. a. $\dfrac{\triangle}{\square} \div \dfrac{\bigcirc}{\triangle} = \dfrac{\triangle\triangle}{\square\bigcirc}$ **b.** $\dfrac{\triangle}{\square} \div \dfrac{\bigcirc}{\triangle} = \dfrac{\bigcirc\square}{\triangle\triangle}$ **c.** $\dfrac{\triangle}{\square} \div \dfrac{\bigcirc}{\triangle} = \dfrac{\bigcirc}{\square}$ **d.** $\dfrac{\triangle}{\square} \div \dfrac{\bigcirc}{\triangle} = \dfrac{\triangle + \triangle}{\square + \bigcirc}$

33. a. $\dfrac{\frac{\triangle + \square}{\bigcirc}}{\frac{\triangle}{\bigcirc}} = \square$ **b.** $\dfrac{\frac{\triangle + \square}{\bigcirc}}{\frac{\triangle}{\bigcirc}} = \dfrac{\triangle\triangle + \triangle\square}{\bigcirc\bigcirc}$ **c.** $\dfrac{\frac{\triangle + \square}{\bigcirc}}{\frac{\triangle}{\bigcirc}} = 1 + \square$ **d.** $\dfrac{\frac{\triangle + \square}{\bigcirc}}{\frac{\triangle}{\bigcirc}} = \dfrac{\triangle + \square}{\triangle}$

My thanks to Kelly Champagne for permission to use her Exercises for 29 through 33.

6.6 RATIONAL EQUATIONS AND PROBLEM SOLVING

OBJECTIVES

1 Solve an equation containing rational expressions for a specified variable.

2 Solve problems by writing equations containing rational expressions.

OBJECTIVE 1 ▶ Solving equations with rational expressions for a specified variable.
In Section 2.3 we solved equations for a specified variable. In this section, we continue practicing this skill by solving equations containing rational expressions for a specified variable. The steps given in Section 2.3 for solving equations for a specified variable are repeated here.

> **Solving Equations for a Specified Variable**
>
> **STEP 1.** Clear the equation of fractions or rational expressions by multiplying each side of the equation by the least common denominator (LCD) of all denominators in the equation.
>
> **STEP 2.** Use the distributive property to remove grouping symbols such as parentheses.
>
> **STEP 3.** Combine like terms on each side of the equation.
>
> **STEP 4.** Use the addition property of equality to rewrite the equation as an equivalent equation with terms containing the specified variable on one side and all other terms on the other side.
>
> **STEP 5.** Use the distributive property and the multiplication property of equality to get the specified variable alone.

EXAMPLE 1   Solve: $\dfrac{1}{x} + \dfrac{1}{y} = \dfrac{1}{z}$ for x.

Solution   To clear this equation of fractions, we multiply both sides of the equation by xyz, the LCD of $\dfrac{1}{x}, \dfrac{1}{y}$, and $\dfrac{1}{z}$.

$$\frac{1}{x} + \frac{1}{y} = \frac{1}{z}$$

$$xyz\left(\frac{1}{x} + \frac{1}{y}\right) = xyz\left(\frac{1}{z}\right) \qquad \text{Multiply both sides by } xyz.$$

$$xyz\left(\frac{1}{x}\right) + xyz\left(\frac{1}{y}\right) = xyz\left(\frac{1}{z}\right) \qquad \text{Use the distributive property.}$$

$$yz + xz = xy \qquad \text{Simplify.}$$

Notice the two terms that contain the specified variable x.

Next, we subtract xz from both sides so that all terms containing the specified variable x are on one side of the equation and all other terms are on the other side.

$$yz = xy - xz$$

Now we use the distributive property to factor x from $xy - xz$ and then the multiplication property of equality to solve for x.

$$yz = x(y - z)$$

$$\frac{yz}{y - z} = x \quad \text{or} \quad x = \frac{yz}{y - z} \qquad \text{Divide both sides by } y - z.$$

PRACTICE
1   Solve: $\dfrac{1}{a} - \dfrac{1}{b} = \dfrac{1}{c}$ for a.

OBJECTIVE 2 ▶ Solving problems modeled by equations with rational expressions. Problem solving sometimes involves modeling a described situation with an equation containing rational expressions. In Examples 2 through 5, we practice solving such problems and use the problem-solving steps first introduced in Section 2.2.

EXAMPLE 2 Finding an Unknown Number

If a certain number is subtracted from the numerator and added to the denominator of $\frac{9}{19}$, the new fraction is equivalent to $\frac{1}{3}$. Find the number.

Solution

1. UNDERSTAND the problem. Read and reread the problem and try guessing the solution. For example, if the unknown number is 3, we have

$$\frac{9-3}{19+3} = \frac{1}{3}$$

To see if this is a true statement, we simplify the fraction on the left side.

$$\frac{6}{22} = \frac{1}{3} \quad \text{or} \quad \frac{3}{11} = \frac{1}{3} \quad \text{False}$$

Since this is not a true statement, 3 is not the correct number. Remember that the purpose of this step is not to guess the correct solution but to gain an understanding of the problem posed.

We will let n = the number to be subtracted from the numerator and added to the denominator.

2. TRANSLATE the problem.

In words:	when the number is subtracted from the numerator and added to the denominator of the fraction $\frac{9}{19}$	this is equivalent to	$\frac{1}{3}$
	↓	↓	↓
Translate:	$\frac{9-n}{19+n}$	=	$\frac{1}{3}$

3. SOLVE the equation for n.

$$\frac{9-n}{19+n} = \frac{1}{3}$$

To solve for n, we begin by multiplying both sides by the LCD of $3(19+n)$.

$$3(19+n) \cdot \frac{9-n}{19+n} = 3(19+n) \cdot \frac{1}{3} \quad \text{Multiply both sides by the LCD.}$$

$$3(9-n) = 19+n \qquad \text{Simplify.}$$

$$27 - 3n = 19 + n$$

$$8 = 4n$$

$$2 = n \qquad \text{Solve.}$$

4. INTERPRET the results.

Check: If we subtract 2 from the numerator and add 2 to the denominator of $\frac{9}{19}$, we have $\frac{9-2}{19+2} = \frac{7}{21} = \frac{1}{3}$, and the problem checks.

State: The unknown number is 2. □

PRACTICE

2 Find a number that when added to the numerator and subtracted from the denominator of $\frac{3}{11}$ results in a fraction equivalent to $\frac{5}{2}$.

A **ratio** is the quotient of two number or two quantities. Since rational expressions are quotients of quantities, rational expressions are ratios, also. A **proportion** is a mathematical statement that two ratios are equal.

EXAMPLE 3   Calculating Homes Heat by Electricity

In the United States, 8 out of every 25 homes are heated by electricity. At this rate, how many homes in a community of 36,000 homes would you predict are heated by electricity? (*Source: 2005 American Housing Survey for the United States*)

Solution

1. UNDERSTAND. Read and reread the problem. Try to estimate a reasonable solution. For example, since 8 is less than $\frac{1}{3}$ of 25, we might reason that the solution would be less than $\frac{1}{3}$ of 36,000 or 12,000.

   Let's let x = number of homes in the community heated by electricity.

2. TRANSLATE.

$$\text{homes heated by electricity} \rightarrow \quad \frac{8}{25} = \frac{x}{36{,}000} \quad \leftarrow \text{homes heated by electricity}$$
$$\text{total homes} \rightarrow \qquad\qquad\qquad\qquad \leftarrow \text{total homes}$$

3. SOLVE. To solve this proportion we can multiply both sides by the LCD, 36,000, or we can set cross products equal. We will set cross products equal.

$$\frac{8}{25} = \frac{x}{36{,}000}$$

$$25x = 8 \cdot 36{,}000$$

$$x = \frac{288{,}000}{25}$$

$$x = 11{,}520$$

4. INTERPRET.

Check: To check, replace x with 11,520 in the proportion and see that a true statement results. Notice that our answer is reasonable since it is less than 12,000 as we stated above.

State: We predict that 11,520 homes are heated by electricity.   □

PRACTICE
3   In the United States, 1 out of 12 homes is heated by fuel oil. At this rate, how many homes in a community of 36,000 homes are heated by fuel oil? (*Source: 2005 American Housing Survey for the United States*)

The following work example leads to an equation containing rational expressions.

EXAMPLE 4   Calculating Work Hours

Melissa Scarlatti can clean the house in 4 hours, whereas her husband, Zack, can do the same job in 5 hours. They have agreed to clean together so that they can finish in time to watch a movie on TV that starts in 2 hours. How long will it take them to clean the house together? Can they finish before the movie starts?

Solution

1. UNDERSTAND. Read and reread the problem. The key idea here is the relationship between the *time* (in hours) it takes to complete the job and the *part of the job* completed in 1 unit of time (1 hour). For example, if the *time* it takes Melissa to complete the job is 4 hours, the part of the job she can complete in 1 hour is $\frac{1}{4}$. Similarly, Zack can complete $\frac{1}{5}$ of the job in 1 hour.

We will let t = *the time* in hours it takes Melissa and Zack to clean the house together. Then $\frac{1}{t}$ represents the *part of the job* they complete in 1 hour. We summarize the given information in a chart.

	Hours to Complete the Job	*Part of Job Completed in 1 Hour*
MELISSA ALONE	4	$\frac{1}{4}$
ZACK ALONE	5	$\frac{1}{5}$
TOGETHER	t	$\frac{1}{t}$

2. TRANSLATE.

In words:	part of job Melissa can complete in 1 hour	added to	part of job Zack can complete in 1 hour	is equal to	part of job they can complete together in 1 hour
	↓	↓	↓	↓	↓
Translate:	$\frac{1}{4}$	$+$	$\frac{1}{5}$	$=$	$\frac{1}{t}$

3. SOLVE.

$$\frac{1}{4} + \frac{1}{5} = \frac{1}{t}$$

$$20t\left(\frac{1}{4} + \frac{1}{5}\right) = 20t\left(\frac{1}{t}\right) \qquad \text{Multiply both sides by the LCD, } 20t.$$

$$5t + 4t = 20$$

$$9t = 20$$

$$t = \frac{20}{9} \quad \text{or} \quad 2\frac{2}{9} \quad \text{Solve.}$$

4. INTERPRET.

Check: The proposed solution is $2\frac{2}{9}$. That is, Melissa and Zack would take $2\frac{2}{9}$ hours to clean the house together. This proposed solution is reasonable since $2\frac{2}{9}$ hours is more than half of Melissa's time and less than half of Zack's time. Check this solution in the originally stated problem.

State: Melissa and Zack can clean the house together in $2\frac{2}{9}$ hours. They cannot complete the job before the movie starts. □

PRACTICE
4   Elissa Juarez can clean the animal cages at the animal shelter where she volunteers in 3 hours. Bill Stiles can do the same job in 2 hours. How long would it take them to clean the cages if they work together?

EXAMPLE 5   **Finding the Speed of a Current**

Steve Deitmer takes $1\frac{1}{2}$ times as long to go 72 miles upstream in his boat as he does to return. If the boat cruises at 30 mph in still water, what is the speed of the current?

Solution

1. UNDERSTAND. Read and reread the problem. Guess a solution. Suppose that the current is 4 mph. The speed of the boat upstream is slowed down by the current: 30 − 4, or 26 mph, and the speed of the boat downstream is speeded up by the current: $30 + 4$, or 34 mph. Next let's find out how long it takes to travel 72 miles upstream and 72 miles downstream. To do so, we use the formula $d = rt$, or $\dfrac{d}{r} = t$.

Upstream

$$\frac{d}{r} = t$$

$$\frac{72}{26} = t$$

$$2\frac{10}{13} = t$$

Downstream

$$\frac{d}{r} = t$$

$$\frac{72}{34} = t$$

$$2\frac{2}{17} = t$$

Since the time upstream $\left(2\dfrac{10}{13} \text{ hours}\right)$ is not $1\dfrac{1}{2}$ times the time downstream $\left(2\dfrac{2}{17} \text{ hours}\right)$, our guess is not correct. We do, however, have a better understanding of the problem.

We will let

$$x = \text{the speed of the current}$$
$$30 + x = \text{the speed of the boat downstream}$$
$$30 - x = \text{the speed of the boat upstream}$$

This information is summarized in the following chart, where we use the formula $\dfrac{d}{r} = t$.

	Distance	Rate	Time $\left(\dfrac{d}{r}\right)$
UPSTREAM	72	$30 - x$	$\dfrac{72}{30 - x}$
DOWNSTREAM	72	$30 + x$	$\dfrac{72}{30 + x}$

2. TRANSLATE. Since the time spent traveling upstream is $1\dfrac{1}{2}$ times the time spent traveling downstream, we have

In words:

time upstream	is	$1\dfrac{1}{2}$	times	times downstream
↓	↓	↓	↓	↓

Translate: $\qquad \dfrac{72}{30 - x} \qquad = \qquad \dfrac{3}{2} \qquad \cdot \qquad \dfrac{72}{30 + x}$

3. SOLVE. $\dfrac{72}{30 - x} = \dfrac{3}{2} \cdot \dfrac{72}{30 + x}$

First we multiply both sides by the LCD, $2(30 + x)(30 - x)$.

$$2(30 + x)(30 - x) \cdot \frac{72}{30 - x} = 2(30 + x)(30 - x)\left(\frac{3}{2} \cdot \frac{72}{30 + x}\right)$$

$$72 \cdot 2(30 + x) = 3 \cdot 72 \cdot (30 - x) \quad \text{Simplify.}$$

$$2(30 + x) = 3(30 - x) \quad \text{Divide both sides by 72.}$$

$$60 + 2x = 90 - 3x \quad \text{Use the distributive property.}$$

$$5x = 30$$

$$x = 6 \quad \text{Solve.}$$

4. INTERPRET.

Check: Check the proposed solution of 6 mph in the originally stated problem.

State: The current's speed is 6 mph.

PRACTICE
5 An airplane flying from Los Angeles to Boston at a speed of 450 mph had a tail-wind assisting its flight. At the same time, there was another flight doing the same speed, going from Boston to Los Angeles. This second flight encountered a headwind. It took the pilot heading west $1\frac{1}{4}$ times as long to travel from Boston to Los Angeles as it took the pilot flying east from Los Angeles to Boston. What was the speed of the wind?

6.6 | EXERCISE SET

Solve each equation for the specified variable. See Example 1.

1. $F = \frac{9}{5}C + 32$ for C (Meteorology)

△ 2. $V = \frac{1}{3}\pi r^2 h$ for h (Volume)

3. $Q = \frac{A - I}{L}$ for I (Finance)

4. $P = 1 - \frac{C}{S}$ for S (Finance)

5. $\frac{1}{R} = \frac{1}{R_1} + \frac{1}{R_2}$ for R (Electronics)

6. $\frac{1}{R} = \frac{1}{R_1} + \frac{1}{R_2}$ for R_1 (Electronics)

7. $S = \frac{n(a + L)}{2}$ for n (Sequences)

8. $S = \frac{n(a + L)}{2}$ for a (Sequences)

△ 9. $A = \frac{h(a + b)}{2}$ for b (Geometry)

△ 10. $A = \frac{h(a + b)}{2}$ for h (Geometry)

11. $\frac{P_1 V_1}{T_1} = \frac{P_2 V_2}{T_2}$ for T_2 (Chemistry)

12. $H = \frac{kA(T_1 - T_2)}{L}$ for T_2 (Physics)

13. $f = \frac{f_1 f_2}{f_1 + f_2}$ for f_2 (Optics)

14. $I = \frac{E}{R + r}$ for r (Electronics)

15. $\lambda = \frac{2L}{n}$ for L (Physics)

16. $S = \frac{a_1 - a_n r}{1 - r}$ for a_1 (Sequences)

17. $\frac{\theta}{\omega} = \frac{2L}{c}$ for c

18. $F = \frac{-GMm}{r^2}$ for M (Physics)

Solve. See Example 2.

19. The sum of a number and 5 times its reciprocal is 6. Find the number(s).

20. The quotient of a number and 9 times its reciprocal is 1. Find the number(s).

21. If a number is added to the numerator of $\frac{12}{41}$ and twice the number is added to the denominator of $\frac{12}{41}$, the resulting fraction is equivalent to $\frac{1}{3}$. Find the number.

22. If a number is subtracted from the numerator of $\frac{13}{8}$ and added to the denominator of $\frac{13}{8}$, the resulting fraction is equivalent to $\frac{2}{5}$. Find the number.

Solve. See Example 3.

23. An Arabian camel can drink 15 gallons of water in 10 minutes. At this rate, how much water can the camel drink in 3 minutes? (*Source:* Grolier, Inc.)

24. An Arabian camel can travel 20 miles in 8 hours, carrying a 300-pound load on its back. At this rate, how far can the camel travel in 10 hours? (*Source:* Grolier, Inc.)

25. In 2005, 5.5 out of every 50 Coast Guard personnel were women. If there are 40,639 total Coast Guard personnel on active duty, estimate the number of women. Round to the nearest whole. (*Source: The World Almanac,* 2007)

26. In 2005, 42.8 out of every 50 Navy personnel were men. If there are 353,496 total Navy personnel on active duty, estimate the number of men. Round to the nearest whole. (*Source: The World Almanac,* 2007)

Solve. See Example 4.

27. An experienced roofer can roof a house in 26 hours. A beginning roofer needs 39 hours to complete the same job. Find how long it takes for the two to do the job together.

28. Alan Cantrell can word process a research paper in 6 hours. With Steve Isaac's help, the paper can be processed in 4 hours. Find how long it takes Steve to word process the paper alone.

29. Three postal workers can sort a stack of mail in 20 minutes, 30 minutes, and 60 minutes, respectively. Find how long it takes them to sort the mail if all three work together.

30. A new printing press can print newspapers twice as fast as the old one can. The old one can print the afternoon edition in 4 hours. Find how long it takes to print the afternoon edition if both printers are operating.

Solve. See Example 5.

31. Mattie Evans drove 150 miles in the same amount of time that it took a turbopropeller plane to travel 600 miles. The speed of the plane was 150 mph faster than the speed of the car. Find the speed of the plane.

32. An F-100 plane and a Toyota truck leave the same town at sunrise and head for a town 450 miles away. The speed of the plane is three times the speed of the truck, and the plane arrives 6 hours ahead of the truck. Find the speed of the truck.

33. The speed of Lazy River's current is 5 mph. If a boat travels 20 miles downstream in the same time that it takes to travel 10 miles upstream, find the speed of the boat in still water.

34. The speed of a boat in still water is 24 mph. If the boat travels 54 miles upstream in the same time that it takes to travel 90 miles downstream, find the speed of the current.

MIXED PRACTICE

Solve.

35. The sum of the reciprocals of two consecutive integers is $-\dfrac{15}{56}$. Find the two integers.

36. The sum of the reciprocals of two consecutive odd integers is $\dfrac{20}{99}$. Find the two integers.

37. One hose can fill a goldfish pond in 45 minutes, and two hoses can fill the same pond in 20 minutes. Find how long it takes the second hose alone to fill the pond.

38. If Sarah Clark can do a job in 5 hours and Dick Belli and Sarah working together can do the same job in 2 hours, find how long it takes Dick to do the job alone.

39. Two trains going in opposite directions leave at the same time. One train travels 15 mph faster than the other. In 6 hours the trains are 630 miles apart. Find the speed of each.

40. The speed of a bicyclist is 10 mph faster than the speed of a walker. If the bicyclist travels 26 miles in the same amount of time that the walker travels 6 miles, find the speed of the bicyclist.

41. A giant tortoise can travel 0.17 miles in 1 hour. At this rate, how long would it take the tortoise to travel 1 mile? Round to the nearest tenth of an hour. (*Source: The World Almanac*)

42. A black mamba snake can travel 88 feet in 3 seconds. At this rate, how long does it take to travel 300 feet (the length of a football field)? Round to the nearest tenth of a second. (*Source: The World Almanac*)

43. A local dairy has three machines to fill half-gallon milk cartons. The machines can fill the daily quota in 5 hours, 6 hours, and 7.5 hours, respectively. Find how long it takes to fill the daily quota if all three machines are running.

44. The inlet pipe of an oil tank can fill the tank in 1 hour, 30 minutes. The outlet pipe can empty the tank in 1 hour. Find how long it takes to empty a full tank if both pipes are open.

45. A plane flies 465 miles with the wind and 345 miles against the wind in the same length of time. If the speed of the wind is 20 mph, find the speed of the plane in still air.

46. Two rockets are launched. The first travels at 9000 mph. Fifteen minutes later the second is launched at 10,000 mph. Find the distance at which both rockets are an equal distance from Earth.

47. Two joggers, one averaging 8 mph and one averaging 6 mph, start from a designated initial point. The slower jogger arrives at the end of the run a half-hour after the other jogger. Find the distance of the run.

48. A semi truck travels 300 miles through the flatland in the same amount of time that it travels 180 miles through the Great Smoky Mountains. The rate of the truck is 20 miles per hour slower in the mountains than in the flatland. Find both the flatland rate and mountain rate.

49. The denominator of a fraction is 1 more than the numerator. If both the numerator and the denominator are decreased by 3, the resulting fraction is equivalent to $\dfrac{4}{5}$. Find the fraction.

50. The numerator of a fraction is 4 less than the denominator. If both the numerator and the denominator are increased by 2, the resulting fraction is equivalent to $\dfrac{2}{3}$. Find the fraction.

51. In 2 minutes, a conveyor belt can move 300 pounds of recyclable aluminum from the delivery truck to a storage area. A smaller belt can move the same quantity of cans the same distance in 6 minutes. If both belts are used, find how long it takes to move the cans to the storage area.

52. Gary Marcus and Tony Alva work at Lombardo's Pipe and Concrete. Mr. Lombardo is preparing an estimate for a customer. He knows that Gary can lay a slab of concrete in 6 hours. Tony can lay the same size slab in 4 hours. If both work on the job and the cost of labor is $45.00 per hour, determine what the labor estimate should be.

53. Smith Engineering is in the process of reviewing the salaries of their surveyors. During this review, the company found that an experienced surveyor can survey a roadbed in 4 hours. An apprentice surveyor needs 5 hours to survey the same stretch of road. If the two work together, find how long it takes them to complete the job.

54. Mr. Dodson can paint his house by himself in four days. His son will need an additional day to complete the job if he works by himself. If they work together, find how long it takes to paint the house.

55. Cyclist Lance Armstrong of the United States won the Tours de France a record seven times. This inspired an amateur cyclist to train for a local road race. He rode the first 20-mile portion of his workout at a constant rate. For the 16-mile cool-down portion of his workout, he reduced his speed by 2 miles per hour. Each portion of the workout took equal time. Find the cyclist's rate during the first portion and his rate during the cool-down portion.

56. The world record for the largest white bass caught is held by Ronald Sprouse of Virginia. The bass weighed 6 pounds 13 ounces. If Ronald rows to his favorite fishing spot 9 miles downstream in the same amount of time that he rows 3 miles upstream and if the current is 6 mph, find how long it takes him to cover the 12 miles.

57. An experienced bricklayer can construct a small wall in 3 hours. An apprentice can complete the job in 6 hours. Find how long it takes if they work together.

58. Scanner A can scan a document in 3 hours. Scanner B takes 5 hours to do the same job. If both scanners are used, how long will it take for the document to be scanned?

59. A marketing manager travels 1080 miles in a corporate jet and then an additional 240 miles by car. If the car ride takes 1 hour longer, and if the rate of the jet is 6 times the rate of the car, find the time the manager travels by jet and find the time she travels by car.

60. In a recent year, 13 out of 20 top grossing movies were rated PG-13. At this rate, how many movies in a year with 599 new releases would you predict to be rated PG-13? Round to the nearest whole movie. (*Source:* Motion Picture Association)

61. In a recent year, 5 out of 7 movies cost between $50 and $99 million to make. At this rate, how many movies in a year with 599 new releases would you predict to cost between $50 and $99 million to make? Round to the nearest whole movie. (*Source:* Motion Picture Association)

REVIEW AND PREVIEW

Solve each equation for x. See Section 2.1.

62. $\dfrac{x}{5} = \dfrac{x+2}{3}$

63. $\dfrac{x}{4} = \dfrac{x+3}{6}$

64. $\dfrac{x-3}{2} = \dfrac{x-5}{6}$

65. $\dfrac{x-6}{4} = \dfrac{x-2}{5}$

CONCEPT EXTENSIONS

Calculating body-mass index (BMI) is a way to gauge whether a person should lose weight. Doctors recommend that body-mass index values fall between 19 and 25. The formula for body-mass index B is $B = \dfrac{705w}{h^2}$, where w is weight in pounds and h is height in inches. Use this formula to answer Exercises 66 and 67.

66. A patient is 5 ft 8 in. tall. What should his or her weight be to have a body-mass index of 25? Round to the nearest whole pound.

67. A doctor recorded a body-mass index of 47 on a patient's chart. Later, a nurse notices that the doctor recorded the patient's weight as 240 pounds but neglected to record the patient's height. Explain how the nurse can use the information from the chart to find the patient's height. Then find the height.

In physics, when the source of a sound is traveling toward an observer, the relationship between the actual pitch a of the sound and the pitch h that the observer hears due to the Doppler effect is described by the formula $h = \dfrac{a}{1 - \dfrac{s}{770}}$, where s is the speed of the sound source in miles per hour. Use this formula to answer Exercise 68.

68. An emergency vehicle has a single-tone siren with the pitch of the musical note E. As it approaches an observer standing by the road, the vehicle is traveling 50 mph. Is the pitch that the observer hears due to the Doppler effect lower or higher than the actual pitch? To which musical note is the pitch that the observer hears closest?

Pitch of an Octave of Musical Notes in Hertz (Hz)	
Note	*Pitch*
Middle C	261.63
D	293.66
E	329.63
F	349.23
G	392.00
A	440.00
B	493.88

Note: Greater numbers indicate higher pitches (acoustically).
(*Source:* American Standards Association)

In electronics, the relationship among the resistances R_1 and R_2 of two resistors wired in a parallel circuit and their combined resistance R is described by the formula $\dfrac{1}{R} = \dfrac{1}{R_1} + \dfrac{1}{R_2}$. Use this formula to solve Exercises 69 through 71.

69. If the combined resistance is 2 ohms and one of the two resistances is 3 ohms, find the other resistance.

70. Find the combined resistance of two resistors of 12 ohms each when they are wired in a parallel circuit.

71. The relationship among resistance of two resistors wired in a parallel circuit and their combined resistance may be extended to three resistors of resistances R_1, R_2, and R_3. Write an equation you believe may describe the relationship, and use it to find the combined resistance if R_1 is 5, R_2 is 6, and R_3 is 2.

6.7 VARIATION AND PROBLEM SOLVING

OBJECTIVES

1 Solve problems involving direct variation.

2 Solve problems involving inverse variation.

3 Solve problems involving joint variation.

4 Solve problems involving combined variation.

OBJECTIVE 1 ▶ Solving problems involving direct variation. A very familiar example of direct variation is the relationship of the circumference C of a circle to its radius r. The formula $C = 2\pi r$ expresses that the circumference is always 2π times the radius. In other words, C is always a constant multiple (2π) of r. Because it is, we say that C **varies directly as r**, that C **varies directly with r**, or that C **is directly proportional to r**.

> **Direct Variation**
>
> y **varies directly as x**, or y **is directly proportional to x**, if there is a nonzero constant k such that
>
> $$y = kx$$
>
> The number k is called the **constant of variation** or the **constant of proportionality**.

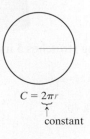

$C = 2\pi r$
↑
constant

In the above definition, the relationship described between x and y is a linear one. In other words, the graph of $y = kx$ is a line. The slope of the line is k, and the line passes through the origin.

For example, the graph of the direct variation equation $C = 2\pi r$ is shown. The horizontal axis represents the radius r, and the vertical axis is the circumference C. From the graph we can read that when the radius is 6 units, the circumference is approximately 38 units. Also, when the circumference is 45 units, the radius is between 7 and 8 units. Notice that as the radius increases, the circumference increases.

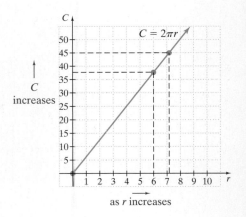

EXAMPLE 1   Suppose that y varies directly as x. If y is 5 when x is 30, find the constant of variation and the direct variation equation.

Solution   Since y varies directly as x, we write $y = kx$. If $y = 5$ when $x = 30$, we have that

$$y = kx$$
$$5 = k(30) \qquad \text{Replace } y \text{ with 5 and } x \text{ with 30.}$$
$$\frac{1}{6} = k \qquad \text{Solve for } k.$$

The constant of variation is $\frac{1}{6}$.

After finding the constant of variation k, the direct variation equation can be written as $y = \frac{1}{6}x$.   □

PRACTICE

1   Suppose that y varies directly as x. If y is 20 when x is 15, find the constant of variation and the direct variation equation.

EXAMPLE 2 Using Direct Variation and Hooke's Law

Hooke's law states that the distance a spring stretches is directly proportional to the weight attached to the spring. If a 40-pound weight attached to the spring stretches the spring 5 inches, find the distance that a 65-pound weight attached to the spring stretches the spring.

Solution

1. UNDERSTAND. Read and reread the problem. Notice that we are given that the distance a spring stretches is **directly proportional** to the weight attached. We let

$$d = \text{the distance stretched}$$
$$w = \text{the weight attached}$$

The constant of variation is represented by k.

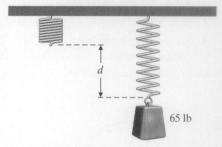

2. TRANSLATE. Because d is directly proportional to w, we write

$$d = kw$$

3. SOLVE. When a weight of 40 pounds is attached, the spring stretches 5 inches. That is, when $w = 40$, $d = 5$.

$$d = kw$$
$$5 = k(40) \quad \text{Replace } d \text{ with 5 and } w \text{ with 40.}$$
$$\frac{1}{8} = k \quad \text{Solve for } k.$$

Now when we replace k with $\frac{1}{8}$ in the equation

$$d = kw, \text{ we have}$$
$$d = \frac{1}{8}w$$

To find the stretch when a weight of 65 pounds is attached, we replace w with 65 to find d.

$$d = \frac{1}{8}(65)$$
$$= \frac{65}{8} = 8\frac{1}{8} \quad \text{or} \quad 8.125$$

4. INTERPRET.

Check: Check the proposed solution of 8.125 inches in the original problem.

State: The spring stetches 8.125 inches when a 65-pound weight is attached. ☐

PRACTICE

2   Use Hooke's law as stated in Example 2. If a 36-pound weight attached to a spring stretches the spring 9 inches, find the distance that a 75-pound weight attached to the spring stretches the spring.

OBJECTIVE 2 ▶ Solving problems involving inverse variation. When y is proportional to the **reciprocal** of another variable x, we say that **y varies inversely as x**, or that **y is inversely proportional to x**. An example of the inverse variation relationship is the relationship between the pressure that a gas exerts and the volume of its container. As the volume of a container decreases, the pressure of the gas it contains increases.

> **Inverse Variation**
>
> **y varies inversely as x**, or **y is inversely proportional to x**, if there is a nonzero constant k such that
>
> $$y = \frac{k}{x}$$
>
> The number k is called the **constant of variation** or the **constant of proportionality.**

Notice that $y = \frac{k}{x}$ is a rational equation. Its graph for $k > 0$ and $x > 0$ is shown. From the graph, we can see that as x increases, y decreases.

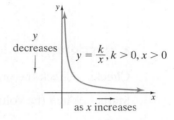

EXAMPLE 3   Suppose that u varies inversely as w. If u is 3 when w is 5, find the constant of variation and the inverse variation equation.

Solution   Since u varies inversely as w, we have $u = \dfrac{k}{w}$. We let $u = 3$ and $w = 5$, and we solve for k.

$$u = \frac{k}{w}$$

$$3 = \frac{k}{5} \qquad \text{Let } u = 3 \text{ and } w = 5.$$

$$15 = k \qquad \text{Multiply both sides by 5.}$$

The constant of variation k is 15. This gives the inverse variation equation

$$u = \frac{15}{w} \qquad\qquad \square$$

PRACTICE
3   Suppose that b varies inversely as a. If b is 5 when a is 9, find the constant of variation and the inverse variation equation.

- ■

EXAMPLE 4   **Using Inverse Variation and Boyle's Law**

Boyle's law says that if the temperature stays the same, the pressure P of a gas is inversely proportional to the volume V. If a cylinder in a steam engine has a pressure of 960 kilopascals when the volume is 1.4 cubic meters, find the pressure when the volume increases to 2.5 cubic meters.

Solution

1. UNDERSTAND. Read and reread the problem. Notice that we are given that the pressure of a gas is *inversely proportional* to the volume. We will let $P =$ the pressure and $V =$ the volume. The constant of variation is represented by k.
2. TRANSLATE. Because P is inversely proportional to V, we write

$$P = \frac{k}{V}$$

When $P = 960$ kilopascals, the volume $V = 1.4$ cubic meters. We use this information to find k.

$$960 = \frac{k}{1.4} \quad \text{Let } P = 960 \text{ and } V = 1.4.$$
$$1344 = k \quad \text{Multiply both sides by 1.4.}$$

Thus, the value of k is 1344. Replacing k with 1344 in the variation equation, we have

$$P = \frac{1344}{V}$$

Next we find P when V is 2.5 cubic meters.

3. SOLVE.

$$P = \frac{1344}{2.5} \quad \text{Let } V = 2.5.$$
$$= 537.6$$

4. INTERPRET.

Check: Check the proposed solution in the original problem.

State: When the volume is 2.5 cubic meters, the pressure is 537.6 kilopascals. □

PRACTICE
4 Use Boyle's law as stated in Example 4. When $P = 350$ kilopascals and $V = 2.8$ cubic meters, find the pressure when the volume decreases to 1.5 cubic meters.

OBJECTIVE 3 ▶ Solving problems involving joint variation. Sometimes the ratio of a variable to the product of many other variables is constant. For example, the ratio of distance traveled to the product of speed and time traveled is always 1.

$$\frac{d}{rt} = 1 \quad \text{or} \quad d = rt$$

Such a relationship is called **joint variation.**

> **Joint Variation**
>
> If the ratio of a variable y to the product of two or more variables is constant, then y **varies jointly as,** or **is jointly proportional to,** the other variables. If
>
> $$y = kxz$$
>
> then the number k is the **constant of variation** or the **constant of proportionality.**

Concept Check ☑
Which type of variation is represented by the equation $xy = 8$? Explain.

a. Direct variation   **b.** Inverse variation   **c.** Joint variation

△ **EXAMPLE 5** **Expressing Surface Area**

The lateral surface area of a cylinder varies jointly as its radius and height. Express this surface area S in terms of radius r and height h.

Solution   Because the surface area varies jointly as the radius r and the height h, we equate S to a constant multiple of r and h.

$$S = krh$$

In the equation, $S = krh$, it can be determined that the constant k is 2π, and we then have the formula $S = 2\pi rh$. (The lateral surface area formula does not include the areas of the two circular bases.)   □

PRACTICE
5   The area of a regular polygon varies jointly as its apothem and its perimeter. Express the area in terms of the apothem a and the perimeter p.

OBJECTIVE 4 ▶ Solving problems involving combined variation. Some examples of variation involve combinations of direct, inverse, and joint variation. We will call these variations **combined variation.**

EXAMPLE 6   Suppose that y varies directly as the square of x. If y is 24 when x is 2, find the constant of variation and the variation equation.

Solution   Since y varies directly as the square of x, we have

$$y = kx^2$$

Now let $y = 24$ and $x = 2$ and solve for k.

$$y = kx^2$$
$$24 = k \cdot 2^2$$
$$24 = 4k$$
$$6 = k$$

The constant of variation is 6, so the variation equation is

$$y = 6x^2$$ □

PRACTICE
6   Suppose that y varies inversely as the cube of x. If y is $\dfrac{1}{2}$ when x is 2, find the constant of variation and the variation equation.

△ **EXAMPLE 7**   Finding Column Weight

The maximum weight that a circular column can support is directly proportional to the fourth power of its diameter and is inversely proportional to the square of its height. A 2-meter-diameter column that is 8 meters in height can support 1 ton. Find the weight that a 1-meter-diameter column that is 4 meters in height can support.

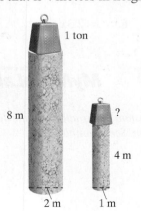

1 ton

8 m

?

4 m

2 m   1 m

Solution

1. **UNDERSTAND.** Read and reread the problem. Let w = weight, d = diameter, h = height, and k = the constant of variation.

2. **TRANSLATE.** Since w is directly proportional to d^4 and inversely proportional to h^2, we have

$$w = \frac{kd^4}{h^2}$$

3. **SOLVE.** To find k, we are given that a 2-meter-diameter column that is 8 meters in height can support 1 ton. That is, $w = 1$ when $d = 2$ and $h = 8$, or

$$1 = \frac{k \cdot 2^4}{8^2} \qquad \text{Let } w = 1, d = 2, \text{ and } h = 8.$$

$$1 = \frac{k \cdot 16}{64}$$

$$4 = k \qquad \text{Solve for } k.$$

Now replace k with 4 in the equation $w = \dfrac{kd^4}{h^2}$ and we have

$$w = \frac{4d^4}{h^2}$$

To find weight w for a 1-meter-diameter column that is 4 meters in height, let $d = 1$ and $h = 4$.

$$w = \frac{4 \cdot 1^4}{4^2}$$

$$w = \frac{4}{16} = \frac{1}{4}$$

4. **INTERPRET.**

Check: Check the proposed solution in the original problem.

State: The 1-meter-diameter column that is 4 meters in height can hold $\frac{1}{4}$ ton of weight. □

PRACTICE
7 Suppose that y varies directly as z and inversely as the cube of x. If y is 15 when $z = 5$ and $x = 3$, find the constant of variation and the variation equation.

VOCABULARY & READINESS CHECK

State whether each equation represents direct, inverse, or joint variation.

1. $y = 5x$ **2.** $y = \dfrac{700}{x}$ **3.** $y = 5xz$ **4.** $y = \dfrac{1}{2}abc$

5. $y = \dfrac{9.1}{x}$ **6.** $y = 2.3x$ **7.** $y = \dfrac{2}{3}x$ **8.** $y = 3.1\,st$

6.7 | EXERCISE SET

If y varies directly as x, find the constant of variation and the direct variation equation for each situation. See Example 1.

1. $y = 4$ when $x = 20$

2. $y = 5$ when $x = 30$

3. $y = 6$ when $x = 4$

4. $y = 12$ when $x = 8$

5. $y = 7$ when $x = \dfrac{1}{2}$

6. $y = 11$ when $x = \dfrac{1}{3}$

7. $y = 0.2$ when $x = 0.8$

8. $y = 0.4$ when $x = 2.5$

72. The volume of a cylinder varies jointly as the height and the square of the radius. If the height is halved and the radius is doubled, determine what happens to the volume.

73. Suppose that y varies directly as x. If x is doubled, what is the effect on y?

74. Suppose that y varies directly as x^2. If x is doubled, what is the effect on y?

Complete the following table for the inverse variation $y = \dfrac{k}{x}$ over each given value of k. Plot the points on a rectangular coordinate system.

x	$\frac{1}{4}$	$\frac{1}{2}$	1	2	4
$y = \dfrac{k}{x}$					

75. $k = 3$ **76.** $k = 1$ **77.** $k = \dfrac{1}{2}$ **78.** $k = 5$

CHAPTER 6 GROUP ACTIVITY

Fastest-Growing Occupations

We reviewed fastest-growing occupations originally in Chapter 2. In this chapter, let's study this important data in terms of percents.

According to U.S. Bureau of Labor Statistics projections, the careers listed in the following table will be among the top twenty-five fastest-growing jobs into the next decade, according to the percent increase in the number of jobs.

Employment (in thousands)				
Occupation	2004	2014	% Change	Rank
Medical assistants	387	589		
Preschool teachers	431	573		
Computer software engineers	800	1168		
Personal and home care aides	701	988		
Physician assistants	62	93		
Network administrators	278	385		
Postsecondary teachers	1628	2153		
Dental hygienists	158	226		
Network systems and data communications analysts	231	357		
Home health aides	624	974		

What do all these fast-growing occupations have in common? They all require knowledge of math! For some careers, such as management analysts, registered nurses, and computer software engineers, the ways math is used on the job may be obvious. For other occupations, the use of math may not be quite as apparent. However, tasks common to many jobs, like filling in a time sheet, writing up an expense or mileage report, planning a budget, figuring a bill, ordering supplies, and even making a work schedule, all require math.

Group Activity

1. Find the percent change in the number of jobs available from 2004 to 2014 for each occupation in the list.

2. Rank these top-ten occupations according to percent growth, from greatest to least.

3. Which occupation will be the fastest growing during this period?

4. How many occupations will have 50% or more positions in 2014 than in 2004?

5. Which of the listed occupations will be the slowest growing during this period?

📖 **STUDY SKILLS BUILDER**

Are You Preparing for a Test on Chapter 6?

Below I have listed some common trouble areas for students in Chapter 6. After studying for your test—but before taking your test—read these.

- Make sure you know the difference in the following:

Simplify: $\dfrac{\dfrac{3}{x}}{\dfrac{1}{x} - \dfrac{5}{y}}$

Solve: $\dfrac{5x}{6} - \dfrac{1}{2} = \dfrac{5x}{12}$

Subtract: $\dfrac{1}{2x} - \dfrac{7}{x-3}$

Multiply numerator and denominator by the LCD.

Multiply both sides by the LCD.

Write each expression as an equivalent expression with the LCD.

$\dfrac{\dfrac{3}{x} \cdot xy}{\dfrac{1}{x} \cdot xy - \dfrac{5}{y} \cdot xy}$

$= \dfrac{3y}{y - 5x}$

$12 \cdot \dfrac{5x}{6} - 12 \cdot \dfrac{1}{2} = 12 \cdot \dfrac{5x}{12}$

$2 \cdot 5x - 6 = 5x$

$10x - 6 = 5x$

$5x = 6$

$x = \dfrac{6}{5}$

$\dfrac{1 \cdot (x-3)}{2x \cdot (x-3)} - \dfrac{7 \cdot 2x}{(x-3) \cdot 2x}$

$= \dfrac{x-3}{2x(x-3)} - \dfrac{14x}{2x(x-3)}$

$= \dfrac{-13x - 3}{2x(x-3)}$

Remember: This is simply a checklist of common trouble areas. For a review of Chapter 6, see the Highlights and Chapter Review at the end of this chapter.

CHAPTER 6 VOCABULARY CHECK

Fill in each blank with one of the words or phrases listed below.

rational expression   equation   complex fraction   opposites   synthetic division
least common denominator   expression   long division   jointly   directly   inversely

1. A rational expression whose numerator, denominator, or both contain one or more rational expressions is called a
_____.

2. To divide a polynomial by a polynomial other than a monomial, we use _____.

3. In the equation $y = kx$, y varies _____ as x.

4. In the equation $y = \dfrac{k}{x}$, y varies _____ as x.

5. The _____ of a list of rational expressions is a polynomial of least degree whose factors include the denominator factors in the list.

6. When a polynomial is to be divided by a binomial of the form $x - c$, a shortcut process called _____ may be used.

7. In the equation $y = kxz$, y varies, _____ as x and z.

8. The expressions $(x - 5)$ and $(5 - x)$ are called _____.

9. A _____ is an expression that can be written as the quotient $\dfrac{P}{Q}$ of two polynomials P and Q as long as Q is not 0.

10. Which is an expression and which is an equation? An example of an _____ is $\dfrac{2}{x} + \dfrac{2}{x^2} = 7$ and an example of an _____ is $\dfrac{2}{x} + \dfrac{5}{x^2}$.

▶ Helpful Hint

Are you preparing for your test? Don't forget to take the Chapter 6 Test on page 409. Then check your answers at the back of the text and use the Chapter Test Prep Video CD to see the fully worked-out solutions to any of the exercises you want to review.

CHAPTER 6 HIGHLIGHTS

DEFINITIONS AND CONCEPTS	EXAMPLES

SECTION 6.1   RATIONAL FUNCTIONS AND MULTIPLYING AND DIVIDING RATIONAL EXPRESSIONS

A rational expression is the quotient $\frac{P}{Q}$ of two polynomials P and Q, as long as Q is not 0.

$$\frac{2x-6}{7}, \quad \frac{t^2-3t+5}{t-1}$$

To Simplify a Rational Expression

Step 1. Completely factor the numerator and the denominator.

Step 2. Apply the fundamental principle of rational expressions.

Simplify.

$$\frac{2x^2+9x-5}{x^2-25} = \frac{(2x-1)(x+5)}{(x-5)(x+5)}$$
$$= \frac{2x-1}{x-5}$$

To Multiply Rational Expressions

Step 1. Completely factor numerators and denominators.

Step 2. Multiply the numerators and multiply the denominators.

Step 3. Apply the fundamental principle of rational expressions.

Multiply $\dfrac{x^3+8}{12x-18} \cdot \dfrac{14x^2-21x}{x^2+2x}$.

$$= \frac{(x+2)(x^2-2x+4)}{6(2x-3)} \cdot \frac{7x(2x-3)}{x(x+2)}$$
$$= \frac{7(x^2-2x+4)}{6}$$

To Divide Rational Expressions

Multiply the first rational expression by the reciprocal of the second rational expression.

Divide $\dfrac{x^2+6x+9}{5xy-5y} \div \dfrac{x+3}{10y}$.

$$= \frac{(x+3)(x+3)}{5y(x-1)} \cdot \frac{2\cdot 5y}{x+3}$$
$$= \frac{2(x+3)}{x-1}$$

A **rational function** is a function described by a rational expression.

$$f(x) = \frac{2x-6}{7}, \quad h(t) = \frac{t^2-3t+5}{t-1}$$

SECTION 6.2   ADDING AND SUBTRACTING RATIONAL EXPRESSIONS

To Add or Subtract Rational Expressions

Step 1. Find the LCD.

Step 2. Write each rational expression as an equivalent rational expression whose denominator is the LCD.

Step 3. Add or subtract numerators and write the result over the common denominator.

Step 4. Simplify the resulting rational expression.

Subtract $\dfrac{3}{x+2} - \dfrac{x+1}{x-3}$.

$$= \frac{3\cdot(x-3)}{(x+2)\cdot(x-3)} - \frac{(x+1)\cdot(x+2)}{(x-3)\cdot(x+2)}$$
$$= \frac{3(x-3)-(x+1)(x+2)}{(x+2)(x-3)}$$
$$= \frac{3x-9-(x^2+3x+2)}{(x+2)(x-3)}$$
$$= \frac{3x-9-x^2-3x-2}{(x+2)(x-3)}$$
$$= \frac{-x^2-11}{(x+2)(x-3)}$$

DEFINITIONS AND CONCEPTS	EXAMPLES

SECTION 6.3   SIMPLIFYING COMPLEX FRACTIONS

Method 1: Simplify the numerator and the denominator so that each is a single fraction. Then perform the indicated division and simplify if possible.

Simplify $\dfrac{\dfrac{x+2}{x}}{x-\dfrac{4}{x}}$.

Method 1: $\dfrac{\dfrac{x+2}{x}}{\dfrac{x\cdot x}{1\cdot x}-\dfrac{4}{x}}=\dfrac{\dfrac{x+2}{x}}{\dfrac{x^2-4}{x}}$

$=\dfrac{x+2}{x}\cdot\dfrac{x}{(x+2)(x-2)}=\dfrac{1}{x-2}$

Method 2: Multiply the numerator and the denominator of the complex fraction by the LCD of the fractions in both the numerator and the denominator. Then simplify if possible.

Method 2: $\dfrac{\left(\dfrac{x+2}{x}\right)\cdot x}{\left(x-\dfrac{4}{x}\right)\cdot x}=\dfrac{x+2}{x\cdot x-\dfrac{4}{x}\cdot x}$

$=\dfrac{x+2}{x^2-4}=\dfrac{x+2}{(x+2)(x-2)}=\dfrac{1}{x-2}$

SECTION 6.4   DIVIDING POLYNOMIALS: LONG DIVISION AND SYNTHETIC DIVISION

To divide a polynomial by a monomial: Divide each term in the polynomial by the monomial.

Divide $\dfrac{12a^5b^3-6a^2b^2+ab}{6a^2b^2}$

$=\dfrac{12a^5b^3}{6a^2b^2}-\dfrac{6a^2b^2}{6a^2b^2}+\dfrac{ab}{6a^2b^2}$

$=2a^3b-1+\dfrac{1}{6ab}$

To divide a polynomial by a polynomial, other than a monomial:

Use long division.

Divide $2x^3-x^2-8x-1$ by $x-2$.

$$
\begin{array}{r}
2x^2+3x-2 \\
x-2{\overline{\smash{\big)}\,2x^3-\ \ x^2-8x-1}} \\
\underline{2x^3-4x^2} \\
3x^2-8x \\
\underline{3x^2-6x} \\
-2x-1 \\
\underline{-2x+4} \\
-5
\end{array}
$$

The quotient is $2x^2+3x-2-\dfrac{5}{x-2}$.

A shortcut method called **synthetic division** may be used to divide a polynomial by a binomial of the form $x-c$.

Use synthetic division to divide $2x^3-x^2-8x-1$ by $x-2$.

$$
\begin{array}{r|rrrr}
2 & 2 & -1 & -8 & -1 \\
 & \downarrow & 4 & 6 & -4 \\
\hline
 & 2 & 3 & -2 & -5
\end{array}
$$

The quotient is $2x^2+3x-2-\dfrac{5}{x-2}$.

DEFINITIONS AND CONCEPTS	EXAMPLES

SECTION 6.5 SOLVING EQUATIONS CONTAINING RATIONAL EXPRESSIONS

To solve an equation containing rational expressions: Multiply both sides of the equation by the LCD of all rational expressions. Then apply the distributive property and simplify. Solve the resulting equation and then check each proposed solution to see whether it makes the denominator 0. If so, it is an **extraneous solution.**

Solve $x - \dfrac{3}{x} = \dfrac{1}{2}$.

$$2x\left(x - \dfrac{3}{x}\right) = 2x\left(\dfrac{1}{2}\right) \quad \text{The LCD is } 2x.$$

$$2x \cdot x - 2x\left(\dfrac{3}{x}\right) = 2x\left(\dfrac{1}{2}\right) \quad \text{Distribute.}$$

$$2x^2 - 6 = x$$

$$2x^2 - x - 6 = 0 \quad \text{Subtract } x.$$

$$(2x + 3)(x - 2) = 0 \quad \text{Factor.}$$

$$x = -\dfrac{3}{2} \quad \text{or} \quad x = 2 \quad \text{Solve.}$$

Both $-\dfrac{3}{2}$ and 2 check. The solutions are 2 and $-\dfrac{3}{2}$.

SECTION 6.6 RATIONAL EQUATIONS AND PROBLEM SOLVING

Solving an Equation for a Specified Variable

Treat the specified variable as the only variable of the equation and solve as usual.

Problem-Solving Steps to Follow

Solve for x.

$$A = \dfrac{2x + 3y}{5}$$

$$5A = 2x + 3y \quad \text{Multiply both sides by 5.}$$

$$5A - 3y = 2x \quad \text{Subtract } 3y \text{ from both sides.}$$

$$\dfrac{5A - 3y}{2} = x \quad \text{Divide both sides by 2.}$$

Jeanee and David Dillon volunteer every year to clean a strip of Lake Ponchartrain Beach. Jeanee can clean all the trash in this area of beach in 6 hours; David takes 5 hours. Find how long it will take them to clean the area of beach together.

1. UNDERSTAND.

1. Read and reread the problem.

Let $x =$ time in hours that it takes Jeanee and David to clean the beach together.

	Hours to Complete	Part Completed in 1 Hour
Jeanee Alone	6	$\dfrac{1}{6}$
David Alone	5	$\dfrac{1}{5}$
Together	x	$\dfrac{1}{x}$

(continued)

DEFINITIONS AND CONCEPTS	EXAMPLES

2. TRANSLATE.

2. In words:

part Jeanee can complete in 1 hour	+	part David can complete in 1 hour	=	part they can complete together in 1 hour
↓		↓		↓

Translate:

$$\frac{1}{6} \quad + \quad \frac{1}{5} \quad = \quad \frac{1}{x}$$

3. SOLVE.

3. $\frac{1}{6} + \frac{1}{5} = \frac{1}{x}$ Multiply both sides by $30x$.

$$5x + 6x = 30$$
$$11x = 30$$
$$x = \frac{30}{11} \quad \text{or} \quad 2\frac{8}{11}$$

4. INTERPRET.

4. *Check* and then *state*. Together, they can clean the beach in $2\frac{8}{11}$ hours.

y **varies directly as** *x*, or *y* is **directly proportional to** *x*, if there is a nonzero constant *k* such that

$$y = kx$$

y **varies inversely as** *x*, or *y* is **inversely proportional to** *x*, if there is a nonzero constant *k* such that

$$y = \frac{k}{x}$$

y **varies jointly as** *x* and *z* or *y* is **jointly proportional to** *x* and *z* if there is a nonzero constant *k* such that

$$y = kxz$$

The circumference of a circle C varies directly as its radius r.

$$C = \underset{k}{2\pi r}$$

Pressure P varies inversely with volume V.

$$P = \frac{k}{V}$$

The lateral surface area S of a cylinder varies jointly as its radius r and height h.

$$S = \underset{k}{2\pi rh}$$

CHAPTER 6 REVIEW

(6.1) *Find the domain for each rational function.*

1. $f(x) = \dfrac{3 - 5x}{7}$

2. $g(x) = \dfrac{2x + 4}{11}$

3. $F(x) = \dfrac{-3x^2}{x - 5}$

4. $h(x) = \dfrac{4x}{3x - 12}$

5. $f(x) = \dfrac{x^3 + 2}{x^2 + 8x}$

6. $G(x) = \dfrac{20}{3x^2 - 48}$

Write each rational expression in lowest terms.

7. $\dfrac{x - 12}{12 - x}$

8. $\dfrac{5x - 15}{25x - 75}$

9. $\dfrac{2x}{2x^2 - 2x}$

10. $\dfrac{x + 7}{x^2 - 49}$

11. $\dfrac{2x^2 + 4x - 30}{x^2 + x - 20}$

12. The average cost (per bookcase) of manufacturing x bookcases is given by the rational function.

$$C(x) = \frac{35x + 4200}{x}$$

a. Find the average cost per bookcase of manufacturing 50 bookcases.

b. Find the average cost per bookcase of manufacturing 100 bookcases.

c. As the number of bookcases increases, does the average cost per bookcase increase or decrease? (See parts (a) and (b).)

Perform each indicated operation. Write your answers in lowest terms.

13. $\dfrac{4 - x}{5} \cdot \dfrac{15}{2x - 8}$

14. $\dfrac{x^2 - 6x + 9}{2x^2 - 18} \cdot \dfrac{4x + 12}{5x - 15}$

15. $\dfrac{a - 4b}{a^2 + ab} \cdot \dfrac{b^2 - a^2}{8b - 2a}$

16. $\dfrac{x^2 - x - 12}{2x^2 - 32} \cdot \dfrac{x^2 + 8x + 16}{3x^2 + 21x + 36}$

17. $\dfrac{4x + 8y}{3} \div \dfrac{5x + 10y}{9}$

18. $\dfrac{x^2 - 25}{3} \div \dfrac{x^2 - 10x + 25}{x^2 - x - 20}$

19. $\dfrac{a - 4b}{a^2 + ab} \div \dfrac{20b - 5a}{b^2 - a^2}$

20. $\dfrac{3x + 3}{x - 1} \div \dfrac{x^2 - 6x - 7}{x^2 - 1}$

21. $\dfrac{2x - x^2}{x^3 - 8} \div \dfrac{x^2}{x^2 + 2x + 4}$

22. $\dfrac{5x - 15}{3 - x} \cdot \dfrac{x + 2}{10x + 20} \cdot \dfrac{x^2 - 9}{x^2 - x - 6}$

(6.2) *Find the LCD of the rational expressions in each list.*

23. $\dfrac{5}{4x^2y^5}, \dfrac{3}{10x^2y^4}, \dfrac{x}{6y^4}$

24. $\dfrac{5}{2x}, \dfrac{7}{x - 2}$

25. $\dfrac{3}{5x}, \dfrac{2}{x - 5}$

26. $\dfrac{1}{5x^3}, \dfrac{4}{x^2 + 3x - 28}, \dfrac{11}{10x^2 - 30x}$

Perform each indicated operation. Write your answers in lowest terms.

27. $\dfrac{4}{x - 4} + \dfrac{x}{x - 4}$

28. $\dfrac{4}{3x^2} + \dfrac{2}{3x^2}$

29. $\dfrac{1}{x - 2} - \dfrac{1}{4 - 2x}$

30. $\dfrac{1}{10 - x} + \dfrac{x - 1}{x - 10}$

31. $\dfrac{x}{9 - x^2} - \dfrac{2}{5x - 15}$

32. $2x + 1 - \dfrac{1}{x - 3}$

33. $\dfrac{2}{a^2 - 2a + 1} + \dfrac{3}{a^2 - 1}$

34. $\dfrac{x}{9x^2 + 12x + 16} - \dfrac{3x + 4}{27x^3 - 64}$

Perform each indicated operation. Write your answers in lowest terms.

35. $\dfrac{2}{x - 1} - \dfrac{3x}{3x - 3} + \dfrac{1}{2x - 2}$

△ **36.** Find the perimeter of the heptagon (a polygon with seven sides).

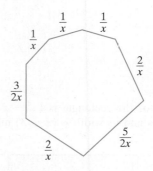

(6.3) *Simplify each complex fraction.*

37. $\dfrac{1 - \dfrac{3x}{4}}{2 + \dfrac{x}{4}}$

38. $\dfrac{\dfrac{x^2}{15}}{\dfrac{x + 1}{5x}}$

39. $\dfrac{2 - \dfrac{3}{2x}}{x - \dfrac{2}{5x}}$

40. $\dfrac{1 + \dfrac{x}{y}}{\dfrac{x^2}{y^2} - 1}$

41. $\dfrac{\dfrac{5}{x} + \dfrac{1}{xy}}{\dfrac{3}{x^2}}$

42. $\dfrac{\dfrac{x}{3} - \dfrac{3}{x}}{1 + \dfrac{3}{x}}$

43. $\dfrac{\dfrac{1}{x - 1} + 1}{\dfrac{1}{x + 1} - 1}$

44. $\dfrac{\dfrac{x - 3}{x + 3} + \dfrac{x + 3}{x - 3}}{\dfrac{x - 3}{x + 3} - \dfrac{x + 3}{x - 3}}$

If $f(x) = \dfrac{3}{x}, x \neq 0,$ *find each of the following*

45. $f(a + h)$

46. $f(a)$

47. Use Exercises 45 and 46 to find $\dfrac{f(a + h) - f(a)}{h}$.

48. Simplify the results of Exercise 47.

(6.4)

49. $(4xy + 2x^2 - 9) \div 4xy$

50. Divide $12xb^2 - 16xb^4$ by $4xb^3$.

51. $(3x^4 - 25x^2 - 20) \div (x - 3)$

52. $(-x^2 + 2x^4 + 5x - 12) \div (x + 2)$

53. $(2x^3 + 3x^2 - 2x + 2) \div (2x + 3)$

54. $(3x^4 + 5x^3 + 7x^2 + 3x - 2) \div (x^2 + x + 2)$

Use synthetic division to find each quotient.

55. $(3x^3 + 12x - 4) \div (x - 2)$

56. $(x^5 - 1) \div (x + 1)$

57. $(x^3 - 81) \div (x - 3)$

58. $(3x^4 - 2x^2 + 10) \div (x + 2)$

If $P(x) = 3x^5 - 9x + 7$, use the remainder theorem to find the following.

59. $P(4)$

60. $P(-5)$

△ **61.** $P\left(-\dfrac{1}{2}\right)$

62. If the area of the rectangle is $(x^4 - x^3 - 6x^2 - 6x + 18)$ square miles and its width is $(x - 3)$ miles, find the length.

$$x^4 - x^3 - 6x^2 - 6x + 18 \text{ square miles} \quad | \quad x - 3 \text{ miles}$$

(6.5) Solve each equation.

63. $\dfrac{3}{x} + \dfrac{1}{3} = \dfrac{5}{x}$

64. $\dfrac{2x + 3}{5x - 9} = \dfrac{3}{2}$

65. $\dfrac{1}{x - 2} - \dfrac{3x}{x^2 - 4} = \dfrac{2}{x + 2}$

66. $\dfrac{7}{x} - \dfrac{x}{7} = 0$

Solve each equation or perform each indicated operation. Simplify.

67. $\dfrac{5}{x^2 - 7x} + \dfrac{4}{2x - 14}$

68. $3 - \dfrac{5}{x} - \dfrac{2}{x^2} = 0$

69. $\dfrac{4}{3 - x} - \dfrac{7}{2x - 6} + \dfrac{5}{x}$

(6.6) Solve each equation for the specified variable.

△ **70.** $A = \dfrac{h(a + b)}{2}$ for a

71. $\dfrac{1}{R} = \dfrac{1}{R_1} + \dfrac{1}{R_2}$ for R_2

72. $I = \dfrac{E}{R + r}$ for R

73. $A = P + Prt$ for r

74. $H = \dfrac{kA(T_1 - T_2)}{L}$ for A

Solve.

75. The sum of a number and twice its reciprocal is 3. Find the number(s).

76. If a number is added to the numerator of $\dfrac{3}{7}$, and twice that number is added to the denominator of $\dfrac{3}{7}$, the result is equivalent to $\dfrac{10}{21}$. Find the number.

77. Three boys can paint a fence in 4 hours, 5 hours, and 6 hours, respectively. Find how long it will take all three boys to paint the fence.

78. If Sue Katz can type a certain number of mailing labels in 6 hours and Tom Neilson and Sue working together can type the same number of mailing labels in 4 hours, find how long it takes Tom alone to type the mailing labels.

79. The speed of a Ranger boat in still water is 32 mph. If the boat travels 72 miles upstream in the same time that it takes to travel 120 miles downstream, find the current of the stream.

80. The speed of a jogger is 3 mph faster than the speed of a walker. If the jogger travels 14 miles in the same amount of time that the walker travels 8 miles, find the speed of the walker.

(6.7) Solve each variation problem.

81. A is directly proportional to B. If $A = 6$ when $B = 14$, find A when $B = 21$.

82. According to Boyle's law, the pressure exerted by a gas is inversely proportional to the volume, as long as the temperature stays the same. If a gas exerts a pressure of 1250 kilopascals when the volume is 2 cubic meters, find the volume when the pressure is 800 kilopascals.

MIXED REVIEW

For expressions, perform the indicated operation and/or simplify. For equations, solve the equation for the unknown variable.

83. $\dfrac{22x + 8}{11x + 4}$

84. $\dfrac{xy - 3x + 2y - 6}{x^2 + 4x + 4}$

85. $\dfrac{2}{5x} \div \dfrac{4 - 18x}{6 - 27x}$

86. $\dfrac{7x + 28}{2x + 4} \div \dfrac{x^2 + 2x - 8}{x^2 - 2x - 8}$

87. $\dfrac{5a^2 - 20}{a^3 + 2a^2 + a + 2} \div \dfrac{7a}{a^3 + a}$

88. $\dfrac{4a + 8}{5a^2 - 20} \cdot \dfrac{3a^2 - 6a}{a + 3} \div \dfrac{2a^2}{5a + 15}$

89. $\dfrac{7}{2x} + \dfrac{5}{6x}$

90. $\dfrac{x - 2}{x + 1} - \dfrac{x - 3}{x - 1}$

91. $\dfrac{2x + 1}{x^2 + x - 6} + \dfrac{2 - x}{x^2 + x - 6}$

92. $\dfrac{2}{x^2 - 16} - \dfrac{3x}{x^2 + 8x + 16} + \dfrac{3}{x + 4}$

93. $\dfrac{\dfrac{1}{x} - \dfrac{2}{3x}}{\dfrac{5}{2x} - \dfrac{1}{3}}$

94. $\dfrac{2}{1 - \dfrac{2}{x}}$

95. $\dfrac{\dfrac{x^2 + 5x - 6}{4x + 3}}{\dfrac{(x + 6)^2}{8x + 6}}$

96. $\dfrac{\dfrac{3}{x - 1} - \dfrac{2}{1 - x}}{\dfrac{2}{x - 1} - \dfrac{2}{x}}$

97. $4 + \dfrac{8}{x} = 8$

98. $\dfrac{x - 2}{x^2 - 7x + 10} = \dfrac{1}{5x - 10} - \dfrac{1}{x - 5}$

99. The denominator of a fraction is 2 more than the numerator. If the numerator is decreased by 3 and the denominator is increased by 5, the resulting fraction is equivalent to $\dfrac{2}{3}$. Find the fraction.

100. The sum of the reciprocals of two consecutive even integers is $-\dfrac{9}{40}$. Find the two integers.

101. The inlet pipe of a water tank can fill the tank in 2 hours and 30 minutes. The outlet pipe can empty the tank in 2 hours. Find how long it takes to empty a full tank if both pipes are open.

102. Timmy Garnica drove 210 miles in the same amount of time that it took a DC-10 jet to travel 1715 miles. The speed of the jet was 430 mph faster than the speed of the car. Find the speed of the jet.

103. Two Amtrak trains traveling on parallel tracks leave Tucson at the same time. In 6 hours the faster train is 382 miles from Tucson and the trains are 112 miles apart. Find how fast each train is traveling.

104. C is inversely proportional to D. If $C = 12$ when $D = 8$, find C when $D = 24$.

105. The surface area of a sphere varies directly as the square of its radius. If the surface area is 36π square inches when the radius is 3 inches, find the surface area when the radius is 4 inches.

106. Divide $(x^3 - x^2 + 3x^4 - 2)$ by $(x - 4)$.

CHAPTER 6 TEST TEST PREP VIDEO

Remember to use the Chapter Test Prep Video CD to see the fully worked-out solutions to any of the exercises you want to review.

Find the domain of each rational function.

1. $f(x) = \dfrac{5x^2}{1 - x}$

2. $g(x) = \dfrac{9x^2 - 9}{x^2 + 4x + 3}$

Write each rational expression in lowest terms.

3. $\dfrac{7x - 21}{24 - 8x}$

4. $\dfrac{x^2 - 4x}{x^2 + 5x - 36}$

5. $\dfrac{x^3 - 8}{x - 2}$

Perform the indicated operation. If possible, simplify your answer.

6. $\dfrac{2x^3 + 16}{6x^2 + 12x} \cdot \dfrac{5}{x^2 - 2x + 4}$

7. $\dfrac{5}{4x^3} + \dfrac{7}{4x^3}$

8. $\dfrac{3x^2 - 12}{x^2 + 2x - 8} \div \dfrac{6x + 18}{x + 4}$

9. $\dfrac{4x - 12}{2x - 9} \div \dfrac{3 - x}{4x^2 - 81} \cdot \dfrac{x + 3}{5x + 15}$

10. $\dfrac{3 + 2x}{10 - x} + \dfrac{13 + x}{x - 10}$

11. $\dfrac{2x^2 + 7}{2x^4 - 18x^2} - \dfrac{6x + 7}{2x^4 - 18x^2}$

12. $\dfrac{3}{x^2 - x - 6} + \dfrac{2}{x^2 - 5x + 6}$

13. $\dfrac{5}{x - 7} - \dfrac{2x}{3x - 21} + \dfrac{x}{2x - 14}$

14. $\dfrac{3x}{5} \cdot \left(\dfrac{5}{x} - \dfrac{5}{2x} \right)$

Simplify each complex fraction.

15. $\dfrac{\dfrac{5}{x} - \dfrac{7}{3x}}{\dfrac{9}{8x} - \dfrac{1}{x}}$

16. $\dfrac{\dfrac{x^2 - 5x + 6}{x + 3}}{\dfrac{x^2 - 4x + 4}{x^2 - 9}}$

Divide.

17. $(4x^2y + 9x + 3xz) \div 3xz$

18. $(4x^3 - 5x) \div (2x + 1)$

19. Use synthetic division to divide $(4x^4 - 3x^3 - x - 1)$ by $(x + 3)$.

20. If $P(x) = 4x^4 + 7x^2 - 2x - 5$, use the remainder theorem to find $P(-2)$.

Solve each equation for x.

21. $\dfrac{x}{x-4} = 3 - \dfrac{4}{x-4}$

22. $\dfrac{3}{x+2} - \dfrac{1}{5x} = \dfrac{2}{5x^2 + 10x}$

23. $\dfrac{x^2+8}{x} - 1 = \dfrac{2(x+4)}{x}$

24. Solve for x: $\dfrac{x+b}{a} = \dfrac{4x-7a}{b}$

25. The product of one more than a number and twice the reciprocal of the number is $\dfrac{12}{5}$. Find the number.

26. If Jan can weed the garden in 2 hours and her husband can weed it in 1 hour and 30 minutes, find how long it takes them to weed the garden together.

27. Suppose that W is inversely proportional to V. If $W = 20$ when $V = 12$, find W when $V = 15$.

28. Suppose that Q is jointly proportional to R and the square of S. If $Q = 24$ when $R = 3$ and $S = 4$, find Q when $R = 2$ and $S = 3$.

29. When an anvil is dropped into a gorge, the speed with which it strikes the ground is directly proportional to the square root of the distance it falls. An anvil that falls 400 feet hits the ground at a speed of 160 feet per second. Find the height of a cliff over the gorge if a dropped anvil hits the ground at a speed of 128 feet per second.

CHAPTER 6 CUMULATIVE REVIEW

1. Translate each phrase to an algebraic expression. Use the variable x to represent each unknown number.

  a. Eight times a number

  b. Three more than eight times a number

  c. The quotient of a number and -7

  d. One and six-tenths subtracted from twice a number

  e. Six less than a number

  f. Twice the sum of four and a number

2. Translate each phrase to an algebraic expression. Use the variable x to represent each unknown number.

  a. One third subtracted from a number

  b. Six less than five times a number

  c. Three more than eight times a number

  d. The quotient of seven and the difference of two and a number.

3. Solve for y: $\dfrac{y}{3} - \dfrac{y}{4} = \dfrac{1}{6}$

4. Solve $\dfrac{x}{7} + \dfrac{x}{5} = \dfrac{12}{5}$

5. In the United States, the annual consumption of cigarettes is declining. The consumption c in billions of cigarettes per year since the year 1990 can be approximated by the formula $c = -9.2t + 527.33$ where t is the number of years after 1990. Use this formula to predict the years that the consumption of cigarettes will be less than 200 billion per year.

6. Olivia has scores of 78, 65, 82, and 79 on her algebra tests. Use an inequality to find the minimum score she can make or her final exam to pass the course with a 78 average or higher, given that the final exam counts as two tests.

7. Solve: $\left| \dfrac{3x+1}{2} \right| = -2$

8. Solve: $\left| \dfrac{2x-1}{3} \right| + 6 = 3$

9. Solve for x: $\left| \dfrac{2(x+1)}{3} \right| \le 0$

10. Solve for x: $\left| \dfrac{3(x-1)}{4} \right| \ge 2$

11. Graph the equation $y = -2x + 3$.

12. Graph the equation $y = -x + 3$.

13. Which of the following relations are also functions?

  a. $\{(-2,5), (2,7), (-3,5), (9,9)\}$

  b.

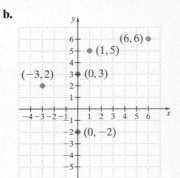

  c.

Input	Correspondence	Output
People in a certain city	Each person's age	The set of nonnegative integers

14. If $f(x) = -x^2 + 3x - 2$, find

   a. $f(0)$ **b.** $f(-3)$ **c.** $f\left(\dfrac{1}{3}\right)$

15. Graph $3x + 4y = -12$ by plotting intercept points.

16. Graph $3x - y = 6$ by plotting x- and y-intercepts.

17. Find an equation of the line with slope -3 containing the point $(1, -5)$. Write the equation in slope–intercept form $y = mx + b$.

18. Find an equation of the line with slope $\dfrac{1}{2}$ containing the point $(-1, 3)$. Use function notation to write the equation.

19. Graph the intersection of $x \geq 1$ and $y \geq 2x - 1$.

20. Graph the union of $2x + y \leq 4$ or $y > 2$.

21. Use the elimination method to solve the system.
$$\begin{cases} 3x - 2y = 10 \\ 4x - 3y = 15 \end{cases}$$

22. Use the substitution method to solve the system.
$$\begin{cases} -2x + 3y = 6 \\ 3x - y = 5 \end{cases}$$

23. Solve the system. $\begin{cases} 2x - 4y + 8z = 2 \\ -x - 3y + z = 11 \\ x - 2y + 4z = 0 \end{cases}$

24. Solve the system. $\begin{cases} 2x - 2y + 4z = 6 \\ -4x - y + z = -8 \\ 3x - y + z = 6 \end{cases}$

25. The measure of the largest angle of a triangle is $80°$ more than the measure of the smallest angle, and the measure of the remaining angle is $10°$ more than the measure of the smallest angle. Find the measure of each angle.

26. Kernersville office supply sold three reams of paper and two boxes of manila folders for $21.90. Also, five reams of paper and one box of manila folders cost $24.25. Find the price of a ream of paper and a box of manila folders.

27. Use matrices to solve the system. $\begin{cases} x + 2y + z = 2 \\ -2x - y + 2z = 5 \\ x + 3y - 2z = -8 \end{cases}$

28. Use matrices to solve the system. $\begin{cases} x + y + z = 9 \\ 2x - 2y + 3z = 2 \\ -3x + y - z = 1 \end{cases}$

29. Evaluate the following.

   a. 7^0 **b.** -7^0

   c. $(2x + 5)^0$ **d.** $2x^0$

30. Simplify the following. Write answers with positive exponents.

   a. $2^{-2} + 3^{-1}$ **b.** $-6a^0$ **c.** $\dfrac{x^{-5}}{x^{-2}}$

31. Simplify each. Assume that a and b are integers and that x and y are not 0.

   a. $x^{-b}(2x^b)^2$ **b.** $\dfrac{(y^{3a})^2}{y^{a-6}}$

32. Simplify each. Assume that a and b are integers and that x and y are not 0.

   a. $3x^{4a}(4x^{-a})^2$ **b.** $\dfrac{(y^{4b})^3}{y^{2b-3}}$

33. Find the degree of each term.

   a. $3x^2$ **b.** $-2^3 x^5$ **c.** y

   d. $12x^2 yz^3$ **e.** 5.27

34. Subtract $(2x - 7)$ from $2x^2 + 8x - 3$

35. Multiply $[3 + (2a + b)]^2$

36. Multiply $[4 + (3x - y)]^2$

37. Factor $ab - 5a + 2b - 12$

38. Factor $xy + 2x - 5y - 10$

39. Factor $2n^2 - 38n + 80$

40. Factor $6x^2 - x - 35$

41. Factor $x^2 + 4x + 4 - y^2$

42. Factor $4x^2 - 4x + 1 - 9y^2$

43. Solve $(x + 2)(x - 6) = 0$

44. Solve $2x(3x + 1)(x - 3) = 0$

45. Simplify

   a. $\dfrac{2x^2}{10x^3 - 2x^2}$

   b. $\dfrac{9x^2 + 13x + 4}{8x^2 + x - 7}$

46. For the graph of $f(x)$, answer the following:

   a. Find the domain and range.

   b. List the x- and y-intercepts.

   c. Find the coordinates of the point with the greatest y-value.

   d. Find the coordinates of the point with the least y-value.

   e. List the x-values whose y-values are equal to 0.

   f. List the x-values whose y-values are less than 0.

   g. Find the solutions of $f(x) = 0$.

47. Subtract $\dfrac{5k}{k^2 - 4} - \dfrac{2}{k^2 + k - 2}$.

48. Subtract $\dfrac{5a}{a^2 - 4} - \dfrac{3}{2 - a}$.

49. Solve: $\dfrac{3}{x} - \dfrac{x + 21}{3x} = \dfrac{5}{3}$.

50. Solve: $\dfrac{3x - 4}{2x} = -\dfrac{8}{x}$.

7 Rational Exponents, Radicals, and Complex Numbers

In this chapter, radical notation is reviewed, and then rational exponents are introduced. As the name implies, rational exponents are exponents that are rational numbers. We present an interpretation of rational exponents that is consistent with the meaning and rules already established for integer exponents, and we present two forms of notation for roots: radical and exponent. We conclude this chapter with complex numbers, a natural extension of the real number system.

What is a zorb? Simply put, a zorb is a large inflated ball within a ball, and zorbing is a recreational activity which may involve rolling down a hill while strapped in a zorb. Zorbing started in New Zealand (as well as bungee jumping) and was invented by Andrew Akers and Dwane van der Sluis. The first site was set up in New Zealand's North Island. This downhill course has a length of about 490 feet, and you can reach speeds of up to 20 mph.

An example of a course is shown in the diagram below, and you can see the mathematics involved. In Section 7.3, Exercise 115, page 436, you will calculate the outer radius of a zorb, which would certainly be closely associated with the cost of production.

7.1 RADICALS AND RADICAL FUNCTIONS

OBJECTIVES

1 Find square roots.

2 Approximate roots.

3 Find cube roots.

4 Find nth roots.

5 Find $\sqrt[n]{a^n}$ where a is a real number.

6 Graph square and cube root functions.

OBJECTIVE 1 ▶ Finding square roots. Recall from Section 1.3 that to find a **square root** of a number a, we find a number that was squared to get a.

Thus, because

$$5^2 = 25 \quad \text{and} \quad (-5)^2 = 25, \text{ then}$$

both 5 and -5 are square roots of 25.

Recall that we denote the **nonnegative,** or **principal, square root** with the **radical sign.**

$$\sqrt{25} = 5$$

We denote the **negative square root** with the **negative radical sign.**

$$-\sqrt{25} = -5$$

An expression containing a radical sign is called a **radical expression.** An expression within, or "under," a radical sign is called a **radicand.**

$$\text{radical expression}: \quad \sqrt{a} \quad \overset{\nearrow \text{radical sign}}{\underset{\searrow \text{radicand}}{}}$$

Principal and Negative Square Roots

If a is a nonnegative number, then

$\sqrt{a}$ is the **principal,** or **nonnegative square root** of a

$-\sqrt{a}$ is the **negative square root** of a

EXAMPLE 1   Simplify. Assume that all variables represent positive numbers.

a. $\sqrt{36}$ **b.** $\sqrt{0}$ **c.** $\sqrt{\dfrac{4}{49}}$ **d.** $\sqrt{0.25}$

e. $\sqrt{x^6}$ **f.** $\sqrt{9x^{12}}$ **g.** $-\sqrt{81}$ **h.** $\sqrt{-81}$

Solution

a. $\sqrt{36} = 6$ because $6^2 = 36$ and 6 is not negative.

b. $\sqrt{0} = 0$ because $0^2 = 0$ and 0 is not negative.

c. $\sqrt{\dfrac{4}{49}} = \dfrac{2}{7}$ because $\left(\dfrac{2}{7}\right)^2 = \dfrac{4}{49}$ and $\dfrac{2}{7}$ is not negative.

d. $\sqrt{0.25} = 0.5$ because $(0.5)^2 = 0.25$.

e. $\sqrt{x^6} = x^3$ because $(x^3)^2 = x^6$.

f. $\sqrt{9x^{12}} = 3x^6$ because $(3x^6)^2 = 9x^{12}$.

g. $-\sqrt{81} = -9$. The negative in front of the radical indicates the negative square root of 81.

h. $\sqrt{-81}$ is not a real number.   □

PRACTICE

1   Simplify. Assume that all variables represent positive numbers.

a. $\sqrt{49}$ **b.** $\sqrt{\dfrac{0}{1}}$ **c.** $\sqrt{\dfrac{16}{81}}$ **d.** $\sqrt{0.64}$

e. $\sqrt{z^8}$ **f.** $\sqrt{16b^4}$ **g.** $-\sqrt{36}$ **h.** $\sqrt{-36}$

Recall from Section 1.3 our discussion of the square root of a negative number. For example, can we simplify $\sqrt{-4}$? That is, can we find a real number whose square is -4? No, there is no real number whose square is -4, and we say that $\sqrt{-4}$ is not a real number. In general:

The square root of a negative number is not a real number.

> ▶ **Helpful Hint**
> - Remember: $\sqrt{0} = 0$
> - Don't forget, the square root of a negative number, such as $\sqrt{-9}$, is not a real number. In Section 7.7, we will see what kind of a number $\sqrt{-9}$ is.

OBJECTIVE 2 ▶ Approximating roots. Recall that numbers such as 1, 4, 9, and 25 are called **perfect squares,** since $1 = 1^2$, $4 = 2^2$, $9 = 3^2$, and $25 = 5^2$. Square roots of perfect square radicands simplify to rational numbers. What happens when we try to simplify a root such as $\sqrt{3}$? Since there is no rational number whose square is 3, then $\sqrt{3}$ is not a rational number. It is called an **irrational number,** and we can find a decimal **approximation** of it. To find decimal approximations, use a calculator. For example, an approximation for $\sqrt{3}$ is

$$\sqrt{3} \approx 1.732$$
$$\uparrow$$
approximation symbol

To see if the approximation is reasonable, notice that since

$$1 < 3 < 4, \text{ then}$$
$$\sqrt{1} < \sqrt{3} < \sqrt{4}, \text{ or}$$
$$1 < \sqrt{3} < 2.$$

We found $\sqrt{3} \approx 1.732$, a number between 1 and 2, so our result is reasonable.

EXAMPLE 2   Use a calculator to approximate $\sqrt{20}$. Round the approximation to 3 decimal places and check to see that your approximation is reasonable.

$$\sqrt{20} \approx 4.472$$

Solution   Is this reasonable? Since $16 < 20 < 25$, then $\sqrt{16} < \sqrt{20} < \sqrt{25}$, or $4 < \sqrt{20} < 5$. The approximation is between 4 and 5 and thus is reasonable.   □

PRACTICE
2   Use a calculator to approximate $\sqrt{45}$. Round the approximation to three decimal places and check to see that your approximation is reasonable.

OBJECTIVE 3 ▶ Finding cube roots. Finding roots can be extended to other roots such as cube roots. For example, since $2^3 = 8$, we call 2 the **cube root** of 8. In symbols, we write

$$\sqrt[3]{8} = 2$$

> **Cube Root**
> The **cube root** of a real number a is written as $\sqrt[3]{a}$, and
> $$\sqrt[3]{a} = b \text{ only if } b^3 = a$$

From this definition, we have

$$\sqrt[3]{64} = 4 \text{ since } 4^3 = 64$$
$$\sqrt[3]{-27} = -3 \text{ since } (-3)^3 = -27$$
$$\sqrt[3]{x^3} = x \text{ since } x^3 = x^3$$

Notice that, unlike with square roots, *it is possible to have a negative radicand when finding a cube root.* This is so because the *cube* of a negative number is a negative number. Therefore, the *cube root* of a negative number is a negative number.

EXAMPLE 3   Find the cube roots.

a. $\sqrt[3]{1}$ **b.** $\sqrt[3]{-64}$ **c.** $\sqrt[3]{\dfrac{8}{125}}$ **d.** $\sqrt[3]{x^6}$ **e.** $\sqrt[3]{-27x^9}$

Solution

a. $\sqrt[3]{1} = 1$ because $1^3 = 1$.

b. $\sqrt[3]{-64} = -4$ because $(-4)^3 = -64$.

c. $\sqrt[3]{\dfrac{8}{125}} = \dfrac{2}{5}$ because $\left(\dfrac{2}{5}\right)^3 = \dfrac{8}{125}$.

d. $\sqrt[3]{x^6} = x^2$ because $(x^2)^3 = x^6$.

e. $\sqrt[3]{-27x^9} = -3x^3$ because $(-3x^3)^3 = -27x^9$.

PRACTICE

3   Find the cube roots.

a. $\sqrt[3]{-1}$ **b.** $\sqrt[3]{27}$ **c.** $\sqrt[3]{\dfrac{27}{64}}$ **d.** $\sqrt[3]{x^{12}}$ **e.** $\sqrt[3]{-8x^3}$

OBJECTIVE 4 ▶ Finding *n*th roots. Just as we can raise a real number to powers other than 2 or 3, we can find roots other than square roots and cube roots. In fact, we can find the ***n*th root** of a number, where *n* is any natural number. In symbols, the *n*th root of *a* is written as $\sqrt[n]{a}$, where *n* is called the **index.** The index 2 is usually omitted for square roots.

> ▶ **Helpful Hint**
>
> If the index is even, such as $\sqrt{\ }$, $\sqrt[4]{\ }$, $\sqrt[6]{\ }$, and so on, the radicand must be non-negative for the root to be a real number. For example,
>
> $$\sqrt[4]{16} = 2, \text{ but } \sqrt[4]{-16} \text{ is not a real number.}$$
> $$\sqrt[6]{64} = 2, \text{ but } \sqrt[6]{-64} \text{ is not a real number.}$$
>
> If the index is odd, such as $\sqrt[3]{\ }$, $\sqrt[5]{\ }$, and so on, the radicand may be any real number. For example,
>
> $$\sqrt[3]{64} = 4 \quad \text{and} \quad \sqrt[3]{-64} = -4$$
> $$\sqrt[5]{32} = 2 \quad \text{and} \quad \sqrt[5]{-32} = -2$$

Concept Check ☑

Which one is not a real number?

a. $\sqrt[3]{-15}$ **b.** $\sqrt[4]{-15}$ **c.** $\sqrt[5]{-15}$ **d.** $\sqrt{(-15)^2}$

EXAMPLE 4   Simplify the following expressions.

a. $\sqrt[4]{81}$ **b.** $\sqrt[5]{-243}$ **c.** $-\sqrt{25}$ **d.** $\sqrt[4]{-81}$ **e.** $\sqrt[3]{64x^3}$

Solution

a. $\sqrt[4]{81} = 3$ because $3^4 = 81$ and 3 is positive.

b. $\sqrt[5]{-243} = -3$ because $(-3)^5 = -243$.

c. $-\sqrt{25} = -5$ because -5 is the opposite of $\sqrt{25}$.

d. $\sqrt[4]{-81}$ is not a real number. There is no real number that, when raised to the fourth power, is -81.

e. $\sqrt[3]{64x^3} = 4x$ because $(4x)^3 = 64x^3$.

PRACTICE
4 Simplify the following expressions.

a. $\sqrt[4]{10000}$ **b.** $\sqrt[5]{-1}$ **c.** $-\sqrt{81}$ **d.** $\sqrt[4]{-625}$ **e.** $\sqrt[3]{27x^9}$

OBJECTIVE 5 ▶ **Finding $\sqrt[n]{a^n}$ where a is a real number.** Recall that the notation $\sqrt{a^2}$ indicates the positive square root of a^2 only. For example,

$$\sqrt{(-5)^2} = \sqrt{25} = 5$$

When variables are present in the radicand and it is unclear whether the variable represents a positive number or a negative number, absolute value bars are sometimes needed to ensure that the result is a positive number. For example,

$$\sqrt{x^2} = |x|$$

This ensures that the result is positive. This same situation may occur when the index is any *even* positive integer. When the index is any *odd* positive integer, absolute value bars are not necessary.

> **Finding $\sqrt[n]{a^n}$**
> If n is an *even* positive integer, then $\sqrt[n]{a^n} = |a|$.
> If n is an *odd* positive integer, then $\sqrt[n]{a^n} = a$.

EXAMPLE 5 Simplify.

a. $\sqrt{(-3)^2}$ **b.** $\sqrt{x^2}$ **c.** $\sqrt[4]{(x-2)^4}$ **d.** $\sqrt[3]{(-5)^3}$

e. $\sqrt[5]{(2x-7)^5}$ **f.** $\sqrt{25x^2}$ **g.** $\sqrt{x^2+2x+1}$

Solution

a. $\sqrt{(-3)^2} = |-3| = 3$ When the index is even, the absolute value bars ensure us that our result is not negative.

b. $\sqrt{x^2} = |x|$

c. $\sqrt[4]{(x-2)^4} = |x-2|$

d. $\sqrt[3]{(-5)^3} = -5$

e. $\sqrt[5]{(2x-7)^5} = 2x-7$ Absolute value bars are not needed when the index is odd.

f. $\sqrt{25x^2} = 5|x|$

g. $\sqrt{x^2+2x+1} = \sqrt{(x+1)^2} = |x+1|$

PRACTICE
5 Simplify.

a. $\sqrt{(-4)^2}$ **b.** $\sqrt{x^{14}}$ **c.** $\sqrt[4]{(x+7)^4}$ **d.** $\sqrt[3]{(-7)^3}$

e. $\sqrt[5]{(3x-5)^5}$ **f.** $\sqrt{49x^2}$ **g.** $\sqrt{x^2+4x+4}$

OBJECTIVE 6 ▶ **Graphing square and cube root functions.** Recall that an equation in x and y describes a function if each x-value is paired with exactly one y-value. With this in mind, does the equation

$$y = \sqrt{x}$$

describe a function? First, notice that replacement values for x must be nonnegative real numbers, since $\sqrt{x}$ is not a real number if $x < 0$. The notation $\sqrt{x}$ denotes the principal square root of x, so for every nonnegative number x, there is exactly one number, $\sqrt{x}$. Therefore, $y = \sqrt{x}$ describes a function, and we may write it as

$$f(x) = \sqrt{x}$$

In general, radical functions are functions of the form

$$f(x) = \sqrt[n]{x}.$$

Recall that the domain of a function in x is the set of all possible replacement values of x. This means that if n is even, the domain is the set of all nonnegative numbers, or $\{x \mid x \geq 0\}$. If n is odd, the domain is the set of all real numbers. Keep this in mind as we find function values.

EXAMPLE 6   If $f(x) = \sqrt{x - 4}$ and $g(x) = \sqrt[3]{x + 2}$, find each function value.

a. $f(8)$ **b.** $f(6)$ **c.** $g(-1)$ **d.** $g(1)$

Solution

a. $f(8) = \sqrt{8 - 4} = \sqrt{4} = 2$ **b.** $f(6) = \sqrt{6 - 4} = \sqrt{2}$

c. $g(-1) = \sqrt[3]{-1 + 2} = \sqrt[3]{1} = 1$ **d.** $g(1) = \sqrt[3]{1 + 2} = \sqrt[3]{3}$ □

PRACTICE

6   If $f(x) = \sqrt{x + 5}$ and $g(x) = \sqrt[3]{x - 3}$, find each function value.

a. $f(11)$ **b.** $f(-1)$ **c.** $g(11)$ **d.** $g(-5)$

> ▶ **Helpful Hint**
>
> Notice that for the function $f(x) = \sqrt{x - 4}$, the domain includes all real numbers that make the radicand ≥ 0. To see what numbers these are, solve $x - 4 \geq 0$ and find that $x \geq 4$. The domain is $\{x \mid x \geq 4\}$.
>
> The domain of the cube root function $g(x) = \sqrt[3]{x + 2}$ is the set of real numbers.

EXAMPLE 7   Graph the square root function $f(x) = \sqrt{x}$.

Solution   To graph, we identify the domain, evaluate the function for several values of x, plot the resulting points, and connect the points with a smooth curve. Since $\sqrt{x}$ represents the nonnegative square root of x, the domain of this function is the set of all nonnegative numbers, $\{x \mid x \geq 0\}$, or $[0, \infty)$. We have approximated $\sqrt{3}$ below to help us locate the point corresponding to $(3, \sqrt{3})$.

x	$f(x) = \sqrt{x}$
0	0
1	1
3	$\sqrt{3} \approx 1.7$
4	2
9	3

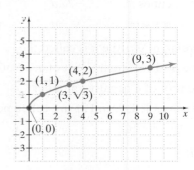

Notice that the graph of this function passes the vertical line test, as expected.   □

PRACTICE

7   Graph the square root function $h(x) = \sqrt{x + 2}$.

The equation $f(x) = \sqrt[3]{x}$ also describes a function. Here x may be any real number, so the domain of this function is the set of all real numbers, or $(-\infty, \infty)$. A few function values are given next.

$$f(0) = \sqrt[3]{0} = 0$$

$$f(1) = \sqrt[3]{1} = 1$$

$$f(-1) = \sqrt[3]{-1} = -1$$

$$f(6) = \sqrt[3]{6}$$

$$f(-6) = \sqrt[3]{-6}$$

Here, there is no rational number whose cube is 6. Thus, the radicals do not simplify to rational numbers.

$$f(8) = \sqrt[3]{8} = 2$$

$$f(-8) = \sqrt[3]{-8} = -2$$

EXAMPLE 8   Graph the function $f(x) = \sqrt[3]{x}$.

Solution   To graph, we identify the domain, plot points, and connect the points with a smooth curve. The domain of this function is the set of all real numbers. The table comes from the function values obtained earlier. We have approximated $\sqrt[3]{6}$ and $\sqrt[3]{-6}$ for graphing purposes.

x	$f(x) = \sqrt[3]{x}$
0	0
1	1
−1	−1
6	$\sqrt[3]{6} \approx 1.8$
−6	$\sqrt[3]{-6} \approx -1.8$
8	2
−8	−2

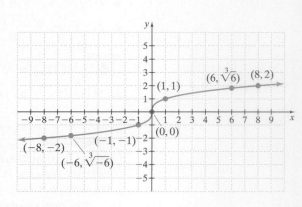

The graph of this function passes the vertical line test, as expected.

PRACTICE
8   Graph the function $f(x) = \sqrt[3]{x} - 4$.

VOCABULARY & READINESS CHECK

Use the choices below to fill in each blank. Not all choices will be used.

is	cubes	$-\sqrt{a}$	radical sign	index
is not	squares	$\sqrt{-a}$	radicand	

1. In the expression $\sqrt[n]{a}$, the n is called the _____, the $\sqrt{}$ is called the _____, and a is called the _____.
2. If $\sqrt{a}$ is the positive square root of a, $a \neq 0$, then _____ is the negative square root of a.
3. The square root of a negative number _____ a real number.
4. Numbers such as 1, 4, 9, and 25 are called perfect _____ where numbers such as 1, 8, 27, and 125 are called perfect _____.

Fill in the blank.

5. The domain of the function $f(x) = \sqrt{x}$ is _____.
6. The domain of the function $f(x) = \sqrt[3]{x}$ is _____.
7. If $f(16) = 4$, the corresponding ordered pair is _____.
8. If $g(-8) = -2$, the corresponding ordered pair is _____.

Choose the correct letter or letters. No pencil is needed, just think your way through these.

9. Which radical is not a real number?

   a. $\sqrt{3}$ **b.** $-\sqrt{11}$ **c.** $\sqrt[3]{-10}$ **d.** $\sqrt{-10}$

10. Which radical(s) simplify to 3?

   a. $\sqrt{9}$ **b.** $\sqrt{-9}$ **c.** $\sqrt[3]{27}$ **d.** $\sqrt[3]{-27}$

11. Which radical(s) simplify to -3?

   a. $\sqrt{9}$ **b.** $\sqrt{-9}$ **c.** $\sqrt[3]{27}$ **d.** $\sqrt[3]{-27}$

12. Which radical does not simplify to a whole number?

   a. $\sqrt{64}$ **b.** $\sqrt[3]{64}$ **c.** $\sqrt{8}$ **d.** $\sqrt[3]{8}$

7.1 EXERCISE SET

MyMathLab   PRACTICE   WATCH   DOWNLOAD   READ   REVIEW

Simplify. Assume that variables represent positive real numbers. See Example 1.

1. $\sqrt{100}$ 2. $\sqrt{400}$

3. $\sqrt{\dfrac{1}{4}}$ 4. $\sqrt{\dfrac{9}{25}}$

5. $\sqrt{0.0001}$ 6. $\sqrt{0.04}$

7. $-\sqrt{36}$ 8. $-\sqrt{9}$

9. $\sqrt{x^{10}}$ 10. $\sqrt{x^{16}}$

11. $\sqrt{16y^6}$ 12. $\sqrt{64y^{20}}$

Use a calculator to approximate each square root to 3 decimal places. Check to see that each approximation is reasonable. See Example 2.

13. $\sqrt{7}$ 14. $\sqrt{11}$

 15. $\sqrt{38}$ 16. $\sqrt{56}$

17. $\sqrt{200}$ 18. $\sqrt{300}$

Find each cube root. See Example 3.

19. $\sqrt[3]{64}$ 20. $\sqrt[3]{27}$

 21. $\sqrt[3]{\dfrac{1}{8}}$ 22. $\sqrt[3]{\dfrac{27}{64}}$

23. $\sqrt[3]{-1}$ 24. $\sqrt[3]{-125}$

25. $\sqrt[3]{x^{12}}$ 26. $\sqrt[3]{x^{15}}$

 27. $\sqrt[3]{-27x^9}$ 28. $\sqrt[3]{-64x^6}$

Find each root. Assume that all variables represent nonnegative real numbers. See Example 4.

29. $-\sqrt[4]{16}$ 30. $\sqrt[5]{-243}$

 31. $\sqrt[4]{-16}$ 32. $\sqrt{-16}$

 33. $\sqrt[5]{-32}$ 34. $\sqrt[5]{-1}$

35. $\sqrt[5]{x^{20}}$ 36. $\sqrt[4]{x^{20}}$

 37. $\sqrt[6]{64x^{12}}$ 38. $\sqrt[5]{-32x^{15}}$

39. $\sqrt{81x^4}$ 40. $\sqrt[4]{81x^4}$

41. $\sqrt[4]{256x^8}$ 42. $\sqrt{256x^8}$

Simplify. Assume that the variables represent any real number. See Example 5.

 43. $\sqrt{(-8)^2}$ 44. $\sqrt{(-7)^2}$

 45. $\sqrt[3]{(-8)^3}$ 46. $\sqrt[5]{(-7)^5}$

47. $\sqrt{4x^2}$ 48. $\sqrt[4]{16x^4}$

49. $\sqrt[3]{x^3}$ 50. $\sqrt[5]{x^5}$

 51. $\sqrt{(x-5)^2}$ 52. $\sqrt{(y-6)^2}$

53. $\sqrt{x^2 + 4x + 4}$

   (*Hint:* Factor the polynomial first.)

54. $\sqrt{x^2 - 8x + 16}$

   (*Hint:* Factor the polynomial first.)

MIXED PRACTICE

Simplify each radical. Assume that all variables represent positive real numbers.

55. $-\sqrt{121}$ 56. $-\sqrt[3]{125}$

57. $\sqrt[3]{8x^3}$ 58. $\sqrt{16x^8}$

59. $\sqrt{y^{12}}$ 60. $\sqrt[3]{y^{12}}$

61. $\sqrt{25a^2b^{20}}$ 62. $\sqrt{9x^4y^6}$

63. $\sqrt[3]{-27x^{12}y^9}$ 64. $\sqrt[3]{-8a^{21}b^6}$

65. $\sqrt[4]{a^{16}b^4}$ 66. $\sqrt[4]{x^8y^{12}}$

 67. $\sqrt[5]{-32x^{10}y^5}$ 68. $\sqrt[5]{-243z^{15}}$

69. $\sqrt{\dfrac{25}{49}}$ 70. $\sqrt{\dfrac{4}{81}}$

71. $\sqrt{\dfrac{x^2}{4y^2}}$ 72. $\sqrt{\dfrac{y^{10}}{9x^6}}$

73. $-\sqrt[3]{\dfrac{z^{21}}{27x^3}}$ 74. $-\sqrt[3]{\dfrac{64a^3}{b^9}}$

75. $\sqrt[4]{\dfrac{x^4}{16}}$ 76. $\sqrt[4]{\dfrac{y^4}{81x^4}}$

If $f(x) = \sqrt{2x+3}$ and $g(x) = \sqrt[3]{x-8}$, find the following function values. See Example 6.

77. $f(0)$ 78. $g(0)$

79. $g(7)$ 80. $f(-1)$

81. $g(-19)$ **82.** $f(3)$
83. $f(2)$ **84.** $g(1)$

Identify the domain and then graph each function. See Example 7.

85. $f(x) = \sqrt{x} + 2$

86. $f(x) = \sqrt{x} - 2$

87. $f(x) = \sqrt{x - 3}$; use the following table.

x	$f(x)$
3	
4	
7	
12	

88. $f(x) = \sqrt{x + 1}$; use the following table.

x	$f(x)$
-1	
0	
3	
8	

Identify the domain and then graph each function. See Example 8.

89. $f(x) = \sqrt[3]{x} + 1$

90. $f(x) = \sqrt[3]{x} - 2$

91. $g(x) = \sqrt[3]{x - 1}$; use the following table.

x	$g(x)$
1	
2	
0	
9	
-7	

92. $g(x) = \sqrt[3]{x + 1}$; use the following table.

x	$g(x)$
-1	
0	
-2	
7	
-9	

REVIEW AND PREVIEW

Simplify each exponential expression. See Sections 5.1 and 5.2.

93. $(-2x^3y^2)^5$ **94.** $(4y^6z^7)^3$

95. $(-3x^2y^3z^5)(20x^5y^7)$ **96.** $(-14a^5bc^2)(2abc^4)$

97. $\dfrac{7x^{-1}y}{14(x^5y^2)^{-2}}$ **98.** $\dfrac{(2a^{-1}b^2)^3}{(8a^2b)^{-2}}$

CONCEPT EXTENSIONS

Which of the following are not real numbers? See the Concept Check in this section.

99. $\sqrt{-17}$ **100.** $\sqrt[3]{-17}$

101. $\sqrt[10]{-17}$ **102.** $\sqrt[15]{-17}$

103. Explain why $\sqrt{-64}$ is not a real number.

104. Explain why $\sqrt[3]{-64}$ is a real number.

For Exercises 105 through 108, do not use a calculator.

105. $\sqrt{160}$ is closest to
   a. 10 **b.** 13 **c.** 20 **d.** 40

106. $\sqrt{1000}$ is closest to
   a. 10 **b.** 30 **c.** 100 **d.** 500

107. The perimeter of the triangle is closest to
   a. 12 **b.** 18
   c. 66 **d.** 132

108. The length of the bent wire is closest to
   a. 5 **b.** $\sqrt{28}$
   c. 7 **d.** 14

The Mosteller formula for calculating adult body surface area is $B = \sqrt{\dfrac{hw}{3131}}$, *where B is an individual's body surface area in square meters, h is the individual's height in inches, and w is the individual's weight in pounds. Use this information to answer Exercises 109 and 110. Round answers to 2 decimal places.*

109. Find the body surface area of an individual who is 66 inches tall and who weighs 135 pounds.

110. Find the body surface area of an individual who is 74 inches tall and who weighs 225 pounds.

111. Suppose that a friend tells you that $\sqrt{13} \approx 5.7$. Without a calculator, how can you convince your friend that he or she must have made an error?

112. Escape velocity is the minimum speed that an object must reach to escape a planet's pull of gravity. Escape velocity v is given by the equation $v = \sqrt{\dfrac{2Gm}{r}}$, where m is the mass of the planet, r is its radius, and G is the universal gravitational constant, which has a value of $G = 6.67 \times 10^{-11}$ m³/kg · sec². The mass of Earth is 5.97×10^{24} kg and its radius is 6.37×10^6 m. Use this information to find the escape velocity for Earth. Round to the nearest whole number. (*Source:* National Space Science Data Center)

Use a graphing calculator to verify the domain of each function and its graph.

113. Exercise 85 **114.** Exercise 86

115. Exercise 89 **116.** Exercise 90

STUDY SKILLS BUILDER

How Are Your Homework Assignments Going?

Remember that it is important to keep up with homework. Why? Many concepts in mathematics build on each other. Often, your understanding of a day's lecture depends on an understanding of the previous day's material.

To complete a homework assignment, remember these four things:

- Attempt all of it.
- Check it.
- Correct it.
- If needed, ask questions about it.

Take a moment and review your completed homework assignments. Answer the exercises below based on this review.

1. Approximate the fraction of your homework you have attempted.

2. Approximate the fraction of your homework you have checked (if possible).

3. If you are able to check your homework, have you corrected it when errors have been found?

4. What do you do, if you do not understand a concept while working on homework?

7.2 RATIONAL EXPONENTS

OBJECTIVES

1 Understand the meaning of $a^{1/n}$.

2 Understand the meaning of $a^{m/n}$.

3 Understand the meaning of $a^{-m/n}$.

4 Use rules for exponents to simplify expressions that contain rational exponents.

5 Use rational exponents to simplify radical expressions.

OBJECTIVE 1 ▶ Understanding the meaning of $a^{1/n}$. So far in this text, we have not defined expressions with rational exponents such as $3^{1/2}$, $x^{2/3}$, and $-9^{-1/4}$. We will define these expressions so that the rules for exponents will apply to these rational exponents as well.

Suppose that $x = 5^{1/3}$. Then

$$x^3 = (5^{1/3})^3 = 5^{1/3 \cdot 3} = 5^1 \text{ or } 5$$

$\underbrace{\qquad}_{\text{using rules}}$
for exponents

Since $x^3 = 5$, then x is the number whose cube is 5, or $x = \sqrt[3]{5}$. Notice that we also know that $x = 5^{1/3}$. This means

$$5^{1/3} = \sqrt[3]{5}$$

Definition of $a^{1/n}$

If n is a positive integer greater than 1 and $\sqrt[n]{a}$ is a real number, then

$$a^{1/n} = \sqrt[n]{a}$$

Notice that the denominator of the rational exponent corresponds to the index of the radical.

EXAMPLE 1   Use radical notation to write the following. Simplify if possible.

a. $4^{1/2}$ **b.** $64^{1/3}$ **c.** $x^{1/4}$ **d.** $0^{1/6}$ **e.** $-9^{1/2}$ **f.** $(81x^8)^{1/4}$ **g.** $(5y)^{1/3}$

Solution

a. $4^{1/2} = \sqrt{4} = 2$ **b.** $64^{1/3} = \sqrt[3]{64} = 4$

c. $x^{1/4} = \sqrt[4]{x}$ **d.** $0^{1/6} = \sqrt[6]{0} = 0$

e. $-9^{1/2} = -\sqrt{9} = -3$ **f.** $(81x^8)^{1/4} = \sqrt[4]{81x^8} = 3x^2$

g. $(5y)^{1/3} = \sqrt[3]{5y}$

PRACTICE
1 Use radical notation to write the following. Simplify if possible.

a. $36^{1/2}$ **b.** $1000^{1/3}$ **c.** $x^{1/5}$ **d.** $1^{1/4}$ **e.** $-64^{1/2}$

f. $(125x^9)^{1/3}$ **g.** $(3x)^{1/4}$

OBJECTIVE 2 ▶ Understanding the meaning of $a^{m/n}$. As we expand our use of exponents to include $\dfrac{m}{n}$, we define their meaning so that rules for exponents still hold true. For example, by properties of exponents,

$$8^{2/3} = (8^{1/3})^2 = \left(\sqrt[3]{8}\right)^2 \quad \text{or}$$
$$8^{2/3} = (8^2)^{1/3} = \sqrt[3]{8^2}$$

> **Definition of $a^{m/n}$**
>
> If m and n are positive integers greater than 1 with $\dfrac{m}{n}$ in lowest terms, then
> $$a^{m/n} = \sqrt[n]{a^m} = \left(\sqrt[n]{a}\right)^m$$
> as long as $\sqrt[n]{a}$ is a real number.

Notice that the denominator n of the rational exponent corresponds to the index of the radical. The numerator m of the rational exponent indicates that the base is to be raised to the mth power. This means

$$8^{2/3} = \sqrt[3]{8^2} = \sqrt[3]{64} = 4 \quad \text{or}$$
$$8^{2/3} = \left(\sqrt[3]{8}\right)^2 = 2^2 = 4$$

From simplifying $8^{2/3}$, can you see that it doesn't matter whether you raise to a power first and then take the nth root or you take the nth root first and then raise to a power?

> ▶ **Helpful Hint**
> Most of the time, $\left(\sqrt[n]{a}\right)^m$ will be easier to calculate than $\sqrt[n]{a^m}$.

EXAMPLE 2 Use radical notation to write the following. Then simplify if possible.

a. $4^{3/2}$ **b.** $-16^{3/4}$ **c.** $(-27)^{2/3}$

d. $\left(\dfrac{1}{9}\right)^{3/2}$ **e.** $(4x - 1)^{3/5}$

Solution

a. $4^{3/2} = \left(\sqrt{4}\right)^3 = 2^3 = 8$ **b.** $-16^{3/4} = -\left(\sqrt[4]{16}\right)^3 = -(2)^3 = -8$

c. $(-27)^{2/3} = \left(\sqrt[3]{-27}\right)^2 = (-3)^2 = 9$ **d.** $\left(\dfrac{1}{9}\right)^{3/2} = \left(\sqrt{\dfrac{1}{9}}\right)^3 = \left(\dfrac{1}{3}\right)^3 = \dfrac{1}{27}$

e. $(4x - 1)^{3/5} = \sqrt[5]{(4x - 1)^3}$

PRACTICE
2 Use radical notation to write the following. Simplify if possible.

a. $16^{3/2}$ **b.** $-1^{3/5}$ **c.** $-(81)^{3/4}$

d. $\left(\dfrac{1}{25}\right)^{3/2}$ **e.** $(3x + 2)^{5/9}$

▶ **Helpful Hint**

The *denominator* of a rational exponent is the index of the corresponding radical. For example, $x^{1/5} = \sqrt[5]{x}$ and $z^{2/3} = \sqrt[3]{z^2}$, or $z^{2/3} = \left(\sqrt[3]{z}\right)^2$.

OBJECTIVE 3 ▶ Understanding the meaning of $a^{-m/n}$. The rational exponents we have given meaning to exclude negative rational numbers. To complete the set of definitions, we define $a^{-m/n}$.

Definition of $a^{-m/n}$

$$a^{-m/n} = \frac{1}{a^{m/n}}$$

as long as $a^{m/n}$ is a nonzero real number.

EXAMPLE 3   Write each expression with a positive exponent, and then simplify.

a. $16^{-3/4}$ **b.** $(-27)^{-2/3}$

Solution

a. $16^{-3/4} = \dfrac{1}{16^{3/4}} = \dfrac{1}{\left(\sqrt[4]{16}\right)^3} = \dfrac{1}{2^3} = \dfrac{1}{8}$

b. $(-27)^{-2/3} = \dfrac{1}{(-27)^{2/3}} = \dfrac{1}{\left(\sqrt[3]{-27}\right)^2} = \dfrac{1}{(-3)^2} = \dfrac{1}{9}$ □

PRACTICE

3   Write each expression with a positive exponent; then simplify.

a. $9^{-3/2}$ **b.** $(-64)^{-2/3}$

▶ **Helpful Hint**

If an expression contains a negative rational exponent, such as $9^{-3/2}$, you may want to first write the expression with a positive exponent and then interpret the rational exponent. Notice that the sign of the base is not affected by the sign of its exponent. For example,

$$9^{-3/2} = \frac{1}{9^{3/2}} = \frac{1}{\left(\sqrt{9}\right)^3} = \frac{1}{27}$$

Also,

$$(-27)^{-1/3} = \frac{1}{(-27)^{1/3}} = -\frac{1}{3}$$

Concept Check ☑

Which one is correct?

a. $-8^{2/3} = \dfrac{1}{4}$ **b.** $8^{-2/3} = -\dfrac{1}{4}$ **c.** $8^{-2/3} = -4$ **d.** $-8^{-2/3} = -\dfrac{1}{4}$

OBJECTIVE 4 ▶ Using rules for exponents to simplify expressions. It can be shown that the properties of integer exponents hold for rational exponents. By using these properties and definitions, we can now simplify expressions that contain rational exponents.

These rules are repeated here for review.

Note: For the remainder of this chapter, we will assume that variables represent positive real numbers. Since this is so, we need not insert absolute value bars when we simplify even roots.

Answer to Concept Check: d

Summary of Exponent Rules

If m and n are rational numbers, and a, b, and c are numbers for which the expressions below exist, then

Product rule for exponents: $\qquad\qquad a^m \cdot a^n = a^{m+n}$

Power rule for exponents: $\qquad\qquad (a^m)^n = a^{m \cdot n}$

Power rules for products and quotients: $\qquad (ab)^n = a^n b^n \qquad$ and

$$\left(\frac{a}{c}\right)^n = \frac{a^n}{c^n}, c \neq 0$$

Quotient rule for exponents: $\qquad\qquad \dfrac{a^m}{a^n} = a^{m-n}, a \neq 0$

Zero exponent: $\qquad\qquad a^0 = 1, a \neq 0$

Negative exponent: $\qquad\qquad a^{-n} = \dfrac{1}{a^n}, a \neq 0$

EXAMPLE 4 Use properties of exponents to simplify. Write results with only positive exponents.

a. $b^{1/3} \cdot b^{5/3}$ $\qquad$ **b.** $x^{1/2} x^{1/3}$ $\qquad$ **c.** $\dfrac{7^{1/3}}{7^{4/3}}$

d. $y^{-4/7} \cdot y^{6/7}$ $\qquad$ **e.** $\dfrac{(2x^{2/5}y^{-1/3})^5}{x^2 y}$

Solution

a. $b^{1/3} \cdot b^{5/3} = b^{(1/3+5/3)} = b^{6/3} = b^2$

b. $x^{1/2} x^{1/3} = x^{(1/2+1/3)} = x^{3/6+2/6} = x^{5/6}$ $\quad$ Use the product rule.

c. $\dfrac{7^{1/3}}{7^{4/3}} = 7^{1/3-4/3} = 7^{-3/3} = 7^{-1} = \dfrac{1}{7}$ $\quad$ Use the quotient rule.

d. $y^{-4/7} \cdot y^{6/7} = y^{-4/7+6/7} = y^{2/7}$ $\qquad$ Use the product rule.

e. We begin by using the power rule $(ab)^m = a^m b^m$ to simplify the numerator.

$$\frac{(2x^{2/5}y^{-1/3})^5}{x^2 y} = \frac{2^5(x^{2/5})^5(y^{-1/3})^5}{x^2 y} = \frac{32x^2 y^{-5/3}}{x^2 y} \quad \text{Use the power rule and simplify}$$

$$= 32x^{2-2}y^{-5/3-3/3} \qquad\qquad \text{Apply the quotient rule.}$$

$$= 32x^0 y^{-8/3}$$

$$= \frac{32}{y^{8/3}}$$

PRACTICE
4 Use properties of exponents to simplify.

a. $y^{2/3} \cdot y^{8/3}$ $\qquad$ **b.** $x^{3/5} \cdot x^{1/4}$ $\qquad$ **c.** $\dfrac{9^{2/7}}{9^{9/7}}$

d. $b^{4/9} \cdot b^{-2/9}$ $\qquad$ **e.** $\dfrac{\left(3x^{1/4}y^{-2/3}\right)^4}{x^4 y}$

EXAMPLE 5 Multiply.

a. $z^{2/3}(z^{1/3} - z^5)$ $\qquad\qquad$ **b.** $(x^{1/3} - 5)(x^{1/3} + 2)$

Solution

a. $z^{2/3}(z^{1/3} - z^5) = z^{2/3}z^{1/3} - z^{2/3}z^5$ Apply the distributive property.

$$= z^{(2/3-1/3)} - z^{(2/3+5)}$$ Use the product rule.

$$= z^{3/3} - z^{(2/3+15/3)}$$

$$= z - z^{17/3}$$

b. $(x^{1/3} - 5)(x^{1/3} + 2) = x^{2/3} + 2x^{1/3} - 5x^{1/3} - 10$ Think of $(x^{1/3} - 5)$ and $(x^{1/3} + 2)$

$$= x^{2/3} - 3x^{1/3} - 10$$ as 2 binomials, and FOIL.

PRACTICE
5   Multiply.

a. $x^{3/5}(x^{1/3} - x^2)$ **b.** $(x^{1/2} + 6)(x^{1/2} - 2)$

EXAMPLE 6   Factor $x^{-1/2}$ from the expression $3x^{-1/2} - 7x^{5/2}$. Assume that all variables represent positive numbers.

Solution

$$3x^{-1/2} - 7x^{5/2} = (x^{-1/2})(3) - (x^{-1/2})(7x^{6/2})$$

$$= x^{-1/2}(3 - 7x^3)$$

To check, multiply $x^{-1/2}(3 - 7x^3)$ to see that the product is $3x^{-1/2} - 7x^{5/2}$.

PRACTICE
6   Factor $x^{-1/5}$ from the expression $2x^{-1/5} - 7x^{4/5}$.

OBJECTIVE 5 ▶ Using rational exponents to simplify radical expressions. Some radical expressions are easier to simplify when we first write them with rational exponents. We can simplify some radical expressions by first writing the expression with rational exponents. Use properties of exponents to simplify, and then convert back to radical notation.

EXAMPLE 7   Use rational exponents to simplify. Assume that variables represent positive numbers.

a. $\sqrt[8]{x^4}$ **b.** $\sqrt[6]{25}$ **c.** $\sqrt[4]{r^2 s^6}$

Solution

a. $\sqrt[8]{x^4} = x^{4/8} = x^{1/2} = \sqrt{x}$

b. $\sqrt[6]{25} = 25^{1/6} = (5^2)^{1/6} = 5^{2/6} = 5^{1/3} = \sqrt[3]{5}$

c. $\sqrt[4]{r^2 s^6} = (r^2 s^6)^{1/4} = r^{2/4} s^{6/4} = r^{1/2} s^{3/2} = (rs^3)^{1/2} = \sqrt{rs^3}$

PRACTICE
7   Use rational exponents to simplify. Assume that the variables represent positive numbers.

a. $\sqrt[9]{x^3}$ **b.** $\sqrt[4]{36}$ **c.** $\sqrt[8]{a^4 b^2}$

EXAMPLE 8   Use rational exponents to write as a single radical.

a. $\sqrt{x} \cdot \sqrt[4]{x}$ **b.** $\dfrac{\sqrt{x}}{\sqrt[3]{x}}$ **c.** $\sqrt[3]{3} \cdot \sqrt{2}$

Solution

a. $\sqrt{x} \cdot \sqrt[4]{x} = x^{1/2} \cdot x^{1/4} = x^{1/2+1/4}$

$\qquad = x^{3/4} = \sqrt[4]{x^3}$

b. $\dfrac{\sqrt{x}}{\sqrt[3]{x}} = \dfrac{x^{1/2}}{x^{1/3}} = x^{1/2-1/3} = x^{3/6-2/6}$

$\qquad = x^{1/6} = \sqrt[6]{x}$

c. $\sqrt[3]{3} \cdot \sqrt{2} = 3^{1/3} \cdot 2^{1/2}$ Write with rational exponents.

$\qquad = 3^{2/6} \cdot 2^{3/6}$ Write the exponents so that they have the same denominator.

$\qquad = (3^2 \cdot 2^3)^{1/6}$ Use $a^n b^n = (ab)^n$

$\qquad = \sqrt[6]{3^2 \cdot 2^3}$ Write with radical notation.

$\qquad = \sqrt[6]{72}$ Multiply $3^2 \cdot 2^3$.   □

PRACTICE
8   Use rational expressions to write each of the following as a single radical.

a. $\sqrt[3]{x} \cdot \sqrt[4]{x}$ b. $\dfrac{\sqrt[3]{y}}{\sqrt[5]{y}}$ c. $\sqrt[3]{5} \cdot \sqrt{3}$

VOCABULARY & READINESS CHECK

Answer each true or false.

1. $9^{-1/2}$ is a positive number. _____

2. $9^{-1/2}$ is a whole number. _____

3. $\dfrac{1}{a^{-m/n}} = a^{m/n}$ (where $a^{m/n}$ is a nonzero real number). _____

Fill in the blank with the correct choice.

4. To simplify $x^{2/3} \cdot x^{1/5}$, _____ the exponents.
   a. add   b. subtract   c. multiply   d. divide

5. To simplify $(x^{2/3})^{1/5}$, _____ the exponents.
   a. add   b. subtract   c. multiply   d. divide

6. To simplify $\dfrac{x^{2/3}}{x^{1/5}}$, _____ the exponents.
   a. add   b. subtract   c. multiply   d. divide

Choose the correct letter for each exercise. Letters will be used more than once. No pencil is needed. Just think about the meaning of each expression.

A = 2, B = −2, C = not a real number

7. $4^{1/2}$ ____   8. $-4^{1/2}$ ____   9. $(-4)^{1/2}$ ____   10. $8^{1/3}$ ____   11. $-8^{1/3}$ ____   12. $(-8)^{1/3}$ ____

7.2 | EXERCISE SET

PRACTICE   WATCH   DOWNLOAD   READ   REVIEW

Use radical notation to write each expression. Simplify if possible. See Example 1.

1. $49^{1/2}$

2. $64^{1/3}$

3. $27^{1/3}$

4. $8^{1/3}$

5. $\left(\dfrac{1}{16}\right)^{1/4}$

6. $\left(\dfrac{1}{64}\right)^{1/2}$

7. $169^{1/2}$

8. $81^{1/4}$

9. $2m^{1/3}$

10. $(2m)^{1/3}$

11. $(9x^4)^{1/2}$

12. $(16x^8)^{1/2}$

13. $(-27)^{1/3}$

14. $-64^{1/2}$

15. $-16^{1/4}$

16. $(-32)^{1/5}$

Use radical notation to write each expression. Simplify if possible. See Example 2.

17. $16^{3/4}$

18. $4^{5/2}$

19. $(-64)^{2/3}$

20. $(-8)^{4/3}$

21. $(-16)^{3/4}$

22. $(-9)^{3/2}$

23. $(2x)^{3/5}$

24. $2x^{3/5}$

25. $(7x + 2)^{2/3}$

26. $(x - 4)^{3/4}$

27. $\left(\dfrac{16}{9}\right)^{3/2}$

28. $\left(\dfrac{49}{25}\right)^{3/2}$

Write with positive exponents. Simplify if possible. See Example 3.

29. $8^{-4/3}$

30. $64^{-2/3}$

31. $(-64)^{-2/3}$

32. $(-8)^{-4/3}$

33. $(-4)^{-3/2}$

34. $(-16)^{-5/4}$

35. $x^{-1/4}$

36. $y^{-1/6}$

37. $\dfrac{1}{a^{-2/3}}$

38. $\dfrac{1}{n^{-8/9}}$

39. $\dfrac{5}{7x^{-3/4}}$

40. $\dfrac{2}{3y^{-5/7}}$

Use the properties of exponents to simplify each expression. Write with positive exponents. See Example 4.

41. $a^{2/3}a^{5/3}$

42. $b^{9/5}b^{8/5}$

43. $x^{-2/5} \cdot x^{7/5}$

44. $y^{4/3} \cdot y^{-1/3}$

45. $3^{1/4} \cdot 3^{3/8}$

46. $5^{1/2} \cdot 5^{1/6}$

47. $\dfrac{y^{1/3}}{y^{1/6}}$

48. $\dfrac{x^{3/4}}{x^{1/8}}$

49. $(4u^2)^{3/2}$

50. $(32^{1/5}x^{2/3})^3$

51. $\dfrac{b^{1/2}b^{3/4}}{-b^{1/4}}$

52. $\dfrac{a^{1/4}a^{-1/2}}{a^{2/3}}$

53. $\dfrac{(x^3)^{1/2}}{x^{7/2}}$

54. $\dfrac{y^{11/3}}{(y^5)^{1/3}}$

55. $\dfrac{(3x^{1/4})^3}{x^{1/12}}$

56. $\dfrac{(2x^{1/5})^4}{x^{3/10}}$

57. $\dfrac{(y^3z)^{1/6}}{y^{-1/2}z^{1/3}}$

58. $\dfrac{(m^2n)^{1/4}}{m^{-1/2}n^{5/8}}$

59. $\dfrac{(x^3y^2)^{1/4}}{(x^{-5}y^{-1})^{-1/2}}$

60. $\dfrac{(a^{-2}b^3)^{1/8}}{(a^{-3}b)^{-1/4}}$

Multiply. See Example 5.

61. $y^{1/2}(y^{1/2} - y^{2/3})$

62. $x^{1/2}(x^{1/2} + x^{3/2})$

63. $x^{2/3}(x - 2)$

64. $3x^{1/2}(x + y)$

65. $(2x^{1/3} + 3)(2x^{1/3} - 3)$

66. $(y^{1/2} + 5)(y^{1/2} + 5)$

Factor the common factor from the given expression. See Example 6.

67. $x^{8/3}; x^{8/3} + x^{10/3}$

68. $x^{3/2}; x^{5/2} - x^{3/2}$

69. $x^{1/5}; x^{2/5} - 3x^{1/5}$

70. $x^{2/7}; x^{3/7} - 2x^{2/7}$

71. $x^{-1/3}; 5x^{-1/3} + x^{2/3}$

72. $x^{-3/4}; x^{-3/4} + 3x^{1/4}$

Use rational exponents to simplify each radical. Assume that all variables represent positive numbers. See Example 7.

73. $\sqrt[6]{x^3}$

74. $\sqrt[9]{a^3}$

75. $\sqrt[6]{4}$

76. $\sqrt[4]{36}$

77. $\sqrt[4]{16x^2}$

78. $\sqrt[8]{4y^2}$

79. $\sqrt[8]{x^4y^4}$

80. $\sqrt[9]{y^6z^3}$

81. $\sqrt[12]{a^8b^4}$

82. $\sqrt[10]{a^5b^5}$

83. $\sqrt[4]{(x + 3)^2}$

84. $\sqrt[8]{(y + 1)^4}$

Use rational expressions to write as a single radical expression. See Example 8.

85. $\sqrt[3]{y} \cdot \sqrt[5]{y^2}$

86. $\sqrt[3]{y^2} \cdot \sqrt[6]{y}$

87. $\dfrac{\sqrt[3]{b^2}}{\sqrt[4]{b}}$

88. $\dfrac{\sqrt[4]{a}}{\sqrt[5]{a}}$

89. $\sqrt[3]{x} \cdot \sqrt[4]{x} \cdot \sqrt[8]{x^3}$

90. $\sqrt[6]{y} \cdot \sqrt[3]{y} \cdot \sqrt[5]{y^2}$

91. $\dfrac{\sqrt[3]{a^2}}{\sqrt[6]{a}}$

92. $\dfrac{\sqrt[5]{b^2}}{\sqrt[10]{b^3}}$

93. $\sqrt{3} \cdot \sqrt[3]{4}$

94. $\sqrt[3]{5} \cdot \sqrt{2}$

95. $\sqrt[5]{7} \cdot \sqrt[3]{y}$

96. $\sqrt[4]{5} \cdot \sqrt[3]{x}$

97. $\sqrt{5r} \cdot \sqrt[3]{s}$

98. $\sqrt[3]{b} \cdot \sqrt[5]{4a}$

REVIEW AND PREVIEW

Write each integer as a product of two integers such that one of the factors is a perfect square. For example, write 18 as $9 \cdot 2$, because 9 is a perfect square.

99. 75

100. 20

101. 48

102. 45

Write each integer as a product of two integers such that one of the factors is a perfect cube. For example, write 24 as $8 \cdot 3$, because 8 is a perfect cube.

103. 16

104. 56

105. 54

106. 80

CONCEPT EXTENSIONS

Basal metabolic rate (BMR) is the number of calories per day a person needs to maintain life. A person's basal metabolic rate $B(w)$ in calories per day can be estimated with the function $B(w) = 70w^{3/4}$, where w is the person's weight in kilograms. Use this information to answer Exercises 107 and 108.

107. Estimate the BMR for a person who weighs 60 kilograms. Round to the nearest calorie. (*Note:* 60 kilograms is approximately 132 pounds.)

108. Estimate the BMR for a person who weighs 90 kilograms. Round to the nearest calorie. (*Note:* 90 kilograms is approximately 198 pounds.)

The number of cellular telephone subscriptions in the United States from 1996 through 2006 can be modeled by the function $f(x) = 33.3x^{4/5}$, where y is the number of cellular telephone subscriptions in millions, x years after 1996. (Source: Based on data from the Cellular Telecommunications & Internet Association, 1994–2000) Use this information to answer Exercises 109 and 110.

109. Use this model to estimate the number of cellular telephone subscriptions in the United States in 2006. Round to the nearest tenth of a million.

110. Predict the number of cellular telephone subscriptions in the United States in 2010. Round to the nearest tenth of a million.

Fill in each box with the correct expression.

111. $\Box \cdot a^{2/3} = a^{3/3}$, or a

112. $\Box \cdot x^{1/8} = x^{4/8}$, or $x^{1/2}$

113. $\dfrac{\Box}{x^{-2/5}} = x^{3/5}$

114. $\dfrac{\Box}{y^{-3/4}} = y^{4/4}$, or y

Use a calculator to write a four-decimal-place approximation of each number.

115. $8^{1/4}$
116. $20^{1/5}$
117. $18^{3/5}$
118. $76^{5/7}$

119. In physics, the speed of a wave traveling over a stretched string with tension t and density u is given by the expression $\dfrac{\sqrt{t}}{\sqrt{u}}$. Write this expression with rational exponents.

120. In electronics, the angular frequency of oscillations in a certain type of circuit is given by the expression $(LC)^{-1/2}$. Use radical notation to write this expression.

7.3 SIMPLIFYING RADICAL EXPRESSIONS

OBJECTIVES

1. Use the product rule for radicals.

2. Use the quotient rule for radicals.

3. Simplify radicals.

4. Use the distance and midpoint formula.

OBJECTIVE 1 ▶ Using the product rule. It is possible to simplify some radicals that do not evaluate to rational numbers. To do so, we use a product rule and a quotient rule for radicals. To discover the product rule, notice the following pattern.

$$\sqrt{9} \cdot \sqrt{4} = 3 \cdot 2 = 6$$
$$\sqrt{9 \cdot 4} = \sqrt{36} = 6$$

Since both expressions simplify to 6, it is true that

$$\sqrt{9} \cdot \sqrt{4} = \sqrt{9 \cdot 4}$$

This pattern suggests the following product rule for radicals.

Product Rule for Radicals

If $\sqrt[n]{a}$ and $\sqrt[n]{b}$ are real numbers, then

$$\sqrt[n]{a} \cdot \sqrt[n]{b} = \sqrt[n]{ab}$$

Notice that the product rule is the relationship $a^{1/n} \cdot b^{1/n} = (ab)^{1/n}$ stated in radical notation.

EXAMPLE 1   Multiply.

a. $\sqrt{3} \cdot \sqrt{5}$ **b.** $\sqrt{21} \cdot \sqrt{x}$ **c.** $\sqrt[3]{4} \cdot \sqrt[3]{2}$

d. $\sqrt[4]{5y^2} \cdot \sqrt[4]{2x^3}$ **e.** $\sqrt{\dfrac{2}{a}} \cdot \sqrt{\dfrac{b}{3}}$

Solution

a. $\sqrt{3} \cdot \sqrt{5} = \sqrt{3 \cdot 5} = \sqrt{15}$

b. $\sqrt{21} \cdot \sqrt{x} = \sqrt{21x}$

c. $\sqrt[3]{4} \cdot \sqrt[3]{2} = \sqrt[3]{4 \cdot 2} = \sqrt[3]{8} = 2$

d. $\sqrt[4]{5y^2} \cdot \sqrt[4]{2x^3} = \sqrt[4]{5y^2 \cdot 2x^3} = \sqrt[4]{10y^2x^3}$

e. $\sqrt{\dfrac{2}{a}} \cdot \sqrt{\dfrac{b}{3}} = \sqrt{\dfrac{2}{a} \cdot \dfrac{b}{3}} = \sqrt{\dfrac{2b}{3a}}$

PRACTICE
1   Multiply.

a. $\sqrt{5} \cdot \sqrt{7}$ **b.** $\sqrt{13} \cdot \sqrt{z}$ **c.** $\sqrt[4]{125} \cdot \sqrt[4]{5}$

d. $\sqrt[3]{5y} \cdot \sqrt[3]{3x^2}$ **e.** $\sqrt{\dfrac{5}{m}} \cdot \sqrt{\dfrac{t}{2}}$

OBJECTIVE 2 ▶ Using the quotient rule. To discover a quotient rule for radicals, notice the following pattern.

$$\sqrt{\dfrac{4}{9}} = \dfrac{2}{3}$$

$$\dfrac{\sqrt{4}}{\sqrt{9}} = \dfrac{2}{3}$$

Since both expressions simplify to $\dfrac{2}{3}$, it is true that

$$\sqrt{\dfrac{4}{9}} = \dfrac{\sqrt{4}}{\sqrt{9}}$$

This pattern suggests the following quotient rule for radicals.

Quotient Rule for Radicals

If $\sqrt[n]{a}$ and $\sqrt[n]{b}$ are real numbers and $\sqrt[n]{b}$ is not zero, then

$$\sqrt[n]{\dfrac{a}{b}} = \dfrac{\sqrt[n]{a}}{\sqrt[n]{b}}$$

Notice that the quotient rule is the relationship $\left(\dfrac{a}{b}\right)^{1/n} = \dfrac{a^{1/n}}{b^{1/n}}$ stated in radical notation. We can use the quotient rule to simplify radical expressions by reading the rule from left to right, or to divide radicals by reading the rule from right to left.

For example,

$$\sqrt{\frac{x}{16}} = \frac{\sqrt{x}}{\sqrt{16}} = \frac{\sqrt{x}}{4} \qquad \text{Using } \sqrt[n]{\frac{a}{b}} = \frac{\sqrt[n]{a}}{\sqrt[n]{b}}$$

$$\frac{\sqrt{75}}{\sqrt{3}} = \sqrt{\frac{75}{3}} = \sqrt{25} = 5 \qquad \text{Using } \frac{\sqrt[n]{a}}{\sqrt[n]{b}} = \sqrt[n]{\frac{a}{b}}$$

Note: *Recall that from Section 7.2 on, we assume that variables represent positive real numbers. Since this is so, we need not insert absolute value bars when we simplify even roots.*

EXAMPLE 2 Use the quotient rule to simplify.

a. $\sqrt{\dfrac{25}{49}}$ **b.** $\sqrt{\dfrac{x}{9}}$ **c.** $\sqrt[3]{\dfrac{8}{27}}$ **d.** $\sqrt[4]{\dfrac{3}{16y^4}}$

Solution

a. $\sqrt{\dfrac{25}{49}} = \dfrac{\sqrt{25}}{\sqrt{49}} = \dfrac{5}{7}$ **b.** $\sqrt{\dfrac{x}{9}} = \dfrac{\sqrt{x}}{\sqrt{9}} = \dfrac{\sqrt{x}}{3}$

c. $\sqrt[3]{\dfrac{8}{27}} = \dfrac{\sqrt[3]{8}}{\sqrt[3]{27}} = \dfrac{2}{3}$ **d.** $\sqrt[4]{\dfrac{3}{16y^4}} = \dfrac{\sqrt[4]{3}}{\sqrt[4]{16y^4}} = \dfrac{\sqrt[4]{3}}{2y}$

PRACTICE
2 Use the quotient rule to simplify.

a. $\sqrt{\dfrac{36}{49}}$ **b.** $\sqrt{\dfrac{z}{16}}$ **c.** $\sqrt[3]{\dfrac{125}{8}}$ **d.** $\sqrt[4]{\dfrac{5}{81x^8}}$

OBJECTIVE 3 ▶ Simplifying radicals. Both the product and quotient rules can be used to simplify a radical. If the product rule is read from right to left, we have that

$$\sqrt[n]{ab} = \sqrt[n]{a} \cdot \sqrt[n]{b}.$$

This is used to simplify the following radicals.

EXAMPLE 3 Simplify the following.

a. $\sqrt{50}$ **b.** $\sqrt[3]{24}$ **c.** $\sqrt{26}$ **d.** $\sqrt[4]{32}$

Solution

a. Factor 50 such that one factor is the largest perfect square that divides 50. The largest perfect square factor of 50 is 25, so we write 50 as $25 \cdot 2$ and use the product rule for radicals to simplify.

$$\sqrt{50} = \sqrt{25 \cdot 2} = \sqrt{25} \cdot \sqrt{2} = 5\sqrt{2}$$

The largest perfect square factor of 50

> ▶ **Helpful Hint**
> Don't forget that, for example, $5\sqrt{2}$ means $5 \cdot \sqrt{2}$.

b. $\sqrt[3]{24} = \sqrt[3]{8 \cdot 3} = \sqrt[3]{8} \cdot \sqrt[3]{3} = 2\sqrt[3]{3}$

The largest perfect cube factor of 24

c. $\sqrt{26}$ The largest perfect square factor of 26 is 1, so $\sqrt{26}$ cannot be simplified further.

d. $\sqrt[4]{32} = \sqrt[4]{16 \cdot 2} = \sqrt[4]{16} \cdot \sqrt[4]{2} = 2\sqrt[4]{2}$

The largest fourth power factor of 32

PRACTICE
3 Simplify the following.

a. $\sqrt{98}$ **b.** $\sqrt[3]{54}$ **c.** $\sqrt{35}$ **d.** $\sqrt[4]{243}$

After simplifying a radical such as a square root, always check the radicand to see that it contains no other perfect square factors. It may, if the largest perfect square factor of the radicand was not originally recognized. For example,

$$\sqrt{200} = \sqrt{4 \cdot 50} = \sqrt{4} \cdot \sqrt{50} = 2\sqrt{50}$$

Notice that the radicand 50 still contains the perfect square factor 25. This is because 4 is not the largest perfect square factor of 200. We continue as follows.

$$2\sqrt{50} = 2\sqrt{25 \cdot 2} = 2 \cdot \sqrt{25} \cdot \sqrt{2} = 2 \cdot 5 \cdot \sqrt{2} = 10\sqrt{2}$$

The radical is now simplified since 2 contains no perfect square factors (other than 1).

> ▶ **Helpful Hint**
>
> To help you recognize largest perfect power factors of a radicand, it will help if you are familiar with some perfect powers. A few are listed below.
>
> | Perfect Squares | 1, | 4, | 9, | 16, | 25, | 36, | 49, | 64, | 81, | 100, | 121, | 144 |
> |---|---|---|---|---|---|---|---|---|---|---|---|---|
> | | 1^2 | 2^2 | 3^2 | 4^2 | 5^2 | 6^2 | 7^2 | 8^2 | 9^2 | 10^2 | 11^2 | 12^2 |
>
> | Perfect Cubes | 1, | 8, | 27, | 64, | 125 |
> |---|---|---|---|---|---|
> | | 1^3 | 2^3 | 3^3 | 4^3 | 5^3 |
>
> | Perfect Fourth Powers | 1, | 16, | 81, | 256 |
> |---|---|---|---|---|
> | | 1^4 | 2^4 | 3^4 | 4^4 |

In general, we say that a radicand of the form $\sqrt[n]{a}$ is simplified when the radicand a contains no factors that are perfect nth powers (other than 1 or -1).

EXAMPLE 4 Use the product rule to simplify.

a. $\sqrt{25x^3}$ **b.** $\sqrt[3]{54x^6y^8}$ **c.** $\sqrt[4]{81z^{11}}$

Solution

a. $\sqrt{25x^3} = \sqrt{25x^2 \cdot x}$ Find the largest perfect square factor.

$= \sqrt{25x^2} \cdot \sqrt{x}$ Apply the product rule.

$= 5x\sqrt{x}$ Simplify.

b. $\sqrt[3]{54x^6y^8} = \sqrt[3]{27 \cdot 2 \cdot x^6 \cdot y^6 \cdot y^2}$ Factor the radicand and identify perfect cube factors.

$= \sqrt[3]{27x^6y^6 \cdot 2y^2}$

$= \sqrt[3]{27x^6y^6} \cdot \sqrt[3]{2y^2}$ Apply the product rule.

$= 3x^2y^2\sqrt[3]{2y^2}$ Simplify.

c. $\sqrt[4]{81z^{11}} = \sqrt[4]{81 \cdot z^8 \cdot z^3}$ Factor the radicand and identify perfect fourth power factors.

$= \sqrt[4]{81z^8} \cdot \sqrt[4]{z^3}$ Apply the product rule.

$= 3z^2\sqrt[4]{z^3}$ Simplify.

PRACTICE
4 Use the product rule to simplify.

a. $\sqrt{36z^7}$ **b.** $\sqrt[3]{32p^4q^7}$ **c.** $\sqrt[4]{16x^{15}}$

EXAMPLE 5 Use the quotient rule to divide, and simplify if possible.

a. $\dfrac{\sqrt{20}}{\sqrt{5}}$ b. $\dfrac{\sqrt{50x}}{2\sqrt{2}}$ c. $\dfrac{7\sqrt[3]{48x^4y^8}}{\sqrt[3]{6y^2}}$ d. $\dfrac{2\sqrt[4]{32a^8b^6}}{\sqrt[4]{a^{-1}b^2}}$

<u>Solution</u>

a. $\dfrac{\sqrt{20}}{\sqrt{5}} = \sqrt{\dfrac{20}{5}}$ Apply the quotient rule.

     $= \sqrt{4}$ Simplify.

     $= 2$ Simplify.

b. $\dfrac{\sqrt{50x}}{2\sqrt{2}} = \dfrac{1}{2} \cdot \sqrt{\dfrac{50x}{2}}$ Apply the quotient rule.

     $= \dfrac{1}{2} \cdot \sqrt{25x}$ Simplify.

     $= \dfrac{1}{2} \cdot \sqrt{25} \cdot \sqrt{x}$ Factor 25x.

     $= \dfrac{1}{2} \cdot 5 \cdot \sqrt{x}$ Simplify.

     $= \dfrac{5}{2}\sqrt{x}$

c. $\dfrac{7\sqrt[3]{48x^4y^8}}{\sqrt[3]{6y^2}} = 7 \cdot \sqrt[3]{\dfrac{48x^4y^8}{6y^2}}$ Apply the quotient rule.

     $= 7 \cdot \sqrt[3]{8x^4y^6}$ Simplify.

     $= 7\sqrt[3]{8x^3y^6 \cdot x}$ Factor.

     $= 7 \cdot \sqrt[3]{8x^3y^6} \cdot \sqrt[3]{x}$ Apply the product rule.

     $= 7 \cdot 2xy^2 \cdot \sqrt[3]{x}$ Simplify.

     $= 14xy^2\sqrt[3]{x}$

d. $\dfrac{2\sqrt[4]{32a^8b^6}}{\sqrt[4]{a^{-1}b^2}} = 2\sqrt[4]{\dfrac{32a^8b^6}{a^{-1}b^2}} = 2\sqrt[4]{32a^9b^4} = 2\sqrt[4]{16 \cdot a^8 \cdot b^4 \cdot 2 \cdot a}$

     $= 2\sqrt[4]{16a^8b^4} \cdot \sqrt[4]{2a} = 2 \cdot 2a^2b \cdot \sqrt[4]{2a} = 4a^2b\sqrt[4]{2a}$

PRACTICE
5 Use the quotient rule to divide and simplify.

a. $\dfrac{\sqrt{80}}{\sqrt{5}}$ b. $\dfrac{\sqrt{98z}}{3\sqrt{2}}$ c. $\dfrac{5\sqrt[3]{40x^5y^7}}{\sqrt[3]{5y}}$ d. $\dfrac{3\sqrt[5]{64x^9y^8}}{\sqrt[5]{x^{-1}y^2}}$

Concept Check ☑

Find and correct the error:

$$\dfrac{\sqrt[3]{27}}{\sqrt{9}} = \sqrt[3]{\dfrac{27}{9}} = \sqrt[3]{3}$$

Answer to Concept Check:
$\dfrac{\sqrt[3]{27}}{\sqrt{9}} = \dfrac{3}{3} = 1$

OBJECTIVE 4 ▶ Using the distance and midpoint formulas. Now that we know how to simplify radicals, we can derive and use the distance formula. The midpoint formula is often confused with the distance formula, so to clarify both, we will also review the midpoint formula.

The Cartesian coordinate system helps us visualize a distance between points. To find the distance between two points, we use the distance formula, which is derived from the Pythagorean theorem.

To find the distance d between two points (x_1, y_1) and (x_2, y_2) as shown to the left, notice that the length of leg a is $x_2 - x_1$ and that the length of leg b is $y_2 - y_1$.

Thus, the Pythagorean theorem tells us that

$$d^2 = a^2 + b^2$$

or

$$d^2 = (x_2 - x_1)^2 + (y_2 - y_1)^2$$

or

$$d = \sqrt{(x_2 - x_1)^2 + (y_2 - y_1)^2}$$

This formula gives us the distance between any two points on the real plane.

> **Distance Formula**
> The distance d between two points (x_1, y_1) and (x_2, y_2) is given by
> $$d = \sqrt{(x_2 - x_1)^2 + (y_2 - y_1)^2}$$

EXAMPLE 6   Find the distance between $(2, -5)$ and $(1, -4)$. Give an exact distance and a three-decimal-place approximation.

Solution   To use the distance formula, it makes no difference which point we call (x_1, y_1) and which point we call (x_2, y_2). We will let $(x_1, y_1) = (2, -5)$ and $(x_2, y_2) = (1, -4)$.

$$
\begin{aligned}
d &= \sqrt{(x_2 - x_1)^2 + (y_2 - y_1)^2} \\
&= \sqrt{(1 - 2)^2 + [-4 - (-5)]^2} \\
&= \sqrt{(-1)^2 + (1)^2} \\
&= \sqrt{1 + 1} \\
&= \sqrt{2} \approx 1.414
\end{aligned}
$$

The distance between the two points is exactly $\sqrt{2}$ units, or approximately 1.414 units.

PRACTICE

6   Find the distance between $P(-3, 7)$ and $Q(-2, 3)$. Give an exact distance and a three-decimal-place approximation.

The **midpoint** of a line segment is the **point** located exactly halfway between the two endpoints of the line segment. On the graph to the left, the point M is the midpoint of line segment PQ. Thus, the distance between M and P equals the distance between M and Q.

Note: We usually need no knowledge of roots to calculate the midpoint of a line segment. We review midpoint here only because it is often confused with the distance between two points.

The x-coordinate of M is at half the distance between the x-coordinates of P and Q, and the y-coordinate of M is at half the distance between the y-coordinates of P and Q. That is, the x-coordinate of M is the average of the x-coordinates of P and Q; the y-coordinate of M is the average of the y-coordinates of P and Q.

> **Midpoint Formula**
>
> The midpoint of the line segment whose endpoints are (x_1, y_1) and (x_2, y_2) is the point with coordinates
>
> $$\left(\frac{x_1 + x_2}{2}, \frac{y_1 + y_2}{2} \right)$$

EXAMPLE 7 Find the midpoint of the line segment that joins points $P(-3, 3)$ and $Q(1, 0)$.

Solution Use the midpoint formula. It makes no difference which point we call (x_1, y_1) or which point we call (x_2, y_2). Let $(x_1, y_1) = (-3, 3)$ and $(x_2, y_2) = (1, 0)$.

$$\text{midpoint} = \left(\frac{x_1 + x_2}{2}, \frac{y_1 + y_2}{2} \right)$$

$$= \left(\frac{-3 + 1}{2}, \frac{3 + 0}{2} \right)$$

$$= \left(\frac{-2}{2}, \frac{3}{2} \right)$$

$$= \left(-1, \frac{3}{2} \right)$$

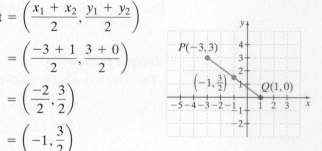

The midpoint of the segment is $\left(-1, \frac{3}{2} \right)$.

PRACTICE
7 Find the midpoint of the line segment that joins points $P(5, -2)$ and $Q(8, -6)$.

> ▶ **Helpful Hint**
>
> The distance between two points is a distance. The midpoint of a line segment is the point halfway between the endpoints of the segment.
>
> distance—measured in units
>
> midpoint—it is a point

VOCABULARY & READINESS CHECK

Use the choices below to fill in each blank. Some choices may be used more than once.

    distance   midpoint   point

1. The _____ of a line segment is a _____ exactly halfway between the two endpoints of the line segment.

2. The _____ formula is $d = \sqrt{(x_2 - x_1)^2 + (y_2 - y_1)^2}$.

3. The _____ formula is $\left(\frac{x_1 + x_2}{2}, \frac{y_1 + y_2}{2} \right)$.

7.4 ADDING, SUBTRACTING, AND MULTIPLYING RADICAL EXPRESSIONS

OBJECTIVES

1 Add or subtract radical expressions.

2 Multiply radical expressions.

OBJECTIVE 1 ▶ Adding or subtracting radical expressions. We have learned that sums or differences of like terms can be simplified. To simplify these sums or differences, we use the distributive property. For example,

$$2x + 3x = (2 + 3)x = 5x \quad \text{and} \quad 7x^2y - 4x^2y = (7 - 4)x^2y = 3x^2y$$

The distributive property can also be used to add **like radicals**.

> **Like Radicals**
> Radicals with the same index and the same radicand are like radicals.

For example, $2\sqrt{7} + 3\sqrt{7} = (2 - 3)\sqrt{7} = 5\sqrt{7}$. Also,

Like radicals

$$5\sqrt{3x} - 7\sqrt{3x} = (5 - 7)\sqrt{3x} = -2\sqrt{3x}$$

The expression $2\sqrt{7} + 2\sqrt[3]{7}$ cannot be simplified further since $2\sqrt{7}$ and $2\sqrt[3]{7}$ are not like radicals.

Unlike radicals

EXAMPLE 1   Add or subtract as indicated. Assume all variables represent positive real numbers.

a. $4\sqrt{11} + 8\sqrt{11}$ **b.** $5\sqrt[3]{3x} - 7\sqrt[3]{3x}$ **c.** $2\sqrt{7} + 2\sqrt[3]{7}$

Solution

a. $4\sqrt{11} + 8\sqrt{11} = (4 + 8)\sqrt{11} = 12\sqrt{11}$

b. $5\sqrt[3]{3x} - 7\sqrt[3]{3x} = (5 - 7)\sqrt[3]{3x} = -2\sqrt[3]{3x}$

c. $2\sqrt{7} + 2\sqrt[3]{7}$

This expression cannot be simplified since $2\sqrt{7}$ and $2\sqrt[3]{7}$ do not contain like radicals.

PRACTICE
1   Add or subtract as indicated.

a. $3\sqrt{17} + 5\sqrt{17}$ **b.** $7\sqrt[3]{5z} - 12\sqrt[3]{5z}$ **c.** $3\sqrt{2} + 5\sqrt[3]{2}$

When adding or subtracting radicals, always check first to see whether any radicals can be simplified.

Concept Check ☑

True or false?

$$\sqrt{a} + \sqrt{b} = \sqrt{a + b}$$

Explain.

Answer to Concept Check:
false; answers may vary

EXAMPLE 2 Add or subtract. Assume that variables represent positive real numbers.

a. $\sqrt{20} + 2\sqrt{45}$ **b.** $\sqrt[3]{54} - 5\sqrt[3]{16} + \sqrt[3]{2}$ **c.** $\sqrt{27x} - 2\sqrt{9x} + \sqrt{72x}$
d. $\sqrt[3]{98} + \sqrt{98}$ **e.** $\sqrt[3]{48y^4} + \sqrt[3]{6y^4}$

Solution First, simplify each radical. Then add or subtract any like radicals.

a. $\sqrt{20} + 2\sqrt{45} = \sqrt{4 \cdot 5} + 2\sqrt{9 \cdot 5}$ Factor 20 and 45.

$\phantom{\sqrt{20} + 2\sqrt{45}} = \sqrt{4} \cdot \sqrt{5} + 2 \cdot \sqrt{9} \cdot \sqrt{5}$ Use the product rule.

$\phantom{\sqrt{20} + 2\sqrt{45}} = 2 \cdot \sqrt{5} + 2 \cdot 3 \cdot \sqrt{5}$ Simplify $\sqrt{4}$ and $\sqrt{9}$.

$\phantom{\sqrt{20} + 2\sqrt{45}} = 2\sqrt{5} + 6\sqrt{5}$ Add like radicals.

$\phantom{\sqrt{20} + 2\sqrt{45}} = 8\sqrt{5}$

b. $\sqrt[3]{54} - 5\sqrt[3]{16} + \sqrt[3]{2}$

$ = \sqrt[3]{27} \cdot \sqrt[3]{2} - 5 \cdot \sqrt[3]{8} \cdot \sqrt[3]{2} + \sqrt[3]{2}$ Factor and use the product rule.

$ = 3 \cdot \sqrt[3]{2} - 5 \cdot 2 \cdot \sqrt[3]{2} + \sqrt[3]{2}$ Simplify $\sqrt[3]{27}$ and $\sqrt[3]{8}$.

$ = 3\sqrt[3]{2} - 10\sqrt[3]{2} + \sqrt[3]{2}$ Write $5 \cdot 2$ as 10.

$ = -6\sqrt[3]{2}$ Combine like radicals.

c. $\sqrt{27x} - 2\sqrt{9x} + \sqrt{72x}$

$ = \sqrt{9} \cdot \sqrt{3x} - 2 \cdot \sqrt{9} \cdot \sqrt{x} + \sqrt{36} \cdot \sqrt{2x}$ Factor and use the product rule.

$ = 3 \cdot \sqrt{3x} - 2 \cdot 3 \cdot \sqrt{x} + 6 \cdot \sqrt{2x}$ Simplify $\sqrt{9}$ and $\sqrt{36}$.

$ = 3\sqrt{3x} - 6\sqrt{x} + 6\sqrt{2x}$ Write $2 \cdot 3$ as 6.

> ▶ **Helpful Hint**
> None of these terms contain like radicals. We can simplify no further.

d. $\sqrt[3]{98} + \sqrt{98} = \sqrt[3]{98} + \sqrt{49} \cdot \sqrt{2}$ Factor and use the product rule.

$\phantom{\sqrt[3]{98} + \sqrt{98}} = \sqrt[3]{98} + 7\sqrt{2}$ No further simplification is possible.

e. $\sqrt[3]{48y^4} + \sqrt[3]{6y^4} = \sqrt[3]{8y^3} \cdot \sqrt[3]{6y} + \sqrt[3]{y^3} \cdot \sqrt[3]{6y}$ Factor and use the product rule.

$\phantom{\sqrt[3]{48y^4} + \sqrt[3]{6y^4}} = 2y\sqrt[3]{6y} + y\sqrt[3]{6y}$ Simplify $\sqrt[3]{8y^3}$ and $\sqrt[3]{y^3}$.

$\phantom{\sqrt[3]{48y^4} + \sqrt[3]{6y^4}} = 3y\sqrt[3]{6y}$ Combine like radicals. ☐

PRACTICE
2 Add or subtract.

a. $\sqrt{24} + 3\sqrt{54}$ **b.** $\sqrt[3]{24} - 4\sqrt[3]{81} + \sqrt[3]{3}$ **c.** $\sqrt{75x} - 3\sqrt{27x} + \sqrt{12x}$
d. $\sqrt{40} + \sqrt[3]{40}$ **e.** $\sqrt[3]{81x^4} + \sqrt[3]{3x^4}$

Let's continue to assume that variables represent positive real numbers.

EXAMPLE 3 Add or subtract as indicated.

a. $\dfrac{\sqrt{45}}{4} - \dfrac{\sqrt{5}}{3}$ **b.** $\sqrt[3]{\dfrac{7x}{8}} + 2\sqrt[3]{7x}$

Solution

a. $\dfrac{\sqrt{45}}{4} - \dfrac{\sqrt{5}}{3} = \dfrac{3\sqrt{5}}{4} - \dfrac{\sqrt{5}}{3}$ To subtract, notice that the LCD is 12.

$ = \dfrac{3\sqrt{5} \cdot 3}{4 \cdot 3} - \dfrac{\sqrt{5} \cdot 4}{3 \cdot 4}$ Write each expression as an equivalent expression with a denominator of 12.

$ = \dfrac{9\sqrt{5}}{12} - \dfrac{4\sqrt{5}}{12}$ Multiply factors in the numerator and the denominator.

$ = \dfrac{5\sqrt{5}}{12}$ Subtract.

b. $\sqrt[3]{\dfrac{7x}{8}} + 2\sqrt[3]{7x} = \dfrac{\sqrt[3]{7x}}{\sqrt[3]{8}} + 2\sqrt[3]{7x}$ Apply the quotient rule for radicals.

$\qquad\qquad\qquad = \dfrac{\sqrt[3]{7x}}{2} + 2\sqrt[3]{7x}$ Simplify.

$\qquad\qquad\qquad = \dfrac{\sqrt[3]{7x}}{2} + \dfrac{2\sqrt[3]{7x} \cdot 2}{2}$ Write each expression as an equivalent expression with a denominator of 2.

$\qquad\qquad\qquad = \dfrac{\sqrt[3]{7x}}{2} + \dfrac{4\sqrt[3]{7x}}{2}$

$\qquad\qquad\qquad = \dfrac{5\sqrt[3]{7x}}{2}$ Add.   □

PRACTICE
3   Add or subtract as indicated.

a. $\dfrac{\sqrt{28}}{3} - \dfrac{\sqrt{7}}{4}$ **b.** $\sqrt[3]{\dfrac{6y}{64}} + 3\sqrt[3]{6y}$

OBJECTIVE 2 ▶ Multiplying radical expressions. We can multiply radical expressions by using many of the same properties used to multiply polynomial expressions. For instance, to multiply $\sqrt{2}(\sqrt{6} - 3\sqrt{2})$, we use the distributive property and multiply $\sqrt{2}$ by each term inside the parentheses.

$\sqrt{2}(\sqrt{6} - 3\sqrt{2}) = \sqrt{2}(\sqrt{6}) - \sqrt{2}(3\sqrt{2})$ Use the distributive property.

$\qquad\qquad\qquad = \sqrt{2 \cdot 6} - 3\sqrt{2 \cdot 2}$

$\qquad\qquad\qquad = \sqrt{2 \cdot 2 \cdot 3} - 3 \cdot 2$ Use the product rule for radicals.

$\qquad\qquad\qquad = 2\sqrt{3} - 6$

EXAMPLE 4   Multiply.

a. $\sqrt{3}(5 + \sqrt{30})$ **b.** $(\sqrt{5} - \sqrt{6})(\sqrt{7} + 1)$ **c.** $(7\sqrt{x} + 5)(3\sqrt{x} - \sqrt{5})$

d. $(4\sqrt{3} - 1)^2$ **e.** $(\sqrt{2x} - 5)(\sqrt{2x} + 5)$ **f.** $(\sqrt{x - 3} + 5)^2$

Solution

a. $\sqrt{3}(5 + \sqrt{30}) = \sqrt{3}(5) + \sqrt{3}(\sqrt{30})$

$\qquad\qquad\qquad = 5\sqrt{3} + \sqrt{3 \cdot 30}$

$\qquad\qquad\qquad = 5\sqrt{3} + \sqrt{3 \cdot 3 \cdot 10}$

$\qquad\qquad\qquad = 5\sqrt{3} + 3\sqrt{10}$

b. To multiply, we can use the FOIL method.

$\qquad\qquad\qquad\qquad\quad$ First $\qquad$ Outer $\qquad$ Inner $\qquad$ Last

$(\sqrt{5} - \sqrt{6})(\sqrt{7} + 1) = \sqrt{5} \cdot \sqrt{7} + \sqrt{5} \cdot 1 - \sqrt{6} \cdot \sqrt{7} - \sqrt{6} \cdot 1$

$\qquad\qquad\qquad\qquad = \sqrt{35} + \sqrt{5} - \sqrt{42} - \sqrt{6}$

c. $(7\sqrt{x} + 5)(3\sqrt{x} - \sqrt{5}) = 7\sqrt{x}(3\sqrt{x}) - 7\sqrt{x}(\sqrt{5}) + 5(3\sqrt{x}) - 5(\sqrt{5})$

$\qquad\qquad\qquad\qquad\qquad = 21x - 7\sqrt{5x} + 15\sqrt{x} - 5\sqrt{5}$

d. $(4\sqrt{3} - 1)^2 = (4\sqrt{3} - 1)(4\sqrt{3} - 1)$

$\qquad\qquad\qquad = 4\sqrt{3}(4\sqrt{3}) - 4\sqrt{3}(1) - 1(4\sqrt{3}) - 1(-1)$

$\qquad\qquad\qquad = 16 \cdot 3 - 4\sqrt{3} - 4\sqrt{3} + 1$

$\qquad\qquad\qquad = 48 - 8\sqrt{3} + 1$

$\qquad\qquad\qquad = 49 - 8\sqrt{3}$

e. $(\sqrt{2x} - 5)(\sqrt{2x} + 5) = \sqrt{2x} \cdot \sqrt{2x} + 5\sqrt{2x} - 5\sqrt{2x} - 5 \cdot 5$

$$= 2x - 25$$

f. $\underbrace{(\underbrace{\sqrt{x-3}}_{a} + 5)^2}_{} = \underbrace{(\underbrace{\sqrt{x-3}}_{a})^2}_{a^2} + \underbrace{2 \cdot}_{+ \, 2 \, \cdot} \underbrace{\sqrt{x-3}}_{a} \cdot \underbrace{5}_{\cdot \, b} + \underbrace{5^2}_{+ \, b^2}$

$$= x - 3 + 10\sqrt{x-3} + 25 \qquad \text{Simplify.}$$

$$= x + 22 + 10\sqrt{x-3} \qquad \text{Combine like terms.} \qquad \square$$

PRACTICE
4 Multiply.

a. $\sqrt{5}(2 + \sqrt{15})$ **b.** $(\sqrt{2} - \sqrt{5})(\sqrt{6} + 2)$

c. $(3\sqrt{z} - 4)(2\sqrt{z} + 3)$ **d.** $(\sqrt{6} - 3)^2$

e. $(\sqrt{5x} + 3)(\sqrt{5x} - 3)$ **f.** $(\sqrt{x+2} + 3)^2$

VOCABULARY & READINESS CHECK

Complete the table with "Like" or "Unlike."

	Terms	Like or Unlike Radical Terms?
1.	$\sqrt{7}, \sqrt[3]{7}$	
2.	$\sqrt[3]{x^2 y}, \sqrt[3]{y x^2}$	
3.	$\sqrt[3]{abc}, \sqrt[3]{cba}$	
4.	$2x\sqrt{5}, 2x\sqrt{10}$	

Simplify. Assume that all variables represent positive real numbers.

5. $2\sqrt{3} + 4\sqrt{3} =$ _____   **6.** $5\sqrt{7} + 3\sqrt{7} =$ _____   **7.** $8\sqrt{x} - \sqrt{x} =$ _____

8. $3\sqrt{y} - \sqrt{y} =$ _____   **9.** $7\sqrt[3]{x} + \sqrt[3]{x} =$ _____   **10.** $8\sqrt[3]{z} + \sqrt[3]{z} =$ _____

Add or subtract if possible.

11. $\sqrt{11} + \sqrt[3]{11} =$ _____   **12.** $9\sqrt{13} - \sqrt[4]{13} =$ _____

13. $8\sqrt[3]{2x} + 3\sqrt[3]{2x} - \sqrt[3]{2x} =$ _____   **14.** $8\sqrt[3]{2x} + 3\sqrt[3]{2x^2} - \sqrt[3]{2x} =$ _____

7.4 | EXERCISE SET

Add or subtract. See Examples 1 through 3.

1. $\sqrt{8} - \sqrt{32}$

2. $\sqrt{27} - \sqrt{75}$

3. $2\sqrt{2x^3} + 4x\sqrt{8x}$

4. $3\sqrt{45x^3} + x\sqrt{5x}$

5. $2\sqrt{50} - 3\sqrt{125} + \sqrt{98}$

6. $4\sqrt{32} - \sqrt{18} + 2\sqrt{128}$

7. $\sqrt[3]{16x} - \sqrt[3]{54x}$

8. $2\sqrt[3]{3a^4} - 3a\sqrt[3]{81a}$

9. $\sqrt{9b^3} - \sqrt{25b^3} + \sqrt{49b^3}$

10. $\sqrt{4x^7} + 9x^2\sqrt{x^3} - 5x\sqrt{x^5}$

11. $\dfrac{5\sqrt{2}}{3} + \dfrac{2\sqrt{2}}{5}$

12. $\dfrac{\sqrt{3}}{2} + \dfrac{4\sqrt{3}}{3}$

13. $\sqrt[3]{\dfrac{11}{8}} - \dfrac{\sqrt[3]{11}}{6}$

14. $\dfrac{2\sqrt[3]{4}}{7} - \dfrac{\sqrt[3]{4}}{14}$

15. $\dfrac{\sqrt{20x}}{9} + \sqrt{\dfrac{5x}{9}}$

16. $\dfrac{3x\sqrt{7}}{5} + \sqrt{\dfrac{7x^2}{100}}$

17. $7\sqrt{9} - 7 + \sqrt{3}$

18. $\sqrt{16} - 5\sqrt{10} + 7$

19. $2 + 3\sqrt{y^2} - 6\sqrt{y^2} + 5$

20. $3\sqrt{7} - \sqrt[3]{x} + 4\sqrt{7} - 3\sqrt[3]{x}$

21. $3\sqrt{108} - 2\sqrt{18} - 3\sqrt{48}$

22. $-\sqrt{75} + \sqrt{12} - 3\sqrt{3}$

23. $-5\sqrt[3]{625} + \sqrt[3]{40}$

24. $-2\sqrt[3]{108} - \sqrt[3]{32}$

25. $\sqrt{9b^3} - \sqrt{25b^3} + \sqrt{16b^3}$

26. $\sqrt{4x^7y^5} + 9x^2\sqrt{x^3y^5} - 5xy\sqrt{x^5y^3}$

27. $5y\sqrt{8y} + 2\sqrt{50y^3}$

28. $3\sqrt{8x^2y^3} - 2x\sqrt{32y^3}$

29. $\sqrt[3]{54xy^3} - 5\sqrt[3]{2xy^3} + y\sqrt[3]{128x}$

30. $2\sqrt[3]{24x^3y^4} + 4x\sqrt[3]{81y^4}$

31. $6\sqrt[3]{11} + 8\sqrt{11} - 12\sqrt{11}$

32. $3\sqrt[3]{5} + 4\sqrt{5}$

33. $-2\sqrt[4]{x^7} + 3\sqrt[4]{16x^7}$

34. $6\sqrt[3]{24x^3} - 2\sqrt[3]{81x^3} - x\sqrt[3]{3}$

35. $\dfrac{4\sqrt{3}}{3} - \dfrac{\sqrt{12}}{3}$

36. $\dfrac{\sqrt{45}}{10} + \dfrac{7\sqrt{5}}{10}$

37. $\dfrac{\sqrt[3]{8x^4}}{7} + \dfrac{3x\sqrt[3]{x}}{7}$

38. $\dfrac{\sqrt[4]{48}}{5x} - \dfrac{2\sqrt[4]{3}}{10x}$

39. $\sqrt{\dfrac{28}{x^2}} + \sqrt{\dfrac{7}{4x^2}}$

40. $\dfrac{\sqrt{99}}{5x} - \sqrt{\dfrac{44}{x^2}}$

41. $\sqrt[3]{\dfrac{16}{27}} - \dfrac{\sqrt[3]{54}}{6}$

42. $\dfrac{\sqrt[3]{3}}{10} + \sqrt[3]{\dfrac{24}{125}}$

43. $-\dfrac{\sqrt[3]{2x^4}}{9} + \sqrt[3]{\dfrac{250x^4}{27}}$

44. $\dfrac{\sqrt[3]{y^5}}{8} + \dfrac{5y\sqrt[3]{y^2}}{4}$

△ **45.** Find the perimeter of the trapezoid.

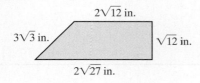

$2\sqrt{12}$ in.

$3\sqrt{3}$ in.

$\sqrt{12}$ in.

$2\sqrt{27}$ in.

△ **46.** Find the perimeter of the triangle.

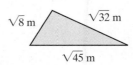

$\sqrt{8}$ m $\sqrt{32}$ m

$\sqrt{45}$ m

Multiply, and then simplify if possible. See Example 4.

47. $\sqrt{7}\left(\sqrt{5} + \sqrt{3}\right)$

48. $\sqrt{5}\left(\sqrt{15} - \sqrt{35}\right)$

49. $\left(\sqrt{5} - \sqrt{2}\right)^2$

50. $\left(3x - \sqrt{2}\right)\left(3x - \sqrt{2}\right)$

51. $\sqrt{3x}\left(\sqrt{3} - \sqrt{x}\right)$

52. $\sqrt{5y}\left(\sqrt{y} + \sqrt{5}\right)$

53. $\left(2\sqrt{x} - 5\right)\left(3\sqrt{x} + 1\right)$

54. $\left(8\sqrt{y} + z\right)\left(4\sqrt{y} - 1\right)$

55. $\left(\sqrt[3]{a} - 4\right)\left(\sqrt[3]{a} + 5\right)$

56. $\left(\sqrt[3]{a} + 2\right)\left(\sqrt[3]{a} + 7\right)$

57. $6\left(\sqrt{2} - 2\right)$

58. $\sqrt{5}\left(6 - \sqrt{5}\right)$

59. $\sqrt{2}\left(\sqrt{2} + x\sqrt{6}\right)$

60. $\sqrt{3}\left(\sqrt{3} - 2\sqrt{5x}\right)$

61. $\left(2\sqrt{7} + 3\sqrt{5}\right)\left(\sqrt{7} - 2\sqrt{5}\right)$

62. $\left(\sqrt{6} - 4\sqrt{2}\right)\left(3\sqrt{6} + \sqrt{2}\right)$

63. $\left(\sqrt{x} - y\right)\left(\sqrt{x} + y\right)$

64. $\left(\sqrt{3x} + 2\right)\left(\sqrt{3x} - 2\right)$

65. $\left(\sqrt{3} + x\right)^2$

66. $\left(\sqrt{y} - 3x\right)^2$

67. $\left(\sqrt{5x} - 2\sqrt{3x}\right)\left(\sqrt{5x} - 3\sqrt{3x}\right)$

68. $\left(5\sqrt{7x} - \sqrt{2x}\right)\left(4\sqrt{7x} + 6\sqrt{2x}\right)$

69. $\left(\sqrt[3]{4} + 2\right)\left(\sqrt[3]{2} - 1\right)$

70. $\left(\sqrt[3]{3} + \sqrt[3]{2}\right)\left(\sqrt[3]{9} - \sqrt[3]{4}\right)$

71. $\left(\sqrt[3]{x} + 1\right)\left(\sqrt[3]{x^2} - \sqrt[3]{x} + 1\right)$

72. $\left(\sqrt[3]{3x} + 2\right)\left(\sqrt[3]{9x^2} - 2\sqrt[3]{3x} + 4\right)$

73. $\left(\sqrt{x - 1} + 5\right)^2$

74. $\left(\sqrt{3x + 1} + 2\right)^2$

75. $\left(\sqrt{2x + 5} - 1\right)^2$

76. $\left(\sqrt{x - 6} - 7\right)^2$

REVIEW AND PREVIEW

Factor each numerator and denominator. Then simplify if possible. See Section 6.1.

77. $\dfrac{2x - 14}{2}$

78. $\dfrac{8x - 24y}{4}$

79. $\dfrac{7x - 7y}{x^2 - y^2}$

80. $\dfrac{x^3 - 8}{4x - 8}$

81. $\dfrac{6a^2b - 9ab}{3ab}$

82. $\dfrac{14r - 28r^2s^2}{7rs}$

83. $\dfrac{-4 + 2\sqrt{3}}{6}$

84. $\dfrac{-5 + 10\sqrt{7}}{5}$

87. **a.** Add: $\sqrt{3} + \sqrt{3}$.
    b. Multiply: $\sqrt{3} \cdot \sqrt{3}$.
    c. Describe the differences in parts **a** and **b**.

88. Multiply: $\left(\sqrt{2} + \sqrt{3} - 1\right)^2$.

89. Explain how simplifying $2x + 3x$ is similar to simplifying $2\sqrt{x} + 3\sqrt{x}$.

90. Explain how multiplying $(x - 2)(x + 3)$ is similar to multiplying $\left(\sqrt{x} - \sqrt{2}\right)\left(\sqrt{x} + 3\right)$.

CONCEPT EXTENSIONS

△ 85. Find the perimeter and area of the rectangle.

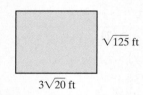

$\sqrt{125}$ ft

$3\sqrt{20}$ ft

△ 86. Find the area and perimeter of the trapezoid. (*Hint:* The area of a trapezoid is the product of half the height $6\sqrt{3}$ meters and the sum of the bases $2\sqrt{63}$ and $7\sqrt{7}$ meters.)

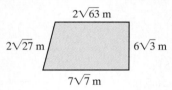

$2\sqrt{63}$ m

$2\sqrt{27}$ m

$6\sqrt{3}$ m

$7\sqrt{7}$ m

📖 **STUDY SKILLS BUILDER**

Have You Decided to Successfully Complete This Course?

Hopefully by now, one of your current goals is to successfully complete this course.

If it is not a goal of yours, ask yourself why? One common reason is fear of failure. Amazingly enough, fear of failure alone can be strong enough to keep many of us from doing our best in any endeavor. Another common reason is that you simply haven't taken the time to make successfully completing this course one of your goals.

Anytime you are registered for a course, successfully completing this course should probably be a goal. How do you do this? Start by writing this goal in your mathematics notebook. Then list steps you will take to ensure success. A great first step is to read or reread Section 1.1 and make a commitment to try the suggestions in this section.

Good luck, and don't forget that a positive attitude will make a big difference.

Let's see how you are doing.

1. Have you made the decision to make "successfully completing this course" a goal of yours? If not, please list reasons that this has not happened. Study your list and talk to your instructor about this.

2. If your answer to Exercise 1 is yes, take a moment and list, in your notebook, further specific goals that will help you achieve this major goal of successfully completing this course. (For example, my goal this semester is not to miss any of my mathematics classes.)

3. Rate your commitment to this course with a number between 1 and 5. Use the diagram below to help.

High Commitment		Average Commitment		Not Committed at All
5	4	3	2	1

4. If you have rated your personal commitment level (from the exercise above) as a 1, 2, or 3, list the reasons why this is so. Then determine whether it is possible to increase your commitment level to a 4 or 5.

7.5 RATIONALIZING DENOMINATORS AND NUMERATORS OF RADICAL EXPRESSIONS

OBJECTIVES

1 Rationalize denominators.

2 Rationalize denominators having two terms.

3 Rationalize numerators.

OBJECTIVE 1 ▶ Rationalizing denominators of radical expressions. Often in mathematics, it is helpful to write a radical expression such as $\dfrac{\sqrt{3}}{\sqrt{2}}$ either without a radical in the denominator or without a radical in the numerator. The process of writing this expression as an equivalent expression but without a radical in the denominator is called **rationalizing the denominator.** To rationalize the denominator of $\dfrac{\sqrt{3}}{\sqrt{2}}$, we use the fundamental principle of fractions and multiply the numerator and the denominator by $\sqrt{2}$. Recall that this is the same as multiplying by $\dfrac{\sqrt{2}}{\sqrt{2}}$, which simplifies to 1.

$$\frac{\sqrt{3}}{\sqrt{2}} = \frac{\sqrt{3} \cdot \sqrt{2}}{\sqrt{2} \cdot \sqrt{2}} = \frac{\sqrt{6}}{\sqrt{4}} = \frac{\sqrt{6}}{2}$$

In this section, we continue to assume that variables represent positive real numbers.

EXAMPLE 1   Rationalize the denominator of each expression.

a. $\dfrac{2}{\sqrt{5}}$ **b.** $\dfrac{2\sqrt{16}}{\sqrt{9x}}$ **c.** $\sqrt[3]{\dfrac{1}{2}}$

Solution

a. To rationalize the denominator, we multiply the numerator and denominator by a factor that makes the radicand in the denominator a perfect square.

$$\frac{2}{\sqrt{5}} = \frac{2 \cdot \sqrt{5}}{\sqrt{5} \cdot \sqrt{5}} = \frac{2\sqrt{5}}{5}$$ The denominator is now rationalized.

b. First, we simplify the radicals and then rationalize the denominator.

$$\frac{2\sqrt{16}}{\sqrt{9x}} = \frac{2(4)}{3\sqrt{x}} = \frac{8}{3\sqrt{x}}$$

To rationalize the denominator, multiply the numerator and denominator by $\sqrt{x}$. Then

$$\frac{8}{3\sqrt{x}} = \frac{8 \cdot \sqrt{x}}{3\sqrt{x} \cdot \sqrt{x}} = \frac{8\sqrt{x}}{3x}$$

c. $\sqrt[3]{\dfrac{1}{2}} = \dfrac{\sqrt[3]{1}}{\sqrt[3]{2}} = \dfrac{1}{\sqrt[3]{2}}$. Now we rationalize the denominator. Since $\sqrt[3]{2}$ is a cube root, we want to multiply by a value that will make the radicand 2 a perfect cube. If we multiply $\sqrt[3]{2}$ by $\sqrt[3]{2^2}$, we get $\sqrt[3]{2^3} = \sqrt[3]{8} = 2$.

$$\frac{1 \cdot \sqrt[3]{2^2}}{\sqrt[3]{2} \cdot \sqrt[3]{2^2}} = \frac{\sqrt[3]{4}}{\sqrt[3]{2^3}} = \frac{\sqrt[3]{4}}{2}$$ Multiply the numerator and denominator by $\sqrt[3]{2^2}$ and then simplify.   □

PRACTICE
1   Rationalize the denominator of each expression.

a. $\dfrac{5}{\sqrt{3}}$ **b.** $\dfrac{3\sqrt{25}}{\sqrt{4x}}$ **c.** $\sqrt[3]{\dfrac{2}{9}}$

Concept Check ✓

Determine by which number both the numerator and denominator can be multiplied to rationalize the denominator of the radical expression.

a. $\dfrac{1}{\sqrt[3]{7}}$ **b.** $\dfrac{1}{\sqrt[4]{8}}$

EXAMPLE 2   Rationalize the denominator of $\sqrt{\dfrac{7x}{3y}}$.

Solution $\sqrt{\dfrac{7x}{3y}} = \dfrac{\sqrt{7x}}{\sqrt{3y}}$ Use the quotient rule. No radical may be simplified further.

$= \dfrac{\sqrt{7x} \cdot \sqrt{3y}}{\sqrt{3y} \cdot \sqrt{3y}}$ Multiply numerator and denominator by $\sqrt{3y}$ so that the radicand in the denominator is a perfect square.

$= \dfrac{\sqrt{21xy}}{3y}$ Use the product rule in the numerator and denominator. Remember that $\sqrt{3y} \cdot \sqrt{3y} = 3y$.   □

PRACTICE
2   Rationalize the denominator of $\sqrt{\dfrac{3z}{5y}}$.

EXAMPLE 3   Rationalize the denominator of $\dfrac{\sqrt[4]{x}}{\sqrt[4]{81y^5}}$.

Solution   First, simplify each radical if possible.

$\dfrac{\sqrt[4]{x}}{\sqrt[4]{81y^5}} = \dfrac{\sqrt[4]{x}}{\sqrt[4]{81y^4} \cdot \sqrt[4]{y}}$ Use the product rule in the denominator.

$= \dfrac{\sqrt[4]{x}}{3y\sqrt[4]{y}}$ Write $\sqrt[4]{81y^4}$ as $3y$.

$= \dfrac{\sqrt[4]{x} \cdot \sqrt[4]{y^3}}{3y\sqrt[4]{y} \cdot \sqrt[4]{y^3}}$ Multiply numerator and denominator by $\sqrt[4]{y^3}$ so that the radicand in the denominator is a perfect fourth power.

$= \dfrac{\sqrt[4]{xy^3}}{3y\sqrt[4]{y^4}}$ Use the product rule in the numerator and denominator.

$= \dfrac{\sqrt[4]{xy^3}}{3y^2}$ In the denominator, $\sqrt[4]{y^4} = y$ and $3y \cdot y = 3y^2$.   □

PRACTICE
3   Rationalize the denominator of $\dfrac{\sqrt[3]{z^2}}{\sqrt[3]{27x^4}}$.

OBJECTIVE 2 ▶ Rationalizing denominators having two terms. Remember the product of the sum and difference of two terms?

$$(a + b)(a - b) = a^2 - b^2$$

These two expressions are called **conjugates** of each other.

Answer to Concept Check:
a. $\sqrt[3]{7^2}$ or $\sqrt[3]{49}$ **b.** $\sqrt[4]{2}$

To rationalize a numerator or denominator that is a sum or difference of two terms, we use conjugates. To see how and why this works, let's rationalize the denominator of the expression $\dfrac{5}{\sqrt{3} - 2}$. To do so, we multiply both the numerator and the denominator by $\sqrt{3} + 2$, the **conjugate** of the denominator $\sqrt{3} - 2$, and see what happens.

$$\frac{5}{\sqrt{3} - 2} = \frac{5(\sqrt{3} + 2)}{(\sqrt{3} - 2)(\sqrt{3} + 2)}$$

$$= \frac{5(\sqrt{3} + 2)}{(\sqrt{3})^2 - 2^2} \qquad \text{Multiply the sum and difference of two terms: } (a + b)(a - b) = a^2 - b^2.$$

$$= \frac{5(\sqrt{3} + 2)}{3 - 4}$$

$$= \frac{5(\sqrt{3} + 2)}{-1}$$

$$= -5(\sqrt{3} + 2) \quad \text{or} \quad -5\sqrt{3} - 10$$

Notice in the denominator that the product of $(\sqrt{3} - 2)$ and its conjugate, $(\sqrt{3} + 2)$, is -1. In general, the product of an expression and its conjugate will contain no radical terms. This is why, when rationalizing a denominator or a numerator containing two terms, we multiply by its conjugate. Examples of conjugates are

$$\sqrt{a} - \sqrt{b} \quad \text{and} \quad \sqrt{a} + \sqrt{b}$$
$$x + \sqrt{y} \quad \text{and} \quad x - \sqrt{y}$$

EXAMPLE 4   Rationalize each denominator.

a. $\dfrac{2}{3\sqrt{2} + 4}$ **b.** $\dfrac{\sqrt{6} + 2}{\sqrt{5} - \sqrt{3}}$ **c.** $\dfrac{2\sqrt{m}}{3\sqrt{x} + \sqrt{m}}$

Solution

a. Multiply the numerator and denominator by the conjugate of the denominator, $3\sqrt{2} + 4$.

$$\frac{2}{3\sqrt{2} + 4} = \frac{2(3\sqrt{2} - 4)}{(3\sqrt{2} + 4)(3\sqrt{2} - 4)}$$

$$= \frac{2(3\sqrt{2} - 4)}{(3\sqrt{2})^2 - 4^2}$$

$$= \frac{2(3\sqrt{2} - 4)}{18 - 16}$$

$$= \frac{2(3\sqrt{2} - 4)}{2}, \quad \text{or} \quad 3\sqrt{2} - 4$$

It is often useful to leave a numerator in factored form to help determine whether the expression can be simplified.

b. Multiply the numerator and denominator by the conjugate of $\sqrt{5} - \sqrt{3}$.

$$\frac{\sqrt{6} + 2}{\sqrt{5} - \sqrt{3}} = \frac{(\sqrt{6} + 2)(\sqrt{5} + \sqrt{3})}{(\sqrt{5} - \sqrt{3})(\sqrt{5} + \sqrt{3})}$$

$$= \frac{\sqrt{6}\sqrt{5} + \sqrt{6}\sqrt{3} + 2\sqrt{5} + 2\sqrt{3}}{(\sqrt{5})^2 - (\sqrt{3})^2}$$

$$= \frac{\sqrt{30} + \sqrt{18} + 2\sqrt{5} + 2\sqrt{3}}{5 - 3}$$

$$= \frac{\sqrt{30} + 3\sqrt{2} + 2\sqrt{5} + 2\sqrt{3}}{2}$$

c. Multiply by the conjugate of $3\sqrt{x} + \sqrt{m}$ to eliminate the radicals from the denominator.

$$\frac{2\sqrt{m}}{3\sqrt{x} + \sqrt{m}} = \frac{2\sqrt{m}(3\sqrt{x} - \sqrt{m})}{(3\sqrt{x} + \sqrt{m})(3\sqrt{x} - \sqrt{m})} = \frac{6\sqrt{mx} - 2m}{(3\sqrt{x})^2 - (\sqrt{m})^2}$$

$$= \frac{6\sqrt{mx} - 2m}{9x - m}$$

PRACTICE
4   Rationalize the denominator.

a. $\dfrac{5}{3\sqrt{5} + 2}$ **b.** $\dfrac{\sqrt{2} + 5}{\sqrt{3} - \sqrt{5}}$ **c.** $\dfrac{3\sqrt{x}}{2\sqrt{x} + \sqrt{y}}$

OBJECTIVE 3 ▶ Rationalizing numerators. As mentioned earlier, it is also often helpful to write an expression such as $\dfrac{\sqrt{3}}{\sqrt{2}}$ as an equivalent expression without a radical in the numerator. This process is called **rationalizing the numerator.** To rationalize the numerator of $\dfrac{\sqrt{3}}{\sqrt{2}}$, we multiply the numerator and the denominator by $\sqrt{3}$.

$$\frac{\sqrt{3}}{\sqrt{2}} = \frac{\sqrt{3} \cdot \sqrt{3}}{\sqrt{2} \cdot \sqrt{3}} = \frac{\sqrt{9}}{\sqrt{6}} = \frac{3}{\sqrt{6}}$$

EXAMPLE 5   Rationalize the numerator of $\dfrac{\sqrt{7}}{\sqrt{45}}$.

Solution   First we simplify $\sqrt{45}$.

$$\frac{\sqrt{7}}{\sqrt{45}} = \frac{\sqrt{7}}{\sqrt{9 \cdot 5}} = \frac{\sqrt{7}}{3\sqrt{5}}$$

Next we rationalize the numerator by multiplying the numerator and the denominator by $\sqrt{7}$.

$$\frac{\sqrt{7}}{3\sqrt{5}} = \frac{\sqrt{7} \cdot \sqrt{7}}{3\sqrt{5} \cdot \sqrt{7}} = \frac{7}{3\sqrt{5 \cdot 7}} = \frac{7}{3\sqrt{35}}$$

PRACTICE
5   Rationalize the numerator of $\dfrac{\sqrt{32}}{\sqrt{80}}$.

EXAMPLE 6   Rationalize the numerator of $\dfrac{\sqrt[3]{2x^2}}{\sqrt[3]{5y}}$.

Solution   The numerator and the denominator of this expression are already simplified. To rationalize the numerator, $\sqrt[3]{2x^2}$, we multiply the numerator and denominator by a factor that will make the radicand a perfect cube. If we multiply $\sqrt[3]{2x^2}$ by $\sqrt[3]{4x}$, we get $\sqrt[3]{8x^3} = 2x$.

$$\frac{\sqrt[3]{2x^2}}{\sqrt[3]{5y}} = \frac{\sqrt[3]{2x^2} \cdot \sqrt[3]{4x}}{\sqrt[3]{5y} \cdot \sqrt[3]{4x}} = \frac{\sqrt[3]{8x^3}}{\sqrt[3]{20xy}} = \frac{2x}{\sqrt[3]{20xy}}$$ □

PRACTICE
6   Rationalize the numerator of $\dfrac{\sqrt[3]{5b}}{\sqrt[3]{2a}}$.

EXAMPLE 7   Rationalize the numerator of $\dfrac{\sqrt{x} + 2}{5}$.

Solution   We multiply the numerator and the denominator by the conjugate of the numerator, $\sqrt{x} + 2$.

$$\frac{\sqrt{x} + 2}{5} = \frac{(\sqrt{x} + 2)(\sqrt{x} - 2)}{5(\sqrt{x} - 2)} \qquad \text{Multiply by } \sqrt{x} - 2, \text{ the conjugate of } \sqrt{x} + 2.$$

$$= \frac{(\sqrt{x})^2 - 2^2}{5(\sqrt{x} - 2)} \qquad (a + b)(a - b) = a^2 - b^2$$

$$= \frac{x - 4}{5(\sqrt{x} - 2)}$$ □

PRACTICE
7   Rationalize the numerator of $\dfrac{\sqrt{x} - 3}{4}$.

VOCABULARY & READINESS CHECK

Use the choices below to fill in each blank. Not all choices will be used.

rationalizing the numerator   conjugate $\dfrac{\sqrt{3}}{\sqrt{3}}$

rationalizing the denominator $\dfrac{5}{5}$

1. The _____ of $a + b$ is $a - b$.

2. The process of writing an equivalent expression, but without a radical in the denominator is called
_____.

3. The process of writing an equivalent expression, but without a radical in the numerator is called
_____.

4. To rationalize the denominator of $\dfrac{5}{\sqrt{3}}$, we multiply by _____.

Find the conjugate of each expression.

5. $\sqrt{2} + x$ **6.** $\sqrt{3} + y$ **7.** $5 - \sqrt{a}$ **8.** $6 - \sqrt{b}$

9. $-7\sqrt{5} + 8\sqrt{x}$ **10.** $-9\sqrt{2} - 6\sqrt{y}$

7.5 EXERCISE SET

PRACTICE   WATCH   DOWNLOAD   READ   REVIEW

Rationalize each denominator. See Examples 1 through 3.

1. $\dfrac{\sqrt{2}}{\sqrt{7}}$

2. $\dfrac{\sqrt{3}}{\sqrt{2}}$

3. $\sqrt{\dfrac{1}{5}}$

4. $\sqrt{\dfrac{1}{2}}$

5. $\sqrt{\dfrac{4}{x}}$

6. $\sqrt{\dfrac{25}{y}}$

7. $\dfrac{4}{\sqrt[3]{3}}$

8. $\dfrac{6}{\sqrt[3]{9}}$

9. $\dfrac{3}{\sqrt{8x}}$

10. $\dfrac{5}{\sqrt{27a}}$

11. $\dfrac{3}{\sqrt[3]{4x^2}}$

12. $\dfrac{5}{\sqrt[3]{3y}}$

13. $\dfrac{9}{\sqrt{3a}}$

14. $\dfrac{x}{\sqrt{5}}$

15. $\dfrac{3}{\sqrt[3]{2}}$

16. $\dfrac{5}{\sqrt[3]{9}}$

17. $\dfrac{2\sqrt{3}}{\sqrt{7}}$

18. $\dfrac{-5\sqrt{2}}{\sqrt{11}}$

19. $\sqrt{\dfrac{2x}{5y}}$

20. $\sqrt{\dfrac{13a}{2b}}$

21. $\sqrt[3]{\dfrac{3}{5}}$

22. $\sqrt[3]{\dfrac{7}{10}}$

23. $\sqrt{\dfrac{3x}{50}}$

24. $\sqrt{\dfrac{11y}{45}}$

25. $\dfrac{1}{\sqrt{12z}}$

26. $\dfrac{1}{\sqrt{32x}}$

27. $\dfrac{\sqrt[3]{2y^2}}{\sqrt[3]{9x^2}}$

28. $\dfrac{\sqrt[3]{3x}}{\sqrt[3]{4y^4}}$

29. $\sqrt[4]{\dfrac{81}{8}}$

30. $\sqrt[4]{\dfrac{1}{9}}$

31. $\sqrt[4]{\dfrac{16}{9x^7}}$

32. $\sqrt[5]{\dfrac{32}{m^6 n^{13}}}$

33. $\dfrac{5a}{\sqrt[5]{8a^9 b^{11}}}$

34. $\dfrac{9y}{\sqrt[4]{4y^9}}$

Rationalize each denominator. See Example 4.

35. $\dfrac{6}{2 - \sqrt{7}}$

36. $\dfrac{3}{\sqrt{7} - 4}$

37. $\dfrac{-7}{\sqrt{x} - 3}$

38. $\dfrac{-8}{\sqrt{y} + 4}$

39. $\dfrac{\sqrt{2} - \sqrt{3}}{\sqrt{2} + \sqrt{3}}$

40. $\dfrac{\sqrt{3} + \sqrt{4}}{\sqrt{2} - \sqrt{3}}$

41. $\dfrac{\sqrt{a} + 1}{2\sqrt{a} - \sqrt{b}}$

42. $\dfrac{2\sqrt{a} - 3}{2\sqrt{a} + \sqrt{b}}$

43. $\dfrac{8}{1 + \sqrt{10}}$

44. $\dfrac{-3}{\sqrt{6} - 2}$

45. $\dfrac{\sqrt{x}}{\sqrt{x} + \sqrt{y}}$

46. $\dfrac{2\sqrt{a}}{2\sqrt{x} - \sqrt{y}}$

47. $\dfrac{2\sqrt{3} + \sqrt{6}}{4\sqrt{3} - \sqrt{6}}$

48. $\dfrac{4\sqrt{5} + \sqrt{2}}{2\sqrt{5} - \sqrt{2}}$

Rationalize each numerator. See Examples 5 and 6.

49. $\sqrt{\dfrac{5}{3}}$

50. $\sqrt{\dfrac{3}{2}}$

51. $\sqrt{\dfrac{18}{5}}$

52. $\sqrt{\dfrac{12}{7}}$

53. $\dfrac{\sqrt{4x}}{7}$

54. $\dfrac{\sqrt{3x^5}}{6}$

55. $\dfrac{\sqrt[3]{5y^2}}{\sqrt[3]{4x}}$

56. $\dfrac{\sqrt[3]{4x}}{\sqrt[3]{z^4}}$

57. $\sqrt{\dfrac{2}{5}}$

58. $\sqrt{\dfrac{3}{7}}$

59. $\dfrac{\sqrt{2x}}{11}$

60. $\dfrac{\sqrt{y}}{7}$

61. $\sqrt[3]{\dfrac{7}{8}}$

62. $\sqrt[3]{\dfrac{25}{2}}$

63. $\dfrac{\sqrt[3]{3x^5}}{10}$

64. $\sqrt[3]{\dfrac{9y}{7}}$

65. $\sqrt{\dfrac{18x^4 y^6}{3z}}$

66. $\sqrt{\dfrac{8x^5 y}{2z}}$

67. When rationalizing the denominator of $\dfrac{\sqrt{5}}{\sqrt{7}}$, explain why both the numerator and the denominator must be multiplied by $\sqrt{7}$.

68. When rationalizing the numerator of $\dfrac{\sqrt{5}}{\sqrt{7}}$, explain why both the numerator and the denominator must be multiplied by $\sqrt{5}$.

Rationalize each numerator. See Example 7.

69. $\dfrac{2 - \sqrt{11}}{6}$

70. $\dfrac{\sqrt{15} + 1}{2}$

71. $\dfrac{2 - \sqrt{7}}{-5}$

72. $\dfrac{\sqrt{5} + 2}{\sqrt{2}}$

73. $\dfrac{\sqrt{x} + 3}{\sqrt{x}}$

74. $\dfrac{5 + \sqrt{2}}{\sqrt{2x}}$

75. $\dfrac{\sqrt{2} - 1}{\sqrt{2} + 1}$

76. $\dfrac{\sqrt{8} - \sqrt{3}}{\sqrt{2} + \sqrt{3}}$

77. $\dfrac{\sqrt{x} + 1}{\sqrt{x} - 1}$

78. $\dfrac{\sqrt{x} + \sqrt{y}}{\sqrt{x} - \sqrt{y}}$

REVIEW AND PREVIEW

Solve each equation. See Sections 2.1 and 5.8.

79. $2x - 7 = 3(x - 4)$ **80.** $9x - 4 = 7(x - 2)$

81. $(x - 6)(2x + 1) = 0$ **82.** $(y + 2)(5y + 4) = 0$

83. $x^2 - 8x = -12$ **84.** $x^3 = x$

CONCEPTS EXTENSIONS

Determine the smallest number both the numerator and denominator should be multiplied by to rationalize the denominator of the radical expression. See the Concept Check in this section.

85. $\dfrac{9}{\sqrt[3]{5}}$ **86.** $\dfrac{5}{\sqrt{27}}$

△ **87.** The formula of the radius r of a sphere with surface area A is

$$r = \sqrt{\dfrac{A}{4\pi}}$$

Rationalize the denominator of the radical expression in this formula.

△ **88.** The formula for the radius r of a cone with height 7 centimeters and volume V is

$$r = \sqrt{\dfrac{3V}{7\pi}}$$

Rationalize the numerator of the radical expression in this formula.

7 cm

r

89. Explain why rationalizing the denominator does not change the value of the original expression.

90. Explain why rationalizing the numerator does not change the value of the original expression.

INTEGRATED REVIEW   RADICALS AND RATIONAL EXPONENTS

Sections 7.1–7.5

Find each root. Throughout this review, assume that all variables represent positive real numbers.

1. $\sqrt{81}$ **2.** $\sqrt[3]{-8}$ **3.** $\sqrt[4]{\dfrac{1}{16}}$ **4.** $\sqrt{x^6}$

5. $\sqrt[3]{y^9}$ **6.** $\sqrt{4y^{10}}$ **7.** $\sqrt[5]{-32y^5}$ **8.** $\sqrt[4]{81b^{12}}$

Use radical notation to rewrite each expression. Simplify if possible.

9. $36^{1/2}$ **10.** $(3y)^{1/4}$ **11.** $64^{-2/3}$ **12.** $(x + 1)^{3/5}$

Use the properties of exponents to simplify each expression. Write with positive exponents.

13. $y^{-1/6} \cdot y^{7/6}$ **14.** $\dfrac{(2x^{1/3})^4}{x^{5/6}}$ **15.** $\dfrac{x^{1/4}x^{3/4}}{x^{-1/4}}$ **16.** $4^{1/3} \cdot 4^{2/5}$

Use rational exponents to simplify each radical.

17. $\sqrt[3]{8x^6}$ **18.** $\sqrt[12]{a^9b^6}$

Use rational exponents to write each as a single radical expression.

19. $\sqrt[4]{x} \cdot \sqrt{x}$ **20.** $\sqrt{5} \cdot \sqrt[3]{2}$

Simplify.

21. $\sqrt{40}$ **22.** $\sqrt[4]{16x^7y^{10}}$ **23.** $\sqrt[3]{54x^4}$ **24.** $\sqrt[5]{-64b^{10}}$

Multiply or divide. Then simplify if possible.

25. $\sqrt{5} \cdot \sqrt{x}$

26. $\sqrt[3]{8x} \cdot \sqrt[3]{8x^2}$

27. $\dfrac{\sqrt{98y^6}}{\sqrt{2y}}$

28. $\dfrac{\sqrt[4]{48a^9b^3}}{\sqrt[4]{ab^3}}$

Perform each indicated operation.

29. $\sqrt{20} - \sqrt{75} + 5\sqrt{7}$

30. $\sqrt[3]{54y^4} - y\sqrt[3]{16y}$

31. $\sqrt{3}\left(\sqrt{5} - \sqrt{2}\right)$

32. $\left(\sqrt{7} + \sqrt{3}\right)^2$

33. $\left(2x - \sqrt{5}\right)\left(2x + \sqrt{5}\right)$

34. $\left(\sqrt{x + 1} - 1\right)^2$

Rationalize each denominator.

35. $\sqrt{\dfrac{7}{3}}$

36. $\dfrac{5}{\sqrt[3]{2x^2}}$

37. $\dfrac{\sqrt{3} - \sqrt{7}}{2\sqrt{3} + \sqrt{7}}$

Rationalize each numerator.

38. $\sqrt{\dfrac{7}{3}}$

39. $\sqrt[3]{\dfrac{9y}{11}}$

40. $\dfrac{\sqrt{x} - 2}{\sqrt{x}}$

7.6 | RADICAL EQUATIONS AND PROBLEM SOLVING

OBJECTIVES

1 Solve equations that contain radical expressions.

2 Use the Pythagorean theorem to model problems.

OBJECTIVE 1 ▶ Solving equations that contain radical expressions. In this section, we present techniques to solve equations containing radical expressions such as

$$\sqrt{2x - 3} = 9$$

We use the power rule to help us solve these radical equations.

> **Power Rule**
>
> If both sides of an equation are raised to the same power, **all** solutions of the original equation are **among** the solutions of the new equation.

This property *does not* say that raising both sides of an equation to a power yields an equivalent equation. A solution of the new equation *may or may not* be a solution of the original equation. For example, $(-2)^2 = 2^2$, but $-2 \neq 2$. Thus, *each solution of the new equation must be checked* to make sure it is a solution of the original equation. Recall that a proposed solution that is not a solution of the original equation is called an **extraneous solution.**

EXAMPLE 1 Solve: $\sqrt{2x - 3} = 9$.

Solution We use the power rule to square both sides of the equation to eliminate the radical.

$$\sqrt{2x - 3} = 9$$
$$\left(\sqrt{2x - 3}\right)^2 = 9^2$$
$$2x - 3 = 81$$
$$2x = 84$$
$$x = 42$$

Now we, check the solution in the original equation.

Check:

$$\sqrt{2x - 3} = 9$$
$$\sqrt{2(42) - 3} \stackrel{?}{=} 9 \quad \text{Let } x = 42.$$
$$\sqrt{84 - 3} \stackrel{?}{=} 9$$
$$\sqrt{81} \stackrel{?}{=} 9$$
$$9 = 9 \quad \text{True}$$

The solution checks, so we conclude that the solution is 42 or the solution set is {42}. $\square$

PRACTICE
1 Solve: $\sqrt{3x - 5} = 7$.

To solve a radical equation, first isolate a radical on one side of the equation.

EXAMPLE 2 Solve: $\sqrt{-10x - 1} + 3x = 0$.

Solution First, isolate the radical on one side of the equation. To do this, we subtract $3x$ from both sides.

$$\sqrt{-10x - 1} + 3x = 0$$
$$\sqrt{-10x - 1} + 3x - 3x = 0 - 3x$$
$$\sqrt{-10x - 1} = -3x$$

Next we use the power rule to eliminate the radical.

$$\left(\sqrt{-10x - 1}\right)^2 = (-3x)^2$$
$$-10x - 1 = 9x^2$$

Since this is a quadratic equation, we can set the equation equal to 0 and try to solve by factoring.

$$9x^2 + 10x + 1 = 0$$
$$(9x + 1)(x + 1) = 0 \quad \text{Factor.}$$
$$9x + 1 = 0 \quad \text{or} \quad x + 1 = 0 \quad \text{Set each factor equal to 0.}$$
$$x = -\frac{1}{9} \quad \text{or} \quad x = -1$$

Check: Let $x = -\frac{1}{9}$.

$$\sqrt{-10x - 1} + 3x = 0$$
$$\sqrt{-10\left(-\frac{1}{9}\right) - 1} + 3\left(-\frac{1}{9}\right) \stackrel{?}{=} 0$$
$$\sqrt{\frac{10}{9} - \frac{9}{9}} - \frac{3}{9} \stackrel{?}{=} 0$$
$$\sqrt{\frac{1}{9}} - \frac{1}{3} \stackrel{?}{=} 0$$
$$\frac{1}{3} - \frac{1}{3} = 0 \quad \text{True}$$

Let $x = -1$.

$$\sqrt{-10x - 1} + 3x = 0$$
$$\sqrt{-10(-1) - 1} + 3(-1) \stackrel{?}{=} 0$$
$$\sqrt{10 - 1} - 3 \stackrel{?}{=} 0$$
$$\sqrt{9} - 3 \stackrel{?}{=} 0$$
$$3 - 3 = 0 \quad \text{True}$$

Both solutions check. The solutions are $-\frac{1}{9}$ and -1 or the solution set is $\left\{-\frac{1}{9}, -1\right\}$.

$\square$

PRACTICE
2 Solve: $\sqrt{3 - 2x} - 4x = 0$.

The following steps may be used to solve a radical equation.

Solving a Radical Equation

STEP 1. Isolate one radical on one side of the equation.

STEP 2. Raise each side of the equation to a power equal to the index of the radical and simplify.

STEP 3. If the equation still contains a radical term, repeat Steps 1 and 2. If not, solve the equation.

STEP 4. Check all proposed solutions in the original equation.

EXAMPLE 3   Solve: $\sqrt[3]{x + 1} + 5 = 3$.

Solution   First we isolate the radical by subtracting 5 from both sides of the equation.

$$\sqrt[3]{x + 1} + 5 = 3$$
$$\sqrt[3]{x + 1} = -2$$

Next we raise both sides of the equation to the third power to eliminate the radical.

$$\left(\sqrt[3]{x + 1}\right)^3 = (-2)^3$$
$$x + 1 = -8$$
$$x = -9$$

The solution checks in the original equation, so the solution is -9. □

PRACTICE
3   Solve: $\sqrt[3]{x - 2} + 1 = 3$.

EXAMPLE 4   Solve: $\sqrt{4 - x} = x - 2$.

Solution

$$\sqrt{4 - x} = x - 2$$
$$\left(\sqrt{4 - x}\right)^2 = (x - 2)^2$$
$$4 - x = x^2 - 4x + 4$$
$$x^2 - 3x = 0 \qquad \text{Write the quadratic equation in standard form.}$$
$$x(x - 3) = 0 \qquad \text{Factor.}$$
$$x = 0 \quad \text{or} \quad x - 3 = 0 \qquad \text{Set each factor equal to 0.}$$
$$x = 3$$

Check:

$$\sqrt{4 - x} = x - 2 \qquad\qquad \sqrt{4 - x} = x - 2$$
$$\sqrt{4 - 0} \stackrel{?}{=} 0 - 2 \quad \text{Let } x = 0. \qquad \sqrt{4 - 3} \stackrel{?}{=} 3 - 2 \quad \text{Let } x = 3.$$
$$2 = -2 \qquad \text{False} \qquad\qquad 1 = 1 \qquad \text{True}$$

The proposed solution 3 checks, but 0 does not. Since 0 is an extraneous solution, the only solution is 3. □

PRACTICE
4   Solve: $\sqrt{16 + x} = x - 4$.

▶ **Helpful Hint**

In Example 4, notice that $(x - 2)^2 = x^2 - 4x + 4$. Make sure binomials are squared correctly.

Concept Check ☑

How can you immediately tell that the equation $\sqrt{2y + 3} = -4$ has no real solution?

EXAMPLE 5   Solve: $\sqrt{2x + 5} + \sqrt{2x} = 3$.

Solution   We get one radical alone by subtracting $\sqrt{2x}$ from both sides.

$$\sqrt{2x + 5} + \sqrt{2x} = 3$$
$$\sqrt{2x + 5} = 3 - \sqrt{2x}$$

Now we use the power rule to begin eliminating the radicals. First we square both sides.

$$\left(\sqrt{2x + 5}\right)^2 = \left(3 - \sqrt{2x}\right)^2$$

$$2x + 5 = 9 - 6\sqrt{2x} + 2x \quad \text{Multiply } \left(3 - \sqrt{2x}\right)\left(3 - \sqrt{2x}\right).$$

There is still a radical in the equation, so we get a radical alone again. Then we square both sides.

$$2x + 5 = 9 - 6\sqrt{2x} + 2x \quad \text{Get the radical alone.}$$
$$6\sqrt{2x} = 4$$
$$36(2x) = 16 \qquad\qquad \text{Square both sides of the equation to eliminate the radical.}$$
$$72x = 16 \qquad\qquad \text{Multiply.}$$
$$x = \frac{16}{72} \qquad\qquad \text{Solve.}$$
$$x = \frac{2}{9} \qquad\qquad \text{Simplify.}$$

The proposed solution, $\frac{2}{9}$, checks in the original equation. The solution is $\frac{2}{9}$.   □

PRACTICE
5   Solve: $\sqrt{8x + 1} + \sqrt{3x} = 2$.

▶ **Helpful Hint**

Make sure expressions are squared correctly. In Example 5, we squared $\left(3 - \sqrt{2x}\right)$ as

$$\left(3 - \sqrt{2x}\right)^2 = \left(3 - \sqrt{2x}\right)\left(3 - \sqrt{2x}\right)$$
$$= 3 \cdot 3 - 3\sqrt{2x} - 3\sqrt{2x} + \sqrt{2x} \cdot \sqrt{2x}$$
$$= 9 - 6\sqrt{2x} + 2x$$

Concept Check ☑

What is wrong with the following solution?

$$\sqrt{2x + 5} + \sqrt{4 - x} = 8$$
$$\left(\sqrt{2x + 5} + \sqrt{4 - x}\right)^2 = 8^2$$
$$(2x + 5) + (4 - x) = 64$$
$$x + 9 = 64$$
$$x = 55$$

Answers to Concept Check:
answers may vary

$\left(\sqrt{2x + 5} + \sqrt{4 - x}\right)^2$ is not $(2x + 5) + (4 - x)$.

OBJECTIVE 2 ▶ **Using the pythagorean theorem.**   Recall that the Pythagorean theorem states that in a right triangle, the length of the hypotenuse squared equals the sum of the lengths of each of the legs squared.

Pythagorean Theorem

If a and b are the lengths of the legs of a right triangle and c is the length of the hypotenuse, then $a^2 + b^2 = c^2$.

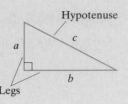

Hypotenuse

c

a

b

Legs

△ **EXAMPLE 6** Find the length of the unknown leg of the right triangle.

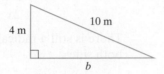

10 m

4 m

b

Solution In the formula $a^2 + b^2 = c^2$, c is the hypotenuse. Here, $c = 10$, the length of the hypotenuse, and $a = 4$. We solve for b. Then $a^2 + b^2 = c^2$ becomes

$$4^2 + b^2 = 10^2$$
$$16 + b^2 = 100$$
$$b^2 = 84 \quad \text{Subtract 16 from both sides.}$$
$$b = \pm\sqrt{84} = \pm\sqrt{4 \cdot 21} = \pm 2\sqrt{21}$$

Since b is a length and thus is positive, we will use the positive value only.

The unknown leg of the triangle is $2\sqrt{21}$ meters long. ☐

PRACTICE
6 Find the length of the unknown leg of the right triangle.

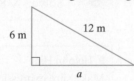

12 m

6 m

a

△ **EXAMPLE 7** **Calculating Placement of a Wire**

A 50-foot supporting wire is to be attached to a 75-foot antenna. Because of surrounding buildings, sidewalks, and roadways, the wire must be anchored exactly 20 feet from the base of the antenna.

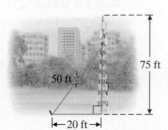

75 ft

50 ft

←20 ft→

50 ft x ft

←20 ft→

a. How high from the base of the antenna is the wire attached?

b. Local regulations require that a supporting wire be attached at a height no less than $\frac{3}{5}$ of the total height of the antenna. From part **a,** have local regulations been met?

Solution

1. **UNDERSTAND.** Read and reread the problem. From the diagram we notice that a right triangle is formed with hypotenuse 50 feet and one leg 20 feet. Let x be the height from the base of the antenna to the attached wire.

2. **TRANSLATE.** Use the Pythagorean theorem.

$$a^2 + b^2 = c^2$$
$$20^2 + x^2 = 50^2 \quad a = 20, c = 50$$

3. **SOLVE.**

$$20^2 + x^2 = 50^2$$
$$400 + x^2 = 2500$$
$$x^2 = 2100 \qquad \text{Subtract 400 from both sides.}$$
$$x = \pm\sqrt{2100}$$
$$= \pm 10\sqrt{21}$$

4. **INTERPRET.** *Check* the work and *state* the solution.

Check: We will use only the positive value, $x = 10\sqrt{21}$ because x represents length. The wire is attached exactly $10\sqrt{21}$ feet from the base of the pole, or approximately 45.8 feet.

State: The supporting wire must be attached at a height no less than $\frac{3}{5}$ of the total height of the antenna. This height is $\frac{3}{5}$(75 feet), or 45 feet. Since we know from part **a** that the wire is to be attached at a height of approximately 45.8 feet, local regulations have been met.   □

PRACTICE
7   Keith Robinson bought two Siamese fighting fish, but when he got home he found he only had one rectangular tank that was 12 in. long, 7 in. wide, and 5 in. deep. Since the fish must be kept separated, he needed to insert a plastic divider in the diagonal of the tank. He already has a piece that is 5 in. in one dimension, but how long must it be to fit corner to corner in the tank?

Graphing Calculator Explorations

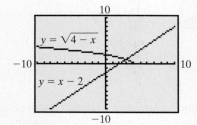

We can use a graphing calculator to solve radical equations. For example, to use a graphing calculator to approximate the solutions of the equation solved in Example 4, we graph the following.

$$Y_1 = \sqrt{4 - x} \qquad \text{and} \qquad Y_2 = x - 2$$

The x-value of the point of intersection is the solution. Use the Intersect feature or the Zoom and Trace features of your graphing calculator to see that the solution is 3.

Use a graphing calculator to solve each radical equation. Round all solutions to the nearest hundredth.

1. $\sqrt{x + 7} = x$

2. $\sqrt{3x + 5} = 2x$

3. $\sqrt{2x + 1} = \sqrt{2x + 2}$

4. $\sqrt{10x - 1} = \sqrt{-10x + 10} - 1$

5. $1.2x = \sqrt{3.1x + 5}$

6. $\sqrt{1.9x^2 - 2.2} = -0.8x + 3$

VOCABULARY & READINESS CHECK

Use the choices below to fill in each blank. Not all choices will be used.

hypotenuse	right	$x^2 + 25$	$16 - 8\sqrt{7x} + 7x$
extraneous solution	legs	$x^2 - 10x + 25$	$16 + 7x$

1. A proposed solution that is not a solution of the original equation is called an _____.
2. The Pythagorean Theorem states that $a^2 + b^2 = c^2$ where a and b are the lengths of the _____ of a _____ triangle and c is the length of the _____.
3. The square of $x - 5$, or $(x - 5)^2 = $ _____.
4. The square of $4 - \sqrt{7x}$, or $(4 - \sqrt{7x})^2 = $ _____.

7.6 EXERCISE SET

MyMathLab® Powered by CourseCompass® and MathXL®

     PRACTICE WATCH DOWNLOAD READ REVIEW

Solve. See Examples 1 and 2.

1. $\sqrt{2x} = 4$
2. $\sqrt{3x} = 3$
3. $\sqrt{x - 3} = 2$
4. $\sqrt{x + 1} = 5$
5. $\sqrt{2x} = -4$
6. $\sqrt{5x} = -5$
7. $\sqrt{4x - 3} - 5 = 0$
8. $\sqrt{x - 3} - 1 = 0$
9. $\sqrt{2x - 3} - 2 = 1$
10. $\sqrt{3x + 3} - 4 = 8$

Solve. See Example 3.

11. $\sqrt[3]{6x} = -3$
12. $\sqrt[3]{4x} = -2$
13. $\sqrt[3]{x - 2} - 3 = 0$
14. $\sqrt[3]{2x - 6} - 4 = 0$

Solve. See Examples 4 and 5.

15. $\sqrt{13 - x} = x - 1$
16. $\sqrt{2x - 3} = 3 - x$
17. $x - \sqrt{4 - 3x} = -8$
18. $2x + \sqrt{x + 1} = 8$
19. $\sqrt{y + 5} = 2 - \sqrt{y - 4}$
20. $\sqrt{x + 3} + \sqrt{x - 5} = 3$
21. $\sqrt{x - 3} + \sqrt{x + 2} = 5$
22. $\sqrt{2x - 4} - \sqrt{3x + 4} = -2$

MIXED PRACTICE

Solve. See Examples 1 through 5.

23. $\sqrt{3x - 2} = 5$
24. $\sqrt{5x - 4} = 9$
25. $-\sqrt{2x} + 4 = -6$
26. $-\sqrt{3x + 9} = -12$
27. $\sqrt{3x + 1} + 2 = 0$
28. $\sqrt{3x + 1} - 2 = 0$
29. $\sqrt[4]{4x + 1} - 2 = 0$
30. $\sqrt[4]{2x - 9} - 3 = 0$
31. $\sqrt{4x - 3} = 7$
32. $\sqrt{3x + 9} = 6$
33. $\sqrt[3]{6x - 3} - 3 = 0$
34. $\sqrt[3]{3x + 4} = 7$
35. $\sqrt[3]{2x - 3} - 2 = -5$
36. $\sqrt[3]{x - 4} - 5 = -7$
37. $\sqrt{x + 4} = \sqrt{2x - 5}$
38. $\sqrt{3y + 6} = \sqrt{7y - 6}$
39. $x - \sqrt{1 - x} = -5$
40. $x - \sqrt{x - 2} = 4$
41. $\sqrt[3]{-6x - 1} = \sqrt[3]{-2x - 5}$
42. $\sqrt[3]{-4x - 3} = \sqrt[3]{-x - 15}$

43. $\sqrt{5x - 1} - \sqrt{x + 2} = 3$
44. $\sqrt{2x - 1} - 4 = -\sqrt{x - 4}$
45. $\sqrt{2x - 1} = \sqrt{1 - 2x}$
46. $\sqrt{7x - 4} = \sqrt{4 - 7x}$
47. $\sqrt{3x + 4} - 1 = \sqrt{2x + 1}$
48. $\sqrt{x - 2} + 3 = \sqrt{4x + 1}$
49. $\sqrt{y + 3} - \sqrt{y - 3} = 1$
50. $\sqrt{x + 1} - \sqrt{x - 1} = 2$

Find the length of the unknown side of each triangle. See Example 6.

△ 51.

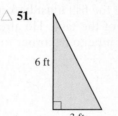

6 ft

3 ft

△ 52.

7 in.

8 in.

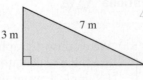

△ 53.

3 m

7 m

△ 54.

4 cm

7 cm

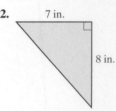

Find the length of the unknown side of each triangle. Give the exact length and a one-decimal-place approximation. See Example 6.

△ 55.

9 m

$11\sqrt{5}$ m

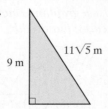

△ 56.

$5\sqrt{3}$ cm

10 cm

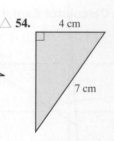

57.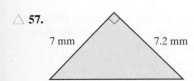

7 mm   7.2 mm

58.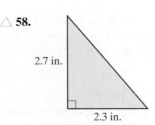

2.7 in.

2.3 in.

Solve. See Example 7. Give exact answers and two-decimal-place approximations where appropriate.

59. A wire is needed to support a vertical pole 15 feet high. The cable will be anchored to a stake 8 feet from the base of the pole. How much cable is needed?

15 ft

8 ft

60. The tallest structure in the United States is a TV tower in Blanchard, North Dakota. Its height is 2063 feet. A 2382-foot length of wire is to be used as a guy wire attached to the top of the tower. Approximate to the nearest foot how far from the base of the tower the guy wire must be anchored. (*Source:* U.S. Geological Survey)

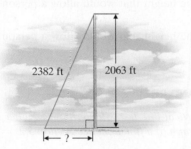

2382 ft   2063 ft

?

61. A spotlight is mounted on the eaves of a house 12 feet above the ground. A flower bed runs between the house and the sidewalk, so the closest the ladder can be placed to the house is 5 feet. How long a ladder is needed so that an electrician can reach the place where the light is mounted?

12 ft

5 ft

62. A wire is to be attached to support a telephone pole. Because of surrounding buildings, sidewalks, and roadways, the wire must be anchored exactly 15 feet from the base of the pole. Telephone company workers have only 30 feet of cable, and 2 feet of that must be used to attach the cable to the pole and

to the stake on the ground. How high from the base of the pole can the wire be attached?

15 ft

63. The radius of the Moon is 1080 miles. Use the formula for the radius *r* of a sphere given its surface area *A*,

$$r = \sqrt{\frac{A}{4\pi}}$$

to find the surface area of the Moon. Round to the nearest square mile. (*Source:* National Space Science Data Center)

64. Police departments find it very useful to be able to approximate the speed of a car when they are given the distance that the car skidded before it came to a stop. If the road surface is wet concrete, the function $S(x) = \sqrt{10.5x}$ is used, where $S(x)$ is the speed of the car in miles per hour and *x* is the distance skidded in feet. Find how fast a car was moving if it skidded 280 feet on wet concrete.

65. The formula $v = \sqrt{2gh}$ gives the velocity *v*, in feet per second, of an object when it falls *h* feet accelerated by gravity *g*, in feet per second squared. If *g* is approximately 32 feet per second squared, find how far an object has fallen if its velocity is 80 feet per second.

66. Two tractors are pulling a tree stump from a field. If two forces *A* and *B* pull at right angles (90°) to each other, the size of the resulting force *R* is given by the formula $R = \sqrt{A^2 + B^2}$. If tractor *A* is exerting 600 pounds of force and the resulting force is 850 pounds, find how much force tractor *B* is exerting.

600 lb   ?

In psychology, it has been suggested that the number S of nonsense syllables that a person can repeat consecutively depends on his or her IQ score I according to the equation $S = 2\sqrt{I} - 9$.

67. Use this relationship to estimate the IQ of a person who can repeat 11 nonsense syllables consecutively.

68. Use this relationship to estimate the IQ of a person who can repeat 15 nonsense syllables consecutively.

*The **period** of a pendulum is the time it takes for the pendulum to make one full back-and-forth swing. The period of a pendulum depends on the length of the pendulum. The formula for the period P, in seconds, is $P = 2\pi\sqrt{\dfrac{l}{32}}$, where l is the length of the pendulum in feet. Use this formula for Exercises 69 through 74.*

69. Find the period of a pendulum whose length is 2 feet. Give an exact answer and a two-decimal-place approximation.

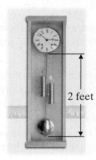

2 feet

70. Klockit sells a 43-inch lyre pendulum. Find the period of this pendulum. Round your answer to 2 decimal places. (*Hint:* First convert inches to feet.)

71. Find the length of a pendulum whose period is 4 seconds. Round your answer to 2 decimal places.

72. Find the length of a pendulum whose period is 3 seconds. Round your answer to 2 decimal places.

73. Study the relationship between period and pendulum length in Exercises 69 through 72 and make a conjecture about this relationship.

74. Galileo experimented with pendulums. He supposedly made conjectures about pendulums of equal length with different bob weights. Try this experiment. Make two pendulums 3 feet long. Attach a heavy weight (lead) to one and a light weight (a cork) to the other. Pull both pendulums back the same angle measure and release. Make a conjecture from your observations. (There is more about pendulums in the Chapter 7 Group Activity.)

If the three lengths of the sides of a triangle are known, Heron's formula can be used to find its area. If a, b, and c are the three lengths of the sides, Heron's formula for area is

$$A = \sqrt{s(s-a)(s-b)(s-c)}$$

where s is half the perimeter of the triangle, or $s = \dfrac{1}{2}(a+b+c)$. Use this formula to find the area of each triangle. Give an exact answer and then a two-decimal place approximation.

△ **75.**

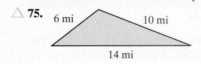

6 mi   10 mi
14 mi

△ **76.**

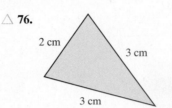

2 cm
3 cm
3 cm

77. Describe when Heron's formula might be useful.

78. In your own words, explain why you think s in Heron's formula is called the *semiperimeter*.

The maximum distance D(h) in kilometers that a person can see from a height h kilometers above the ground is given by the function $D(h) = 111.7\sqrt{h}$. Use this function for Exercises 79 and 80. Round your answers to two decimal places.

79. Find the height that would allow a person to see 80 kilometers.

80. Find the height that would allow a person to see 40 kilometers.

REVIEW AND PREVIEW

Use the vertical line test to determine whether each graph represents the graph of a function. See Section 3.2.

81.

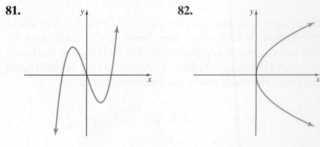

82.

83.

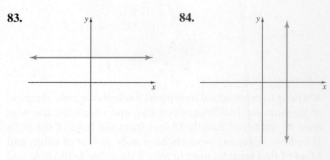

84.

85.

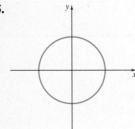

86.

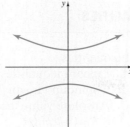

Simplify. See Section 6.3.

87. $\dfrac{\dfrac{x}{6}}{\dfrac{2x}{3} + \dfrac{1}{2}}$

88. $\dfrac{\dfrac{1}{y} + \dfrac{4}{5}}{\dfrac{-3}{20}}$

89. $\dfrac{\dfrac{z}{5} + \dfrac{1}{10}}{\dfrac{z}{20} - \dfrac{z}{5}}$

90. $\dfrac{\dfrac{1}{y} + \dfrac{1}{x}}{\dfrac{1}{y} - \dfrac{1}{x}}$

CONCEPT EXTENSIONS

91. Find the error in the following solution and correct. See the Concept Check in this section.

$$\sqrt{5x - 1} + 4 = 7$$
$$(\sqrt{5x - 1} + 4)^2 = 7^2$$
$$5x - 1 + 16 = 49$$
$$5x = 34$$
$$x = \frac{34}{5}$$

92. Explain why proposed solutions of radical equations must be checked.

93. Solve: $\sqrt{\sqrt{x + 3} + \sqrt{x}} = \sqrt{3}$

94. The cost $C(x)$ in dollars per day to operate a small delivery service is given by $C(x) = 80\sqrt[3]{x} + 500$, where x is the number of deliveries per day. In July, the manager decides that it is necessary to keep delivery costs below $1620.00. Find the greatest number of deliveries this company can make per day and still keep overhead below $1620.00.

95. Consider the equations $\sqrt{2x} = 4$ and $\sqrt[3]{2x} = 4$.

  a. Explain the difference in solving these equations.

  b. Explain the similarity in solving these equations.

Example

For Exercises 96 through 99, see the example below.

Solve $(t^2 - 3t) - 2\sqrt{t^2 - 3t} = 0$.

Solution

Substitution can be used to make this problem somewhat simpler. Since $t^2 - 3t$ occurs more than once, let $x = t^2 - 3t$.

$$(t^2 - 3t) - 2\sqrt{t^2 - 3t} = 0$$
$$x - 2\sqrt{x} = 0$$
$$x = 2\sqrt{x}$$
$$x^2 = (2\sqrt{x})^2$$
$$x^2 = 4x$$
$$x^2 - 4x = 0$$
$$x(x - 4) = 0$$
$$x = 0 \quad \text{or} \quad x - 4 = 0$$
$$x = 4$$

Now we "undo" the substitution.

$x = 0$ Replace x with $t^2 - 3t$.

$$t^2 - 3t = 0$$
$$t(t - 3) = 0$$
$$t = 0 \quad \text{or} \quad t - 3 = 0$$
$$t = 3$$

$x = 4$ Replace x with $t^2 - 3t$.

$$t^2 - 3t = 4$$
$$t^2 - 3t - 4 = 0$$
$$(t - 4)(t + 1) = 0$$
$$t - 4 = 0 \quad \text{or} \quad t + 1 = 0$$
$$t = 4 \qquad\qquad t = -1$$

In this problem, we have four possible solutions: 0, 3, 4, and -1. All four solutions check in the original equation, so the solutions are $-1, 0, 3, 4$.

Solve. See the preceding example.

96. $3\sqrt{x^2 - 8x} = x^2 - 8x$

97. $\sqrt{(x^2 - x) + 7} = 2(x^2 - x) - 1$

98. $7 - (x^2 - 3x) = \sqrt{(x^2 - 3x) + 5}$

99. $x^2 + 6x = 4\sqrt{x^2 + 6x}$

THE BIGGER PICTURE   SOLVING EQUATIONS AND INEQUALITIES

Continue your outline from Sections 2.4, 2.5, 2.7, 5.8, and 6.5. Write how to recognize and how to solve equations with radicals in your own words. For example:

Solving Equations and Inequalities

I. Equations
  A. Linear equations (Sec. 2.1)
  B. Absolute value equations (Sec. 2.6)
  C. Quadratic and higher degree equations (Sec. 5.8)
  D. Equations with rational expressions (Sec. 6.5)
  E. Equations with radicals: Equation contains at least one root of a variable expression.

$$\sqrt{5x + 10} - 2 = x \qquad \text{Radical equation}$$
$$\sqrt{5x + 10} = x + 2 \qquad \text{Isolate the radical.}$$
$$\left(\sqrt{5x + 10}\right)^2 = (x + 2)^2 \qquad \text{Square both sides.}$$
$$5x + 10 = x^2 + 4x + 4 \qquad \text{Simplify.}$$
$$0 = x^2 - x - 6 \qquad \text{Write in standard form.}$$
$$0 = (x - 3)(x + 2) \qquad \text{Factor.}$$
$$x - 3 = 0 \quad \text{or} \quad x + 2 = 0 \qquad \text{Set each factor equal to 0.}$$
$$x = 3 \quad \text{or} \quad x = -2 \qquad \text{Solve.}$$

Both solutions check.

II. Inequalities
  A. Linear inequalities (Sec. 2.4)
  B. Compound inequalities (Sec. 2.5)
  C. Absolute value inequalities (Sec. 2.7)

Solve. Write inequality solutions in interval notation.

1. $\dfrac{x}{4} + \dfrac{x + 18}{20} = \dfrac{x - 5}{5}$

2. $|3x - 5| = 10$

3. $2x^2 - x = 45$

4. $-6 \le -5x - 1 \le 10$

5. $4(x - 1) + 3x > 1 + 2(x - 6)$

6. $\sqrt{x} + 14 = x - 6$

7. $x \ge 10 \quad \text{or} \quad -x < 5$

8. $\sqrt{3x - 1} + 4 = 1$

9. $|x - 2| > 15$

10. $5x - 4[x - 2(3x + 1)] = 25$

7.7 COMPLEX NUMBERS

OBJECTIVES

1 Write square roots of negative numbers in the form *bi*.

2 Add or subtract complex numbers.

3 Multiply complex numbers.

4 Divide complex numbers.

5 Raise *i* to powers.

OBJECTIVE 1 ▶ Writing numbers in the form *bi*. Our work with radical expressions has excluded expressions such as $\sqrt{-16}$ because $\sqrt{-16}$ is not a real number; there is no real number whose square is -16. In this section, we discuss a number system that includes roots of negative numbers. This number system is the **complex number system,** and it includes the set of real numbers as a subset. The complex number system allows us to solve equations such as $x^2 + 1 = 0$ that have no real number solutions. The set of complex numbers includes the **imaginary unit.**

Imaginary Unit
The imaginary unit, written *i*, is the number whose square is -1. That is,

$$i^2 = -1 \quad \text{and} \quad i = \sqrt{-1}$$

To write the square root of a negative number in terms of *i*, use the property that if *a* is a positive number, then

$$\sqrt{-a} = \sqrt{-1} \cdot \sqrt{a}$$
$$= i \cdot \sqrt{a}$$

Using *i*, we can write $\sqrt{-16}$ as

$$\sqrt{-16} = \sqrt{-1 \cdot 16} = \sqrt{-1} \cdot \sqrt{16} = i \cdot 4, \text{ or } 4i$$

EXAMPLE 1   Write with i notation.

a. $\sqrt{-36}$ b. $\sqrt{-5}$ c. $-\sqrt{-20}$

> **Helpful Hint**
> Since $\sqrt{5}i$ can easily be confused with $\sqrt{5i}$, we write $\sqrt{5}i$ as $i\sqrt{5}$.

Solution

a. $\sqrt{-36} = \sqrt{-1 \cdot 36} = \sqrt{-1} \cdot \sqrt{36} = i \cdot 6$, or $6i$

b. $\sqrt{-5} = \sqrt{-1(5)} = \sqrt{-1} \cdot \sqrt{5} = i\sqrt{5}$.

c. $-\sqrt{-20} = -\sqrt{-1 \cdot 20} = -\sqrt{-1} \cdot \sqrt{4 \cdot 5} = -i \cdot 2\sqrt{5} = -2i\sqrt{5}$

PRACTICE
1   Write with i notation.

a. $\sqrt{-4}$ b. $\sqrt{-7}$ c. $-\sqrt{-18}$

The product rule for radicals does not necessarily hold true for imaginary numbers. *To multiply square roots of negative numbers, first we write each number in terms of the imaginary unit i.* For example, to multiply $\sqrt{-4}$ and $\sqrt{-9}$, we first write each number in the form bi.

$$\sqrt{-4}\sqrt{-9} = 2i(3i) = 6i^2 = 6(-1) = -6 \quad \text{Correct}$$

We will also use this method to simplify quotients of square roots of negative numbers. Why? The product rule does not work for this example. In other words,

$$\sqrt{-4} \cdot \sqrt{-9} = \sqrt{(-4)(-9)} = \sqrt{36} = 6 \quad \text{Incorrect}$$

EXAMPLE 2   Multiply or divide as indicated.

a. $\sqrt{-3} \cdot \sqrt{-5}$ b. $\sqrt{-36} \cdot \sqrt{-1}$ c. $\sqrt{8} \cdot \sqrt{-2}$ d. $\dfrac{\sqrt{-125}}{\sqrt{5}}$

Solution

a. $\sqrt{-3} \cdot \sqrt{-5} = i\sqrt{3}\left(i\sqrt{5}\right) = i^2\sqrt{15} = -1\sqrt{15} = -\sqrt{15}$

b. $\sqrt{-36} \cdot \sqrt{-1} = 6i(i) = 6i^2 = 6(-1) = -6$

c. $\sqrt{8} \cdot \sqrt{-2} = 2\sqrt{2}\left(i\sqrt{2}\right) = 2i\left(\sqrt{2}\sqrt{2}\right) = 2i(2) = 4i$

d. $\dfrac{\sqrt{-125}}{\sqrt{5}} = \dfrac{i\sqrt{125}}{\sqrt{5}} = i\sqrt{25} = 5i$

PRACTICE
2   Multiply or divide as indicated.

a. $\sqrt{-5} \cdot \sqrt{-6}$ b. $\sqrt{-9} \cdot \sqrt{-1}$ c. $\sqrt{125} \cdot \sqrt{-5}$ d. $\dfrac{\sqrt{-27}}{\sqrt{3}}$

Now that we have practiced working with the imaginary unit, we define complex numbers.

> **Complex Numbers**
> A **complex number** is a number that can be written in the form $a + bi$, where a and b are real numbers.

Notice that the set of real numbers is a subset of the complex numbers since any real number can be written in the form of a complex number. For example,

$$16 = 16 + 0i$$

In general, a complex number $a + bi$ is a real number if $b = 0$. Also, a complex number is called a **pure imaginary number** if $a = 0$ and $b \neq 0$. For example,

$$3i = 0 + 3i \quad \text{and} \quad i\sqrt{7} = 0 + i\sqrt{7}$$

are pure imaginary numbers.

The following diagram shows the relationship between complex numbers and their subsets.

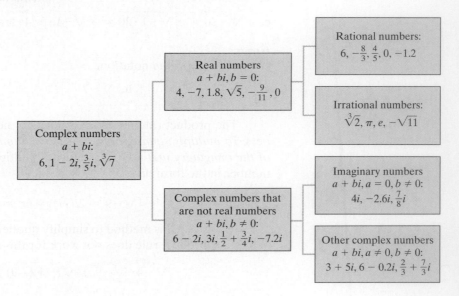

Concept Check ☑

True or false? Every complex number is also a real number.

OBJECTIVE 2 ▶ **Adding or subtracting complex numbers.** Two complex numbers $a + bi$ and $c + di$ are equal if and only if $a = c$ and $b = d$. Complex numbers can be added or subtracted by adding or subtracting their real parts and then adding or subtracting their imaginary parts.

Sum or Difference of Complex Numbers

If $a + bi$ and $c + di$ are complex numbers, then their sum is

$$(a + bi) + (c + di) = (a + c) + (b + d)i$$

Their difference is

$$(a + bi) - (c + di) = a + bi - c - di = (a - c) + (b - d)i$$

EXAMPLE 3 Add or subtract the complex numbers. Write the sum or difference in the form $a + bi$.

a. $(2 + 3i) + (-3 + 2i)$ **b.** $5i - (1 - i)$ **c.** $(-3 - 7i) - (-6)$

Solution

a. $(2 + 3i) + (-3 + 2i) = (2 - 3) + (3 + 2)i = -1 + 5i$

b. $5i - (1 - i) = 5i - 1 + i$

$\qquad\qquad\qquad = -1 + (5 + 1)i$

$\qquad\qquad\qquad = -1 + 6i$

Answer to Concept Check:

false

c. $(-3 - 7i) - (-6) = -3 - 7i + 6$
$$= (-3 + 6) - 7i$$
$$= 3 - 7i$$ □

3 Add or subtract the complex numbers. Write the sum or difference in the form $a + bi$.

a. $(3 - 5i) + (-4 + i)$ **b.** $4i - (3 - i)$ **c.** $(-5 - 2i) - (-8)$

OBJECTIVE 3 ▶ Multiplying complex numbers. To multiply two complex numbers of the form $a + bi$, we multiply as though they are binomials. Then we use the relationship $i^2 = -1$ to simplify.

EXAMPLE 4 Multiply the complex numbers. Write the product in the form $a + bi$.

a. $-7i \cdot 3i$ **b.** $3i(2 - i)$ **c.** $(2 - 5i)(4 + i)$
d. $(2 - i)^2$ **e.** $(7 + 3i)(7 - 3i)$

Solution

a. $-7i \cdot 3i = -21i^2$
$$= -21(-1) \quad \text{Replace } i^2 \text{ with } -1.$$
$$= 21$$

b. $3i(2 - i) = 3i \cdot 2 - 3i \cdot i \quad \text{Use the distributive property.}$
$$= 6i - 3i^2 \quad \text{Multiply.}$$
$$= 6i - 3(-1) \quad \text{Replace } i^2 \text{ with } -1.$$
$$= 6i + 3$$
$$= 3 + 6i$$

     Use the FOIL order below. (First, Outer, Inner, Last)

c. $(2 - 5i)(4 + i) = 2(4) + 2(i) - 5i(4) - 5i(i)$
                        F   O   I   L
$$= 8 + 2i - 20i - 5i^2$$
$$= 8 - 18i - 5(-1) \quad\quad i^2 = -1$$
$$= 8 - 18i + 5$$
$$= 13 - 18i$$

d. $(2 - i)^2 = (2 - i)(2 - i)$
$$= 2(2) - 2(i) - 2(i) + i^2$$
$$= 4 - 4i + (-1) \quad\quad i^2 = -1$$
$$= 3 - 4i$$

e. $(7 + 3i)(7 - 3i) = 7(7) - 7(3i) + 3i(7) - 3i(3i)$
$$= 49 - 21i + 21i - 9i^2$$
$$= 49 - 9(-1) \quad\quad i^2 = -1$$
$$= 49 + 9$$
$$= 58$$ □

4 Multiply the complex numbers. Write the product in the form $a + bi$.

a. $-4i \cdot 5i$ **b.** $5i(2 + i)$ **c.** $(2 + 3i)(6 - i)$
d. $(3 - i)^2$ **e.** $(9 + 2i)(9 - 2i)$

Notice that if you add, subtract, or multiply two complex numbers, just like real numbers, the result is a complex number.

OBJECTIVE 4 ▶ Dividing complex numbers. From Example 4e, notice that the product of $7 + 3i$ and $7 - 3i$ is a real number. These two complex numbers are called **complex conjugates** of one another. In general, we have the following definition.

Complex Conjugates

The complex numbers $(a + bi)$ and $(a - bi)$ are called **complex conjugates** of each other, and $(a + bi)(a - bi) = a^2 + b^2$.

To see that the product of a complex number $a + bi$ and its conjugate $a - bi$ is the real number $a^2 + b^2$, we multiply.

$$(a + bi)(a - bi) = a^2 - abi + abi - b^2 i^2$$
$$= a^2 - b^2(-1)$$
$$= a^2 + b^2$$

We use complex conjugates to divide by a complex number.

EXAMPLE 5   Divide. Write in the form $a + bi$.

a. $\dfrac{2 + i}{1 - i}$ **b.** $\dfrac{7}{3i}$

Solution

a. Multiply the numerator and denominator by the complex conjugate of $1 - i$ to eliminate the imaginary number in the denominator.

$$\frac{2 + i}{1 - i} = \frac{(2 + i)(1 + i)}{(1 - i)(1 + i)}$$

$$= \frac{2(1) + 2(i) + 1(i) + i^2}{1^2 - i^2}$$

$$= \frac{2 + 3i - 1}{1 + 1} \qquad \text{Here, } i^2 = -1.$$

$$= \frac{1 + 3i}{2} \quad \text{or} \quad \frac{1}{2} + \frac{3}{2}i$$

b. Multiply the numerator and denominator by the conjugate of $3i$. Note that $3i = 0 + 3i$, so its conjugate is $0 - 3i$ or $-3i$.

$$\frac{7}{3i} = \frac{7(-3i)}{(3i)(-3i)} = \frac{-21i}{-9i^2} = \frac{-21i}{-9(-1)} = \frac{-21i}{9} = \frac{-7i}{3} \quad \text{or} \quad 0 - \frac{7}{3}i \qquad \square$$

PRACTICE

5   Divide. Write in the form $a + bi$.

a. $\dfrac{4 - i}{3 + i}$ **b.** $\dfrac{5}{2i}$

▶ Helpful Hint

Recall that division can be checked by multiplication.

To check that $\dfrac{2 + i}{1 - i} = \dfrac{1}{2} + \dfrac{3}{2}i$, in Example 5a, multiply $\left(\dfrac{1}{2} + \dfrac{3}{2}i\right)(1 - i)$ to verify that the product is $2 + i$.

OBJECTIVE 5 ▶ Finding powers of *i*. We can use the fact that $i^2 = -1$ to find higher powers of *i*. To find i^3, we rewrite it as the product of i^2 and *i*.

$$i^3 = i^2 \cdot i = (-1)i = -i$$
$$i^4 = i^2 \cdot i^2 = (-1) \cdot (-1) = 1$$

We continue this process and use the fact that $i^4 = 1$ and $i^2 = -1$ to simplify i^5 and i^6.

$$i^5 = i^4 \cdot i = 1 \cdot i = i$$
$$i^6 = i^4 \cdot i^2 = 1 \cdot (-1) = -1$$

If we continue finding powers of *i*, we generate the following pattern. Notice that the values i, -1, $-i$, and 1 repeat as *i* is raised to higher and higher powers.

$i^1 = i$	$i^5 = i$	$i^9 = i$
$i^2 = -1$	$i^6 = -1$	$i^{10} = -1$
$i^3 = -i$	$i^7 = -i$	$i^{11} = -i$
$i^4 = 1$	$i^8 = 1$	$i^{12} = 1$

This pattern allows us to find other powers of *i*. To do so, we will use the fact that $i^4 = 1$ and rewrite a power of *i* in terms of i^4. For example,

$$i^{22} = i^{20} \cdot i^2 = (i^4)^5 \cdot i^2 = 1^5 \cdot (-1) = 1 \cdot (-1) = -1.$$

EXAMPLE 6   Find the following powers of *i*.

a. i^7 **b.** i^{20} **c.** i^{46} **d.** i^{-12}

Solution

a. $i^7 = i^4 \cdot i^3 = 1(-i) = -i$

b. $i^{20} = (i^4)^5 = 1^5 = 1$

c. $i^{46} = i^{44} \cdot i^2 = (i^4)^{11} \cdot i^2 = 1^{11}(-1) = -1$

d. $i^{-12} = \dfrac{1}{i^{12}} = \dfrac{1}{(i^4)^3} = \dfrac{1}{(1)^3} = \dfrac{1}{1} = 1$

PRACTICE
6   Find the following powers of *i*.

a. i^9 **b.** i^{16} **c.** i^{34} **d.** i^{-24}

VOCABULARY & READINESS CHECK

Use the choices below to fill in each blank. Not all choices will be used.

-1	$\sqrt{-1}$	real	imaginary unit
1	$\sqrt{1}$	complex	pure imaginary

1. A _____ number is one that can be written in the form $a + bi$ where a and b are real numbers.

2. In the complex number system, *i* denotes the _____.

3. $i^2 =$ _____

4. $i =$ _____

5. A complex number, $a + bi$, is a _____ number if $b = 0$.

6. A complex number, $a + bi$, is a _____ number if $a = 0$ and $b \neq 0$.

Simplify. See Example 1.

7. $\sqrt{-81}$ **8.** $\sqrt{-49}$ **9.** $\sqrt{-7}$ **10.** $\sqrt{-3}$

11. $-\sqrt{16}$ **12.** $-\sqrt{4}$ **13.** $\sqrt{-64}$ **14.** $\sqrt{-100}$

7.7 EXERCISE SET

MyMathLab   PRACTICE   WATCH   DOWNLOAD   READ   REVIEW

Write in terms of i. See Example 1.

1. $\sqrt{-24}$

2. $\sqrt{-32}$

3. $-\sqrt{-36}$

4. $-\sqrt{-121}$

5. $8\sqrt{-63}$

6. $4\sqrt{-20}$

7. $-\sqrt{54}$

8. $\sqrt{-63}$

Multiply or divide. See Example 2.

9. $\sqrt{-2} \cdot \sqrt{-7}$

10. $\sqrt{-11} \cdot \sqrt{-3}$

11. $\sqrt{-5} \cdot \sqrt{-10}$

12. $\sqrt{-2} \cdot \sqrt{-6}$

13. $\sqrt{16} \cdot \sqrt{-1}$

14. $\sqrt{3} \cdot \sqrt{-27}$

15. $\dfrac{\sqrt{-9}}{\sqrt{3}}$

16. $\dfrac{\sqrt{49}}{\sqrt{-10}}$

17. $\dfrac{\sqrt{-80}}{\sqrt{-10}}$

18. $\dfrac{\sqrt{-40}}{\sqrt{-8}}$

Add or subtract. Write the sum or difference in the form a + bi. See Example 3.

19. $(4 - 7i) + (2 + 3i)$

20. $(2 - 4i) - (2 - i)$

21. $(6 + 5i) - (8 - i)$

22. $(8 - 3i) + (-8 + 3i)$

23. $6 - (8 + 4i)$

24. $(9 - 4i) - 9$

Multiply. Write the product in the form a + bi. See Example 4.

25. $-10i \cdot -4i$

26. $-2i \cdot -11i$

27. $6i(2 - 3i)$

28. $5i(4 - 7i)$

29. $\left(\sqrt{3} + 2i\right)\left(\sqrt{3} - 2i\right)$

30. $\left(\sqrt{5} - 5i\right)\left(\sqrt{5} + 5i\right)$

31. $(4 - 2i)^2$

32. $(6 - 3i)^2$

Write each quotient in the form a + bi. See Example 5.

33. $\dfrac{4}{i}$

34. $\dfrac{5}{6i}$

35. $\dfrac{7}{4 + 3i}$

36. $\dfrac{9}{1 - 2i}$

37. $\dfrac{3 + 5i}{1 + i}$

38. $\dfrac{6 + 2i}{4 - 3i}$

39. $\dfrac{5 - i}{3 - 2i}$

40. $\dfrac{6 - i}{2 + i}$

MIXED PRACTICE

Perform each indicated operation. Write the result in the form a + bi.

41. $(7i)(-9i)$

42. $(-6i)(-4i)$

43. $(6 - 3i) - (4 - 2i)$

44. $(-2 - 4i) - (6 - 8i)$

45. $-3i(-1 + 9i)$

46. $-5i(-2 + i)$

47. $\dfrac{4 - 5i}{2i}$

48. $\dfrac{6 + 8i}{3i}$

49. $(4 + i)(5 + 2i)$

50. $(3 + i)(2 + 4i)$

51. $(6 - 2i)(3 + i)$

52. $(2 - 4i)(2 - i)$

53. $(8 - 3i) + (2 + 3i)$

54. $(7 + 4i) + (4 - 4i)$

55. $(1 - i)(1 + i)$

56. $(6 + 2i)(6 - 2i)$

57. $\dfrac{16 + 15i}{-3i}$

58. $\dfrac{2 - 3i}{-7i}$

59. $(9 + 8i)^2$

60. $(4 - 7i)^2$

61. $\dfrac{2}{3 + i}$

62. $\dfrac{5}{3 - 2i}$

63. $(5 - 6i) - 4i$

64. $(6 - 2i) + 7i$

65. $\dfrac{2 - 3i}{2 + i}$

66. $\dfrac{6 + 5i}{6 - 5i}$

67. $(2 + 4i) + (6 - 5i)$

68. $(5 - 3i) + (7 - 8i)$

69. $(\sqrt{3} + 2i)(\sqrt{3} - 2i)$

70. $(\sqrt{5} - 5i)(\sqrt{5} + 5i)$

71. $(4 - 2i)^2$

72. $(6 - 3i)^2$

Find each power of i. See Example 6.

73. i^8

74. i^{10}

75. i^{21}

76. i^{15}

77. i^{11}

78. i^{40}

79. i^{-6}

80. i^{-9}

81. $(2i)^6$

82. $(5i)^4$

83. $(-3i)^5$

84. $(-2i)^7$

REVIEW AND PREVIEW

Recall that the sum of the measures of the angles of a triangle is 180°. Find the unknown angle in each triangle.

△ **85.**

△ **86.**

Use synthetic division to divide the following. See Section 6.4.

87. $(x^3 - 6x^2 + 3x - 4) \div (x - 1)$

88. $(5x^4 - 3x^2 + 2) \div (x + 2)$

Thirty people were recently polled about their average monthly balance in their checking accounts. The results of this poll are shown in the following histogram. Use this graph to answer Exercises 89 through 94. See Section 1.2.

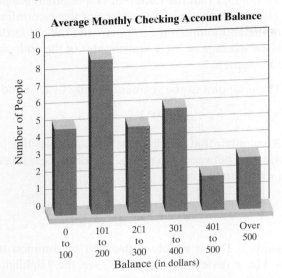

Average Monthly Checking Account Balance

89. How many people polled reported an average checking balance of $201 to $300?

90. How many people polled reported an average checking balance of $0 to $100?

91. How many people polled reported an average checking balance of $200 or less?

92. How many people polled reported an average checking balance of $301 or more?

93. What percent of people polled reported an average checking balance of $201 to $300?

94. What percent of people polled reported an average checking balance of $0 to $100?

CONCEPT EXTENSIONS

Write in the form $a + bi$.

95. $i^3 - i^4$

96. $i^8 - i^7$

97. $i^6 + i^8$

98. $i^4 + i^{12}$

99. $2 + \sqrt{-9}$

100. $5 - \sqrt{-16}$

101. $\dfrac{6 + \sqrt{-18}}{3}$

102. $\dfrac{4 - \sqrt{-8}}{2}$

103. $\dfrac{5 - \sqrt{-75}}{10}$

104. Describe how to find the conjugate of a complex number.

105. Explain why the product of a complex number and its complex conjugate is a real number.

Simplify.

106. $\left(8 - \sqrt{-3}\right) - \left(2 + \sqrt{-12}\right)$

107. $\left(8 - \sqrt{-4}\right) - \left(2 + \sqrt{-16}\right)$

108. Determine whether $2i$ is a solution of $x^2 + 4 = 0$.

109. Determine whether $-1 + i$ is a solution of $x^2 + 2x = -2$.

CHAPTER 7 GROUP ACTIVITY

Heron of Alexandria

Heron (also Hero) was a Greek mathematician and engineer. He lived and worked in Alexandria, Egypt, around 75 A.D. During his prolific work life, Heron developed a rotary steam engine called an aeolipile, a surveying tool called a dioptra, as well as a wind organ and a fire engine. As an engineer, he must have had the need to approximate square roots because he described an iterative method for doing so in his work *Metrica*. Heron's method for approximating a square root can be summarized as follows:

Suppose that x is not a perfect square and a^2 is the nearest perfect square to x. For a rough estimate of the value of $\sqrt{x}$, find the value of $y_1 = \dfrac{1}{2}\left(a + \dfrac{x}{a}\right)$. This estimate can be improved by calculating a second estimate using the first estimate y_1 in place of a: $y_2 = \dfrac{1}{2}\left(y_1 + \dfrac{x}{y_1}\right)$.

Repeating this process several times will give more and more accurate estimates of $\sqrt{x}$.

Critical Thinking

1. a. Which perfect square is closest to 80?

   b. Use Heron's method for approximating square roots to calculate the first estimate of the square root of 80. Give an exact decimal answer.

   c. Use the first estimate of the square root of 80 to find a more refined second estimate. Round this second estimate to 6 decimal places.

   d. Use a calculator to find the actual value of the square root of 80. List all digits shown on your calculator's display.

   e. Compare the actual value from part (d) to the values of the first and second estimates. What do you notice?

   f. How many iterations of this process are necessary to get an estimate that differs no more than one digit from the actual value recorded in part (d)?

2. Repeat Question 1 for finding an estimate of the square root of 30.

3. Repeat Question 1 for finding an estimate of the square root of 4572.

4. Why would this iterative method have been important to people of Heron's era? Would you say that this method is as important today? Why or why not?

STUDY SKILLS BUILDER

Are You Prepared for a Test on Chapter 7?

Below I have listed some common trouble areas for students in Chapter 7. After studying for your test, but before taking your test, read these.

- Remember how to convert an expression with rational expressions to one with radicals and one with radicals to one with rational expressions.

$$7^{2/3} = \sqrt[3]{7^2} \text{ or } (\sqrt[3]{7})^2$$

$$\sqrt[5]{4^3} = 4^{3/5}$$

- Remember the difference between $\sqrt{x} + \sqrt{x}$ and $\sqrt{x} \cdot \sqrt{x}, x > 0$.

$$\sqrt{x} + \sqrt{x} = 2\sqrt{x}$$
$$\sqrt{x} \cdot \sqrt{x} = x$$

- Don't forget the difference between rationalizing the denominator of $\sqrt{\dfrac{2}{x}}$ and rationalizing the denominator

of $\dfrac{\sqrt{2}}{\sqrt{x}+1}, x > 0$.

$$\sqrt{\frac{2}{x}} = \frac{\sqrt{2}}{\sqrt{x}} = \frac{\sqrt{2} \cdot \sqrt{x}}{\sqrt{x} \cdot \sqrt{x}} = \frac{\sqrt{2x}}{x}$$

$$\frac{\sqrt{2}}{\sqrt{x}+1} = \frac{\sqrt{2}(\sqrt{x}-1)}{(\sqrt{x}+1)(\sqrt{x}-1)} = \frac{\sqrt{2}(\sqrt{x}-1)}{x-1}$$

- Remember that the midpoint of a segment is a *point*. The x-coordinate is the average of the x-coordinates of the endpoints of the segment and the y-coordinate is the average of the y-coordinates of the endpoints of the segment.

The midpoint of the segment joining $(-1, 5)$ and $(3, 4)$ is $\left(\dfrac{-1+3}{2}, \dfrac{5+4}{2}\right)$ or $\left(1, \dfrac{9}{2}\right)$.

- Remember that the distance formula gives the *distance* between two points. The distance between $(-1, 5)$ and $(3, 4)$ is

$$\sqrt{(3-(-1))^2 + (4-5)^2} = \sqrt{4^2 + (-1)^2}$$
$$= \sqrt{16+1} = \sqrt{17} \text{ units}$$

Remember: This is simply a checklist of common trouble areas. For a review of Chapter 7, see the Highlights and Chapter Review at the end of this chapter.

CHAPTER 7 VOCABULARY CHECK

Fill in each blank with one of the words or phrases listed below.

index   rationalizing   conjugate   principal square root   cube root   midpoint

complex number   like radicals   radicand   imaginary unit   distance

1. The _____ of $\sqrt{3} + 2$ is $\sqrt{3} - 2$.

2. The _____ of a nonnegative number a is written as $\sqrt{a}$.

3. The process of writing a radical expression as an equivalent expression but without a radical in the denominator is called _____ the denominator.

4. The _____ written i, is the number whose square is -1.

5. The _____ of a number is written as $\sqrt[3]{a}$.

6. In the notation $\sqrt[n]{a}$, n is called the _____ and a is called the _____.

7. Radicals with the same index and the same radicand are called _____.

8. A _____ is a number that can be written in the form $a + bi$, where a and b are real numbers.

9. The _____ formula is $d = \sqrt{(x_2 - x_1)^2 + (y_2 - y_1)^2}$.

10. The _____ formula is $\left(\dfrac{x_1 + x_2}{2}, \dfrac{y_1 + y_2}{2}\right)$.

▶ **Helpful Hint**

Are you preparing for your test? Don't forget to take the Chapter 7 Test on page 475. Then check your answers at the back of the text and use the Chapter Test Prep Video CD to see the fully worked-out solutions to any of the exercises you want to review.

CHAPTER 7 HIGHLIGHTS

DEFINITIONS AND CONCEPTS	EXAMPLES

SECTION 7.1   RADICALS AND RADICAL FUNCTIONS

The **positive,** or **principal, square root** of a nonnegative number a is written as $\sqrt{a}$.

$$\sqrt{a} = b \text{ only if } b^2 = a \text{ and } b \geq 0$$

The **negative square root of** a is written as $-\sqrt{a}$.

The **cube root** of a real number a is written as $\sqrt[3]{a}$.

$$\sqrt[3]{a} = b \text{ only if } b^3 = a$$

If n is an even positive integer, then $\sqrt[n]{a^n} = |a|$.

If n is an odd positive integer, then $\sqrt[n]{a^n} = a$.

A **radical function** in x is a function defined by an expression containing a root of x.

$$\sqrt{36} = 6 \qquad \sqrt{\frac{9}{100}} = \frac{3}{10}$$

$$-\sqrt{36} = -6 \qquad \sqrt{0.04} = 0.2$$

$$\sqrt[3]{27} = 3 \qquad \sqrt[3]{-\frac{1}{8}} = -\frac{1}{2}$$

$$\sqrt[3]{y^6} = y^2 \qquad \sqrt[3]{64x^9} = 4x^3$$

$$\sqrt{(-3)^2} = |-3| = 3$$

$$\sqrt[3]{(-7)^3} = -7$$

If $\quad f(x) = \sqrt{x} + 2$,

$$f(1) = \sqrt{(1)} + 2 = 1 + 2 = 3$$

$$f(3) = \sqrt{(3)} + 2 \approx 3.73$$

SECTION 7.2   RATIONAL EXPONENTS

$a^{1/n} = \sqrt[n]{a}$ if $\sqrt[n]{a}$ is a real number.

If m and n are positive integers greater than 1 with $\dfrac{m}{n}$ in lowest terms and $\sqrt[n]{a}$ is a real number, then

$$a^{m/n} = (a^{1/n})^m = \left(\sqrt[n]{a}\right)^m$$

$a^{-m/n} = \dfrac{1}{a^{m/n}}$ as long as $a^{m/n}$ is a nonzero number.

Exponent rules are true for rational exponents.

$$81^{1/2} = \sqrt{81} = 9$$

$$(-8x^3)^{1/3} = \sqrt[3]{-8x^3} = -2x$$

$$4^{5/2} = \left(\sqrt{4}\right)^5 = 2^5 = 32$$

$$27^{2/3} = \left(\sqrt[3]{27}\right)^2 = 3^2 = 9$$

$$16^{-3/4} = \frac{1}{16^{3/4}} = \frac{1}{\left(\sqrt[4]{16}\right)^3} = \frac{1}{2^3} = \frac{1}{8}$$

$$x^{2/3} \cdot x^{-5/6} = x^{2/3-5/6} = x^{-1/6} = \frac{1}{x^{1/6}}$$

$$(8^4)^{1/2} = 8^2 = 64$$

$$\frac{a^{4/5}}{a^{-2/5}} = a^{4/5-(-2/5)} = a^{6/5}$$

DEFINITIONS AND CONCEPTS	EXAMPLES

SECTION 7.3 SIMPLIFYING RADICAL EXPRESSIONS

Product and Quotient Rules

If $\sqrt[n]{a}$ and $\sqrt[n]{b}$ are real numbers,

$$\sqrt[n]{a} \cdot \sqrt[n]{b} = \sqrt[n]{a \cdot b}$$

$$\frac{\sqrt[n]{a}}{\sqrt[n]{b}} = \sqrt[n]{\frac{a}{b}}, \text{ provided } \sqrt[n]{b} \neq 0$$

A radical of the form $\sqrt[n]{a}$ is **simplified** when a contains no factors that are perfect nth powers.

Multiply or divide as indicated:

$$\sqrt{11} \cdot \sqrt{3} = \sqrt{33}$$

$$\frac{\sqrt[3]{40x}}{\sqrt[3]{5x}} = \sqrt[3]{8} = 2$$

$$\sqrt{40} = \sqrt{4 \cdot 10} = 2\sqrt{10}$$

$$\sqrt{36x^5} = \sqrt{36x^4 \cdot x} = 6x^2\sqrt{x}$$

$$\sqrt[3]{24x^7y^3} = \sqrt[3]{8x^6y^3 \cdot 3x} = 2x^2y\sqrt[3]{3x}$$

$$\sqrt{36x^4 \cdot x} = 6x^2\sqrt{x}$$

Distance Formula

The distance d between two points (x_1, y_1) and (x_2, y_2) is given by

$$d = \sqrt{(x_2 - x_1)^2 + (y_2 - y_1)^2}$$

Find the distance between points $(-1, 6)$ and $(-2, -4)$.
Let $(x_1, y_1) = (-1, 6)$ and $(x_2, y_2) = (-2, -4)$.

$$d = \sqrt{(x_2 - x_1)^2 + (y_2 - y_1)^2}$$

$$= \sqrt{(-2 - (-1))^2 + (-4 - 6)^2}$$

$$= \sqrt{1 + 100} = \sqrt{101}$$

Midpoint Formula

The midpoint of the line segment whose endpoints are (x_1, y_1) and (x_2, y_2) is the point with coordinates

$$\left(\frac{x_1 + x_2}{2}, \frac{y_1 + y_2}{2} \right)$$

Find the midpoint of the line segment whose endpoints are $(-1, 6)$ and $(-2, -4)$.

$$\left(\frac{-1 + (-2)}{2}, \frac{6 + (-4)}{2} \right)$$

The midpoint is $\left(-\frac{3}{2}, 1 \right)$.

SECTION 7.4 ADDING, SUBTRACTING, AND MULTIPLYING RADICAL EXPRESSIONS

Radicals with the same index and the same radicand are **like radicals.**

The distributive property can be used to add like radicals.

$$5\sqrt{6} + 2\sqrt{6} = (5 + 2)\sqrt{6} = 7\sqrt{6}$$

$$= \sqrt[3]{3x} - 10\sqrt[3]{3x} + 3\sqrt[3]{10x}$$

$$= (-1 - 10)\sqrt[3]{3x} + 3\sqrt[3]{10x}$$

$$= -11\sqrt[3]{3x} + 3\sqrt[3]{10x}$$

Radical expressions are multiplied by using many of the same properties used to multiply polynomials.

Multiply:

$$(\sqrt{5} - \sqrt{2x})(\sqrt{2} + \sqrt{2x})$$

$$= \sqrt{10} + \sqrt{10x} - \sqrt{4x} - 2x$$

$$= \sqrt{10} + \sqrt{10x} - 2\sqrt{x} - 2x$$

$$(2\sqrt{3} - \sqrt{8x})(2\sqrt{3} + \sqrt{8x})$$

$$= 4(3) - 8x = 12 - 8x$$

DEFINITIONS AND CONCEPTS	EXAMPLES

SECTION 7.5 RATIONALIZING DENOMINATORS AND NUMERATORS OF RADICAL EXPRESSIONS

The **conjugate** of $a + b$ is $a - b$.

The conjugate of $\sqrt{7} + \sqrt{3}$ is $\sqrt{7} - \sqrt{3}$.

The process of writing the denominator of a radical expression without a radical is called **rationalizing the denominator.**

Rationalize each denominator.

$$\frac{\sqrt{5}}{\sqrt{3}} = \frac{\sqrt{5} \cdot \sqrt{3}}{\sqrt{3} \cdot \sqrt{3}} = \frac{\sqrt{15}}{3}$$

$$\frac{6}{\sqrt{7} + \sqrt{3}} = \frac{6(\sqrt{7} - \sqrt{3})}{(\sqrt{7} + \sqrt{3})(\sqrt{7} - \sqrt{3})}$$

$$= \frac{6(\sqrt{7} - \sqrt{3})}{7 - 3}$$

$$= \frac{6(\sqrt{7} - \sqrt{3})}{4} = \frac{3(\sqrt{7} - \sqrt{3})}{2}$$

The process of writing the numerator of a radical expression without a radical is called **rationalizing the numerator.**

Rationalize each numerator:

$$\frac{\sqrt[3]{9}}{\sqrt[3]{5}} = \frac{\sqrt[3]{9} \cdot \sqrt[3]{3}}{\sqrt[3]{5} \cdot \sqrt[3]{3}} = \frac{\sqrt[3]{27}}{\sqrt[3]{15}} = \frac{3}{\sqrt[3]{15}}$$

$$\frac{\sqrt{9} + \sqrt{3x}}{12} = \frac{(\sqrt{9} + \sqrt{3x})(\sqrt{9} - \sqrt{3x})}{12(\sqrt{9} - \sqrt{3x})}$$

$$= \frac{9 - 3x}{12(\sqrt{9} - \sqrt{3x})}$$

$$= \frac{3(3 - x)}{3 \cdot 4(3 - \sqrt{3x})} = \frac{3 - x}{4(3 - \sqrt{3x})}$$

SECTION 7.6 RADICAL EQUATIONS AND PROBLEM SOLVING

To Solve a Radical Equation

Step 1. Write the equation so that one radical is by itself on one side of the equation.

Step 2. Raise each side of the equation to a power equal to the index of the radical and simplify.

Step 3. If the equation still contains a radical, repeat Steps 1 and 2. If not, solve the equation.

Step 4. Check all proposed solutions in the original equation.

Solve: $x = \sqrt{4x + 9} + 3$.

1. $x - 3 = \sqrt{4x + 9}$

2. $(x - 3)^2 = (\sqrt{4x + 9})^2$

$x^2 - 6x + 9 = 4x + 9$

3. $x^2 - 10x = 0$

$x(x - 10) = 0$

$x = 0 \quad \text{or} \quad x = 10$

4. The proposed solution 10 checks, but 0 does not. The solution is 10.

(continued)

DEFINITIONS AND CONCEPTS	EXAMPLES

SECTION 7.7 COMPLEX NUMBERS

$$i^2 = -1 \text{ and } i = \sqrt{-1}$$

A **complex number** is a number that can be written in the form $a + bi$, where a and b are real numbers.

Simplify: $\sqrt{-9}$.

$$\sqrt{-9} = \sqrt{-1 \cdot 9} = \sqrt{-1} \cdot \sqrt{9} = i \cdot 3 \text{ or } 3i$$

Complex Numbers	*Written in Form a + bi*
12	$12 + 0i$
$-5i$	$0 + (-5)i$
$-2 - 3i$	$-2 + (-3)i$

Multiply,

$$\sqrt{-3} \cdot \sqrt{-7} = i\sqrt{3} \cdot i\sqrt{7}$$
$$= i^2\sqrt{21}$$
$$= -\sqrt{21}$$

To add or subtract complex numbers, add or subtract their real parts and then add or subtract their imaginary parts.

To multiply complex numbers, multiply as though they are binomials.

Perform each indicated operation.

$$(-3 + 2i) - (7 - 4i) = -3 + 2i - 7 + 4i$$
$$= -10 + 6i$$

$$(-7 - 2i)(6 + i) = -42 - 7i - 12i - 2i^2$$
$$= -42 - 19i - 2(-1)$$
$$= -42 - 19i + 2$$
$$= -40 - 19i$$

The complex numbers $(a + bi)$ and $(a - bi)$ are called **complex conjugates.**

The complex conjugate of

$$(3 + 6i) \text{ is } (3 - 6i).$$

Their product is a real number:

$$(3 - 6i)(3 + 6i) = 9 - 36i^2$$
$$= 9 - 36(-1) = 9 + 36 = 45$$

To divide complex numbers, multiply the numerator and the denominator by the conjugate of the denominator.

Divide.

$$\frac{4}{2 - i} = \frac{4(2 + i)}{(2 - i)(2 + i)}$$
$$= \frac{4(2 + i)}{4 - i^2}$$
$$= \frac{4(2 + i)}{5}$$
$$= \frac{8 + 4i}{5} = \frac{8}{5} + \frac{4}{5}i$$

CHAPTER 7 REVIEW

(7.1) *Find the root. Assume that all variables represent positive numbers.*

1. $\sqrt{81}$

2. $\sqrt[4]{81}$

3. $\sqrt[3]{-8}$

4. $\sqrt[4]{-16}$

5. $-\sqrt{\dfrac{1}{49}}$

6. $\sqrt{x^{64}}$

7. $-\sqrt{36}$

8. $\sqrt[3]{64}$

9. $\sqrt[3]{-a^6 b^9}$

10. $\sqrt{16a^4 b^{12}}$

11. $\sqrt[5]{32a^5 b^{10}}$

12. $\sqrt[5]{-32x^{15}y^{20}}$

13. $\sqrt{\dfrac{x^{12}}{36y^2}}$

14. $\sqrt[3]{\dfrac{27y^3}{z^{12}}}$

Simplify. Use absolute value bars when necessary.

15. $\sqrt{(-x)^2}$

16. $\sqrt[4]{(x^2 - 4)^4}$

17. $\sqrt[3]{(-27)^3}$

18. $\sqrt[5]{(-5)^5}$

19. $-\sqrt[5]{x^5}$

20. $\sqrt[4]{16(2y + z)^{12}}$

21. $\sqrt{25(x-y)^{10}}$

22. $\sqrt[5]{-y^5}$

23. $\sqrt[9]{-x^9}$

Identify the domain and then graph each function.

24. $f(x) = \sqrt{x} + 3$

25. $g(x) = \sqrt[3]{x} - 3$; use the accompanying table.

x	-5	2	3	4	11
$g(x)$					

(7.2) Evaluate the following.

26. $\left(\dfrac{1}{81}\right)^{1/4}$

27. $\left(-\dfrac{1}{27}\right)^{1/3}$

28. $(-27)^{-1/3}$

29. $(-64)^{-1/3}$

30. $-9^{3/2}$

31. $64^{-1/3}$

32. $(-25)^{5/2}$

33. $\left(\dfrac{25}{49}\right)^{-3/2}$

34. $\left(\dfrac{8}{27}\right)^{-2/3}$

35. $\left(-\dfrac{1}{36}\right)^{-1/4}$

Write with rational exponents.

36. $\sqrt[3]{x^2}$

37. $\sqrt[5]{5x^2y^3}$

Write with radical notation.

38. $y^{4/5}$

39. $5(xy^2z^5)^{1/3}$

40. $(x+2y)^{-1/2}$

Simplify each expression. Assume that all variables represent positive numbers. Write with only positive exponents.

41. $a^{1/3}a^{4/3}a^{1/2}$

42. $\dfrac{b^{1/3}}{b^{4/3}}$

43. $(a^{1/2}a^{-2})^3$

44. $(x^{-3}y^6)^{1/3}$

45. $\left(\dfrac{b^{3/4}}{a^{-1/2}}\right)^8$

46. $\dfrac{x^{1/4}x^{-1/2}}{x^{2/3}}$

47. $\left(\dfrac{49c^{5/3}}{a^{-1/4}b^{5/6}}\right)^{-1}$

48. $a^{-1/4}(a^{5/4} - a^{9/4})$

Use a calculator and write a three-decimal-place approximation.

49. $\sqrt{20}$

50. $\sqrt[3]{-39}$

51. $\sqrt[4]{726}$

52. $56^{1/3}$

53. $-78^{3/4}$

54. $105^{-2/3}$

Use rational exponents to write each radical with the same index. Then multiply.

55. $\sqrt[3]{2} \cdot \sqrt{7}$

56. $\sqrt[3]{3} \cdot \sqrt[4]{x}$

(7.3) Perform the indicated operations and then simplify if possible. For the remainder of this review, assume that variables represent positive numbers only.

57. $\sqrt{3} \cdot \sqrt{8}$

58. $\sqrt[3]{7y} \cdot \sqrt[3]{x^2z}$

59. $\dfrac{\sqrt{44x^3}}{\sqrt{11x}}$

60. $\dfrac{\sqrt[4]{a^6b^{13}}}{\sqrt[4]{a^2b}}$

Simplify.

61. $\sqrt{60}$

62. $-\sqrt{75}$

63. $\sqrt[3]{162}$

64. $\sqrt[3]{-32}$

65. $\sqrt{36x^7}$

66. $\sqrt[3]{24a^5b^7}$

67. $\sqrt{\dfrac{p^{17}}{121}}$

68. $\sqrt[3]{\dfrac{y^5}{27x^6}}$

69. $\sqrt[4]{\dfrac{xy^6}{81}}$

70. $\sqrt{\dfrac{2x^3}{49y^4}}$

△ 71. The formula for the radius r of a circle of area A is

$$r = \sqrt{\dfrac{A}{\pi}}$$

a. Find the exact radius of a circle whose area is 25 square meters.

b. Approximate to two decimal places the radius of a circle whose area is 104 square inches.

Find the distance between each pair of points. Give an exact value and a three-decimal-place approximation.

72. $(-6, 3)$ and $(8, 4)$

73. $(-4, -6)$ and $(-1, 5)$

74. $(-1, 5)$ and $(2, -3)$

75. $(-\sqrt{2}, 0)$ and $(0, -4\sqrt{6})$

76. $(-\sqrt{5}, -\sqrt{11})$ and $(-\sqrt{5}, -3\sqrt{11})$

77. $(7.4, -8.6)$ and $(-1.2, 5.6)$

Find the midpoint of each line segment whose endpoints are given.

78. $(2, 6); (-12, 4)$

79. $(-6, -5); (-9, 7)$

80. $(4, -6); (-15, 2)$

81. $\left(0, -\dfrac{3}{8}\right); \left(\dfrac{1}{10}, 0\right)$

82. $\left(\dfrac{3}{4}, -\dfrac{1}{7}\right); \left(-\dfrac{1}{4}, -\dfrac{3}{7}\right)$

83. $(\sqrt{3}, -2\sqrt{6})$ and $(\sqrt{3}, -4\sqrt{6})$

(7.4) Perform the indicated operation.

84. $2\sqrt{50} - 3\sqrt{125} + \sqrt{98}$

85. $x\sqrt{75xy} - \sqrt{27x^3y}$

86. $\sqrt[3]{128} + \sqrt[3]{250}$

87. $3\sqrt[4]{32a^5} - a\sqrt[4]{162a}$

88. $\dfrac{5}{\sqrt{4}} + \dfrac{\sqrt{3}}{3}$

89. $\sqrt{\dfrac{8}{x^2}} - \sqrt{\dfrac{50}{16x^2}}$

90. $2\sqrt{32x^2y^3} - xy\sqrt{98y}$

91. $2a\sqrt[4]{32b^5} - 3b\sqrt[4]{162a^4b} + \sqrt[4]{2a^4b^5}$

Multiply and then simplify if possible.

92. $\sqrt{3}\left(\sqrt{27} - \sqrt{3}\right)$

93. $\left(\sqrt{x} - 3\right)^2$

94. $\left(\sqrt{5} - 5\right)\left(2\sqrt{5} + 2\right)$

95. $\left(2\sqrt{x} - 3\sqrt{y}\right)\left(2\sqrt{x} + 3\sqrt{y}\right)$

96. $\left(\sqrt{a} + 3\right)\left(\sqrt{a} - 3\right)$

97. $\left(\sqrt[3]{a} + 2\right)^2$

98. $\left(\sqrt[3]{5x} + 9\right)\left(\sqrt[3]{5x} - 9\right)$

99. $\left(\sqrt[3]{a} + 4\right)\left(\sqrt[3]{a^2} - 4\sqrt[3]{a} + 16\right)$

(7.5) *Rationalize each denominator.*

100. $\dfrac{3}{\sqrt{7}}$

101. $\sqrt{\dfrac{x}{12}}$

102. $\dfrac{5}{\sqrt[3]{4}}$

103. $\sqrt{\dfrac{24x^5}{3y^2}}$

104. $\sqrt[3]{\dfrac{15x^6y^7}{z^2}}$

105. $\dfrac{5}{2 - \sqrt{7}}$

106. $\dfrac{3}{\sqrt{y} - 2}$

107. $\dfrac{\sqrt{2} - \sqrt{3}}{\sqrt{2} + \sqrt{3}}$

Rationalize each numerator.

108. $\dfrac{\sqrt{11}}{3}$

109. $\sqrt{\dfrac{18}{y}}$

110. $\dfrac{\sqrt[3]{9}}{7}$

111. $\sqrt{\dfrac{24x^5}{3y^2}}$

112. $\sqrt[3]{\dfrac{xy^2}{10z}}$

113. $\dfrac{\sqrt{x} + 5}{-3}$

(7.6) *Solve each equation for the variable.*

114. $\sqrt{y - 7} = 5$

115. $\sqrt{2x} + 10 = 4$

116. $\sqrt[3]{2x - 6} = 4$

117. $\sqrt{x + 6} = \sqrt{x + 2}$

118. $2x - 5\sqrt{x} = 3$

119. $\sqrt{x + 9} = 2 + \sqrt{x - 7}$

Find each unknown length.

△ **120.**

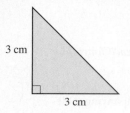

3 cm

3 cm

△ **121.**

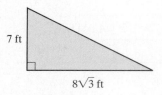

7 ft

$8\sqrt{3}$ ft

122. Beverly Hillis wants to determine the distance x across a pond on her property. She is able to measure the distances shown on the following diagram. Find how wide the lake is at the crossing point, indicated by the triangle, to the nearest tenth of a foot.

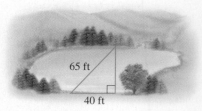

65 ft

40 ft

△ **123.** A pipe fitter needs to connect two underground pipelines that are offset by 3 feet, as pictured in the diagram. Neglecting the joints needed to join the pipes, find the length of the shortest possible connecting pipe rounded to the nearest hundredth of a foot.

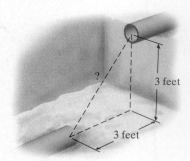

3 feet

3 feet

?

(7.7) *Perform the indicated operation and simplify. Write the result in the form $a + bi$.*

124. $\sqrt{-8}$

125. $-\sqrt{-6}$

126. $\sqrt{-4} + \sqrt{-16}$

127. $\sqrt{-2} \cdot \sqrt{-5}$

128. $(12 - 6i) + (3 + 2i)$

129. $(-8 - 7i) - (5 - 4i)$

130. $(2i)^6$

131. $-3i(6 - 4i)$

132. $(3 + 2i)(1 + i)$

133. $(2 - 3i)^2$

134. $\left(\sqrt{6} - 9i\right)\left(\sqrt{6} + 9i\right)$

135. $\dfrac{2 + 3i}{2i}$

136. $\dfrac{1 + i}{-3i}$

MIXED REVIEW

Simplify. Use absolute value bars when necessary.

137. $\sqrt[3]{x^3}$

138. $\sqrt{(x+2)^2}$

Simplify. Assume that all variables represent positive real numbers. If necessary, write answers with positive exponents only.

139. $-\sqrt{100}$

140. $\sqrt[3]{-x^{12}y^3}$

141. $\sqrt[4]{\dfrac{y^{20}}{16x^{12}}}$

142. $9^{1/2}$

143. $64^{-1/2}$

144. $\left(\dfrac{27}{64}\right)^{-2/3}$

145. $\dfrac{(x^{2/3}x^{-3})^3}{x^{-1/2}}$

146. $\sqrt{200x^9}$

147. $\sqrt{\dfrac{3n^3}{121m^{10}}}$

148. $3\sqrt{20} - 7x\sqrt[3]{40} + 3\sqrt[3]{5x^3}$

149. $(2\sqrt{x} - 5)^2$

150. Find the distance between $(-3, 5)$ and $(-8, 9)$.

151. Find the midpoint of the line segment joining $(-3, 8)$ and $(11, 24)$.

Rationalize each denominator.

152. $\dfrac{7}{\sqrt{13}}$

153. $\dfrac{2}{\sqrt{x} + 3}$

Solve.

154. $\sqrt{x} + 2 = x$

CHAPTER 7 TEST

Remember to use the Chapter Test Prep Video CD to see the fully worked-out solutions to any of the exercises you want to review.

Raise to the power or find the root. Assume that all variables represent positive numbers. Write with only positive exponents.

1. $\sqrt{216}$

2. $-\sqrt[4]{x^{64}}$

3. $\left(\dfrac{1}{125}\right)^{1/3}$

4. $\left(\dfrac{1}{125}\right)^{-1/3}$

5. $\left(\dfrac{8x^3}{27}\right)^{2/3}$

6. $\sqrt[3]{-a^{18}b^9}$

7. $\left(\dfrac{64c^{4/3}}{a^{-2/3}b^{5/6}}\right)^{1/2}$

8. $a^{-2/3}(a^{5/4} - a^3)$

Find the root. Use absolute value bars when necessary.

9. $\sqrt[4]{(4xy)^4}$

10. $\sqrt[3]{(-27)^3}$

Rationalize the denominator. Assume that all variables represent positive numbers.

11. $\sqrt{\dfrac{9}{y}}$

12. $\dfrac{4 - \sqrt{x}}{4 + 2\sqrt{x}}$

13. $\dfrac{\sqrt[3]{ab}}{\sqrt[3]{ab^2}}$

14. Rationalize the numerator of $\dfrac{\sqrt{6} + x}{8}$ and simplify.

Perform the indicated operations. Assume that all variables represent positive numbers.

15. $\sqrt{125x^3} - 3\sqrt{20x^3}$

16. $\sqrt{3}(\sqrt{16} - \sqrt{2})$

17. $(\sqrt{x} + 1)^2$

18. $(\sqrt{2} - 4)(\sqrt{3} + 1)$

19. $(\sqrt{5} + 5)(\sqrt{5} - 5)$

Use a calculator to approximate each to three decimal places.

20. $\sqrt{561}$

21. $386^{-2/3}$

Solve

22. $x = \sqrt{x - 2} + 2$

23. $\sqrt{x^2 - 7} + 3 = 0$

24. $\sqrt[3]{x + 5} = \sqrt[3]{2x - 1}$

Perform the indicated operation and simplify. Write the result in the form $a + bi$.

25. $\sqrt{-2}$

26. $-\sqrt{-8}$

27. $(12 - 6i) - (12 - 3i)$

28. $(6 - 2i)(6 + 2i)$

29. $(4 + 3i)^2$

30. $\dfrac{1 + 4i}{1 - i}$

△ **31.** Find x.

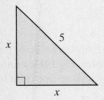

32. Identify the domain of $g(x)$. Then complete the accompanying table and graph $g(x)$.

$$g(x) = \sqrt{x + 2}$$

x	-2	-1	2	7
$g(x)$				

33. Find the distance between the points $(-6, 3)$ and $(-8, -7)$.

34. Find the distance between the points $(-2\sqrt{5}, \sqrt{10})$ and $(-\sqrt{5}, 4\sqrt{10})$.

35. Find the midpoint of the line segment whose endpoints are $(-2, -5)$ and $(-6, 12)$.

36. Find the midpoint of the line segment whose endpoints are $\left(-\dfrac{2}{3}, -\dfrac{1}{5}\right)$ and $\left(-\dfrac{1}{3}, \dfrac{4}{5}\right)$.

Solve.

37. The function $V(r) = \sqrt{2.5r}$ can be used to estimate the maximum safe velocity V in miles per hour at which a car can travel if it is driven along a curved road with a *radius of curvature r* in feet. To the nearest whole number, find the maximum safe speed if a cloverleaf exit on an expressway has a radius of curvature of 300 feet.

38. Use the formula from Exercise 37 to find the radius of curvature if the safe velocity is 30 mph.

CHAPTER 7 CUMULATIVE REVIEW

1. Simplify each expression.

  a. $3xy - 2xy + 5 - 7 + xy$

  b. $7x^2 + 3 - 5(x^2 - 4)$

  c. $(2.1x - 5.6) - (-x - 5.3)$

  d. $\frac{1}{2}(4a - 6b) - \frac{1}{3}(9a + 12b - 1) + \frac{1}{4}$

2. Simplify each expression.

  a. $2(x - 3) + (5x + 3)$

  b. $4(3x + 2) - 3(5x - 1)$

  c. $7x + 2(x - 7) - 3x$

3. Solve for x: $\dfrac{x + 5}{2} + \dfrac{1}{2} = 2x - \dfrac{x - 3}{8}$

4. Solve: $\dfrac{a - 1}{2} + a = 2 - \dfrac{2a + 7}{8}$

5. A part-time salesperson earns $600 per month plus a commission of 20% of sales. Find the minimum amount of sales needed to receive a total income of at least $1500 per month.

6. The Smith family owns a lake house 121.5 miles from home. If it takes them $4\frac{1}{2}$ hours round-trip to drive from their house to their lake house, find their average speed.

7. Solve: $2|x| + 25 = 23$

8. Solve: $|3x - 2| + 5 = 5$

9. Solve: $\left|\dfrac{x}{3} - 1\right| - 7 \geq -5$

10. Solve: $\left|\dfrac{x}{2} - 1\right| \leq 0.$

11. Graph the equation $y = |x|$.

12. Graph $y = |x - 2|$.

13. Determine the domain and range of each relation.

  a. $\{(2, 3), (2, 4), (0, -1), (3, -1)\}$

  b.

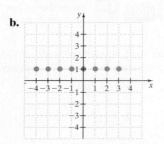

  c.

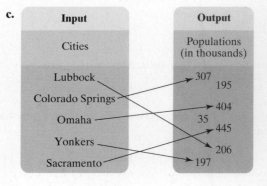

14. Find the domain and the range of each relation. Use the vertical line test to determine whether each graph is the graph of a function.

  a.

  b.

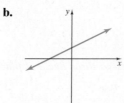

c.

(−2, 0)   (2, 0)

15. Graph $y = -3$.

16. Graph $f(x) = -2$.

17. Find the slope of the line $x = -5$.

18. Find the slope of $y = -3$.

19. Use the substitution method to solve the system.

$$\begin{cases} -\dfrac{x}{6} + \dfrac{y}{2} = \dfrac{1}{2} \\ \dfrac{x}{3} - \dfrac{y}{6} = -\dfrac{3}{4} \end{cases}$$

20. Use the substitution method to solve the system.

$$\begin{cases} \dfrac{x}{6} - \dfrac{y}{2} = 1 \\ \dfrac{x}{3} - \dfrac{y}{4} = 2 \end{cases}$$

21. Use the product rule to simplify.

a. $2^2 \cdot 2^5$

b. $x^7 x^3$

c. $y \cdot y^2 \cdot y^4$

22. At a seasonal clearance sale, Nana Long spent $33.75. She paid $3.50 for tee-shirts and $4.25 for shorts. If she bought 9 items, how many of each item did she buy?

23. Use scientific notation to simplify $\dfrac{2000 \times 0.000021}{700}$.

24. Use scientific notation to simplify and write the answer in scientific notation $\dfrac{0.0000035 \times 4000}{0.28}$.

25. If $P(x) = 3x^2 - 2x - 5$, find the following.

a. $P(1)$

b. $P(-2)$

26. Subtract $(2x - 5)$ from the sum of $(5x^2 - 3x + 6)$ and $(4x^2 + 5x - 3)$.

27. Multiply and simplify the product if possible.

a. $(x + 3)(2x + 5)$

b. $(2x - 3)(5x^2 - 6x + 7)$

28. Multiply and simplify the product if possible.

a. $(y - 2)(3y + 4)$

b. $(3y - 1)(2y^2 + 3y - 1)$

29. Find the GCF of $20x^3 y$, $10x^2 y^2$, and $35x^3$.

30. Factor $x^3 - x^2 + 4x - 4$

31. Simplify each rational expression.

a. $\dfrac{x^3 + 8}{2 + x}$

b. $\dfrac{2y^2 + 2}{y^3 - 5y^2 + y - 5}$

32. Simplify each rational expression.

a. $\dfrac{a^3 - 8}{2 - a}$

b. $\dfrac{3a^2 - 3}{a^3 + 5a^2 - a - 5}$

33. Perform the indicated operation.

a. $\dfrac{2}{x^2 y} + \dfrac{5}{3x^3 y}$

b. $\dfrac{3}{x + 2} + \dfrac{2x}{x - 2}$

c. $\dfrac{2x - 6}{x - 1} - \dfrac{4}{1 - x}$

34. Perform the indicated operations.

a. $\dfrac{3}{xy^2} - \dfrac{2}{3x^2 y}$

b. $\dfrac{5x}{x + 3} - \dfrac{2x}{x - 3}$

c. $\dfrac{x}{x - 2} - \dfrac{5}{2 - x}$

35. Simplify each complex fraction.

a. $\dfrac{\dfrac{5x}{x + 2}}{\dfrac{10}{x - 2}}$

b. $\dfrac{\dfrac{x}{y^2} + \dfrac{1}{y}}{\dfrac{y}{x^2} + \dfrac{1}{x}}$

36. Simplify each complex fraction.

a. $\dfrac{\dfrac{y - 2}{16}}{\dfrac{2y + 3}{12}}$

b. $\dfrac{\dfrac{x}{16} - \dfrac{1}{x}}{1 - \dfrac{4}{x}}$

37. Divide $10x^3 - 5x^2 + 20x$ by $5x$.

38. Divide $x^3 - 2x^2 + 3x - 6$ by $x - 2$.

39. Use synthetic division to divide $2x^3 - x^2 - 13x + 1$ by $x - 3$.

40. Use synthetic division to divide $4y^3 - 12y^2 - y + 12$ by $y - 3$.

41. Solve: $\dfrac{x + 6}{x - 2} = \dfrac{2(x + 2)}{x - 2}$.

42. Solve: $\dfrac{28}{9 - a^2} = \dfrac{2a}{a - 3} + \dfrac{6}{a + 3}$.

43. Solve: $\dfrac{1}{x} + \dfrac{1}{y} = \dfrac{1}{z}$ for x.

44. Solve: $A = \dfrac{h(a + b)}{2}$ for a.

45. Suppose that u varies inversely as w. If u is 3 when w is 5, find the constant of variation and the inverse variation equation.

46. Suppose that y varies directly as x. If $y = 0.51$ when $x = 3$, find the constant of variation and the direct variation equation.

47. Write each expression with a positive exponent, and then simplify.

   a. $16^{-3/4}$

   b. $(-27)^{-2/3}$

48. Write each expression with a positive exponent, and then simplify.

   a. $(81)^{-3/4}$

   b. $(-125)^{-2/3}$

49. Rationalize the numerator of $\dfrac{\sqrt{x} + 2}{5}$.

50. Add or subtract.

   a. $\sqrt{36a^3} - \sqrt{144a^3} + \sqrt{4a^3}$

   b. $\sqrt[3]{128ab^3} - 3\sqrt[3]{2ab^3} + b\sqrt[3]{16a}$

   c. $\dfrac{\sqrt[3]{81}}{10} + \sqrt[3]{\dfrac{192}{125}}$

8

Quadratic Equations and Functions

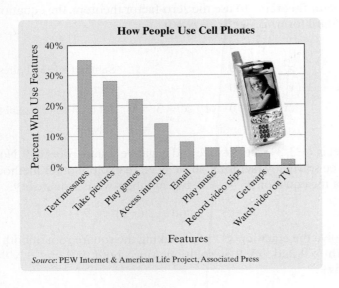

How People Use Cell Phones

Source: PEW Internet & American Life Project, Associated Press

The growth of cell phones, shown below, can be approximated by a quadratic function. More interesting information is probably given on the graph above. As shown, the cell phone is certainly no longer just a phone.

On page 523, Section 8.5, Exercises 79 and 80, you will have the opportunity to use the quadratic function below and discuss its limitations.

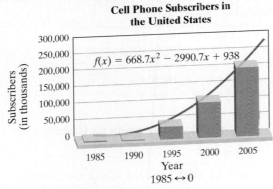

Cell Phone Subscribers in the United States

$$f(x) = 668.7x^2 - 2990.7x + 938$$

Year
$1985 \leftrightarrow 0$

Source: CTIA – The Wireless Association

An important part of the study of algebra is learning to model and solve problems. Often, the model of a problem is a quadratic equation or a function containing a second-degree polynomial. In this chapter, we continue the work begun in Chapter 5, when we solved polynomial equations in one variable by factoring. Two additional methods of solving quadratic equations are analyzed, as well as methods of solving non-linear inequalities in one variable.

8.1 SOLVING QUADRATIC EQUATIONS BY COMPLETING THE SQUARE

OBJECTIVES

1 Use the square root property to solve quadratic equations.

2 Solve quadratic equations by completing the square.

3 Use quadratic equations to solve problems.

OBJECTIVE 1 ▶ Using the square root property. In Chapter 5, we solved quadratic equations by factoring. Recall that a **quadratic,** or **second-degree, equation** is an equation that can be written in the form $ax^2 + bx + c = 0$, where a, b, and c are real numbers and a is not 0. To solve a quadratic equation such as $x^2 = 9$ by factoring, we use the zero-factor theorem. To use the zero-factor theorem, the equation must first be written in standard form, $ax^2 + bx + c = 0$.

$$x^2 = 9$$
$$x^2 - 9 = 0 \qquad \text{Subtract 9 from both sides.}$$
$$(x + 3)(x - 3) = 0 \qquad \text{Factor.}$$
$$x + 3 = 0 \quad \text{or} \quad x - 3 = 0 \qquad \text{Set each factor equal to 0.}$$
$$x = -3 \qquad\qquad x = 3 \qquad \text{Solve.}$$

The solution set is $\{-3, 3\}$, the positive and negative square roots of 9. Not all quadratic equations can be solved by factoring, so we need to explore other methods. Notice that the solutions of the equation $x^2 = 9$ are two numbers whose square is 9.

$$3^2 = 9 \qquad \text{and} \qquad (-3)^2 = 9$$

Thus, we can solve the equation $x^2 = 9$ by taking the square root of both sides. Be sure to include both $\sqrt{9}$ and $-\sqrt{9}$ as solutions since both $\sqrt{9}$ and $-\sqrt{9}$ are numbers whose square is 9.

$$x^2 = 9$$
$$\sqrt{x^2} = \pm\sqrt{9} \quad \text{The notation } \pm\sqrt{9} \text{ (read as "plus or minus } \sqrt{9}\text{")}$$
$$x = \pm 3 \qquad \text{indicates the pair of numbers } +\sqrt{9} \text{ and } -\sqrt{9}.$$

This illustrates the square root property.

▶ **Helpful Hint**

The notation ± 3, for example, is read as "plus or minus 3." It is a shorthand notation for the pair of numbers $+3$ and -3.

Square Root Property

If b is a real number and if $a^2 = b$, then $a = \pm\sqrt{b}$.

EXAMPLE 1 Use the square root property to solve $x^2 = 50$.

Solution

$$x^2 = 50$$
$$x = \pm\sqrt{50} \quad \text{Use the square root property.}$$
$$x = \pm 5\sqrt{2} \quad \text{Simplify the radical.}$$

Check:

Let $x = 5\sqrt{2}$.

$$x^2 = 50$$
$$\left(5\sqrt{2}\right)^2 \stackrel{?}{=} 50$$
$$25 \cdot 2 \stackrel{?}{=} 50$$
$$50 = 50 \quad \text{True}$$

Let $x = -5\sqrt{2}$.

$$x^2 = 50$$
$$\left(-5\sqrt{2}\right)^2 \stackrel{?}{=} 50$$
$$25 \cdot 2 \stackrel{?}{=} 50$$
$$50 = 50 \quad \text{True}$$

The solutions are $5\sqrt{2}$ and $-5\sqrt{2}$, or the solution set is $\{-5\sqrt{2}, 5\sqrt{2}\}$. ☐

PRACTICE

1 Use the square root property to solve $x^2 = 18$.

EXAMPLE 2   Use the square root property to solve $2x^2 - 14 = 0$.

Solution   First we get the squared variable alone on one side of the equation.

$$2x^2 - 14 = 0$$
$$2x^2 = 14 \qquad \text{Add 14 to both sides.}$$
$$x^2 = 7 \qquad \text{Divide both sides by 2.}$$
$$x = \pm\sqrt{7} \qquad \text{Use the square root property.}$$

Check to see that the solutions are $\sqrt{7}$ and $-\sqrt{7}$, or the solution set is $\{-\sqrt{7}, \sqrt{7}\}$.   □

PRACTICE
2   Use the square root property to solve $3x^2 - 30 = 0$.

EXAMPLE 3   Use the square root property to solve $(x + 1)^2 = 12$.

Solution
$$(x + 1)^2 = 12$$
$$x + 1 = \pm\sqrt{12} \qquad \text{Use the square root property.}$$
$$x + 1 = \pm2\sqrt{3} \qquad \text{Simplify the radical.}$$
$$x = -1 \pm 2\sqrt{3} \qquad \text{Subtract 1 from both sides.}$$

Check: Below is a check for $-1 + 2\sqrt{3}$. The check for $-1 - 2\sqrt{3}$ is almost the same and is left for you to do on your own.

$$(x + 1)^2 = 12$$
$$\left(-1 + 2\sqrt{3} + 1\right)^2 \stackrel{?}{=} 12$$
$$\left(2\sqrt{3}\right)^2 \stackrel{?}{=} 12$$
$$4 \cdot 3 \stackrel{?}{=} 12$$
$$12 = 12 \quad \text{True}$$

The solutions are $-1 + 2\sqrt{3}$ and $-1 - 2\sqrt{3}$.   □

PRACTICE
3   Use the square root property to solve $(x + 3)^2 = 20$.

EXAMPLE 4   Use the square root property to solve $(2x - 5)^2 = -16$.

Solution
$$(2x - 5)^2 = -16$$
$$2x - 5 = \pm\sqrt{-16} \qquad \text{Use the square root property.}$$
$$2x - 5 = \pm4i \qquad \text{Simplify the radical.}$$
$$2x = 5 \pm 4i \qquad \text{Add 5 to both sides.}$$
$$x = \frac{5 \pm 4i}{2} \qquad \text{Divide both sides by 2.}$$

The solutions are $\dfrac{5 + 4i}{2}$ and $\dfrac{5 - 4i}{2}$.   □

PRACTICE
4   Use the square root property to solve $(5x - 2)^2 = -9$.

Concept Check ☑

How do you know just by looking that $(x - 2)^2 = -4$ has complex, but not real solutions?

Answer to Concept Check:
answers may vary

OBJECTIVE 2 ▶ Solving by completing the square. Notice from Examples 3 and 4 that, if we write a quadratic equation so that one side is the square of a binomial, we can solve by using the square root property. To write the square of a binomial, we write perfect square trinomials. Recall that a perfect square trinomial is a trinomial that can be factored into two identical binomial factors.

Perfect Square Trinomials	*Factored Form*
$x^2 + 8x + 16$	$(x + 4)^2$
$x^2 - 6x + 9$	$(x - 3)^2$
$x^2 + 3x + \dfrac{9}{4}$	$\left(x + \dfrac{3}{2}\right)^2$

Notice that for each perfect square trinomial, **the constant term of the trinomial is the square of half the coefficient of the x-term.** For example,

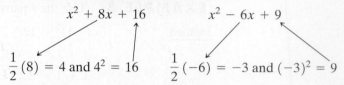

$$\frac{1}{2}(8) = 4 \text{ and } 4^2 = 16 \qquad \frac{1}{2}(-6) = -3 \text{ and } (-3)^2 = 9$$

The process of writing a quadratic equation so that one side is a perfect square trinomial is called **completing the square.**

EXAMPLE 5   Solve $p^2 + 2p = 4$ by completing the square.

Solution   First, add the square of half the coefficient of p to both sides so that the resulting trinomial will be a perfect square trinomial. The coefficient of p is 2.

$$\frac{1}{2}(2) = 1 \quad \text{and} \quad 1^2 = 1$$

Add 1 to both sides of the original equation.

$$p^2 + 2p = 4$$
$$p^2 + 2p + 1 = 4 + 1 \qquad \text{Add 1 to both sides.}$$
$$(p + 1)^2 = 5 \qquad \text{Factor the trinomial; simplify the right side.}$$

We may now use the square root property and solve for p.

$$p + 1 = \pm\sqrt{5} \qquad \text{Use the square root property.}$$
$$p = -1 \pm \sqrt{5} \quad \text{Subtract 1 from both sides.}$$

Notice that there are two solutions: $-1 + \sqrt{5}$ and $-1 - \sqrt{5}$.   □

PRACTICE
5   Solve $b^2 + 4b = 3$ by completing the square.

EXAMPLE 6   Solve $m^2 - 7m - 1 = 0$ for m by completing the square.

Solution   First, add 1 to both sides of the equation so that the left side has no constant term.

$$m^2 - 7m - 1 = 0$$
$$m^2 - 7m = 1$$

Now find the constant term that makes the left side a perfect square trinomial by squaring half the coefficient of m. Add this constant to both sides of the equation.

$$\frac{1}{2}(-7) = -\frac{7}{2} \quad \text{and} \quad \left(-\frac{7}{2}\right)^2 = \frac{49}{4}$$

$$m^2 - 7m + \frac{49}{4} = 1 + \frac{49}{4} \qquad \text{Add } \frac{49}{4} \text{ to both sides of the equation.}$$

$$\left(m - \frac{7}{2}\right)^2 = \frac{53}{4}$$ Factor the perfect square trinomial and simplify the right side.

$$m - \frac{7}{2} = \pm\sqrt{\frac{53}{4}}$$ Apply the square root property.

$$m = \frac{7}{2} \pm \frac{\sqrt{53}}{2}$$ Add $\frac{7}{2}$ to both sides and simplify $\sqrt{\frac{53}{4}}$.

$$m = \frac{7 \pm \sqrt{53}}{2}$$ Simplify.

The solutions are $\dfrac{7 + \sqrt{53}}{2}$ and $\dfrac{7 - \sqrt{53}}{2}$.   □

PRACTICE
6   Solve $p^2 - 3p + 1 = 0$ by completing the square.

EXAMPLE 7   Solve: $2x^2 - 8x + 3 = 0$.

Solution   Our procedure for finding the constant term to complete the square works only if the coefficient of the squared variable term is 1. Therefore, to solve this equation, the first step is to divide both sides by 2, the coefficient of x^2.

$$2x^2 - 8x + 3 = 0$$

$$x^2 - 4x + \frac{3}{2} = 0$$ Divide both sides by 2.

$$x^2 - 4x = -\frac{3}{2}$$ Subtract $\frac{3}{2}$ from both sides.

Next find the square of half of -4.

$$\frac{1}{2}(-4) = -2 \quad \text{and} \quad (-2)^2 = 4$$

Add 4 to both sides of the equation to complete the square.

$$x^2 - 4x + 4 = -\frac{3}{2} + 4$$

$$(x - 2)^2 = \frac{5}{2}$$ Factor the perfect square and simplify the right side.

$$x - 2 = \pm\sqrt{\frac{5}{2}}$$ Apply the square root property.

$$x - 2 = \pm\frac{\sqrt{10}}{2}$$ Rationalize the denominator.

$$x = 2 \pm \frac{\sqrt{10}}{2}$$ Add 2 to both sides.

$$= \frac{4}{2} \pm \frac{\sqrt{10}}{2}$$ Find the common denominator.

$$= \frac{4 \pm \sqrt{10}}{2}$$ Simplify.

The solutions are $\dfrac{4 + \sqrt{10}}{2}$ and $\dfrac{4 - \sqrt{10}}{2}$.   □

PRACTICE
7   Solve: $3x^2 - 12x + 1 = 0$.

The following steps may be used to solve a quadratic equation such as $ax^2 + bx + c = 0$ by completing the square. This method may be used whether or not the polynomial $ax^2 + bx + c$ is factorable.

> **Solving a Quadratic Equation in *x* by Completing the Square**
>
> **STEP 1.** If the coefficient of x^2 is 1, go to Step 2. Otherwise, divide both sides of the equation by the coefficient of x^2.
>
> **STEP 2.** Isolate all variable terms on one side of the equation.
>
> **STEP 3.** Complete the square for the resulting binomial by adding the square of half of the coefficient of *x* to both sides of the equation.
>
> **STEP 4.** Factor the resulting perfect square trinomial and write it as the square of a binomial.
>
> **STEP 5.** Use the square root property to solve for *x*.

EXAMPLE 8 Solve $3x^2 - 9x + 8 = 0$ by completing the square.

Solution $3x^2 - 9x + 8 = 0$

STEP 1. $x^2 - 3x + \dfrac{8}{3} = 0$ Divide both sides of the equation by 3.

STEP 2. $x^2 - 3x = -\dfrac{8}{3}$ Subtract $\dfrac{8}{3}$ from both sides.

Since $\dfrac{1}{2}(-3) = -\dfrac{3}{2}$ and $\left(-\dfrac{3}{2}\right)^2 = \dfrac{9}{4}$, we add $\dfrac{9}{4}$ to both sides of the equation.

STEP 3. $x^2 - 3x + \dfrac{9}{4} = -\dfrac{8}{3} + \dfrac{9}{4}$

STEP 4. $\left(x - \dfrac{3}{2}\right)^2 = -\dfrac{5}{12}$ Factor the perfect square trinomial.

STEP 5. $x - \dfrac{3}{2} = \pm\sqrt{-\dfrac{5}{12}}$ Apply the square root property.

$\qquad x - \dfrac{3}{2} = \pm\dfrac{i\sqrt{5}}{2\sqrt{3}}$ Simplify the radical.

$\qquad x - \dfrac{3}{2} = \pm\dfrac{i\sqrt{15}}{6}$ Rationalize the denominator.

$\qquad\qquad x = \dfrac{3}{2} \pm \dfrac{i\sqrt{15}}{6}$ Add $\dfrac{3}{2}$ to both sides.

$\qquad\qquad = \dfrac{9}{6} \pm \dfrac{i\sqrt{15}}{6}$ Find a common denominator.

$\qquad\qquad = \dfrac{9 \pm i\sqrt{15}}{6}$ Simplify.

The solutions are $\dfrac{9 + i\sqrt{15}}{6}$ and $\dfrac{9 - i\sqrt{15}}{6}$.

PRACTICE

8 Solve $2x^2 - 5x + 7 = 0$ by completing the square.

OBJECTIVE 3 ▶ Solving problems modeled by quadratic equations. Recall the **simple interest** formula $I = Prt$, where *I* is the interest earned, *P* is the principal, *r* is the rate of interest, and *t* is time in years. If \$100 is invested at a simple interest rate of 5% annually, at the end of 3 years the total interest *I* earned is

$$I = P \cdot r \cdot t$$

or

$$I = 100 \cdot 0.05 \cdot 3 = \$15$$

and the new principal is

$$\$100 + \$15 = \$115$$

Most of the time, the interest computed on money borrowed or money deposited is **compound interest.** Compound interest, unlike simple interest, is computed on original principal *and* on interest already earned. To see the difference between simple interest and compound interest, suppose that $100 is invested at a rate of 5% compounded annually. To find the total amount of money at the end of 3 years, we calculate as follows.

$$I = P \cdot r \cdot t$$

First year: Interest = $100 \cdot 0.05 \cdot 1 = \$5.00$
New principal = $100.00 + \$5.00 = \$105.00$

Second year: Interest = $105.00 \cdot 0.05 \cdot 1 = \$5.25$
New principal = $105.00 + \$5.25 = \$110.25$

Third year: Interest = $110.25 \cdot 0.05 \cdot 1 \approx \$5.51$
New principal = $110.25 + \$5.51 = \$115.76$

At the end of the third year, the total compound interest earned is $15.76, whereas the total simple interest earned is $15.

It is tedious to calculate compound interest as we did above, so we use a compound interest formula. The formula for calculating the total amount of money when interest is compounded annually is

$$A = P(1 + r)^t$$

where P is the original investment, r is the interest rate per compounding period, and t is the number of periods. For example, the amount of money A at the end of 3 years if $100 is invested at 5% compounded annually is

$$A = \$100(1 + 0.05)^3 \approx \$100(1.1576) = \$115.76$$

as we previously calculated.

EXAMPLE 9   Finding Interest Rates

Use the formula $A = P(1 + r)^t$ to find the interest rate r if $2000 compounded annually grows to $2420 in 2 years.

Solution

1. UNDERSTAND the problem. Since the $2000 is compounded annually, we use the compound interest formula. For this example, make sure that you understand the formula for compounding interest annually.

2. TRANSLATE. We substitute the given values into the formula.

$$A = P(1 + r)^t$$
$$2420 = 2000(1 + r)^2 \qquad \text{Let } A = 2420, P = 2000, \text{ and } t = 2.$$

3. SOLVE. Solve the equation for r.

$$2420 = 2000(1 - r)^2$$
$$\frac{2420}{2000} = (1 + r)^2 \qquad \text{Divide both sides by 2000.}$$
$$\frac{121}{100} = (1 + r)^2 \qquad \text{Simplify the fraction.}$$
$$\pm\sqrt{\frac{121}{100}} = 1 + r \qquad \text{Use the square root property.}$$

$$\pm\frac{11}{10} = 1 + r \qquad \text{Simplify.}$$

$$-1 \pm \frac{11}{10} = r$$

$$-\frac{10}{10} \pm \frac{11}{10} = r$$

$$\frac{1}{10} = r \quad \text{or} \quad -\frac{21}{10} = r$$

4. INTERPRET. The rate cannot be negative, so we reject $-\frac{21}{10}$.

Check: $\frac{1}{10} = 0.10 = 10\%$ per year. If we invest $2000 at 10% compounded annually, in 2 years the amount in the account would be $2000(1 + 0.10)^2 = 2420$ dollars, the desired amount.

State: The interest rate is 10% compounded annually.

9 Use the formula from Example 9 to find the interest rate r if $5000 compounded annually grows to $5618 in 2 years.

Graphing Calculator Explorations

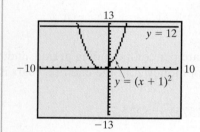

In Section 5.8, we showed how we can use a grapher to approximate real number solutions of a quadratic equation written in standard form. We can also use a grapher to solve a quadratic equation when it is not written in standard form. For example, to solve $(x + 1)^2 = 12$, the quadratic equation in Example 3, we graph the following on the same set of axes. Use Xmin = -10, Xmax = 10, Ymin = -13, and Ymax = 13.

$$Y_1 = (x + 1)^2 \quad \text{and} \quad Y_2 = 12$$

Use the Intersect feature or the Zoom and Trace features to locate the points of intersection of the graphs. (See your manuals for specific instructions.) The x-values of these points are the solutions of $(x + 1)^2 = 12$. The solutions, rounded to two decimal places, are 2.46 and -4.46.

Check to see that these numbers are approximations of the exact solutions $-1 \pm 2\sqrt{3}$.

Use a graphing calculator to solve each quadratic equation. Round all solutions to the nearest hundredth.

1. $x(x - 5) = 8$ **2.** $x(x + 2) = 5$

3. $x^2 + 0.5x = 0.3x + 1$ **4.** $x^2 - 2.6x = -2.2x + 3$

5. Use a graphing calculator and solve $(2x - 5)^2 = -16$, Example 4 in this section, using the window

$$Xmin = -20$$
$$Xmax = 20$$
$$Xscl = 1$$
$$Ymin = -20$$
$$Ymax = 20$$
$$Yscl = 1$$

Explain the results. Compare your results with the solution found in Example 4.

6. What are the advantages and disadvantages of using a graphing calculator to solve quadratic equations?

VOCABULARY & READINESS CHECK

Use the choices below to fill in each blank. Not all choices will be used.

binomial $\sqrt{b}$ $\pm\sqrt{b}$ b^2 9   25   completing the square

quadratic $-\sqrt{b}$ $\dfrac{b}{2}$ $\left(\dfrac{b}{2}\right)^2$ 3   5

1. By the square root property, if b is a real number, and $a^2 = b$, then $a =$ _____.

2. A _____ equation can be written in the form $ax^2 + bx + c = 0, a \neq 0$.

3. The process of writing a quadratic equation so that one side is a perfect square trinomial is called _____.

4. A perfect square trinomial is one that can be factored as a _____ squared.

5. To solve $x^2 + 6x = 10$ by completing the square, add _____ to both sides.

6. To solve $x^2 + bx = c$ by completing the square, add _____ to both sides.

Fill in the blank with the number needed to make the expression a perfect square trinomial.

7. $m^2 + 2m +$ _____   **8.** $m^2 - 2m +$ _____   **9.** $y^2 - 14y +$ _____   **10.** $z^2 + z +$ _____

8.1 | EXERCISE SET

Use the square root property to solve each equation. These equations have real-number solutions. See Examples 1 through 3.

1. $x^2 = 16$

2. $x^2 = 49$

3. $x^2 - 7 = 0$

4. $x^2 - 11 = 0$

5. $x^2 = 18$

6. $y^2 = 20$

7. $3z^2 - 30 = 0$

8. $2x^2 - 4 = 0$

9. $(x + 5)^2 = 9$

10. $(y - 3)^2 = 4$

11. $(z - 6)^2 = 18$

12. $(y + 4)^2 = 27$

13. $(2x - 3)^2 = 8$

14. $(4x + 9)^2 = 6$

Use the square root property to solve each equation. See Examples 1 through 4.

15. $x^2 + 9 = 0$

16. $x^2 + 4 = 0$

17. $x^2 - 6 = 0$

18. $y^2 - 10 = 0$

19. $2z^2 + 16 = 0$

20. $3p^2 + 36 = 0$

21. $(x - 1)^2 = -16$

22. $(y + 2)^2 = -25$

23. $(z + 7)^2 = 5$

24. $(x + 10)^2 = 11$

25. $(x + 3)^2 = -8$

26. $(y - 4)^2 = -18$

Add the proper constant to each binomial so that the resulting trinomial is a perfect square trinomial. Then factor the trinomial.

27. $x^2 + 16x +$ _____   **28.** $y^2 + 2y +$ _____

29. $z^2 - 12z +$ _____   **30.** $x^2 - 8x +$ _____

31. $p^2 + 9p +$ _____   **32.** $n^2 + 5n +$ _____

33. $x^2 + x +$ _____   **34.** $y^2 - y +$ _____

MIXED PRACTICE

Solve each equation by completing the square. These equations have real number solutions. See Examples 5 through 7.

35. $x^2 + 8x = -15$

36. $y^2 + 6y = -8$

37. $x^2 + 6x + 2 = 0$

38. $x^2 - 2x - 2 = 0$

39. $x^2 + x - 1 = 0$

40. $x^2 + 3x - 2 = 0$

41. $x^2 + 2x - 5 = 0$

42. $y^2 + y - 7 = 0$

43. $3p^2 - 12p + 2 = 0$

44. $2x^2 + 14x - 1 = 0$

45. $4y^2 - 12y - 2 = 0$

46. $6x^2 - 3 = 6x$

47. $2x^2 + 7x = 4$

48. $3x^2 - 4x = 4$

49. $x^2 - 4x - 5 = 0$

50. $y^2 + 6y - 8 = 0$

51. $x^2 + 8x + 1 = 0$

52. $x^2 - 10x + 2 = 0$

53. $3y^2 + 6y - 4 = 0$

54. $2y^2 + 12y + 3 = 0$

55. $2x^2 - 3x - 5 = 0$

56. $5x^2 + 3x - 2 = 0$

Solve each equation by completing the square. See Examples 5 through 8.

57. $y^2 + 2y + 2 = 0$

58. $x^2 + 4x + 6 = 0$

59. $x^2 - 6x + 3 = 0$

60. $x^2 - 7x - 1 = 0$

61. $2a^2 + 8a = -12$

62. $3x^2 + 12x = -14$

63. $5x^2 + 15x - 1 = 0$

64. $16y^2 + 16y - 1 = 0$

65. $2x^2 - x + 6 = 0$

66. $4x^2 - 2x + 5 = 0$

67. $x^2 + 10x + 28 = 0$

68. $y^2 + 8y + 18 = 0$

69. $z^2 + 3z - 4 = 0$

70. $y^2 + y - 2 = 0$

71. $2x^2 - 4x = -3$

72. $9x^2 - 36x = -40$

73. $3x^2 + 3x = 5$

74. $5y^2 - 15y = 1$

Use the formula $A = P(1 + r)^t$ to solve Exercises 75 through 78. See Example 9.

75. Find the rate r at which $3000 compounded annually grows to $4320 in 2 years.

76. Find the rate r at which $800 compounded annually grows to $882 in 2 years.

77. Find the rate at which $15,000 compounded annually grows to $16,224 in 2 years.

78. Find the rate at which $2000 compounded annually grows to $2880 in 2 years.

79. In your own words, what is the difference between simple interest and compound interest?

Neglecting air resistance, the distance s(t) in feet traveled by a freely falling object is given by the function $s(t) = 16t^2$, where t is time in seconds. Use this formula to solve Exercises 80 through 83. Round answers to two decimal places.

80. The Petronas Towers in Kuala Lumpur, built in 1997, are the tallest buildings in Malaysia. Each tower is 1483 feet tall. How long would it take an object to fall to the ground from the top of one of the towers? (*Source:* Council on Tall Buildings and Urban Habitat, Lehigh University)

81. The height of the Chicago Beach Tower Hotel, built in 1998 in Dubai, United Arab Emirates, is 1053 feet. How long would it take an object to fall to the ground from the top of the building? (*Source:* Council on Tall Buildings and Urban Habitat, Lehigh University)

82. The height of the Nurek Dam in Tajikistan (part of the former USSR that borders Afghanistan) is 984 feet. How long would it take an object to fall from the top to the base of the dam? (*Source:* U.S. Committee on Large Dams of the International Commission on Large Dams)

83. The Hoover Dam, located on the Colorado River on the border of Nevada and Arizona near Las Vegas, is 725 feet tall. How long would it take an object to fall from the top to the base of the dam? (*Source:* U.S. Committee on Large Dams of the International Commission on Large Dams)

84. If you are depositing money in an account that pays 4%, would you prefer the interest to be simple or compound? Explain why.

85. If you are borrowing money at a rate of 10%, would you prefer the interest to be simple or compound? Explain why.

REVIEW AND PREVIEW

Simplify each expression. See Section 7.1.

86. $\dfrac{3}{4} - \sqrt{\dfrac{25}{16}}$

87. $\dfrac{3}{5} + \sqrt{\dfrac{16}{25}}$

88. $\dfrac{1}{2} - \sqrt{\dfrac{9}{4}}$ **89.** $\dfrac{9}{10} - \sqrt{\dfrac{49}{100}}$

Simplify each expression. See Section 7.5.

90. $\dfrac{6 + 4\sqrt{5}}{2}$ **91.** $\dfrac{10 - 20\sqrt{3}}{2}$

92. $\dfrac{3 - 9\sqrt{2}}{6}$ **93.** $\dfrac{12 - 8\sqrt{7}}{16}$

Evaluate $\sqrt{b^2 - 4ac}$ for each set of values. See Section 7.3.

94. $a = 2, b = 4, c = -1$ **95.** $a = 1, b = 6, c = 2$

96. $a = 3, b = -1, c = -2$ **97.** $a = 1, b = -3, c = -1$

CONCEPT EXTENSIONS

Without solving, determine whether the solutions of each equation are real numbers or complex, but not real numbers. See the Concept Check in this section.

98. $(x + 1)^2 = -1$

99. $(y - 5)^2 = -9$

100. $3z^2 = 10$

101. $4x^2 = 17$

102. $(2y - 5)^2 + 7 = 3$

103. $(3m + 2)^2 + 4 = 1$

Find two possible missing terms so that each is a perfect square trinomial.

104. $x^2 + + 16$ **105.** $y^2 + + 9$

106. $z^2 + + \dfrac{25}{4}$ **107.** $x^2 + + \dfrac{1}{4}$

Solve.

△ **108.** The area of a square room is 225 square feet. Find the dimensions of the room.

△ **109.** The area of a circle is 36π square inches. Find the radius of the circle.

△ **110.** An isosceles right triangle has legs of equal length. If the hypotenuse is 20 centimeters long, find the length of each leg.

△ **111.** A 27-inch TV is advertised in the *Daily Sentry* newspaper. If 27 inches is the measure of the diagonal of the picture tube, find the measure of each side of the picture tube.

A common equation used in business is a demand equation. It expresses the relationship between the unit price of some commodity and the quantity demanded. For Exercises 112 and 113, p represents the unit price and x represents the quantity demanded in thousands.

112. A manufacturing company has found that the demand equation for a certain type of scissors is given by the equation $p = -x^2 + 47$. Find the demand for the scissors if the price is \$11 per pair.

113. Acme, Inc., sells desk lamps and has found that the demand equation for a certain style of desk lamp is given by the equation $p = -x^2 + 15$. Find the demand for the desk lamp if the price is \$7 per lamp.

8.2 SOLVING QUADRATIC EQUATIONS BY THE QUADRATIC FORMULA

OBJECTIVES

1 Solve quadratic equations by using the quadratic formula.

2 Determine the number and type of solutions of a quadratic equation by using the discriminant.

3 Solve geometric problems modeled by quadratic equations.

OBJECTIVE 1 ▶ Solving quadratic equations by using the quadratic formula. Any quadratic equation can be solved by completing the square. Since the same sequence of steps is repeated each time we complete the square, let's complete the square for a general quadratic equation, $ax^2 + bx + c = 0, a \neq 0$. By doing so, we find a pattern for the solutions of a quadratic equation known as the **quadratic formula.**

Recall that to complete the square for an equation such as $ax^2 + bx + c = 0$, we first divide both sides by the coefficient of x^2.

$$ax^2 + bx + c = 0$$

$$x^2 + \dfrac{b}{a}x + \dfrac{c}{a} = 0 \qquad \text{Divide both sides by } a, \text{ the coefficient of } x^2.$$

$$x^2 + \dfrac{b}{a}x = -\dfrac{c}{a} \qquad \text{Subtract the constant } \dfrac{c}{a} \text{ from both sides.}$$

Next, find the square of half $\dfrac{b}{a}$, the coefficient of x.

$$\frac{1}{2}\left(\frac{b}{a}\right) = \frac{b}{2a} \quad \text{and} \quad \left(\frac{b}{2a}\right)^2 = \frac{b^2}{4a^2}$$

Add this result to both sides of the equation.

$$x^2 + \frac{b}{a}x + \frac{b^2}{4a^2} = -\frac{c}{a} + \frac{b^2}{4a^2} \qquad \text{Add } \frac{b^2}{4a^2} \text{ to both sides.}$$

$$x^2 + \frac{b}{a}x + \frac{b^2}{4a^2} = \frac{-c \cdot 4a}{a \cdot 4a} + \frac{b^2}{4a^2} \qquad \begin{array}{l}\text{Find a common denominator}\\\text{on the right side.}\end{array}$$

$$x^2 + \frac{b}{a}x + \frac{b^2}{4a^2} = \frac{b^2 - 4ac}{4a^2} \qquad \text{Simplify the right side.}$$

$$\left(x + \frac{b}{2a}\right)^2 = \frac{b^2 - 4ac}{4a^2} \qquad \begin{array}{l}\text{Factor the perfect square}\\\text{trinomial on the left side.}\end{array}$$

$$x + \frac{b}{2a} = \pm\sqrt{\frac{b^2 - 4ac}{4a^2}} \qquad \text{Apply the square root property.}$$

$$x + \frac{b}{2a} = \pm\frac{\sqrt{b^2 - 4ac}}{2a} \qquad \text{Simplify the radical.}$$

$$x = -\frac{b}{2a} \pm \frac{\sqrt{b^2 - 4ac}}{2a} \qquad \text{Subtract } \frac{b}{2a} \text{ from both sides.}$$

$$x = \frac{-b \pm \sqrt{b^2 - 4ac}}{2a} \qquad \text{Simplify.}$$

This equation identifies the solutions of the general quadratic equation in standard form and is called the quadratic formula. It can be used to solve any equation written in standard form $ax^2 + bx + c = 0$ as long as a is not 0.

> **Quadratic Formula**
>
> A quadratic equation written in the form $ax^2 + bx + c = 0$ has the solutions
> $$x = \frac{-b \pm \sqrt{b^2 - 4ac}}{2a}$$

EXAMPLE 1   Solve $3x^2 + 16x + 5 = 0$ for x.

Solution   This equation is in standard form, so $a = 3$, $b = 16$, and $c = 5$. Substitute these values into the quadratic formula.

$$x = \frac{-b \pm \sqrt{b^2 - 4ac}}{2a} \qquad \text{Quadratic formula}$$

$$= \frac{-16 \pm \sqrt{16^2 - 4(3)(5)}}{2 \cdot 3} \qquad \text{Use } a = 3, b = 16, \text{ and } c = 5.$$

$$= \frac{-16 \pm \sqrt{256 - 60}}{6}$$

$$= \frac{-16 \pm \sqrt{196}}{6} = \frac{-16 \pm 14}{6}$$

$$x = \frac{-16 + 14}{6} = -\frac{1}{3} \quad \text{or} \quad x = \frac{-16 - 14}{6} = -\frac{30}{6} = -5$$

The solutions are $-\dfrac{1}{3}$ and -5, or the solution set is $\left\{-\dfrac{1}{3}, -5\right\}$.

PRACTICE
1   Solve $3x^2 - 5x - 2 = 0$ for x.

EXAMPLE 2   Solve: $2x^2 - 4x = 3$.

Solution   First write the equation in standard form by subtracting 3 from both sides.

$$2x^2 - 4x - 3 = 0$$

Now $a = 2$, $b = -4$, and $c = -3$. Substitute these values into the quadratic formula.

$$x = \frac{-b \pm \sqrt{b^2 - 4ac}}{2a}$$

$$= \frac{-(-4) \pm \sqrt{(-4)^2 - 4(2)(-3)}}{2 \cdot 2}$$

$$= \frac{4 \pm \sqrt{16 + 24}}{4}$$

$$= \frac{4 \pm \sqrt{40}}{4} = \frac{4 \pm 2\sqrt{10}}{4}$$

$$= \frac{2\left(2 \pm \sqrt{10}\right)}{2 \cdot 2} = \frac{2 \pm \sqrt{10}}{2}$$

The solutions are $\dfrac{2 + \sqrt{10}}{2}$ and $\dfrac{2 - \sqrt{10}}{2}$, or the solution set is $\left\{\dfrac{2 - \sqrt{10}}{2}, \dfrac{2 + \sqrt{10}}{2}\right\}$.

PRACTICE
2   Solve: $3x^2 - 8x = 2$.

▶ **Helpful Hint**

To simplify the expression $\dfrac{4 \pm 2\sqrt{10}}{4}$ in the preceding example, note that 2 is factored out of both terms of the numerator *before* simplifying.

$$\frac{4 \pm 2\sqrt{10}}{4} = \frac{2\left(2 \pm \sqrt{10}\right)}{2 \cdot 2} = \frac{2 \pm \sqrt{10}}{2}$$

Concept Check ✓
For the quadratic equation $x^2 = 7$, which substitution is correct?

a. $a = 1, b = 0,$ and $c = -7$

b. $a = 1, b = 0,$ and $c = 7$

c. $a = 0, b = 0,$ and $c = 7$

d. $a = 1, b = 1,$ and $c = -7$

EXAMPLE 3   Solve: $\dfrac{1}{4}m^2 - m + \dfrac{1}{2} = 0$.

Solution   We could use the quadratic formula with $a = \dfrac{1}{4}$, $b = -1$, and $c = \dfrac{1}{2}$. Instead, we find a simpler, equivalent standard form equation whose coefficients are not fractions. Multiply both sides of the equation by the LCD 4 to clear fractions.

$$4\left(\frac{1}{4}m^2 - m + \frac{1}{2}\right) = 4 \cdot 0$$

$$m^2 - 4m + 2 = 0 \qquad \text{Simplify.}$$

Substitute $a = 1$, $b = -4$, and $c = 2$ into the quadratic formula and simplify.

$$m = \frac{-(-4) \pm \sqrt{(-4)^2 - 4(1)(2)}}{2 \cdot 1} = \frac{4 \pm \sqrt{16 - 8}}{2}$$

$$= \frac{4 \pm \sqrt{8}}{2} = \frac{4 \pm 2\sqrt{2}}{2} = \frac{2\left(2 \pm \sqrt{2}\right)}{2}$$

$$= 2 \pm \sqrt{2}$$

The solutions are $2 + \sqrt{2}$ and $2 - \sqrt{2}$. □

PRACTICE
3 Solve: $\frac{1}{8}x^2 - \frac{1}{4}x - 2 = 0$.

EXAMPLE 4 Solve: $x = -3x^2 - 3$.

Solution The equation in standard form is $3x^2 + x + 3 = 0$. Thus, let $a = 3$, $b = 1$, and $c = 3$ in the quadratic formula.

$$x = \frac{-1 \pm \sqrt{1^2 - 4(3)(3)}}{2 \cdot 3} = \frac{-1 \pm \sqrt{1 - 36}}{6} = \frac{-1 \pm \sqrt{-35}}{6} = \frac{-1 \pm i\sqrt{35}}{6}$$

The solutions are $\dfrac{-1 + i\sqrt{35}}{6}$ and $\dfrac{-1 - i\sqrt{35}}{6}$. □

PRACTICE
4 Solve: $x = -2x^2 - 2$.

Concept Check ☑

What is the first step in solving $-3x^2 = 5x - 4$ using the quadratic formula?

In Example 1, the equation $3x^2 + 16x + 5 = 0$ had 2 real roots, $-\frac{1}{3}$ and -5. In Example 4, the equation $3x^2 + x + 3 = 0$ (written in standard form) had no real roots. How do their related graphs compare? Recall that the x-intercepts of $f(x) = 3x^2 + 16x + 5$ occur where $f(x) = 0$ or where $3x^2 + 16x + 5 = 0$. Since this equation has 2 real roots, the graph has 2 x-intercepts. Similarly, since the equation $3x^2 + x + 3 = 0$ has no real roots, the graph of $f(x) = 3x^2 + x + 3$ has no x-intercepts.

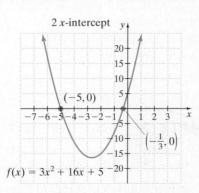

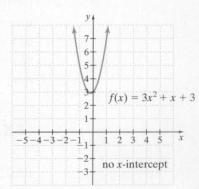

OBJECTIVE 2 ▶ Using the discriminant. In the quadratic formula, $x = \dfrac{-b \pm \sqrt{b^2 - 4ac}}{2a}$, the radicand $b^2 - 4ac$ is called the **discriminant** because, by knowing its value, we can **discriminate** among the possible number and type of solutions of a quadratic equation. Possible values of the discriminant and their meanings are summarized next.

Answer to Concept Check:
Write the equation in standard form.

Discriminant

The following table corresponds the discriminant $b^2 - 4ac$ of a quadratic equation of the form $ax^2 + bx + c = 0$ with the number and type of solutions of the equation.

$b^2 - 4ac$	*Number and Type of Solutions*
Positive	Two real solutions
Zero	One real solution
Negative	Two complex but not real solutions

EXAMPLE 5   Use the discriminant to determine the number and type of solutions of each quadratic equation.

a. $x^2 + 2x + 1 = 0$ **b.** $3x^2 + 2 = 0$ **c.** $2x^2 - 7x - 4 = 0$

Solution

a. In $x^2 + 2x + 1 = 0$, $a = 1$, $b = 2$, and $c = 1$. Thus,

$$b^2 - 4ac = 2^2 - 4(1)(1) = 0$$

Since $b^2 - 4ac = 0$, this quadratic equation has one real solution.

b. In this equation, $a = 3$, $b = 0$, $c = 2$. Then $b^2 - 4ac = 0 - 4(3)(2) = -24$. Since $b^2 - 4ac$ is negative, the quadratic equation has two complex but not real solutions.

c. In this equation, $a = 2$, $b = -7$, and $c = -4$. Then

$$b^2 - 4ac = (-7)^2 - 4(2)(-4) = 81$$

Since $b^2 - 4ac$ is positive, the quadratic equation has two real solutions.   □

PRACTICE
5   Use the discriminant to determine the number and type of solutions of each quadratic equation.

a. $x^2 - 6x + 9 = 0$ **b.** $x^2 - 3x - 1 = 0$ **c.** $7x^2 + 11 = 0$

The discriminant helps us determine the number and type of solutions of a quadratic equation, $ax^2 + bx + c = 0$. Recall that the solutions of this equation are the same as the x-intercepts of its related graph $f(x) = ax^2 + bx + c$. This means that the discriminant of $ax^2 + bx + c = 0$ also tells us the number of x-intercepts for the graph of $f(x) = ax^2 + bx + c$, or equivalently $y = ax^2 + bx + c$.

Graph of $f(x) = ax^2 + bx + c$ or $y = ax^2 + bx + c$

$b^2 - 4ac > 0$, $f(x)$ has two x-intercepts	$b^2 - 4ac = 0$, $f(x)$ has one x-intercept	$b^2 - 4ac < 0$, $f(x)$ has no x-intercepts

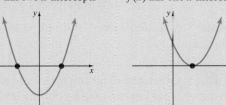
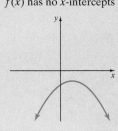

OBJECTIVE 3 ▶ Solving problems modeled by quadratic equations. The quadratic formula is useful in solving problems that are modeled by quadratic equations.

△ **EXAMPLE 6   Calculating Distance Saved**

At a local university, students often leave the sidewalk and cut across the lawn to save walking distance. Given the diagram below of a favorite place to cut across the lawn, approximate how many feet of walking distance a student saves by cutting across the lawn instead of walking on the sidewalk.

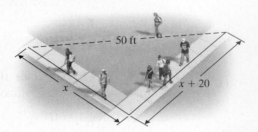

Solution

1. **UNDERSTAND.** Read and reread the problem. In the diagram, notice that a triangle is formed. Since the corner of the block forms a right angle, we use the Pythagorean theorem for right triangles. You may want to review this theorem.

2. **TRANSLATE.** By the Pythagorean theorem, we have

   In words: $(\text{leg})^2 + (\text{leg})^2 = (\text{hypotenuse})^2$

   Translate: $x^2 + (x + 20)^2 = 50^2$

3. **SOLVE.** Use the quadratic formula to solve.

   $$x^2 + x^2 + 40x + 400 = 2500 \quad \text{Square } (x + 20) \text{ and } 50.$$
   $$2x^2 + 40x - 2100 = 0 \quad \text{Set the equation equal to 0.}$$
   $$x^2 + 20x - 1050 = 0 \quad \text{Divide by 2.}$$

   Here, $a = 1, b = 20, c = -1050$. By the quadratic formula,

   $$x = \frac{-20 \pm \sqrt{20^2 - 4(1)(-1050)}}{2 \cdot 1}$$
   $$= \frac{-20 \pm \sqrt{400 + 4200}}{2} = \frac{-20 \pm \sqrt{4600}}{2}$$
   $$= \frac{-20 \pm \sqrt{100 \cdot 46}}{2} = \frac{-20 \pm 10\sqrt{46}}{2}$$
   $$= -10 \pm 5\sqrt{46} \quad \text{Simplify.}$$

4. **INTERPRET.**

Check: Your calculations in the quadratic formula. The length of a side of a triangle can't be negative, so we reject $-10 - 5\sqrt{46}$. Since $-10 + 5\sqrt{46} \approx 24$ feet, the walking distance along the sidewalk is

$$x + (x + 20) \approx 24 + (24 + 20) = 68 \text{ feet.}$$

State: A student saves about $68 - 50$ or 18 feet of walking distance by cutting across the lawn. □

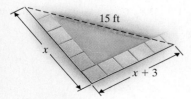

PRACTICE
6   Given the diagram, approximate to the nearest foot how many feet of walking distance a person can save by cutting across the lawn instead of walking on the sidewalk.

EXAMPLE 7 **Calculating Landing Time**

An object is thrown upward from the top of a 200-foot cliff with a velocity of 12 feet per second. The height h in feet of the object after t seconds is

$$h = -16t^2 + 12t + 200$$

How long after the object is thrown will it strike the ground? Round to the nearest tenth of a second.

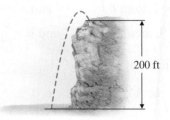

200 ft

Solution

1. UNDERSTAND. Read and reread the problem.

2. TRANSLATE. Since we want to know when the object strikes the ground, we want to know when the height $h = 0$, or

$$0 = -16t^2 + 12t + 200$$

3. SOLVE. First we divide both sides of the equation by -4.

$$0 = 4t^2 - 3t - 50 \quad \text{Divide both sides by } -4.$$

Here, $a = 4$, $b = -3$, and $c = -50$. By the quadratic formula,

$$t = \frac{-(-3) \pm \sqrt{(-3)^2 - 4(4)(-50)}}{2 \cdot 4}$$

$$= \frac{3 \pm \sqrt{9 + 800}}{8}$$

$$= \frac{3 \pm \sqrt{809}}{8}$$

4. INTERPRET.

Check: We check our calculations from the quadratic formula. Since the time won't be negative, we reject the proposed solution

$$\frac{3 - \sqrt{809}}{8}.$$

State: The time it takes for the object to strike the ground is exactly

$$\frac{3 + \sqrt{809}}{8} \text{ seconds} \approx 3.9 \text{ seconds}. \qquad \square$$

PRACTICE

7 A toy rocket is shot upward at the edge of a building, 45 feet high, with an initial velocity of 20 feet per second. The height h in feet of the rocket after t seconds is

$$h = -16t^2 + 20t + 45$$

How long after the rocket is launched will it strike the ground? Round to the nearest tenth of a second.

VOCABULARY & READINESS CHECK

Fill in each blank.

1. The quadratic formula is _____.

2. For $2x^2 + x + 1 = 0$, if $a = 2$, then $b =$ ____ and $c =$ ____.

3. For $5x^2 - 5x - 7 = 0$, if $a = 5$, then $b =$ ____ and $c =$ ____.

4. For $7x^2 - 4 = 0$, if $a = 7$, then $b =$ ____ and $c =$ ____.

5. For $x^2 + 9 = 0$, if $c = 9$, then $a =$ ____ and $b =$ ____.

6. The correct simplified form of $\dfrac{5 \pm 10\sqrt{2}}{5}$ is _____.

     a. $1 \pm 10\sqrt{2}$ **b.** $2\sqrt{2}$ **c.** $1 \pm 2\sqrt{2}$ **d.** $\pm 5\sqrt{2}$

8.2 | EXERCISE SET

Use the quadratic formula to solve each equation. These equations have real number solutions only. See Examples 1 through 3.

1. $m^2 + 5m - 6 = 0$

2. $p^2 + 11p - 12 = 0$

3. $2y = 5y^2 - 3$

4. $5x^2 - 3 = 14x$

5. $x^2 - 6x + 9 = 0$

6. $y^2 + 10y + 25 = 0$

7. $x^2 + 7x + 4 = 0$

8. $y^2 + 5y + 3 = 0$

9. $8m^2 - 2m = 7$

10. $11n^2 - 9n = 1$

11. $3m^2 - 7m = 3$

12. $x^2 - 13 = 5x$

13. $\dfrac{1}{2}x^2 - x - 1 = 0$

14. $\dfrac{1}{6}x^2 + x + \dfrac{1}{3} = 0$

15. $\dfrac{2}{5}y^2 + \dfrac{1}{5}y = \dfrac{3}{5}$

16. $\dfrac{1}{8}x^2 + x = \dfrac{5}{2}$

17. $\dfrac{1}{3}y^2 = y + \dfrac{1}{6}$

18. $\dfrac{1}{2}y^2 = y + \dfrac{1}{2}$

19. $x^2 + 5x = -2$

20. $y^2 - 8 = 4y$

21. $(m + 2)(2m - 6) = 5(m - 1) - 12$

22. $7p(p - 2) + 2(p + 4) = 3$

MIXED PRACTICE

Use the quadratic formula to solve each equation. These equations have real solutions and complex, but not real, solutions. See Examples 1 through 4.

23. $x^2 + 6x + 13 = 0$

24. $x^2 + 2x + 2 = 0$

25. $(x + 5)(x - 1) = 2$

26. $x(x + 6) = 2$

27. $6 = -4x^2 + 3x$

28. $2 = -9x^2 - x$

29. $\dfrac{x^2}{3} - x = \dfrac{5}{3}$

30. $\dfrac{x^2}{2} - 3 = -\dfrac{9}{2}x$

31. $10y^2 + 10y + 3 = 0$

32. $3y^2 + 6y + 5 = 0$

33. $x(6x + 2) = 3$

34. $x(7x + 1) = 2$

35. $\dfrac{2}{5}y^2 + \dfrac{1}{5}y + \dfrac{3}{5} = 0$

36. $\dfrac{1}{8}x^2 + x + \dfrac{5}{2} = 0$

37. $\dfrac{1}{2}y^2 = y - \dfrac{1}{2}$

38. $\dfrac{2}{3}x^2 - \dfrac{20}{3}x = -\dfrac{100}{6}$

39. $(n - 2)^2 = 2n$

40. $\left(p - \dfrac{1}{2}\right)^2 = \dfrac{p}{2}$

Use the discriminant to determine the number and types of solutions of each equation. See Example 5.

41. $x^2 - 5 = 0$

42. $x^2 - 7 = 0$

43. $4x^2 + 12x = -9$

44. $9x^2 + 1 = 6x$

45. $3x = -2x^2 + 7$

46. $3x^2 = 5 - 7x$

47. $6 = 4x - 5x^2$

48. $8x = 3 - 9x^2$

49. $9x - 2x^2 + 5 = 0$

50. $5 - 4x + 12x^2 = 0$

Solve. See Examples 6 and 7.

51. Nancy, Thelma, and John Varner live on a corner lot. Often, neighborhood children cut across their lot to save walking distance. Given the diagram below, approximate to the nearest foot how many feet of walking distance is saved by cutting across their property instead of walking around the lot.

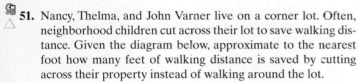

52. Given the diagram below, approximate to the nearest foot how many feet of walking distance a person saves by cutting across the lawn instead of walking on the sidewalk.

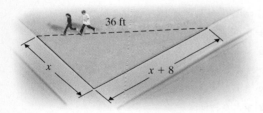

53. The hypotenuse of an isosceles right triangle is 2 centimeters longer than either of its legs. Find the exact length of each side. (*Hint:* An isosceles right triangle is a right triangle whose legs are the same length.)

54. The hypotenuse of an isosceles right triangle is one meter longer than either of its legs. Find the length of each side.

55. Bailey's rectangular dog pen for his Irish setter must have an area of 400 square feet. Also, the length must be 10 feet longer than the width. Find the dimensions of the pen.

56. An entry in the Peach Festival Poster Contest must be rectangular and have an area of 1200 square inches. Furthermore, its length must be 20 inches longer than its width. Find the dimensions each entry must have.

57. A holding pen for cattle must be square and have a diagonal length of 100 meters.

   a. Find the length of a side of the pen.

   b. Find the area of the pen.

58. A rectangle is three times longer than it is wide. It has a diagonal of length 50 centimeters.

   a. Find the dimensions of the rectangle.

   b. Find the perimeter of the rectangle.

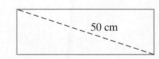

59. The heaviest reported door in the world is the 708.6 ton radiation shield door in the National Institute for Fusion Science at Toki, Japan. If the height of the door is 1.1 feet longer than its width, and its front area (neglecting depth) is 1439.9 square feet, find its width and height [Interesting note: the door is 6.6 feet thick.] (*Source: Guiness World Records*)

60. Christi and Robbie Wegmann are constructing a rectangular stained glass window whose length is 7.3 inches longer than its width. If the area of the window is 569.9 square inches, find its width and length.

61. The base of a triangle is four more than twice its height. If the area of the triangle is 42 square centimeters, find its base and height.

62. If a point B divides a line segment such that the smaller portion is to the larger portion as the larger is to the whole, the whole is the length of the *golden ratio*.

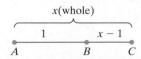

$$\overbrace{\underset{A}{\bullet}\underset{}{\underline{\quad 1 \quad}}\underset{B}{\bullet}\underset{}{\underline{\quad x-1 \quad}}\underset{C}{\bullet}}^{x(\text{whole})}$$

The golden ratio was thought by the Greeks to be the most pleasing to the eye, and many of their buildings contained numerous examples of the golden ratio. The value of the golden ratio is the positive solution of

$$\begin{matrix}(\text{smaller}) \\ (\text{larger})\end{matrix} \quad \frac{x-1}{1} = \frac{1}{x} \quad \begin{matrix}(\text{larger}) \\ (\text{whole})\end{matrix}$$

Find this value.

The Wollomombi Falls in Australia have a height of 1100 feet. A pebble is thrown upward from the top of the falls with an initial velocity of 20 feet per second. The height of the pebble h after t seconds is given by the equation $h = -16t^2 + 20t + 1100$. Use this equation for Exercises 63 and 64.

63. How long after the pebble is thrown will it hit the ground? Round to the nearest tenth of a second.

64. How long after the pebble is thrown will it be 550 feet from the ground? Round to the nearest tenth of a second.

A ball is thrown downward from the top of a 180-foot building with an initial velocity of 20 feet per second. The height of the ball h after t seconds is given by the equation $h = -16t^2 - 20t + 180$. Use this equation to answer Exercises 65 and 66.

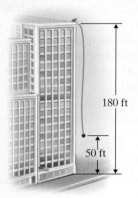

65. How long after the ball is thrown will it strike the ground? Round the result to the nearest tenth of a second.

66. How long after the ball is thrown will it be 50 feet from the ground? Round the result to the nearest tenth of a second.

REVIEW AND PREVIEW

Solve each equation. See Sections 6.6 and 7.6.

67. $\sqrt{5x-2} = 3$

68. $\sqrt{y+2} + 7 = 12$

69. $\frac{1}{x} + \frac{2}{5} = \frac{7}{x}$

70. $\frac{10}{z} = \frac{5}{z} - \frac{1}{3}$

Factor. See Section 5.7.

71. $x^4 + x^2 - 20$

72. $2y^4 + 11y^2 - 6$

73. $z^4 - 13z^2 + 36$

74. $x^4 - 1$

CONCEPT EXTENSIONS

For each quadratic equation, choose the correct substitution for a, b, and c in the standard form $ax^2 + bx + c = 0$.

75. $x^2 = -10$

    a. $a = 1, b = 0, c = -10$

    b. $a = 1, b = 0, c = 10$

    c. $a = 0, b = 1, c = -10$

    d. $a = 1, b = 1, c = 10$

76. $x^2 + 5 = -x$

    a. $a = 1, b = 5, c = -1$

    b. $a = 1, b = -1, c = 5$

    c. $a = 1, b = 5, c = 1$

    d. $a = 1, b = 1, c = 5$

77. Solve Exercise 1 by factoring. Explain the result.

78. Solve Exercise 2 by factoring. Explain the result.

Use the quadratic formula and a calculator to approximate each solution to the nearest tenth.

79. $2x^2 - 6x + 3 = 0$

80. $3.6x^2 + 1.8x - 4.3 = 0$

The accompanying graph shows the daily low temperatures for one week in New Orleans, Louisiana.

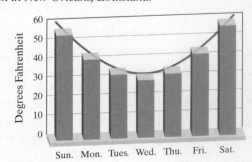

81. Which day of the week shows the greatest decrease in low temperature?

82. Which day of the week shows the greatest increase in low temperature?

83. Which day of the week had the lowest low temperature?

84. Use the graph to estimate the low temperature on Thursday.

Notice that the shape of the temperature graph is similar to the curve drawn. In fact, this graph can be modeled by the quadratic function $f(x) = 3x^2 - 18x + 56$, where $f(x)$ is the temperature in degrees Fahrenheit and x is the number of days from Sunday. (This graph is shown in blue.) Use this function to answer Exercises 85 and 86.

85. Use the quadratic function given to approximate the temperature on Thursday. Does your answer agree with the graph?

86. Use the function given and the quadratic formula to find when the temperature was $35°$ F. [*Hint:* Let $f(x) = 35$ and solve for x.] Round your answer to one decimal place and interpret your result. Does your answer agree with the graph?

87. The number of Starbucks stores can be modeled by the quadratic function $f(x) = 115x^2 + 711x + 3946$, where $f(x)$ is the number of Starbucks and x is the number of years after 2000. (*Source: Starbuck's Annual Report 2006*)

   a. Find the number of Starbucks in 2004.

   b. If the trend described by the model continues, predict the years after 2000 in which the number of Starbucks will be 25,000. Round to the nearest whole year.

88. The number of visitors to U.S. theme parks can be modeled by the quadratic equation $v(x) = 0.25x^2 + 2.6x + 315.6$, where $v(x)$ is the number of visitors (in millions) and x is the number of years after 2000. (*Source:* Price Waterhouse Coopers)

   a. Find the number of visitors to U.S. theme parks in 2005. Round to the nearest million.

   b. Find the projected number of visitors to U.S. theme parks in 2010. Round to the nearest million.

The solutions of the quadratic equation $ax^2 + bx + c = 0$ are $\dfrac{-b + \sqrt{b^2 - 4ac}}{2a}$ and $\dfrac{-b - \sqrt{b^2 - 4ac}}{2a}$.

89. Show that the sum of these solutions is $\dfrac{-b}{a}$.

90. Show that the product of these solutions is $\dfrac{c}{a}$.

Use the quadratic formula to solve each quadratic equation.

91. $3x^2 - \sqrt{12}x + 1 = 0$,
   (*Hint:* $a = 3, b = -\sqrt{12}, c = 1$)

92. $5x^2 + \sqrt{20}x + 1 = 0$

93. $x^2 + \sqrt{2}x + 1 = 0$

94. $x^2 - \sqrt{2}x + 1 = 0$

95. $2x^2 - \sqrt{3}x - 1 = 0$

96. $7x^2 + \sqrt{7}x - 2 = 0$

97. Use a graphing calculator to solve Exercises 63 and 65.

98. Use a graphing calculator to solve Exercises 64 and 66.

Recall that the discriminant also tells us the number of x-intercepts of the related function.

99. Check the results of Exercise 49 by graphing
   $y = 9x - 2x^2 + 5$.

100. Check the results of Exercise 50 by graphing
   $y = 5 - 4x + 12x^2$.

📖 STUDY SKILLS BUILDER

How Well Do You Know Your Textbook?

Let's check to see whether you are familiar with your textbook yet. For help, see Section 1.1 in this text.

1. What does the 🔲 icon mean?

2. What does the ＼ icon mean?

3. What does the △ icon mean?

4. Where can you find a review for each chapter? What answers to this review can be found in the back of your text?

5. Each chapter contains an overview of the chapter along with examples. What is this feature called?

6. Each chapter contains a review of vocabulary. What is this feature called?

7. There are free CDs in your text. What content is contained on these CDs?

8. What is the location of the section that is entirely devoted to study skills?

9. There are Practice Problems that are contained in the margin of the text. What are they and how can they be used?

8.3 SOLVING EQUATIONS BY USING QUADRATIC METHODS

OBJECTIVES

1 Solve various equations that are quadratic in form.

2 Solve problems that lead to quadratic equations.

OBJECTIVE 1 ▶ Solving equations that are quadratic in form. In this section, we discuss various types of equations that can be solved in part by using the methods for solving quadratic equations.

Once each equation is simplified, you may want to use these steps when deciding what method to use to solve the quadratic equation.

Solving a Quadratic Equation

STEP 1. If the equation is in the form $(ax + b)^2 = c$, use the square root property and solve. If not, go to Step 2.

STEP 2. Write the equation in standard form: $ax^2 + bx + c = 0$.

STEP 3. Try to solve the equation by the factoring method. If not possible, go to Step 4.

STEP 4. Solve the equation by the quadratic formula.

The first example is a radical equation that becomes a quadratic equation once we square both sides.

EXAMPLE 1   Solve: $x - \sqrt{x} - 6 = 0$.

Solution   Recall that to solve a radical equation, first get the radical alone on one side of the equation. Then square both sides.

$$
\begin{aligned}
x - 6 &= \sqrt{x} \qquad &\text{Add } \sqrt{x} \text{ to both sides.}\\
(x - 6)^2 &= \left(\sqrt{x}\right)^2 \qquad &\text{Square both sides.}\\
x^2 - 12x + 36 &= x\\
x^2 - 13x + 36 &= 0 \qquad &\text{Set the equation equal to 0.}\\
(x - 9)(x - 4) &= 0
\end{aligned}
$$

$$x - 9 = 0 \quad \text{or} \quad x - 4 = 0$$
$$x = 9 \qquad\qquad x = 4$$

Check:

Let $x = 9$	Let $x = 4$
$x - \sqrt{x} - 6 = 0$	$x - \sqrt{x} - 6 = 0$
$9 - \sqrt{9} - 6 \overset{?}{=} 0$	$4 - \sqrt{4} - 6 \overset{?}{=} 0$
$9 - 3 - 6 \overset{?}{=} 0$	$4 - 2 - 6 \overset{?}{=} 0$
$0 = 0$ True	$-4 = 0$ False

The solution is 9 or the solution set is {9}.

PRACTICE

1   Solve: $x - \sqrt{x + 1} - 5 = 0$.

EXAMPLE 2   Solve: $\dfrac{3x}{x - 2} - \dfrac{x + 1}{x} = \dfrac{6}{x(x - 2)}$.

Solution   In this equation, x cannot be either 2 or 0, because these values cause denominators to equal zero. To solve for x, we first multiply both sides of the equation by

$x(x-2)$ to clear the fractions. By the distributive property, this means that we multiply each term by $x(x-2)$.

$$x(x-2)\left(\frac{3x}{x-2}\right) - x(x-2)\left(\frac{x+1}{x}\right) = x(x-2)\left[\frac{6}{x(x-2)}\right]$$

$$3x^2 - (x-2)(x+1) = 6 \qquad \text{Simplify.}$$
$$3x^2 - (x^2 - x - 2) = 6 \qquad \text{Multiply.}$$
$$3x^2 - x^2 + x + 2 = 6$$
$$2x^2 + x - 4 = 0 \qquad \text{Simplify.}$$

This equation cannot be factored using integers, so we solve by the quadratic formula.

$$x = \frac{-1 \pm \sqrt{1^2 - 4(2)(-4)}}{2 \cdot 2} \qquad \begin{array}{l}\text{Use } a = 2, b = 1, \text{ and } c = -4 \\ \text{in the quadratic formula.}\end{array}$$
$$= \frac{-1 \pm \sqrt{1 + 32}}{4} \qquad \text{Simplify.}$$
$$= \frac{-1 \pm \sqrt{33}}{4}$$

Neither proposed solution will make the denominators 0.

The solutions are $\dfrac{-1 + \sqrt{33}}{4}$ and $\dfrac{-1 - \sqrt{33}}{4}$ or the solution set is $\left\{\dfrac{-1 + \sqrt{33}}{4},\right.$ $\left.\dfrac{-1 - \sqrt{33}}{4}\right\}$. □

PRACTICE
2 Solve: $\dfrac{5x}{x+1} - \dfrac{x+4}{x} = \dfrac{3}{x(x+1)}$.

EXAMPLE 3 Solve: $p^4 - 3p^2 - 4 = 0$.

Solution First we factor the trinomial.

$$p^4 - 3p^2 - 4 = 0$$
$$(p^2 - 4)(p^2 + 1) = 0 \qquad\qquad\qquad \text{Factor.}$$
$$(p - 2)(p + 2)(p^2 + 1) = 0 \qquad\qquad \text{Factor further.}$$
$$p - 2 = 0 \quad \text{or} \quad p + 2 = 0 \quad \text{or} \quad p^2 + 1 = 0 \qquad \begin{array}{l}\text{Set each factor equal} \\ \text{to 0 and solve.}\end{array}$$
$$p = 2 \qquad\qquad\quad p = -2 \qquad\qquad p^2 = -1$$
$$p = \pm\sqrt{-1} = \pm i$$

The solutions are $2, -2, i$ and $-i$. □

PRACTICE
3 Solve: $p^4 - 7p^2 - 144 = 0$.

> ▶ **Helpful Hint**
> Example 3 can be solved using substitution also. Think of $p^4 - 3p^2 - 4 = 0$ as
> $$(p^2)^2 - 3p^2 - 4 = 0 \qquad \begin{array}{l}\text{Then let } x = p^2, \text{ and solve and substitute back.} \\ \text{The solutions will be the same.}\end{array}$$
> $$x^2 - 3x - 4 = 0$$

Concept Check ✓

a. True or false? The maximum number of solutions that a quadratic equation can have is 2.

b. True or false? The maximum number of solutions that an equation in quadratic form can have is 2.

EXAMPLE 4   Solve: $(x - 3)^2 - 3(x - 3) - 4 = 0$.

Solution   Notice that the quantity $(x - 3)$ is repeated in this equation. Sometimes it is helpful to substitute a variable (in this case other than x) for the repeated quantity. We will let $y = x - 3$. Then

$$(x - 3)^2 - 3(x - 3) - 4 = 0$$

becomes

$$y^2 - 3y - 4 = 0 \quad \text{Let } x - 3 = y.$$
$$(y - 4)(y + 1) = 0 \quad \text{Factor.}$$

To solve, we use the zero factor property.

$$y - 4 = 0 \quad \text{or} \quad y + 1 = 0 \quad \text{Set each factor equal to 0.}$$
$$y = 4 \qquad\qquad y = -1 \quad \text{Solve.}$$

> **▶ Helpful Hint**
>
> When using substitution, don't forget to substitute back to the original variable.

To find values of x, we substitute back. That is, we substitute $x - 3$ for y.

$$x - 3 = 4 \quad \text{or} \quad x - 3 = -1$$
$$x = 7 \qquad\qquad x = 2$$

Both 2 and 7 check. The solutions are 2 and 7.   □

PRACTICE
4   Solve: $(x + 2)^2 - 2(x + 2) - 3 = 0$.

EXAMPLE 5   Solve: $x^{2/3} - 5x^{1/3} + 6 = 0$.

Solution   The key to solving this equation is recognizing that $x^{2/3} = (x^{1/3})^2$. We replace $x^{1/3}$ with m so that

$$(x^{1/3})^2 - 5x^{1/3} + 6 = 0$$

becomes

$$m^2 - 5m + 6 = 0$$

Now we solve by factoring.

$$m^2 - 5m + 6 = 0$$
$$(m - 3)(m - 2) = 0 \qquad\qquad \text{Factor.}$$
$$m - 3 = 0 \quad \text{or} \quad m - 2 = 0 \quad \text{Set each factor equal to 0.}$$
$$m = 3 \qquad\qquad m = 2$$

Since $m = x^{1/3}$, we have

$$x^{1/3} = 3 \qquad \text{or} \quad x^{1/3} = 2$$
$$x = 3^3 = 27 \quad \text{or} \qquad x = 2^3 = 8$$

Both 8 and 27 check. The solutions are 8 and 27.   □

PRACTICE
5   Solve: $x^{2/3} - 5x^{1/3} + 4 = 0$.

OBJECTIVE 2 ▶ Solving problems that lead to quadratic equations. The next example is a work problem. This problem is modeled by a rational equation that simplifies to a quadratic equation.

EXAMPLE 6   **Finding Work Time**

Together, an experienced word processor and an apprentice word processor can create a word document in 6 hours. Alone, the experienced word processor can create the document 2 hours faster than the apprentice word processor can. Find the time in which each person can create the word document alone.

Solution

1. **UNDERSTAND.** Read and reread the problem. The key idea here is the relationship between the *time* (hours) it takes to complete the job and the *part of the job* completed in one unit of time (hour). For example, because they can complete the job together in 6 hours, the *part of the job* they can complete in 1 hour is $\frac{1}{6}$.

Let

x = the *time* in hours it takes the apprentice word processor to complete the job alone

$x - 2$ = the *time* in hours it takes the experienced word processor to complete the job alone

We can summarize in a chart the information discussed

	Total Hours to Complete Job	Part of Job Completed in 1 Hour
Apprentice Word Processor	x	$\frac{1}{x}$
Experienced Word Processor	$x - 2$	$\frac{1}{x - 2}$
Together	6	$\frac{1}{6}$

2. **TRANSLATE.**

In words:	part of job completed by apprentice word processor in 1 hour	added to	part of job completed by experienced word processor in 1 hour	is equal to	part of job completed together in 1 hour
	↓	↓	↓	↓	↓
Translate:	$\frac{1}{x}$	$+$	$\frac{1}{x - 2}$	$=$	$\frac{1}{6}$

3. **SOLVE.**

$$\frac{1}{x} + \frac{1}{x - 2} = \frac{1}{6}$$

$$6x(x - 2)\left(\frac{1}{x} + \frac{1}{x - 2}\right) = 6x(x - 2) \cdot \frac{1}{6} \qquad \text{Multiply both sides by the LCD } 6x(x - 2).$$

$$6x(x - 2) \cdot \frac{1}{x} + 6x(x - 2) \cdot \frac{1}{x - 2} = 6x(x - 2) \cdot \frac{1}{6} \qquad \text{Use the distributive property.}$$

$$6(x - 2) + 6x = x(x - 2)$$

$$6x - 12 + 6x = x^2 - 2x$$

$$0 = x^2 - 14x + 12$$

Now we can substitute $a = 1$, $b = -14$, and $c = 12$ into the quadratic formula and simplify.

$$x = \frac{-(-14) \pm \sqrt{(-14)^2 - 4(1)(12)}}{2 \cdot 1} = \frac{14 \pm \sqrt{148}}{2}^{*}$$

(*This expression can be simplified further, but this will suffice as we are approximating.)

Using a calculator or a square root table, we see that $\sqrt{148} \approx 12.2$ rounded to one decimal place. Thus,

$$x \approx \frac{14 \pm 12.2}{2}$$

$$x \approx \frac{14 + 12.2}{2} = 13.1 \quad \text{or} \quad x \approx \frac{14 - 12.2}{2} = 0.9$$

4. INTERPRET.

Check: If the apprentice word processor completes the job alone in 0.9 hours, the experienced word processor completes the job alone in $x - 2 = 0.9 - 2 = -1.1$ hours. Since this is not possible, we reject the solution of 0.9. The approximate solution thus is 13.1 hours.

State: The apprentice word processor can complete the job alone in approximately 13.1 hours, and the experienced word processor can complete the job alone in approximately

$$x - 2 = 13.1 - 2 = 11.1 \text{ hours.} \qquad \square$$

PRACTICE

6 Together, Katy and Steve can groom all the dogs at the Barkin' Doggie Day Care in 4 hours. Alone, Katy can groom the dogs 1 hour faster than Steve can groom the dogs alone. Find the time in which each of them can groom the dogs alone.

EXAMPLE 7 **Finding Driving Speeds**

Beach and Fargo are about 400 miles apart. A salesperson travels from Fargo to Beach one day at a certain speed. She returns to Fargo the next day and drives 10 mph faster. Her total travel time was $14\frac{2}{3}$ hours. Find her speed to Beach and the return speed to Fargo.

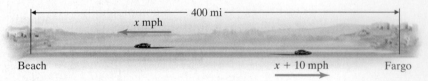

Solution

1. UNDERSTAND. Read and reread the problem. Let

$$x = \text{the speed to Beach, so}$$
$$x + 10 = \text{the return speed to Fargo.}$$

Then organize the given information in a table.

> **Helpful Hint**
>
> Since $d = rt$, then $t = \dfrac{d}{r}$. The time column was completed using $\dfrac{d}{r}$.

	distance	=	rate	·	time	
To Beach	400		x		$\dfrac{400}{x}$	← distance ← rate
Return to Fargo	400		$x + 10$		$\dfrac{400}{x + 10}$	← distance ← rate

2. TRANSLATE.

In words:

time to Beach	+	return time to Fargo	=	$14\frac{2}{3}$ hours

Translate: $\dfrac{400}{x} + \dfrac{400}{x+10} = \dfrac{44}{3}$

3. SOLVE.

$$\frac{400}{x} + \frac{400}{x+10} = \frac{44}{3}$$

$$\frac{100}{x} + \frac{100}{x+10} = \frac{11}{3} \qquad \text{Divide both sides by 4.}$$

$$3x(x+10)\left(\frac{100}{x} + \frac{100}{x+10}\right) = 3x(x+10)\cdot\frac{11}{3} \qquad \begin{array}{l}\text{Multiply both sides by}\\ \text{the LCD } 3x(x+10).\end{array}$$

$$3x(x+10)\cdot\frac{100}{x} + 3x(x+10)\cdot\frac{100}{x+10} = 3x(x+10)\cdot\frac{11}{3} \qquad \begin{array}{l}\text{Use the distributive}\\ \text{property.}\end{array}$$

$$3(x+10)\cdot 100 + 3x\cdot 100 = x(x-10)\cdot 11$$

$$300x + 3000 + 300x = 11x^2 + 110x$$

$$0 = 11x^2 - 490x - 3000 \qquad \text{Set equation equal to 0.}$$

$$0 = (11x + 60)(x - 50) \qquad \text{Factor.}$$

$$11x + 60 = 0 \quad \text{or} \quad x - 50 = 0 \qquad \begin{array}{l}\text{Set each factor equal}\\ \text{to 0.}\end{array}$$

$$x = -\frac{60}{11} \text{ or } -5\frac{5}{11}; \quad x = 50$$

4. INTERPRET.

Check: The speed is not negative, so it's not $-5\frac{5}{11}$. The number 50 does check.

State: The speed to Beach was 50 mph and her return speed to Fargo was 60 mph. □

PRACTICE
7 The 36-km S-shaped Hangzhou Bay Bridge is the longest cross-sea bridge in the world, linking Ningbo and Shanghai, China. A merchant drives over the bridge one morning from Ningbo to Shanghai in very heavy traffic and returns home that night driving 50 km per hour faster. The total travel time was 1.3 hours. Find the speed to Shanghai and the return speed to Ningbo.

8.3 EXERCISE SET

PRACTICE   WATCH   DOWNLOAD   READ   REVIEW

Solve. See Example 1.

1. $2x = \sqrt{10 + 3x}$

2. $3x = \sqrt{8x + 1}$

3. $x - 2\sqrt{x} = 8$

4. $x - \sqrt{2x} = 4$

5. $\sqrt{9x} = x + 2$

6. $\sqrt{16x} = x + 3$

Solve. See Example 2.

7. $\dfrac{2}{x} + \dfrac{3}{x-1} = 1$

8. $\dfrac{6}{x^2} = \dfrac{3}{x+1}$

9. $\dfrac{3}{x} + \dfrac{4}{x+2} = 2$

10. $\dfrac{5}{x-2} + \dfrac{4}{x+2} = 1$

11. $\dfrac{7}{x^2 - 5x + 6} = \dfrac{2x}{x-3} - \dfrac{x}{x-2}$

12. $\dfrac{11}{2x^2 + x - 15} = \dfrac{5}{2x-5} - \dfrac{x}{x+3}$

Solve. See Example 3.

13. $p^4 - 16 = 0$

14. $x^4 + 2x^2 - 3 = 0$

15. $4x^4 + 11x^2 = 3$

16. $z^4 = 81$

17. $z^4 - 13z^2 + 36 = 0$

18. $9x^4 + 5x^2 - 4 = 0$

Solve. See Examples 4 and 5.

19. $x^{2/3} - 3x^{1/3} - 10 = 0$

20. $x^{2/3} + 2x^{1/3} + 1 = 0$

21. $(5n + 1)^2 + 2(5n + 1) - 3 = 0$

22. $(m - 6)^2 + 5(m - 6) + 4 = 0$

23. $2x^{2/3} - 5x^{1/3} = 3$

24. $3x^{2/3} + 11x^{1/3} = 4$

25. $1 + \dfrac{2}{3t - 2} = \dfrac{8}{(3t - 2)^2}$

26. $2 - \dfrac{7}{x + 6} = \dfrac{15}{(x + 6)^2}$

27. $20x^{2/3} - 6x^{1/3} - 2 = 0$

28. $4x^{2/3} + 16x^{1/3} = -15$

MIXED PRACTICE

Solve. See Examples 1 through 5.

29. $a^4 - 5a^2 + 6 = 0$

30. $x^4 - 12x^2 + 11 = 0$

31. $\dfrac{2x}{x - 2} + \dfrac{x}{x + 3} = -\dfrac{5}{x + 3}$

32. $\dfrac{5}{x - 3} + \dfrac{x}{x + 3} = \dfrac{19}{x^2 - 9}$

33. $(p + 2)^2 = 9(p + 2) - 20$

34. $2(4m - 3)^2 - 9(4m - 3) = 5$

35. $2x = \sqrt{11x + 3}$

36. $4x = \sqrt{2x + 3}$

37. $x^{2/3} - 8x^{1/3} + 15 = 0$

38. $x^{2/3} - 2x^{1/3} - 8 = 0$

39. $y^3 + 9y - y^2 - 9 = 0$

40. $x^3 + x - 3x^2 - 3 = 0$

41. $2x^{2/3} + 3x^{1/3} - 2 = 0$

42. $6x^{2/3} - 25x^{1/3} - 25 = 0$

43. $x^{-2} - x^{-1} - 6 = 0$

44. $y^{-2} - 8y^{-1} + 7 = 0$

45. $x - \sqrt{x} = 2$

46. $x - \sqrt{3x} = 6$

47. $\dfrac{x}{x - 1} + \dfrac{1}{x + 1} = \dfrac{2}{x^2 - 1}$

48. $\dfrac{x}{x - 5} + \dfrac{5}{x + 5} = -\dfrac{1}{x^2 - 25}$

49. $p^4 - p^2 - 20 = 0$

50. $x^4 - 10x^2 + 9 = 0$

51. $(x + 3)(x^2 - 3x + 9) = 0$

52. $(x - 6)(x^2 + 6x + 36) = 0$

53. $1 = \dfrac{4}{x - 7} + \dfrac{5}{(x - 7)^2}$

54. $3 + \dfrac{1}{2p + 4} = \dfrac{10}{(2p + 4)^2}$

55. $27y^4 + 15y^2 = 2$

56. $8z^4 + 14z^2 = -5$

Solve. See Examples 6 and 7.

57. A jogger ran 3 miles, decreased her speed by 1 mile per hour, and then ran another 4 miles. If her total time jogging was $1\dfrac{3}{5}$ hours, find her speed for each part of her run.

58. Mark Keaton's workout consists of jogging for 3 miles, and then riding his bike for 5 miles at a speed 4 miles per hour faster than he jogs. If his total workout time is 1 hour, find his jogging speed and his biking speed.

59. A Chinese restaurant in Mandeville, Louisiana, has a large goldfish pond around the restaurant. Suppose that an inlet pipe and a hose together can fill the pond in 8 hours. The inlet pipe alone can complete the job in one hour less time than the hose alone. Find the time that the hose can complete the job alone and the time that the inlet pipe can complete the job alone. Round each to the nearest tenth of an hour.

60. A water tank on a farm in Flatonia, Texas, can be filled with a large inlet pipe and a small inlet pipe in 3 hours. The large inlet pipe alone can fill the tank in 2 hours less time than the small inlet pipe alone. Find the time to the nearest tenth of an hour each pipe can fill the tank alone.

61. Roma Sherry drove 330 miles from her hometown to Tucson. During her return trip, she was able to increase her speed by 11 mph. If her return trip took 1 hour less time, find her original speed and her speed returning home.

62. A salesperson drove to Portland, a distance of 300 miles. During the last 80 miles of his trip, heavy rainfall forced him to decrease his speed by 15 mph. If his total driving time was 6 hours, find his original speed and his speed during the rainfall.

63. Bill Shaughnessy and his son Billy can clean the house together in 4 hours. When the son works alone, it takes him an hour longer to clean than it takes his dad alone. Find how long to the nearest tenth of an hour it takes the son to clean alone.

64. Together, Noodles and Freckles eat a 50-pound bag of dog food in 30 days. Noodles by himself eats a 50-pound bag in 2 weeks less time than Freckles does by himself. How many days to the nearest whole day would a 50-pound bag of dog food last Freckles?

65. The product of a number and 4 less than the number is 96. Find the number.

66. A whole number increased by its square is two more than twice itself. Find the number.

△ **67.** Suppose that an open box is to be made from a square sheet of cardboard by cutting out squares from each corner as shown and then folding along the dotted lines. If the box is to have a volume of 300 cubic centimeters, find the original dimensions of the sheet of cardboard.

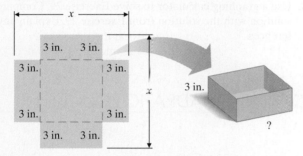

a. The ? in the drawing above will be the length (and also the width) of the box as shown. Represent this length in terms of x.

b. Use the formula for volume of a box, $V = l \cdot w \cdot h$, to write an equation in x.

c. Solve the equation for x and give the dimensions of the sheet of cardboard. Check your solution.

△ **68.** Suppose that an open box is to be made from a square sheet of cardboard by cutting out squares from each corner as shown and then folding along the dotted lines. If the box is to have a volume of 128 cubic inches, find the original dimensions of the sheet of cardboard.

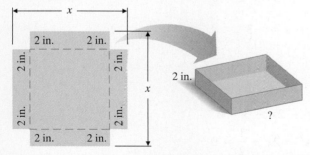

a. The ? in the drawing above will be the length (and also the width) of the box as shown. Represent this length in terms of x.

b. Use the formula for volume of a box, $V = l \cdot w \cdot h$, to write an equation in x.

c. Solve the equation for x and give the dimensions of the sheet of cardboard. Check your solution.

△ **69.** A sprinkler that sprays water in a circular motion is to be used to water a square garden. If the area of the garden is 920 square feet, find the smallest whole number *radius* that the sprinkler can be adjusted to so that the entire garden is watered.

△ **70.** Suppose that a square field has an area of 6270 square feet. See Exercise 69 and find a new sprinkler radius.

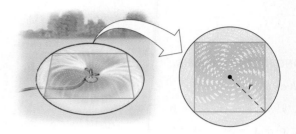

REVIEW AND PREVIEW

Solve each inequality. See Section 2.4.

71. $\dfrac{5x}{3} + 2 \le 7$

72. $\dfrac{2x}{3} + \dfrac{1}{6} \ge 2$

73. $\dfrac{y - 1}{15} > -\dfrac{2}{5}$

74. $\dfrac{z - 2}{12} < \dfrac{1}{4}$

Find the domain and range of each graphed relation. Decide which relations are also functions. See Section 3.2.

75.

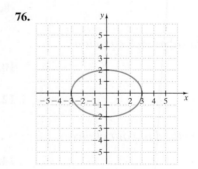

76.

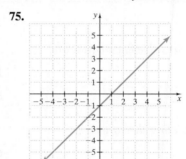

77.

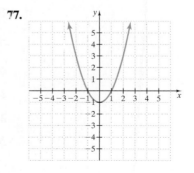

78.

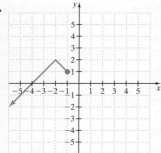

CONCEPT EXTENSIONS

Solve.

79. $y^3 + 9y - y^2 - 9 = 0$

80. $x^3 + x - 3x^2 - 3 = 0$

81. $x^{-2} - x^{-1} - 6 = 0$

82. $y^{-2} - 8y^{-1} + 7 = 0$

83. $2x^3 = -54$

84. $y^3 - 216 = 0$

85. Write a polynomial equation that has three solutions: 2, 5, and −7.

86. Write a polynomial equation that has three solutions: 0, $2i$, and $-2i$.

87. At the 2007 Grand Prix of Long Beach auto race, Simon Pagenaud posted the fastest lap speed, but Sebastian Bourdais won the race. One lap through the streets of Long Beach is 10,391 feet (1.968 miles) long. Pagenaud's fastest lap speed was 0.55 foot per second faster than Bourdais's fastest lap speed. Traveling at these fastest speeds, Bourdais would have taken 0.25 second longer than Pagenaud to complete a lap. (*Source:* Championship Auto Racing Teams, Inc.)

　a. Find Sebastian Bourdais's fastest lap speed during the race. Round to two decimal places.

　b. Find Simon Pagenaud's fastest last speed during the race. Round to two decimal places.

　c. Convert each speed to miles per hour. Round to one decimal place.

88. Use a graphing calculator to solve Exercise 29. Compare the solution with the solution from Exercise 29. Explain any differences.

INTEGRATED REVIEW　SUMMARY ON SOLVING QUADRATIC EQUATIONS

Sections 8.1–8.3

Use the square root property to solve each equation.

1. $x^2 - 10 = 0$

2. $x^2 - 14 = 0$

3. $(x - 1)^2 = 8$

4. $(x + 5)^2 = 12$

Solve each equation by completing the square.

5. $x^2 + 2x - 12 = 0$

6. $x^2 - 12x + 11 = 0$

7. $3x^2 + 3x = 5$

8. $16y^2 + 16y = 1$

Use the quadratic formula to solve each equation

9. $2x^2 - 4x + 1 = 0$

10. $\frac{1}{2}x^2 + 3x + 2 = 0$

11. $x^2 + 4x = -7$

12. $x^2 + x = -3$

Solve each equation. Use a method of your choice.

13. $x^2 + 3x + 6 = 0$

14. $2x^2 + 18 = 0$

15. $x^2 + 17x = 0$

16. $4x^2 - 2x - 3 = 0$

17. $(x - 2)^2 = 27$

18. $\frac{1}{2}x^2 - 2x + \frac{1}{2} = 0$

19. $3x^2 + 2x = 8$

20. $2x^2 = -5x - 1$

21. $x(x - 2) = 5$

22. $x^2 - 31 = 0$

23. $5x^2 - 55 = 0$

24. $5x^2 + 55 = 0$

25. $x(x + 5) = 66$

26. $5x^2 + 6x - 2 = 0$

27. $2x^2 + 3x = 1$

△ **28.** The diagonal of a square room measures 20 feet. Find the exact length of a side of the room. Then approximate the length to the nearest tenth of a foot.

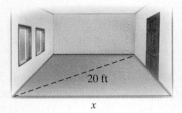

29. Together, Jack and Lucy Hoag can prepare a crawfish boil for a large party in 4 hours. Lucy alone can complete the job in 2 hours less time than Jack alone. Find the time that each person can prepare the crawfish boil alone. Round each time to the nearest tenth of an hour.

30. Diane Gray exercises at Total Body Gym. On the treadmill, she runs 5 miles, then increases her speed by 1 mile per hour and runs an additional 2 miles. If her total time on the tread mill is $1\frac{1}{3}$ hours, find her speed during each part of her run.

8.4 NONLINEAR INEQUALITIES IN ONE VARIABLE

OBJECTIVES

1 Solve polynomial inequalities of degree 2 or greater.

2 Solve inequalities that contain rational expressions with variables in the denominator.

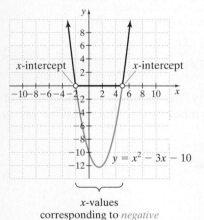

x-values corresponding to *negative* y-values

OBJECTIVE 1 ▶ Solving polynomial inequalities. Just as we can solve linear inequalities in one variable, so can we also solve quadratic inequalities in one variable. A **quadratic inequality** is an inequality that can be written so that one side is a quadratic expression and the other side is 0. Here are examples of quadratic inequalities in one variable. Each is written in **standard form.**

$$x^2 - 10x + 7 \leq 0 \qquad 3x^2 + 2x - 6 > 0$$
$$2x^2 + 9x - 2 < 0 \qquad x^2 - 3x + 11 \geq 0$$

A solution of a quadratic inequality in one variable is a value of the variable that makes the inequality a true statement.

The value of an expression such as $x^2 - 3x - 10$ will sometimes be positive, sometimes negative, and sometimes 0, depending on the value substituted for x. To solve the inequality $x^2 - 3x - 10 < 0$, we are looking for all values of x that make the expression $x^2 - 3x - 10$ **less than 0,** or **negative.** To understand how we find these values, we'll study the graph of the quadratic function $y = x^2 - 3x - 10$.

Notice that the x-values for which y is positive are separated from the x values for which y is negative by the x-intercepts. (Recall that the x-intercepts correspond to values of x for which $y = 0$.) Thus, the solution set of $x^2 - 3x - 10 < 0$ consists of all real numbers from -2 to 5, or in interval notation, $(-2, 5)$.

It is not necessary to graph $y = x^2 - 3x - 10$ to solve the related inequality $x^2 - 3x - 10 < 0$. Instead, we can draw a number line representing the x-axis and keep the following in mind: *A region on the number line for which the value of $x^2 - 3x - 10$ is positive is separated from a region on the number line for which the value of $x^2 - 3x - 10$ is negative by a value for which the expression is 0.*

Let's find these values for which the expression is 0 by solving the related equation:

$$x^2 - 3x - 10 = 0$$
$$(x - 5)(x + 2) = 0 \qquad \text{Factor.}$$
$$x - 5 = 0 \quad \text{or} \quad x + 2 = 0 \qquad \text{Set each factor equal to 0.}$$
$$x = 5 \quad x = -2 \qquad \text{Solve.}$$

These two numbers -2 and 5, divide the number line into three regions. We will call the regions A, B, and C. These regions are important because, if the value of $x^2 - 3x - 10$ is negative when a number from a region is substituted for x, then $x^2 - 3x - 10$ is negative when any number in that region is substituted for x. The same is true if the value of $x^2 - 3x - 10$ is positive for a particular value of x in a region.

To see whether the inequality $x^2 - 3x - 10 < 0$ is true or false in each region, we choose a test point from each region and substitute its value for x in the inequality

$x^2 - 3x - 10 < 0$. If the resulting inequality is true, the region containing the test point is a solution region.

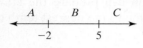

Region	Test Point Value	$(x - 5)(x + 2) < 0$	Result
A	−3	$(-8)(-1) < 0$	False
B	0	$(-5)(2) < 0$	True
C	6	$(1)(8) < 0$	False

The values in region *B* satisfy the inequality. The numbers −2 and 5 are not included in the solution set since the inequality symbol is $<$. The solution set is $(-2, 5)$, and its graph is shown.

$$\underset{\text{F } -2 \quad \text{T} \quad 5 \text{ F}}{\overset{A \qquad B \qquad C}{\xleftarrow{\hspace{1cm}(\hspace{1cm})\hspace{1cm}}\rightarrow}}$$

EXAMPLE 1   Solve: $(x + 3)(x - 3) > 0$.

Solution   First we solve the related equation, $(x + 3)(x - 3) = 0$.

$$(x + 3)(x - 3) = 0$$
$$x + 3 = 0 \quad \text{or} \quad x - 3 = 0$$
$$x = -3 \qquad\qquad x = 3$$

The two numbers −3 and 3 separate the number line into three regions, *A*, *B*, and *C*.
   Now we substitute the value of a test point from each region. If the test value satisfies the inequality, every value in the region containing the test value is a solution.

Region	Test Point Value	$(x + 3)(x - 3) > 0$	Result
A	−4	$(-1)(-7) > 0$	True
B	0	$(3)(-3) > 0$	False
C	4	$(7)(1) > 0$	True

The points in regions *A* and *C* satisfy the inequality. The numbers −3 and 3 are not included in the solution since the inequality symbol is $>$. The solution set is $(-\infty, -3) \cup (3, \infty)$, and its graph is shown.

$$\underset{\text{T } -3 \quad \text{F} \quad 3 \text{ T}}{\overset{A \qquad B \qquad C}{\xleftarrow{\hspace{1cm}) \hspace{1cm}(\hspace{1cm}}\rightarrow}}$$

□

PRACTICE
1   Solve: $(x - 4)(x + 3) > 0$.

The following steps may be used to solve a polynomial inequality.

Solving a Polynomial Inequality

STEP 1. Write the inequality in standard form and then solve the related equation.

STEP 2. Separate the number line into regions with the solutions from Step 1.

STEP 3. For each region, choose a test point and determine whether its value satisfies the *original inequality*.

STEP 4. The solution set includes the regions whose test point value is a solution. If the inequality symbol is $\leq$ or $\geq$, the values from Step 1 are solutions; if $<$ or $>$, they are not.

Concept Check ☑

When choosing a test point in Step 4, why would the solutions from Step 2 not make good choices for test points?

EXAMPLE 2   Solve: $x^2 - 4x \leq 0$.

Solution   First we solve the related equation, $x^2 - 4x = 0$.

$$x^2 - 4x = 0$$
$$x(x - 4) = 0$$
$$x = 0 \quad \text{or} \quad x = 4$$

The numbers 0 and 4 separate the number line into three regions, A, B, and C.

We check a test value in each region in the original inequality. Values in region B satisfy the inequality. The numbers 0 and 4 are included in the solution since the inequality symbol is $\leq$. The solution set is $[0, 4]$, and its graph is shown.

PRACTICE
2   Solve: $x^2 - 8x \leq 0$.

EXAMPLE 3   Solve: $(x + 2)(x - 1)(x - 5) \leq 0$.

Solution   First we solve $(x + 2)(x - 1)(x - 5) = 0$. By inspection, we see that the solutions are $-2, 1$ and 5. They separate the number line into four regions, A, B, C, and D. Next we check test points from each region.

Region	Test Point Value	$(x + 2)(x - 1)(x - 5) \leq 0$	Result
A	-3	$(-1)(-4)(-8) \leq 0$	True
B	0	$(2)(-1)(-5) \leq 0$	False
C	2	$(4)(1)(-3) \leq 0$	True
D	6	$(8)(5)(1) \leq 0$	False

The solution set is $(-\infty, -2] \cup [1, 5]$, and its graph is shown. We include the numbers -2, 1, and 5 because the inequality symbol is $\leq$.

PRACTICE
3   Solve: $(x + 3)(x - 2)(x + 1) \leq 0$.

OBJECTIVE 2 ▶ Solving rational inequalities.   Inequalities containing rational expressions with variables in the denominator are solved by using a similar procedure.

Answer to Concept Check:
The solutions found in Step 2 have a value of 0 in the original inequality.

EXAMPLE 4   Solve: $\dfrac{x+2}{x-3} \le 0$.

Solution   First we find all values that make the denominator equal to 0. To do this, we solve $x - 3 = 0$ and find that $x = 3$.

Next, we solve the related equation $\dfrac{x+2}{x-3} = 0$.

$$\dfrac{x+2}{x-3} = 0$$

$$x + 2 = 0 \qquad \text{Multiply both sides by the LCD, } x - 3.$$

$$x = -2$$

Now we place these numbers on a number line and proceed as before, checking test point values in the original inequality.

$$
\begin{array}{ccc}
A & B & C \\
\hline
\\
-2 & & 3
\end{array}
$$

Choose -3 from region A.   **Choose 0 from region B.**   **Choose 4 from region C.**

$\dfrac{x+2}{x-3} \le 0$	$\dfrac{x+2}{x-3} \le 0$	$\dfrac{x+2}{x-3} \le 0$
$\dfrac{-3+2}{-3-3} \le 0$	$\dfrac{0+2}{0-3} \le 0$	$\dfrac{4+2}{4-3} \le 0$
$\dfrac{-1}{-6} \le 0$	$-\dfrac{2}{3} \le 0$ True	$6 \le 0$ False
$\dfrac{1}{6} \le 0$ False		

The solution set is $[-2, 3)$. This interval includes -2 because -2 satisfies the original inequality. This interval does not include 3, because 3 would make the denominator 0.

$$
\begin{array}{ccc}
A & B & C \\
\hline
\\
\text{F } -2 \;\; \text{T} & 3 & \text{F}
\end{array}
$$

□

PRACTICE
4   Solve: $\dfrac{x-5}{x+4} \le 0$.

The following steps may be used to solve a rational inequality with variables in the denominator.

Solving a Rational Inequality

STEP 1. Solve for values that make all denominators 0.

STEP 2. Solve the related equation.

STEP 3. Separate the number line into regions with the solutions from Steps 1 and 2.

STEP 4. For each region, choose a test point and determine whether its value satisfies the _original inequality_.

STEP 5. The solution set includes the regions whose test point value is a solution. Check whether to include values from Step 2. Be sure _not_ to include values that make any denominator 0.

EXAMPLE 5   Solve: $\dfrac{5}{x+1} < -2$.

Solution   First we find values for x that make the denominator equal to 0.

$$x + 1 = 0$$
$$x = -1$$

Next we solve $\dfrac{5}{x+1} = -2$.

$$(x+1) \cdot \dfrac{5}{x+1} = (x+1) \cdot -2 \quad \text{Multiply both sides by the LCD, } x+1.$$
$$5 = -2x - 2 \qquad \text{Simplify.}$$
$$7 = -2x$$
$$-\dfrac{7}{2} = x$$

We use these two solutions to divide a number line into three regions and choose test points. Only a test point value from region B satisfies the _original inequality_. The solution set is $\left(-\dfrac{7}{2}, -1\right)$, and its graph is shown.

PRACTICE
5   Solve: $\dfrac{7}{x+3} < 5$.

VOCABULARY & READINESS CHECK

Write the graphed solution set in interval notation.

1.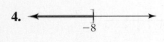
   _____

2.
   _____

3.
   _____

4.
   _____

5.
   _____

6.
   _____

8.4 | EXERCISE SET

MyMathLab _Powered by CourseCompass™ and MathXL™_

 PRACTICE   WATCH   DOWNLOAD   READ   REVIEW

Solve each quadratic inequality. Write the solution set in interval notation. See Examples 1 through 3.

1. $(x+1)(x+5) > 0$

2. $(x+1)(x+5) \le 0$

3. $(x-3)(x+4) \le 0$

4. $(x+4)(x-1) > 0$

5. $x^2 - 7x + 10 \le 0$

6. $x^2 + 8x + 15 \ge 0$

7. $3x^2 + 16x < -5$

8. $2x^2 - 5x < 7$

9. $(x-6)(x-4)(x-2) > 0$

10. $(x-6)(x-4)(x-2) \le 0$

11. $x(x-1)(x+4) \le 0$

12. $x(x-6)(x+2) > 0$

13. $(x^2-9)(x^2-4) > 0$

14. $(x^2-16)(x^2-1) \le 0$

Solve each inequality. Write the solution set in interval notation. See Example 4.

15. $\dfrac{x + 7}{x - 2} < 0$

16. $\dfrac{x - 5}{x - 6} > 0$

17. $\dfrac{5}{x + 1} > 0$

18. $\dfrac{3}{y - 5} < 0$

19. $\dfrac{x + 1}{x - 4} \geq 0$

20. $\dfrac{x + 1}{x - 4} \leq 0$

Solve each inequality. Write the solution set in interval notation. See Example 5.

21. $\dfrac{3}{x - 2} < 4$

22. $\dfrac{-2}{y + 3} > 2$

23. $\dfrac{x^2 + 6}{5x} \geq 1$

24. $\dfrac{y^2 + 15}{8y} \leq 1$

MIXED PRACTICE

Solve each inequality. Write the solution set in interval notation.

25. $(x - 8)(x + 7) > 0$

26. $(x - 5)(x + 1) < 0$

27. $(2x - 3)(4x + 5) \leq 0$

28. $(6x + 7)(7x - 12) > 0$

29. $x^2 > x$

30. $x^2 < 25$

31. $(2x - 8)(x + 4)(x - 6) \leq 0$

32. $(3x - 12)(x + 5)(2x - 3) \geq 0$

33. $6x^2 - 5x \geq 6$

34. $12x^2 + 11x \leq 15$

35. $4x^3 + 16x^2 - 9x - 36 > 0$

36. $x^3 + 2x^2 - 4x - 8 < 0$

37. $x^4 - 26x^2 + 25 \geq 0$

38. $16x^4 - 40x^2 + 9 \leq 0$

39. $(2x - 7)(3x + 5) > 0$

40. $(4x - 9)(2x + 5) < 0$

41. $\dfrac{x}{x - 10} < 0$

42. $\dfrac{x + 10}{x - 10} > 0$

43. $\dfrac{x - 5}{x + 4} \geq 0$

44. $\dfrac{x - 3}{x + 2} \leq 0$

45. $\dfrac{x(x + 6)}{(x - 7)(x + 1)} \geq 0$

46. $\dfrac{(x - 2)(x + 2)}{(x + 1)(x - 4)} \leq 0$

47. $\dfrac{-1}{x - 1} > -1$

48. $\dfrac{4}{y + 2} < -2$

49. $\dfrac{x}{x + 4} \leq 2$

50. $\dfrac{4x}{x - 3} \geq 5$

51. $\dfrac{z}{z - 5} \geq 2z$

52. $\dfrac{p}{p + 4} \leq 3p$

53. $\dfrac{(x + 1)^2}{5x} > 0$

54. $\dfrac{(2x - 3)^2}{x} < 0$

REVIEW AND PREVIEW

Recall that the graph of $f(x) + K$ is the same as the graph of $f(x)$ shifted K units upward if $K > 0$ and $|K|$ units downward if $K < 0$. Use the graph of $f(x) = |x|$ below to sketch the graph of each function. See Section 3.6.

55. $g(x) = |x| + 2$

56. $H(x) = |x| - 2$

57. $F(x) = |x| - 1$

58. $h(x) = |x| + 5$

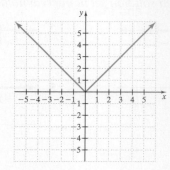

Use the graph of $f(x) = x^2$ below to sketch the graph of each function.

59. $F(x) = x^2 - 3$

60. $h(x) = x^2 - 4$

61. $H(x) = x^2 + 1$

62. $g(x) = x^2 + 3$

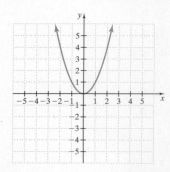

CONCEPT EXTENSIONS

63. Explain why $\dfrac{x+2}{x-3} > 0$ and $(x+2)(x-3) > 0$ have the same solutions.

64. Explain why $\dfrac{x+2}{x-3} \geq 0$ and $(x+2)(x-3) \geq 0$ do not have the same solutions.

Find all numbers that satisfy each of the following.

65. A number minus its reciprocal is less than zero. Find the numbers.

66. Twice a number added to its reciprocal is nonnegative. Find the numbers.

67. The total profit function $P(x)$ for a company producing x thousand units is given by

$$P(x) = -2x^2 + 26x - 44$$

Find the values of x for which the company makes a profit. [*Hint:* The company makes a profit when $P(x) > 0$.]

68. A projectile is fired straight up from the ground with an initial velocity of 80 feet per second. Its height $s(t)$ in feet at any time t is given by the function

$$s(t) = -16t^2 + 80t$$

Find the interval of time for which the height of the projectile is greater than 96 feet.

Use a graphing calculator to check each exercise.

69. Exercise 25

70. Exercise 26

71. Exercise 37

72. Exercise 38

THE BIGGER PICTURE   SOLVING EQUATIONS AND INEQUALITIES

Continue your outline from Sections 2.4, 2.5, 2.7, 5.8, 6.5, and 7.6. Write how to recognize and how to solve quadratic equations and nonlinear inequalities in your own words. For example:

Solving Equations and Inequalities

I. Equations

 A. Linear equations (Sec. 2.1)

 B. Absolute value equations (Sec. 2.6)

 C. Quadratic and higher degree equations (Sec. 5.8, 8.1, 8.2, 8.3)

Solving by Factoring:
$$2x^2 - 7x = 9$$
$$2x^2 - 7x - 9 = 0$$
$$(2x - 9)(x + 1) = 0$$
$$2x - 9 = 0$$
or $\quad x + 1 = 0$
$$x = \frac{9}{2} \quad \text{or} \quad x = -1$$

Solving by the Quadratic Formula:
$$2x^2 + x - 2 = 0$$
$$a = 2, b = 1, c = -2$$
$$x = \frac{-1 \pm \sqrt{(1)^2 - 4(2)(-2)}}{2 \cdot 2}$$
$$x = \frac{-1 \pm \sqrt{17}}{4}$$

 D. Equations with rational expressions (Sec. 6.5)

 E. Equations with radicals (Sec. 7.6)

II. Inequalities

 A. Linear inequalities (Sec. 2.4)

 B. Compound inequalities (Sec. 2.5)

 C. Absolute value inequalities (Sec. 2.7)

D. Nonlinear inequalities

Polynomial Inequality
$$x^2 - x < 6$$
$$x^2 - x - 6 < 0$$
$$(x - 3)(x + 2) < 0$$

✗ ✓ ✗
−2   3

$(-2, 3)$

Rational Inequality with variable in denominator
$$\frac{x-5}{x+1} \geq 0$$

✓ ✗ ✓
−1   5

$(-\infty, -1) \cup [5, \infty)$

Solve. Write solutions to inequalities in interval notation.

1. $|x - 8| = |2x + 1|$

2. $0 < -x + 7 < 3$

3. $\sqrt{3x - 11} + 3 = x$

4. $x(3x + 1) = 1$

5. $\dfrac{x+2}{x-7} \leq 0$

6. $x(x - 6) + 4 = x^2 - 2(3 - x)$

7. $x(5x - 36) = -7$

8. $2x^2 - 4 \geq 7x$

9. $\left|\dfrac{x-7}{3}\right| > 5$

10. $2(x - 5) + 4 < 1 + 7(x - 5) - x$

8.5 QUADRATIC FUNCTIONS AND THEIR GRAPHS

OBJECTIVES

1 Graph quadratic functions of the form $f(x) = x^2 + k$.

2 Graph quadratic functions of the form $f(x) = (x - h)^2$.

3 Graph quadratic functions of the form $f(x) = (x - h)^2 + k$.

4 Graph quadratic functions of the form $f(x) = ax^2$.

5 Graph quadratic functions of the form $f(x) = a(x - h)^2 + k$.

OBJECTIVE 1 ▸ Graphing $f(x) = x^2 + k$. We first graphed the quadratic equation $y = x^2$ in Section 3.1. In Section 3.2, we learned that this graph defines a function, and we wrote $y = x^2$ as $f(x) = x^2$. In these sections, we discovered that the graph of a quadratic function is a parabola opening upward or downward. In this section, we continue our study of quadratic functions and their graphs. (Much of the contents of this section is a review of shifting and reflecting techniques from Section 3.6.)

First, let's recall the definition of a quadratic function.

> **Quadratic Function**
>
> A quadratic function is a function that can be written in the form $f(x) = ax^2 + bx + c$, where a, b, and c are real numbers and $a \neq 0$.

Notice that equations of the form $y = ax^2 + bx + c$, where $a \neq 0$, define quadratic functions, since y is a function of x or $y = f(x)$.

Recall that if $a > 0$, the parabola opens upward and if $a < 0$, the parabola opens downward. Also, the vertex of a parabola is the lowest point if the parabola opens upward and the highest point if the parabola opens downward. The axis of symmetry is the vertical line that passes through the vertex.

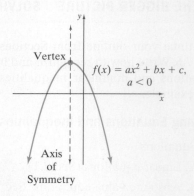

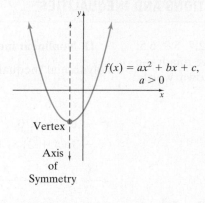

EXAMPLE 1 Graph $f(x) = x^2$ and $g(x) = x^2 + 6$ on the same set of axes.

Solution First we construct a table of values for $f(x)$ and plot the points. Notice that for each x-value, the corresponding value of $g(x)$ must be 6 more than the corresponding value of $f(x)$ since $f(x) = x^2$ and $g(x) = x^2 + 6$. In other words, the graph of $g(x) = x^2 + 6$ is the same as the graph of $f(x) = x^2$ shifted upward 6 units. The axis of symmetry for both graphs is the y-axis.

x	$f(x) = x^2$	$g(x) = x^2 + 6$
-2	4	10
-1	1	7
0	0	6
1	1	7
2	4	10

Each y-value is increased by 6.

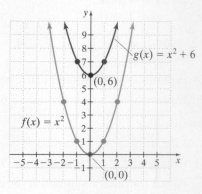

PRACTICE

1 Graph $f(x) = x^2$ and $g(x) = x^2 - 4$ on the same set of axes.

In general, we have the following properties.

> **Graphing the Parabola Defined by $f(x) = x^2 + k$**
>
> If k is positive, the graph of $f(x) = x^2 + k$ is the graph of $y = x^2$ shifted upward k units.
> If k is negative, the graph of $f(x) = x^2 + k$ is the graph of $y = x^2$ shifted downward $|k|$ units.
> The vertex is $(0, k)$, and the axis of symmetry is the y-axis.

EXAMPLE 2   Graph each function.

a. $F(x) = x^2 + 2$ **b.** $g(x) = x^2 - 3$

Solution

a. $F(x) = x^2 + 2$

The graph of $F(x) = x^2 + 2$ is obtained by shifting the graph of $y = x^2$ upward 2 units.

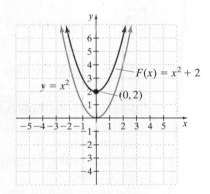

b. $g(x) = x^2 - 3$

The graph of $g(x) = x^2 - 3$ is obtained by shifting the graph of $y = x^2$ downward 3 units.

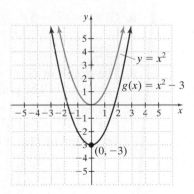

PRACTICE

2   Graph each function.

a. $f(x) = x^2 - 5$ **b.** $g(x) = x^2 + 3$

OBJECTIVE 2 ▶ Graphing $f(x) = (x - h)^2$. Now we will graph functions of the form $f(x) = (x - h)^2$.

EXAMPLE 3 Graph $f(x) = x^2$ and $g(x) = (x - 2)^2$ on the same set of axes.

Solution By plotting points, we see that for each x-value, the corresponding value of $g(x)$ is the same as the value of $f(x)$ when the x-value is increased by 2. Thus, the graph of $g(x) = (x - 2)^2$ is the graph of $f(x) = x^2$ shifted to the right 2 units. The axis of symmetry for the graph of $g(x) = (x - 2)^2$ is also shifted 2 units to the right and is the line $x = 2$.

x	$f(x) = x^2$	x	$g(x) = (x - 2)^2$
-2	4	0	4
-1	1	1	1
0	0	2	0
1	1	3	1
2	4	4	4

Each x-value
Increased by 2
corresponds to
same y-value.

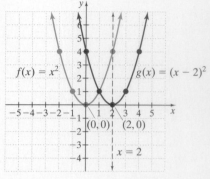

PRACTICE

3 Graph $f(x) = x^2$ and $g(x) = (x + 6)^2$ on the same set of axes.

In general, we have the following properties.

Graphing the Parabola Defined by $f(x) = (x - h)^2$

If h is positive, the graph of $f(x) = (x - h)^2$ is the graph of $y = x^2$ shifted to the right h units.

If h is negative, the graph of $f(x) = (x - h)^2$ is the graph of $y = x^2$ shifted to the left $|h|$ units.

The vertex is $(h, 0)$, and the axis of symmetry is the vertical line $x = h$.

EXAMPLE 4 Graph each function.

a. $G(x) = (x - 3)^2$ **b.** $F(x) = (x + 1)^2$

Solution

a. The graph of $G(x) = (x - 3)^2$ is obtained by shifting the graph of $y = x^2$ to the right 3 units. The graph of $G(x)$ is below on the left.

b. The equation $F(x) = (x + 1)^2$ can be written as $F(x) = [x - (-1)]^2$. The graph of $F(x) = [x - (-1)]^2$ is obtained by shifting the graph of $y = x^2$ to the left 1 unit. The graph of $F(x)$ is below on the right.

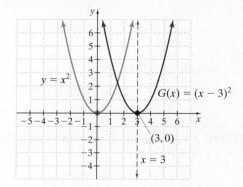 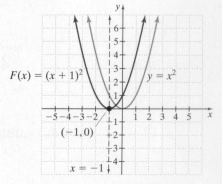

PRACTICE
4   Graph each function.

a. $G(x) = (x + 4)^2$ **b.** $H(x) = (x - 7)^2$

OBJECTIVE 3 ▶ Graphing $f(x) = (x - h)^2 + k$. As we will see in graphing functions of the form $f(x) = (x - h)^2 + k$, it is possible to combine vertical and horizontal shifts.

> **Graphing the Parabola Defined by $f(x) = (x - h)^2 + k$**
> The parabola has the same shape as $y = x^2$.
> The vertex is (h, k), and the axis of symmetry is the vertical line $x = h$.

EXAMPLE 5   Graph $F(x) = (x - 3)^2 + 1$.

Solution   The graph of $F(x) = (x - 3)^2 + 1$ is the graph of $y = x^2$ shifted 3 units to the right and 1 unit up. The vertex is then $(3, 1)$, and the axis of symmetry is $x = 3$. A few ordered pair solutions are plotted to aid in graphing.

x	$F(x) = (x - 3)^2 + 1$
1	5
2	2
4	2
5	5

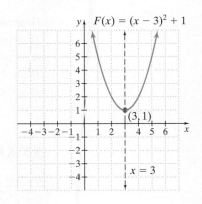

PRACTICE
5   Graph $f(x) = (x + 2)^2 + 2$.

OBJECTIVE 4 ▶ Graphing $f(x) = ax^2$. Next, we discover the change in the shape of the graph when the coefficient of x^2 is not 1.

EXAMPLE 6   Graph $f(x) = x^2$, $g(x) = 3x^2$, and $h(x) = \frac{1}{2}x^2$ on the same set of axes.

Solution   Comparing the tables of values, we see that for each x-value, the corresponding value of $g(x)$ is triple the corresponding value of $f(x)$. Similarly, the value of $h(x)$ is half the value of $f(x)$.

x	$f(x) = x^2$
-2	4
-1	1
0	0
1	1
2	4

x	$g(x) = 3x^2$
-2	12
-1	3
0	0
1	3
2	12

x	$h(x) = \frac{1}{2}x^2$
-2	2
-1	$\frac{1}{2}$
0	0
1	$\frac{1}{2}$
2	2

The result is that the graph of $g(x) = 3x^2$ is narrower than the graph of $f(x) = x^2$ and the graph of $h(x) = \dfrac{1}{2}x^2$ is wider. The vertex for each graph is $(0, 0)$, and the axis of symmetry is the y-axis.

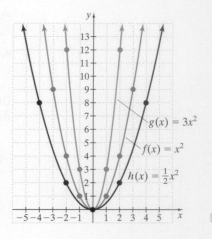

$g(x) = 3x^2$

$f(x) = x^2$

$h(x) = \frac{1}{2}x^2$

PRACTICE
6 Graph $f(x) = x^2$, $g(x) = 4x^2$, and $h(x) = \dfrac{1}{4}x^2$ on the same set of axes.

Graphing the Parabola Defined by $f(x) = ax^2$

If a is positive, the parabola opens upward, and if a is negative, the parabola opens downward.

If $|a| > 1$, the graph of the parabola is narrower than the graph of $y = x^2$.

If $|a| < 1$, the graph of the parabola is wider than the graph of $y = x^2$.

EXAMPLE 7 Graph $f(x) = -2x^2$.

Solution Because $a = -2$, a negative value, this parabola opens downward. Since $|-2| = 2$ and $2 > 1$, the parabola is narrower than the graph of $y = x^2$. The vertex is $(0, 0)$, and the axis of symmetry is the y-axis. We verify this by plotting a few points.

x	$f(x) = -2x^2$
-2	-8
-1	-2
0	0
1	-2
2	-8

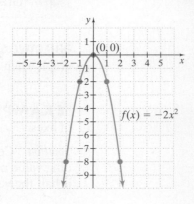

$f(x) = -2x^2$

PRACTICE
7 Graph $f(x) = -\dfrac{1}{2}x^2$.

OBJECTIVE 5 ▶ Graphing $f(x) = a(x - h)^2 + k$. Now we will see the shape of the graph of a quadratic function of the form $f(x) = a(x - h)^2 + k$.

EXAMPLE 8   Graph $g(x) = \frac{1}{2}(x + 2)^2 + 5$. Find the vertex and the axis of symmetry.

<u>Solution</u>   The function $g(x) = \frac{1}{2}(x + 2)^2 + 5$ may be written as $g(x) = \frac{1}{2}[x - (-2)]^2 + 5$. Thus, this graph is the same as the graph of $y = x^2$ shifted 2 units to the left and 5 units up, and it is wider because a is $\frac{1}{2}$. The vertex is $(-2, 5)$, and the axis of symmetry is $x = -2$. We plot a few points to verify.

x	$g(x) = \frac{1}{2}(x + 2)^2 + 5$
-4	7
-3	$5\frac{1}{2}$
-2	5
-1	$5\frac{1}{2}$
0	7

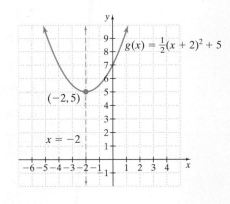

PRACTICE
8   Graph $h(x) = \frac{1}{3}(x - 4)^2 - 3$.

In general, the following holds.

Graph of a Quadratic Function

The graph of a quadratic function written in the form $f(x) = a(x - h)^2 + k$ is a parabola with vertex (h, k). If $a > 0$, the parabola opens upward, and if $a < 0$, the parabola opens downward. The axis of symmetry is the line whose equation is $x = h$.

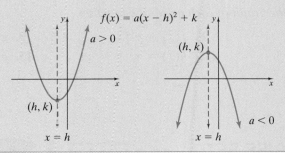

Concept Check ✓
Which description of the graph of $f(x) = -0.35(x + 3)^2 - 4$ is correct?

a. The graph opens downward and has its vertex at $(-3, 4)$.
b. The graph opens upward and has its vertex at $(-3, 4)$.
c. The graph opens downward and has its vertex at $(-3, -4)$.
d. The graph is narrower than the graph of $y = x^2$.

Answer to Concept Check: c

Graphing Calculator Explorations

Use a graphing calculator to graph the first function of each pair that follows. Then use its graph to predict the graph of the second function. Check your prediction by graphing both on the same set of axes.

1. $F(x) = \sqrt{x}; G(x) = \sqrt{x} + 1$

2. $g(x) = x^3; H(x) = x^3 - 2$

3. $H(x) = |x|; f(x) = |x - 5|$

4. $h(x) = x^3 + 2; g(x) = (x - 3)^3 + 2$

5. $f(x) = |x + 4|; F(x) = |x + 4| + 3$

6. $G(x) = \sqrt{x} - 2; g(x) = \sqrt{x - 4} - 2$

VOCABULARY & READINESS CHECK

Use the choices below to fill in each blank. Some choices will be used more than once.

upward   highest   parabola   downward   lowest   quadratic

1. A _____ function is one that can be written in the form $f(x) = ax^2 + bx + c, a \neq 0$.

2. The graph of a quadratic function is a _____ opening _____ or _____.

3. If $a > 0$, the graph of the quadratic function opens _____.

4. If $a < 0$, the graph of the quadratic function opens _____.

5. The vertex of a parabola is the _____ point if $a > 0$.

6. The vertex of a parabola is the _____ point if $a < 0$.

State the vertex of the graph of each quadratic function.

7. $f(x) = x^2$ **8.** $f(x) = -5x^2$ **9.** $g(x) = (x - 2)^2$ **10.** $g(x) = (x + 5)^2$

11. $f(x) = 2x^2 + 3$ **12.** $h(x) = x^2 - 1$ **13.** $g(x) = (x + 1)^2 + 5$ **14.** $h(x) = (x - 10)^2 - 7$

8.5 EXERCISE SET

PRACTICE   WATCH   DOWNLOAD   READ   REVIEW

MIXED PRACTICE

Sketch the graph of each quadratic function. Label the vertex, and sketch and label the axis of symmetry. See Examples 1 through 5.

1. $f(x) = x^2 - 1$ **2.** $g(x) = x^2 + 3$

3. $h(x) = x^2 + 5$ **4.** $h(x) = x^2 - 4$

5. $g(x) = x^2 + 7$ **6.** $f(x) = x^2 - 2$

7. $f(x) = (x - 5)^2$ **8.** $g(x) = (x + 5)^2$

9. $h(x) = (x + 2)^2$ **10.** $H(x) = (x - 1)^2$

11. $G(x) = (x + 3)^2$ **12.** $f(x) = (x - 6)^2$

13. $f(x) = (x - 2)^2 + 5$ **14.** $g(x) = (x - 6)^2 + 1$

15. $h(x) = (x + 1)^2 + 4$ **16.** $G(x) = (x + 3)^2 + 3$

17. $g(x) = (x + 2)^2 - 5$ **18.** $h(x) = (x + 4)^2 - 6$

Sketch the graph of each quadratic function. Label the vertex, and sketch and label the axis of symmetry. See Examples 6 and 7.

19. $g(x) = -x^2$ **20.** $f(x) = 5x^2$

21. $h(x) = \frac{1}{3}x^2$ **22.** $f(x) = -\frac{1}{4}x^2$

23. $H(x) = 2x^2$ **24.** $g(x) = -3x^2$

Sketch the graph of each quadratic function. Label the vertex, and sketch and label the axis of symmetry. See Example 8.

25. $f(x) = 2(x - 1)^2 + 3$ **26.** $g(x) = 4(x - 4)^2 + 2$

27. $h(x) = -3(x + 3)^2 + 1$ **28.** $f(x) = -(x - 2)^2 - 6$

29. $H(x) = \dfrac{1}{2}(x - 6)^2 - 3$ **30.** $G(x) = \dfrac{1}{5}(x + 4)^2 + 3$

MIXED PRACTICE

Sketch the graph of each quadratic function. Label the vertex, and sketch and label the axis of symmetry.

31. $f(x) = -(x - 2)^2$ **32.** $g(x) = -(x + 6)^2$

33. $F(x) = -x^2 + 4$ **34.** $H(x) = -x^2 + 10$

35. $F(x) = 2x^2 - 5$ **36.** $g(x) = \dfrac{1}{2}x^2 - 2$

37. $h(x) = (x - 6)^2 + 4$ **38.** $f(x) = (x - 5)^2 + 2$

39. $F(x) = \left(x + \dfrac{1}{2}\right)^2 - 2$ **40.** $H(x) = \left(x + \dfrac{1}{2}\right)^2 - 3$

41. $F(x) = \dfrac{3}{2}(x + 7)^2 + 1$ **42.** $g(x) = -\dfrac{3}{2}(x - 1)^2 - 5$

43. $f(x) = \dfrac{1}{4}x^2 - 9$ **44.** $H(x) = \dfrac{3}{4}x^2 - 2$

45. $G(x) = 5\left(x + \dfrac{1}{2}\right)^2$ **46.** $F(x) = 3\left(x - \dfrac{3}{2}\right)^2$

47. $h(x) = -(x - 1)^2 - 1$ **48.** $f(x) = -3(x + 2)^2 + 2$

49. $g(x) = \sqrt{3}(x + 5)^2 + \dfrac{3}{4}$ **50.** $G(x) = \sqrt{5}(x - 7)^2 - \dfrac{1}{2}$

51. $h(x) = 10(x + 4)^2 - 6$ **52.** $h(x) = 8(x + 1)^2 + 9$

53. $f(x) = -2(x - 4)^2 + 5$ **54.** $G(x) = -4(x + 9)^2 - 1$

REVIEW AND PREVIEW

Add the proper constant to each binomial so that the resulting trinomial is a perfect square trinomial. See Section 8.1.

55. $x^2 + 8x$ **56.** $y^2 + 4y$

57. $z^2 - 16z$ **58.** $x^2 - 10x$

59. $y^2 + y$ **60.** $z^2 - 3z$

Solve by completing the square. See Section 8.1.

61. $x^2 + 4x = 12$ **62.** $y^2 + 6y = -5$

63. $z^2 + 10z - 1 = 0$ **64.** $x^2 + 14x + 20 = 0$

65. $z^2 - 8z = 2$ **66.** $y^2 - 10y = 3$

CONCEPT EXTENSIONS

Solve. See the Concept Check in this section.

67. Which description of $f(x) = -213(x - 0.1)^2 + 3.6$ is correct?

Graph Opens	Vertex
a. upward	$(0.1, 3.6)$
b. upward	$(-213, 3.6)$
c. downward	$(0.1, 3.6)$
d. downward	$(-0.1, 3.6)$

68. Which description of $f(x) = 5\left(x + \dfrac{1}{2}\right)^2 + \dfrac{1}{2}$ is correct?

Graph Opens	Vertex
a. upward	$\left(\dfrac{1}{2}, \dfrac{1}{2}\right)$
b. upward	$\left(-\dfrac{1}{2}, \dfrac{1}{2}\right)$
c. downward	$\left(\dfrac{1}{2}, -\dfrac{1}{2}\right)$
d. downward	$\left(-\dfrac{1}{2}, -\dfrac{1}{2}\right)$

Write the equation of the parabola that has the same shape as $f(x) = 5x^2$ but with the following vertex.

69. $(2, 3)$ **70.** $(1, 6)$

71. $(-3, 6)$ **72.** $(4, -1)$

The shifting properties covered in this section apply to the graphs of all functions. Given the accompanying graph of $y = f(x)$, sketch the graph of each of the following.

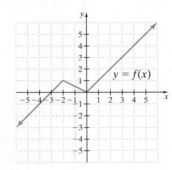

73. $y = f(x) + 1$ **74.** $y = f(x) - 2$

75. $y = f(x - 3)$ **76.** $y = f(x + 3)$

77. $y = f(x + 2) + 2$ **78.** $y = f(x - 1) + 1$

79. The quadratic function $f(x) = 668.7x^2 - 2990.7x + 938$ approximates the U.S. growth of cell phone subscribers between 1985 and 2005 where x is the number of years past 1985 and $f(x)$ is the number of subscribers in thousands.

   a. Use this function to approximate the number of subscribers in 2004.

   b. Use this function to predict the number of subscribers in 2007.

80. Use the function in Exercise 79.

   a. Predict the number of cell phone subscribers in 2010.

   b. Look up the current population of the U.S.

   c. Based on your answers for parts **a.** and **b.**, discuss some limitations of using this quadratic function to predict data.

8.6 FURTHER GRAPHING OF QUADRATIC FUNCTIONS

OBJECTIVE 1 ▶ **Writing quadratic functions in the form $y = a(x - h)^2 + k$.** We know that the graph of a quadratic function is a parabola. If a quadratic function is written in the form

$$f(x) = a(x - h)^2 + k$$

we can easily find the vertex (h, k) and graph the parabola. To write a quadratic function in this form, complete the square. (See Section 8.1 for a review of completing the square.)

EXAMPLE 1 Graph $f(x) = x^2 - 4x - 12$. Find the vertex and any intercepts.

Solution The graph of this quadratic function is a parabola. To find the vertex of the parabola, we will write the function in the form $y = (x - h)^2 + k$. To do this, we complete the square on the binomial $x^2 - 4x$. To simplify our work, we let $f(x) = y$.

$$y = x^2 - 4x - 12 \quad \text{Let } f(x) = y.$$

$$y + 12 = x^2 - 4x \qquad \text{Add 12 to both sides to get the } x\text{-variable terms alone.}$$

Now we add the square of half of -4 to both sides.

$$\frac{1}{2}(-4) = -2 \quad \text{and} \quad (-2)^2 = 4$$

$$y + 12 + 4 = x^2 - 4x + 4 \qquad \text{Add 4 to both sides.}$$

$$y + 16 = (x - 2)^2 \qquad \text{Factor the trinomial.}$$

$$y = (x - 2)^2 - 16 \qquad \text{Subtract 16 from both sides.}$$

$$f(x) = (x - 2)^2 - 16 \qquad \text{Replace } y \text{ with } f(x).$$

From this equation, we can see that the vertex of the parabola is $(2, -16)$, a point in quadrant IV, and the axis of symmetry is the line $x = 2$.

Notice that $a = 1$. Since $a > 0$, the parabola opens upward. This parabola opening upward with vertex $(2, -16)$ will have two x-intercepts and one y-intercept. (See the Helpful Hint after this example.)

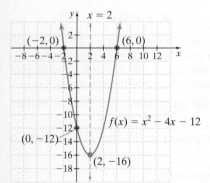

x-intercepts: let y or $f(x) = 0$	y-intercept: let $x = 0$
$f(x) = x^2 - 4x - 12$	$f(x) = x^2 - 4x - 12$
$0 = x^2 - 4x - 12$	$f(0) = 0^2 - 4 \cdot 0 - 12$
$0 = (x - 6)(x + 2)$	$= -12$
$0 = x - 6 \quad \text{or} \quad 0 = x + 2$	
$6 = x \qquad\qquad -2 = x$	

The two x-intercepts are $(6, 0)$ and $(-2, 0)$. The y-intercept is $(0, -12)$. The sketch of $f(x) = x^2 - 4x - 12$ is shown.

Notice that the axis of symmetry is always halfway between the x-intercepts. For the example above, halfway between -2 and 6 is $\dfrac{-2 + 6}{2} = 2$, and the axis of symmetry is $x = 2$. □

PRACTICE

1 Graph $g(x) = x^2 - 2x - 3$. Find the vertex and any intercepts.

▶ **Helpful Hint**

Parabola Opens Upward

Vertex in I or II: no x-intercept

Vertex in III or IV: 2 x-intercepts

Parabola Opens Downward

Vertex in I or II: 2 x-intercepts

Vertex in III or IV: no x-intercept.

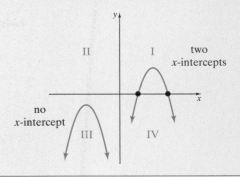

EXAMPLE 2   Graph $f(x) = 3x^2 + 3x + 1$. Find the vertex and any intercepts.

Solution   Replace $f(x)$ with y and complete the square on x to write the equation in the form $y = a(x - h)^2 + k$.

$$y = 3x^2 + 3x + 1 \quad \text{Replace } f(x) \text{ with } y.$$
$$y - 1 = 3x^2 + 3x \qquad \text{Isolate } x\text{-variable terms.}$$

Factor 3 from the terms $3x^2 + 3x$ so that the coefficient of x^2 is 1.

$$y - 1 = 3(x^2 + x) \quad \text{Factor out 3.}$$

The coefficient of x in the parentheses above is 1. Then $\frac{1}{2}(1) = \frac{1}{2}$ and $\left(\frac{1}{2}\right)^2 = \frac{1}{4}$.

Since we are adding $\frac{1}{4}$ inside the parentheses, we are really adding $3\left(\frac{1}{4}\right)$, so we *must* add $3\left(\frac{1}{4}\right)$ to the left side.

$$y - 1 + 3\left(\frac{1}{4}\right) = 3\left(x^2 + x + \frac{1}{4}\right)$$

$$y - \frac{1}{4} = 3\left(x + \frac{1}{2}\right)^2 \qquad \text{Simplify the left side and factor the right side.}$$

$$y = 3\left(x + \frac{1}{2}\right)^2 + \frac{1}{4} \quad \text{Add } \frac{1}{4} \text{ to both sides.}$$

$$f(x) = 3\left(x + \frac{1}{2}\right)^2 + \frac{1}{4} \quad \text{Replace } y \text{ with } f(x).$$

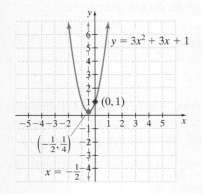

Then $a = 3$, $h = -\frac{1}{2}$, and $k = \frac{1}{4}$. This means that the parabola opens upward with vertex $\left(-\frac{1}{2}, \frac{1}{4}\right)$ and that the axis of symmetry is the line $x = -\frac{1}{2}$.

To find the y-intercept, let $x = 0$. Then

$$f(0) = 3(0)^2 + 3(0) + 1 = 1$$

Thus the y-intercept is $(0, 1)$.

This parabola has no x-intercepts since the vertex is in the second quadrant and opens upward. Use the vertex, axis of symmetry, and y-intercept to sketch the parabola.   □

PRACTICE

2   Graph $g(x) = 4x^2 + 4x + 3$. Find the vertex and any intercepts.

EXAMPLE 3 Graph $f(x) = -x^2 - 2x + 3$. Find the vertex and any intercepts.

Solution We write $f(x)$ in the form $a(x - h)^2 + k$ by completing the square. First we replace $f(x)$ with y.

$$f(x) = -x^2 - 2x + 3$$

$$y = -x^2 - 2x + 3$$

$$y - 3 = -x^2 - 2x \qquad \text{Subtract 3 from both sides to get the } x\text{-variable terms alone.}$$

$$y - 3 = -1(x^2 + 2x) \qquad \text{Factor } -1 \text{ from the terms } -x^2 - 2x.$$

The coefficient of x is 2. Then $\frac{1}{2}(2) = 1$ and $1^2 = 1$. We add 1 to the right side inside the parentheses and add $-1(1)$ to the left side.

$$y - 3 - 1(1) = -1(x^2 + 2x + 1)$$

$$y - 4 = -1(x + 1)^2 \qquad \text{Simplify the left side and factor the right side.}$$

$$y = -1(x + 1)^2 + 4 \qquad \text{Add 4 to both sides.}$$

$$\underline{f(x) = -1(x + 1)^2 + 4} \qquad \text{Replace } y \text{ with } f(x).$$

> ▶ **Helpful Hint**
>
> This can be written as
> $f(x) = -1[x - (-1)]^2 + 4$.
> Notice that the vertex is $(-1, 4)$.

Since $a = -1$, the parabola opens downward with vertex $(-1, 4)$ and axis of symmetry $x = -1$.

To find the y-intercept, we let $x = 0$ and solve for y. Then

$$f(0) = -0^2 - 2(0) + 3 = 3$$

Thus, $(0, 3)$ is the y-intercept.

To find the x-intercepts, we let y or $f(x) = 0$ and solve for x.

$$f(x) = -x^2 - 2x + 3$$

$$0 = -x^2 - 2x + 3 \qquad \text{Let } f(x) = 0.$$

Now we divide both sides by -1 so that the coefficient of x^2 is 1.

$$\frac{0}{-1} = \frac{-x^2}{-1} - \frac{2x}{-1} + \frac{3}{-1} \qquad \text{Divide both sides by } -1.$$

$$0 = x^2 + 2x - 3 \qquad \text{Simplify.}$$

$$0 = (x + 3)(x - 1) \qquad \text{Factor.}$$

$$x + 3 = 0 \quad \text{or} \quad x - 1 = 0 \qquad \text{Set each factor equal to 0.}$$

$$x = -3 \qquad\qquad x = 1 \qquad \text{Solve.}$$

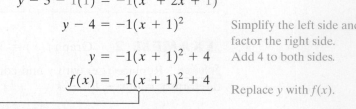

The x-intercepts are $(-3, 0)$ and $(1, 0)$. Use these points to sketch the parabola. ☐

PRACTICE
3 Graph $g(x) = -x^2 + 5x + 6$. Find the vertex and any intercepts.

OBJECTIVE 2 ▶ Deriving a formula for finding the vertex. There is also a formula that may be used to find the vertex of a parabola. Now that we have practiced completing the square, we will show that the x-coordinate of the vertex of the graph of $f(x)$ or $y = ax^2 + bx + c$ can be found by the formula $x = \frac{-b}{2a}$. To do so, we complete the square on x and write the equation in the form $y = a(x - h)^2 + k$.

First, isolate the x-variable terms by subtracting c from both sides.

$$y = ax^2 + bx + c$$

$$y - c = ax^2 + bx$$

Next, factor a from the terms $ax^2 + bx$.

$$y - c = a\left(x^2 + \frac{b}{a}x\right)$$

Next, add the square of half of $\frac{b}{a}$, or $\left(\frac{b}{2a}\right)^2 = \frac{b^2}{4a^2}$, to the right side inside the parentheses. Because of the factor a, what we really added was $a\left(\frac{b^2}{4a^2}\right)$ and this must be added to the left side.

$$y - c + a\left(\frac{b^2}{4a^2}\right) = a\left(x^2 + \frac{b}{a}x + \frac{b^2}{4a^2}\right)$$

$$y - c + \frac{b^2}{4a} = a\left(x + \frac{b}{2a}\right)^2 \qquad \text{Simplify the left side and factor the right side.}$$

$$y = a\left(x + \frac{b}{2a}\right)^2 + c - \frac{b^2}{4a} \qquad \text{Add } c \text{ to both sides and subtract } \frac{b^2}{4a} \text{ from both sides.}$$

Compare this form with $f(x)$ or $y = a(x - h)^2 + k$ and see that h is $\frac{-b}{2a}$, which means that the x-coordinate of the vertex of the graph of $f(x) = ax^2 + bx + c$ is $\frac{-b}{2a}$.

> **Vertex Formula**
>
> The graph of $f(x) = ax^2 + bx + c$, when $a \neq 0$, is a parabola with vertex
>
> $$\left(\frac{-b}{2a}, f\left(\frac{-b}{2a}\right)\right)$$

Let's use this formula to find the vertex of the parabola we graphed in Example 1.

EXAMPLE 4 Find the vertex of the graph of $f(x) = x^2 - 4x - 12$.

<u>Solution</u> In the quadratic function $f(x) = x^2 - 4x - 12$, notice that $a = 1, b = -4$, and $c = -12$. Then

$$\frac{-b}{2a} = \frac{-(-4)}{2(1)} = 2$$

The x-value of the vertex is 2. To find the corresponding $f(x)$ or y-value, find $f(2)$. Then

$$f(2) = 2^2 - 4(2) - 12 = 4 - 8 - 12 = -16$$

The vertex is $(2, -16)$. These results agree with our findings in Example 1. □

PRACTICE
4 Find the vertex of the graph of $g(x) = x^2 - 2x - 3$.

OBJECTIVE 3 ▶ Finding minimum and maximum values. The vertex of a parabola gives us some important information about its corresponding quadratic function. The quadratic function whose graph is a parabola that opens upward has a minimum value, and the quadratic function whose graph is a parabola that opens downward has a maximum value. The $f(x)$ or y-value of the vertex is the minimum or maximum value of the function.

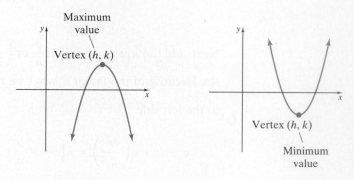

Concept Check ☑

Without making any calculations, tell whether the graph of $f(x) = 7 - x - 0.3x^2$ has a maximum value or a minimum value. Explain your reasoning.

EXAMPLE 5 Finding Maximum Height

A rock is thrown upward from the ground. Its height in feet above ground after t seconds is given by the function $f(t) = -16t^2 + 20t$. Find the maximum height of the rock and the number of seconds it took for the rock to reach its maximum height.

Solution

1. UNDERSTAND. The maximum height of the rock is the largest value of $f(t)$. Since the function $f(t) = -16t^2 + 20t$ is a quadratic function, its graph is a parabola. It opens downward since $-16 < 0$. Thus, the maximum value of $f(t)$ is the $f(t)$ or y-value of the vertex of its graph.

2. TRANSLATE. To find the vertex (h, k), notice that for $f(t) = -16t^2 + 20t$, $a = -16, b = 20$, and $c = 0$. We will use these values and the vertex formula

$$\left(\frac{-b}{2a}, f\left(\frac{-b}{2a}\right)\right)$$

3. SOLVE.

$$h = \frac{-b}{2a} = \frac{-20}{-32} = \frac{5}{8}$$

$$f\left(\frac{5}{8}\right) = -16\left(\frac{5}{8}\right)^2 + 20\left(\frac{5}{8}\right)$$

$$= -16\left(\frac{25}{64}\right) + \frac{25}{2}$$

$$= -\frac{25}{4} + \frac{50}{4} = \frac{25}{4}$$

4. INTERPRET. The graph of $f(t)$ is a parabola opening downward with vertex $\left(\frac{5}{8}, \frac{25}{4}\right)$. This means that the rock's maximum height is $\frac{25}{4}$ feet, or $6\frac{1}{4}$ feet, which was reached in $\frac{5}{8}$ second. □

PRACTICE

5 A ball is tossed upward from the ground. Its height in feet above ground after t seconds is given by the function $h(t) = -16t^2 + 24t$. Find the maximum height of the ball and the number of seconds it took for the ball to reach the maximum height.

Answer to Concept Check:
$f(x)$ has a maximum value since it opens downward.

VOCABULARY & READINESS CHECK

Fill in each blank.

1. If a quadratic function is in the form $f(x) = a(x - h)^2 + k$, the vertex of its graph is _____.

2. The graph of $f(x) = ax^2 + bx + c, a \neq 0$ is a parabola whose vertex has *x*-value of _____.

	Parabola Opens	*Vertex Location*	*Number of x-intercept(s)*	*Number of y-intercept(s)*
3.	up	Q I		
4.	up	Q III		
5.	down	Q II		
6.	down	Q IV		
7.	up	*x*-axis		
8.	down	*x*-axis		
9.		Q III	0	
10.		Q I	2	
11.		Q IV	2	
12.		Q II	0	

8.6 | EXERCISE SET

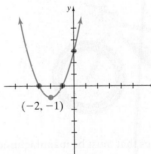

Find the vertex of the graph of each quadratic function. See Examples 1 through 4.

1. $f(x) = x^2 + 8x + 7$

2. $f(x) = x^2 + 6x + 5$

3. $f(x) = -x^2 + 10x + 5$

4. $f(x) = -x^2 - 8x + 2$

5. $f(x) = 5x^2 - 10x + 3$

6. $f(x) = -3x^2 + 6x + 4$

7. $f(x) = -x^2 + x + 1$

8. $f(x) = x^2 - 9x + 8$

Match each function with its graph. See Examples 1 through 4.

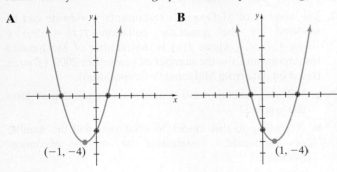

C

$(-2, -1)$

D

$(2, -1)$

9. $f(x) = x^2 - 4x + 3$ **10.** $f(x) = x^2 + 2x - 3$

11. $f(x) = x^2 - 2x - 3$ **12.** $f(x) = x^2 + 4x + 3$

MIXED PRACTICE

Find the vertex of the graph of each quadratic function. Determine whether the graph opens upward or downward, find any intercepts, and sketch the graph. See Examples 1 through 4.

13. $f(x) = x^2 + 4x - 5$ **14.** $f(x) = x^2 + 2x - 3$

15. $f(x) = -x^2 + 2x - 1$ **16.** $f(x) = -x^2 + 4x - 4$

17. $f(x) = x^2 - 4$ **18.** $f(x) = x^2 - 1$

19. $f(x) = 4x^2 + 4x - 3$ **20.** $f(x) = 2x^2 - x - 3$

21. $f(x) = x^2 + 8x + 15$ **22.** $f(x) = x^2 + 10x + 9$

23. $f(x) = x^2 - 6x + 5$

24. $f(x) = x^2 - 4x + 3$

25. $f(x) = x^2 - 4x + 5$

26. $f(x) = x^2 - 6x + 11$

27. $f(x) = 2x^2 + 4x + 5$

28. $f(x) = 3x^2 + 12x + 16$

29. $f(x) = -2x^2 + 12x$

30. $f(x) = -4x^2 + 8x$

31. $f(x) = x^2 + 1$

32. $f(x) = x^2 + 4$

33. $f(x) = x^2 - 2x - 15$

34. $f(x) = x^2 - x - 12$

35. $f(x) = -5x^2 + 5x$

36. $f(x) = 3x^2 - 12x$

37. $f(x) = -x^2 + 2x - 12$

38. $f(x) = -x^2 + 8x - 17$

39. $f(x) = 3x^2 - 12x + 15$

40. $f(x) = 2x^2 - 8x + 11$

41. $f(x) = x^2 + x - 6$

42. $f(x) = x^2 + 3x - 18$

43. $f(x) = -2x^2 - 3x + 35$

44. $f(x) = 3x^2 - 13x - 10$

Solve. See Example 5.

45. If a projectile is fired straight upward from the ground with an initial speed of 96 feet per second, then its height h in feet after t seconds is given by the equation

$$h(t) = -16t^2 + 96t$$

Find the maximum height of the projectile.

46. If Rheam Gaspar throws a ball upward with an initial speed of 32 feet per second, then its height h in feet after t seconds is given by the equation

$$h(t) = -16t^2 + 32t$$

Find the maximum height of the ball.

47. The cost C in dollars of manufacturing x bicycles at Holladay's Production Plant is given by the function

$$C(x) = 2x^2 - 800x + 92{,}000.$$

a. Find the number of bicycles that must be manufactured to minimize the cost.

b. Find the minimum cost.

48. The Utah Ski Club sells calendars to raise money. The profit P, in cents, from selling x calendars is given by the equation $P(x) = 360x - x^2$.

a. Find how many calendars must be sold to maximize profit.

b. Find the maximum profit.

49. Find two numbers whose sum is 60 and whose product is as large as possible. [*Hint:* Let x and $60 - x$ be the two positive numbers. Their product can be described by the function $f(x) = x(60 - x)$.]

50. Find two numbers whose sum is 11 and whose product is as large as possible. (Use the hint for Exercise 49.)

51. Find two numbers whose difference is 10 and whose product is as small as possible. (Use the hint for Exercise 49.)

52. Find two numbers whose difference is 8 and whose product is as small as possible.

△ 53. The length and width of a rectangle must have a sum of 40. Find the dimensions of the rectangle that will have the maximum area. (Use the hint for Exercise 49.)

△ 54. The length and width of a rectangle must have a sum of 50. Find the dimensions of the rectangle that will have maximum area.

REVIEW AND PREVIEW

Sketch the graph of each function. See Section 8.5.

55. $f(x) = x^2 + 2$

56. $f(x) = (x - 3)^2$

57. $g(x) = x + 2$

58. $h(x) = x - 3$

59. $f(x) = (x + 5)^2 + 2$

60. $f(x) = 2(x - 3)^2 + 2$

61. $f(x) = 3(x - 4)^2 + 1$

62. $f(x) = (x + 1)^2 + 4$

63. $f(x) = -(x - 4)^2 + \dfrac{3}{2}$

64. $f(x) = -2(x + 7)^2 + \dfrac{1}{2}$

CONCEPT EXTENSIONS

Without calculating, tell whether each graph has a minimum value or a maximum value. See the Concept Check in the section.

65. $f(x) = 2x^2 - 5$

66. $g(x) = -7x^2 + x + 1$

67. $F(x) = 3 - \dfrac{1}{2}x^2$

68. $G(x) = 3 - \dfrac{1}{2}x + 0.8x^2$

Find the vertex of the graph of each quadratic function. Determine whether the graph opens upward or downward, find the y-intercept, approximate the x-intercepts to one decimal place, and sketch the graph.

69. $f(x) = x^2 + 10x + 15$

70. $f(x) = x^2 - 6x + 4$

71. $f(x) = 3x^2 - 6x + 7$

72. $f(x) = 2x^2 + 4x - 1$

Find the maximum or minimum value of each function. Approximate to two decimal places.

73. $f(x) = 2.3x^2 - 6.1x + 3.2$

74. $f(x) = 7.6x^2 + 9.8x - 2.1$

75. $f(x) = -1.9x^2 + 5.6x - 2.7$

76. $f(x) = -5.2x^2 - 3.8x + 5.1$

77. The number of McDonald's restaurants worldwide can be modeled by the quadratic equation $f(x) = -96x^2 + 1018x + 28{,}824$, where $f(x)$ is the number of McDonald's restaurants and x is the number of years after 2000. (*Source:* Based on data from McDonald's Corporation)

a. Will this function have a maximum or minimum? How can you tell?

b. According to this model, in what year will the number of McDonald's restaurants be at its maximum/minimum?

c. What is the maximum/minimum number of McDonald's restaurants predicted?

78. Methane is a gas produced by landfills, natural gas systems, and coal mining that contributes to the greenhouse effect and global warming. Projected methane emissions in the United States can be modeled by the quadratic function

$$f(x) = -0.072x^2 + 1.93x + 173.9$$

where $f(x)$ is the amount of methane produced in million metric tons and x is the number of years after 2000. (*Source:* Based on data from the U.S. Environmental Protection Agency, 2000–2020)

a. According to this model, what will U.S. emissions of methane be in 2009? (Round to 2 decimal places.)

b. Will this function have a maximum or a minimum? How can you tell?

c. In what year will methane emissions in the United States be at their maximum/minimum? Round to the nearest whole year.

d. What is the level of methane emissions for that year? (Use your rounded answer from part c.) (Round this answer to 2 decimals places.)

Use a graphing calculator to check each exercise.

79. Exercise 27   **80.** Exercise 28

81. Exercise 37   **82.** Exercise 38

CHAPTER 8 GROUP ACTIVITY

Fitting a Quadratic Model to Data

Throughout the twentieth century, the eating habits of Americans changed noticeably. Americans started consuming less whole milk and butter, and started consuming more skim and low-fat milk and margarine. We also started eating more poultry and fish. In this project, you will have the opportunity to investigate trends in per capita consumption of poultry during the twentieth century. This project may be completed by working in groups or individually.

We will start by finding a quadratic model, $y = ax^2 + bx + c$, that has ordered pair solutions that correspond to the data for U.S. per capita consumption of poultry given in the table. To do so, substitute each data pair into the equation. Each time, the result is an equation in three unknowns: a, b, and c. Because there are three pairs of data, we can form a system of three linear equations in three unknowns. Solving for the values of a, b, and c gives a quadratic model that represents the given data.

U.S. per Capita Consumption of Poultry (in Pounds)

Year	x	Poultry Consumption, y (in pounds)
1909	9	11
1957	57	22
2005	105	66

(*Source:* Economic Research Service, U.S. Department of Agriculture)

1. Write the system of equations that must be solved to find the values of a, b, and c needed for a quadratic model of the given data.

2. Solve the system of equations for a, b, and c. Recall the various methods of solving linear systems used in Chapter 4. You might consider using matrices, Cramer's rule, or a graphing calculator to do so. Round to the nearest thousandth.

3. Write the quadratic model for the data. Note that the variable x represents the number of years after 1900.

4. In 1939, the actual U.S. per capita consumption of poultry was 12 pounds per person. Based on this information, how accurate do you think this model is for years other than those given in the table?

5. Use your model to estimate the per capita consumption of poultry in 1950.

6. According to the model, in what year was per capita consumption of poultry 50 pounds per person?

7. In what year was the per capita consumption of poultry at its lowest level? What was that level?

8. Who might be interested in a model like this and how would it be helpful?

STUDY SKILLS BUILDER

Are You Preparing for a Test on Chapter 8?

Below I have listed some common trouble areas for students in Chapter 8. After studying for your test—but before taking your test—read these.

- Don't forget that to solve a quadratic equation such as $x^2 + 6x = 1$, by completing the square, add the square of half of 6 to both sides.

$$x^2 + 6x = 1$$
$$x^2 + 6x + 9 = 1 + 9 \qquad \text{Add 9 to both sides, } \left(\frac{1}{2}(6) = 3 \text{ and } 3^2 = 9\right)$$
$$(x + 3)^2 = 10$$
$$x + 3 = \pm\sqrt{10}$$
$$x = -3 \pm \sqrt{10}$$

- Remember to write a quadratic equation in standard form $(ax^2 + bx + c = 0)$ before using the quadratic formula to solve.

$$x(4x - 1) = 1$$
$$4x^2 - x - 1 = 0 \qquad\qquad\qquad\qquad \text{Write in standard form.}$$
$$x = \frac{-(-1) \pm \sqrt{(-1)^2 - 4(4)(-1)}}{2 \cdot 4} \qquad \text{Use the quadratic formula with } a = 4, b = -1, \text{ and } c = -1.$$
$$x = \frac{1 \pm \sqrt{17}}{8} \qquad\qquad\qquad\qquad \text{Simplify.}$$

- Review the steps for solving a quadratic equation in general on page 500.
- Don't forget how to graph a quadratic function in the form $f(x) = a(x - h)^2 + k$.

The graph of $f(x) = -2(x - 3)^2 - 1$

| opens downward | shift 3 units right | shift 1 unit down |

narrower

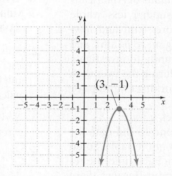

Remember: This is simply a checklist of common trouble areas. For a review of Chapter 8, see the Highlights and Chapter Review at the end of this chapter.

CHAPTER 8 VOCABULARY CHECK

Fill in each blank with one of the words or phrases listed below.

quadratic formula	quadratic	discriminant	$\pm\sqrt{b}$
completing the square	quadratic inequality	(h, k)	$(0, k)$
$(h, 0)$	$\dfrac{-b}{2a}$		

1. The _____ helps us find the number and type of solutions of a quadratic equation.

2. If $a^2 = b$, then $a = $ _____

3. The graph of $f(x) = ax^2 + bx + c$ where a is not 0 is a parabola whose vertex has x-value of _____.

4. A(n) _____ is an inequality that can be written so that one side is a quadratic expression and the other side is 0.

5. The process of writing a quadratic equation so that one side is a perfect square trinomial is called

_____ .

6. The graph of $f(x) = x^2 + k$ has vertex _____ .

7. The graph of $f(x) = (x - h)^2$ has vertex _____ .

8. The graph of $f(x) = (x - h)^2 + k$ has vertex _____ .

9. The formula $x = \dfrac{-b \pm \sqrt{b^2 - 4ac}}{2a}$ is called the _____ .

10. A _____ equation is one that can be written in the form $ax^2 + bx + c = 0$ where $a, b,$ and c are real numbers and a is not 0.

> **▶ Helpful Hint**
>
> Are you preparing for your test? Don't forget to take the Chapter 8 Test on page 537. Then check your answers at the back of the text and use the Chapter Test Prep Video CD to see the fully worked-out solutions to any of the exercises you want to review.

CHAPTER 8 HIGHLIGHTS

DEFINITIONS AND CONCEPTS	EXAMPLES

SECTION 8.1 SOLVING QUADRATIC EQUATIONS BY COMPLETING THE SQUARE

Square root property	Solve: $(x + 3)^2 = 14$.
If b is a real number and if $a^2 = b$, then $a = \pm\sqrt{b}$.	$x + 3 = \pm\sqrt{14}$
	$x = -3 \pm \sqrt{14}$
To solve a quadratic equation in x by completing the square	Solve: $3x^2 - 12x - 18 = 0$.
Step 1. If the coefficient of x^2 is not 1, divide both sides of the equation by the coefficient of x^2.	**1.** $x^2 - 4x - 6 = 0$
Step 2. Isolate the variable terms.	**2.** $x^2 - 4x = 6$
Step 3. Complete the square by adding the square of half of the coefficient of x to both sides.	**3.** $\dfrac{1}{2}(-4) = -2$ and $(-2)^2 = 4$
	$x^2 - 4x + 4 = 6 + 4$
Step 4. Write the resulting trinomial as the square of a binomial.	**4.** $(x - 2)^2 = 10$
Step 5. Apply the square root property and solve for x.	**5.** $x - 2 = \pm\sqrt{10}$
	$x = 2 \pm \sqrt{10}$

SECTION 8.2 SOLVING QUADRATIC EQUATIONS BY THE QUADRATIC FORMULA

A quadratic equation written in the form $ax^2 + bx + c = 0$ has solutions	Solve: $x^2 - x - 3 = 0$.
$$x = \dfrac{-b \pm \sqrt{b^2 - 4ac}}{2a}$$	$a = 1, b = -1, c = -3$
	$x = \dfrac{-(-1) \pm \sqrt{(-1)^2 - 4(1)(-3)}}{2 \cdot 1}$
	$x = \dfrac{1 \pm \sqrt{13}}{2}$

| **DEFINITIONS AND CONCEPTS** | **EXAMPLES** |

SECTION 8.3   SOLVING EQUATIONS BY USING QUADRATIC METHODS

Substitution is often helpful in solving an equation that contains a repeated variable expression.

Solve: $(2x + 1)^2 - 5(2x + 1) + 6 = 0$.

Let $m = 2x + 1$. Then

$$m^2 - 5m + 6 = 0 \qquad \text{Let } m = 2x + 1.$$

$$(m - 3)(m - 2) = 0$$

$$m = 3 \quad \text{or} \quad m = 2$$

$$2x + 1 = 3 \quad \text{or} \quad 2x + 1 = 2 \quad \text{Substitute back.}$$

$$x = 1 \quad \text{or} \quad x = \frac{1}{2}$$

SECTION 8.4   NONLINEAR INEQUALITIES IN ONE VARIABLE

To solve a polynomial inequality

Step 1. Write the inequality in standard form.

Step 2. Solve the related equation.

Step 3. Use solutions from Step 2 to separate the number line into regions.

Step 4. Use test points to determine whether values in each region satisfy the original inequality.

Step 5. Write the solution set as the union of regions whose test point value is a solution.

Solve: $x^2 \geq 6x$.

1. $x^2 - 6x \geq 0$

2. $x^2 - 6x = 0$

$x(x - 6) = 0$

$x = 0 \quad \text{or} \quad x = 6$

3.

4.

Region	Test Point Value	$x^2 \geq 6x$	Result
A	-2	$(-2)^2 \geq 6(-2)$	True
B	1	$1^2 \geq 6(1)$	False
C	7	$7^2 \geq 6(7)$	True

5.

The solution set is $(-\infty, 0] \cup [6, \infty)$.

To solve a rational inequality

Step 1. Solve for values that make all denominators 0.

Step 2. Solve the related equation.

Step 3. Use solutions from Steps 1 and 2 to separate the number line into regions.

Step 4. Use test points to determine whether values in each region satisfy the original inequality.

Step 5. Write the solution set as the union of regions whose test point value is a solution.

Solve: $\dfrac{6}{x - 1} < -2$.

1. $x - 1 = 0$ Set denominator equal to 0.

$x = 1$

2. $\dfrac{6}{x - 1} = -2$

$6 = -2(x - 1)$ Multiply by $(x - 1)$.

$6 = -2x + 2$

$4 = -2x$

$-2 = x$

3.

4. Only a test value from region B satisfies the original inequality.

5.

The solution set is $(-2, 1)$.

| **DEFINITIONS AND CONCEPTS** | **EXAMPLES** |

Graph of a quadratic function

The graph of a quadratic function written in the form $f(x) = a(x - h)^2 + k$ is a parabola with vertex (h, k). If $a > 0$, the parabola opens upward; if $a < 0$, the parabola opens downward. The axis of symmetry is the line whose equation is $x = h$.

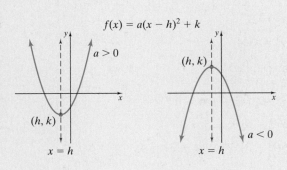

Graph $g(x) = 3(x - 1)^2 + 4$.

The graph is a parabola with vertex $(1, 4)$ and axis of symmetry $x = 1$. Since $a = 3$ is positive, the graph opens upward.

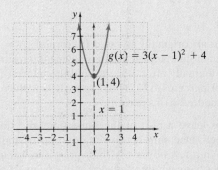

The graph of $f(x) = ax^2 + bx + c$, where $a \neq 0$, is a parabola with vertex

$$\left(\frac{-b}{2a}, f\left(\frac{-b}{2a} \right) \right)$$

Graph $f(x) = x^2 - 2x - 8$. Find the vertex and x- and y-intercepts.

$$\frac{-b}{2a} = \frac{-(-2)}{2 \cdot 1} = 1$$

$$f(1) = 1^2 - 2(1) - 8 = -9$$

The vertex is $(1, -9)$.

$$0 = x^2 - 2x - 8$$

$$0 = (x - 4)(x + 2)$$

$$x = 4 \quad \text{or} \quad x = -2$$

The x-intercepts are $(4, 0)$ and $(-2, 0)$.

$$f(0) = 0^2 - 2 \cdot 0 - 8 = -8$$

The y-intercept is $(0, -8)$.

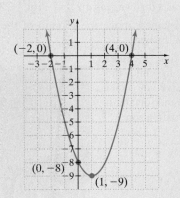

CHAPTER 8 REVIEW

(8.1) *Solve by factoring.*

1. $x^2 - 15x + 14 = 0$ **2.** $7a^2 = 29a + 30$

Solve by using the square root property.

3. $4m^2 = 196$ **4.** $(5x - 2)^2 = 2$

Solve by completing the square.

5. $z^2 + 3z + 1 = 0$

6. $(2x + 1)^2 = x$

7. If P dollars are originally invested, the formula $A = P(1 + r)^2$ gives the amount A in an account paying interest rate r compounded annually after 2 years. Find the interest rate r such that \$2500 increases to \$2717 in 2 years. Round the result to the nearest hundredth of a percent.

△ **8.** Two ships leave a port at the same time and travel at the same speed. One ship is traveling due north and the other due east. In a few hours, the ships are 150 miles apart. How many miles has each ship traveled? Give an exact answer and a one-decimal-place approximation.

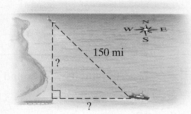

(8.2) *If the discriminant of a quadratic equation has the given value, determine the number and type of solutions of the equation.*

9. -8 **10.** 48

11. 100   **12.** 0

Solve by using the quadratic formula.

13. $x^2 - 16x + 64 = 0$ **14.** $x^2 + 5x = 0$

15. $2x^2 + 3x = 5$ **16.** $9a^2 + 4 = 2a$

17. $6x^2 + 7 = 5x$ **18.** $(2x - 3)^2 = x$

19. Cadets graduating from military school usually toss their hats high into the air at the end of the ceremony. One cadet threw his hat so that its distance $d(t)$ in feet above the ground t seconds after it was thrown was $d(t) = -16t^2 + 30t + 6$.

   a. Find the distance above the ground of the hat 1 second after it was thrown.

   b. Find the time it takes the hat to hit the ground. Give an exact time and a one-decimal-place approximation.

△ **20.** The hypotenuse of an isosceles right triangle is 6 centimeters longer than either of the legs. Find the length of the legs.

(8.3) *Solve each equation for the variable.*

21. $x^3 = 27$

22. $y^3 = -64$

23. $\dfrac{5}{x} + \dfrac{6}{x - 2} = 3$

24. $x^4 - 21x^2 - 100 = 0$

25. $x^{2/3} - 6x^{1/3} + 5 = 0$

26. $5(x + 3)^2 - 19(x + 3) = 4$

27. $a^6 - a^2 = a^4 - 1$

28. $y^{-2} + y^{-1} = 20$

29. Two postal workers, Jerome Grant and Tim Bozik, can sort a stack of mail in 5 hours. Working alone, Tim can sort the mail in 1 hour less time than Jerome can. Find the time that each postal worker can sort the mail alone. Round the result to one decimal place.

30. A negative number decreased by its reciprocal is $-\dfrac{24}{5}$. Find the number.

(8.4) *Solve each inequality for x. Write each solution set in interval notation.*

31. $2x^2 - 50 \le 0$

32. $\dfrac{1}{4}x^2 < \dfrac{1}{16}$

33. $\dfrac{x - 5}{x - 6} < 0$

34. $(x^2 - 16)(x^2 - 1) > 0$

35. $\dfrac{(4x + 3)(x - 5)}{x(x + 6)} > 0$

36. $(x + 5)(x - 6)(x + 2) \le 0$

37. $x^3 + 3x^2 - 25x - 75 > 0$

38. $\dfrac{x^2 + 4}{3x} \le 1$

39. $\dfrac{(5x + 6)(x - 3)}{x(6x - 5)} < 0$

40. $\dfrac{3}{x - 2} > 2$

(8.5) *Sketch the graph of each function. Label the vertex and the axis of symmetry.*

41. $f(x) = x^2 - 4$

42. $g(x) = x^2 + 7$

43. $H(x) = 2x^2$

44. $h(x) = -\dfrac{1}{3}x^2$

45. $F(x) = (x - 1)^2$

46. $G(x) = (x + 5)^2$

47. $f(x) = (x - 4)^2 - 2$

48. $f(x) = -3(x - 1)^2 + 1$

(8.6) *Sketch the graph of each function. Find the vertex and the intercepts.*

49. $f(x) = x^2 + 10x + 25$

50. $f(x) = -x^2 + 6x - 9$

51. $f(x) = 4x^2 - 1$

52. $f(x) = -5x^2 + 5$

 53. Find the vertex of the graph of $f(x) = -3x^2 - 5x + 4$. Determine whether the graph opens upward or downward, find the y-intercept, approximate the x-intercepts to one decimal place, and sketch the graph.

54. The function $h(t) = -16t^2 + 120t + 300$ gives the height in feet of a projectile fired from the top of a building in t seconds.

  a. When will the object reach a height of 350 feet? Round your answer to one decimal place.

  b. Explain why part **a** has two answers.

55. Find two numbers whose product is as large as possible, given that their sum is 420.

56. Write an equation of a quadratic function whose graph is a parabola that has vertex $(-3, 7)$ and that passes through the origin.

MIXED REVIEW

Solve each equation.

57. $x^2 - x - 30 = 0$

58. $10x^2 = 3x + 4$

59. $9y^2 = 36$

60. $(9n + 1)^2 = 9$

61. $x^2 + x + 7 = 0$

62. $(3x - 4)^2 = 10x$

63. $x^2 + 11 = 0$

64. $(5a - 2)^2 - a = 0$

65. $\dfrac{7}{8} = \dfrac{8}{x^2}$

66. $x^{2/3} - 6x^{1/3} = -8$

67. $(2x - 3)(4x + 5) \geq 0$

68. $\dfrac{x(x + 5)}{4x - 3} \geq 0$

69. $\dfrac{3}{x - 2} > 2$

70. The total amount of passenger traffic at Phoenix Sky Harbor International Airport in Phoenix, Arizona, during the period 1980 through 2005 can be modeled by the equation $y = 6.46x^2 + 1236.5x + 7289$, where y is the number of passengers enplaned and deplaned in thousands and x is the number of years after 1980. (*Source*: Based on data from The City of Phoenix Aviation Department, 1980–2005)

  a. Estimate the passenger traffic at Phoenix Sky Harbor International Airport in 2000.

  b. According to this model, in what year will passenger traffic at Phoenix Sky Harbor International Airport reach 60,000,000 passengers?

CHAPTER 8 TEST TEST PREP VIDEO

Remember to use the Chapter Test Prep Video CD to see the fully worked-out solutions to any of the exercises you want to review.

Solve each equation for the variable.

1. $5x^2 - 2x = 7$

2. $(x + 1)^2 = 10$

3. $m^2 - m + 8 = 0$

4. $u^2 - 6u + 2 = 0$

5. $7x^2 + 8x + 1 = 0$

6. $y^2 - 3y = 5$

7. $\dfrac{4}{x + 2} + \dfrac{2x}{x - 2} = \dfrac{6}{x^2 - 4}$

8. $x^5 + 3x^4 = x + 3$

9. $x^6 + 1 = x^4 + x^2$

10. $(x + 1)^2 - 15(x + 1) + 56 = 0$

Solve the equation for the variable by completing the square.

11. $x^2 - 6x = -2$

12. $2a^2 + 5 = 4a$

Solve each inequality for x. Write the solution set in interval notation.

13. $2x^2 - 7x > 15$

14. $(x^2 - 16)(x^2 - 25) \geq 0$

15. $\dfrac{5}{x+3} < 1$

16. $\dfrac{7x-14}{x^2-9} \leq 0$

Graph each function. Label the vertex.

17. $f(x) = 3x^2$

18. $G(x) = -2(x-1)^2 + 5$

Graph each function. Find and label the vertex, y-intercept, and x-intercepts (if any).

19. $h(x) = x^2 - 4x + 4$

20. $F(x) = 2x^2 - 8x + 9$

21. Dave and Sandy Hartranft can paint a room together in 4 hours. Working alone, Dave can paint the room in 2 hours less time than Sandy can. Find how long it takes Sandy to paint the room alone.

22. A stone is thrown upward from a bridge. The stone's height in feet, $s(t)$, above the water t seconds after the stone is thrown is a function given by the equation $s(t) = -16t^2 + 32t + 256$.

a. Find the maximum height of the stone.

b. Find the time it takes the stone to hit the water. Round the answer to two decimal places.

23. Given the diagram shown, approximate to the nearest foot how many feet of walking distance a person saves by cutting across the lawn instead of walking on the sidewalk.

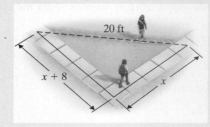

CHAPTER 8 CUMULATIVE REVIEW

1. Write each sentence using mathematical symbols.

a. The sum of 5 and y is greater than or equal to 7.

b. 11 is not equal to z.

c. 20 is less than the difference of 5 and twice x.

2. Solve $|3x - 2| = -5$.

3. Find the slope of the line containing the points $(0, 3)$ and $(2, 5)$. Graph the line.

4. Use the elimination method to solve the system.
$$\begin{cases} -6x + y = 5 \\ 4x - 2y = 6 \end{cases}$$

5. Use the elimination method to solve the system:
$$\begin{cases} x - 5y = -12 \\ -x + y = 4 \end{cases}$$

6. Simplify. Use positive exponents to write each answer.

a. $(a^{-2}bc^3)^{-3}$

b. $\left(\dfrac{a^{-4}b^2}{c^3}\right)^{-2}$

c. $\left(\dfrac{3a^8b^2}{12a^5b^5}\right)^{-2}$

7. Multiply.

a. $(2x - 7)(3x - 4)$

b. $(3x^2 + y)(5x^2 - 2y)$

8. Multiply.

a. $(4a - 3)(7a - 2)$

b. $(2a + b)(3a - 5b)$

9. Factor.

a. $8x^2 + 4$

b. $5y - 2z^4$

c. $6x^2 - 3x^3 + 12x^4$

10. Factor.

a. $9x^3 + 27x^2 - 15x$

b. $2x(3y - 2) - 5(3y - 2)$

c. $2xy + 6x - y - 3$

Factor the polynomials in Exercises 11 through 14.

11. $x^2 - 12x + 35$

12. $x^2 - 2x - 48$.

13. $3a^2x - 12abx + 12b^2x$

14. Factor. $2ax^2 - 12axy + 18ay^2$

15. Solve $3(x^2 + 4) + 5 = -6(x^2 + 2x) + 13$.

16. Solve $2(a^2 + 2) - 8 = -2a(a - 2) - 5$.

17. Solve $x^3 = 4x$.

18. Find the vertex and any intercepts of $f(x) = x^2 + x - 12$.

19. Simplify $\dfrac{2x^2}{10x^3 - 2x^2}$.

20. Simplify $\dfrac{x^2 - 4x + 4}{2 - x}$.

21. Add $\dfrac{2x - 1}{2x^2 - 9x - 5} + \dfrac{x + 3}{6x^2 - x - 2}$.

22. Subtract $\dfrac{a+1}{a^2-6a+8} - \dfrac{3}{16-a^2}$

23. Simplify $\dfrac{x^{-1}+2xy^{-1}}{x^{-2}-x^{-2}y^{-1}}$.

24. Simplify $\dfrac{(2a)^{-1}+b^{-1}}{a^{-1}+(2b)^{-1}}$.

25. Divide $\dfrac{3x^5y^2-15x^3y-x^2y-6x}{x^2y}$.

26. Divide $x^3-3x^2-10x+24$ by $x+3$.

27. If $P(x) = 2x^3-4x^2+5$

  a. Find $P(2)$ by substitution.

  b. Use synthetic division to find the remainder when $P(x)$ is divided by $x-2$.

28. If $P(x) = 4x^3-2x^2+3$,

  a. Find $P(-2)$ by substitution.

  b. Use synthetic division to find the remainder when $P(x)$ is divided by $x+2$.

29. Solve $\dfrac{4x}{5} + \dfrac{3}{2} = \dfrac{3x}{10}$.

30. Solve $\dfrac{x+3}{x^2+5x+6} = \dfrac{3}{2x+4} - \dfrac{1}{x+3}$.

31. If a certain number is subtracted from the numerator and added to the denominator of $\dfrac{9}{19}$, the new fraction is equivalent to $\dfrac{1}{3}$. Find the number.

32. Mr. Briley can roof his house in 24 hours. His son can roof the same house in 40 hours. If they work together, how long will it take to roof the house?

33. Suppose that y varies directly as x. If y is 5 when x is 30, find the constant of variation and the direct variation equation.

34. Suppose that y varies inversely as x. If y is 8 when x is 14, find the constant of variation and the inverse variation equation.

35. Simplify.

  a. $\sqrt{(-3)^2}$ **b.** $\sqrt{x^2}$

  c. $\sqrt[4]{(x-2)^4}$ **d.** $\sqrt[3]{(-5)^3}$

  e. $\sqrt[5]{(2x-7)^5}$ **f.** $\sqrt{25x^2}$

  g. $\sqrt{x^2+2x+1}$

36. Simplify. Assume that the variables represent any real number.

  a. $\sqrt{(-2)^2}$ **b.** $\sqrt{y^2}$

  c. $\sqrt[4]{(a-3)^4}$ **d.** $\sqrt[3]{(-6)^3}$

  e. $\sqrt[5]{(3x-1)^5}$

37. Use rational exponents to simplify. Assume that variables represent positive numbers.

  a. $\sqrt[8]{x^4}$ **b.** $\sqrt[6]{25}$

  c. $\sqrt[4]{r^2s^6}$

38. Use rational exponents to simplify. Assume that variables represent positive numbers.

  a. $\sqrt[4]{5^2}$ **b.** $\sqrt[12]{x^3}$

  c. $\sqrt[6]{x^2y^4}$

39. Use the product rule to simplify.

  a. $\sqrt{25x^3}$ **b.** $\sqrt[3]{54x^6y^8}$

  c. $\sqrt[4]{81z^{11}}$

40. Use the product rule to simplify. Assume that variables represent positive numbers.

  a. $\sqrt{64a^5}$ **b.** $\sqrt[3]{24a^7b^9}$

  c. $\sqrt[4]{48x^9}$

41. Rationalize the denominator of each expression.

  a. $\dfrac{2}{\sqrt{5}}$ **b.** $\dfrac{2\sqrt{16}}{\sqrt{9x}}$

  c. $\sqrt[3]{\dfrac{1}{2}}$

42. Multiply. Simplify if possible.

  a. $(\sqrt{3}-4)(2\sqrt{3}+2)$

  b. $(\sqrt{5}-x)^2$

  c. $(\sqrt{a}+b)(\sqrt{a}-b)$

43. Solve $\sqrt{2x+5} + \sqrt{2x} = 3$.

44. Solve $\sqrt{x-2} = \sqrt{4x+1} - 3$.

45. Divide. Write in the form $a+bi$.

  a. $\dfrac{2+i}{1-i}$ **b.** $\dfrac{7}{3i}$

46. Write each product in the form of $a+bi$.

  a. $3i(5-2i)$

  b. $(6-5i)^2$

  c. $(\sqrt{3}+2i)(\sqrt{3}-2i)$

47. Use the square root property to solve $(x+1)^2 = 12$.

48. Use the square root property to solve $(y-1)^2 = 24$.

49. Solve $x - \sqrt{x} - 6 = 0$.

50. Use the quadratic formula to solve $m^2 = 4m+8$.

9

Exponential and Logarithmic Functions

In this chapter, we discuss two closely related functions: exponential and logarithmic functions. These functions are vital to applications in economics, finance, engineering, the sciences, education, and other fields. Models of tumor growth and learning curves are two examples of the uses of exponential and logarithmic functions.

p H (Potential of Hydrogen) is a measure of the acidity or alkalinity of a solution. Solutions with a pH less than 7 are considered acidic, those with a pH greater than 7 are considered basic (alkaline) and those equal to 7 are defined as "neutral." The pH scale is logarithmic and some examples are in the table below. Since pH is dependent on ionic activity, it can't easily be measured. One of the oldest ways to measure the pH of a solution is litmus paper. Litmus is a water-soluble mixture of different dyes extracted from lichens.

In Section 9.4, Exercise 106, page 572, we will calculate the pH for lemonade.

Representative pH values

Substance	pH
Hydrochloric Acid, 10M	−1.0
Lead-acid battery	0.5
Gastric acid	1.5 – 2.0
Lemon juice	2.4
Cola	2.5
Vinegar	2.9
Orange or apple juice	3.5
Tomato Juice	4.0
Beer	4.5
Acid Rain	<5.0
Coffee	5.0
Tea or healthy skin	5.5
Milk	6.5
Pure Water	7.0
Healthy human saliva	6.5 – 7.4
Blood	7.34 – 7.45
Seawater	7.7 – 8.3
Hand soap	9.0 – 10.0
Household ammonia	11.5
Bleach	12.5
Household lye	13.5

9.1 THE ALGEBRA OF FUNCTIONS; COMPOSITE FUNCTIONS

OBJECTIVES

1 Add, subtract, multiply, and divide functions.

2 Construct composite functions.

OBJECTIVE 1 ▶ Adding, subtracting, multiplying, and dividing functions. As we have seen in earlier chapters, it is possible to add, subtract, multiply, and divide functions. Although we have not stated it as such, the sums, differences, products, and quotients of functions are themselves functions. For example, if $f(x) = 3x$ and $g(x) = x + 1$, their product, $f(x) \cdot g(x) = 3x(x + 1) = 3x^2 + 3x$, is a new function. We can use the notation $(f \cdot g)(x)$ to denote this new function. Finding the sum, difference, product, and quotient of functions to generate new functions is called the **algebra of functions.**

Algebra of Functions

Let f and g be functions. New functions from f and g are defined as follows.

Sum	$(f + g)(x) = f(x) + g(x)$
Difference	$(f - g)(x) = f(x) - g(x)$
Product	$(f \cdot g)(x) = f(x) \cdot g(x)$
Quotient	$\left(\dfrac{f}{g}\right)(x) = \dfrac{f(x)}{g(x)}, \quad g(x) \neq 0$

EXAMPLE 1 If $f(x) = x - 1$ and $g(x) = 2x - 3$, find

a. $(f + g)(x)$ **b.** $(f - g)(x)$ **c.** $(f \cdot g)(x)$ **d.** $\left(\dfrac{f}{g}\right)(x)$

Solution Use the algebra of functions and replace $f(x)$ by $x - 1$ and $g(x)$ by $2x - 3$. Then we simplify.

a. $(f + g)(x) = f(x) + g(x)$
$$= (x - 1) + (2x - 3)$$
$$= 3x - 4$$

b. $(f - g)(x) = f(x) - g(x)$
$$= (x - 1) - (2x - 3)$$
$$= x - 1 - 2x + 3$$
$$= -x + 2$$

c. $(f \cdot g)(x) = f(x) \cdot g(x)$
$$= (x - 1)(2x - 3)$$
$$= 2x^2 - 5x + 3$$

d. $\left(\dfrac{f}{g}\right)(x) = \dfrac{f(x)}{g(x)} = \dfrac{x - 1}{2x - 3}$, where $x \neq \dfrac{3}{2}$

PRACTICE

1 If $f(x) = x + 2$ and $g(x) = 3x + 5$, find

a. $(f + g)(x)$ **b.** $(f - g)(x)$ **c.** $(f \cdot g)(x)$ **d.** $\left(\dfrac{f}{g}\right)(x)$

There is an interesting but not surprising relationship between the graphs of functions and the graphs of their sum, difference, product, and quotient. For example, the graph of $(f + g)(x)$ can be found by adding the graph of $f(x)$ to the graph of $g(x)$. We add two graphs by adding y-values of corresponding x-values.

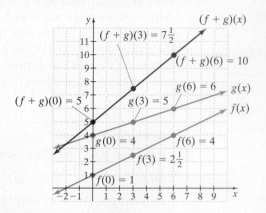

OBJECTIVE 2 ▶ Constructing composite functions. Another way to combine functions is called **function composition.** To understand this new way of combining functions, study the diagrams below. The left diagram shows degrees Celsius $f(x)$ as a function of degrees Fahrenheit x. The right diagram shows Kelvins $g(x)$ as a function of degrees Celsius x. (The Kelvin scale is a temperature scale devised by Lord Kelvin in 1848.) The function represented by the first diagram we will call f, and the second function we will call g.

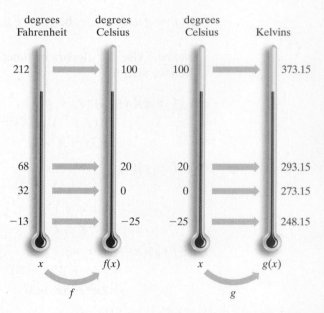

Suppose that we want a function that shows a direct conversion from degrees Fahrenheit to Kelvins. In other words, suppose that a function is needed that shows Kelvins as a function of degrees Fahrenheit. This can easily be done because the output of the first function $f(x)$ is the same as the input of the second function. If we use $f(x)$ to represent this, then we get the left diagram.

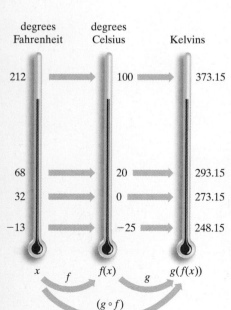

For example $g(f(-13)) = 248.15$, and so on.

Since the output of the first function is used as the input of the second function, we write the new function as $g(f(x))$. The new function is formed from the composition of the other two functions. The mathematical symbol for this composition is $(g \circ f)(x)$. Thus, $(g \circ f)(x) = g(f(x))$.

It is possible to find an equation for the composition of the two functions f and g. In other words, we can find a function that converts degrees Fahrenheit directly to

Kelvins. The function $f(x) = \dfrac{5}{9}(x - 32)$ converts degrees Fahrenheit to degrees Celsius, and the function $g(x) = x + 273.15$ converts degrees Celsius to Kelvins. Thus,

$$(g \circ f)(x) = g(f(x)) = g\left(\frac{5}{9}(x - 32)\right) = \frac{5}{9}(x - 32) + 273.15$$

In general, the notation $g(f(x))$ means "g composed with f" and can be written as $(g \circ f)(x)$. Also $f(g(x))$, or $(f \circ g)(x)$, means "f composed with g."

Composition of Functions

The composition of functions f and g is

$$(f \circ g)(x) = f(g(x))$$

▶ **Helpful Hint**

$(f \circ g)(x)$ does not mean the same as $(f \cdot g)(x)$.

$$(f \circ g)(x) = f(g(x)) \text{ while } (f \cdot g)(x) = f(x) \cdot g(x)$$

$\qquad\qquad\quad\uparrow\qquad\qquad\qquad\qquad\qquad\uparrow$

$\qquad$ Composition of functions $\qquad$ Multiplication of functions

---

EXAMPLE 2 If $f(x) = x^2$ and $g(x) = x + 3$, find each composition.

a. $(f \circ g)(2)$ and $(g \circ f)(2)$ **b.** $(f \circ g)(x)$ and $(g \circ f)(x)$

Solution

a. $(f \circ g)(2) = f(g(2))$

$\qquad\qquad\quad = f(5)$ $\qquad$ Replace $g(2)$ with 5. [Since $g(x) = x + 3$, then

$\qquad\qquad\quad = 5^2 = 25$ $\qquad g(2) = 2 + 3 = 5.]$

$(g \circ f)(2) = g(f(2))$

$\qquad\qquad\quad = g(4)$ $\qquad$ Since $f(x) = x^2$, then $f(2) = 2^2 = 4$.

$\qquad\qquad\quad = 4 + 3 = 7$

b. $(f \circ g)(x) = f(g(x))$

$\qquad\qquad\quad = f(x + 3)$ $\qquad$ Replace $g(x)$ with $x + 3$.

$\qquad\qquad\quad = (x + 3)^2$ $\qquad f(x + 3) = (x + 3)^2$

$\qquad\qquad\quad = x^2 + 6x + 9$ $\quad$ Square $(x + 3)$.

$(g \circ f)(x) = g(f(x))$

$\qquad\qquad\quad = g(x^2)$ $\qquad\qquad$ Replace $f(x)$ with x^2.

$\qquad\qquad\quad = x^2 + 3$ $\qquad\quad g(x^2) = x^2 + 3$

PRACTICE

2 If $f(x) = x^2 + 1$ and $g(x) = 3x - 5$, find

a. $(f \circ g)(4)$ **b.** $(f \circ g)(x)$

$\quad (g \circ f)(4)$ $\qquad (g \circ f)(x)$

EXAMPLE 3 If $f(x) = |x|$ and $g(x) = x - 2$, find each composition.

a. $(f \circ g)(x)$ **b.** $(g \circ f)(x)$

Solution

a. $(f \circ g)(x) = f(g(x)) = f(x - 2) = |x - 2|$
b. $(g \circ f)(x) = g(f(x)) = g(|x|) = |x| - 2$

> ▶ **Helpful Hint**
> In Examples 2 and 3, notice that $(g \circ f)(x) \neq (f \circ g)(x)$. In general, $(g \circ f)(x)$ *may* or *may not* equal $(f \circ g)(x)$.

PRACTICE

3 If $f(x) = x^2 + 5$ and $g(x) = x + 3$, find each composition.

a. $(f \circ g)(x)$ **b.** $(g \circ f)(x)$

EXAMPLE 4 If $f(x) = 5x$, $g(x) = x - 2$, and $h(x) = \sqrt{x}$, write each function as a composition using two of the given functions.

a. $F(x) = \sqrt{x - 2}$ **b.** $G(x) = 5x - 2$

Solution

a. Notice the order in which the function F operates on an input value x. First, 2 is subtracted from x. This is the function $g(x) = x - 2$. Then the square root *of that result* is taken. The square root function is $h(x) = \sqrt{x}$. This means that $F = h \circ g$. To check, we find $h \circ g$.

$$F(x) = (h \circ g)(x) = h(g(x)) = h(x - 2) = \sqrt{x - 2}$$

b. Notice the order in which the function G operates on an input value x. First, x is multiplied by 5, and then 2 is subtracted from the result. This means that $G = g \circ f$. To check, we find $g \circ f$.

$$G(x) = (g \circ f)(x) = g(f(x)) = g(5x) = 5x - 2$$

PRACTICE

4 If $f(x) = 3x$, $g(x) = x - 4$, and $h(x) = |x|$, write each function as a composition using two of the given functions.

a. $F(x) = |x - 4|$ **b.** $G(x) = 3x - 4$

Graphing Calculator Explorations

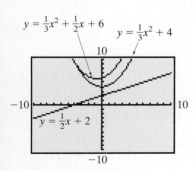

If $f(x) = \dfrac{1}{2}x + 2$ and $g(x) = \dfrac{1}{3}x^2 + 4$, then

$$(f + g)(x) = f(x) + g(x)$$
$$= \left(\frac{1}{2}x + 2\right) + \left(\frac{1}{3}x^2 + 4\right)$$
$$= \frac{1}{3}x^2 + \frac{1}{2}x + 6.$$

To visualize this addition of functions with a graphing calculator, graph

$$Y_1 = \frac{1}{2}x + 2, \qquad Y_2 = \frac{1}{3}x^2 + 4, \qquad Y_3 = \frac{1}{3}x^2 + \frac{1}{2}x + 6$$

Use a TABLE feature to verify that for a given x value, $Y_1 + Y_2 = Y_3$. For example, verify that when $x = 0$, $Y_1 = 2$, $Y_2 = 4$, and $Y_3 = 2 + 4 = 6$.

VOCABULARY & READINESS CHECK

Match each function with its definition.

1. $(f \circ g)(x)$ **4.** $(g \circ f)(x)$ **A.** $g(f(x))$ **D.** $\dfrac{f(x)}{g(x)}, g(x) \neq 0$

2. $(f \cdot g)(x)$ **5.** $\left(\dfrac{f}{g}\right)(x)$ **B.** $f(x) + g(x)$ **E.** $f(x) \cdot g(x)$

3. $(f - g)(x)$ **6.** $(f + g)(x)$ **C.** $f(g(x))$ **F.** $f(x) - g(x)$

9.1 | EXERCISE SET

PRACTICE   WATCH   DOWNLOAD   READ   REVIEW

---

*For the functions f and g, find **a.** $(f + g)(x)$, **b.** $(f - g)(x)$,*
***c.** $(f \cdot g)(x)$, and **d.** $\left(\dfrac{f}{g}\right)(x)$. See Example 1.*

1. $f(x) = x - 7, g(x) = 2x + 1$

2. $f(x) = x + 4, g(x) = 5x - 2$

3. $f(x) = x^2 + 1, g(x) = 5x$

4. $f(x) = x^2 - 2, g(x) = 3x$

5. $f(x) = \sqrt{x}, g(x) = x + 5$

6. $f(x) = \sqrt[3]{x}, g(x) = x - 3$

7. $f(x) = -3x, g(x) = 5x^2$

8. $f(x) = 4x^3, g(x) = -6x$

If $f(x) = x^2 - 6x + 2, g(x) = -2x$, and $h(x) = \sqrt{x}$, find each composition. See Example 2.

9. $(f \circ g)(2)$ **10.** $(h \circ f)(-2)$

11. $(g \circ f)(-1)$ **12.** $(f \circ h)(1)$

13. $(g \circ h)(0)$ **14.** $(h \circ g)(0)$

Find $(f \circ g)(x)$ and $(g \circ f)(x)$. See Examples 2 and 3.

15. $f(x) = x^2 + 1, g(x) = 5x$

16. $f(x) = x - 3, g(x) = x^2$

17. $f(x) = 2x - 3, g(x) = x + 7$

18. $f(x) = x + 10, g(x) = 3x + 1$

19. $f(x) = x^3 + x - 2, g(x) = -2x$

20. $f(x) = -4x, g(x) = x^3 + x^2 - 6$

21. $f(x) = |x|; g(x) = 10x - 3$

22. $f(x) = |x|; g(x) = 14x - 8$

23. $f(x) = \sqrt{x}, g(x) = -5x + 2$

24. $f(x) = 7x - 1, g(x) = \sqrt[3]{x}$

If $f(x) = 3x, g(x) = \sqrt{x}$, and $h(x) = x^2 + 2$, write each function as a composition using two of the given functions. See Example 4.

25. $H(x) = \sqrt{x^2 + 2}$

26. $G(x) = \sqrt{3x}$

27. $F(x) = 9x^2 + 2$

28. $H(x) = 3x^2 + 6$

29. $G(x) = 3\sqrt{x}$

30. $F(x) = x + 2$

Find $f(x)$ and $g(x)$ so that the given function $h(x) = (f \circ g)(x)$.

31. $h(x) = (x + 2)^2$

32. $h(x) = |x - 1|$

33. $h(x) = \sqrt{x + 5} + 2$

34. $h(x) = (3x + 4)^2 + 3$

35. $h(x) = \dfrac{1}{2x - 3}$

36. $h(x) = \dfrac{1}{x + 10}$

REVIEW AND PREVIEW

Solve each equation for y. See Section 2.3.

37. $x = y + 2$ **38.** $x = y - 5$

39. $x = 3y$ **40.** $x = -6y$

41. $x = -2y - 7$ **42.** $x = 4y + 7$

CONCEPT EXTENSIONS

Given that $f(-1) = 4$ $g(-1) = -4$

$$f(0) = 5 \qquad g(0) = -3$$
$$f(2) = 7 \qquad g(2) = -1$$
$$f(7) = 1 \qquad g(7) = 4$$

Find each function value.

43. $(f + g)(2)$ **44.** $(f - g)(7)$

45. $(f \circ g)(2)$ **46.** $(g \circ f)(2)$

47. $(f \cdot g)(7)$ **48.** $(f \cdot g)(0)$

49. $\left(\dfrac{f}{g}\right)(-1)$ **50.** $\left(\dfrac{g}{f}\right)(-1)$

51. If you are given $f(x)$ and $g(x)$, explain in your own words how to find $(f \circ g)(x)$, and then how to find $(g \circ f)(x)$.

52. Given $f(x)$ and $g(x)$, describe in your own words the difference between $(f \circ g)(x)$ and $(f \cdot g)(x)$.

Solve.

53. Business people are concerned with cost functions, revenue functions, and profit functions. Recall that the profit $P(x)$ obtained from x units of a product is equal to the revenue $R(x)$ from selling the x units minus the cost $C(x)$ of manufacturing the x units. Write an equation expressing this relationship among $C(x)$, $R(x)$, and $P(x)$.

54. Suppose the revenue $R(x)$ for x units of a product can be described by $R(x) = 25x$, and the cost $C(x)$ can be described by $C(x) = 50 + x^2 + 4x$. Find the profit $P(x)$ for x units. (See Exercise 53.)

📖 STUDY SKILLS BUILDER

Tips for Studying for an Exam

To prepare for an exam, try the following study techniques.

- Start the study process days before your exam.
- Make sure that you are up-to-date on your assignments.
- If there is a topic that you are unsure of, use one of the many resources that are available to you. For example,

    See your instructor.

    Visit a learning resource center on campus.

    Read the textbook material and examples on the topic.

    View a video on the topic.

- Reread your notes and carefully review the Chapter Highlights at the end of any chapter.
- Work the review exercises at the end of the chapter. Check your answers and correct any mistakes. If you have trouble, use a resource listed above.
- Find a quiet place to take the Chapter Test found at the end of the chapter. Do not use any resources when taking this sample test. This way, you will have a clear indication of how prepared you are for your exam.

Check your answers and make sure that you correct any missed exercises.

- Get lots of rest the night before the exam. It's hard to show how well you know the material if your brain is foggy from lack of sleep.

Good luck and keep a positive attitude.

Let's see how you did on your last exam.

1. How many days before your last exam did you start studying?

2. Were you up-to-date on your assignments at that time or did you need to catch up on assignments?

3. List the most helpful text supplement (if you used one).

4. List the most helpful campus supplement (if you used one).

5. List your process for preparing for a mathematics test.

6. Was this process helpful? In other words, were you satisfied with your performance on your exam?

7. If not, what changes can you make in your process that will make it more helpful to you?

9.2 INVERSE FUNCTIONS

OBJECTIVES

1   Determine whether a function is a one-to-one function.

2   Use the horizontal line test to decide whether a function is a one-to-one function.

3   Find the inverse of a function.

4   Find the equation of the inverse of a function.

5   Graph functions and their inverses.

6   Determine whether two functions are inverses of each other.

OBJECTIVE 1 ▶ Determining whether a function is one-to-one. In the next section, we begin a study of two new functions: exponential and logarithmic functions. As we learn more about these functions, we will discover that they share a special relation to each other: They are inverses of each other.

Before we study these functions, we need to learn about inverses. We begin by defining one-to-one functions.

Study the following diagram.

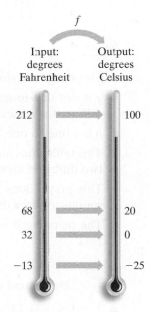

Recall that since each degrees Fahrenheit (input) corresponds to exactly one degrees Celsius (output), this pairing of inputs and outputs does describe a function. Also notice that each output corresponds to exactly one input. This type of function is given a special name—a one-to-one function.

Does the set $f = \{(0, 1), (2, 2), (-3, 5), (7, 6)\}$ describe a one-to-one function? It is a function since each x-value corresponds to a unique y-value. For this particular function f, each y-value also corresponds to a unique x-value. Thus, this function is also a **one-to-one function.**

> **One-to-One Function**
>
> For a **one-to-one function,** each x-value (input) corresponds to only one y-value (output), and each y-value (output) corresponds to only one x-value (input).

EXAMPLE 1   Determine whether each function described is one-to-one.

a. $f = \{(6, 2), (5, 4), (-1, 0), (7, 3)\}$

b. $g = \{(3, 9), (-4, 2), (-3, 9), (0, 0)\}$

c. $h = \{(1, 1), (2, 2), (10, 10), (-5, -5)\}$

d.

Mineral (Input)	Talc	Gypsum	Diamond	Topaz	Stibnite
Hardness on the Mohs Scale (Output)	1	2	10	8	2

e.

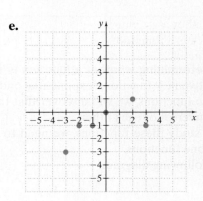

f.

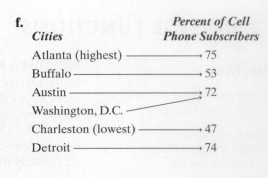

Cities	Percent of Cell Phone Subscribers
Atlanta (highest)	75
Buffalo	53
Austin	72
Washington, D.C.	
Charleston (lowest)	47
Detroit	74

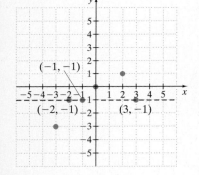

Solution

a. *f* is one-to-one since each *y*-value corresponds to only one *x*-value.

b. *g* is not one-to-one because the *y*-value 9 in $(3, 9)$ and $(-3, 9)$ corresponds to two different *x*-values.

c. *h* is a one-to-one function since each *y*-value corresponds to only one *x*-value.

d. This table does not describe a one-to-one function since the output 2 corresponds to two different inputs, gypsum and stibnite.

e. This graph does not describe a one-to-one function since the *y*-value -1 corresponds to three different *x*-values, $-2, -1,$ and 3.

f. The mapping is not one-to-one since 72% corresponds to Austin and Washington, D.C.

PRACTICE

1 Determine whether each function described is one-to-one.

a. $f = \{(4, -3), (3, -4), (2, 7), (5, 0)\}$

b. $g = \{(8, 4), (-2, 0), (6, 4), (2, 6)\}$

c. $h = \{(2, 4), (1, 3), (4, 6), (-2, 4)\}$

d.

Year	1950	1963	1968	1975	1997	2002
Federal Minimum Wage	$0.75	$1.25	$1.60	$2.10	$5.15	$5.15

e.

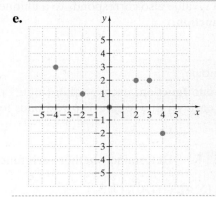

f.

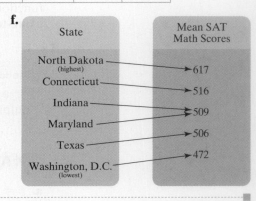

State	Mean SAT Math Scores
North Dakota (highest)	617
Connecticut	516
Indiana	509
Maryland	506
Texas	472
Washington, D.C. (lowest)	

OBJECTIVE 2 ▶ Using the horizontal line test. Recall that we recognize the graph of a function when it passes the vertical line test. Since every *x*-value of the function corresponds to exactly one *y*-value, each vertical line intersects the function's graph at most once. The graph shown (left), for instance, is the graph of a function.

Is this function a *one-to-one* function? The answer is no. To see why not, notice that the *y*-value of the ordered pair $(-3, 3)$, for example, is the same as the *y*-value of the ordered pair $(3, 3)$. In other words, the *y*-value 3 corresponds to two *x*-values, -3 and 3. This function is therefore not one-to-one.

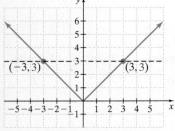

Not a one-to-one function.

To test whether a graph is the graph of a one-to-one function, apply the vertical line test to see if it is a function, and then apply a similar **horizontal line test** to see if it is a one-to-one function.

Horizontal Line Test

If every horizontal line intersects the graph of a function at most once, then the function is a one-to-one function.

EXAMPLE 2   Determine whether each graph is the graph of a one-to-one function.

a.

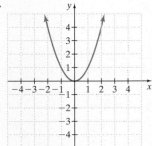

b.

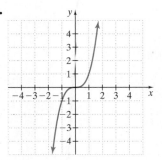

c.

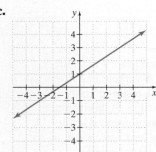

d.

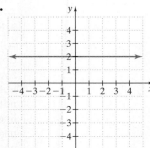

e.

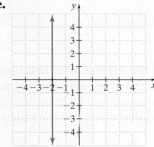

Solution   Graphs **a, b, c,** and **d** all pass the vertical line test, so only these graphs are graphs of functions. But, of these, only **b** and **c** pass the horizontal line test, so only **b** and **c** are graphs of one-to-one functions.   □

PRACTICE
2   Determine whether each graph is the graph of a one-to-one function.

a.

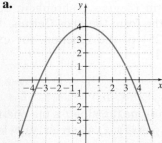

b.

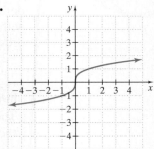

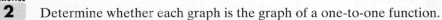

c.

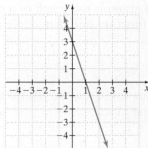

d.

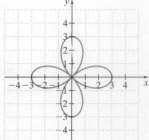

e.

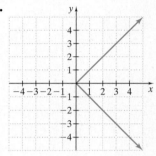

> ▶ **Helpful Hint**
>
> All linear equations are one-to-one functions except those whose graphs are horizontal or vertical lines. A vertical line does not pass the vertical line test and hence is not the graph of a function. A horizontal line is the graph of a function but does not pass the horizontal line test and hence is not the graph of a one-to-one function.
>
>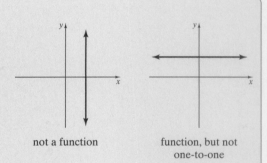
>
> not a function   function, but not one-to-one

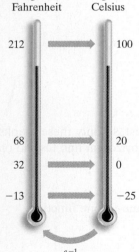

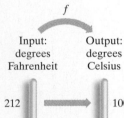

f

Input: degrees Fahrenheit   Output: degrees Celsius

212 → 100

68 → 20

32 → 0

−13 → −25

f^{-1}

OBJECTIVE 3 ▶ Finding the inverse of a function. One-to-one functions are special in that their graphs pass both the vertical and horizontal line tests. They are special, too, in another sense: For each one-to-one function, we can find its **inverse function** by switching the coordinates of the ordered pairs of the function, or the inputs and the outputs. For example,

the inverse of the one-to-one function $f = \{(2, -3), (5, 10), (9, 1)\}$ is $\{(-3, 2), (10, 5), (1, 9)\}$.

For a function f, we use the notation f^{-1}, read "f inverse," to denote its inverse function. Notice that since the coordinates of each ordered pair have been switched, the domain (set of inputs) of f is the range (set of outputs) of f^{-1}, and the range of f is the domain of f^{-1}.

The diagram to the left shows the inverse of the one-to-one function f with ordered pairs of the form (degrees Fahrenheit, degrees Celsuis) is the function f^{-1} with ordered pairs of the form (degrees Celsius, degrees Fahrenheit). Notice that the ordered pair $(-13, -25)$ of the function, for example, becomes the ordered pair $(-25, -13)$ of its inverse.

> **Inverse Function**
>
> The inverse of a one-to-one function f is the one-to-one function f^{-1} that consists of the set of all ordered pairs (y, x) where (x, y) belongs to f.

▶ **Helpful Hint**
If a function is not one-to-one, it does not have an inverse function.

EXAMPLE 3 Find the inverse of the one-to-one function.
$$f = \{(0,1),(-2,7),(3,-6),(4,4)\}$$

Solution $f^{-1} = \{(1,0),(7,-2),(-6,3),(4,4)\}$

Switch coordinates of each ordered pair.

PRACTICE
3 Find the inverse of the one-to-one function.
$$f(x) = \{(3,4),(-2,0),(2,8),(6,6)\}$$

▶ **Helpful Hint**
The symbol f^{-1} is the single symbol used to denote the inverse of the function f.
It is read as "f inverse." This symbol *does not mean* $\dfrac{1}{f}$.

Concept Check ☑
Suppose that f is a one-to-one function and that $f(1) = 5$.
a. Write the corresponding ordered pair.
b. Write one point that we know must belong to the inverse function f^{-1}.

OBJECTIVE 4 ▶ Finding the equation of the inverse of a function. If a one-to-one function f is defined as a set of ordered pairs, we can find f^{-1} by interchanging the x- and y-coordinates of the ordered pairs. If a one-to-one function f is given in the form of an equation, we can find f^{-1} by using a similar procedure.

Finding the Inverse of a One-to-One Function f(x)
STEP 1. Replace $f(x)$ with y.
STEP 2. Interchange x and y.
STEP 3. Solve the equation for y.
STEP 4. Replace y with the notation $f^{-1}(x)$.

EXAMPLE 4 Find an equation of the inverse of $f(x) = x + 3$.
Solution $f(x) = x + 3$
STEP 1. $y = x + 3$ Replace $f(x)$ with y.
STEP 2. $x = y + 3$ Interchange x and y.
STEP 3. $x - 3 = y$ Solve for y.
STEP 4. $f^{-1}(x) = x - 3$ Replace y with $f^{-1}(x)$.

Answer to Concept Check:
a. $(1,5)$, **b.** $(5,1)$

The inverse of $f(x) = x + 3$ is $f^{-1}(x) = x - 3$. Notice that, for example,

$$f(1) = 1 + 3 = 4 \quad \text{and} \quad f^{-1}(4) = 4 - 3 = 1$$

Ordered pair: $(1, 4)$ Ordered pair: $(4, 1)$

The coordinates are
switched, as expected.

PRACTICE
4 Find the equation of the inverse of $f(x) = 6 - x$.

EXAMPLE 5 Find the equation of the inverse of $f(x) = 3x - 5$. Graph f and f^{-1} on the same set of axes.

Solution $f(x) = 3x - 5$

STEP 1. $y = 3x - 5$ Replace $f(x)$ with y.

STEP 2. $x = 3y - 5$ Interchange x and y.

STEP 3. $3y = x + 5$ Solve for y.

$$y = \frac{x + 5}{3}$$

STEP 4. $f^{-1}(x) = \dfrac{x + 5}{3}$ Replace y with $f^{-1}(x)$.

Now we graph $f(x)$ and $f^{-1}(x)$ on the same set of axes. Both $f(x) = 3x - 5$ and $f^{-1}(x) = \dfrac{x + 5}{3}$ are linear functions, so each graph is a line.

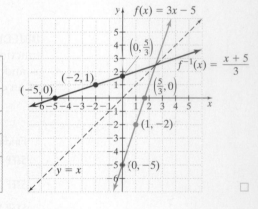

$f(x) = 3x - 5$	
x	$y = f(x)$
1	-2
0	-5
$\dfrac{5}{3}$	0

$f^{-1}(x) = \dfrac{x + 5}{3}$	
x	$y = f^{-1}(x)$
-2	1
-5	0
0	$\dfrac{5}{3}$

PRACTICE
5 Find the equation of the inverse of $f(x) = 5x + 2$. Graph f and f^{-1} on the same set of axes.

OBJECTIVE 5 ▶ Graphing inverse functions. Notice that the graphs of f and f^{-1} in Example 5 are mirror images of each other, and the "mirror" is the dashed line $y = x$. This is true for every function and its inverse. For this reason, we say that *the graphs of f and f^{-1} are symmetric about the line $y = x$.*

To see why this happens, study the graph of a few ordered pairs and their switched coordinates in the diagram to the right.

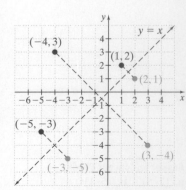

EXAMPLE 6   Graph the inverse of each function.

Solution   The function is graphed in blue and the inverse is graphed in red.

a.

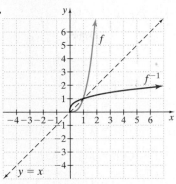

b.

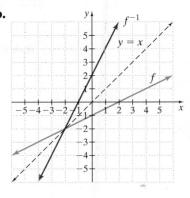

PRACTICE
6   Graph the inverse of each function.

a.

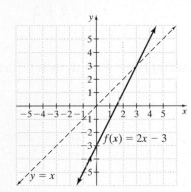

b.

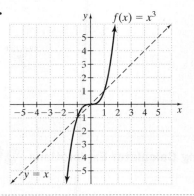

OBJECTIVE 6 ▶ Determining whether functions are inverses of each other. Notice in the table of values in Example 5 that $f(0) = -5$ and $f^{-1}(-5) = 0$, as expected. Also, for example, $f(1) = -2$ and $f^{-1}(-2) = 1$. In words, we say that for some input x, the function f^{-1} takes the output of x, called $f(x)$, back to x.

$$x \to f(x) \quad \text{and} \quad f^{-1}(f(x)) \to x$$

$$f(0) = -5 \quad \text{and} \quad f^{-1}(-5) = 0$$
$$f(1) = -2 \quad \text{and} \quad f^{-1}(-2) = 1$$

In general,

If f is a one-to-one function, then the inverse of f is the function f^{-1} such that

$$(f^{-1} \circ f)(x) = x \quad \text{and} \quad (f \circ f^{-1})(x) = x$$

EXAMPLE 7 Show that if $f(x) = 3x + 2$, then $f^{-1}(x) = \dfrac{x - 2}{3}$.

$\underline{\textit{Solution}}$ See that $(f^{-1} \circ f)(x) = x$ and $(f \circ f^{-1})(x) = x$.

$$(f^{-1} \circ f)(x) = f^{-1}(f(x))$$
$$= f^{-1}(3x + 2) \qquad \text{Replace } f(x) \text{ with } 3x + 2.$$
$$= \frac{3x + 2 - 2}{3}$$
$$= \frac{3x}{3}$$
$$= x$$

$$(f \circ f^{-1})(x) = f(f^{-1}(x))$$
$$= f\left(\frac{x - 2}{3}\right) \qquad \text{Replace } f^{-1}(x) \text{ with } \frac{x - 2}{3}.$$
$$= 3\left(\frac{x - 2}{3}\right) + 2$$
$$= x - 2 + 2$$
$$= x$$

PRACTICE
7 Show that if $f(x) = 4x - 1$, then $f^{-1}(x) = \dfrac{x + 1}{4}$.

Graphing Calculator Explorations

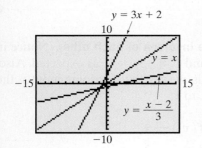

$y = 3x + 2$

$y = x$

$y = \dfrac{x - 2}{3}$

A graphing calculator can be used to visualize the results of Example 7. Recall that the graph of a function f and its inverse f^{-1} are mirror images of each other across the line $y = x$. To see this for the function from Example 7, use a square window and graph

the given function: $Y_1 = 3x + 2$

its inverse: $Y_2 = \dfrac{x - 2}{3}$

and the line: $Y_3 = x$

Exercises will follow in Exercise Set 9.2.

VOCABULARY & READINESS CHECK

Use the choices below to fill in each blank. Some choices will not be used and some will be used more than once.

vertical	$(3, 7)$	$(11, 2)$	$y = x$	x
horizontal	$(7, 3)$	$(2, 11)$	$\dfrac{1}{f}$	the inverse of f

1. If $f(2) = 11$, the corresponding ordered pair is _____.
2. The symbol f^{-1} means _____.
3. If $(7, 3)$ is an ordered pair solution of $f(x)$, and $f(x)$ has an inverse, then an ordered pair solution of $f^{-1}(x)$ is _____.
4. To tell whether a graph is the graph of a function, use the _____ line test.
5. To tell whether the graph of a function is also a one-to-one function, use the _____ line test.
6. The graphs of f and f^{-1} are symmetric about the _____ line.
7. Two functions are inverse of each other if $(f \circ f^{-1})(x) =$ _____ and $(f^{-1} \circ f)(x) =$ _____.

9.2 EXERCISE SET

PRACTICE   WATCH   DOWNLOAD   READ   REVIEW

Determine whether each function is a one-to-one function. If it is one-to-one, list the inverse function by switching coordinates, or inputs and outputs. See Examples 1 and 3.

1. $f = \{(-1, -1), (1, 1), (0, 2), (2, 0)\}$

2. $g = \{(8, 6), (9, 6), (3, 4), (-4, 4)\}$

3. $h = \{(10, 10)\}$

4. $r = \{(1, 2), (3, 4), (5, 6), (6, 7)\}$

5. $f = \{(11, 12), (4, 3), (3, 4), (6, 6)\}$

6. $g = \{(0, 3), (3, 7), (6, 7), (-2, -2)\}$

7.

Month of 2007 (Input)	January	February	March	April
Unemployment Rate in Percent	4.6	4.6	4.4	4.4

(*Source:* Bureau of Labor Statistics, U.S. Department of Housing and Urban Development)

8.

State (Input)	Wisconsin	Ohio	Georgia	Colorado	California	Arizona
Electoral Votes (Output)	10	20	15	9	55	10

9.

State (Input)	California	Maryland	Nevada	Florida	North Dakota
Rank in Population (Output)	1	19	35	4	48

(*Source:* U.S. Bureau of the Census)

 10.

Shape (Input)	Triangle	Pentagon	Quadrilateral	Hexagon	Decagon
Number of Sides (Output)	3	5	4	6	10

(*Source:* U.S. Bureau of the Census)

Given the one-to-one function $f(x) = x^3 + 2$, *find the following.* [*Hint: You do not need to find the equation for* $f^{-1}(x)$.]

11. a. $f(1)$
    b. $f^{-1}(3)$

12. a. $f(0)$
    b. $f^{-1}(2)$

13. a. $f(-1)$
    b. $f^{-1}(1)$

14. a. $f(-2)$
    b. $f^{-1}(-6)$

Determine whether the graph of each function is the graph of a one-to-one function. See Example 2.

 15.

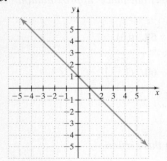

16.

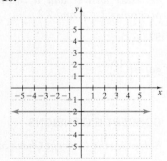

17.

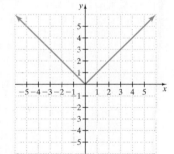

18.

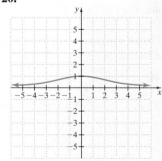

19.

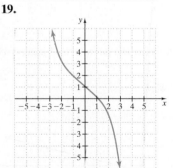

20.

21.

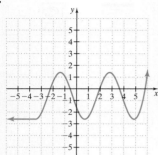

22.

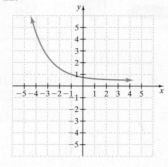

MIXED PRACTICE

Each of the following functions is one-to-one. Find the inverse of each function and graph the function and its inverse on the same set of axes. See Examples 4 and 5.

23. $f(x) = x + 4$

24. $f(x) = x - 5$

25. $f(x) = 2x - 3$

26. $f(x) = 4x + 9$

27. $f(x) = \frac{1}{2}x - 1$

28. $f(x) = -\frac{1}{2}x + 2$

29. $f(x) = x^3$

30. $f(x) = x^3 - 1$

Find the inverse of each one-to-one function. See Examples 4 and 5.

31. $f(x) = 5x + 2$

32. $f(x) = 6x - 1$

33. $f(x) = \frac{x - 2}{5}$

34. $f(x) = \frac{4x - 3}{2}$

35. $f(x) = \sqrt[3]{x}$

36. $f(x) = \sqrt[3]{x + 1}$

37. $f(x) = \frac{5}{3x + 1}$

38. $f(x) = \frac{7}{2x + 4}$

39. $f(x) = (x + 2)^3$

40. $f(x) = (x - 5)^3$

Graph the inverse of each function on the same set of axes. See Example 6.

41.

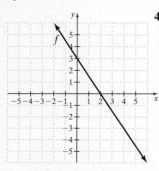

42.

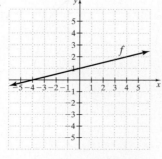

43.

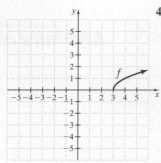

44.

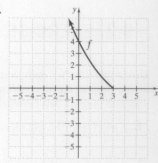

45.

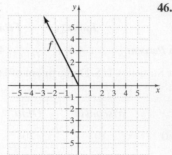

46.

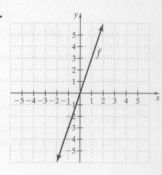

Solve. See Example 7.

47. If $f(x) = 2x + 1$, show that $f^{-1}(x) = \dfrac{x - 1}{2}$.

48. If $f(x) = 3x - 10$, show that $f^{-1}(x) = \dfrac{x + 10}{3}$.

49. If $f(x) = x^3 + 6$, show that $f^{-1}(x) = \sqrt[3]{x - 6}$.

50. If $f(x) = x^3 - 5$, show that $f^{-1}(x) = \sqrt[3]{x + 5}$.

REVIEW AND PREVIEW

Evaluate each of the following. See Section 7.2.

51. $25^{1/2}$

52. $49^{1/2}$

53. $16^{3/4}$

54. $27^{2/3}$

55. $9^{-3/2}$

56. $81^{-3/4}$

If $f(x) = 3^x$, find the following. In Exercises 59 and 60, give an exact answer and a two-decimal-place approximation. See Sections 3.2, 5.1, and 7.2.

57. $f(2)$

58. $f(0)$

59. $f\left(\dfrac{1}{2}\right)$

60. $f\left(\dfrac{2}{3}\right)$

CONCEPT EXTENSIONS

Solve. See the Concept Check in this section.

61. Suppose that f is a one-to-one function and that $f(2) = 9$.

    a. Write the corresponding ordered pair.

    b. Name one ordered-pair that we know is a solution of the inverse of f, or f^{-1}.

62. Suppose that F is a one-to-one function and that $F\left(\dfrac{1}{2}\right) = -0.7$.

    a. Write the corresponding ordered pair.

    b. Name one ordered pair that we know is a solution of the inverse of F, or F^{-1}.

For Exercises 63 and 64,

a. *Write the ordered pairs for $f(x)$ whose points are highlighted. (Include the points whose coordinates are given.)*

b. *Write the corresponding ordered pairs for the inverse of f, f^{-1}.*

c. *Graph the ordered pairs for f^{-1} found in part **b**.*

d. *Graph $f^{-1}(x)$ by drawing a smooth curve through the plotted points.*

63.

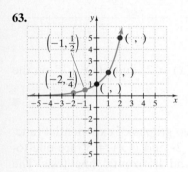

64.

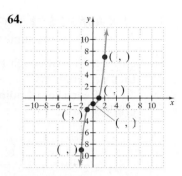

65. If you are given the graph of a function, describe how you can tell from the graph whether a function has an inverse.

66. Describe the appearance of the graphs of a function and its inverse.

Find the inverse of each given one-to-one function. Then use a graphing calculator to graph the function and its inverse on a square window.

67. $f(x) = 3x + 1$

68. $f(x) = -2x - 6$

69. $f(x) = \sqrt[3]{x + 1}$

70. $f(x) = x^3 - 3$

9.3 EXPONENTIAL FUNCTIONS

OBJECTIVES

1 Graph exponential functions.

2 Solve equations of the form $b^x = b^y$.

3 Solve problems modeled by exponential equations.

OBJECTIVE 1 ▶ Graphing exponential functions. In earlier chapters, we gave meaning to exponential expressions such as 2^x, where x is a rational number. For example,

$$2^3 = 2 \cdot 2 \cdot 2 \qquad \text{Three factors; each factor is 2}$$
$$2^{3/2} = (2^{1/2})^3 = \sqrt{2} \cdot \sqrt{2} \cdot \sqrt{2} \qquad \text{Three factors; each factor is } \sqrt{2}$$

When x is an irrational number (for example, $\sqrt{3}$), what meaning can we give to $2^{\sqrt{3}}$?

It is beyond the scope of this book to give precise meaning to 2^x if x is irrational. We can confirm your intuition and say that $2^{\sqrt{3}}$ is a real number, and since $1 < \sqrt{3} < 2$, then $2^1 < 2^{\sqrt{3}} < 2^2$. We can also use a calculator and approximate $2^{\sqrt{3}}$: $2^{\sqrt{3}} \approx 3.321997$. In fact, as long as the base b is positive, b^x is a real number for all real numbers x. Finally, the rules of exponents apply whether x is rational or irrational, as long as b is positive. In this section, we are interested in functions of the form $f(x) = b^x$, where $b > 0$. A function of this form is called an **exponential function.**

Exponential Function

A function of the form

$$f(x) = b^x$$

is called an **exponential function** if $b > 0$, b is not 1, and x is a real number.

Next, we practice graphing exponential functions.

EXAMPLE 1 Graph the exponential functions defined by $f(x) = 2^x$ and $g(x) = 3^x$ on the same set of axes.

Solution Graph each function by plotting points. Set up a table of values for each of the two functions.

If each set of points is plotted and connected with a smooth curve, the following graphs result.

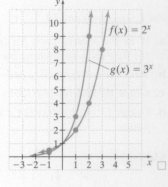

$f(x) = 2^x$	x	0	1	2	3	−1	−2
	$f(x)$	1	2	4	8	$\frac{1}{2}$	$\frac{1}{4}$

$g(x) = 3^x$	x	0	1	2	3	−1	−2
	$g(x)$	1	3	9	27	$\frac{1}{3}$	$\frac{1}{9}$

PRACTICE
1 Graph the exponential functions defined by $f(x) = 2^x$ and $g(x) = 7^x$ on the same set of axes.

A number of things should be noted about the two graphs of exponential functions in Example 1. First, the graphs show that $f(x) = 2^x$ and $g(x) = 3^x$ are one-to-one functions since each graph passes the vertical and horizontal line tests. The y-intercept of each graph is $(0, 1)$, but neither graph has an x-intercept. From the graph, we can also see that the domain of each function is all real numbers and that the range is $(0, \infty)$. We can also see that as x-values are increasing, y-values are increasing also.

EXAMPLE 2 Graph the exponential functions $y = \left(\frac{1}{2}\right)^x$ and $y = \left(\frac{1}{3}\right)^x$ on the same set of axes.

Solution As before, plot points and connect them with a smooth curve.

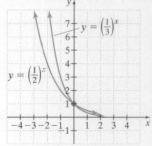

$y = \left(\frac{1}{2}\right)^x$	x	0	1	2	3	−1	−2
	y	1	$\frac{1}{2}$	$\frac{1}{4}$	$\frac{1}{8}$	2	4

$y = \left(\frac{1}{3}\right)^x$	x	0	1	2	3	−1	−2
	y	1	$\frac{1}{3}$	$\frac{1}{9}$	$\frac{1}{27}$	3	9

PRACTICE
2 Graph the exponential functions $f(x) = \left(\frac{1}{3}\right)^x$ and $g(x) = \left(\frac{1}{5}\right)^x$ on the same set of axes.

Each function in Example 2 again is a one-to-one function. The y-intercept of both is $(0, 1)$. The domain is the set of all real numbers, and the range is $(0, \infty)$.

Notice the difference between the graphs of Example 1 and the graphs of Example 2. An exponential function is always increasing if the base is greater than 1.

When the base is between 0 and 1, the graph is always decreasing. The following figures summarize these characteristics of exponential functions.

$$f(x) = b^x, \quad b > 0, \quad b \neq 1$$

- one-to-one function
- domain: $(-\infty, \infty)$
- y-intercept $(0, 1)$
- range: $(0, \infty)$
- no x-intercept

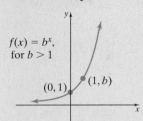

$f(x) = b^x,$
for $b > 1$

$(0, 1)$ $(1, b)$

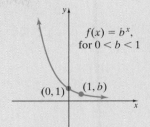

$f(x) = b^x,$
for $0 < b < 1$

$(0, 1)$ $(1, b)$

EXAMPLE 3   Graph the exponential function $f(x) = 3^{x+2}$.

Solution   As before, we find and plot a few ordered pair solutions. Then we connect the points with a smooth curve.

$y = 3^{x+2}$	
x	y
0	9
-1	3
-2	1
-3	$\dfrac{1}{3}$
-4	$\dfrac{1}{9}$

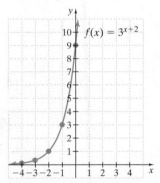

$f(x) = 3^{x+2}$

PRACTICE
3   Graph the exponential function $f(x) = 2^{x+3}$.

Concept Check ✓
Which functions are exponential functions?

a. $f(x) = x^3$ **b.** $g(x) = \left(\dfrac{2}{3}\right)^x$ **c.** $h(x) = 5^{x-2}$ **d.** $w(x) = (2x)^2$

OBJECTIVE 2 ▶ **Solving equations of the form** $b^x = b^y$. We have seen that an exponential function $y = b^x$ is a one-to-one function. Another way of stating this fact is a property that we can use to solve exponential equations.

Uniqueness of b^x
Let $b > 0$ and $b \neq 1$. Then $b^x = b^y$ is equivalent to $x = y$.

EXAMPLE 4   Solve each equation for x.

a. $2^x = 16$ **b.** $9^x = 27$ **c.** $4^{x+3} = 8^x$

Solution

a. We write 16 as a power of 2 and then use the uniqueness of b^x to solve.

$$2^x = 16$$
$$2^x = 2^4$$

Since the bases are the same and are nonnegative, by the uniqueness of b^x, we then have that the exponents are equal. Thus,

$$x = 4$$

The solution is 4, or the solution set is $\{4\}$.

b. Notice that both 9 and 27 are powers of 3.

$$9^x = 27$$
$$(3^2)^x = 3^3 \quad \text{Write 9 and 27 as powers of 3.}$$
$$3^{2x} = 3^3$$
$$2x = 3 \quad \text{Apply the uniqueness of } b^x.$$
$$x = \frac{3}{2} \quad \text{Divide by 2.}$$

To check, replace x with $\frac{3}{2}$ in the original expression, $9^x = 27$. The solution is $\frac{3}{2}$.

c. Write both 4 and 8 as powers of 2.

$$4^{x+3} = 8^x$$
$$(2^2)^{x+3} = (2^3)^x$$
$$2^{2x+6} = 2^{3x}$$
$$2x + 6 = 3x \quad \text{Apply the uniqueness of } b^x.$$
$$6 = x \quad \text{Subtract } 2x \text{ from both sides.}$$

The solution is 6.

PRACTICE
4 Solve each equation for x.

a. $3^x = 9$ **b.** $8^x = 16$ **c.** $125^x = 25^{x-2}$

There is one major problem with the preceding technique. Often the two sides of an equation cannot easily be written as powers of a common base. We explore how to solve an equation such as $4 = 3^x$ with the help of **logarithms** later.

OBJECTIVE 3 ▶ Solving problems modeled by exponential equations. The bar graph below shows the increase in the number of cellular phone users. Notice that the graph of the exponential function $y = 110.6(1.132)^x$ approximates the heights of the bars.

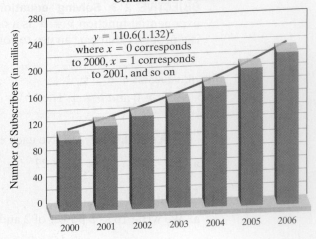

Cellular Phone Subscribers

$y = 110.6(1.132)^x$
where $x = 0$ corresponds
to 2000, $x = 1$ corresponds
to 2001, and so on

Source: Cellular Telecommunications & Internet Association

Note: Compare this Chapter 9 graph with the Chapter 8 opener graph, page 479, on the bottom of the page. Notice how using different data years leads to different models—one quadratic and one exponential.

The graph on the previous page shows just one example of how the world abounds with patterns that can be modeled by exponential functions. To make these applications realistic, we use numbers that warrant a calculator. Another application of an exponential function has to do with interest rates on loans.

The exponential function defined by $A = P\left(1 + \dfrac{r}{n}\right)^{nt}$ models the dollars A accrued (or owed) after P dollars are invested (or loaned) at an annual rate of interest r compounded n times each year for t years. This function is known as the compound interest formula.

EXAMPLE 5   **Using the Compound Interest Formula**

Find the amount owed at the end of 5 years if $1600 is loaned at a rate of 9% compounded monthly.

Solution   We use the formula $A = P\left(1 + \dfrac{r}{n}\right)^{nt}$, with the following values.

$P = \$1600$ (the amount of the loan)
$r = 9\% = 0.09$ (the annual rate of interest)
$n = 12$ (the number of times interest is compounded each year)
$t = 5$ (the duration of the loan, in years)

$A = P\left(1 + \dfrac{r}{n}\right)^{nt}$ Compound interest formula

$= 1600\left(1 + \dfrac{0.09}{12}\right)^{12(5)}$ Substitute known values.

$= 1600(1.0075)^{60}$

To approximate A, use the $\boxed{y^x}$ or $\boxed{\wedge}$ key on your calculator.

$$\boxed{2505.0896}$$

Thus, the amount A owed is approximately $2505.09.   □

PRACTICE
5   Find the amount owed at the end of 4 years if $3000 is loaned at a rate of 7% compounded semiannually (twice a year).

- -

EXAMPLE 6   **Estimating Percent of Radioactive Material**

As a result of the Chernobyl nuclear accident, radioactive debris was carried through the atmosphere. One immediate concern was the impact that the debris had on the milk supply. The percent y of radioactive material in raw milk after t days is estimated by $y = 100(2.7)^{-0.1t}$. Estimate the expected percent of radioactive material in the milk after 30 days.

Solution   Replace t with 30 in the given equation.

$y = 100(2.7)^{-0.1t}$

$= 100(2.7)^{-0.1(30)}$ Let $t = 30$.

$= 100(2.7)^{-3}$

To approximate the percent y, the following keystrokes may be used on a scientific calculator.

| 2.7 | y^x | 3 | + / − | = | × | 100 | = |

The display should read

| 5.0805263 |

Thus, approximately 5% of the radioactive material still remained in the milk supply after 30 days.

PRACTICE

6 If a single sheet of glass prevents 5% of the incoming light from passing through it, then the percent p of light that passes through n successive sheets of glass is given approximately by the function $p(n) = 100(2.7)^{-0.05n}$. Estimate the expected percent of light that will pass through 10 sheets of glass. Round to the nearest hundredth of a percent.

Graphing Calculator Explorations

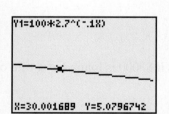

We can use a graphing calculator and its TRACE feature to solve Example 6 graphically.

To estimate the expected percent of radioactive material in the milk after 30 days, enter $Y_1 = 100(2.7)^{-0.1x}$. (The variable t in Example 6 is changed to x here to better accomodate our work on the graphing calculator.) The graph does not appear on a standard viewing window, so we need to determine an appropriate viewing window. Because it doesn't make sense to look at radioactivity *before* the Chernobyl nuclear accident, we use Xmin = 0. We are interested in finding the percent of radioactive material in the milk when $x = 30$, so we choose Xmax = 35 to leave enough space to see the graph at $x = 30$. Because the values of y are percents, it seems appropriate that $0 \le y \le 100$. (We also use Xscl = 1 and Yscl = 10.) Now we graph the function.

We can use the TRACE feature to obtain an approximation of the expected percent of radioactive material in the milk when $x = 30$. (A TABLE feature may also be used to approximate the percent.) To obtain a better approximation, let's use the ZOOM feature several times to zoom in near $x = 30$.

The percent of radioactive material in the milk 30 days after the Chernobyl accident was 5.08%, accurate to two decimal places.

Use a graphing calculator to find each percent. Approximate your solutions so that they are accurate to two decimal places.

1. Estimate the expected percent of radioactive material in the milk 2 days after the Chernobyl nuclear accident.

2. Estimate the expected percent of radioactive material in the milk 10 days after the Chernobyl nuclear accident.

3. Estimate the expected percent of radioactive material in the milk 15 days after the Chernobyl nuclear accident.

4. Estimate the expected percent of radioactive material in the milk 25 days after the Chernobyl nuclear accident.

VOCABULARY & READINESS CHECK

Use the choices to fill in each blank.

1. A function such as $f(x) = 2^x$ is a(n) _____ function.

    A. linear   **B.** quadratic   **C.** exponential

2. If $7^x = 7^y$, then _____.

    A. $x = 7^y$ **B.** $x = y$ **C.** $y = 7^x$ **D.** $7 = 7^y$

Answer the questions about the graph of $y = 2^x$, shown to the right.

3. Is this a one-to-one function? _____

4. Is there an x-intercept? _____ If so, name the coordinates. _____

5. Is there a y-intercept? _____ If so, name the coordinates. _____

6. The domain of this function, in interval notation, is _____ .

7. The range of this function, in interval notation, is _____ .

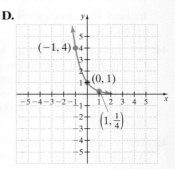

9.3 | EXERCISE SET

 MyMathLab  PRACTICE   WATCH   DOWNLOAD   READ   REVIEW

Graph each exponential function. See Examples 1 through 3.

1. $y = 4^x$ **2.** $y = 5^x$

3. $y = 2^x + 1$ **4.** $y = 3^x - 1$

5. $y = \left(\dfrac{1}{4}\right)^x$ **6.** $y = \left(\dfrac{1}{5}\right)^x$

7. $y = \left(\dfrac{1}{2}\right)^x - 2$ **8.** $y = \left(\dfrac{1}{3}\right)^x + 2$

9. $y = -2^x$ **10.** $y = -3^x$

11. $y = -\left(\dfrac{1}{4}\right)^x$ **12.** $y = -\left(\dfrac{1}{5}\right)^x$

13. $f(x) = 2^{x+1}$ **14.** $f(x) = 3^{x-1}$

15. $f(x) = 4^{x-2}$ **16.** $f(x) = 2^{x+3}$

Match each exponential equation with its graph below or in the next column. See Examples 1 through 3.

17. $f(x) = \left(\dfrac{1}{2}\right)^x$ **18.** $f(x) = \left(\dfrac{1}{4}\right)^x$

19. $f(x) = 2^x$ **20.** $f(x) = 3^x$

A.

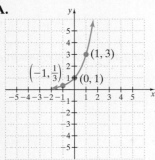

B.

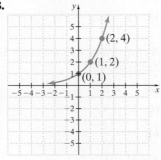

C.

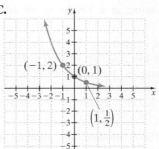

D.

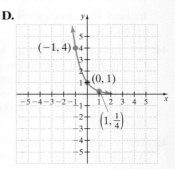

Solve each equation for x. See Example 4.

21. $3^x = 27$ **22.** $6^x = 36$

23. $16^x = 8$ **24.** $64^x = 16$

25. $32^{2x-3} = 2$ **26.** $9^{2x+1} = 81$

27. $\dfrac{1}{4} = 2^{3x}$ **28.** $\dfrac{1}{27} = 3^{2x}$

29. $5^x = 625$ **30.** $2^x = 64$

31. $4^x = 8$ **32.** $32^x = 4$

33. $27^{x+1} = 9$ **34.** $125^{x-2} = 25$

35. $81^{x-1} = 27^{2x}$ **36.** $4^{3x-7} = 32^{2x}$

Solve. Unless otherwise indicated, round results to one decimal place. See Example 6.

37. One type of uranium has a daily radioactive decay rate of 0.4%. If 30 pounds of this uranium is available today, find how much will still remain after 50 days. Use $y = 30(2.7)^{-0.004t}$, and let t be 50.

38. The nuclear waste from an atomic energy plant decays at a rate of 3% each century. If 150 pounds of nuclear waste is disposed of, find how much of it will still remain after 10 centuries. Use $y = 150(2.7)^{-0.03t}$, and let t be 10.

39. National Park Service personnel are trying to increase the size of the bison population of Theodore Roosevelt National Park. If 260 bison currently live in the park, and if the population's rate of growth is 2.5% annually, find how many bison (rounded to the nearest whole) there should be in 10 years. Use $y = 260(2.7)^{0.025t}$.

40. The size of the rat population of a wharf area grows at a rate of 8% monthly. If there are 200 rats in January, find how many rats (rounded to the nearest whole) should be expected by next January. Use $y = 200(2.7)^{0.08t}$.

41. A rare isotope of a nuclear material is very unstable, decaying at a rate of 15% each second. Find how much isotope remains 10 seconds after 5 grams of the isotope is created. Use $y = 5(2.7)^{-0.15t}$.

42. An accidental spill of 75 grams of radioactive material in a local stream has led to the presence of radioactive debris decaying at a rate of 4% each day. Find how much debris still remains after 14 days. Use $y = 75(2.7)^{-0.04t}$.

43. The atmospheric pressure p, in Pascals, on a weather balloon decreases with increasing height. This pressure, measured in millimeters of mercury, is related to the number of kilometers h above sea level by the function $p(h) = 760(2.7)^{-0.145h}$. Round to the nearest tenth of a Pascal.

a. Find the atmospheric pressure at a height of 1 kilometer.

b. Find the atmospheric pressure at a height of 10 kilometers.

44. An unusually wet spring has caused the size of the Cape Cod mosquito population to increase by 8% each day. If an estimated 200,000 mosquitoes are on Cape Cod on May 12, find how many mosquitoes will inhabit the Cape on May 25. Use $y = 200,000(2.7)^{0.08t}$. Round to the nearest thousand.

45. The equation $y = 84,949(1.096)^x$ models the number of American college students who study abroad each year from 1995 through 2006. In the equation, y is the number of American students studying abroad and x represents the number of years after 1995. Round answers to the nearest whole. (*Source:* Based on data from Institute of International Education, Open Doors 2006)

a. Estimate the number of American students studying abroad in 2000.

b. Assuming this equation continues to be valid in the future, use this equation to predict the number of American students studying abroad in 2020.

46. Carbon dioxide (CO_2) is a greenhouse gas that contributes to global warming. Partially due to the combustion of fossil fuels, the amount of CO_2 in Earth's atmosphere has been increasing by 0.4% annually over the past century. In 2000, the concentration of CO_2 in the atmosphere was 369.4 parts per million by volume. To make the following predictions, use $y = 369.4(1.004)^t$ where y is the concentration of CO_2 in parts per million and t is the number of years after 2000. Round answers to the nearest tenth. (*Sources:* Based on data from the United Nations Environment Programme and the Carbon Dioxide Information Analysis Center)

a. Predict the concentration of CO_2 in the atmosphere in the year 2006.

b. Predict the concentration of CO_2 in the atmosphere in the year 2030.

Solve. Use $A = P\left(1 + \dfrac{r}{n}\right)^{nt}$. *Round answers to two decimal places. See Example 5.*

47. Find the amount Erica owes at the end of 3 years if $6000 is loaned to her at a rate of 8% compounded monthly.

48. Find the amount owed at the end of 5 years if $3000 is loaned at a rate of 10% compounded quarterly.

49. Find the total amount Janina has in a college savings account if $2000 was invested and earned 6% compounded semiannually for 12 years.

50. Find the amount accrued if $500 is invested and earns 7% compounded monthly for 4 years.

The formula $y = 18(1.24)^x$ *gives the number of cellular phone users y (in millions) in the United States for the years 1994 through 2006. In this formula, x = 0 corresponds to 1994, x = 1 corresponds to 1995, and so on. Use this formula to solve Exercises 51 and 52. Round results to the nearest whole million.*

51. Use this model to predict the number of cellular phone users in the year 2010.

52. Use this model to predict the number of cellular phone users in the year 2014.

REVIEW AND PREVIEW

Solve each equation. See Sections 2.1 and 5.8.

53. $5x - 2 = 18$

54. $3x - 7 = 11$

55. $3x - 4 = 3(x + 1)$

56. $2 - 6x = 6(1 - x)$

57. $x^2 + 6 = 5x$

58. $18 = 11x - x^2$

By inspection, find the value for x that makes each statement true. See Section 5.1.

59. $2^x = 8$

60. $3^x = 9$

61. $5^x = \dfrac{1}{5}$

62. $4^x = 1$

CONCEPT EXTENSIONS

63. Explain why the graph of an exponential function $y = b^x$ contains the point $(1, b)$.

64. Explain why an exponential function $y = b^x$ has a y-intercept of $(0, 1)$.

Graph.

65. $y = |3^x|$

66. $y = \left|\left(\dfrac{1}{3}\right)^x\right|$

67. $y = 3^{|x|}$

68. $y = \left(\dfrac{1}{3}\right)^{|x|}$

69. Graph $y = 2^x$ and $y = \left(\dfrac{1}{2}\right)^{-x}$ on the same set of axes. Describe what you see and why.

70. Graph $y = 2^x$ and $x = 2^y$ on the same set of axes. Describe what you see.

Use a graphing calculator to solve. Estimate each result to two decimal places.

71. Verify the results of Exercise 37.

72. From Exercise 37, estimate the number of pounds of uranium that will be available after 100 days.

73. From Exercise 37, estimate the number of pounds of uranium that will be available after 120 days.

74. Verify the results of Exercise 42.

75. From Exercise 42, estimate the amount of debris that remains after 10 days.

76. From Exercise 42, estimate the amount of debris that remains after 20 days.

9.4 LOGARITHMIC FUNCTIONS

OBJECTIVES

1. Write exponential equations with logarithmic notation and write logarithmic equations with exponential notation.

2. Solve logarithmic equations by using exponential notation.

3. Identify and graph logarithmic functions.

OBJECTIVE 1 ▶ Using logarithmic notation. Since the exponential function $f(x) = 2^x$ is a one-to-one function, it has an inverse.

We can create a table of values for f^{-1} by switching the coordinates in the accompanying table of values for $f(x) = 2^x$.

$$f(x) = 2^x$$

x	$y = f(x)$
-3	$\dfrac{1}{8}$
-2	$\dfrac{1}{4}$
-1	$\dfrac{1}{2}$
0	1
1	2
2	4
3	8

x	$y = f^{-1}(x)$
$\dfrac{1}{8}$	-3
$\dfrac{1}{4}$	-2
$\dfrac{1}{2}$	-1
1	0
2	1
4	2
8	3

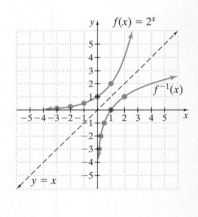

The graphs of $f(x)$ and its inverse are shown above. Notice that the graphs of f and f^{-1} are symmetric about the line $y = x$, as expected.

Now we would like to be able to write an equation for f^{-1}. To do so, we follow the steps for finding an inverse.

$$f(x) = 2^x$$

STEP 1. Replace $f(x)$ by y. $y = 2^x$

STEP 2. Interchange x and y. $x = 2^y$

STEP 3. Solve for y.

At this point, we are stuck. To solve this equation for y, a new notation, the **logarithmic notation,** is needed. The symbol $\log_b x$ means "the power to which b is raised in order to produce a result of x."

$$\log_b x = y \quad \text{means} \quad b^y = x$$

We say that $\log_b x$ is "the logarithm of x to the base b" or "the log of x to the base b."

Logarithmic Definition

If $b > 0$ and $b \neq 1$, then

$$y = \log_b x \text{ means } x = b^y$$

for every $x > 0$ and every real number y.

▶ **Helpful Hint**

Notice that a *logarithm* is an *exponent*. In other words, $\log_3 9$ is the *power* that we raise 3 to in order to get 9.

Before returning to the function $x = 2^y$ and solving it for y in terms of x, let's practice using the new notation $\log_b x$.

It is important to be able to write exponential equations from logarithmic notation, and vice versa. The following table shows examples of both forms.

Logarithmic Equation	*Corresponding Exponential Equation*
$\log_3 9 = 2$	$3^2 = 9$
$\log_6 1 = 0$	$6^0 = 1$
$\log_2 8 = 3$	$2^3 = 8$
$\log_4 \dfrac{1}{16} = -2$	$4^{-2} = \dfrac{1}{16}$
$\log_8 2 = \dfrac{1}{3}$	$8^{1/3} = 2$

EXAMPLE 1 Write as an exponential equation.

a. $\log_5 25 = 2$ **b.** $\log_6 \dfrac{1}{6} = -1$ **c.** $\log_2 \sqrt{2} = \dfrac{1}{2}$ **d.** $\log_7 x = 5$

Solution

a. $\log_5 25 = 2$ means $5^2 = 25$

b. $\log_6 \dfrac{1}{6} = -1$ means $6^{-1} = \dfrac{1}{6}$

c. $\log_2 \sqrt{2} = \dfrac{1}{2}$ means $2^{1/2} = \sqrt{2}$

d. $\log_7 x = 5$ means $7^5 = x$

PRACTICE

1 Write as an exponential equation.

a. $\log_3 81 = 4$ **b.** $\log_5 \dfrac{1}{5} = -1$ **c.** $\log_7 \sqrt{7} = \dfrac{1}{2}$ **d.** $\log_{13} y = 4$

EXAMPLE 2 Write as a logarithmic equation.

a. $9^3 = 729$ **b.** $6^{-2} = \dfrac{1}{36}$ **c.** $5^{1/3} = \sqrt[3]{5}$ **d.** $\pi^4 = x$

Solution

a. $9^3 = 729$ means $\log_9 729 = 3$

b. $6^{-2} = \dfrac{1}{36}$ means $\log_6 \dfrac{1}{36} = -2$

c. $5^{1/3} = \sqrt[3]{5}$ means $\log_5 \sqrt[3]{5} = \dfrac{1}{3}$

d. $\pi^4 = x$ means $\log_\pi x = 4$

PRACTICE
2   Write as a logarithmic equation.

a. $4^3 = 64$ **b.** $6^{1/3} = \sqrt[3]{6}$ **c.** $5^{-3} = \dfrac{1}{125}$ **d.** $\pi^7 = z$

EXAMPLE 3   Find the value of each logarithmic expression.

a. $\log_4 16$ **b.** $\log_{10} \dfrac{1}{10}$ **c.** $\log_9 3$

Solution

a. $\log_4 16 = 2$ because $4^2 = 16$

b. $\log_{10} \dfrac{1}{10} = -1$ because $10^{-1} = \dfrac{1}{10}$

c. $\log_9 3 = \dfrac{1}{2}$ because $9^{1/2} = \sqrt{9} = 3$

PRACTICE
3   Find the value of each logarithmic expression.

a. $\log_3 9$ **b.** $\log_2 \dfrac{1}{8}$ **c.** $\log_{49} 7$

▶ Helpful Hint

Another method for evaluating logarithms such as those in Example 3 is to set the expression equal to x and then write them in exponential form to find x. For example:

a. $\log_4 16 = x$ means $4^x = 16$. Since $4^2 = 16$, $x = 2$ or $\log_4 16 = 2$.

b. $\log_{10} \dfrac{1}{10} = x$ means $10^x = \dfrac{1}{10}$. Since $10^{-1} = \dfrac{1}{10}$, $x = -1$ or $\log_{10} \dfrac{1}{10} = -1$.

c. $\log_9 3 = x$ means $9^x = 3$. Since $9^{1/2} = 3$, $x = \dfrac{1}{2}$ or $\log_9 3 = \dfrac{1}{2}$.

OBJECTIVE 2 ▶ Solving logarithmic equations. The ability to interchange the logarithmic and exponential forms of a statement is often the key to solving logarithmic equations.

EXAMPLE 4   Solve each equation for x.

a. $\log_4 \dfrac{1}{4} = x$ **b.** $\log_5 x = 3$ **c.** $\log_x 25 = 2$ **d.** $\log_3 1 = x$ **e.** $\log_b 1 = x$

Solution

a. $\log_4 \dfrac{1}{4} = x$ means $4^x = \dfrac{1}{4}$. Solve $4^x = \dfrac{1}{4}$ for x.

$$4^x = \dfrac{1}{4}$$

$$4^x = 4^{-1}$$

Since the bases are the same, by the uniqueness of b^x, we have that

$$x = -1$$

The solution is -1 or the solution set is $\{-1\}$. To check, see that $\log_4 \frac{1}{4} = -1$, since $4^{-1} = \frac{1}{4}$.

b. $\log_5 x = 3$

     $5^3 = x$ Write as an exponential equation.

     $125 = x$

The solution is 125.

c. $\log_x 25 = 2$

     $x^2 = 25$ Write as an exponential equation. Here $x > 0$, $x \neq 1$.

     $x = 5$

Even though $(-5)^2 = 25$, the base b of a logarithm must be positive. The solution is 5.

d. $\log_3 1 = x$

     $3^x = 1$ Write as an exponential equation.

     $3^x = 3^0$ Write 1 as 3^0.

     $x = 0$ Use the uniqueness of b^x.

The solution is 0.

e. $\log_b 1 = x$

     $b^x = 1$ Write as an exponential equation. Here, $b > 0$ and $b \neq 1$.

     $b^x = b^0$ Write 1 as b^0.

     $x = 0$ Apply the uniqueness of b^x.

The solution is 0.

PRACTICE

4   Solve each equation for x.

a. $\log_5 \frac{1}{25} = x$ **b.** $\log_x 8 = 3$ **c.** $\log_6 x = 2$

d. $\log_{13} 1 = x$ **e.** $\log_h 1 = x$

In Example 4e we proved an important property of logarithms. That is, $\log_b 1$ is always 0. This property as well as two important others are given next.

Properties of Logarithms

If b is a real number, $b > 0$, and $b \neq 1$, then

1. $\log_b 1 = 0$
2. $\log_b b^x = x$
3. $b^{\log_b x} = x$

To see that **2.** $\log_b b^x = x$, change the logarithmic form to exponential form. Then, $\log_b b^x = x$ means $b^x = b^x$. In exponential form, the statement is true, so in logarithmic form, the statement is also true. To understand **3.** $b^{\log_b x} = x$, write this exponential equation as an equivalent logarithm.

EXAMPLE 5   Simplify.

a. $\log_3 3^2$ **b.** $\log_7 7^{-1}$ **c.** $5^{\log_5 3}$ **d.** $2^{\log_2 6}$

Solution

a. From Property 2, $\log_3 3^2 = 2$.
b. From Property 2, $\log_7 7^{-1} = -1$.
c. From Property 3, $5^{\log_5 3} = 3$.
d. From Property 3, $2^{\log_2 6} = 6$.   □

PRACTICE
5   Simplify.

a. $\log_5 5^4$ **b.** $\log_9 9^{-2}$ **c.** $6^{\log_6 5}$ **d.** $7^{\log_7 4}$

OBJECTIVE 3 ▶ Graphing logarithmic functions. Let us now return to the function $f(x) = 2^x$ and write an equation for its inverse, $f^{-1}(x)$. Recall our earlier work.

$$f(x) = 2^x$$

STEP 1.   Replace $f(x)$ by y. $y = 2^x$

STEP 2.   Interchange x and y. $x = 2^y$

Having gained proficiency with the notation $\log_b x$, we can now complete the steps for writing the inverse equation by writing $x = 2^y$ as an equivalent logarithm.

STEP 1.   Solve for y. $y = \log_2 x$

STEP 2.   Replace y with $f^{-1}(x)$. $f^{-1}(x) = \log_2 x$

Thus, $f^{-1}(x) = \log_2 x$ defines a function that is the inverse function of the function $f(x) = 2^x$. The function $f^{-1}(x)$ or $y = \log_2 x$ is called a **logarithmic function.**

> **Logarithmic Function**
>
> If x is a positive real number, b is a constant positive real number, and b is not 1, then a **logarithmic function** is a function that can be defined by
>
> $$f(x) = \log_b x$$
>
> The domain of f is the set of positive real numbers, and the range of f is the set of real numbers.

Concept Check ☑

Let $f(x) = \log_3 x$ and $g(x) = 3^x$. These two functions are inverses of each other. Since $(2, 9)$ is an ordered pair solution of $g(x)$ or $g(2) = 9$, what ordered pair do we know to be a solution of $f(x)$? Also, find $f(9)$. Explain why.

We can explore logarithmic functions by graphing them.

EXAMPLE 6   Graph the logarithmic function $y = \log_2 x$.

Solution   First we write the equation with exponential notation as $2^y = x$. Then we find some ordered pair solutions that satisfy this equation. Finally, we plot the points and connect them with a smooth curve. The domain of this function is $(0, \infty)$, and the range is all real numbers.

Answer to Concept Check:
$(9, 2)$; $f(9) = 2$; answers may vary

Since $x = 2^y$ is solved for x, we choose y-values and compute corresponding x-values.

If $y = 0, x = 2^0 = 1$

If $y = 1, x = 2^1 = 2$

If $y = 2, x = 2^2 = 4$

If $y = -1, x = 2^{-1} = \frac{1}{2}$

$x = 2^y$	y
1	0
2	1
4	2
$\frac{1}{2}$	-1

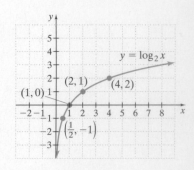

Notice that the x-intercept is $(1, 0)$ and there is no y-intercept.

PRACTICE

6 Graph the logarithmic function $y = \log_7 x$.

EXAMPLE 7 Graph the logarithmic function $f(x) = \log_{1/3} x$.

Solution Replace $f(x)$ with y, and write the result with exponential notation.

$$f(x) = \log_{1/3} x$$
$$y = \log_{1/3} x \quad \text{Replace } f(x) \text{ with } y.$$
$$\left(\frac{1}{3}\right)^y = x \quad \text{Write in exponential form.}$$

Now we can find ordered pair solutions that satisfy $\left(\frac{1}{3}\right)^y = x$, plot these points, and connect them with a smooth curve.

If $y = 0, x = \left(\frac{1}{3}\right)^0 = 1$

If $y = 1, x = \left(\frac{1}{3}\right)^1 = \frac{1}{3}$

If $y = -1, x = \left(\frac{1}{3}\right)^{-1} = 3$

If $y = -2, x = \left(\frac{1}{3}\right)^{-2} = 9$

$x = \left(\frac{1}{3}\right)^y$	y
1	0
$\frac{1}{3}$	1
3	-1
9	-2

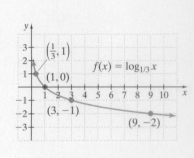

The domain of this function is $(0, \infty)$, and the range is the set of all real numbers. The x-intercept is $(1, 0)$ and there is no y-intercept.

PRACTICE

7 Graph the logarithmic function $y = \log_{1/4} x$.

The following figures summarize characteristics of logarithmic functions.

$$f(x) = \log_b x, b > 0, b \neq 1$$

- one-to-one function
- x-intercept $(1, 0)$
- no y-intercept
- domain: $(0, \infty)$
- range: $(-\infty, \infty)$

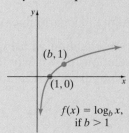

$f(x) = \log_b x$, if $b > 1$

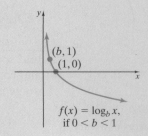

$f(x) = \log_b x$, if $0 < b < 1$

VOCABULARY & READINESS CHECK

Use the choices to fill in each blank.

1. A function, such as $y = \log_2 x$ is a(n) _____ function.

    A. linear   **B.** logarithmic   **C.** quadratic   **D.** exponential

2. If $y = \log_2 x$, then _____.

    A. $x = y$ **B.** $2^x = y$ **C.** $2^y = x$ **D.** $2y = x$

Answer the questions about the graph of $y = \log_2 x$, shown to the left.

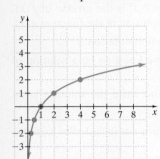

3. Is this a one-to-one function? _____

4. Is there an x-intercept? _____ If so, name the coordinates. _____

5. Is there a y-intercept? _____ If so, name the coordinates. _____

6. The domain of this function, in interval notation, is _____.

7. The range of this function, in interval notation, is _____.

9.4 | EXERCISE SET

Write each as an exponential equation. See Example 1.

1. $\log_6 36 = 2$

2. $\log_2 32 = 5$

3. $\log_3 \dfrac{1}{27} = -3$

4. $\log_5 \dfrac{1}{25} = -2$

5. $\log_{10} 1000 = 3$

6. $\log_{10} 10 = 1$

7. $\log_9 x = 4$

8. $\log_8 y = 7$

9. $\log_\pi \dfrac{1}{\pi^2} = -2$

10. $\log_e \dfrac{1}{e} = -1$

11. $\log_7 \sqrt{7} = \dfrac{1}{2}$

12. $\log_{11} \sqrt[4]{11} = \dfrac{1}{4}$

13. $\log_{0.7} 0.343 = 3$

14. $\log_{1.2} 1.44 = 2$

15. $\log_3 \dfrac{1}{81} = -4$

16. $\log_{1/4} 16 = -2$

Write each as a logarithmic equation. See Example 2.

17. $2^4 = 16$

18. $5^3 = 125$

19. $10^2 = 100$

20. $10^4 = 10{,}000$

21. $\pi^3 = x$

22. $\pi^5 = y$

23. $10^{-1} = \dfrac{1}{10}$

24. $10^{-2} = \dfrac{1}{100}$

25. $4^{-2} = \dfrac{1}{16}$

26. $3^{-4} = \dfrac{1}{81}$

27. $5^{1/2} = \sqrt{5}$

28. $4^{1/3} = \sqrt[3]{4}$

Find the value of each logarithmic expression. See Examples 3 and 5.

29. $\log_2 8$

30. $\log_3 9$

31. $\log_3 \dfrac{1}{9}$

32. $\log_2 \dfrac{1}{32}$

33. $\log_{25} 5$

34. $\log_8 \dfrac{1}{2}$

35. $\log_{1/2} 2$

36. $\log_{2/3} \dfrac{4}{9}$

37. $\log_6 1$

38. $\log_9 9$

39. $\log_{10} 100$

40. $\log_{10} \dfrac{1}{10}$

41. $\log_3 81$

42. $\log_2 16$

43. $\log_4 \dfrac{1}{64}$

44. $\log_3 \dfrac{1}{9}$

Solve. See Example 4.

45. $\log_3 9 = x$

46. $\log_2 8 = x$

47. $\log_3 x = 4$

48. $\log_2 x = 3$

49. $\log_x 49 = 2$

50. $\log_x 8 = 3$

51. $\log_2 \dfrac{1}{8} = x$

52. $\log_3 \dfrac{1}{81} = x$

53. $\log_3 \dfrac{1}{27} = x$

54. $\log_5 \dfrac{1}{125} = x$

55. $\log_8 x = \dfrac{1}{3}$

56. $\log_9 x = \dfrac{1}{2}$

57. $\log_4 16 = x$

58. $\log_2 16 = x$

59. $\log_{3/4} x = 3$

60. $\log_{2/3} x = 2$

61. $\log_x 100 = 2$

62. $\log_x 27 = 3$

63. $\log_2 2^4 = x$

64. $\log_6 6^{-2} = x$

65. $3^{\log_3 5} = x$

66. $5^{\log_5 7} = x$

67. $\log_x \dfrac{1}{7} = \dfrac{1}{2}$

68. $\log_x 2 = -\dfrac{1}{3}$

Simplify. See Example 5.

69. $\log_5 5^3$

70. $\log_6 6^2$

71. $2^{\log_2 3}$

72. $7^{\log_7 4}$

73. $\log_9 9$

74. $\log_8 (8)^{-1}$

Graph each logarithmic function. Label any intercepts. See Examples 6 and 7.

75. $y = \log_3 x$

76. $y = \log_8 x$

77. $f(x) = \log_{1/4} x$

78. $f(x) = \log_{1/2} x$

79. $f(x) = \log_5 x$

80. $f(x) = \log_6 x$

81. $f(x) = \log_{1/6} x$

82. $f(x) = \log_{1/5} x$

REVIEW AND PREVIEW

Simplify each rational expression. See Section 6.1.

83. $\dfrac{x + 3}{3 + x}$

84. $\dfrac{x - 5}{5 - x}$

85. $\dfrac{x^2 - 8x + 16}{2x - 8}$

86. $\dfrac{x^2 - 3x - 10}{2 + x}$

Add or subtract as indicated. See Section 6.2.

87. $\dfrac{2}{x} + \dfrac{3}{x^2}$

88. $\dfrac{3x}{x + 3} + \dfrac{9}{x + 3}$

89. $\dfrac{m^2}{m + 1} - \dfrac{1}{m + 1}$

90. $\dfrac{5}{y + 1} - \dfrac{4}{y - 1}$

CONCEPT EXTENSIONS

Solve. See the Concept Check in this section.

91. Let $f(x) = \log_5 x$. Then $g(x) = 5^x$ is the inverse of $f(x)$. The ordered pair $(2, 25)$ is a solution of the function $g(x)$.

    a. Write this solution using function notation.

    b. Write an ordered pair that we know to be a solution of $f(x)$.

    c. Use the answer to part b and write the solution using function notation.

92. Let $f(x) = \log_{0.3} x$. Then $g(x) = 0.3^x$ is the inverse of $f(x)$. The ordered pair $(3, 0.027)$ is a solution of the function $g(x)$.

    a. Write this solution using function notation.

    b. Write an ordered pair that we know to be a solution of $f(x)$.

    c. Use the answer to part b and write the solution using function notation.

93. Explain why negative numbers are not included as logarithmic bases.

94. Explain why 1 is not included as a logarithmic base.

Solve by first writing as an exponential.

95. $\log_7 (5x - 2) = 1$ **96.** $\log_3 (2x + 4) = 2$

97. Simplify: $\log_3 (\log_5 125)$ **98.** Simplify: $\log_7 (\log_4 (\log_2 16))$

Graph each function and its inverse function on the same set of axes. Label any intercepts.

99. $y = 4^x$; $y = \log_4 x$

100. $y = 3^x$; $y = \log_3 x$

101. $y = \left(\dfrac{1}{3}\right)^x$; $y = \log_{1/3} x$

102. $y = \left(\dfrac{1}{2}\right)^x$; $y = \log_{1/2} x$

103. Explain why the graph of the function $y = \log_b x$ contains the point $(1, 0)$ no matter what b is.

104. $\log_3 10$ is between which two integers? Explain your answer.

105. The formula $\log_{10}(1 - k) = \dfrac{-0.3}{H}$ models the relationship between the half-life H of a radioactive material and its rate of decay k. Find the rate of decay of the iodine isotope I-131 if its half-life is 8 days. Round to four decimal places.

106. The formula $\text{pH} = -\log_{10}(\text{H}^+)$ provides the pH for a liquid, where H^+ stands for the concentration of hydronium ions. Find the pH of lemonade, whose concentration of hydronium ions is 0.0050 moles/liter.

9.5 PROPERTIES OF LOGARITHMS

OBJECTIVES

1 Use the product property of logarithms.

2 Use the quotient property of logarithms.

3 Use the power property of logarithms.

4 Use the properties of logarithms together.

In the previous section we explored some basic properties of logarithms. We now introduce and explore additional properties. Because a logarithm is an exponent, logarithmic properties are just restatements of exponential properties.

OBJECTIVE 1 ▶ Using the product property. The first of these properties is called the **product property of logarithms,** because it deals with the logarithm of a product.

Product Property of Logarithms

If x, y, and b are positive real numbers and $b \neq 1$, then

$$\log_b xy = \log_b x + \log_b y$$

To prove this, let $\log_b x = M$ and $\log_b y = N$. Now write each logarithm with exponential notation.

$$\log_b x = M \qquad \text{is equivalent to} \qquad b^M = x$$
$$\log_b y = N \qquad \text{is equivalent to} \qquad b^N = y$$

Multiply the left sides and the right sides of the exponential equations, and we have that

$$xy = (b^M)(b^N) = b^{M+N}$$

If we write the equation $xy = b^{M+N}$ in equivalent logarithmic form, we have

$$\log_b xy = M + N$$

But since $M = \log_b x$ and $N = \log_b y$, we can write

$$\log_b xy = \log_b x + \log_b y \quad \text{Let } M = \log_b x \text{ and } N = \log_b y.$$

In other words, the logarithm of a product is the sum of the logarithms of the factors. This property is sometimes used to simplify logarithmic expressions.

In the examples that follow, assume that variables represent positive numbers.

EXAMPLE 1   Write each sum as a single logarithm.

a. $\log_{11} 10 + \log_{11} 3$ **b.** $\log_3 \dfrac{1}{2} + \log_3 12$ **c.** $\log_2(x + 2) + \log_2 x$

Solution

In each case, both terms have a common logarithmic base.

a. $\log_{11} 10 + \log_{11} 3 = \log_{11}(10 \cdot 3)$ Apply the product property.
$$= \log_{11} 30$$

b. $\log_3 \dfrac{1}{2} + \log_3 12 = \log_3 \left(\dfrac{1}{2} \cdot 12 \right) = \log_3 6$

c. $\log_2(x + 2) + \log_2 x = \log_2[(x + 2) \cdot x] = \log_2(x^2 + 2x)$

▶ **Helpful Hint**

Check your logarithm properties. Make sure you understand that $\log_2(x + 2)$ _is not_ $\log_2 x + \log_2 2$.

PRACTICE
1   Write each sum as a single logarithm.

a. $\log_8 5 + \log_8 3$

b. $\log_2 \dfrac{1}{3} + \log_2 18$

c. $\log_5(x - 1) + \log_5(x + 1)$

OBJECTIVE 2 ▶ **Using the quotient property.** The second property is the **quotient property of logarithms.**

Quotient Property of Logarithms

If x, y, and b are positive real numbers and $b \neq 1$, then

$$\log_b \frac{x}{y} = \log_b x - \log_b y$$

The proof of the quotient property of logarithms is similar to the proof of the product property. Notice that the quotient property says that the logarithm of a quotient is the difference of the logarithms of the dividend and divisor.

Concept Check ☑

Which of the following is the correct way to rewrite $\log_5 \frac{7}{2}$?

a. $\log_5 7 - \log_5 2$ **b.** $\log_5 (7 - 2)$ **c.** $\dfrac{\log_5 7}{\log_5 2}$ **d.** $\log_5 14$

EXAMPLE 2   Write each difference as a single logarithm.

a. $\log_{10} 27 - \log_{10} 3$ **b.** $\log_5 8 - \log_5 x$ **c.** $\log_3(x^2 + 5) - \log_3(x^2 + 1)$

Solution   All terms have a common logarithmic base.

a. $\log_{10} 27 - \log_{10} 3 = \log_{10} \dfrac{27}{3} = \log_{10} 9$

b. $\log_5 8 - \log_5 x = \log_5 \dfrac{8}{x}$

c. $\log_3(x^2 + 5) - \log_3(x^2 + 1) = \log_3 \dfrac{x^2 + 5}{x^2 + 1}$ Apply the quotient property.   ☐

PRACTICE
2   Write each difference as a single logarithm.

a. $\log_5 18 - \log_5 6$ **b.** $\log_6 x - \log_6 3$ **c.** $\log_4(x^2 + 1) - \log_4(x^2 + 3)$

OBJECTIVE 3 ▶ **Using the power property.** The third and final property we introduce is the **power property of logarithms.**

Power Property of Logarithms

If x and b are positive real numbers, $b \neq 1$, and r is a real number, then

$$\log_b x^r = r \log_b x$$

EXAMPLE 3   Use the power property to rewrite each expression.

a. $\log_5 x^3$ **b.** $\log_4 \sqrt{2}$

Solution

a. $\log_5 x^3 = 3 \log_5 x$ **b.** $\log_4 \sqrt{2} = \log_4 2^{1/2} = \dfrac{1}{2} \log_4 2$ ☐

PRACTICE
3   Use the power property to rewrite each expression.

a. $\log_7 x^8$ **b.** $\log_5 \sqrt[4]{7}$

OBJECTIVE 4 ▶ Using the properties together. Many times we must use more than one property of logarithms to simplify a logarithmic expression.

EXAMPLE 4   Write as a single logarithm.

a. $2 \log_5 3 + 3 \log_5 2$ **b.** $3 \log_9 x - \log_9(x + 1)$ **c.** $\log_4 25 + \log_4 3 - \log_4 5$

Solution   In each case, all terms have a common logarithmic base.

a. $2 \log_5 3 + 3 \log_5 2 = \log_5 3^2 + \log_5 2^3$ Apply the power property.

$\qquad\qquad\qquad\qquad = \log_5 9 + \log_5 8$

$\qquad\qquad\qquad\qquad = \log_5(9 \cdot 8)$ Apply the product property.

$\qquad\qquad\qquad\qquad = \log_5 72$

b. $3 \log_9 x - \log_9(x - 1) = \log_9 x^3 - \log_9(x + 1)$ Apply the power property.

$\qquad\qquad\qquad\qquad\qquad = \log_9 \dfrac{x^3}{x + 1}$ Apply the quotient property.

c. Use both the product and quotient properties.

$\log_4 25 + \log_4 3 - \log_4 5 = \log_4(25 \cdot 3) - \log_4 5$ Apply the product property.

$\qquad\qquad\qquad\qquad\qquad = \log_4 75 - \log_4 5$ Simplify.

$\qquad\qquad\qquad\qquad\qquad = \log_4 \dfrac{75}{5}$ Apply the quotient property.

$\qquad\qquad\qquad\qquad\qquad = \log_4 15$ Simplify.   □

PRACTICE
4   Write as a single logarithm.

a. $2 \log_5 4 + 5 \log_5 2$ **b.** $2 \log_8 x - \log_8(x + 3)$ **c.** $\log_7 12 + \log_7 5 - \log_7 4$

EXAMPLE 5   Write each expression as sums or differences of multiples of logarithms.

a. $\log_3 \dfrac{5 \cdot 7}{4}$ **b.** $\log_2 \dfrac{x^5}{y^2}$

Solution

a. $\log_3 \dfrac{5 \cdot 7}{4} = \log_3(5 \cdot 7) - \log_3 4$ Apply the quotient property.

$\qquad\qquad = \log_3 5 + \log_3 7 - \log_3 4$ Apply the product property.

b. $\log_2 \dfrac{x^5}{y^2} = \log_2(x^5) - \log_2(y^2)$ Apply the quotient property.

$\qquad\qquad = 5 \log_2 x - 2 \log_2 y$ Apply the power property.   □

PRACTICE
5   Write each expression as sums or differences of multiples of logarithms.

a. $\log_5 \dfrac{4 \cdot 3}{7}$ **b.** $\log_4 \dfrac{a^2}{b^5}$

▶ **Helpful Hint**

Notice that we are not able to simplify further a logarithmic expression such as $\log_5(2x - 1)$. None of the basic properties gives a way to write the logarithm of a difference in some equivalent form.

Concept Check ☑

What is wrong with the following?

$$\log_{10}(x^2 + 5) = \log_{10} x^2 + \log_{10} 5$$
$$= 2 \log_{10} x + \log_{10} 5$$

Use a numerical example to demonstrate that the result is incorrect.

EXAMPLE 6 If $\log_b 2 = 0.43$ and $\log_b 3 = 0.68$, use the properties of logarithms to evaluate.

a. $\log_b 6$ **b.** $\log_b 9$ **c.** $\log_b \sqrt{2}$

Solution

a. $\log_b 6 = \log_b(2 \cdot 3)$ Write 6 as $2 \cdot 3$.
$\quad\quad\quad = \log_b 2 + \log_b 3$ Apply the product property.
$\quad\quad\quad = 0.43 + 0.68$ Substitute given values.
$\quad\quad\quad = 1.11$ Simplify.

b. $\log_b 9 = \log_b 3^2$ Write 9 as 3^2.
$\quad\quad\quad = 2 \log_b 3$
$\quad\quad\quad = 2(0.68)$ Substitute 0.68 for $\log_b 3$.
$\quad\quad\quad = 1.36$ Simplify.

c. First, recall that $\sqrt{2} = 2^{1/2}$. Then

$\log_b \sqrt{2} = \log_b 2^{1/2}$ Write $\sqrt{2}$ as $2^{1/2}$.
$\quad\quad\quad = \dfrac{1}{2} \log_b 2$ Apply the power property.
$\quad\quad\quad = \dfrac{1}{2}(0.43)$ Substitute the given value.
$\quad\quad\quad = 0.215$ Simplify.

PRACTICE
6 If $\log_b 5 = 0.83$ and $\log_b 3 = 0.56$, use the properties of logarithms to evaluate.

a. $\log_b 15$ **b.** $\log_b 25$ **c.** $\log_b \sqrt{3}$

A summary of the basic properties of logarithms that we have developed so far is given next.

Properties of Logarithms

If x, y, and b are positive real numbers, $b \neq 1$, and r is a real number, then

1. $\log_b 1 = 0$ **2.** $\log_b b^x = x$

3. $b^{\log_b x} = x$ **4.** $\log_b xy = \log_b x + \log_b y$ Product property.

5. $\log_b \dfrac{x}{y} = \log_b x - \log_b y$ Quotient property.   **6.** $\log_b x^r = r \log_b x$ Power property.

Answer to Concept Check:
The properties do not give any way to simplify the logarithm of a sum; answers may vary.

VOCABULARY & READINESS CHECK

Select the correct choice.

1. $\log_b 12 + \log_b 3 = \log_b$ _____
   a. 36   **b.** 15   **c.** 4   **d.** 9

2. $\log_b 12 - \log_b 3 = \log_b$ ___
   a. 36   **b.** 15   **c.** 4   **d.** 9

3. $7 \log_b 2 =$ _____
   a. $\log_b 14$ **b.** $\log_b 2^7$ **c.** $\log_b 7^2$ **d.** $(\log_b 2)^7$

4. $\log_b 1 =$ ___
   a. b **b.** 1   **c.** 0   **d.** no answer

5. $b^{\log_b x} =$ ___
   a. x **b.** b **c.** 1   **d.** 0

6. $\log_5 5^2 =$ ___
   a. 25   **b.** 2   **c.** 5^{5^2} **d.** 32

9.5 EXERCISE SET

PRACTICE   WATCH   DOWNLOAD   READ   REVIEW

Write each sum as a single logarithm. Assume that variables represent positive numbers. See Example 1.

1. $\log_5 2 + \log_5 7$

2. $\log_3 8 + \log_3 4$

3. $\log_4 9 + \log_4 x$

4. $\log_2 x + \log_2 y$

5. $\log_6 x + \log_6 (x + 1)$

6. $\log_5 y^3 + \log_5 (y - 7)$

7. $\log_{10} 5 + \log_{10} 2 + \log_{10} (x^2 + 2)$

8. $\log_6 3 + \log_6 (x + 4) + \log_6 5$

Write each difference as a single logarithm. Assume that variables represent positive numbers. See Examples 2 and 4.

9. $\log_5 12 - \log_5 4$

10. $\log_7 20 - \log_7 4$

11. $\log_3 8 - \log_3 2$

12. $\log_5 12 - \log_5 3$

13. $\log_2 x - \log_2 y$

14. $\log_3 12 - \log_3 z$

15. $\log_2 (x^2 + 6) - \log_2 (x^2 + 1)$

16. $\log_7 (x + 9) - \log_7 (x^2 + 10)$

Use the power property to rewrite each expression. See Example 3.

17. $\log_3 x^2$

18. $\log_2 x^5$

19. $\log_4 5^{-1}$

20. $\log_6 7^{-2}$

21. $\log_5 \sqrt{y}$

22. $\log_5 \sqrt[3]{x}$

MIXED PRACTICE

Write each as a single logarithm. Assume that variables represent positive numbers. See Example 4.

23. $\log_2 5 + \log_2 x^3$

24. $\log_5 2 + \log_5 y^2$

25. $3 \log_4 2 + \log_4 6$

26. $2 \log_3 5 + \log_3 2$

27. $3 \log_5 x + 6 \log_5 z$

28. $2 \log_7 y + 6 \log_7 z$

29. $\log_4 2 + \log_4 10 - \log_4 5$

30. $\log_6 18 + \log_6 2 - \log_6 9$

31. $\log_7 6 + \log_7 3 - \log_7 4$

32. $\log_8 5 + \log_8 15 - \log_8 20$

33. $\log_{10} x - \log_{10} (x + 1) + \log_{10} (x^2 - 2)$

34. $\log_9 (4x) - \log_9 (x - 3) + \log_9 (x^3 + 1)$

35. $3 \log_2 x + \dfrac{1}{2} \log_2 x - 2 \log_2 (x + 1)$

36. $2 \log_5 x + \dfrac{1}{3} \log_5 x - 3 \log_5 (x + 5)$

37. $2 \log_8 x - \dfrac{2}{3} \log_8 x + 4 \log_8 x$

38. $5 \log_6 x - \dfrac{3}{4} \log_6 x + 3 \log_6 x$

MIXED PRACTICE

Write each expression as a sum or difference of logarithms. Assume that variables represent positive numbers. See Example 5.

39. $\log_3 \dfrac{4y}{5}$

40. $\log_7 \dfrac{5x}{4}$

41. $\log_4 \dfrac{2}{9z}$

42. $\log_9 \dfrac{7}{8y}$

43. $\log_2 \dfrac{x^3}{y}$

44. $\log_5 \dfrac{x}{y^4}$

45. $\log_b \sqrt{7x}$

46. $\log_b \sqrt{\dfrac{3}{y}}$

47. $\log_6 x^4 y^5$

48. $\log_2 y^3 z$

49. $\log_5 x^3 (x + 1)$

50. $\log_3 x^2 (x - 9)$

51. $\log_6 \dfrac{x^2}{x + 3}$

52. $\log_3 \dfrac{(x + 5)^2}{x}$

If $\log_b 3 = 0.5$ and $\log_b 5 = 0.7$, evaluate each expression. See Example 6.

53. $\log_b 15$

54. $\log_b 25$

55. $\log_b \dfrac{5}{3}$

56. $\log_b \dfrac{3}{5}$

57. $\log_b \sqrt{5}$

58. $\log_b \sqrt[4]{3}$

If $\log_b 2 = 0.43$ and $\log_b 3 = 0.68$, evaluate each expression. See Example 6.

59. $\log_b 8$

60. $\log_b 81$

61. $\log_b \dfrac{3}{9}$

62. $\log_b \dfrac{4}{32}$

63. $\log_b \sqrt{\dfrac{2}{3}}$

64. $\log_b \sqrt{\dfrac{3}{2}}$

REVIEW AND PREVIEW

65. Graph the functions $y = 10^x$ and $y = \log_{10} x$ on the same set of axes. See Section 9.4.

Evaluate each expression. See Section 9.4.

66. $\log_{10} 100$

67. $\log_{10} \dfrac{1}{10}$

68. $\log_7 7^2$

69. $\log_7 \sqrt{7}$

CONCEPT EXTENSIONS

Solve. See the Concept Checks in this section.

70. Which of the following is the correct way to rewrite $\log_3 \dfrac{14}{11}$?

   a. $\dfrac{\log_3 14}{\log_3 11}$ **b.** $\log_3 14 - \log_3 11$

   c. $\log_3 (14 - 11)$ **d.** $\log_3 154$

71. Which of the following is the correct way to rewrite $\log_9 \dfrac{21}{3}$?

   a. $\log_9 7$ **b.** $\log_9 (21 - 3)$

   c. $\dfrac{\log_9 21}{\log_9 3}$ **d.** $\log_9 21 - \log_9 3$

Answer the following true or false. Study your logarithm properties carefully before answering.

72. $\log_2 x^3 = 3 \log_2 x$

73. $\log_3(x + y) = \log_3 x + \log_3 y$

74. $\dfrac{\log_7 10}{\log_7 5} = \log_7 2$

75. $\log_7 \dfrac{14}{8} = \log_7 14 - \log_7 8$

76. $\dfrac{\log_7 x}{\log_7 y} = (\log_7 x) - (\log_7 y)$

77. $(\log_3 6) \cdot (\log_3 4) = \log_3 24$

78. It is true that $\log 8 = \log(8 \cdot 1) = \log 8 + \log 1$. Explain how $\log 8$ can equal $\log 8 + \log 1$.

INTEGRATED REVIEW FUNCTIONS AND PROPERTIES OF LOGARITHMS

Sections 9.1–9.5

If $f(x) = x - 6$ and $g(x) = x^2 + 1$, find each value.

1. $(f + g)(x)$

2. $(f - g)(x)$

3. $(f \cdot g)(x)$

4. $\left(\dfrac{f}{g}\right)(x)$

If $f(x) = \sqrt{x}$ and $g(x) = 3x - 1$, find each function.

5. $(f \circ g)(x)$

6. $(g \circ f)(x)$

Determine whether each is a one-to-one function. If it is, find its inverse.

7. $f = \{(-2, 6), (4, 8), (2, -6), (3, 3)\}$

8. $g = \{(4, 2), (-1, 3), (5, 3), (7, 1)\}$

Determine whether the graph of each function is one-to-one.

9.

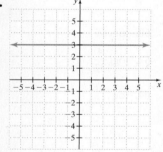

10.

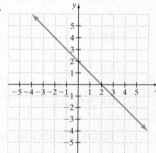

11.

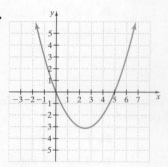

Each function listed is one-to-one. Find the inverse of each function.

12. $f(x) = 3x$

13. $f(x) = x + 4$

14. $f(x) = 5x - 1$

15. $f(x) = 3x + 2$

Graph each function.

16. $y = \left(\dfrac{1}{2}\right)^x$

17. $y = 2^x + 1$

18. $y = \log_3 x$

19. $y = \log_{1/3} x$

Solve.

20. $2^x = 8$

21. $9 = 3^{x-5}$

22. $4^{x-1} = 8^{x+2}$

23. $25^x = 125^{x-1}$

24. $\log_4 16 = x$

25. $\log_{49} 7 = x$

26. $\log_2 x = 5$

27. $\log_x 64 = 3$

28. $\log_x \dfrac{1}{125} = -3$

29. $\log_3 x = -2$

Write each as a single logarithm.

30. $5 \log_2 x$

31. $x \log_2 5$

32. $3 \log_5 x - 5 \log_5 y$

33. $9 \log_5 x + 3 \log_5 y$

34. $\log_2 x + \log_2(x - 3) - \log_2(x^2 + 4)$

35. $\log_3 y - \log_3(y + 2) + \log_3(y^3 + 11)$

Write each expression as sums or differences of multiples of logarithms.

36. $\log_7 \dfrac{9x^2}{y}$

37. $\log_6 \dfrac{5y}{z^2}$

9.6 COMMON LOGARITHMS, NATURAL LOGARITHMS, AND CHANGE OF BASE

OBJECTIVES

1 Identify common logarithms and approximate them by calculator.

2 Evaluate common logarithms of powers of 10.

3 Identify natural logarithms and approximate them by calculator.

4 Evaluate natural logarithms of powers of e.

5 Use the change of base formula.

In this section we look closely at two particular logarithmic bases. These two logarithmic bases are used so frequently that logarithms to their bases are given special names. **Common logarithms** are logarithms to base 10. **Natural logarithms** are logarithms to base e, which we introduce in this section. The work in this section is based on the use of the calculator, which has both the common "log" $\boxed{\text{LOG}}$ and the natural "log" $\boxed{\text{LN}}$ keys.

OBJECTIVE 1 ▶ **Approximating common logarithms.** Logarithms to base 10, common logarithms, are used frequently because our number system is a base 10 decimal system. The notation $\log x$ means the same as $\log_{10} x$.

> **Common Logarithms**
>
> $$\log x \text{ means } \log_{10} x$$

EXAMPLE 1 Use a calculator to approximate log 7 to four decimal places.

Solution Press the following sequence of keys.

$$\boxed{7} \ \boxed{\text{LOG}} \quad \text{or} \quad \boxed{\text{LOG}} \ \boxed{7} \ \boxed{\text{ENTER}}$$

To four decimal places.

$$\log 7 \approx 0.8451 \qquad \square$$

PRACTICE
1 Use a calculator to approximate log 15 to four decimal places.

OBJECTIVE 2 ▶ **Evaluating common logarithms of powers of 10.** To evaluate the common log of a power of 10, a calculator is not needed. According to the property of logarithms,

$$\log_b b^x = x$$

It follows that if b is replaced with 10, we have

$$\log 10^x = x$$

> ▶ **Helpful Hint**
> Remember that $\log 10^x$ means $\log_{10} 10^x = x$.

EXAMPLE 2 Find the exact value of each logarithm.

a. $\log 10$ **b.** $\log 1000$ **c.** $\log \dfrac{1}{10}$ **d.** $\log \sqrt{10}$

Solution

a. $\log 10 = \log 10^1 = 1$ **b.** $\log 1000 = \log 10^3 = 3$

c. $\log \dfrac{1}{10} = \log 10^{-1} = -1$ **d.** $\log \sqrt{10} = \log 10^{1/2} = \dfrac{1}{2}$

PRACTICE
2 Find the exact value of each logarithm.

a. $\log \dfrac{1}{100}$ **b.** $\log 100{,}000$ **c.** $\log \sqrt[5]{10}$ **d.** $\log 0.001$

As we will soon see, equations containing common logs are useful models of many natural phenomena.

EXAMPLE 3 Solve $\log x = 1.2$ for x. Give an exact solution, and then approximate the solution to four decimal places.

Solution Remember that the base of a common log is understood to be 10.

$$\log x = 1.2$$

$$10^{1.2} = x \qquad \text{Write with exponential notation.}$$

> **Helpful Hint**
> The understood base is 10.

The exact solution is $10^{1.2}$. To four decimal places, $x \approx 15.8489$.

PRACTICE
3 Solve $\log x = 3.4$ for x. Give an exact solution, and then approximate the solution to four decimal places.

The Richter scale measures the intensity, or magnitude, of an earthquake. The formula for the magnitude R of an earthquake is $R = \log\left(\dfrac{a}{T}\right) + B$, where a is the amplitude in micrometers of the vertical motion of the ground at the recording station, T is the number of seconds between successive seismic waves, and B is an adjustment factor that takes into account the weakening of the seismic wave as the distance increases from the epicenter of the earthquake.

EXAMPLE 4 **Finding the Magnitude of an Earthquake**

Find an earthquake's magnitude on the Richter scale if a recording station measures an amplitude of 300 micrometers and 2.5 seconds between waves. Assume that B is 4.2. Approximate the solution to the nearest tenth.

Solution Substitute the known values into the formula for earthquake intensity.

$$R = \log\left(\dfrac{a}{T}\right) + B \qquad \text{Richter scale formula}$$

$$= \log\left(\dfrac{300}{2.5}\right) + 4.2 \qquad \text{Let } a = 300, T = 2.5, \text{ and } B = 4.2.$$

$$= \log(120) + 4.2$$

$$\approx 2.1 + 4.2 \qquad \text{Approximate log 120 by 2.1.}$$

$$= 6.3$$

This earthquake had a magnitude of 6.3 on the Richter scale.

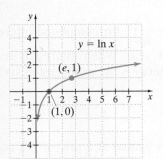

y = ln x

(e, 1)

(1, 0)

PRACTICE
4   Find an earthquake's magnitude on the Richter scale if a recording station measures an amplitude of 450 micrometers and 4.2 seconds between waves with $B = 3.6$. Approximate the solution to the nearest tenth.

OBJECTIVE 3 ▶ **Approximating natural logarithms.** Natural logarithms are also frequently used, especially to describe natural events; hence the label "natural logarithm." Natural logarithms are logarithms to the base e, which is a constant approximately equal to 2.7183. The number e is an irrational number, as is π. The notation $\log_e x$ is usually abbreviated to $\ln x$. (The abbreviation ln is read "el en.")

Natural Logarithms

$$\ln x \text{ means } \log_e x$$

The graph of $y = \ln x$ is shown to the left.

EXAMPLE 5   Use a calculator to approximate ln 8 to four decimal places.

Solution   Press the following sequence of keys.

| 8 | LN | or | LN | 8 | ENTER |

To four decimal places,

$$\ln 8 \approx 2.0794$$

PRACTICE
5   Use a calculator to approximate ln 13 to four decimal places.

OBJECTIVE 4 ▶ **Evaluating natural logarithms of powers of e.** As a result of the property $\log_b b^x = x$, we know that $\log_e e^x = x$, or **ln $e^x = x$.**
Since $\ln e^x = x$, then $\ln e^5 = 5$, $\ln e^{22} = 22$ and so on. Also,

$$\ln e^1 = 1 \text{ or simply } \ln e = 1.$$

That is why the graph of $y = \ln x$ shown on the previous page passes through $(e, 1)$.
If $x = e$, then $y = \ln e = 1$, thus the ordered pair is $(e, 1)$.

EXAMPLE 6   Find the exact value of each natural logarithm.

a. $\ln e^3$ **b.** $\ln \sqrt[5]{e}$

Solution

a. $\ln e^3 = 3$ **b.** $\ln \sqrt[5]{e} = \ln e^{1/5} = \dfrac{1}{5}$

PRACTICE
6   Find the exact value of each natural logarithm.

a. $\ln e^4$ **b.** $\ln \sqrt[3]{e}$

EXAMPLE 7   Solve $\ln 3x = 5$. Give an exact solution, and then approximate the solution to four decimal places.

Solution   Remember that the base of a natural logarithm is understood to be e.

$$\ln 3x = 5$$
$$e^5 = 3x \qquad \text{Write with exponential notation.}$$
$$\dfrac{e^5}{3} = x \qquad \text{Solve for } x.$$

▶ **Helpful Hint**
The understood base is e.

The exact solution is $\dfrac{e^5}{3}$. To four decimal places,

$$x \approx 49.4711.$$

PRACTICE
7 Solve $\ln 5x = 8$. Give an exact solution, and then approximate the solution to four decimal places.

Recall from Section 9.3 the formula $A = P\left(1 + \dfrac{r}{n}\right)^{nt}$ for compound interest, where n represents the number of compoundings per year. When interest is compounded continuously, the formula $A = Pe^{rt}$ is used, where r is the annual interest rate and interest is compounded continuously for t years.

EXAMPLE 8 Finding Final Loan Payment

Find the amount owed at the end of 5 years if $1600 is loaned at a rate of 9% compounded continuously.

Solution Use the formula $A = Pe^{rt}$, where

$$P = \$1600 \text{ (the size of the loan)}$$
$$r = 9\% = 0.09 \text{ (the rate of interest)}$$
$$t = 5 \text{ (the 5-year duration of the loan)}$$
$$A = Pe^{rt}$$
$$= 1600e^{0.09(5)} \quad \text{Substitute in known values.}$$
$$= 1600e^{0.45}$$

Now we can use a calculator to approximate the solution.

$$A \approx 2509.30$$

The total amount of money owed is $2509.30.

PRACTICE
8 Find the amount owed at the end of 4 years if $2400 is borrowed at a rate of 6% compounded continuously.

OBJECTIVE 5 ▶ Using the change of base formula. Calculators are handy tools for approximating natural and common logarithms. Unfortunately, some calculators cannot be used to approximate logarithms to bases other than e or 10—at least not directly. In such cases, we use the change of base formula.

> **Change of Base**
> If a, b, and c are positive real numbers and neither b nor c is 1, then
>
> $$\log_b a = \frac{\log_c a}{\log_c b}$$

EXAMPLE 9 Approximate $\log_5 3$ to four decimal places.

Solution Use the change of base property to write $\log_5 3$ as a quotient of logarithms to base 10.

$$\log_5 3 = \frac{\log 3}{\log 5} \quad \text{Use the change of base property. In the change of base property, we let } a = 3, b = 5, \text{ and } c = 10.$$

$$\approx \frac{0.4771213}{0.69897} \quad \text{Approximate logarithms by calculator.}$$

$$\approx 0.6826062 \quad \text{Simplify by calculator.}$$

To four decimal places, $\log_5 3 \approx 0.6826$.

PRACTICE
9   Approximate $\log_8 5$ to four decimal places.

Answer to Concept Check:

$$f(x) = \frac{\log x}{\log 5}$$

Concept Check ✓

If a graphing calculator cannot directly evaluate logarithms to base 5, describe how you could use the graphing calculator to graph the function $f(x) = \log_5 x$.

VOCABULARY & READINESS CHECK

Use the choices to fill in each blank.

1. The base of log 7 is ____.
   a. e **b.** 7   **c.** 10   **d.** no answer

2. The base of ln 7 is ____.
   a. e **b.** 7   **c.** 10   **d.** no answer

3. $\log_{10} 10^7 =$ ____.
   a. e **b.** 7   **c.** 10   **d.** no answer

4. $\log_7 1 =$ ____.
   a. e **b.** 7   **c.** 10   **d.** 0

5. $\log_e e^5 =$ ____.
   a. e **b.** 5   **c.** 0   **d.** 1

6. Study exercise 5 to the left. Then answer: $\ln e^5 =$ ____.
   a. e **b.** 5   **c.** 0   **d.** 1

7. $\log_2 7 =$ _____   (There may be more than one answer.)

   a. $\dfrac{\log 7}{\log 2}$ **b.** $\dfrac{\ln 7}{\ln 2}$ **c.** $\dfrac{\log 2}{\log 7}$ **d.** $\log \dfrac{7}{2}$

9.6 | EXERCISE SET

MIXED PRACTICE

Use a calculator to approximate each logarithm to four decimal places. See Examples 1 and 5.

1. log 8   **2.** log 6

3. log 2.31   **4.** log 4.86

5. ln 2   **6.** ln 3

7. ln 0.0716   **8.** ln 0.0032

9. log 12.6   **10.** log 25.9

11. ln 5   **12.** ln 7

13. log 41.5   **14.** ln 41.5

15. Use a calculator and try to approximate log 0. Describe what happens and explain why.

16. Use a calculator and try to approximate ln 0. Describe what happens and explain why.

MIXED PRACTICE

Find the exact value. See Examples 2 and 6.

17. log 100   **18.** log 10,000

19. $\log\left(\dfrac{1}{1000}\right)$ **20.** $\log\left(\dfrac{1}{100}\right)$

21. $\ln e^2$ **22.** $\ln e^4$

23. $\ln \sqrt[4]{e}$ **24.** $\ln \sqrt[5]{e}$

25. $\log 10^3$ **26.** $\log 10^7$

27. $\ln e^{-7}$ **28.** $\ln e^{-5}$

29. log 0.0001   **30.** log 0.001

31. $\ln \sqrt{e}$ **32.** $\log \sqrt{10}$

Solve each equation for x. Give an exact solution and a four-decimal-place approximation. See Examples 3 and 7.

33. $\ln 2x = 7$ **34.** $\ln 5x = 9$

35. $\log x = 1.3$ **36.** $\log x = 2.1$

37. $\log 2x = 1.1$ **38.** $\log 3x = 1.3$

39. $\ln x = 1.4$ **40.** $\ln x = 2.1$

41. $\ln(3x - 4) = 2.3$

42. $\ln(2x + 5) = 3.4$

43. $\log x = 2.3$

44. $\log x = 3.1$

45. $\ln x = -2.3$

46. $\ln x = -3.7$

47. $\log(2x + 1) = -0.5$

48. $\log(3x - 2) = -0.8$

49. $\ln 4x = 0.18$

50. $\ln 3x = 0.76$

Approximate each logarithm to four decimal places. See Example 9.

51. $\log_2 3$

52. $\log_3 2$

53. $\log_{1/2} 5$

54. $\log_{1/3} 2$

55. $\log_4 9$

56. $\log_9 4$

57. $\log_3 \dfrac{1}{6}$

58. $\log_6 \dfrac{2}{3}$

59. $\log_8 6$

60. $\log_6 8$

Use the formula $R = \log\left(\dfrac{a}{T}\right) + B$ to find the intensity R on the Richter scale of the earthquakes that fit the descriptions given. Round answers to one decimal place. See Example 4.

61. Amplitude a is 200 micrometers, time T between waves is 1.6 seconds, and B is 2.1.

62. Amplitude a is 150 micrometers, time T between waves is 3.6 seconds, and B is 1.9.

63. Amplitude a is 400 micrometers, time T between waves is 2.6 seconds, and B is 3.1.

64. Amplitude a is 450 micrometers, time T between waves is 4.2 seconds, and B is 2.7.

Use the formula $A = Pe^{rt}$ to solve. See Example 8.

65. Find how much money Dana Jones has after 12 years if $1400 is invested at 8% interest compounded continuously.

66. Determine the size of an account in which $3500 earns 6% interest compounded continuously for 1 year.

67. Find the amount of money Barbara Mack owes at the end of 4 years if 6% interest is compounded continuously on her $2000 debt.

68. Find the amount of money for which a $2500 certificate of deposit is redeemable if it has been paying 10% interest compounded continuously for 3 years.

REVIEW AND PREVIEW

Solve each equation for x. See Sections 2.1, 2.3, and 5.8.

69. $6x - 3(2 - 5x) = 6$

70. $2x + 3 = 5 - 2(3x - 1)$

71. $2x + 3y = 6x$

72. $4x - 8y = 10x$

73. $x^2 + 7x = -6$

74. $x^2 + 4x = 12$

Solve each system of equations. See Section 4.1.

75. $\begin{cases} x + 2y = -4 \\ 3x - y = 9 \end{cases}$

76. $\begin{cases} 5x + y = 5 \\ -3x - 2y = -10 \end{cases}$

CONCEPT EXTENSIONS

77. Without using a calculator, explain which of log 50 or ln 50 must be larger and why.

78. Without using a calculator, explain which of $\log 50^{-1}$ or $\ln 50^{-1}$ must be larger and why.

Graph each function by finding ordered pair solutions, plotting the solutions, and then drawing a smooth curve through the plotted points.

79. $f(x) = e^x$

80. $f(x) = e^{2x}$

81. $f(x) = e^{-3x}$

82. $f(x) = e^{-x}$

83. $f(x) = e^x + 2$

84. $f(x) = e^x - 3$

85. $f(x) = e^{x-1}$

86. $f(x) = e^{x+4}$

87. $f(x) = 3e^x$

88. $f(x) = -2e^x$

89. $f(x) = \ln x$

90. $f(x) = \log x$

91. $f(x) = -2 \log x$

92. $f(x) = 3 \ln x$

93. $f(x) = \log(x + 2)$

94. $f(x) = \log(x - 2)$

95. $f(x) = \ln x - 3$

96. $f(x) = \ln x + 3$

97. Graph $f(x) = e^x$ (Exercise 79), $f(x) = e^x + 2$ (Exercise 83), and $f(x) = e^x - 3$ (Exercise 84) on the same screen. Discuss any trends shown on the graphs.

98. Graph $f(x) = \ln x$ (Exercise 89), $f(x) = \ln x - 3$ (Exercise 95), and $f(x) = \ln x + 3$ (Exercise 96). Discuss any trends shown on the graphs.

📖 STUDY SKILLS BUILDER

What to Do the Day of an Exam?

On the day of an exam, don't forget to try the following:

- Allow yourself plenty of time to arrive.
- Read the directions on the test carefully.
- Read each problem carefully as you take your test. Make sure that you answer the question asked.
- Watch your time and pace yourself so that you may attempt each problem on your test.
- Check your work and answers.
- ***Do not turn your test in early.*** If you have extra time, spend it double-checking your work.

Good luck!

Answer the following questions based on your most recent mathematics exam, whenever that was.

1. How soon before class did you arrive?

2. Did you read the directions on the test carefully?

3. Did you make sure you answered the question asked for each problem on the exam?

4. Were you able to attempt each problem on your exam?

5. If your answer to Question 4 is no, list reasons why.

6. Did you have extra time on your exam?

7. If your answer to Question 6 is yes, describe how you spent that extra time.

9.7 EXPONENTIAL AND LOGARITHMIC EQUATIONS AND APPLICATIONS

OBJECTIVES

1 Solve exponential equations.

2 Solve logarithmic equations.

3 Solve problems that can be modeled by exponential and logarithmic equations.

OBJECTIVE 1 ▶ Solving exponential equations. In Section 9.3 we solved exponential equations such as $2^x = 16$ by writing 16 as a power of 2 and applying the uniqueness of b^x.

$$2^x = 16$$
$$2^x = 2^4 \quad \text{Write 16 as } 2^4.$$
$$x = 4 \quad \text{Use the uniqueness of } b^x.$$

Solving the equation in this manner is possible since 16 is a power of 2. If solving an equation such as $2^x = a \ number,$ where the number is not a power of 2, we use logarithms. For example, to solve an equation such as $3^x = 7$, we use the fact that $f(x) = \log_b x$ is a one-to-one function. Another way of stating this fact is as a property of equality.

> **Logarithm Property of Equality**
>
> Let a, b, and c be real numbers such that $\log_b a$ and $\log_b c$ are real numbers and b is not 1. Then
>
> $$\log_b a = \log_b c \text{ is equivalent to } a = c$$

EXAMPLE 1   Solve: $3^x = 7$.

Solution   To solve, we use the logarithm property of equality and take the logarithm of both sides. For this example, we use the common logarithm.

$$3^x = 7$$
$$\log 3^x = \log 7 \quad \text{Take the common log of both sides.}$$
$$x \log 3 = \log 7 \quad \text{Apply the power property of logarithms.}$$
$$x = \frac{\log 7}{\log 3} \quad \text{Divide both sides by } \log 3.$$

The exact solution is $\dfrac{\log 7}{\log 3}$. If a decimal approximation is preferred,

$$\frac{\log 7}{\log 3} \approx \frac{0.845098}{0.4771213} \approx 1.7712 \text{ to four decimal places.}$$

The solution is $\dfrac{\log 7}{\log 3}$, or *approximately* 1.7712.   □

PRACTICE

1   Solve: $5^x = 9$.

OBJECTIVE 2 ▶ Solving logarithmic equations. By applying the appropriate properties of logarithms, we can solve a broad variety of logarithmic equations.

EXAMPLE 2   Solve: $\log_4(x - 2) = 2$.

Solution   Notice that $x - 2$ must be positive, so x must be greater than 2. With this in mind, we first write the equation with exponential notation.

$$\log_4(x - 2) = 2$$
$$4^2 = x - 2$$
$$16 = x - 2$$
$$18 = x \quad \text{Add 2 to both sides.}$$

Check: To check, we replace x with 18 in the original equation.

$$\log_4(x - 2) = 2$$
$$\log_4(18 - 2) \stackrel{?}{=} 2 \quad \text{Let } x = 18.$$
$$\log_4 16 \stackrel{?}{=} 2$$
$$4^2 = 16 \quad \text{True}$$

The solution is 18.

PRACTICE
2 Solve: $\log_2(x - 1) = 5$.

EXAMPLE 3 Solve: $\log_2 x + \log_2(x - 1) = 1$.

Solution Notice that $x - 1$ must be positive, so x must be greater than 1. We use the product property on the left side of the equation.

$$\log_2 x + \log_2(x - 1) = 1$$
$$\log_2 x(x - 1) = 1 \quad \text{Apply the product property.}$$
$$\log_2(x^2 - x) = 1$$

Next we write the equation with exponential notation and solve for x.

$$2^1 = x^2 - x$$
$$0 = x^2 - x - 2 \qquad \text{Subtract 2 from both sides.}$$
$$0 = (x - 2)(x + 1) \qquad \text{Factor.}$$
$$0 = x - 2 \quad \text{or} \quad 0 = x + 1 \quad \text{Set each factor equal to 0.}$$
$$2 = x \qquad\qquad -1 = x$$

Recall that -1 cannot be a solution because x must be greater than 1. If we forgot this, we would still reject -1 after checking. To see this, we replace x with -1 in the original equation.

$$\log_2 x + \log_2(x - 1) = 1$$
$$\log_2(-1) + \log_2(-1 - 1) \stackrel{?}{=} 1 \quad \text{Let } x = -1.$$

Because the logarithm of a negative number is undefined, -1 is rejected. Check to see that the solution is 2.

PRACTICE
3 Solve: $\log_5 x + \log_5(x + 4) = 1$.

EXAMPLE 4 Solve: $\log(x + 2) - \log x = 2$.

We use the quotient property of logarithms on the left side of the equation.

Solution $\log(x + 2) - \log x = 2$

$$\log \frac{x + 2}{x} = 2 \qquad \text{Apply the quotient property.}$$
$$10^2 = \frac{x + 2}{x} \qquad \text{Write using exponential notation.}$$
$$100 = \frac{x + 2}{x} \qquad \text{Simplify.}$$
$$100x = x + 2 \qquad \text{Multiply both sides by } x.$$
$$99x = 2 \qquad \text{Subtract } x \text{ from both sides.}$$
$$x = \frac{2}{99} \qquad \text{Divide both sides by 99.}$$

Verify that the solution is $\frac{2}{99}$.

PRACTICE
4 Solve: $\log(x + 3) - \log x = 1$.

OBJECTIVE 3 ▶ **Solving problems modeled by exponential and logarithmic equations.**
Logarithmic and exponential functions are used in a variety of scientific, technical, and business settings. A few examples follow.

EXAMPLE 5 **Estimating Population Size**

The population size y of a community of lemmings varies according to the relationship $y = y_0 e^{0.15t}$. In this formula, t is time in months, and y_0 is the initial population at time 0. Estimate the population after 6 months if there were originally 5000 lemmings.

Solution We substitute 5000 for y_0 and 6 for t.

$$y = y_0 e^{0.15t}$$
$$= 5000 e^{0.15(6)} \qquad \text{Let } t = 6 \text{ and } y_0 = 5000.$$
$$= 5000 e^{0.9} \qquad \text{Multiply.}$$

Using a calculator, we find that $y \approx 12{,}298.016$. In 6 months the population will be approximately 12,300 lemmings. □

PRACTICE
5 The population size y of a group of rabbits varies according to the relationship $y = y_0 e^{0.916t}$. In this formula, t is time in years and y_0 is the initial population at time $t = 0$. Estimate the population in three years if there were originally 60 rabbits.

EXAMPLE 6 **Doubling an Investment**

How long does it take an investment of $2000 to double if it is invested at 5% interest compounded quarterly? The necessary formula is $A = P\left(1 + \dfrac{r}{n}\right)^{nt}$, where A is the accrued (or owed) amount, P is the principal invested, r is the annual rate of interest, n is the number of compounding periods per year, and t is the number of years.

Solution We are given that $P = \$2000$ and $r = 5\% = 0.05$. Compounding quarterly means 4 times a year, so $n = 4$. The investment is to double, so A must be $4000. Substitute these values and solve for t.

$$A = P\left(1 + \frac{r}{n}\right)^{nt}$$

$$4000 = 2000\left(1 + \frac{0.05}{4}\right)^{4t} \qquad \text{Substitute in known values.}$$
$$4000 = 2000(1.0125)^{4t} \qquad \text{Simplify } 1 + \frac{0.05}{4}.$$
$$2 = (1.0125)^{4t} \qquad \text{Divide both sides by 2000.}$$
$$\log 2 = \log 1.0125^{4t} \qquad \text{Take the logarithm of both sides.}$$
$$\log 2 = 4t(\log 1.0125) \qquad \text{Apply the power property.}$$
$$\frac{\log 2}{4 \log 1.0125} = t \qquad \text{Divide both sides by } 4 \log 1.0125.$$
$$13.949408 \approx t \qquad \text{Approximate by calculator.}$$

Thus, it takes nearly 14 years for the money to double in value. □

PRACTICE
6 How long does it take for an investment of $3000 to double if it is invested at 7% interest compounded monthly? Round to the nearest whole year.

Graphing Calculator Explorations

Use a graphing calculator to find how long it takes an investment of $1500 to triple if it is invested at 8% interest compounded monthly.

First, let $P = \$1500$, $r = 0.08$, and $n = 12$ (for 12 months) in the formula

$$A = P\left(1 + \frac{r}{n}\right)^{nt}$$

Notice that when the investment has tripled, the accrued amount A is $4500. Thus,

$$4500 = 1500\left(1 + \frac{0.08}{12}\right)^{12t}$$

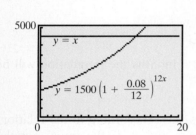

Determine an appropriate viewing window and enter and graph the equations

$$Y_1 = 1500\left(1 + \frac{0.08}{12}\right)^{12x}$$

and

$$Y_2 = 4500$$

The point of intersection of the two curves is the solution. The x-coordinate tells how long it takes for the investment to triple.

Use a TRACE feature or an INTERSECT feature to approximate the co-ordinates of the point of intersection of the two curves. It takes approximately 13.78 years, or 13 years and 9 months, for the investment to triple in value to $4500.

Use this graphical solution method to solve each problem. Round each answer to the nearest hundredth.

1. Find how long it takes an investment of $5000 to grow to $6000 if it is invested at 5% interest compounded quarterly.

2. Find how long it takes an investment of $1000 to double if it is invested at 4.5% interest compounded daily. (Use 365 days in a year.)

3. Find how long it takes an investment of $10,000 to quadruple if it is invested at 6% interest compounded monthly.

4. Find how long it takes $500 to grow to $800 if it is invested at 4% interest compounded semiannually.

9.7 EXERCISE SET

 MyMathLab

PRACTICE   WATCH   DOWNLOAD   READ   REVIEW

Solve each equation. Give an exact solution, and also approximate the solution to four decimal places. See Example 1.

1. $3^x = 6$

2. $4^x = 7$

3. $3^{2x} = 3.8$

4. $5^{3x} = 5.6$

5. $2^{x-3} = 5$

6. $8^{x-2} = 12$

7. $9^x = 5$

8. $3^x = 11$

9. $4^{x+7} = 3$

10. $6^{x+3} = 2$

MIXED PRACTICE

Solve each equation. See Examples 1 through 4.

11. $7^{3x-4} = 11$

12. $5^{2x-6} = 12$

13. $e^{6x} = 5$

14. $e^{2x} = 8$

15. $\log_2(x + 5) = 4$

16. $\log_6(x^2 - x) = 1$

17. $\log_3 x^2 = 4$

18. $\log_2 x^2 = 6$

19. $\log_4 2 + \log_4 x = 0$

20. $\log_3 5 + \log_3 x = 1$

21. $\log_2 6 - \log_2 x = 3$

22. $\log_4 10 - \log_4 x = 2$

23. $\log_4 x + \log_4(x + 6) = 2$

24. $\log_3 x + \log_3(x + 6) = 3$

25. $\log_5(x + 3) - \log_5 x = 2$

26. $\log_6(x + 2) - \log_6 x = 2$

27. $\log_3(x - 2) = 2$

28. $\log_2(x - 5) = 3$

29. $\log_4(x^2 - 3x) = 1$

30. $\log_8(x^2 - 2x) = 1$

31. $\ln 5 + \ln x = 0$

32. $\ln 3 + \ln(x - 1) = 0$

33. $3 \log x - \log x^2 = 2$

34. $2 \log x - \log x = 3$

35. $\log_2 x + \log_2(x + 5) = 1$

36. $\log_4 x + \log_4(x + 7) = 1$

37. $\log_4 x - \log_4(2x - 3) = 3$

38. $\log_2 x - \log_2(3x + 5) = 4$

39. $\log_2 x + \log_2(3x + 1) = 1$

40. $\log_3 x + \log_3(x - 8) = 2$

Solve. See Example 5.

41. The size of the wolf population at Isle Royale National Park increases at a rate of 4.3% per year. If the size of the current population is 83 wolves, find how many there should be in 5 years. Use $y = y_0 e^{0.043t}$ and round to the nearest whole.

42. The number of victims of a flu epidemic is increasing at a rate of 7.5% per week. If 20,000 persons are currently infected, find in how many days we can expect 45,000 to have the flu. Use $y = y_0 e^{0.075t}$ and round to the nearest whole. (*Hint: Don't forget to convert your answer to days.*)

43. The size of the population of Belize is increasing at a rate of 2.3% per year. If 294,380 people lived in Belize in 2007, find how many inhabitants there will be by 2015. Round to the nearest thousand. Use $y = y_0 e^{0.023t}$. (*Source: CIA 2007 World Factbook*)

44. In 2007, 1730 million people were citizens of India. Find how long it will take India's population to reach a size of 2000 million (that is, 2 billion) if the population size is growing at a rate of 1.6% per year. Use $y = y_0 e^{0.016t}$ and round to the nearest tenth. (*Source: U.S. Bureau of the Census, International Data Base*)

45. In 2007, Germany had a population of 82,400 thousand. At that time, Germany's population was declining at a rate of 0.033% per year. If this continues, how long will it take Germany's population to reach 82,000 thousand? Use $y = y_0 e^{-0.00033t}$ and round to the nearest tenth. (*Source: CIA 2007 World Factbook*)

46. The population of the United States has been increasing at a rate of 0.894% per year. If there were 301,140,000 people living in the United States in 2007, how many inhabitants will there be by 2020? Use $y = y_0 e^{0.00894t}$ and round to the nearest ten-thousand. (*Source: CIA 2007 World Factbook*)

Use the formula $A = P\left(1 + \dfrac{r}{n}\right)^{rt}$ to solve these compound interest problems. Round to the nearest tenth. See Example 6.

47. Find how long it takes $600 to double if it is invested at 7% interest compounded monthly.

48. Find how long it takes $600 to double if it is invested at 12% interest compounded monthly.

49. Find how long it takes a $1200 investment to earn $200 interest if it is invested at 9% interest compounded quarterly.

50. Find how long it takes a $1500 investment to earn $200 interest if it is invested at 10% compounded semiannually.

51. Find how long it takes $1000 to double if it is invested at 8% interest compounded semiannually.

52. Find how long it takes $1000 to double if it is invested at 8% interest compounded monthly.

The formula $w = 0.00185h^{2.67}$ is used to estimate the normal weight w of a boy h inches tall. Use this formula to solve the height-weight problems. Round to the nearest tenth.

53. Find the expected weight of a boy who is 35 inches tall.

54. Find the expected weight of a boy who is 43 inches tall.

55. Find the expected height of a boy who weighs 85 pounds.

56. Find the expected height of a boy who weighs 140 pounds.

The formula $P = 14.7e^{-0.21x}$ gives the average atmospheric pressure P, in pounds per square inch, at an altitude x, in miles above sea level. Use this formula to solve these pressure problems. Round answers to the nearest tenth.

57. Find the average atmospheric pressure of Denver, which is 1 mile above sea level.

58. Find the average atmospheric pressure of Pikes Peak, which is 2.7 miles above sea level.

59. Find the elevation of a Delta jet if the atmospheric pressure outside the jet is 7.5 lb/in.^{2}.

60. Find the elevation of a remote Himalayan peak if the atmospheric pressure atop the peak is 6.5 lb/in.^{2}.

Psychologists call the graph of the formula $t = \dfrac{1}{c}\ln\left(\dfrac{A}{A-N}\right)$ the learning curve, since the formula relates time t passed, in weeks, to a measure N of learning achieved, to a measure A of maximum learning possible, and to a measure c of an individual's learning style. Round to the nearest week.

61. Norman is learning to type. If he wants to type at a rate of 50 words per minute (N is 50) and his expected maximum rate is 75 words per minute (A is 75), find how many weeks it should take him to achieve his goal. Assume that c is 0.09.

62. An experiment with teaching chimpanzees sign language shows that a typical chimp can master a maximum of 65 signs. Find how many weeks it should take a chimpanzee to master 30 signs if c is 0.03.

63. Janine is working on her dictation skills. She wants to take dictation at a rate of 150 words per minute and believes that the maximum rate she can hope for is 210 words per minute. Find how many weeks it should take her to achieve the 150 words per minute level if c is 0.07.

64. A psychologist is measuring human capability to memorize nonsense syllables. Find how many weeks it should take a subject to learn 15 nonsense syllables if the maximum possible to learn is 24 syllables and c is 0.17.

REVIEW AND PREVIEW

If $x = -2$, $y = 0$, and $z = 3$, find the value of each expression. See Section 1.3.

65. $\dfrac{x^2 - y + 2z}{3x}$

66. $\dfrac{x^3 - 2y + z}{2z}$

67. $\dfrac{3z - 4x + y}{x + 2z}$

68. $\dfrac{4y - 3x + z}{2x + y}$

Find the inverse function of each one-to-one function. See Section 9.2.

69. $f(x) = 5x + 2$

70. $f(x) = \dfrac{x - 3}{4}$

CONCEPT EXTENSIONS

The formula $y = y_0e^{kt}$ gives the population size y of a population that experiences an annual rate of population growth k (given as a decimal). In this formula, t is time in years and y_0 is the initial population at time 0. Use this formula to solve Exercises 71 and 72.

71. In 2000, the population of Arizona was 5,130,632. By 2006, the population had grown to 6,123,106. Find the annual rate of population growth over this period. Round your answer to the nearest tenth of a percent. (*Source:* State of Arizona)

72. In 2000, the population of Nevada was 2,018,456. By 2006, the population had grown to 2,495,529. Find the annual rate of population growth over this period. Round your answer to the nearest tenth of a percent. (*Source:* State of Nevada)

73. When solving a logarithmic equation, explain why you must check possible solutions in the original equation.

74. Solve $5^x = 9$ by taking the common logarithm of both sides of the equation. Next, solve this equation by taking the natural logarithm of both sides. Compare your solutions. Are they the same? Why or why not?

Use a graphing calculator to solve each equation. For example, to solve Exercise 75, let $Y_1 = e^{0.3x}$ and $Y_2 = 8$, and graph the equations. The x-value of the point of intersection is the solution. Round all solutions to two decimal places.

75. $e^{0.3x} = 8$

76. $10^{0.5x} = 7$

77. $2\log(-5.6x + 1.3) + x + 1 = 0$

78. $\ln(1.3x - 2.1) + 3.5x - 5 = 0$

79. Check Exercise 11. Graph $7^{3x-4} - 11 = 0$

80. Check Exercise 12. Graph $5^{2x-6} - 12 = 0$

81. Check Exercise 31.

82. Check Exercise 32.

THE BIGGER PICTURE   SOLVING EQUATIONS AND INEQUALITIES

Continue your outline from Sections 2.4, 2.5, 2.7, 5.8, 6.5, 7.6, and 8.4. Write how to recognize and how to solve exponential and logarithmic equations in your own words. For example:

Solving Equations and Inequalities

I. Equations

  A. Linear equations (Sec. 2.1)

  B. Absolute value equations (Sec. 2.6)

  C. Quadratic and higher degree equations (Sec. 5.8 and Chapter 8)

  D. Equations with rational expressions (Sec. 6.5)

  E. Equations with radicals (Sec. 7.6)

  F. Exponential Equations—equations with variables in the exponent.

1. If we can write both expressions with the same base, then set the exponents equal to each other and solve

$$9^x = 27^{x+1}$$
$$(3^2)^x = (3^3)^{x+1}$$
$$3^{2x} = 3^{3x+3}$$
$$2x = 3x + 3$$
$$-3 = x$$

2. If we can't write both expressions with the same base, then solve using logarithms

$$5^x = 7$$
$$\log 5^x = \log 7$$
$$x \log 5 = \log 7$$
$$x = \frac{\log 7}{\log 5}$$
$$x \approx 1.2091$$

  G. Logarithmic Equations—equations with logarithms of variable expressions

$\log 7 + \log(x + 3) = 2$ Write equation so that single logarithm on
$\log 7(x + 3) = 2$ one side and constant on the other side.
      $10^2 = 7(x + 3)$ Use definition of logarithm.
      $100 = 7x + 21$ Multiply.
      $79 = 7x$
      $\frac{79}{7} = x$ Solve.

II. Inequalities

  A. Linear inequalities (Sec. 2.4)

  B. Compound inequalities (Sec. 2.5)

  C. Absolute value inequalities (Sec. 2.7)

  D. Nonlinear inequalities (Sec. 8.4)

    1. Polynomial inequalities

    2. Rational inequalities

Solve. Write solutions to inequalities in interval notation.

1. $8^x = 2^{x-3}$

2. $11^x = 5$

3. $-7x + 3 \le -5x + 13$

4. $-7 \le 3x + 6 \le 0$

5. $|5y + 3| < 3$

6. $(x - 6)(5x + 1) = 0$

7. $\log_{13} 8 + \log_{15}(x - 1) = 1$

8. $\left|\dfrac{3x - 1}{4}\right| = 2$

9. $|7x + 1| > -2$

10. $x^2 = 4$

11. $(x + 5)^2 = 3$

12. $\log_7(4x^2 - 27x) = 1$

CHAPTER 9 GROUP ACTIVITY

Sound Intensity

The decibel (dB) measures sound intensity, or the relative loudness or strength of a sound. One decibel is the smallest difference in sound levels that is detectable by humans. The decibel is a logarithmic unit. This means that for approximately every 3-decibel increase in sound intensity, the relative loudness of the sound is doubled. For example, a 35 dB sound is twice as loud as a 32 dB sound.

In the modern world, noise pollution has increasingly become a concern. Sustained exposure to high sound intensities can lead to hearing loss. Regular exposure to 90 dB sounds can eventually lead to loss of hearing. Sounds of 130 dB and more can cause permanent loss of hearing instantaneously.

The relative loudness of a sound D in decibels is given by the equation

$$D = 10\log_{10}\frac{I}{10^{-16}}$$

where I is the intensity of a sound given in watts per square centimeter. Some sound intensities of common noises are listed in the table in order of increasing sound intensity.

Group Activity

1. Work together to create a table of the relative loudness (in decibels) of the sounds listed in the table.

2. Research the loudness of other common noises. Add these sounds and their decibel levels to your table. Be sure to list the sounds in order of increasing sound intensity.

Some Sound Intensities of Common Noises		
Noise	*Intensity (watts/cm²)*	*Decibels*
Whispering	10^{-15}	
Rustling leaves	$10^{-14.2}$	
Normal conversation	10^{-13}	
Background noise in a quiet residence	$10^{-12.2}$	
Typewriter	10^{-11}	
Air conditioning	10^{-10}	
Freight train at 50 feet	$10^{-8.5}$	
Vacuum cleaner	10^{-8}	
Nearby thunder	10^{-7}	
Air hammer	$10^{-6.5}$	
Jet plane at takeoff	10^{-6}	
Threshold of pain	10^{-4}	

 STUDY SKILLS BUILDER

Are You Prepared for a Test on Chapter 9?

Below I have listed some common trouble areas for students in Chapter 9. After studying for your test—but before taking your test—read these.

- Don't forget how to find the composition of two functions.

  If $f(x) = x^2 + 5$ and $g(x) = 3x$, then

  $$(f \circ g)(x) = f[g(x)] = f(3x)$$
  $$= (3x)^2 + 5 = 9x^2 + 5$$
  $$(g \circ f)(x) = g[f(x)] = g(x^2 + 5)$$
  $$= 3(x^2 + 5) = 3x^2 + 15$$

- Don't forget that f^{-1} is a special notation used to denote the inverse of a function.

  Let's find the inverse of the one-to-one function $f(x) = 3x - 5$.

$$
\begin{aligned}
f(x) &= 3x - 5 \\
y &= 3x - 5 \quad \text{Replace } f(x) \text{ with } y. \\
x &= 3y - 5 \quad \text{Interchange } x \text{ and } y. \\
x + 5 &= 3y \\
\frac{x + 5}{3} &= y \quad \text{Solve for } y. \\
f^{-1}(x) &= \frac{x + 5}{3} \quad \text{Replace } y \text{ with } f^{-1}(x).
\end{aligned}
$$

- Don't forget that $y = \log_b x$ means $b^y = x$.

  Thus, $3 = \log_5 125$ means $5^3 = 125$.

- Remember rules for logarithms.

  $$\log_b 3x = \log_b 3 + \log_b x$$

  $\log_b(3 + x)$ cannot be simplified in the same manner.

Remember: This is simply a checklist of common trouble areas. For a review of Chapter 9, see the Highlights and Chapter Review at the end of this chapter.

CHAPTER 9 VOCABULARY CHECK

Fill in each blank with one of the words or phrases listed below.

inverse   common   composition   symmetric   exponential
vertical   logarithmic   natural   horizontal

1. For each one-to-one function, we can find its _____ function by switching the coordinates of the ordered pairs of the function.

2. The _____ of functions f and g is $(f \circ g)(x) = f(g(x))$.

3. A function of the form $f(x) = b^x$ is called an _____ function if $b > 0$, b is not 1, and x is a real number.

4. The graphs of f and f^{-1} are _____ about the line $y = x$.

5. _____ logarithms are logarithms to base e.

6. _____ logarithms are logarithms to base 10.

7. To see whether a graph is the graph of a one-to-one function, apply the _____ line test to see if it is a function, and then apply the _____ line test to see if it is a one-to-one function.

8. A _____ function is a function that can be defined by $f(x) = \log_b x$ where x is a positive real number, b is a constant positive real number, and b is not 1.

> ▶ **Helpful Hint**
>
> Are you preparing for your test? Don't forget to take the Chapter 9 Test on page 599. Then check your answers at the back of the text and use the Chapter Test Prep Video CD to see the fully worked-out solutions to any of the exercises you want to review.

CHAPTER 9 HIGHLIGHTS

DEFINITIONS AND CONCEPTS	EXAMPLES

SECTION 9.1   THE ALGEBRA OF FUNCTIONS; COMPOSITE FUNCTIONS

Algebra of Functions

Sum $(f + g)(x) = f(x) + g(x)$

Difference $(f - g)(x) = f(x) - g(x)$

Product $(f \cdot g)(x) = f(x) \cdot g(x)$

Quotient $\left(\dfrac{f}{g}\right)(x) = \dfrac{f(x)}{g(x)}, g(x) \neq 0$

Composite Functions

The notation $(f \circ g)(x)$ means "f composed with g."

$$(f \circ g)(x) = f(g(x))$$
$$(g \circ f)(x) = g(f(x))$$

If $f(x) = 7x$ and $g(x) = x^2 + 1$,

$$(f + g)(x) = f(x) + g(x) = 7x + x^2 + 1$$
$$(f - g)(x) = f(x) - g(x) = 7x - (x^2 + 1)$$
$$= 7x - x^2 - 1$$
$$(f \cdot g)(x) = f(x) \cdot g(x) = 7x(x^2 + 1)$$
$$= 7x^3 + 7x$$
$$\left(\frac{f}{g}\right)(x) = \frac{f(x)}{g(x)} = \frac{7x}{x^2 + 1}$$

If $f(x) = x^2 + 1$ and $g(x) = x - 5$, find $(f \circ g)(x)$.

$$(f \circ g)(x) = f(g(x))$$
$$= f(x - 5)$$
$$= (x - 5)^2 + 1$$
$$= x^2 - 10x + 26$$

SECTION 9.2   INVERSE FUNCTIONS

If f is a function, then f is a **one-to-one function** only if each y-value (output) corresponds to only one x-value (input).

Horizontal Line Test

If every horizontal line intersects the graph of a function at most once, then the function is a one-to-one function.

Determine whether each graph is a one-to-one function.

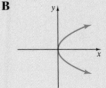

A   **B**

C

Graphs **A** and **C** pass the vertical line test, so only these are graphs of functions. Of graphs **A** and **C,** only graph **A** passes the horizontal line test, so only graph **A** is the graph of a one-to-one function.

(continued)

DEFINITIONS AND CONCEPTS	EXAMPLES

The **inverse** of a one-to-one function f is the one-to-one function f^{-1} that is the set of all ordered pairs (b, a) such that (a, b) belongs to f.

To Find the Inverse of a One-to-One Function f(x)

Step 1. Replace $f(x)$ with y.
Step 2. Interchange x and y.
Step 3. Solve for y.
Step 4. Replace y with $f^{-1}(x)$.

Find the inverse of $f(x) = 2x + 7$.

$$y = 2x + 7 \quad \text{Replace } f(x) \text{ with } y.$$

$$x = 2y + 7 \quad \text{Interchange } x \text{ and } y.$$

$$2y = x - 7 \quad \text{Solve for } y.$$

$$y = \frac{x - 7}{2}$$

$$f^{-1}(x) = \frac{x - 7}{2} \quad \text{Replace } y \text{ with } f^{-1}(x).$$

The inverse of $f(x) = 2x + 7$ is $f^{-1}(x) = \frac{x - 7}{2}$.

SECTION 9.3 EXPONENTIAL FUNCTIONS

A function of the form $f(x) = b^x$ is an **exponential function,** where $b > 0$, $b \neq 1$, and x is a real number.

Graph the exponential function $y = 4^x$.

x	y
-2	$\dfrac{1}{16}$
-1	$\dfrac{1}{4}$
0	1
1	4
2	16

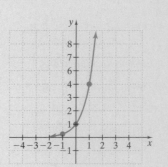

Uniqueness of b^x

If $b > 0$ and $b \neq 1$, then $b^x = b^y$ is equivalent to $x = y$.

Solve $2^{x+5} = 8$.

$$2^{x+5} = 2^3 \quad \text{Write 8 as } 2^3.$$

$$x + 5 = 3 \quad \text{Use the uniqueness of } b^x.$$

$$x = -2 \quad \text{Subtract 5 from both sides.}$$

SECTION 9.4 LOGARITHMIC FUNCTIONS

Logarithmic Definition

If $b > 0$ and $b \neq 1$, then

$$y = \log_b x \quad \text{means} \quad x = b^y$$

for any positive number x and real number y.

Properties of Logarithms

If b is a real number, $b > 0$ and $b \neq 1$, then

$$\log_b 1 = 0, \quad \log_b b^x = x, \quad b^{\log_b x} = x$$

Logarithmic Form	*Corresponding Exponential Statement*
$\log_5 25 = 2$	$5^2 = 25$
$\log_9 3 = \dfrac{1}{2}$	$9^{1/2} = 3$

$$\log_5 1 = 0, \quad \log_7 7^2 = 2, \quad 3^{\log_3 6} = 6$$

DEFINITIONS AND CONCEPTS	EXAMPLES

SECTION 9.4 LOGARITHMIC FUNCTIONS (continued)

Logarithmic Function

If $b > 0$ and $b \neq 1$, then a **logarithmic function** is a function that can be defined as

$$f(x) = \log_b x$$

The domain of f is the set of positive real numbers, and the range of f is the set of real numbers.

Graph $y = \log_3 x$.

Write $y = \log_3 x$ as $3^y = x$. Plot the ordered pair solutions listed in the table, and connect them with a smooth curve.

x	y
3	1
1	0
$\dfrac{1}{3}$	-1
$\dfrac{1}{9}$	-2

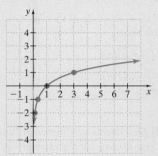

SECTION 9.5 PROPERTIES OF LOGARITHMS

Let x, y, and b be positive numbers and $b \neq 1$.

Product Property

$$\log_b xy = \log_b x + \log_b y$$

Quotient Property

$$\log_b \frac{x}{y} = \log_b x - \log_b y$$

Power Property

$$\log_b x^r = r \log_b x$$

Write as a single logarithm.

$2 \log_5 6 + \log_5 x - \log_5(y + 2)$

$= \log_5 6^2 + \log_5 x - \log_5(y + 2)$ Power property

$= \log_5 36 \cdot x - \log_5(y + 2)$ Product property

$= \log_5 \dfrac{36x}{y + 2}$ Quotient property

SECTION 9.6 COMMON LOGARITHMS, NATURAL LOGARITHMS, AND CHANGE OF BASE

Common Logarithms

$$\log x \quad \text{means} \quad \log_{10} x$$

Natural Logarithms

$$\ln x \quad \text{means} \quad \log_e x$$

Continuously Compounded Interest Formula

$$A = Pe^{rt}$$

where r is the annual interest rate for P dollars invested for t years.

$\log 5 = \log_{10} 5 \approx 0.69897$

$\ln 7 = \log_e 7 \approx 1.94591$

Find the amount in an account at the end of 3 years if $1000 is invested at an interest rate of 4% compounded continuously.

Here, $t = 3$ years, $P = \$1000$, and $r = 0.04$.

$$A = Pe^{rt}$$
$$= 1000e^{0.04(3)}$$
$$\approx \$1127.50$$

SECTION 9.7 EXPONENTIAL AND LOGARITHMIC EQUATIONS AND APPLICATIONS

Logarithm Property of Equality

Let $\log_b a$ and $\log_b c$ be real numbers and $b \neq 1$. Then

$$\log_b a = \log_b c \text{ is equivalent to } a = c$$

Solve $2^x = 5$.

$\log 2^x = \log 5$ Log property of equality

$x \log 2 = \log 5$ Power property

$x = \dfrac{\log 5}{\log 2}$ Divide both sides by log 2.

$x \approx 2.3219$ Use a calculator.

CHAPTER 9 REVIEW

(9.1) If $f(x) = x - 5$ and $g(x) = 2x + 1$, find

1. $(f + g)(x)$ **2.** $(f - g)(x)$

3. $(f \cdot g)(x)$ **4.** $\left(\dfrac{g}{f}\right)(x)$

If $f(x) = x^2 - 2$, $g(x) = x + 1$, and $h(x) = x^3 - x^2$, find each composition.

5. $(f \circ g)(x)$ **6.** $(g \circ f)(x)$
7. $(h \circ g)(2)$ **8.** $(f \circ f)(x)$
9. $(f \circ g)(-1)$ **10.** $(h \circ h)(2)$

(9.2) Determine whether each function is a one-to-one function. If it is one-to-one, list the elements of its inverse.

11. $h = \{(-9, 14), (6, 8), (-11, 12), (15, 15)\}$

12. $f = \{(-5, 5), (0, 4), (13, 5), (11, -6)\}$

13.

U.S. Region (Input)	West	Midwest	South	Northeast
Rank in Automobile Thefts (Output)	2	4	1	3

 14.

Shape (Input)	Square	Triangle	Parallelogram	Rectangle
Number of Sides (Output)	4	3	4	4

Given that $f(x) = \sqrt{x + 2}$ is a one-to-one function, find the following.

15. a. $f(7)$

    b. $f^{-1}(3)$

16. a. $f(-1)$

    b. $f^{-1}(1)$

Determine whether each function is a one-to-one function.

17.

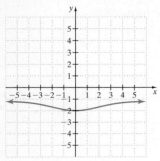

18.

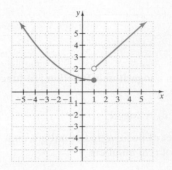

19.

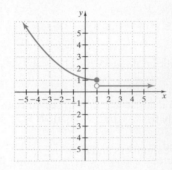

20.

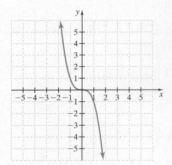

Find an equation defining the inverse function of the given one-to-one function.

21. $f(x) = x - 9$ **22.** $f(x) = x + 8$
23. $f(x) = 6x + 11$ **24.** $f(x) = 12x$
25. $f(x) = x^3 - 5$ **26.** $f(x) = \sqrt[3]{x + 2}$
27. $g(x) = \dfrac{12x - 7}{6}$ **28.** $r(x) = \dfrac{13}{2}x - 4$

On the same set of axes, graph the given one-to-one function and its inverse.

29. $g(x) = \sqrt{x}$ **30.** $h(x) = 5x - 5$

31. Find the inverse of the one-to-one function $f(x) = 2x - 3$. Then graph both $f(x)$ and $f^{-1}(x)$ with a square window.

(9.3) Solve each equation for x.

32. $4^x = 64$ **33.** $3^x = \dfrac{1}{9}$

34. $2^{3x} = \dfrac{1}{16}$

35. $5^{2x} = 125$

36. $9^{x+1} = 243$

37. $8^{3x-2} = 4$

Graph each exponential function.

38. $y = 3^x$

39. $y = \left(\dfrac{1}{3}\right)^x$

40. $y = 4 \cdot 2^x$

41. $y = 2^x + 4$

Use the formula $A = P\left(1 + \dfrac{r}{n}\right)^{nt}$ to solve the interest problems. In this formula,

$\qquad A = $ amount accrued (or owed)

$\qquad P = $ principal invested (or loaned)

$\qquad r = $ rate of interest

$\qquad n = $ number of compounding periods per year

$\qquad t = $ time in years

42. Find the amount accrued if \$1600 is invested at 9% interest compounded semiannually for 7 years.

43. A total of \$800 is invested in a 7% certificate of deposit for which interest is compounded quarterly. Find the value that this certificate will have at the end of 5 years.

44. Use a graphing calculator to verify the results of Exercise 40.

(9.4) *Write each equation with logarithmic notation.*

45. $49 = 7^2$

46. $2^{-4} = \dfrac{1}{16}$

Write each logarithmic equation with exponential notation.

47. $\log_{1/2} 16 = -4$

48. $\log_{0.4} 0.064 = 3$

Solve for x.

49. $\log_4 x = -3$

50. $\log_3 x = 2$

51. $\log_3 1 = x$

52. $\log_4 64 = x$

53. $\log_x 64 = 2$

54. $\log_x 81 = 4$

55. $\log_4 4^5 = x$

56. $\log_7 7^{-2} = x$

57. $5^{\log_5 4} = x$

58. $2^{\log_2 9} = x$

59. $\log_2(3x - 1) = 4$

60. $\log_3(2x + 5) = 2$

61. $\log_4(x^2 - 3x) = 1$

62. $\log_8(x^2 + 7x) = 1$

Graph each pair of equations on the same coordinate system.

63. $y = 2^x$ and $y = \log_2 x$

64. $y = \left(\dfrac{1}{2}\right)^x$ and $y = \log_{1/2} x$

(9.5) *Write each of the following as single logarithms.*

65. $\log_3 8 + \log_3 4$

66. $\log_2 6 + \log_2 3$

67. $\log_7 15 - \log_7 20$

68. $\log 18 - \log 12$

69. $\log_{11} 8 + \log_{11} 3 - \log_{11} 6$

70. $\log_5 14 + \log_5 3 - \log_5 21$

71. $2 \log_5 x - 2 \log_5(x + 1) + \log_5 x$

72. $4 \log_3 x - \log_3 x + \log_3(x + 2)$

Use properties of logarithms to write each expression as a sum or difference of multiples of logarithms.

73. $\log_3 \dfrac{x^3}{x + 2}$

74. $\log_4 \dfrac{x + 5}{x^2}$

75. $\log_2 \dfrac{3x^2 y}{z}$

76. $\log_7 \dfrac{yz^3}{x}$

If $\log_b 2 = 0.36$ and $\log_b 5 = 0.83$, find the following.

77. $\log_b 50$

78. $\log_b \dfrac{4}{5}$

(9.6) *Use a calculator to approximate the logarithm to four decimal places.*

79. $\log 3.6$

80. $\log 0.15$

81. $\ln 1.25$

82. $\ln 4.63$

Find the exact value.

83. $\log 1000$

84. $\log \dfrac{1}{10}$

85. $\ln \dfrac{1}{e}$

86. $\ln e^4$

Solve each equation for x.

87. $\ln(2x) = 2$

88. $\ln(3x) = 1.6$

89. $\ln(2x - 3) = -1$

90. $\ln(3x + 1) = 2$

Use the formula $\ln \dfrac{I}{I_0} = -kx$ to solve radiation problems. In this formula,

$\qquad x = $ depth in millimeters

$\qquad I = $ intensity of radiation

$\qquad I_0 = $ initial intensity

$\qquad k = $ a constant measure dependent on the material

Round answers to two decimal places.

91. Find the depth at which the intensity of the radiation passing through a lead shield is reduced to 3% of the original intensity if the value of k is 2.1.

92. If k is 3.2, find the depth at which 2% of the original radiation will penetrate.

Approximate the logarithm to four decimal places.

93. $\log_5 1.6$

94. $\log_3 4$

Use the formula $A = Pe^{rt}$ to solve the interest problems in which interest is compounded continuously. In this formula,

A = amount accrued (or owed)
P = principal invested (or loaned)
r = rate of interest
t = time in years

95. Bank of New York offers a 5-year, 6% continuously compounded investment option. Find the amount accrued if $1450 is invested.

96. Find the amount to which a $940 investment grows if it is invested at 11% compounded continuously for 3 years.

(9.7) Solve each exponential equation for x. Give an exact solution and also approximate the solution to four decimal places.

97. $3^{2x} = 7$

98. $6^{3x} = 5$

99. $3^{2x+1} = 6$

100. $4^{3x+2} = 9$

101. $5^{3x-5} = 4$

102. $8^{4x-2} = 3$

103. $2 \cdot 5^{x-1} = 1$

104. $3 \cdot 4^{x+5} = 2$

Solve the equation for x.

105. $\log_5 2 + \log_5 x = 2$

106. $\log_3 x + \log_3 10 = 2$

107. $\log(5x) - \log(x + 1) = 4$

108. $\ln(3x) - \ln(x - 3) = 2$

109. $\log_2 x + \log_2 2x - 3 = 1$

110. $-\log_6(4x + 7) + \log_6 x = 1$

Use the formula $y = y_0 e^{kt}$ to solve the population growth problems. In this formula,

y = size of population
y_0 = initial count of population
k = rate of growth written as a decimal
t = time

Round each answer to the nearest whole.

111. The population of mallard ducks in Nova Scotia is expected to grow at a rate of 6% per week during the spring migration. If 155,000 ducks are already in Nova Scotia, find how many are expected by the end of 4 weeks.

112. The population of Armenia is declining at a rate of 0.129% per year. If the population in 2007 was 2,971,650, find the expected population by the year 2015. (*Source:* U.S. Bureau of the Census, International Data Base)

113. China is experiencing an annual growth rate of 0.606%. In 2007, the population of China was 1,321,851,888. How long will it take for the population to be 1,500,000,000? Round to the nearest tenth. (*Source: CIA 2007 World Factbook*)

114. In 2007, Canada had a population of 33,390,141. How long will it take for Canada to double its population if the growth rate is 0.9% annually? Round to the nearest tenth. (*Source: CIA 2007 World Factbook*)

115. Malaysia's population is increasing at a rate of 1.8% per year. How long will it take the 2007 population of 24,821,286 to double in size? Round to the nearest tenth. (*Source: CIA 2007 World Factbook*)

Use the compound interest equation $A = P\left(1 + \dfrac{r}{n}\right)^{nt}$ to solve the following. (See the directions for Exercises 42 and 43 for an explanation of this formula. Round answers to the nearest tenth.)

116. Find how long it will take a $5000 investment to grow to $10,000 if it is invested at 8% interest compounded quarterly.

117. An investment of $6000 has grown to $10,000 while the money was invested at 6% interest compounded monthly. Find how long it was invested.

Use a graphing calculator to solve each equation. Round all solutions to two decimal places.

118. $e^x = 2$ **119.** $10^{0.3x} = 7$

MIXED REVIEW

Solve each equation.

120. $3^x = \dfrac{1}{81}$ **121.** $7^{4x} = 49$

122. $8^{3x-2} = 32$ **123.** $\log_4 4 = x$

124. $\log_3 x = 4$ **125.** $\log_5(x^2 - 4x) = 1$

126. $\log_4(3x - 1) = 2$ **127.** $\ln x = -3.2$

128. $\log_5 x + \log_5 10 = 2$ **129.** $\ln x - \ln 2 = 1$

130. $\log_6 x - \log_6(4x + 7) = 1$

CHAPTER 9 TEST

If $f(x) = x$ and $g(x) = 2x - 3$, find the following.

1. $(f \cdot g)(x)$

2. $(f - g)(x)$

If $f(x) = x$, $g(x) = x - 7$, and $h(x) = x^2 - 6x + 5$, find the following.

3. $(f \circ h)(0)$

4. $(g \circ f)(x)$

5. $(g \circ h)(x)$

On the same set of axes, graph the given one-to-one function and its inverse.

6. $f(x) = 7x - 14$

Determine whether the given graph is the graph of a one-to-one function.

7.

8.

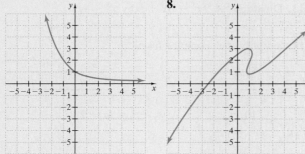

Determine whether each function is one-to-one. If it is one-to-one, find an equation or a set of ordered pairs that defines the inverse function of the given function.

9. $f(x) = 6 - 2x$

10. $f = \{(0,0), (2,3), (-1,5)\}$

11.

Word (Input)	Dog	Cat	House	Desk	Circle
First Letter of Word (Output)	d	c	h	d	c

Use the properties of logarithms to write each expression as a single logarithm.

12. $\log_3 6 + \log_3 4$

13. $\log_5 x + 3\log_5 x - \log_5(x + 1)$

14. Write the expression $\log_6 \dfrac{2x}{y^3}$ as the sum or difference of multiples of logarithms.

15. If $\log_b 3 = 0.79$ and $\log_b 5 = 1.16$, find the value of $\log_b \dfrac{3}{25}$.

16. Approximate $\log_7 8$ to four decimal places.

17. Solve $8^{x-1} = \dfrac{1}{64}$ for x. Give an exact solution.

18. Solve $3^{2x+5} = 4$ for x. Give an exact solution, and also approximate the solution to four decimal places.

Solve each logarithmic equation for x. Give an exact solution.

19. $\log_3 x = -2$

20. $\ln\sqrt{e} = x$

21. $\log_8(3x - 2) = 2$

22. $\log_5 x + \log_5 3 = 2$

23. $\log_4(x + 1) - \log_4(x - 2) = 3$

24. Solve $\ln(3x + 7) = 1.31$ accurate to four decimal places.

25. Graph $y = \left(\dfrac{1}{2}\right)^x + 1$.

26. Graph the functions $y = 3^x$ and $y = \log_3 x$ on the same coordinate system.

Use the formula $A = P\left(1 + \dfrac{r}{n}\right)^{nt}$ to solve Exercises 27 and 28.

27. Find the amount in the account if \$4000 is invested for 3 years at 9% interest compounded monthly.

28. Find how long it will take \$2000 to grow to \$3000 if the money is invested at 7% interest compounded semiannually. Round to the nearest whole.

Use the population growth formula $y = y_0 e^{kt}$ to solve Exercises 29 and 30.

29. The prairie dog population of the Grand Rapids area now stands at 57,000 animals. If the population is growing at a rate of 2.6% annually, find how many prairie dogs there will be in that area 5 years from now.

30. In an attempt to save an endangered species of wood duck, naturalists would like to increase the wood duck population from 400 to 1000 ducks. If the annual population growth rate is 6.2%, find how long it will take the naturalists to reach their goal. Round to the nearest whole year.

31. The formula $\log(1 + k) = \dfrac{0.3}{D}$ relates the doubling time D, in days, and the growth rate k for a population of mice. Find the rate at which the population is increasing if the doubling time is 56 days. Round to the nearest tenth of a percent.

CHAPTER 9 CUMULATIVE REVIEW

1. Multiply.

    a. $(-8)(-1)$ **b.** $(-2)\dfrac{1}{6}$

    c. $-1.2(0.3)$ **d.** $0(-11)$

    e. $\left(\dfrac{1}{5}\right)\left(-\dfrac{10}{11}\right)$ **f.** $(7)(1)(-2)(-3)$

    g. $8(-2)(0)$

2. Solve: $\dfrac{1}{3}(x-2) = \dfrac{1}{4}(x+1)$

3. Graph $y = x^2$.

4. Find the equation of a line through $(-2, 6)$ and perpendicular to $f(x) = -3x + 4$. Write the equation using function notation.

5. Solve the system.

$$\begin{cases} x - 5y - 2z = 6 \\ -2x + 10y + 4z = -12 \\ \dfrac{1}{2}x - \dfrac{5}{2}y - z = 3 \end{cases}$$

6. Line l and line m are parallel lines cut by transversal t. Find the values of x and y.

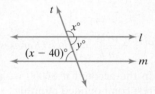

7. Use the quotient rule to simplify.

    a. $\dfrac{x^7}{x^4}$ **b.** $\dfrac{5^8}{5^2}$

    c. $\dfrac{20x^6}{4x^5}$ **d.** $\dfrac{12y^{10}z^7}{14y^8z^7}$

8. Use the power rules to simplify the following. Use positive exponents to write all results.

    a. $(4a^3)^2$ **b.** $\left(-\dfrac{2}{3}\right)^3$

    c. $\left(\dfrac{4a^5}{b^3}\right)^3$ **d.** $\left(\dfrac{3^{-2}}{x}\right)^{-3}$

    e. $(a^{-2}b^3c^{-4})^{-2}$

9. For the ICL Production Company, the rational function $C(x) = \dfrac{2.6x + 10,000}{x}$ describes the company's cost per disc of pressing x compact discs. Find the cost per disc for pressing:

    a. 100 compact discs

    b. 1000 compact discs

10. Multiply.

    a. $(3x - 1)^2$

    b. $\left(\dfrac{1}{2}x + 3\right)\left(\dfrac{1}{2}x - 3\right)$

    c. $(2x - 5)(6x + 7)$

11. Add or subtract.

    a. $\dfrac{x}{4} + \dfrac{5x}{4}$ **b.** $\dfrac{5}{7z^2} + \dfrac{x}{7z^2}$

    c. $\dfrac{x^2}{x+7} - \dfrac{49}{x+7}$ **d.** $\dfrac{x}{3y^2} - \dfrac{x+1}{3y^2}$

12. Perform the indicated operations and simplify if possible.

$$\dfrac{5}{x-2} + \dfrac{3}{x^2 + 4x + 4} - \dfrac{6}{x+2}$$

13. Divide $3x^4 + 2x^3 - 8x + 6$ by $x^2 - 1$.

14. Simplify each complex fraction.

    a. $\dfrac{\dfrac{a}{5}}{\dfrac{a-1}{10}}$ **b.** $\dfrac{\dfrac{3}{2+a} + \dfrac{6}{2-a}}{\dfrac{5}{a+2} - \dfrac{1}{a-2}}$

    c. $\dfrac{x^{-1} + y^{-1}}{xy}$

15. Solve: $\dfrac{2x}{2x-1} + \dfrac{1}{x} = \dfrac{1}{2x-1}$

16. Divide $x^3 - 8$ by $x - 2$.

17. Steve Deitmer takes $1\dfrac{1}{2}$ times as long to go 72 miles upstream in his boat as he does to return. If the boat cruises at 30 mph in still water, what is the speed of the current?

18. Use synthetic division to divide: $(8x^2 - 12x - 7) \div (x - 2)$

19. Simplify the following expressions.

    a. $\sqrt[4]{81}$ **b.** $\sqrt[5]{-243}$

    c. $-\sqrt{25}$ **d.** $\sqrt[4]{-81}$

    e. $\sqrt[3]{64x^3}$

20. Solve $\dfrac{1}{a+5} = \dfrac{1}{3a+6} - \dfrac{a+2}{a^2 + 7x + 10}$

21. Use rational exponents to write as a single radical.

    a. $\sqrt{x} \cdot \sqrt[4]{x}$ **b.** $\dfrac{\sqrt{x}}{\sqrt[3]{x}}$ **c.** $\sqrt[3]{3} \cdot \sqrt{2}$

22. Suppose that y varies directly as x. If $y = \dfrac{1}{2}$ when $x = 12$, find the constant of variation and the direct variation equation.

23. Multiply.

   a. $\sqrt{3}\left(5 + \sqrt{30}\right)$

   b. $\left(\sqrt{5} - \sqrt{6}\right)\left(\sqrt{7} + 1\right)$

   c. $\left(7\sqrt{x} + 5\right)\left(3\sqrt{x} - \sqrt{5}\right)$

   d. $\left(4\sqrt{3} - 1\right)^2$

   e. $\left(\sqrt{2x} - 5\right)\left(\sqrt{2x} + 5\right)$

   f. $\left(\sqrt{x - 3} + 5\right)^2$

24. Find each root. Assume that all variables represent non-negative real numbers.

   a. $\sqrt[4]{81}$ **b.** $\sqrt[3]{-27}$ **c.** $\sqrt{\dfrac{9}{64}}$

   d. $\sqrt[4]{x^{12}}$ **e.** $\sqrt[3]{-125y^6}$

25. Rationalize the denominator of $\dfrac{\sqrt[4]{x}}{\sqrt[4]{81y^5}}$.

26. Multiply.

   a. $a^{1/4}\left(a^{3/4} - a^{7/4}\right)$

   b. $\left(x^{1/2} - 3\right)\left(x^{1/2} + 5\right)$

27. Solve $\sqrt{4 - x} = x - 2$.

28. Use the quotient rule to divide and simplify if possible.

   a. $\dfrac{\sqrt{54}}{\sqrt{6}}$ **b.** $\dfrac{\sqrt{108a^2}}{3\sqrt{3}}$

   c. $\dfrac{3\sqrt[3]{81a^5b^{10}}}{\sqrt[3]{3b^4}}$

29. Solve $3x^2 - 9x + 8 = 0$ by completing the square.

30. Add or subtract as indicated.

   a. $\dfrac{\sqrt{20}}{3} + \dfrac{\sqrt{5}}{4}$

   b. $\sqrt[3]{\dfrac{24x}{27}} - \dfrac{\sqrt[3]{3x}}{2}$

31. Solve $\dfrac{3x}{x - 2} - \dfrac{x + 1}{x} = \dfrac{6}{x(x - 2)}$.

32. Rationalize the denominator. $\sqrt[3]{\dfrac{27}{m^4n^8}}$

33. Solve $x^2 - 4x \le 0$.

34. Find the length of the unknown side of the triangle.

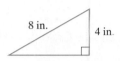

35. Graph $F(x) = (x - 3)^2 + 1$.

36. Find the following powers of i.

   a. i^8 **b.** i^{21}

   c. i^{42} **d.** i^{-13}

37. If $f(x) = x - 1$ and $g(x) = 2x - 3$, find

   a. $(f + g)(x)$ **b.** $(f - g)(x)$

   c. $(f \cdot g)(x)$ **d.** $\left(\dfrac{f}{g}\right)(x)$

38. Solve $4x^2 + 8x - 1 = 0$ by completing the square.

39. Find an equation of the inverse of $f(x) = x + 3$.

40. Solve by using the quadratic formula. $\left(x - \dfrac{1}{2}\right)^2 = \dfrac{x}{2}$

41. Find the value of each logarithmic expression.

   a. $\log_4 16$ **b.** $\log_{10}\dfrac{1}{10}$ **c.** $\log_9 3$

42. Graph $f(x) = -(x + 1)^2 + 1$. Find the vertex and the axis of symmetry.

10 Conic Sections

In Chapter 8, we analyzed some of the important connections between a parabola and its equation. Parabolas are interesting in their own right but are more interesting still because they are part of a collection of curves known as conic sections. This chapter is devoted to quadratic equations in two variables and their conic section graphs: the parabola, circle, ellipse, and hyperbola.

When the sun rises above the horizon on June 21 or 22, thousands of people gather to witness and celebrate summer solstice at Stonehenge. Stonehenge is a megalithic ruin located on the Salisbury Plain in Wiltshire, England. It is a series of earth, timber and stone structures that were constructed, revised, and reconstructed over a period of 1400 years or so. Although no one can say for certain what its true purpose was, there have been multiple theories. The best-known theory is the one from eighteenth century British antiquarian, William Stukeley. He believed that Stonehenge was a temple, possibly an ancient cult center for the Druids. Despite the fact that we don't know its purpose for certain, Stonehenge acts as a prehistoric timepiece, allowing us to theorize what it would have been like during the Neolithic Period, and who could have built this megalithic wonder. In Exercise 72 on page 610, we will explore the dimensions of the outer stone circle, known as the Sarsen circle, or Stonehenge. (*Source:* The Discovery Channel)

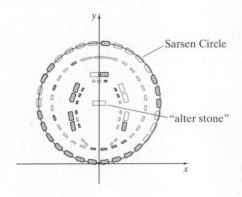

10.1 THE PARABOLA AND THE CIRCLE

OBJECTIVES

1 Graph parabolas of the form $x = a(y - k)^2 + h$ and $y = a(x - h)^2 + k$.

2 Graph circles of the form $(x - h)^2 + (y - k)^2 = r^2$.

3 Write the equation of a circle, given its center and radius.

4 Find the center and the radius of a circle, given its equation.

Conic sections derive their name because each conic section is the intersection of a right circular cone and a plane. The circle, parabola, ellipse, and hyperbola are the conic sections.

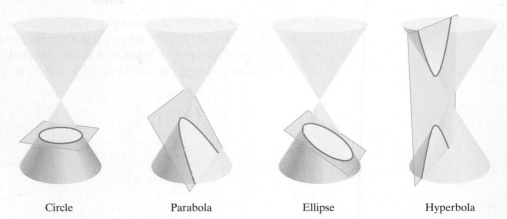

Circle   Parabola   Ellipse   Hyperbola

OBJECTIVE 1 ▶ Graphing parabolas in standard form. Thus far, we have seen that $f(x)$ or $y = a(x - h)^2 + k$ is the equation of a parabola that opens upward if $a > 0$ or downward if $a < 0$. Parabolas can also open left or right, or even on a slant. Equations of these parabolas are not functions of x, of course, since a parabola opening any way other than upward or downward fails the vertical line test. In this section, we introduce parabolas that open to the left and to the right. Parabolas opening on a slant will not be developed in this book.

Just as $y = a(x - h)^2 + k$ is the equation of a parabola that opens upward or downward, $x = a(y - k)^2 + h$ is the equation of a parabola that opens to the right or to the left. The parabola opens to the right if $a > 0$ and to the left if $a < 0$. The parabola has vertex (h, k), and its axis of symmetry is the line $y = k$.

Parabolas

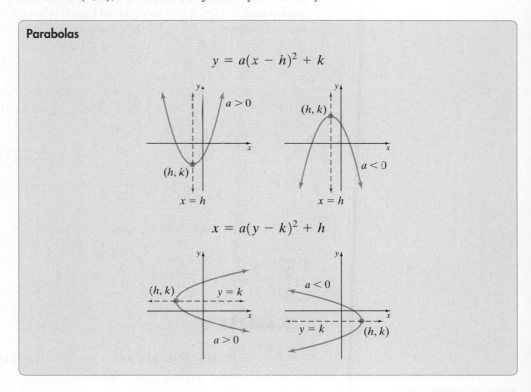

The equations $y = a(x - h)^2 + k$ and $x = a(y - k)^2 + h$ are called **standard forms.**

Concept Check ☑

Does the graph of the parabola given by the equation $x = -3y^2$ open to the left, to the right, upward, or downward?

EXAMPLE 1 Graph the parabola $x = 2y^2$.

Solution   Written in standard form, the equation $x = 2y^2$ is $x = 2(y - 0)^2 + 0$ with $a = 2, h = 0$, and $k = 0$. Its graph is a parabola with vertex $(0,0)$, and its axis of symmetry is the line $y = 0$. Since $a > 0$, this parabola opens to the right. The table shows a few more ordered pair solutions of $x = 2y^2$. Its graph is also shown.

x	y
8	-2
2	-1
0	0
2	1
8	2

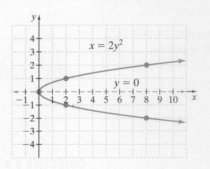

PRACTICE 1   Graph the parabola $x = \frac{1}{2}y^2$.

EXAMPLE 2   Graph the parabola $x = -3(y - 1)^2 + 2$.

Solution   The equation $x = -3(y - 1)^2 + 2$ is in the form $x = a(y - k)^2 + h$ with $a = -3, k = 1$, and $h = 2$. Since $a < 0$, the parabola opens to the left. The vertex (h, k) is $(2, 1)$, and the axis of symmetry is the line $y = 1$. When $y = 0, x = -1$, so the x-intercept is $(-1, 0)$. Again, we obtain a few ordered pair solutions and then graph the parabola.

x	y
2	1
-1	0
-1	2
-10	3
-10	-1

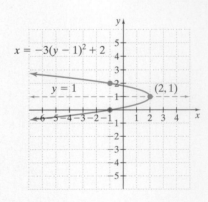

PRACTICE 2   Graph the parabola $x = -2(y + 4)^2 - 1$.

EXAMPLE 3   Graph $y = -x^2 - 2x + 15$.

Solution   Complete the square on x to write the equation in standard form.

$$y - 15 = -x^2 - 2x \qquad \text{Subtract 15 from both sides.}$$

$$y - 15 = -1(x^2 + 2x) \qquad \text{Factor } -1 \text{ from the terms } -x^2 - 2x.$$

Answer to Concept Check:
to the left

The coefficient of x is 2. Find the square of half of 2.

$$\frac{1}{2}(2) = 1 \quad \text{and} \quad 1^2 = 1$$

$$y - 15 - 1(1) = -1(x^2 + 2x + 1) \quad \text{Add } -1(1) \text{ to both sides.}$$

$$y - 16 = -1(x + 1)^2 \qquad \begin{array}{l}\text{Simplify the left side and} \\ \text{factor the right side.}\end{array}$$

$$y = -(x + 1)^2 + 16 \qquad \text{Add 16 to both sides.}$$

The equation is now in standard form $y = a(x - h)^2 + k$ with $a = -1, h = -1$, and $k = 16$.

The vertex is then (h, k), or $(-1, 16)$.

A second method for finding the vertex is by using the formula $\dfrac{-b}{2a}$.

$$x = \frac{-(-2)}{2(-1)} = \frac{2}{-2} = -1$$

$$y = -(-1)^2 - 2(-1) + 15 = -1 + 2 + 15 = 16$$

Again, we see that the vertex is $(-1, 16)$, and the axis of symmetry is the vertical line $x = -1$. The y-intercept is $(0, 15)$. Now we can use a few more ordered pair solutions to graph the parabola.

x	y
-1	16
0	15
-2	15
1	12
-3	12
3	0
-5	0

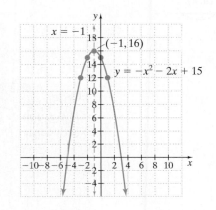

PRACTICE

3   Graph $y = -x^2 + 4x + 6$.

EXAMPLE 4   Graph $x = 2y^2 + 4y + 5$.

Solution   Notice that this equation is quadratic in y, so its graph is a parabola that opens to the left or the right. We can complete the square on y or we can use the formula $\dfrac{-b}{2a}$ to find the vertex.

Since the equation is quadratic in y, the formula gives us the y-value of the vertex.

$$y = \frac{-4}{2 \cdot 2} = \frac{-4}{4} = -1$$

$$x = 2(-1)^2 + 4(-1) + 5 = 2 \cdot 1 - 4 + 5 = 3$$

The vertex is $(3, -1)$, and the axis of symmetry is the line $y = -1$. The parabola opens to the right since $a > 0$. The x-intercept is $(5, 0)$.

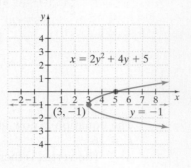

$x = 2y^2 + 4y + 5$

PRACTICE

4   Graph $x = 3y^2 + 6y + 4$.

OBJECTIVE 2 ▶ Graphing circles in standard form. Another conic section is the **circle.** A circle is the set of all points in a plane that are the same distance from a fixed point called the **center.** The distance is called the **radius** of the circle. To find a standard equation for a circle, let (h, k) represent the center of the circle, and let (x, y) represent any point on the circle. The distance between (h, k) and (x, y) is defined to be the circle's radius, r units. We can find this distance r by using the distance formula.

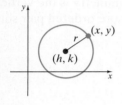

$$r = \sqrt{(x - h)^2 + (y - k)^2}$$

$$r^2 = (x - h)^2 + (y - k)^2 \qquad \text{Square both sides.}$$

Circle

The graph of $(x - h)^2 + (y - k)^2 = r^2$ is a circle with center (h, k) and radius r.

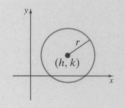

The equation $(x - h)^2 + (y - k)^2 = r^2$ is called **standard form.**

If an equation can be written in the standard form

$$(x - h)^2 + (y - k)^2 = r^2$$

then its graph is a circle, which we can draw by graphing the center (h, k) and using the radius r.

▶ Helpful Hint

Notice that the radius is the *distance* from the center of the circle to any point of the circle. Also notice that the *midpoint* of a diameter of a circle is the center of the circle.

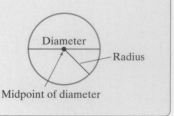

EXAMPLE 5 Graph $x^2 + y^2 = 4$.

Solution The equation can be written in standard form as

$$(x - 0)^2 + (y - 0)^2 = 2^2$$

The center of the circle is $(0, 0)$, and the radius is 2. Its graph is shown.

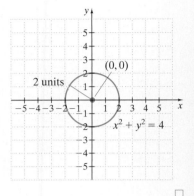

PRACTICE
5 Graph $x^2 + y^2 = 25$.

> ▶ **Helpful Hint**
>
> Notice the difference between the equation of a circle and the equation of a parabola. The equation of a circle contains both x^2 and y^2 terms on the same side of the equation with equal coefficients. The equation of a parabola has either an x^2 term or a y^2 term but not both.

EXAMPLE 6 Graph $(x + 1)^2 + y^2 = 8$.

Solution The equation can be written as $(x + 1)^2 + (y - 0)^2 = 8$ with $h = -1$, $k = 0$, and $r = \sqrt{8}$. The center is $(-1, 0)$, and the radius is $\sqrt{8} = 2\sqrt{2} \approx 2.8$.

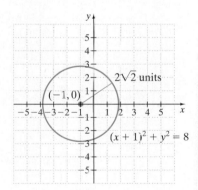

PRACTICE
6 Graph $(x - 3)^2 + (y + 2)^2 = 4$.

Concept Check ☑

In the graph of the equation $(x - 3)^2 + (y - 2)^2 = 5$, what is the distance between the center of the circle and any point on the circle?

Answer to Concept Check:
$\sqrt{5}$ units

OBJECTIVE 3 ▶ Writing equations of circles. Since a circle is determined entirely by its center and radius, this information is all we need to write the equation of a circle.

EXAMPLE 7   Find an equation of the circle with center $(-7, 3)$ and radius 10.

Solution   Using the given values $h = -7$, $k = 3$, and $r = 10$, we write the equation

$$(x - h)^2 + (y - k)^2 = r^2$$

or

$$[x - (-7)]^2 + (y - 3)^2 = 10^2 \quad \text{Substitute the given values.}$$

or

$$(x + 7)^2 + (y - 3)^2 = 100$$

PRACTICE
7   Find the equation of a circle with center $(-2, -5)$ and radius 9.

OBJECTIVE 4 ▶ Finding the center and the radius of a circle. To find the center and the radius of a circle from its equation, write the equation in standard form. To write the equation of a circle in standard form, we complete the square on both x and y.

EXAMPLE 8   Graph $x^2 + y^2 + 4x - 8y = 16$.

Solution   Since this equation contains x^2 and y^2 terms on the same side of the equation with equal coefficients, its graph is a circle. To write the equation in standard form, group the terms involving x and the terms involving y, and then complete the square on each variable.

$$(x^2 + 4x) + (y^2 - 8y) = 16$$

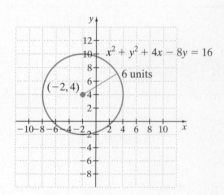

Thus, $\frac{1}{2}(4) = 2$ and $2^2 = 4$. Also, $\frac{1}{2}(-8) = -4$ and $(-4)^2 = 16$. Add 4 and then 16 to both sides.

$$(x^2 + 4x + 4) + (y^2 - 8y + 16) = 16 + 4 + 16$$
$$(x + 2)^2 + (y - 4)^2 = 36 \quad \text{Factor.}$$

This circle has the center $(-2, 4)$ and radius 6, as shown.

PRACTICE
8   Graph $x^2 + y^2 + 6x - 2y = 6$.

Graphing Calculator Explorations

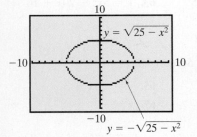

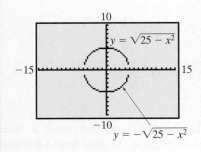

To graph an equation such as $x^2 + y^2 = 25$ with a graphing calculator, we first solve the equation for y.

$$x^2 + y^2 = 25$$
$$y^2 = 25 - x^2$$
$$y = \pm\sqrt{25 - x^2}$$

The graph of $y = \sqrt{25 - x^2}$ will be the top half of the circle, and the graph of $y = -\sqrt{25 - x^2}$ will be the bottom half of the circle.

To graph, press $\boxed{Y=}$ and enter $Y_1 = \sqrt{25 - x^2}$ and $Y_2 = -\sqrt{25 - x^2}$. Insert parentheses around $25 - x^2$ so that $\sqrt{25 - x^2}$ and not $\sqrt{25} - x^2$ is graphed.

The top graph to the left does not appear to be a circle because we are currently using a standard window and the screen is rectangular. This causes the tick marks on the x-axis to be farther apart than the tick marks on the y-axis and, thus, creates the distorted circle. If we want the graph to appear circular, we must define a square window by using a feature of the graphing calculator or by redefining the window to show the x-axis from -15 to 15 and the y-axis from -10 to 10. Using a square window, the graph appears as shown on the bottom to the left.

Use a graphing calculator to graph each circle.

1. $x^2 + y^2 = 55$

2. $x^2 + y^2 = 20$

3. $5x^2 + 5y^2 = 50$

4. $6x^2 + 6y^2 = 105$

5. $2x^2 + 2y^2 - 34 = 0$

6. $4x^2 + 4y^2 - 48 = 0$

7. $7x^2 + 7y^2 - 89 = 0$

8. $3x^2 + 3y^2 - 35 = 0$

VOCABULARY & READINESS CHECK

Use the choices below to fill in each blank. Some choices may be used more than once.

radius	center	vertex
diameter	circle	conic sections

1. The circle, parabola, ellipse, and hyperbola are called the _____.

2. For a parabola that opens upward the lowest point is the _____.

3. A _____ is the set of all points in a plane that are the same distance from a fixed point. The fixed point is called the _____.

4. The midpoint of a diameter of a circle is the _____.

5. The distance from the center of a circle to any point of the circle is called the _____.

6. Twice a circle's radius is its _____.

The graph of each equation is a parabola. Determine whether the parabola opens upward, downward, to the left, or to the right.

7. $y = x^2 - 7x + 5$

8. $y = -x^2 + 16$

9. $x = -y^2 - y + 2$

10. $x = 3y^2 + 2y - 5$

11. $y = -x^2 + 2x + 1$

12. $x = -y^2 + 2y - 6$

10.1 EXERCISE SET

The graph of each equation is a parabola. Find the vertex of the parabola and sketch its graph. See Examples 1 through 4.

1. $x = 3y^2$
2. $x = -2y^2$
3. $x = (y - 2)^2 + 3$
4. $x = (y - 4)^2 - 1$
5. $y = 3(x - 1)^2 + 5$
6. $x = -4(y - 2)^2 + 2$
7. $x = y^2 + 6y + 8$
8. $x = y^2 - 6y + 6$
9. $y = x^2 + 10x + 20$
10. $y = x^2 + 4x - 5$
11. $x = -2y^2 + 4y + 6$
12. $x = 3y^2 + 6y + 7$

The graph of each equation is a circle. Find the center and the radius, and then sketch. See Examples 5, 6, and 8.

13. $x^2 + y^2 = 9$
14. $x^2 + y^2 = 100$
15. $x^2 + (y - 2)^2 = 1$
16. $(x - 3)^2 + y^2 = 9$
17. $(x - 5)^2 + (y + 2)^2 = 1$
18. $(x + 3)^2 + (y + 3)^2 = 4$
19. $x^2 + y^2 + 6y = 0$
20. $x^2 + 10x + y^2 = 0$
21. $x^2 + y^2 + 2x - 4y = 4$
22. $x^2 + 6x - 4y + y^2 = 3$
23. $x^2 + y^2 - 4x - 8y - 2 = 0$
24. $x^2 + y^2 - 2x - 6y - 5 = 0$

Write an equation of the circle with the given center and radius. See Example 7.

25. $(2, 3); 6$
26. $(-7, 6); 2$
27. $(0, 0); \sqrt{3}$
28. $(0, -6); \sqrt{2}$
29. $(-5, 4); 3\sqrt{5}$
30. the origin; $4\sqrt{7}$

31. Explain the error in the statement: The graph of $x^2 + (y + 3)^2 = 10$ is a circle with center $(0, -3)$ and radius 5.

MIXED PRACTICE

Sketch the graph of each equation. If the graph is a parabola, find its vertex. If the graph is a circle, find its center and radius.

32. $x = y^2 + 2$
33. $x = y^2 - 3$
34. $y = (x + 3)^2 + 3$
35. $y = (x - 2)^2 - 2$
36. $x^2 + y^2 = 49$
37. $x^2 + y^2 = 1$
38. $x = (y - 1)^2 + 4$
39. $x = (y + 3)^2 - 1$
40. $(x + 3)^2 + (y - 1)^2 = 9$
41. $(x - 2)^2 + (y - 2)^2 = 16$
42. $x = -2(y + 5)^2$
43. $x = -(y - 1)^2$
44. $x^2 + (y + 5)^2 = 5$
45. $(x - 4)^2 + y^2 = 7$
46. $y = 3(x - 4)^2 + 2$
47. $y = 5(x + 5)^2 + 3$
48. $2x^2 + 2y^2 = \dfrac{1}{2}$
49. $\dfrac{x^2}{8} + \dfrac{y^2}{8} = 2$
50. $y = x^2 - 2x - 15$
51. $y = x^2 + 7x + 6$
52. $x^2 + y^2 + 6x + 10y - 2 = 0$
53. $x^2 + y^2 + 2x + 12y - 12 = 0$
54. $x = y^2 + 6y + 2$
55. $x = y^2 + 8y - 4$
56. $x^2 + y^2 - 8y + 5 = 0$
57. $x^2 - 10y + y^2 + 4 = 0$
58. $x = -2y^2 - 4y$
59. $x = -3y^2 + 30y$

60. $\dfrac{x^2}{3} + \dfrac{y^2}{3} = 2$
61. $5x^2 + 5y^2 = 25$
62. $y = 4x^2 - 40x + 105$
63. $y = 5x^2 - 20x + 16$

REVIEW AND PREVIEW

Graph each equation. See Section 3.3.

64. $y = 2x + 5$
65. $y = -3x + 3$
66. $y = 3$
67. $x = -2$

Rationalize each denominator and simplify, if possible. See Section 7.5.

68. $\dfrac{1}{\sqrt{3}}$
69. $\dfrac{\sqrt{5}}{\sqrt{8}}$
70. $\dfrac{4\sqrt{7}}{\sqrt{6}}$
71. $\dfrac{10}{\sqrt{5}}$

CONCEPT EXTENSIONS

72. **The Sarsen Circle:** The the first image that comes to mind when one thinks of Stonehenge is the very large sandstone blocks with sandstone lintels across the top. The Sarsen Circle of Stonehenge is the outer circle of the sandstone blocks, each of which weighs up to 50 tons. There were originally 30 of these monolithic blocks, but only 17 remain upright to this day. The "altar stone" lies at the center of this circle, which has a diameter of 33 meters.

    a. What is the radius of the Sarsen circle?

    b. What is the circumference of the Sarsen circle? Round your result to 2 decimal places.

    c. Since there were originally 30 Sarsen stones located on the circumference, how far apart would the centers of the stones have been? Round to the nearest tenth of a meter.

    d. Using the axes in the drawing, what are the coordinates of the center of the circle?

    e. Use parts **a** and **d** to write the equation of the Sarsen circle.

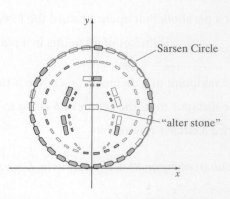

73. Opened in 2000 to honor the millennium, the British Airways London Eye is the world's biggest observation wheel. Each of the 32 enclosed capsules, which each hold 25 passengers, completes a full rotation every 30 minutes. Its diameter is

135 meters, and it is constructed on London's South Bank, to allow passengers to enter the Eye at ground level. (*Source: Guinness Book of World Records*)

a. What is the radius of the London Eye?

b. How close is the wheel to the ground?

c. How high is the center of the wheel from the ground?

d. Using the axes in the drawing, what are the coordinates of the center of the wheel?

e. Use parts **a** and **d** to write the equation of the Eye.

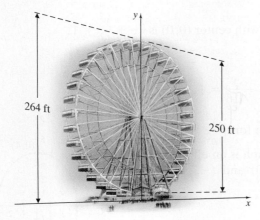

74. In 1893, Pittsburgh bridge builder George Ferris designed and built a gigantic revolving steel wheel whose height was 264 feet and diameter was 250 feet. This Ferris wheel opened at the 1893 exposition in Chicago. It had 36 wooden cars, each capable of holding 60 passengers. (*Source: The Handy Science Answer Book*)

a. What was the radius of this Ferris wheel?

b. How close is the wheel to the ground?

c. How high is the center of the wheel from the ground?

d. Using the axes in the drawing, what are the coordinates of the center of the wheel?

e. Use parts **a** and **d** to write the equation of the wheel.

75. As of this writing, the world's largest-diameter Ferris wheel currently in operation is the Star of Nanchung in Jiangxi Province, China. It has 60 compartments, each of which carries eight people. It is 160 meters tall, and the diameter of the wheel is 153 meters. (*Source: China News Agency*)

a. What is the radius of this Ferris wheel?

b. How close is the wheel to the ground?

c. How high is the center of the wheel from the ground?

d. Using the axes in the drawing, what are the coordinates of the center of the wheel?

e. Use parts **a** and **d** to write the equation of the wheel.

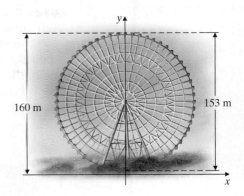

76. If you are given a list of equations of circles and parabolas and none are in standard form, explain how you would determine which is an equation of a circle and which is an equation of a parabola. Explain also how you would distinguish the upward or downward parabolas from the left-opening or right-opening parabolas.

Solve.

77. Cindy Brown, an architect, is drawing plans on grid paper for a circular pool with a fountain in the middle. The paper is marked off in centimeters, and each centimeter represents 1 foot. On the paper, the diameter of the "pool" is 20 centimeters, and "fountain" is the point $(0, 0)$.

a. Sketch the architect's drawing. Be sure to label the axes.

b. Write an equation that describes the circular pool.

c. Cindy plans to place a circle of lights around the fountain such that each light is 5 feet from the fountain. Write an equation for the circle of lights and sketch the circle on your drawing.

78. A bridge constructed over a bayou has a supporting arch in the shape of a parabola. Find an equation of the parabolic arch if the length of the road over the arch is 100 meters and the maximum height of the arch is 40 meters.

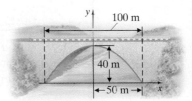

Use a graphing calculator to verify each exercise. Use a square viewing window.

79. Exercise 61.

80. Exercise 60.

81. Exercise 63.

82. Exercise 62.

10.2 THE ELLIPSE AND THE HYPERBOLA

OBJECTIVES

1 Define and graph an ellipse.

2 Define and graph a hyperbola.

OBJECTIVE 1 ▶ Graphing ellipses. An **ellipse** can be thought of as the set of points in a plane such that the sum of the distances of those points from two fixed points is constant. Each of the two fixed points is called a **focus.** (The plural of focus is **foci.**) The point midway between the foci is called the **center.**

An ellipse may be drawn by hand by using two thumbtacks, a piece of string, and a pencil. Secure the two thumbtacks in a piece of cardboard, for example, and tie each end of the string to a tack. Use your pencil to pull the string tight and draw the ellipse. The two thumbtacks are the foci of the drawn ellipse.

Ellipse with Center (0, 0)

The graph of an equation of the form $\frac{x^2}{a^2} + \frac{y^2}{b^2} = 1$ is an ellipse with center $(0, 0)$.

The x-intercepts are $(a, 0)$ and $(-a, 0)$, and the y-intercepts are $(0, b)$, and $(0, -b)$.

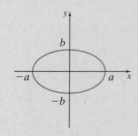

The **standard form** of an ellipse with center $(0, 0)$ is $\frac{x^2}{a^2} + \frac{y^2}{b^2} = 1$.

EXAMPLE 1 Graph $\frac{x^2}{9} + \frac{y^2}{16} = 1$.

Solution The equation is of the form $\frac{x^2}{a^2} + \frac{y^2}{b^2} = 1$, with $a = 3$ and $b = 4$, so its graph is an ellipse with center $(0, 0)$, x-intercepts $(3, 0)$ and $(-3, 0)$, and y-intercepts $(0, 4)$ and $(0, -4)$.

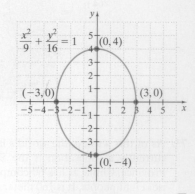

PRACTICE
1 Graph $\frac{x^2}{25} + \frac{y^2}{4} = 1$.

EXAMPLE 2   Graph $4x^2 + 16y^2 = 64$.

<u>Solution</u>   Although this equation contains a sum of squared terms in x and y on the same side of an equation, this is not the equation of a circle since the coefficients of x^2 and y^2 are not the same. The graph of this equation is an ellipse. Since the standard form of the equation of an ellipse has 1 on one side, divide both sides of this equation by 64.

$$4x^2 + 16y^2 = 64$$

$$\frac{4x^2}{64} + \frac{16y^2}{64} = \frac{64}{64} \quad \text{Divide both sides by 64.}$$

$$\frac{x^2}{16} + \frac{y^2}{4} = 1 \quad \text{Simplify.}$$

We now recognize the equation of an ellipse with $a = 4$ and $b = 2$. This ellipse has center $(0, 0)$, x-intercepts $(4, 0)$ and $(-4, 0)$, and y-intercepts $(0, 2)$ and $(0, -2)$.

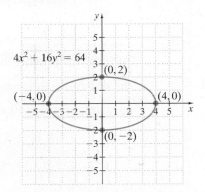

PRACTICE
2   Graph $9x^2 + 4y^2 = 36$.

The center of an ellipse is not always $(0, 0)$, as shown in the next example.

EXAMPLE 3   Graph $\dfrac{(x + 3)^2}{25} + \dfrac{(y - 2)^2}{36} = 1$.

<u>Solution</u>   The center of this ellipse is found in a way that is similar to finding the center of a circle. This ellipse has center $(-3, 2)$. Notice that $a = 5$ and $b = 6$. To find four points on the graph of the ellipse, first graph the center, $(-3, 2)$. Since $a = 5$, count 5 units right and then 5 units left of the point with coordinates $(-3, 2)$. Next, since $b = 6$, start at $(-3, 2)$ and count 6 units up and then 6 units down to find two more points on the ellipse.

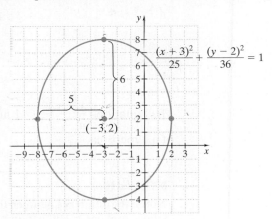

PRACTICE
3   Graph $\dfrac{(x - 4)^2}{49} + \dfrac{(y + 1)^2}{81} = 1$.

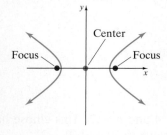

Concept Check ☑

In the graph of the equation $\frac{x^2}{64} + \frac{y^2}{36} = 1$, which distance is longer: the distance between the *x*-intercepts or the distance between the *y*-intercepts? How much longer? Explain.

OBJECTIVE 2 ▶ Graphing hyperbolas. The final conic section is the **hyperbola.** A hyperbola is the set of points in a plane such that the absolute value of the difference of the distances from two fixed points is constant. Each of the two fixed points is called a **focus.** The point midway between the foci is called the **center.**

Using the distance formula, we can show that the graph of $\frac{x^2}{a^2} - \frac{y^2}{b^2} = 1$ is a hyperbola with center (0, 0) and *x*-intercepts $(a, 0)$ and $(-a, 0)$. Also, the graph of $\frac{y^2}{b^2} - \frac{x^2}{a^2} = 1$ is a hyperbola with center (0,0) and *y*-intercepts $(0, b)$ and $(0, -b)$.

Hyperbola with Center (0, 0)

The graph of an equation of the form $\frac{x^2}{a^2} - \frac{y^2}{b^2} = 1$ is a hyperbola with center (0,0) and *x*-intercepts $(a, 0)$ and $(-a, 0)$.

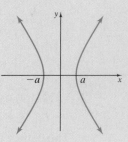

The graph of an equation of the form $\frac{y^2}{b^2} - \frac{x^2}{a^2} = 1$ is a hyperbola with center (0,0) and *y*-intercepts $(0, b)$ and $(0, -b)$.

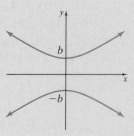

The equations $\frac{x^2}{a^2} - \frac{y^2}{b^2} = 1$ and $\frac{y^2}{b^2} - \frac{x^2}{a^2} = 1$ are the **standard forms** for the equation of a hyperbola.

▶ **Helpful Hint**

Notice the difference between the equation of an ellipse and a hyperbola. The equation of the ellipse contains x^2 and y^2 terms on the same side of the equation with same-sign coefficients. For a hyperbola, the coefficients on the same side of the equation have different signs.

Answer to Concept Check:
x-intercepts, by 4 units

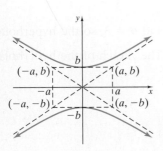

Graphing a hyperbola such as $\dfrac{y^2}{b^2} - \dfrac{x^2}{a^2} = 1$ is made easier by recognizing one of its important characteristics. Examining the figure to the left, notice how the sides of the branches of the hyperbola extend indefinitely and seem to approach the dashed lines in the figure. These dashed lines are called the **asymptotes** of the hyperbola.

To sketch these lines, or asymptotes, draw a rectangle with vertices (a, b), $(-a, b)$, $(a, -b)$, and $(-a, -b)$. The asymptotes of the hyperbola are the extended diagonals of this rectangle.

EXAMPLE 4 Graph $\dfrac{x^2}{16} - \dfrac{y^2}{25} = 1$.

Solution This equation has the form $\dfrac{x^2}{a^2} - \dfrac{y^2}{b^2} = 1$, with $a = 4$ and $b = 5$. Thus, its graph is a hyperbola that opens to the left and right. It has center $(0, 0)$ and x-intercepts $(4, 0)$ and $(-4, 0)$. To aid in graphing the hyperbola, we first sketch its asymptotes. The extended diagonals of the rectangle with corners $(4, 5)$, $(4, -5)$, $(-4, 5)$, and $(-4, -5)$ are the asymptotes of the hyperbola. Then we use the asymptotes to aid in sketching the hyperbola.

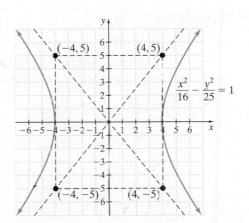

PRACTICE
4 Graph $\dfrac{x^2}{9} - \dfrac{y^2}{16} = 1$.

EXAMPLE 5 Graph $4y^2 - 9x^2 = 36$.

Solution Since this is a difference of squared terms in x and y on the same side of the equation, its graph is a hyperbola, as opposed to an ellipse or a circle. The standard form of the equation of a hyperbola has a 1 on one side, so divide both sides of the equation by 36.

$$4y^2 - 9x^2 = 36$$

$$\frac{4y^2}{36} - \frac{9x^2}{36} = \frac{36}{36} \qquad \text{Divide both sides by 36.}$$

$$\frac{y^2}{9} - \frac{x^2}{4} = 1 \qquad \text{Simplify.}$$

The equation is of the form $\dfrac{y^2}{b^2} - \dfrac{x^2}{a^2} = 1$, with $a = 2$ and $b = 3$, so the hyperbola is centered at $(0, 0)$ with y-intercepts $(0, 3)$ and $(0, -3)$. The sketch of the hyperbola is shown.

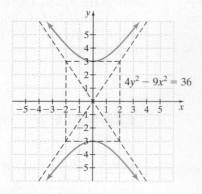

PRACTICE

5　Graph $9y^2 - 25x^2 = 225$.

Graphing Calculator Explorations

To find the graph of an ellipse by using a graphing calculator, use the same procedure as for graphing a circle. For example, to graph $x^2 + 3y^2 = 22$, first solve for y.

$$3y^2 = 22 - x^2$$

$$y^2 = \frac{22 - x^2}{3}$$

$$y = \pm\sqrt{\frac{22 - x^2}{3}}$$

Next press the $\boxed{Y=}$ key and enter $Y_1 = \sqrt{\dfrac{22 - x^2}{3}}$ and $Y_2 = -\sqrt{\dfrac{22 - x^2}{3}}$.

(Insert two sets of parentheses in the radicand as $\sqrt{((22 - x^2)/3)}$ so that the desired graph is obtained.) The graph appears as follows.

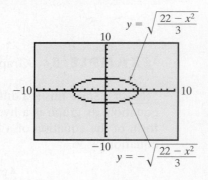

Use a graphing calculator to graph each ellipse.

1. $10x^2 + y^2 = 32$　　　　　　　**2.** $x^2 + 6y^2 = 35$

3. $20x^2 + 5y^2 = 100$　　　　　　**4.** $4y^2 + 12x^2 = 48$

5. $7.3x^2 + 15.5y^2 = 95.2$　　　　**6.** $18.8x^2 + 36.1y^2 = 205.8$

VOCABULARY & READINESS CHECK

Use the choices below to fill in each blank. Some choices will be used more than once and some not at all.

ellipse	$(0, 0)$	focus	$(a, 0)$ and $(-a, 0)$	$(0, a)$ and $(0, -a)$
hyperbola	center	x	$(b, 0)$ and $(-b, 0)$	$(0, b)$ and $(0, -b)$
		y		

1. A(n) _____ is the set of points in a plane such that the absolute value of the differences of their distances from two fixed points is constant.

2. A(n) _____ is the set of points in a plane such that the sum of their distances from two fixed points is constant.

For exercises 1 and 2 above,

3. The two fixed points are each called a _____.

4. The point midway between the foci is called the _____.

5. The graph of $\dfrac{x^2}{a^2} - \dfrac{y^2}{b^2} = 1$ is a(n) _____ with center _____ and _____-intercepts of _____.

6. The graph of $\dfrac{x^2}{b^2} + \dfrac{y^2}{a^2} = 1$ is a(n) _____ with center _____ and x-intercepts of _____.

Identify the graph of each equation as an ellipse or a hyperbola.

7. $\dfrac{x^2}{16} + \dfrac{y^2}{4} = 1$

8. $\dfrac{x^2}{16} - \dfrac{y^2}{4} = 1$

9. $x^2 - 5y^2 = 3$

10. $-x^2 + 5y^2 = 3$

11. $-\dfrac{y^2}{25} + \dfrac{x^2}{36} = 1$

12. $\dfrac{y^2}{25} + \dfrac{x^2}{36} = 1$

10.2 | EXERCISE SET

Sketch the graph of each equation. See Examples 1 and 2.

1. $\dfrac{x^2}{4} + \dfrac{y^2}{25} = 1$

2. $\dfrac{x^2}{16} + \dfrac{y^2}{9} = 1$

3. $\dfrac{x^2}{9} + y^2 = 1$

4. $x^2 + \dfrac{y^2}{4} = 1$

5. $9x^2 + y^2 = 36$

6. $x^2 + 4y^2 = 16$

7. $4x^2 + 25y^2 = 100$

8. $36x^2 + y^2 = 36$

Sketch the graph of each equation. See Example 3.

9. $\dfrac{(x + 1)^2}{36} + \dfrac{(y - 2)^2}{49} = 1$

10. $\dfrac{(x - 3)^2}{9} + \dfrac{(y + 3)^2}{16} = 1$

11. $\dfrac{(x - 1)^2}{4} + \dfrac{(y - 1)^2}{25} = 1$

12. $\dfrac{(x + 3)^2}{16} + \dfrac{(y + 2)^2}{4} = 1$

Sketch the graph of each equation. See Examples 4 and 5.

13. $\dfrac{x^2}{4} - \dfrac{y^2}{9} = 1$

14. $\dfrac{x^2}{36} - \dfrac{y^2}{36} = 1$

15. $\dfrac{y^2}{25} - \dfrac{x^2}{16} = 1$

16. $\dfrac{y^2}{25} - \dfrac{x^2}{49} = 1$

17. $x^2 - 4y^2 = 16$

18. $4x^2 - y^2 = 36$

19. $16y^2 - x^2 = 16$

20. $4y^2 - 25x^2 = 100$

21. If you are given a list of equations of circles, parabolas, ellipses, and hyperbolas, explain how you could distinguish the different conic sections from their equations.

MIXED PRACTICE

Identify whether each equation, when graphed, will be a parabola, circle, ellipse, or hyperbola. Sketch the graph of each equation.

22. $(x - 7)^2 + (y - 2)^2 = 4$

23. $y = x^2 + 4$

24. $y = x^2 + 12x + 36$

25. $\dfrac{x^2}{4} + \dfrac{y^2}{9} = 1$

26. $\dfrac{y^2}{9} - \dfrac{x^2}{9} = 1$

27. $\dfrac{x^2}{16} - \dfrac{y^2}{4} = 1$

28. $\dfrac{x^2}{16} + \dfrac{y^2}{4} = 1$

29. $x^2 + y^2 = 16$

30. $x = y^2 + 4y - 1$

31. $x = -y^2 + 6y$

32. $9x^2 - 4y^2 = 36$

33. $9x^2 + 4y^2 = 36$

34. $\dfrac{(x - 1)^2}{49} + \dfrac{(y + 2)^2}{25} = 1$

35. $y^2 = x^2 + 16$

36. $\left(x + \dfrac{1}{2}\right)^2 + \left(y - \dfrac{1}{2}\right)^2 = 1$

37. $y = -2x^2 + 4x - 3$

REVIEW AND PREVIEW

Solve each inequality. See Section 2.5.

38. $x < 5$ and $x < 1$ **39.** $x < 5$ or $x < 1$

40. $2x - 1 \geq 7$ or $-3x \leq -6$ **41.** $2x - 1 \geq 7$ and $-3x \leq -6$

Perform the indicated operations. See Sections 5.1 and 5.3.

42. $(2x^3)(-4x^2)$ **43.** $2x^3 - 4x^3$

44. $-5x^2 + x^2$ **45.** $(-5x^2)(x^2)$

CONCEPT EXTENSIONS

The graph of each equation is an ellipse. Determine which distance is longer. The distance between the x-intercepts or the distance between the y-intercepts. How much longer? See the Concept Check in this section.

46. $\dfrac{x^2}{16} + \dfrac{y^2}{25} = 1$ **47.** $\dfrac{x^2}{100} + \dfrac{y^2}{49} = 1$

48. $4x^2 + y^2 = 16$ **49.** $x^2 + 4y^2 = 36$

50. We know that $x^2 + y^2 = 25$ is the equation of a circle. Rewrite the equation so that the right side is equal to 1. Which type of conic section does this equation form resemble? In fact, the circle is a special case of this type of conic section. Describe the conditions under which this type of conic section is a circle.

The orbits of stars, planets, comets, asteroids, and satellites all have the shape of one of the conic sections. Astronomers use a measure called eccentricity to describe the shape and elongation of an orbital path. For the circle and ellipse, eccentricity e is calculated with the formula $e = \dfrac{c}{d}$, where $c^2 = |a^2 - b^2|$ and d is the larger value of a or b. For a hyperbola, eccentricity e is calculated with the formula $e = \dfrac{c}{d}$, where $c^2 = a^2 + b^2$ and the value of d is equal to a if the hyperbola has x-intercepts or equal to b if the hyperbola has y-intercepts. Use equations A–H to answer Exercises 51–60.

A. $\dfrac{x^2}{36} - \dfrac{y^2}{13} = 1$ **B.** $\dfrac{x^2}{4} + \dfrac{y^2}{4} = 1$ **C.** $\dfrac{x^2}{25} + \dfrac{y^2}{16} = 1$

D. $\dfrac{y^2}{25} - \dfrac{x^2}{39} = 1$ **E.** $\dfrac{x^2}{17} + \dfrac{y^2}{81} = 1$ **F.** $\dfrac{x^2}{36} + \dfrac{y^2}{36} = 1$

G. $\dfrac{x^2}{16} - \dfrac{y^2}{65} = 1$ **H.** $\dfrac{x^2}{144} + \dfrac{y^2}{140} = 1$

51. Identify the type of conic section represented by each of the equations A–H.

52. For each of the equations A–H, identify the values of a^2 and b^2.

53. For each of the equations A–H, calculate the value of c^2 and c.

54. For each of the equations A–H, find the value of d.

55. For each of the equations A–H, calculate the eccentricity e.

56. What do you notice about the values of e for the equations you identified as ellipses?

57. What do you notice about the values of e for the equations you identified as circles?

58. What do you notice about the values of e for the equations you identified as hyperbolas?

59. The eccentricity of a parabola is exactly 1. Use this information and the observations you made in Exercises 31, 32, and 33 to describe a way that could be used to identify the type of conic section based on its eccentricity value.

60. Graph each of the conic sections given in equations A–H. What do you notice about the shape of the ellipses for increasing values of eccentricity? Which is the most elliptical? Which is the least elliptical, that is, the most circular?

61. A planet's orbit about the Sun can be described as an ellipse. Consider the Sun as the origin of a rectangular coordinate system. Suppose that the x-intercepts of the elliptical path of the planet are ±130,000,000 and that the y-intercepts are ±125,000,000. Write the equation of the elliptical path of the planet.

62. Comets orbit the Sun in elongated ellipses. Consider the Sun as the origin of a rectangular coordinate system. Suppose that the equation of the path of the comet is

$$\dfrac{(x - 1{,}782{,}000{,}000)^2}{3.42 \cdot 10^{23}} + \dfrac{(y - 356{,}400{,}000)^2}{1.368 \cdot 10^{22}} = 1$$

Find the center of the path of the comet.

63. Use a graphing calculator to verify Exercise 33.

64. Use a graphing calculator to verify Exercise 6.

For Exercises 65 through 70, see the example below.

Example

Sketch the graph of $\dfrac{(x - 2)^2}{25} - \dfrac{(y - 1)^2}{9} = 1$.

Solution

This hyperbola has center $(2, 1)$. Notice that $a = 5$ and $b = 3$.

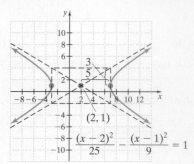

$$\dfrac{(x-2)^2}{25} - \dfrac{(x-1)^2}{9} = 1$$

Sketch the graph of each equation.

65. $\dfrac{(x - 1)^2}{4} - \dfrac{(y + 1)^2}{25} = 1$ **66.** $\dfrac{(x + 2)^2}{9} - \dfrac{(y - 1)^2}{4} = 1$

67. $\dfrac{y^2}{16} - \dfrac{(x + 3)^2}{9} = 1$ **68.** $\dfrac{(y + 4)^2}{4} - \dfrac{x^2}{25} = 1$

69. $\dfrac{(x + 5)^2}{16} - \dfrac{(y + 2)^2}{25} = 1$ **70.** $\dfrac{(x - 3)^2}{9} - \dfrac{(y - 2)^2}{4} = 1$

INTEGRATED REVIEW GRAPHING CONIC SECTIONS

Following is a summary of conic sections.

Conic Sections	Standard Form	Graph
Parabola	$y = a(x - h)^2 + k$	
Parabola	$x = a(y - k)^2 + h$	
Circle	$(x - h)^2 + (y - k)^2 = r^2$	
Ellipse center $(0, 0)$	$\dfrac{x^2}{a^2} + \dfrac{y^2}{b^2} = 1$	
Hyperbola center $(0, 0)$	$\dfrac{x^2}{a^2} - \dfrac{y^2}{b^2} = 1$	
Hyperbola center $(0, 0)$	$\dfrac{y^2}{b^2} - \dfrac{x^2}{a^2} = 1$	

Identify whether each equation, when graphed, will be a parabola, circle, ellipse, or hyperbola. Then graph each equation.

1. $(x - 7)^2 + (y - 2)^2 = 4$

2. $y = x^2 + 4$

3. $y = x^2 + 12x + 36$

4. $\dfrac{x^2}{4} + \dfrac{y^2}{9} = 1$

5. $\dfrac{y^2}{9} - \dfrac{x^2}{9} = 1$

6. $\dfrac{x^2}{16} - \dfrac{y^2}{4} = 1$

7. $\dfrac{x^2}{16} + \dfrac{y^2}{4} = 1$

8. $x^2 + y^2 = 16$

9. $x = y^2 + 4y - 1$

10. $x = -y^2 + 6y$

11. $9x^2 - 4y^2 = 36$

12. $9x^2 + 4y^2 = 36$

13. $\dfrac{(x - 1)^2}{49} + \dfrac{(y + 2)^2}{25} = 1$

14. $y^2 = x^2 + 16$

15. $\left(x + \dfrac{1}{2}\right)^2 + \left(y - \dfrac{1}{2}\right)^2 = 1$

10.3 SOLVING NONLINEAR SYSTEMS OF EQUATIONS

In Section 4.1, we used graphing, substitution, and elimination methods to find solutions of systems of linear equations in two variables. We now apply these same methods to nonlinear systems of equations in two variables. A **nonlinear system of equations** is a system of equations at least one of which is not linear. Since we will be graphing the equations in each system, we are interested in real number solutions only.

OBJECTIVE 1 ▶ Solving nonlinear systems by substitution. First, nonlinear systems are solved by the substitution method.

EXAMPLE 1 Solve the system

$$\begin{cases} x^2 - 3y = 1 \\ x - y = 1 \end{cases}$$

Solution   We can solve this system by substitution if we solve one equation for one of the variables. Solving the first equation for x is not the best choice since doing so introduces a radical. Also, solving for y in the first equation introduces a fraction. We solve the second equation for y.

$$x - y = 1 \quad \text{Second equation}$$
$$x - 1 = y \quad \text{Solve for } y.$$

Replace y with $x - 1$ in the first equation, and then solve for x.

$$x^2 - 3y = 1 \quad \text{First equation}$$
$$x^2 - 3(x - 1) = 1 \quad \text{Replace } y \text{ with } x - 1.$$
$$x^2 - 3x + 3 = 1$$
$$x^2 - 3x + 2 = 0$$
$$(x - 2)(x - 1) = 0$$
$$x = 2 \quad \text{or} \quad x = 1$$

Let $x = 2$ and then let $x = 1$ in the equation $y = x - 1$ to find corresponding y-values.

Let $x = 2$.   Let $x = 1$.
$$y = x - 1 \qquad\qquad y = x - 1$$
$$y = 2 - 1 = 1 \qquad\qquad y = 1 - 1 = 0$$

The solutions are $(2, 1)$ and $(1, 0)$ or the solution set is $\{(2, 1), (1, 0)\}$. Check both solutions in both equations. Both solutions satisfy both equations, so both are solutions of the system. The graph of each equation in the system is shown next. Intersections of the graphs are at $(2, 1)$ and $(1, 0)$.

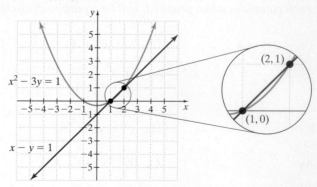

PRACTICE
1   Solve the system $\begin{cases} x^2 - 4y = 4 \\ x + y = -1 \end{cases}$.

EXAMPLE 2   Solve the system

$$\begin{cases} y = \sqrt{x} \\ x^2 + y^2 = 6 \end{cases}$$

Solution   This system is ideal for substitution since y is expressed in terms of x in the first equation. Notice that if $y = \sqrt{x}$, then both x and y must be nonnegative if they are real numbers. Substitute $\sqrt{x}$ for y in the second equation, and solve for x.

$$x^2 + y^2 = 6$$
$$x^2 + \left(\sqrt{x}\right)^2 = 6 \quad \text{Let } y = \sqrt{x}$$
$$x^2 + x = 6$$
$$x^2 + x - 6 = 0$$
$$(x + 3)(x - 2) = 0$$
$$x = -3 \quad \text{or} \quad x = 2$$

The solution -3 is discarded because we have noted that x must be nonnegative. To see this, let $x = -3$ in the first equation. Then let $x = 2$ in the first equation to find a corresponding y-value.

Let $x = -3$.

$$y = \sqrt{x}$$
$$y = \sqrt{-3} \quad \text{Not a real number}$$

Let $x = 2$.

$$y = \sqrt{x}$$
$$y = \sqrt{2}$$

Since we are interested only in real number solutions, the only solution is $\left(2, \sqrt{2}\right)$. Check to see that this solution satisfies both equations. The graph of each equation in the system is shown next.

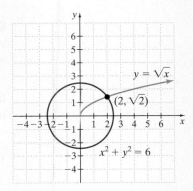

PRACTICE
2   Solve the system $\begin{cases} y = -\sqrt{x} \\ x^2 + y^2 = 20 \end{cases}$.

EXAMPLE 3   Solve the system

$$\begin{cases} x^2 + y^2 = 4 \\ x + y = 3 \end{cases}$$

Solution   We use the substitution method and solve the second equation for x.

$$x + y = 3 \qquad \text{Second equation}$$
$$x = 3 - y$$

Now we let $x = 3 - y$ in the first equation.

$$x^2 + y^2 = 4 \quad \text{First equation}$$

$$(3 - y)^2 + y^2 = 4 \quad \text{Let } x = 3 - y.$$
$$9 - 6y + y^2 + y^2 = 4$$
$$2y^2 - 6y + 5 = 0$$

By the quadratic formula, where $a = 2$, $b = -6$, and $c = 5$, we have

$$y = \frac{6 \pm \sqrt{(-6)^2 - 4 \cdot 2 \cdot 5}}{2 \cdot 2} = \frac{6 \pm \sqrt{-4}}{4}$$

Since $\sqrt{-4}$ is not a real number, there is no real solution, or $\varnothing$. Graphically, the circle and the line do not intersect, as shown below.

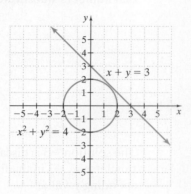

PRACTICE 3 Solve the system $\begin{cases} x^2 + y^2 = 9 \\ x - y = 5 \end{cases}$.

Concept Check ☑

Without solving, how can you tell that $x^2 + y^2 = 9$ and $x^2 + y^2 = 16$ do not have any points of intersection?

OBJECTIVE 2 ▶ Solving nonlinear systems by elimination. Some nonlinear systems may be solved by the elimination method.

EXAMPLE 4 Solve the system

$$\begin{cases} x^2 + 2y^2 = 10 \\ x^2 - y^2 = 1 \end{cases}$$

Solution We will use the elimination, or addition, method to solve this system. To eliminate x^2 when we add the two equations, multiply both sides of the second equation by -1. Then

$$\begin{cases} x^2 + 2y^2 = 10 \\ (-1)(x^2 - y^2) = -1 \cdot 1 \end{cases} \text{ is equivalent to } \begin{cases} x^2 + 2y^2 = 10 \\ -x^2 + y^2 = -1 \end{cases}$$

$$3y^2 = 9 \qquad \text{Add.}$$
$$y^2 = 3 \qquad \text{Divide both sides by 3.}$$
$$y = \pm\sqrt{3}$$

To find the corresponding x-values, we let $y = \sqrt{3}$ and $y = -\sqrt{3}$ in either original equation. We choose the second equation.

Let $y = \sqrt{3}$.

$$x^2 - y^2 = 1$$
$$x^2 - \left(\sqrt{3}\right)^2 = 1$$
$$x^2 - 3 = 1$$
$$x^2 = 4$$
$$x = \pm\sqrt{4} = \pm 2$$

Let $y = -\sqrt{3}$.

$$x^2 - y^2 = 1$$
$$x^2 - \left(-\sqrt{3}\right)^2 = 1$$
$$x^2 - 3 = 1$$
$$x^2 = 4$$
$$x = \pm\sqrt{4} = \pm 2$$

Answer to Concept Check:
$x^2 + y^2 = 9$ is a circle inside the circle $x^2 + y^2 = 16$, therefore they do not have any points of intersection.

The solutions are $\left(2, \sqrt{3}\right)$, $\left(-2, \sqrt{3}\right)$, $\left(2, -\sqrt{3}\right)$, and $\left(-2, -\sqrt{3}\right)$. Check all four ordered pairs in both equations of the system. The graph of each equation in this system is shown.

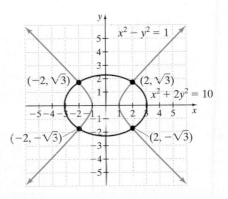

PRACTICE
4   Solve the system $\begin{cases} x^2 + 4y^2 = 16 \\ x^2 - y^2 = 1 \end{cases}$.

10.3 EXERCISE SET

MIXED PRACTICE

Solve each nonlinear system of equations for real solutions. See Examples 1 through 4.

1. $\begin{cases} x^2 + y^2 = 25 \\ 4x + 3y = 0 \end{cases}$

2. $\begin{cases} x^2 + y^2 = 25 \\ 3x + 4y = 0 \end{cases}$

3. $\begin{cases} x^2 + 4y^2 = 10 \\ y = x \end{cases}$

4. $\begin{cases} 4x^2 + y^2 = 10 \\ y = x \end{cases}$

5. $\begin{cases} y^2 = 4 - x \\ x - 2y = 4 \end{cases}$

6. $\begin{cases} x^2 + y^2 = 4 \\ x + y = -2 \end{cases}$

7. $\begin{cases} x^2 + y^2 = 9 \\ 16x^2 - 4y^2 = 64 \end{cases}$

8. $\begin{cases} 4x^2 + 3y^2 = 35 \\ 5x^2 + 2y^2 = 42 \end{cases}$

9. $\begin{cases} x^2 + 2y^2 = 2 \\ x - y = 2 \end{cases}$

10. $\begin{cases} x^2 + 2y^2 = 2 \\ x^2 - 2y^2 = 6 \end{cases}$

11. $\begin{cases} y = x^2 - 3 \\ 4x - y = 6 \end{cases}$

12. $\begin{cases} y = x + 1 \\ x^2 - y^2 = 1 \end{cases}$

13. $\begin{cases} y = x^2 \\ 3x + y = 10 \end{cases}$

14. $\begin{cases} 6x - y = 5 \\ xy = 1 \end{cases}$

15. $\begin{cases} y = 2x^2 + 1 \\ x + y = -1 \end{cases}$

16. $\begin{cases} x^2 + y^2 = 9 \\ x + y = 5 \end{cases}$

17. $\begin{cases} y = x^2 - 4 \\ y = x^2 - 4x \end{cases}$

18. $\begin{cases} x = y^2 - 3 \\ x = y^2 - 3y \end{cases}$

19. $\begin{cases} 2x^2 + 3y^2 = 14 \\ -x^2 + y^2 = 3 \end{cases}$

20. $\begin{cases} 4x^2 - 2y^2 = 2 \\ -x^2 + y^2 = 2 \end{cases}$

21. $\begin{cases} x^2 + y^2 = 1 \\ x^2 + (y + 3)^2 = 4 \end{cases}$

22. $\begin{cases} x^2 + 2y^2 = 4 \\ x^2 - y^2 = 4 \end{cases}$

23. $\begin{cases} y = x^2 + 2 \\ y = -x^2 + 4 \end{cases}$

24. $\begin{cases} x = -y^2 - 3 \\ x = y^2 - 5 \end{cases}$

25. $\begin{cases} 3x^2 + y^2 = 9 \\ 3x^2 - y^2 = 9 \end{cases}$

26. $\begin{cases} x^2 + y^2 = 25 \\ x = y^2 - 5 \end{cases}$

27. $\begin{cases} x^2 + 3y^2 = 6 \\ x^2 - 3y^2 = 10 \end{cases}$

28. $\begin{cases} x^2 + y^2 = 1 \\ y = x^2 - 9 \end{cases}$

29. $\begin{cases} x^2 + y^2 = 36 \\ y = \dfrac{1}{6}x^2 - 6 \end{cases}$

30. $\begin{cases} x^2 + y^2 = 16 \\ y = -\dfrac{1}{4}x^2 + 4 \end{cases}$

REVIEW AND PREVIEW

Graph each inequality in two variables. See Section 3.7.

31. $x > -3$

32. $y \le 1$

33. $y < 2x - 1$

34. $3x - y \le 4$

Find the perimeter of each geometric figure. See Section 5.3.

△ **35.**

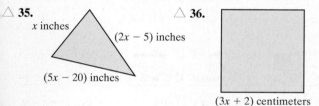

x inches

$(2x - 5)$ inches

$(5x - 20)$ inches

△ **36.**

$(3x + 2)$ centimeters

△ **37.** $(x^2 + 3x + 1)$ meters

x^2 meters

△ **38.**

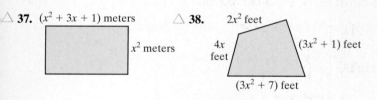

$2x^2$ feet

$4x$ feet

$(3x^2 + 1)$ feet

$(3x^2 + 7)$ feet

CONCEPT EXTENSIONS

For the exercises below, see the Concept Check in this section.

39. Without graphing, how can you tell that the graph of $x^2 + y^2 = 1$ and $x^2 + y^2 = 4$ do not have any points of intersection?

40. Without solving, how can you tell that the graphs of $y = 2x + 3$ and $y = 2x + 7$ do not have any points of intersection?

41. How many real solutions are possible for a system of equations whose graphs are a circle and a parabola? Draw diagrams to illustrate each possibility.

42. How many real solutions are possible for a system of equations whose graphs are an ellipse and a line? Draw diagrams to illustrate each possibility.

Solve.

43. The sum of the squares of two numbers is 130. The difference of the squares of the two numbers is 32. Find the two numbers.

44. The sum of the squares of two numbers is 20. Their product is 8. Find the two numbers.

△ **45.** During the development stage of a new rectangular keypad for a security system, it was decided that the area of the rectangle should be 285 square centimeters and the perimeter should be 68 centimeters. Find the dimensions of the keypad.

△ **46.** A rectangular holding pen for cattle is to be designed so that its perimeter is 92 feet and its area is 525 feet. Find the dimensions of the holding pen.

*Recall that in business, a demand function expresses the quantity of a commodity demanded as a function of the commodity's unit price. A supply function expresses the quantity of a commodity supplied as a function of the commodity's unit price. When the quantity produced and supplied is equal to the quantity demanded, then we have what is called **market equilibrium.***

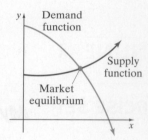

47. The demand function for a certain compact disc is given by the function

$$p = -0.01x^2 - 0.2x + 9$$

and the corresponding supply function is given by

$$p = 0.01x^2 - 0.1x + 3$$

where p is in dollars and x is in thousands of units. Find the equilibrium quantity and the corresponding price by solving the system consisting of the two given equations.

48. The demand function for a certain style of picture frame is given by the function

$$p = -2x^2 + 90$$

and the corresponding supply function is given by

$$p = 9x + 34$$

where p is in dollars and x is in thousands of units. Find the equilibrium quantity and the corresponding price by solving the system consisting of the two given equations.

🖩 *Use a graphing calculator to verify the results of each exercise.*

49. Exercise 3.

50. Exercise 4.

51. Exercise 23.

52. Exercise 24.

STUDY SKILLS BUILDER

Are You Prepared for Your Final Exam?

To prepare for your final exam, try the following study techniques:

- Review the material that you will be responsible for on your exam. This includes material from your textbook, your notebook, and any handouts from your instructor.
- Review any formulas that you may need to memorize.
- Check to see if your instructor or mathematics department will be conducting a final exam review.
- Check with your instructor to see whether final exams from previous semesters/quarters are available to students for review.

- Use your previously taken exams as a practice final exam. To do so, rewrite the test questions in mixed order on blank sheets of paper. This will help you prepare for exam conditions.
- If you are unsure of a few concepts, see your instructor or visit a learning lab for assistance. Also, view the video segment of any troublesome sections.
- If you need further exercises to work, try the Cumulative Reviews at the end of the chapters.

Once again, good luck! I hope you have enjoyed this textbook and your mathematics course.

10.4 NONLINEAR INEQUALITIES AND SYSTEMS OF INEQUALITIES

OBJECTIVES

1 Graph a nonlinear inequality.

2 Graph a system of nonlinear inequalities.

OBJECTIVE 1 ▶ Graphing nonlinear inequalities. We can graph a nonlinear inequality in two variables such as $\frac{x^2}{9} + \frac{y^2}{16} \le 1$ in a way similar to the way we graphed a linear inequality in two variables in Section 3.6. First, we graph the related equation $\frac{x^2}{9} + \frac{y^2}{16} = 1$. The graph of the equation is our boundary. Then, using test points, we determine and shade the region whose points satisfy the inequality.

EXAMPLE 1   Graph $\frac{x^2}{9} + \frac{y^2}{16} \le 1$.

Solution   First, graph the equation $\frac{x^2}{9} + \frac{y^2}{16} = 1$. Sketch a solid curve since the graph of $\frac{x^2}{9} + \frac{y^2}{16} \le 1$ includes the graph of $\frac{x^2}{9} + \frac{y^2}{16} = 1$. The graph is an ellipse, and it divides the plane into two regions, the "inside" and the "outside" of the ellipse. To determine which region contains the solutions, select a test point in either region and determine whether the coordinates of the point satisfy the inequality. We choose $(0, 0)$ as the test point.

$$\frac{x^2}{9} + \frac{y^2}{16} \le 1$$

$$\frac{0^2}{9} + \frac{0^2}{16} \le 1 \quad \text{Let } x = 0 \text{ and } y = 0.$$

$$0 \le 1 \quad \text{True}$$

Since this statement is true, the solution set is the region containing $(0, 0)$. The graph of the solution set includes the points on and inside the ellipse, as shaded in the figure.

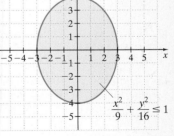

PRACTICE
1   Graph $\frac{x^2}{36} + \frac{y^2}{16} \ge 1$.

EXAMPLE 2   Graph $4y^2 > x^2 + 16$.

Solution   The related equation is $4y^2 = x^2 + 16$. Subtract x^2 from both sides and divide both sides by 16, and we have $\dfrac{y^2}{4} - \dfrac{x^2}{16} = 1$, which is a hyperbola. Graph the hyperbola as a dashed curve since the graph of $4y^2 > x^2 + 16$ does *not* include the graph of $4y^2 = x^2 + 16$. The hyperbola divides the plane into three regions. Select a test point in each region—not on a boundary line—to determine whether that region contains solutions of the inequality.

Test Region A with $(0, 4)$	*Test Region B with* $(0, 0)$	*Test Region C with* $(0, -4)$
$4y^2 > x^2 + 16$	$4y^2 > x^2 + 16$	$4y^2 > x^2 + 16$
$4(4)^2 > 0^2 + 16$	$4(0)^2 > 0^2 + 16$	$4(-4)^2 > 0^2 + 16$
$64 > 16$ True	$0 > 16$ False	$64 > 16$ True

The graph of the solution set includes the shaded regions A and C only, not the boundary.

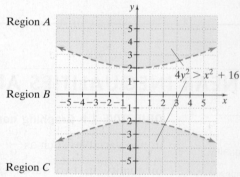

PRACTICE
2   Graph $16y^2 > 9x^2 + 144$.

OBJECTIVE 2 ▶ Graphing systems of nonlinear inequalities. In Section 3.6 we graphed systems of linear inequalities. Recall that the graph of a system of inequalities is the intersection of the graphs of the inequalities.

EXAMPLE 3   Graph the system
$$\begin{cases} x \le 1 - 2y \\ y \le x^2 \end{cases}$$

Solution   We graph each inequality on the same set of axes. The intersection is shown in the third graph on the following page. It is the darkest shaded (appears purple) region along with its boundary lines. The coordinates of the points of intersection can be found by solving the related system.
$$\begin{cases} x = 1 - 2y \\ y = x^2 \end{cases}$$

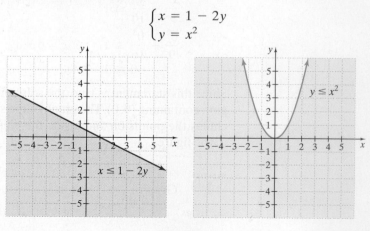

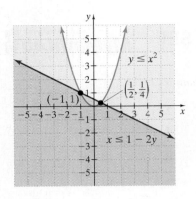

PRACTICE
3   Graph the system $\begin{cases} y \geq x^2 \\ y \leq -3x + 2 \end{cases}$

EXAMPLE 4   Graph the system

$$\begin{cases} x^2 + y^2 < 25 \\ \dfrac{x^2}{9} - \dfrac{y^2}{25} < 1 \\ \qquad\quad y < x - 3 \end{cases}$$

Solution   We graph each inequality. The graph of $x^2 + y^2 < 25$ contains points "inside" the circle that has center $(0, 0)$ and radius 5. The graph of $\dfrac{x^2}{9} - \dfrac{y^2}{25} < 1$ is the region between the two branches of the hyperbola with x-intercepts -3 and 3 and center $(0, 0)$. The graph of $y < x + 3$ is the region "below" the line with slope 1 and y-intercept $(0, 3)$. The graph of the solution set of the system is the intersection of all the graphs, the darkest shaded region shown. The boundary of this region is not part of the solution.

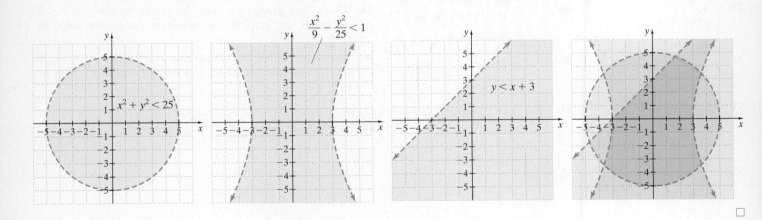

PRACTICE
4   Graph the system $\begin{cases} x^2 + y^2 < 16 \\ \dfrac{x^2}{4} - \dfrac{y^2}{9} < 1 \\ y < x + 3 \end{cases}$

10.4 | EXERCISE SET

PRACTICE   WATCH   DOWNLOAD   READ   REVIEW

Graph each inequality. See Examples 1 and 2.

1. $y < x^2$

2. $y < -x^2$

3. $x^2 + y^2 \geq 16$

4. $x^2 + y^2 < 36$

5. $\dfrac{x^2}{4} - y^2 < 1$

6. $x^2 - \dfrac{y^2}{9} \geq 1$

7. $y > (x - 1)^2 - 3$

8. $y > (x + 3)^2 + 2$

9. $x^2 + y^2 \leq 9$

10. $x^2 + y^2 > 4$

11. $y > -x^2 + 5$

12. $y < -x^2 + 5$

13. $\dfrac{x^2}{4} + \dfrac{y^2}{9} \leq 1$

14. $\dfrac{x^2}{25} + \dfrac{y^2}{4} \geq 1$

15. $\dfrac{y^2}{4} - x^2 \leq 1$

16. $\dfrac{y^2}{16} - \dfrac{x^2}{9} > 1$

17. $y < (x - 2)^2 + 1$

18. $y > (x - 2)^2 + 1$

19. $y \leq x^2 + x - 2$

20. $y > x^2 + x - 2$

Graph each system. See Examples 3 and 4.

21. $\begin{cases} 4x + 3y \geq 12 \\ x^2 + y^2 < 16 \end{cases}$

22. $\begin{cases} 3x - 4y \leq 12 \\ x^2 + y^2 < 16 \end{cases}$

23. $\begin{cases} x^2 + y^2 \leq 9 \\ x^2 + y^2 \geq 1 \end{cases}$

24. $\begin{cases} x^2 + y^2 \geq 9 \\ x^2 + y^2 \geq 16 \end{cases}$

25. $\begin{cases} y > x^2 \\ y \geq 2x + 1 \end{cases}$

26. $\begin{cases} y \leq -x^2 + 3 \\ y \leq 2x - 1 \end{cases}$

27. $\begin{cases} x^2 + y^2 > 9 \\ \quad y > x^2 \end{cases}$

28. $\begin{cases} x^2 + y^2 \leq 9 \\ \quad y < x^2 \end{cases}$

29. $\begin{cases} \dfrac{x^2}{4} + \dfrac{y^2}{9} \geq 1 \\ x^2 + y^2 \geq 4 \end{cases}$

30. $\begin{cases} x^2 + (y - 2)^2 \geq 9 \\ \dfrac{x^2}{4} + \dfrac{y^2}{25} < 1 \end{cases}$

31. $\begin{cases} x^2 - y^2 \geq 1 \\ \quad y \geq 0 \end{cases}$

32. $\begin{cases} x^2 - y^2 \geq 1 \\ \quad x \geq 0 \end{cases}$

33. $\begin{cases} x + y \geq 1 \\ 2x + 3y < 1 \\ \quad x > -3 \end{cases}$

34. $\begin{cases} x - y < -1 \\ 4x - 3y > 0 \\ \quad y > 0 \end{cases}$

35. $\begin{cases} x^2 - y^2 < 1 \\ \dfrac{x^2}{16} + y^2 \leq 1 \\ \quad x \geq -2 \end{cases}$

36. $\begin{cases} x^2 - y^2 \geq 1 \\ \dfrac{x^2}{16} + \dfrac{y^2}{4} \leq 1 \\ \quad y \geq 1 \end{cases}$

REVIEW AND PREVIEW

Determine which graph is the graph of a function. See Section 3.2.

37.

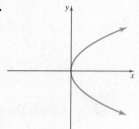

38.

39.

40.

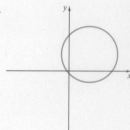

Find each function value if $f(x) = 3x^2 - 2$. See Section 3.2.

41. $f(-1)$

42. $f(-3)$

43. $f(a)$

44. $f(b)$

CONCEPT EXTENSIONS

45. Discuss how graphing a linear inequality such as $x + y < 9$ is similar to graphing a nonlinear inequality such as $x^2 + y^2 < 9$.

46. Discuss how graphing a linear inequality such as $x + y < 9$ is different from graphing a nonlinear inequality such as $x^2 + y^2 < 9$.

47. Graph the system $\begin{cases} y \leq x^2 \\ y \geq x + 2 \\ x \geq 0 \\ y \geq 0 \end{cases}$.

CHAPTER 10 GROUP ACTIVITY

Modeling Conic Sections

In this project, you will have the opportunity to construct and investigate a model of an ellipse. You will need two thumbtacks or nails, graph paper, cardboard, tape, string, a pencil, and a ruler. This project may be completed by working in groups or individually.

Follow these steps, answering any questions as you go.

1. Draw an x-axis and a y-axis on the graph paper as shown in Figure 1.

2. Place the graph paper on the cardboard and attach it with tape.

3. Locate two points on the *x*-axis, each about $1\frac{1}{2}$ inches from the origin and on opposite sides of the origin (see Figure 1). Insert thumbtacks (or nails) at each of these locations.

4. Fasten a 9-inch piece of string to the thumbtacks as shown in Figure 2. Use your pencil to draw and keep the string taut while you carefully move the pencil in a path all around the thumbtacks.

5. Using the grid of the graph paper as a guide, find an approximate equation of the ellipse you drew.

6. Experiment by moving the tacks closer together or farther apart and drawing new ellipses. What do you observe?

7. Write a paragraph explaining why the figure drawn by the pencil is an ellipse. How might you use the same materials to draw a circle?

8. (Optional) Choose one of the ellipses you drew with the string and pencil. Use a ruler to draw any six tangent lines to the ellipse. (A line is tangent to the ellipse if it intersects, or just touches, the ellipse at only one point. See Figure 3.) Extend the tangent lines to yield six points of intersection among the tangents. Use a straightedge to draw a line connecting each pair of opposite points of intersection. What do you observe? Repeat with a different ellipse. Can you make a conjecture about the relationship among the lines that connect opposite points of intersection?

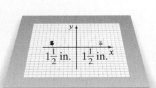

Figure 1

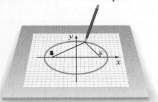

Figure 2

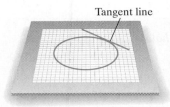
Tangent line

Figure 3

 STUDY SKILLS BUILDER

Are You Prepared for a Test on Chapter 10?

Below I have listed some common trouble areas for students in Chapter 10. After studying for your test—but before taking your test—read these.

- Don't forget to review all the standard forms for the conic sections.

- Don't forget that both methods, substitution and elimination, are available for solving nonlinear systems of equations.

$$\begin{cases} x^2 + y^2 = 7 \\ 2x^2 - 3y^2 = 4 \end{cases} \text{ is equivalent to}$$

$$\begin{cases} 3x^2 + 3y^2 = 21 \\ 2x^2 - 3y^2 = 4 \end{cases}$$
$$\underline{5x^2 = 25}$$
$$x^2 = 5$$
$$x = \pm\sqrt{5}$$

Let $x = \pm\sqrt{5}$ in either original equation, and $y = \pm\sqrt{2}$, the solution set is $\{(\sqrt{5}, \sqrt{2}), (-\sqrt{5}, \sqrt{2}), (\sqrt{5}, -\sqrt{2}), (-\sqrt{5}, -\sqrt{2})\}$.

Remember: This is simply a checklist of common trouble areas. For a review of Chapter 10, see the Highlights and Chapter Review at the end of this chapter.

CHAPTER 10 VOCABULARY CHECK

Fill in each blank with one of the words or phrases listed below.

circle   radius   center

ellipse   hyperbola   nonlinear system of equations

1. A(n) _____ is the set of all points in a plane that are the same distance from a fixed point, called the _____ .

2. A _____ is a system of equations at least one of which is not linear.

3. A(n) _____ is the set of points on a plane such that the sum of the distances of those points from two fixed points is a constant.

4. In a circle, the distance from the center to a point of the circle is called its _____ .

5. A(n) _____ is the set of points in a plane such that the absolute value of the difference of the distance from two fixed points is constant.

▶ **Helpful Hint**

Are you preparing for your test? Don't forget to take the Chapter 10 Test on page 633. Then check your answers at the back of the text and use the Chapter Test Prep Video CD to see the fully worked-out solutions to any of the exercises you want to review.

CHAPTER 10 HIGHLIGHTS

DEFINITIONS AND CONCEPTS	EXAMPLES

SECTION 10.1   THE PARABOLA AND THE CIRCLE

Parabolas

$$y = a(x - h)^2 + k$$

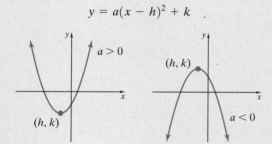

$$x = a(y - k)^2 + h$$

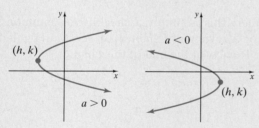

Graph

$$x = 3y^2 - 12y + 13.$$

$$x - 13 = 3y^2 - 12y$$

$$x - 13 + 3(4) = 3(y^2 - 4y + 4) \quad \text{Add } 3(4) \text{ to}$$

$$x = 3(y - 2)^2 + 1 \quad \text{both sides.}$$

Since $a = 3$, this parabola opens to the right with vertex $(1, 2)$. Its axis of symmetry is $y = 2$. The x-intercept is $(13, 0)$.

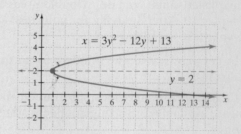

Circle

The graph of $(x - h)^2 + (y - k)^2 = r^2$ is a circle with center (h, k) and radius r.

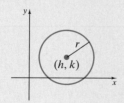

Graph $x^2 + (y + 3)^2 = 5$.

This equation can be written as

$$(x - 0)^2 + (y + 3)^2 = 5 \text{ with } h = 0,$$
$$k = -3, \text{ and } r = \sqrt{5}.$$

The center of this circle is $(0, -3)$, and the radius is $\sqrt{5}$.

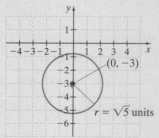

DEFINITIONS AND CONCEPTS	EXAMPLES

Ellipse with Center $(0, 0)$

The graph of an equation of the form $\dfrac{x^2}{a^2} + \dfrac{y^2}{b^2} = 1$ is an ellipse with center $(0, 0)$. The x-intercepts are $(a, 0)$ and $(-a, 0)$, and the y-intercepts are $(0, b)$ and $(0, -b)$.

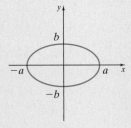

Graph $4x^2 + 9y^2 = 36$.

$$\dfrac{x^2}{9} + \dfrac{y^2}{4} = 1 \quad \text{Divide by 36.}$$

$$\dfrac{x^2}{3^2} + \dfrac{y^2}{2^2} = 1$$

The ellipse has center $(0, 0)$, x-intercepts $(3, 0)$ and $(-3, 0)$, and y-intercepts $(0, 2)$ and $(0, -2)$.

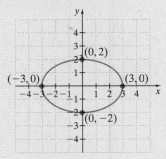

Hyperbola with Center $(0, 0)$

The graph of an equation of the form $\dfrac{x^2}{a^2} - \dfrac{y^2}{b^2} = 1$ is a hyperbola with center $(0, 0)$ and x-intercepts $(a, 0)$ and $(-a, 0)$.

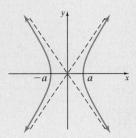

Graph $\dfrac{x^2}{9} - \dfrac{y^2}{4} = 1$. Here $a = 3$ and $b = 2$.

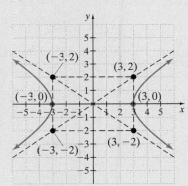

The graph of an equation of the form $\dfrac{y^2}{b^2} - \dfrac{x^2}{a^2} = 1$ is a hyperbola with center $(0, 0)$ and y-intercepts $(0, b)$ and $(0, -b)$.

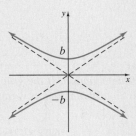

| **DEFINITIONS AND CONCEPTS** | **EXAMPLES** |

SECTION 10.3   SOLVING NONLINEAR SYSTEMS OF EQUATIONS

A **nonlinear system of equations** is a system of equations at least one of which is not linear. Both the substitution method and the elimination method may be used to solve a nonlinear system of equations.

Solve the nonlinear system $\begin{cases} y = x + 2 \\ 2x^2 + y^2 = 3 \end{cases}$.

Substitute $x + 2$ for y in the second equation.

$$2x^2 + y^2 = 3$$
$$2x^2 + (x + 2)^2 = 3$$
$$2x^2 + x^2 + 4x + 4 = 3$$
$$3x^2 + 4x + 1 = 0$$
$$(3x + 1)(x + 1) = 0$$
$$x = -\frac{1}{3}, x = -1$$

If $x = -\frac{1}{3}$, $y = x + 2 = -\frac{1}{3} + 2 = \frac{5}{3}$.

If $x = -1$, $y = x + 2 = -1 + 2 = 1$.

The solutions are $\left(-\frac{1}{3}, \frac{5}{3}\right)$ and $(-1, 1)$.

SECTION 10.4   NONLINEAR INEQUALITIES AND SYSTEMS OF INEQUALITIES

The graph of a system of inequalities is the intersection of the graphs of the inequalities.

Graph the system $\begin{cases} x \geq y^2 \\ x + y \leq 4 \end{cases}$.

The graph of the system is the pink shaded region along with its boundary lines.

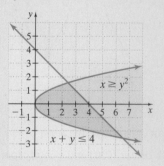

CHAPTER 10 REVIEW

(10.1) *Write an equation of the circle with the given center and radius.*

1. center $(-4, 4)$ radius 3

2. center $(5, 0)$, radius 5

3. center $(-7, -9)$, radius $\sqrt{11}$

4. center $(0, 0)$, radius $\frac{7}{2}$

Sketch the graph of the equation. If the graph is a circle, find its center. If the graph is a parabola, find its vertex.

5. $x^2 + y^2 = 7$

6. $x = 2(y - 5)^2 + 4$

7. $x = -(y + 2)^2 + 3$

8. $(x - 1)^2 + (y - 2)^2 = 4$

9. $y = -x^2 + 4x + 10$

10. $x = -y^2 - 4y + 6$

11. $x = \frac{1}{2}y^2 + 2y + 1$

12. $y = -3x^2 + \frac{1}{2}x + 4$

13. $x^2 + y^2 + 2x + y = \dfrac{3}{4}$ **14.** $x^2 + y^2 - 3y = \dfrac{7}{4}$

15. $4x^2 + 4y^2 + 16x + 8y = 1$

(10.2) Sketch the graph of each equation.

16. $x^2 + \dfrac{y^2}{4} = 1$ **17.** $x^2 - \dfrac{y^2}{4} = 1$

18. $\dfrac{x^2}{5} + \dfrac{y^2}{5} = 1$ **19.** $\dfrac{x^2}{5} - \dfrac{y^2}{5} = 1$

20. $-5x^2 + 25y^2 = 125$ **21.** $4y^2 + 9x^2 = 36$

22. $x^2 - y^2 = 1$ **23.** $\dfrac{(x+3)^2}{9} + \dfrac{(y-4)^2}{25} = 1$

24. $y^2 = x^2 + 9$ **25.** $x^2 = 4y^2 - 16$

26. $100 - 25x^2 = 4y^2$

(10.3) Solve each system of equations.

27. $\begin{cases} y = 2x - 4 \\ y^2 = 4x \end{cases}$

28. $\begin{cases} x^2 + y^2 = 4 \\ x - y = 4 \end{cases}$

29. $\begin{cases} y = x + 2 \\ y = x^2 \end{cases}$

30. $\begin{cases} x^2 + 4y^2 = 16 \\ x^2 + y^2 = 4 \end{cases}$

31. $\begin{cases} 4x - y^2 = 0 \\ 2x^2 + y^2 = 16 \end{cases}$

32. $\begin{cases} x^2 + 2y = 9 \\ 5x - 2y = 5 \end{cases}$

33. $\begin{cases} y = 3x^2 + 5x - 4 \\ y = 3x^2 - x + 2 \end{cases}$

34. $\begin{cases} x^2 - 3y^2 = 1 \\ 4x^2 + 5y^2 = 21 \end{cases}$

△ **35.** Find the length and the width of a room whose area is 150 square feet and whose perimeter is 50 feet.

36. What is the greatest number of real solutions possible for a system of two equations whose graphs are an ellipse and a hyperbola?

(10.4) Graph the inequality or system of inequalities.

37. $y \le -x^2 + 3$ **38.** $x^2 + y^2 < 9$

39. $\begin{cases} 2x \le 4 \\ x + y \ge 1 \end{cases}$ **40.** $\dfrac{x^2}{4} + \dfrac{y^2}{9} \ge 1$

41. $\begin{cases} x^2 + y^2 < 4 \\ x^2 - y^2 \le 1 \end{cases}$ **42.** $\begin{cases} x^2 + y^2 \le 16 \\ x^2 + y^2 \ge 4 \end{cases}$

MIXED REVIEW

43. Write an equation of the circle with center $(-7, 8)$ and radius 5.

Graph each equation.

44. $3x^2 + 6x + 3y^2 = 9$ **45.** $y = x^2 + 6x + 9$

46. $x = y^2 + 6y + 9$ **47.** $\dfrac{y^2}{4} - \dfrac{x^2}{16} = 1$

48. $\dfrac{y^2}{4} + \dfrac{x^2}{16} = 1$ **49.** $\dfrac{(x-2)^2}{4} + (y-1)^2 = 1$

50. $y^2 = x^2 + 6$ **51.** $y^2 + x^2 = 4x + 6$

52. $x^2 + y^2 - 8y = 0$ **53.** $6(x-2)^2 + 9(y+5)^2 = 36$

54. $\dfrac{x^2}{16} - \dfrac{y^2}{25} = 1$

Solve each system of equations.

55. $\begin{cases} y = x^2 - 5x + 1 \\ y = -x + 6 \end{cases}$

56. $\begin{cases} x^2 + y^2 = 10 \\ 9x^2 + y^2 = 18 \end{cases}$

Graph each inequality or system of inequalities.

57. $x^2 - y^2 < 1$ **58.** $\begin{cases} y > x^2 \\ x + y \ge 3 \end{cases}$

CHAPTER 10 TEST TEST PREP VIDEO ⟳ Remember to use the Chapter Test Prep Video CD to see the fully worked-out solutions to any of the exercises you want to review.

Sketch the graph of each equation.

1. $x^2 + y^2 = 36$ **2.** $x^2 - y^2 = 36$

3. $16x^2 + 9y^2 = 144$ **4.** $y = x^2 - 8x + 16$

5. $x^2 + y^2 + 6x = 16$ **6.** $x = y^2 + 8y - 3$

7. $\dfrac{(x-4)^2}{16} + \dfrac{(y-3)^2}{9} = 1$ **8.** $y^2 - x^2 = 1$

Solve each system.

9. $\begin{cases} x^2 + y^2 = 26 \\ x^2 - 2y^2 = 23 \end{cases}$ **10.** $\begin{cases} y = x^2 - 5x + 6 \\ y = 2x \end{cases}$

Graph the solution of each system.

11. $\begin{cases} 2x + 5y \geq 10 \\ y \geq x^2 + 1 \end{cases}$

12. $\begin{cases} \dfrac{x^2}{4} + y^2 \leq 1 \\ x + y > 1 \end{cases}$

13. $\begin{cases} x^2 + y^2 \geq 4 \\ x^2 + y^2 < 16 \\ y \geq 0 \end{cases}$

14. A bridge has an arch in the shape of a half-ellipse. If the equation of the ellipse, measured in feet, is $100x^2 + 225y^2 = 22{,}500$, find the height of the arch from the road and the width of the arch.

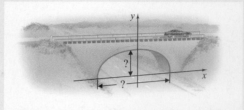

CHAPTER 10 CUMULATIVE REVIEW

1. Use the associative property of multiplication to write an expression equivalent to $4 \cdot (9y)$. Then simplify the equivalent expression.

2. Solve $3x + 4 > 1$ and $2x - 5 \leq 9$. Write the solution in interval notation.

3. Graph $x = -2y$ by plotting intercepts.

4. Find the slope of the line that goes through $(3, 2)$ and $(1, -4)$.

5. Use the elimination method to solve the system:
$$\begin{cases} 3x + \dfrac{y}{2} = 2 \\ 6x + y = 5 \end{cases}$$

6. Two planes leave Greensboro, one traveling north and the other south. After 2 hours they are 650 miles apart. If one plane is flying 25 mph faster than the other, what is the speed of each?

7. Use the power rules to simplify the following. Use positive exponents to write all results.

a. $(5x^2)^3$

b. $\left(\dfrac{2}{3}\right)^3$

c. $\left(\dfrac{3p^4}{q^5}\right)^2$

d. $\left(\dfrac{2^{-3}}{y}\right)^{-2}$

e. $(x^{-5}y^2z^{-1})^7$

8. Use the quotient rule to simplify.

a. $\dfrac{4^8}{4^3}$

b. $\dfrac{y^{11}}{y^5}$

c. $\dfrac{32x^7}{4x^6}$

d. $\dfrac{18a^{12}b^6}{12a^8b^6}$

9. Solve $2x^2 = \dfrac{17}{3}x + 1$.

10. Factor.

a. $3y^2 + 14y + 15$

b. $20a^5 + 54a^4 + 10a^3$

c. $(y - 3)^2 - 2(y - 3) - 8$

11. Perform each indicated operation. $\dfrac{7}{x - 1} + \dfrac{10x}{x^2 - 1} - \dfrac{5}{x + 1}$

12. Perform the indicated operation and simplify if possible.
$$\dfrac{2}{3a - 15} - \dfrac{a}{25 - a^2}$$

13. Simplify each complex fraction.

a. $\dfrac{\frac{2x}{27y^2}}{\frac{6x^2}{9}}$

b. $\dfrac{\frac{5x}{x + 2}}{\frac{10}{x - 2}}$

c. $\dfrac{\frac{x}{y^2} + \frac{1}{y}}{\frac{y}{x^2} + \frac{1}{x}}$

14. Simplify each complex fraction.

a. $(a^{-1} - b^{-1})^{-1}$

b. $\dfrac{2 - \frac{1}{x}}{4x - \frac{1}{x}}$

15. Divide $2x^2 - x - 10$ by $x + 2$.

16. Solve $\dfrac{2}{x + 3} = \dfrac{1}{x^2 - 9} - \dfrac{1}{x - 3}$

17. Use the remainder theorem and synthetic division to find $P(4)$ if
$$P(x) = 4x^6 - 25x^5 + 35x^4 + 17x^2.$$

18. Suppose that y varies inversely as x. If $y = 3$ when $x = \dfrac{2}{3}$, find the constant of variation and the direct variation equation.

19. Solve: $\dfrac{2x}{x - 3} + \dfrac{6 - 2x}{x^2 - 9} = \dfrac{x}{x + 3}$.

20. Simplify the following expressions. Assume that all variables represent nonnegative real numbers.

a. $\sqrt[5]{-32}$

b. $\sqrt[4]{625}$

c. $-\sqrt{36}$

d. $-\sqrt[3]{-27x^3}$

e. $\sqrt{144y^2}$

21. Melissa Scarlatti can clean the house in 4 hours, whereas her husband, Zack, can do the same job in 5 hours. They have agreed to clean together so that they can finish in time to watch a movie on TV that starts in 2 hours. How long will it take them to clean the house together? Can they finish before the movie starts?

22. Use the quotient rule to simplify.

  a. $\dfrac{\sqrt{32}}{\sqrt{4}}$ **b.** $\dfrac{\sqrt[3]{240y^2}}{5\sqrt[3]{3y^{-4}}}$

  c. $\dfrac{\sqrt[5]{64x^9y^2}}{\sqrt[5]{2x^2y^{-8}}}$

23. Find the cube roots.

  a. $\sqrt[3]{1}$ **b.** $\sqrt[3]{-64}$

  c. $\sqrt[3]{\dfrac{8}{125}}$ **d.** $\sqrt[3]{x^6}$

  e. $\sqrt[3]{-27x^9}$

24. Multiply and simplify if possible.

  a. $\sqrt{5}\left(2 + \sqrt{15}\right)$

  b. $\left(\sqrt{3} - \sqrt{5}\right)\left(\sqrt{7} - 1\right)$

  c. $\left(2\sqrt{5} - 1\right)^2$

  d. $\left(3\sqrt{2} + 5\right)\left(3\sqrt{2} - 5\right)$

25. Multiply.

  a. $z^{2/3}\left(z^{1/3} - z^5\right)$

  b. $(x^{1/3} - 5)(x^{1/3} + 2)$

26. Rationalize the denominator. $\dfrac{-2}{\sqrt{3} + 3}$

27. Use the quotient rule to divide, and simplify if possible.

  a. $\dfrac{\sqrt{20}}{\sqrt{5}}$ **b.** $\dfrac{\sqrt{50x}}{2\sqrt{2}}$

  c. $\dfrac{7\sqrt[3]{48x^4y^8}}{\sqrt[3]{6y^2}}$ **d.** $\dfrac{2\sqrt[4]{32a^8b^6}}{\sqrt[4]{a^{-1}b^2}}$

28. Solve: $\sqrt{2x - 3} = x - 3$.

29. Add or subtract as indicated.

  a. $\dfrac{\sqrt{45}}{4} - \dfrac{\sqrt{5}}{3}$ **b.** $\sqrt[3]{\dfrac{7x}{8}} + 2\sqrt[3]{7x}$

30. Use the discriminant to determine the number and type of solutions for $9x^2 - 6x = -4$.

31. Rationalize the denominator of $\sqrt{\dfrac{7x}{3y}}$.

32. Solve: $\dfrac{4}{x - 2} - \dfrac{x}{x + 2} = \dfrac{16}{x^2 - 4}$.

33. Solve: $\sqrt{2x - 3} = 9$.

34. Solve: $x^3 + 2x^2 - 4x \geq 8$.

35. Find the following powers of i.

  a. i^7 **b.** i^{20}

  c. i^{46} **d.** i^{-12}

36. Graph $f(x) = (x + 2)^2 - 1$

37. Solve $p^2 + 2p = 4$ by completing the square.

38. Find the maximum value of $f(x) = -x^2 - 6x + 4$.

39. Solve: $\dfrac{1}{4}m^2 - m + \dfrac{1}{2} = 0$.

40. Find the inverse of $f(x) = \dfrac{x + 1}{2}$.

41. Solve: $p^4 - 3p^2 - 4 = 0$.

42. If $f(x) = x^2 - 3x + 2$ and $g(x) = -3x + 5$, find

  a. $(f \circ g)(x)$

  b. $(f \circ g)(-2)$

  c. $(g \circ f)(x)$

  d. $(g \circ f)(5)$

43. Solve: $\dfrac{x + 2}{x - 3} \leq 0$.

44. Graph $4x^2 + 9y^2 = 36$.

45. Graph $g(x) = \dfrac{1}{2}(x + 2)^2 + 5$. Find the vertex and the axis of symmetry.

46. Solve each equation for x.

  a. $64^x = 4$

  b. $125^{x-3} = 25$

  c. $\dfrac{1}{81} = 3^{2x}$

47. Find the vertex of the graph of $f(x) = x^2 - 4x - 12$.

48. Graph the system: $\begin{cases} x + 2y < 8 \\ \quad y \geq x^2 \end{cases}$

49. Find the distance between $(2, -5)$ and $(1, -4)$. Give an exact distance and a three-decimal-place approximation.

50. Solve the system $\begin{cases} x^2 + y^2 = 36 \\ \quad y = x + 6 \end{cases}$

CHAPTER

11 Sequences, Series, and the Binomial Theorem

Having explored in some depth the concept of function, we turn now in this final chapter to *sequences*. In one sense, a sequence is simply an ordered list of numbers. In another sense, a sequence is itself a function. Phenomena modeled by such functions are everywhere around us. The starting place for all mathematics is the sequence of natural numbers: 1, 2, 3, 4, and so on.

Sequences lead us to *series,* which are a sum of ordered numbers. Through series we gain new insight, for example about the expansion of a binomial $(a + b)^n$, the concluding topic of this book.

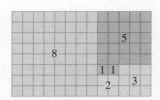

A tiling with squares whose sides are successive Fibonacci numbers in length

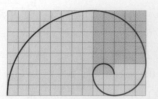

A Fibonacci spiral, created by drawing arcs connecting the opposite corners of squares in the Fibonacci tiling

The Fibonacci Sequence is a special sequence in which the first two terms are 1 and each term thereafter is the sum of the two previous terms:

$$1, 1, 2, 3, 5, 8, 13, 21, \ldots$$

The Fibonacci numbers are named after Leonardo of Pisa, known as Fibonacci, although there is some evidence that these numbers had been described earlier in India.

There are numerous interesting facts about this sequence, and some are shown on the diagrams on this page. In Section 11.1, page 640, Exercise 46, you will have the opportunity to check a formula for this sequence.

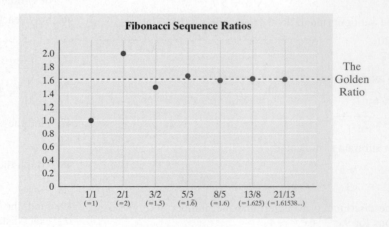

The ratio of successive numbers in the Fibonacci Sequence approaches a number called the golden ratio or golden number, which is approximately 1.618034.

26. Solve each equation.

   a. $\log_2 32 = x$ **b.** $\log_4 \dfrac{1}{64} = x$

   c. $\log_{\frac{1}{2}} x = 5$

27. Simplify.

   a. $\log_3 3^2$ **b.** $\log_7 7^{-1}$

   c. $5^{\log_5 3}$ **d.** $2^{\log_2 6}$

28. Solve each equation for x.

   a. $4^x = 64$ **b.** $8^x = 32$

   c. $9^{x+4} = 243^x$

29. Write each sum as a single logarithm.

   a. $\log_{11} 10 + \log_{11} 3$

   b. $\log_3 \dfrac{1}{2} + \log_3 12$

   c. $\log_2(x + 2) + \log_2 x$

30. Find the exact value.

   a. $\log 100{,}000$ **b.** $\log 10^{-3}$

   c. $\ln \sqrt[5]{e}$ **d.** $\ln e^4$

31. Find the amount owed at the end of 5 years if $1600 is loaned at a rate of 9% compounded continuously.

32. Write each expression as a single logarithm.

   a. $\log_6 5 + \log_6 4$

   b. $\log_8 12 - \log_8 4$

   c. $2 \log_2 x + 3 \log_2 x - 2 \log_2(x - 1)$

33. Solve: $3^x = 7$.

34. Using $A = P\left(1 + \dfrac{r}{n}\right)^{nt}$, find how long it takes $5000 to double if it is invested at 2% interest compounded quarterly. Round to the nearest tenth.

35. Solve: $\log_4(x - 2) = 2$.

36. Solve: $\log_4 10 - \log_4 x = 2$.

37. Graph $\dfrac{x^2}{16} - \dfrac{y^2}{25} = 1$.

38. Find the distance between $(8, 5)$ and $(-2, 4)$.

39. Solve the system $\begin{cases} y = \sqrt{x} \\ x^2 + y^2 = 6 \end{cases}$.

40. Solve the system $\begin{cases} x^2 + y^2 = 36 \\ x - y = 6 \end{cases}$.

41. Graph $\dfrac{x^2}{9} + \dfrac{y^2}{16} \le 1$.

42. Graph $\begin{cases} y \ge x^2 \\ y \le 4 \end{cases}$.

43. Write the first five terms of the sequence whose general term is given by $a_n = n^2 - 1$.

44. If the general term of a sequence is $a_n = \dfrac{n}{n + 4}$, find a_8.

45. Find the eleventh term of the arithmetic sequence whose first three terms are $2, 9$, and 16.

46. Find the sixth term of the geometric sequence $2, 10, 50, \ldots$.

47. Evaluate.

   a. $\displaystyle\sum_{i=0}^{6} \dfrac{i - 2}{2}$ **b.** $\displaystyle\sum_{i=3}^{5} 2^i$

48. Evaluate.

   a. $\displaystyle\sum_{i=0}^{4} i(i + 1)$ **b.** $\displaystyle\sum_{i=0}^{3} 2^i$

49. Find the sum of the first 30 positive integers.

50. Find the third term of the expansion of $(x - y)^6$.

Appendix A

The Bigger Picture/Practice Final Exam

A.1 THE BIGGER PICTURE—SOLVING EQUATIONS AND INEQUALITIES

I. Equations

A. Linear Equations (Sec. 2.1)

$$5(x - 2) = \frac{4(2x + 1)}{3}$$
$$3 \cdot 5(x - 2) = \not{3} \cdot \frac{4(2x + 1)}{\not{3}}$$
$$15x - 30 = 8x + 4$$
$$7x = 34$$
$$x = \frac{34}{7}$$

B. Absolute Value Equations (Sec. 2.6)

$$|3x - 1| = 8$$

$3x - 1 = 8$ or $3x - 1 = -8$

$3x = 9$ or $3x = -7$

$x = 3$ or $x = -\dfrac{7}{3}$

$$|x - 5| = |x + 1|$$

$x - 5 = x + 1$ or $x - 5 = -(x + 1)$

$\underbrace{-5 = 1}$ or $x - 5 = -x - 1$

No solution   or $2x = 4$

            $x = 2$

C. Quadratic and Higher-Degree Equations (Secs. 5.8, 8.1, 8.2, 8.3)

$$2x^2 - 7x = 9$$
$$2x^2 - 7x - 9 = 0$$
$$(2x - 9)(x + 1) = 0$$
$2x - 9 = 0$ or $x + 1 = 0$

$x = \dfrac{9}{2}$ or $x = -1$

$$2x^2 + x - 2 = 0$$
$$a = 2, \quad b = 1, \quad c = -2$$
$$x = \frac{-1 \pm \sqrt{1^2 - 4(2)(-2)}}{2 \cdot 2}$$
$$x = \frac{-1 \pm \sqrt{17}}{4}$$

D. Equations with Rational Expressions (Sec. 6.5)

$$\frac{7}{x - 1} + \frac{3}{x + 1} = \frac{x + 3}{x^2 - 1}$$
$$\not{(x - 1)}(x + 1) \cdot \frac{7}{\not{x - 1}} + (x - 1)\not{(x + 1)} \cdot \frac{3}{\not{x + 1}}$$
$$= \not{(x - 1)}\not{(x + 1)} \cdot \frac{x + 3}{\not{(x - 1)}\not{(x + 1)}}$$
$$7(x + 1) + 3(x - 1) = x + 3$$
$$7x + 7 + 3x - 3 = x + 3$$
$$9x = -1$$
$$x = -\frac{1}{9}$$

672

E. Equations with Radicals (Sec. 7.6)

$$\sqrt{5x + 10} - 2 = x$$
$$\sqrt{5x + 10} = x + 2$$
$$(\sqrt{5x + 10})^2 = (x + 2)^2$$
$$5x + 10 = x^2 + 4x + 4$$
$$0 = x^2 - x - 6$$
$$0 = (x - 3)(x + 2)$$
$$x - 3 = 0 \quad \text{or} \quad x + 2 = 0$$
$$x = 3 \quad \text{or} \quad x = -2$$

Both solutions check.

F. Exponential Equations (Secs. 9.3, 9.7)

$$9^x = 27^{x+1} \qquad\qquad 5^x = 7$$
$$(3^2)^x = (3^3)^{x+1} \qquad \log 5^x = \log 7$$
$$3^{2x} = 3^{3x+3} \qquad\quad x \log 5 = \log 7$$
$$2x = 3x + 3 \qquad\qquad x = \frac{\log 7}{\log 5}$$
$$-3 = x$$

G. Logarithmic Equations (Sec. 9.7)

$$\log 7 + \log(x + 3) = \log 5$$
$$\log 7(x + 3) = \log 5$$
$$7(x + 3) = 5$$
$$7x + 21 = 5$$
$$7x = -16$$
$$x = \frac{-16}{7}$$

II. Inequalities

A. Linear Inequalities (Sec. 2.4)

$$-3(x + 2) \geq 6$$
$$-3x - 6 \geq 6$$
$$-3x \geq 12$$
$$\frac{-3x}{-3} \leq \frac{12}{-3}$$
$$x \leq -4 \quad \text{or} \quad (-\infty, -4]$$

B. Compound Inequalities (Sec. 2.5)

$$x \leq 3 \quad \text{and} \quad x < -7 \qquad\qquad x \leq 3 \quad \text{or} \quad x < -7$$

$$(-\infty, -7) \qquad\qquad\qquad (-\infty, 3]$$

C. Absolute Value Inequalities (Sec. 2.7)

$$|x - 5| - 8 < -2 \qquad\qquad |2x + 1| \geq 17$$
$$|x - 5| < 6 \qquad 2x + 1 \geq 17 \quad \text{or} \quad 2x + 1 \leq -17$$
$$-6 < x - 5 < 6 \qquad\quad 2x \geq 16 \quad \text{or} \qquad 2x \leq -18$$
$$-1 < x < 11 \qquad\qquad x \geq 8 \quad \text{or} \qquad x \leq -9$$
$$(-1, 11) \qquad\qquad (-\infty, -9] \cup [8, \infty)$$

D. Nonlinear Inequalities (Sec. 8.4)

$$x^2 - x < 6$$
$$x^2 - x - 6 < 0$$
$$(x - 3)(x + 2) < 0$$

$$\frac{x - 5}{x + 1} \geq 0$$

$$(-2, 3)$$

$$(-\infty, -1) \cup [5, \infty)$$

A.2 PRACTICE FINAL EXAM

Simplify. If needed, write answers with positive exponents only.

1. $\sqrt{216}$

2. $\dfrac{(4 - \sqrt{16}) - (-7 - 20)}{-2(1 - 4)^2}$

3. $\left(\dfrac{1}{125}\right)^{-1/3}$

4. $(-9x)^{-2}$

5. $\dfrac{\dfrac{5}{x} - \dfrac{7}{3x}}{\dfrac{9}{8x} - \dfrac{1}{x}}$

6. $\dfrac{6^{-1}a^2b^{-3}}{3^{-2}a^{-5}b^2}$

7. $\left(\dfrac{64c^{4/3}}{a^{-2/3}b^{5/6}}\right)^{1/2}$

Factor completely.

8. $3x^2y - 27y^3$

9. $16y^3 - 2$

10. $x^2y - 9y - 3x^2 + 27$

Perform the indicated operations and simplify if possible.

11. $(4x^3y - 3x - 4) - (9x^3y + 8x + 5)$

12. $(6m + n)^2$

13. $(2x - 1)(x^2 - 6x + 4)$

14. $\dfrac{3x^2 - 12}{x^2 + 2x - 8} \div \dfrac{6x + 18}{x + 4}$

15. $\dfrac{2x^2 + 7}{2x^4 - 18x^2} - \dfrac{6x + 7}{2x^4 - 18x^2}$

16. $\dfrac{3}{x^2 - x - 6} + \dfrac{2}{x^2 - 5x + 6}$

17. $\sqrt{125x^3} - 3\sqrt{20x^3}$

18. $(\sqrt{5} + 5)(\sqrt{5} - 5)$

19. $(4x^3 - 5x) \div (2x + 1)$ [Use long division.]

Solve each equation or inequality. Write inequality solutions using interval notation.

20. $9(x + 2) = 5[11 - 2(2 - x) + 3]$

21. $|6x - 5| - 3 = -2$

22. $3n(7n - 20) = 96$

23. $-3 < 2(x - 3) \leq 4$

24. $|3x + 1| > 5$

25. $\dfrac{x^2 + 8}{x} - 1 = \dfrac{2(x + 4)}{x}$

26. $y^2 - 3y = 5$

27. $x = \sqrt{x - 2} + 2$

28. $2x^2 - 7x > 15$

29. Solve the system: $\begin{cases} \dfrac{x}{2} + \dfrac{y}{4} = -\dfrac{3}{4} \\ x + \dfrac{3}{4}y = -4 \end{cases}$

Graph the following.

30. $4x + 6y = 7$

31. $2x - y > 5$

32. $y = -3$

33. $g(x) = -|x + 2| - 1$. Also, find the domain and range of this function.

34. $h(x) = x^2 - 4x + 4$. Label the vertex and any intercepts.

35. $f(x) = \begin{cases} -\dfrac{1}{2}x & \text{if } x \leq 0 \\ 2x - 3 & \text{if } x > 0 \end{cases}$. Also, find the domain and range of this function.

Write equations of the following lines. Write each equation using function notation.

36. through $(4, -2)$ and $(6, -3)$

37. through $(-1, 2)$ and perpendicular to $3x - y = 4$

Find the distance or midpoint.

38. Find the distance between the points $(-6, 3)$ and $(-8, -7)$.

39. Find the midpoint of the line segment whose endpoints are $(-2, -5)$ and $(-6, 12)$.

Rationalize each denominator. Assume that variables represent positive numbers.

40. $\sqrt{\dfrac{9}{y}}$

41. $\dfrac{4 - \sqrt{x}}{4 + 2\sqrt{x}}$

Solve.

42. The most populous city in the United States is New York, although it is only the third most populous city in the world. Tokyo is the most populous city in the world. Second place is held by Seoul, Korea. Seoul's population is 1.3 million more than New York's and Tokyo's is 10.2 million less than twice the population of New York. If the sum of the populations of these three cities is 78.3 million, find the population of each city.

43. Write the area of the shaded region as a factored polynomial.

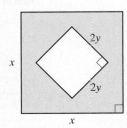

44. The product of one more than a number and twice the reciprocal of the number is $\frac{12}{5}$. Find the number.

45. Suppose that W is inversely proportional to V. If $W = 20$ when $V = 12$, find W when $V = 15$.

46. Given the diagram shown, approximate to the nearest foot how many feet of walking distance a person saves by cutting across the lawn instead of walking on the sidewalk.

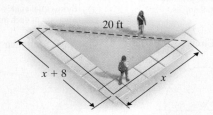

47. A stone is thrown upward from a bridge. The stone's height in feet, $s(t)$, above the water t seconds after the stone is thrown is a function given by the equation

$$s(t) = -16t^2 + 32t + 256$$

a. Find the maximum height of the stone.
b. Find the time it takes the stone to hit the water. Round the answer to two decimal places.

48. The research department of a company that manufactures children's fruit drinks is experimenting with a new flavor. A 17.5% fructose solution is needed, but only 10% and 20% solutions are available. How many gallons of a 10% fructose solution should be mixed with a 20% fructose solution to obtain 20 gallons of a 17.5% fructose solution?

Complex Numbers: Chapter 7

Perform the indicated operation and simplify. Write the result in the form $a + bi$.

49. $-\sqrt{-8}$

50. $(12 - 6i) - (12 - 3i)$

51. $(4 + 3i)^2$

52. $\dfrac{1 + 4i}{1 - i}$

Inverse, Exponential, and Logarithmic Functions: Chapter 9

53. If $g(x) = x - 7$ and $h(x) = x^2 - 6x + 5$, find $(g \circ h)(x)$.

54. Decide whether $f(x) = 6 - 2x$ is a one-to-one function. If it is, find its inverse.

55. Use properties of logarithms to write the expression as a single logarithm.

$$\log_5 x + 3\log_5 x - \log_5(x + 1)$$

Solve. Give exact solutions.

56. $8^{x-1} = \dfrac{1}{64}$

57. $3^{2x-5} = 4$ Give an exact solution and a 4-decimal place approximation.

58. $\log_8(3x - 2) = 2$

59. $\log_4(x + 1) - \log_4(x - 2) = 3$

60. $\ln\sqrt{e} = x$

61. Graph $y = \left(\dfrac{1}{2}\right)^x + 1$

62. The prairie dog population of the Grand Rapids area now stands at 57,000 animals. If the population is growing at a rate of 2.6% annually, use the formula $y = y_0 e^{kt}$ to find how many prairie dogs there will be in that area 5 years from now.

Conic Sections: Chapter 10

Sketch the graph of each equation.

63. $x^2 - y^2 = 36$

64. $16x^2 + 9y^2 = 144$

65. $x^2 - y^2 + 6x = 16$

66. Solve the system:
$$\begin{cases} x^2 + y^2 = 26 \\ x^2 - 2y^2 = 23 \end{cases}$$

Sequences, Series, and the Binomial Theorem: Chapter 11

67. Find the first five terms of the sequence $a_n = \dfrac{(-1)^n}{n + 4}$.

68. Find the partial sum, S_5, of the sequence $a_n = 5(2)^{n-1}$.

69. Find S_∞ of the sequence $\dfrac{3}{2}, -\dfrac{3}{4}, \dfrac{3}{8}, \ldots$

70. Find $\displaystyle\sum_{i=1}^{4} i(i - 2)$

71. Expand: $(2x + y)^5$

Appendix B

Geometry

B.1 GEOMETRIC FORMULAS

Rectangle

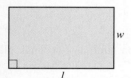

Perimeter: $P = 2l + 2w$
Area: $A = lw$

Square

Perimeter: $P = 4s$
Area: $A = s^2$

Triangle

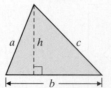

Perimeter: $P = a + b + c$
Area: $A = \frac{1}{2}bh$

Sum of Angles of Triangle

$A + B + C = 180°$
The sum of the measures of the three angles is 180°.

Right Triangles

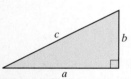

Perimeter: $P = a + b + c$
Area: $A = \frac{1}{2}ab$
One 90° (right) angle

Pythagorean Theorem (for right triangles)

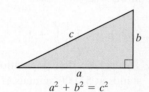

$a^2 + b^2 = c^2$

Isosceles Triangle

Triangle has:
two equal sides and
two equal angles.

Equilateral Triangle

Triangle has:
three equal sides and
three equal angles.
Measure of each angle is 60°.

Trapezoid

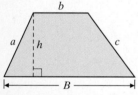

Perimeter: $P = a + b + c + B$
Area: $A = \frac{1}{2}h(B + b)$

Parallelogram

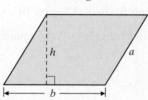

Perimeter: $P = 2a + 2b$
Area: $A = bh$

Circle

Circumference: $C = \pi d$
$C = 2\pi r$
Area: $A = \pi r^2$

Rectangular Solid

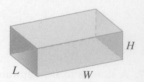

Volume: $V = LWH$
Surface Area:
$S = 2LW + 2HL + 2HW$

Cube

Volume: $V = s^3$
Surface Area: $S = 6s^2$

Cone

Volume: $V = \frac{1}{3}\pi r^2 h$
Lateral Surface Area:
$S = \pi r \sqrt{r^2 + h^2}$

Right Circular Cylinder

Volume: $V = \pi r^2 h$
Surface Area: $S = 2\pi r^2 + 2\pi rh$

Sphere

Volume: $V = \frac{4}{3}\pi r^3$
Surface Area: $S = 4\pi r^2$

Other Formulas

Distance: $d = rt (r = \text{rate}, t = \text{time})$
Percent: $p = br (p = \text{percentage}, b = \text{base}, r = \text{rate})$

Compound Interest: $A = P\left(1 + \dfrac{r}{n}\right)^{nt}$

$(P = \text{principal}, r = \text{annual interest rate}, t = \text{time in years}, n = \text{number of compoundings per year})$

Temperature: $F = \dfrac{9}{5}C + 32 \quad C = \dfrac{5}{9}(F - 32)$

Simple Interest: $I = Prt$
$(P = \text{principal}, r = \text{annual interest rate}, t = \text{time in years})$

B.2 REVIEW OF GEOMETRIC FIGURES

Plane figures have length and width but no thickness or depth

Name	Description	Figure
Polygon	Union of three or more coplanar line segments that intersect with each other only at each endpoint, with each endpoint shared by two segments.	
Triangle	Polygon with three sides (sum of measures of three angles is 180°).	
Scalene Triangle	Triangle with no sides of equal length.	
Isosceles Triangle	Triangle with two sides of equal length.	
Equilateral Triangle	Triangle with all sides of equal length.	
Right Triangle	Triangle that contains a right angle.	hypotenuse, leg, leg
Quadrilateral	Polygon with four sides (sum of measures of four angles is 360°).	
Trapezoid	Quadrilateral with exactly one pair of opposite sides parallel.	base, leg, parallel sides, leg, base
Isosceles Trapezoid	Trapezoid with legs of equal length.	
Parallelogram	Quadrilateral with both pairs of opposite sides parallel and equal in length.	

(continued)

Plane figures have length and width but no thickness or depth (continued)

Name	Description	Figure
Rhombus	Parallelogram with all sides of equal length.	
Rectangle	Parallelogram with four right angles.	
Square	Rectangle with all sides of equal length.	
Circle	All points in a plane the same distance from a fixed point called the **center.**	radius, center, diameter

Solids have length, width, and depth

Name	Description	Figure
Rectangular Solid	A solid with six sides, all of which are rectangles.	
Cube	A rectangular solid whose six sides are squares.	
Sphere	All points the same distance from a fixed point, called the center.	radius, center
Right Circular Cylinder	A cylinder with two circular bases that are perpendicular to its altitude.	
Right Circular Cone	A cone with a circular base that is perpendicular to its altitude.	

B.3 REVIEW OF VOLUME AND SURFACE AREA

A **convex solid** is a set of points, S, not all in one plane, such that for any two points A and B in S, all points between A and B are also in S. In this appendix, we will find the volume and surface area of special types of solids called polyhedrons. A solid formed by the intersection of a finite number of planes is called a **polyhedron.** The box below is an example of a polyhedron.

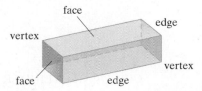

Each of the plane regions of the polyhedron is called a **face** of the polyhedron. If the intersection of two faces is a line segment, this line segment is an **edge** of the polyhedron. The intersections of the edges are the **vertices** of the polyhedron.

Volume is a measure of the space of a solid. The volume of a box or can, for example, is the amount of space inside. Volume can be used to describe the amount of juice in a pitcher or the amount of concrete needed to pour a foundation for a house.

The volume of a solid is the number of **cubic units** in the solid. A cubic centimeter and a cubic inch are illustrated.

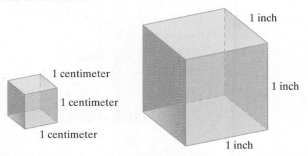

The **surface area** of a polyhedron is the sum of the areas of the faces of the polyhedron. For example, each face of the cube to the left above has an area of 1 square centimeter. Since there are 6 faces of the cube, the sum of the areas of the faces is 6 square centimeters. Surface area can be used to describe the amount of material needed to cover or form a solid. Surface area is measured in square units.

Formulas for finding the volumes, V, and surface areas, SA, of some common solids are given next.

Volume and Surface Area Formulas of Common Solids	
Solid	*Formulas*
RECTANGULAR SOLID	$V = lwh$ $SA = 2lh + 2wh + 2lw$ where h = height, w = width, l = length
CUBE	$V = s^3$ $SA = 6s^2$ where s = side

(*continued*)

Volume and Surface Area Formulas of Common Solids *(continued)*

Solid	Formulas
SPHERE 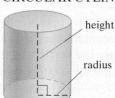 radius	$V = \dfrac{4}{3}\pi r^3$ $SA = 4\pi r^2$ where r = radius
CIRCULAR CYLINDER 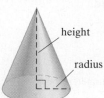 height radius	$V = \pi r^2 h$ $SA = 2\pi rh + 2\pi r^2$ where h = height, r = radius
CONE 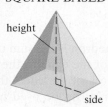 height radius	$V = \dfrac{1}{3}\pi r^2 h$ $SA = \pi r\sqrt{r^2 + h^2} + \pi r^2$ where h = height, r = radius
SQUARE-BASED PYRAMID height side	$V = \dfrac{1}{3}s^2 h$ $SA = B + \dfrac{1}{2}pl$ where B = area of base; p = perimeter of base, h = height, s = side, l = slant height

▶ **Helpful Hint**
Volume is measured in cubic units. Surface area is measured in square units.

EXAMPLE 1   Find the volume and surface area of a rectangular box that is 12 inches long, 6 inches wide, and 3 inches high.

3 in.
6 in.
12 in.

Solution   Let h = 3 in., l = 12 in., and w = 6 in.

$$V = lwh$$

$$V = 12 \text{ inches} \cdot 6 \text{ inches} \cdot 3 \text{ inches} = 216 \text{ cubic inches}$$

The volume of the rectangular box is 216 cubic inches.

$$
\begin{aligned}
SA &= 2lh + 2wh + 2lw \\
&= 2(12 \text{ in.})(3 \text{ in.}) + 2(6 \text{ in.})(3 \text{ in.}) + 2(12 \text{ in.})(6 \text{ in.}) \\
&= 72 \text{ sq in.} + 36 \text{ sq in.} + 144 \text{ sq in.} \\
&= 252 \text{ sq in.}
\end{aligned}
$$

The surface area of the rectangular box is 252 square inches.

EXAMPLE 2   Find the volume and surface area of a ball of radius 2 inches. Give the exact volume and surface area and then use the approximation $\frac{22}{7}$ for π.

<u>Solution</u>

2 in.

$$V = \frac{4}{3}\pi r^3 \qquad \text{Formula for volume of a sphere}$$

$$V = \frac{4}{3}\pi(2 \text{ in.})^3 \qquad \text{Let } r = 2 \text{ inches.}$$

$$= \frac{32}{3}\pi \text{ cu in.} \qquad \text{Simplify.}$$

$$\approx \frac{32}{3}\cdot\frac{22}{7} \text{ cu in.} \qquad \text{Approximate } \pi \text{ with } \frac{22}{7}.$$

$$= \frac{704}{21} \text{ or } 33\frac{11}{21} \text{ cu in.}$$

The volume of the sphere is exactly $\frac{32}{3}\pi$ cubic inches or approximately $33\frac{11}{21}$ cubic inches.

$$SA = 4\pi r^2 \qquad \text{Formula for surface area}$$

$$SA = 4\pi(2 \text{ in.})^2 \qquad \text{Let } r = 2 \text{ inches.}$$

$$= 16\pi \text{ sq in.} \qquad \text{Simplify.}$$

$$\approx 16\cdot\frac{22}{7} \text{ sq in.} \qquad \text{Approximate } \pi \text{ with } \frac{22}{7}.$$

$$= \frac{352}{7} \text{ or } 50\frac{2}{7} \text{ sq in.}$$

The surface area of the sphere is exactly 16π square inches or approximately $50\frac{2}{7}$ square inches.

☐

APPENDIX B.3 | EXERCISE SET

MyMathLab ▸ *Powered by CourseCompass™ and MathXL®*

MathXL PRACTICE   WATCH   DOWNLOAD   READ   REVIEW

Find the volume and surface area of each solid. See Examples 1 and 2. For formulas that contain π, give an exact answer and then approximate using $\frac{22}{7}$ for π.

1.

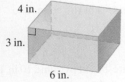

4 in.
3 in.
6 in.

2.

3 mi

5. (For surface area, use 3.14 for π and approximate to two decimal places.)

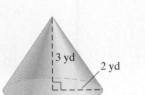

3 yd
2 yd

3.

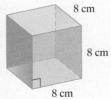

8 cm
8 cm
8 cm

4.

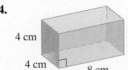

4 cm
4 cm
8 cm

6.

10 ft
6 ft

7.

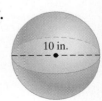

10 in.

8. Find the volume only.

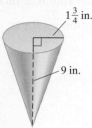

$1\frac{3}{4}$ in.

9 in.

9.

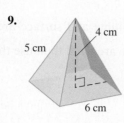

5 cm

4 cm

6 cm

10.

1 ft

Solve.

11. Find the volume of a cube with edges of $1\frac{1}{3}$ inches.

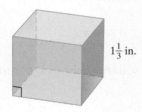

$1\frac{1}{3}$ in.

12. A water storage tank is in the shape of a cone with the pointed end down. If the radius is 14 ft and the depth of the tank is 15 ft, approximate the volume of the tank in cubic feet. Use $\frac{22}{7}$ for π.

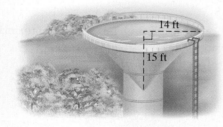

14 ft

15 ft

13. Find the surface area of a rectangular box 2 ft by 1.4 ft by 3 ft.

14. Find the surface area of a box in the shape of a cube that is 5 ft on each side.

15. Find the volume of a pyramid with a square base 5 in. on a side and a height of 1.3 in.

16. Approximate to the nearest hundredth the volume of a sphere with a radius of 2 cm. Use 3.14 for π.

17. A paperweight is in the shape of a square-based pyramid 20 cm tall. If an edge of the base is 12 cm, find the volume of the paperweight.

18. A bird bath is made in the shape of a hemisphere (half-sphere). If its radius is 10 in., approximate the volume. Use $\frac{22}{7}$ for π.

10 in.

19. Find the exact surface area of a sphere with a radius of 7 in.

20. A tank is in the shape of a cylinder 8 ft tall and 3 ft in radius. Find the exact surface area of the tank.

21. Find the volume of a rectangular block of ice 2 ft by $2\frac{1}{2}$ ft by $1\frac{1}{2}$ ft.

22. Find the capacity (volume in cubic feet) of a rectangular ice chest with inside measurements of 3 ft by $1\frac{1}{2}$ ft by $1\frac{3}{4}$ ft.

23. An ice cream cone with a 4-cm diameter and 3-cm depth is filled exactly level with the top of the cone. Approximate how much ice cream (in cubic centimeters) is in the cone. Use $\frac{22}{7}$ for π.

24. A child's toy is in the shape of a square-based pyramid 10 in. tall. If an edge of the base is 7 in., find the volume of the toy.

Appendix C

Stretching and Compressing Graphs of Absolute Value Functions

In Section 3.6, we learned to shift and reflect graphs of common functions: $f(x) = x$, $f(x) = x^2$, $f(x) = |x|$ and $f(x) = \sqrt{x}$. Since other common functions are studied throughout this text, in this Appendix we concentrate on the absolute value function.

Recall that the graph of $h(x) = -|x - 1| + 2$, for example, is the same as the graph of $f(x) = |x|$ reflected about the x-axis, moved 1 unit to the right and 2 units upward. In other words,

$$h(x) = -|x - 1| + 2$$

opens
downward

(1, 2) location of vertex of
V-shape

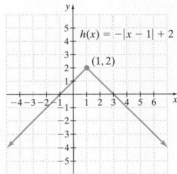

Let's now study the graphs of a few other absolute value functions.

EXAMPLE 1   Graph $h(x) = 2|x|$, and $g(x) = \dfrac{1}{2}|x|$.

Solution   Let's find and plot ordered-pair solutions for the functions.

x	h(x)	g(x)
−2	4	1
−1	2	$\dfrac{1}{2}$
0	0	0
1	2	$\dfrac{1}{2}$
2	4	2

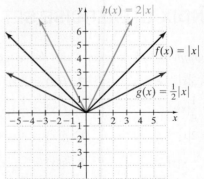

Notice that the graph of $h(x) = 2|x|$ is narrower than the graph of $f(x) = |x|$ and the graph of $g(x) = \dfrac{1}{2}x$ is wider than the graph of $f(x) = |x|$.

683

In general, for the absolute function, we have the following

> **The Graph of the Absolute Value Function**
> The graph of $f(x) = a|x - h| + k$
> - Has vertex (h, k) and is V-shaped.
> - Opens up if $a > 0$ and down if $a < 0$.
> - If $|a| < 1$, the graph is wider than the graph of $y = |x|$.
> - If $|a| > 1$, the graph is narrower than the graph of $y = |x|$.

EXAMPLE 2   Graph $f(x) = -\dfrac{1}{3}|x + 2| + 4$.

Solution   Let's write this function in the form $f(x) = a|x - h| + k$. For our function, we have $f(x) = -\dfrac{1}{3}|x - (-2)| + 4$. Thus,

- vertex is $(-2, 4)$
- since $a < 0$, V-shape opens down
- since $|a| = \left| -\dfrac{1}{3} \right| = \dfrac{1}{3} < 1$, the graph is wider than $y = |x|$

We will also find and plot ordered-pair solutions.

If $x = -5, f(-5) = -\dfrac{1}{3}|-5 + 2| + 4$, or 3

If $x = 1, f(1) = -\dfrac{1}{3}|1 + 2| + 4$, or 3

If $x = 3, f(3) = -\dfrac{1}{3}|3 + 2| + 4$, or $\dfrac{7}{3}$, or $2\dfrac{1}{3}$

x	$f(x)$
-5	3
1	3
3	$2\dfrac{1}{3}$

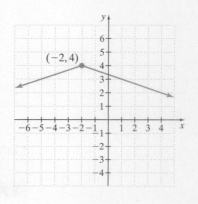

APPENDIX C | EXERCISE SET    PRACTICE   WATCH   DOWNLOAD   READ   REVIEW

Sketch the graph of each function. Label the vertex of the V-shape.

1. $f(x) = 3|x|$

2. $f(x) = 5|x|$

3. $f(x) = \dfrac{1}{4}|x|$

4. $f(x) = \dfrac{1}{3}|x|$

5. $g(x) = 2|x| + 3$

6. $g(x) = 3|x| + 2$

7. $h(x) = -\dfrac{1}{2}|x|$

8. $h(x) = -\dfrac{1}{3}|x|$

9. $f(x) = 4|x - 1|$

10. $f(x) = 3|x - 2|$

11. $g(x) = -\dfrac{1}{3}|x| - 2$

12. $g(x) = -\dfrac{1}{2}|x| - 3$

13. $f(x) = -2|x - 3| + 4$

14. $f(x) = -3|x - 1| + 5$

15. $f(x) = \dfrac{2}{3}|x + 2| - 5$

16. $f(x) = \dfrac{3}{4}|x + 1| - 4$

Appendix D

Solving Systems of Equations Using Determinants

We have solved systems of two linear equations in two variables in four different ways: graphically, by substitution, by elimination, and by matrices. Now we analyze another method called **Cramer's rule.**

OBJECTIVE 1 ▶ Evaluating 2 × 2 determinants. Recall that a matrix is a rectangular array of numbers. If a matrix has the same number of rows and columns, it is called a **square matrix.** Examples of square matrices are

$$\begin{bmatrix} 1 & 6 \\ 5 & 2 \end{bmatrix} \qquad \begin{bmatrix} 2 & 4 & 1 \\ 0 & 5 & 2 \\ 3 & 6 & 9 \end{bmatrix}$$

A **determinant** is a real number associated with a square matrix. The determinant of a square matrix is denoted by placing vertical bars about the array of numbers. Thus,

The determinant of the square matrix $\begin{bmatrix} 1 & 6 \\ 5 & 2 \end{bmatrix}$ is $\begin{vmatrix} 1 & 6 \\ 5 & 2 \end{vmatrix}$.

The determinant of the square matrix $\begin{bmatrix} 2 & 4 & 1 \\ 0 & 5 & 2 \\ 3 & 6 & 9 \end{bmatrix}$ is $\begin{vmatrix} 2 & 4 & 1 \\ 0 & 5 & 2 \\ 3 & 6 & 9 \end{vmatrix}$.

We define the determinant of a 2 × 2 matrix first. (Recall that 2 × 2 is read "two by two." It means that the matrix has 2 rows and 2 columns.)

Determinant of a 2 × 2 Matrix

$$\begin{vmatrix} a & b \\ c & d \end{vmatrix} = ad - bc$$

EXAMPLE 1   Evaluate each determinant

a. $\begin{vmatrix} -1 & 2 \\ 3 & -4 \end{vmatrix}$ **b.** $\begin{vmatrix} 2 & 0 \\ 7 & -5 \end{vmatrix}$

Solution   First we identify the values of $a, b, c,$ and d. Then we perform the evaluation.

a. Here $a = -1, b = 2, c = 3,$ and $d = -4$.

$$\begin{vmatrix} -1 & 2 \\ 3 & -4 \end{vmatrix} = ad - bc = (-1)(-4) - (2)(3) = -2$$

b. In this example, $a = 2, b = 0, c = 7,$ and $d = -5$.

$$\begin{vmatrix} 2 & 0 \\ 7 & -5 \end{vmatrix} = ad - bc = 2(-5) - (0)(7) = -10 \qquad \square$$

685

OBJECTIVE 2 ▶ Using Cramer's rule to solve a system of two linear equations. To develop Cramer's rule, we solve the system $\begin{cases} ax + by = h \\ cx + dy = k \end{cases}$ using elimination. First, we eliminate y by multiplying both sides of the first equation by d and both sides of the second equation by $-b$ so that the coefficients of y are opposites. The result is that

$$\begin{cases} d(ax + by) = d \cdot h \\ -b(cx + dy) = -b \cdot k \end{cases} \quad \text{simplifies to} \quad \begin{cases} adx + bdy = hd \\ -bcx - bdy = -kb \end{cases}$$

We now add the two equations and solve for x.

$$
\begin{aligned}
adx + bdy &= hd \\
\underline{-bcx - bdy} &= \underline{-kb} \\
adx - bcx &= hd - kb \quad \text{Add the equations.} \\
(ad - bc)x &= hd - kb \\
x &= \frac{hd - kb}{ad - bc} \quad \text{Solve for } x.
\end{aligned}
$$

When we replace x with $\dfrac{hd - kb}{ad - bc}$ in the equation $ax + by = h$ and solve for y, we find that $y = \dfrac{ak - ch}{ad - bc}$.

Notice that the numerator of the value of x is the determinant of

$$\begin{vmatrix} h & b \\ k & d \end{vmatrix} = hd - kb$$

Also, the numerator of the value of y is the determinant of

$$\begin{vmatrix} a & h \\ c & k \end{vmatrix} = ak - hc$$

Finally, the denominators of the values of x and y are the same and are the determinant of

$$\begin{vmatrix} a & b \\ c & d \end{vmatrix} = ad - bc$$

This means that the values of x and y can be written in determinant notation:

$$x = \frac{\begin{vmatrix} h & b \\ k & d \end{vmatrix}}{\begin{vmatrix} a & b \\ c & d \end{vmatrix}} \quad \text{and} \quad y = \frac{\begin{vmatrix} a & h \\ c & k \end{vmatrix}}{\begin{vmatrix} a & b \\ c & d \end{vmatrix}}$$

For convenience, we label the determinants D, D_x, and D_y.

x-coefficients

y-coefficients

$$\begin{vmatrix} a & b \\ c & d \end{vmatrix} = D \qquad \begin{vmatrix} h & b \\ k & d \end{vmatrix} = D_x \qquad \begin{vmatrix} a & h \\ c & k \end{vmatrix} = D_y$$

x-column replaced by constants

y-column replaced by constants

These determinant formulas for the coordinates of the solution of a system are known as **Cramer's rule.**

> ### Cramer's Rule for Two Linear Equations in Two Variables
>
> The solution of the system $\begin{cases} ax + by = h \\ cx + dy = k \end{cases}$ is given by
>
> $$x = \frac{\begin{vmatrix} h & b \\ k & d \end{vmatrix}}{\begin{vmatrix} a & b \\ c & d \end{vmatrix}} = \frac{D_x}{D} \qquad y = \frac{\begin{vmatrix} a & h \\ c & k \end{vmatrix}}{\begin{vmatrix} a & b \\ c & d \end{vmatrix}} = \frac{D_y}{D}$$
>
> as long as $D = ad - bc$ is not 0.

When $D = 0$, the system is either inconsistent or the equations are dependent. When this happens, we need to use another method to see which is the case.

EXAMPLE 2   Use Cramer's rule to solve the system

$$\begin{cases} 3x + 4y = -7 \\ x - 2y = -9 \end{cases}$$

Solution   First we find D, D_x, and D_y.

$$\begin{cases} \overset{a}{\downarrow} \overset{b}{\downarrow} \overset{h}{\downarrow} \\ 3x + 4y = -7 \\ x - 2y = -9 \\ \underset{c}{\uparrow} \underset{d}{\uparrow} \underset{k}{\uparrow} \end{cases}$$

$$D = \begin{vmatrix} a & b \\ c & d \end{vmatrix} = \begin{vmatrix} 3 & 4 \\ 1 & -2 \end{vmatrix} = 3(-2) - 4(1) = -10$$

$$D_x = \begin{vmatrix} h & b \\ k & d \end{vmatrix} = \begin{vmatrix} -7 & 4 \\ -9 & -2 \end{vmatrix} = (-7)(-2) - 4(-9) = 50$$

$$D_y = \begin{vmatrix} a & h \\ c & d \end{vmatrix} = \begin{vmatrix} 3 & -7 \\ 1 & -9 \end{vmatrix} = 3(-9) - (-7)(1) = -20$$

Then $x = \dfrac{D_x}{D} = \dfrac{50}{-10} = -5$ and $y = \dfrac{D_y}{D} = \dfrac{-20}{-10} = 2.$

The ordered pair solution is $(-5, 2)$.

As always, check the solution in both original equations.   □

EXAMPLE 3   Use Cramer's rule to solve the system

$$\begin{cases} 5x + y = 5 \\ -7x - 2y = -7 \end{cases}$$

Solution   First we find D, D_x. and D_y.

$$D = \begin{vmatrix} 5 & 1 \\ -7 & -2 \end{vmatrix} = 5(-2) - (-7)(1) = -3$$

$$D_x = \begin{vmatrix} 5 & 1 \\ -7 & -2 \end{vmatrix} = 5(-2) - (-7)(1) = -3$$

$$D_y = \begin{vmatrix} 5 & 5 \\ -7 & -7 \end{vmatrix} = 5(-7) - 5(-7) = 0$$

Then

$$x = \frac{D_x}{D} = \frac{-3}{-3} = 1 \qquad y = \frac{D_y}{D} = \frac{0}{-3} = 0$$

The ordered pair solution is $(1, 0)$.

OBJECTIVE 3 ▶ Evaluating 3 × 3 determinants. A 3×3 determinant can be used to solve a system of three equations in three variables. The determinant of a 3×3 matrix, however, is considerably more complex than a 2×2 one.

Determinant of a 3 × 3 Matrix

$$\begin{vmatrix} a_1 & b_1 & c_1 \\ a_2 & b_2 & c_2 \\ a_3 & b_3 & c_3 \end{vmatrix} = a_1 \cdot \begin{vmatrix} b_2 & c_2 \\ b_3 & c_3 \end{vmatrix} - a_2 \cdot \begin{vmatrix} b_1 & c_1 \\ b_3 & c_3 \end{vmatrix} + a_3 \cdot \begin{vmatrix} b_1 & c_1 \\ b_2 & c_2 \end{vmatrix}$$

Notice that the determinant of a 3×3 matrix is related to the determinants of three 2×2 matrices. Each determinant of these 2×2 matrices is called a **minor,** and every element of a 3×3 matrix has a minor associated with it. For example, the minor of c_2 is the determinant of the 2×2 matrix found by deleting the row and column containing c_2.

$$\begin{matrix} a_1 & b_1 & c_1 \\ a_2 & b_2 & c_2 \\ a_3 & b_3 & c_3 \end{matrix} \qquad \text{The minor of } c_2 \text{ is} \qquad \begin{vmatrix} a_1 & b_1 \\ a_3 & b_3 \end{vmatrix}$$

Also, the minor of element a_1 is the determinant of the 2×2 matrix that has no row or column containing a_1.

$$\begin{matrix} a_1 & b_1 & c_1 \\ a_2 & b_2 & c_2 \\ a_3 & b_3 & c_3 \end{matrix} \qquad \text{The minor of } a_1 \text{ is} \qquad \begin{vmatrix} b_2 & c_2 \\ b_3 & c_3 \end{vmatrix}$$

So the determinant of a 3×3 matrix can be written as

$$a_1 \cdot (\text{minor of } a_1) - a_2 \cdot (\text{minor of } a_2) + a_3 \cdot (\text{minor of } a_3)$$

Finding the determinant by using minors of elements in the first column is called **expanding** by the minors of the first column. *The value of a determinant can be found by expanding by the minors of any row or column.* The following **array of signs** is helpful in determining whether to add or subtract the product of an element and its minor.

$$\begin{matrix} + & - & + \\ - & + & - \\ + & - & + \end{matrix}$$

If an element is in a position marked $+$, we add. If marked $-$, we subtract.

Answer to Concept Check:

$$\begin{matrix} + & - & + & - \\ - & + & - & + \\ + & - & + & - \\ - & + & - & + \end{matrix}$$

Concept Check ☑

Suppose you are interested in finding the determinant of a 4×4 matrix. Study the pattern shown in the array of signs for a 3×3 matrix. Use the pattern to expand the array of signs for use with a 4×4 matrix.

EXAMPLE 4   Evaluate by expanding by the minors of the given row or column.

$$\begin{vmatrix} 0 & 5 & 1 \\ 1 & 3 & -1 \\ -2 & 2 & 4 \end{vmatrix}$$

a. First column

b. Second row

Solution

a. The elements of the first column are $0, 1,$ and -2. The first column of the array of signs is $+, -, +$.

$$\begin{vmatrix} 0 & 5 & 1 \\ 1 & 3 & -1 \\ -2 & 2 & 4 \end{vmatrix} = 0 \cdot \begin{vmatrix} 3 & -1 \\ 2 & 4 \end{vmatrix} - 1 \cdot \begin{vmatrix} 5 & 1 \\ 2 & 4 \end{vmatrix} + (-2) \cdot \begin{vmatrix} 5 & 1 \\ 3 & -1 \end{vmatrix}$$

$$= 0(12 - (-2)) - 1(20 - 2) + (-2)(-5 - 3)$$

$$= 0 - 18 + 16 = -2$$

b. The elements of the second row are $1, 3,$ and -1. This time, the signs begin with $-$ and again alternate.

$$\begin{vmatrix} 0 & 5 & 1 \\ 1 & 3 & -1 \\ -2 & 2 & 4 \end{vmatrix} = -1 \cdot \begin{vmatrix} 5 & 1 \\ 2 & 4 \end{vmatrix} + 3 \cdot \begin{vmatrix} 0 & 1 \\ -2 & 4 \end{vmatrix} - (-1) \cdot \begin{vmatrix} 0 & 5 \\ -2 & 2 \end{vmatrix}$$

$$= -1(20 - 2) + 3(0 - (-2)) - (-1)(0 - (-10))$$

$$= -18 + 6 + 10 = -2$$

Notice that the determinant of the 3×3 matrix is the same regardless of the row or column you select to expand by.   □

Concept Check ☑

Why would expanding by minors of the second row be a good choice for the determinant

$$\begin{vmatrix} 3 & 4 & -2 \\ 5 & 0 & 0 \\ 6 & -3 & 7 \end{vmatrix}?$$

OBJECTIVE 4 ▶ Using Cramer's rule to solve a system of three linear equations. A system of three equations in three variables may be solved with Cramer's rule also. Using the elimination process to solve a system with unknown constants as coefficients leads to the following.

Cramer's Rule for Three Equations in Three Variables

The solution of the system $\begin{cases} a_1x + b_1y + c_1z = k_1 \\ a_2x + b_2y + c_2z = k_2 \\ a_3x + b_3y + c_3z = k_3 \end{cases}$ is given by

$$x = \frac{D_x}{D} \qquad y = \frac{D_y}{D} \qquad \text{and} \qquad z = \frac{D_z}{D}$$

where

$$D = \begin{vmatrix} a_1 & b_1 & c_1 \\ a_2 & b_2 & c_2 \\ a_3 & b_3 & c_3 \end{vmatrix} \qquad D_x = \begin{vmatrix} k_1 & b_1 & c_1 \\ k_2 & b_2 & c_2 \\ k_3 & b_3 & c_3 \end{vmatrix}$$

$$D_y = \begin{vmatrix} a_1 & k_1 & c_1 \\ a_2 & k_2 & c_2 \\ a_3 & k_3 & c_3 \end{vmatrix} \qquad D_z = \begin{vmatrix} a_1 & b_1 & k_1 \\ a_2 & b_2 & k_2 \\ a_3 & b_3 & k_3 \end{vmatrix}$$

as long as D is not 0.

Answer to Concept Check:

Two elements of the second row are 0, which makes calculations easier.

EXAMPLE 5   Use Cramer's rule to solve the system

$$\begin{cases} x - 2y + z = 4 \\ 3x + y - 2z = 3 \\ 5x + 5y + 3z = -8 \end{cases}$$

Solution   First we find D, D_x, D_y, and D_z. Beginning with D, we expand by the minors of the first column.

$$D = \begin{vmatrix} 1 & -2 & 1 \\ 3 & 1 & -2 \\ 5 & 5 & 3 \end{vmatrix} = 1 \cdot \begin{vmatrix} 1 & -2 \\ 5 & 3 \end{vmatrix} - 3 \cdot \begin{vmatrix} -2 & 1 \\ 5 & 3 \end{vmatrix} + 5 \cdot \begin{vmatrix} -2 & 1 \\ 1 & -2 \end{vmatrix}$$

$$= 1(3 - (-10)) - 3(-6 - 5) + 5(4 - 1)$$

$$= 13 + 33 + 15 = 61$$

$$D_x = \begin{vmatrix} 4 & -2 & 1 \\ 3 & 1 & -2 \\ -8 & 5 & 3 \end{vmatrix} = 4 \cdot \begin{vmatrix} 1 & -2 \\ 5 & 3 \end{vmatrix} - 3 \cdot \begin{vmatrix} -2 & 1 \\ 5 & 3 \end{vmatrix} + (-8) \cdot \begin{vmatrix} -2 & 1 \\ 1 & -2 \end{vmatrix}$$

$$= 4(3 - (-10)) - 3(-6 - 5) + (-8)(4 - 1)$$

$$= 52 + 33 - 24 = 61$$

$$D_y = \begin{vmatrix} 1 & 4 & 1 \\ 3 & 3 & -2 \\ 5 & -8 & 3 \end{vmatrix} = 1 \cdot \begin{vmatrix} 3 & -2 \\ -8 & 3 \end{vmatrix} - 3 \cdot \begin{vmatrix} 4 & 1 \\ -8 & 3 \end{vmatrix} + 5 \cdot \begin{vmatrix} 4 & 1 \\ 3 & -2 \end{vmatrix}$$

$$= 1(9 - 16) - 3(12 - (-8)) + 5(-8 - 3)$$

$$= -7 - 60 - 55 = -122$$

$$D_z = \begin{vmatrix} 1 & -2 & 4 \\ 3 & 1 & 3 \\ 5 & 5 & -8 \end{vmatrix} = 1 \cdot \begin{vmatrix} 1 & 3 \\ 5 & -8 \end{vmatrix} - 3 \cdot \begin{vmatrix} -2 & 4 \\ 5 & -8 \end{vmatrix} + 5 \cdot \begin{vmatrix} -2 & 4 \\ 1 & 3 \end{vmatrix}$$

$$= 1(-8 - 15) - 3(16 - 20) + 5(-6 - 4)$$

$$= -23 + 12 - 50 = -61$$

From these determinants, we calculate the solution:

$$x = \frac{D_x}{D} = \frac{61}{61} = 1 \quad y = \frac{D_y}{D} = \frac{-122}{61} = -2 \quad z = \frac{D_z}{D} = \frac{-61}{61} = -1$$

The ordered triple solution is $(1, -2, -1)$. Check this solution by verifying that it satisfies each equation of the system.   ☐

VOCABULARY & READINESS CHECK

Evaluate each determinant mentally.

1. $\begin{vmatrix} 7 & 2 \\ 0 & 8 \end{vmatrix}$

2. $\begin{vmatrix} 6 & 0 \\ 1 & 2 \end{vmatrix}$

3. $\begin{vmatrix} -4 & 2 \\ 0 & 8 \end{vmatrix}$

4. $\begin{vmatrix} 5 & 0 \\ 3 & -5 \end{vmatrix}$

5. $\begin{vmatrix} -2 & 0 \\ 3 & -10 \end{vmatrix}$

6. $\begin{vmatrix} -1 & 4 \\ 0 & -18 \end{vmatrix}$

APPENDIX D | EXERCISE SET *MyMathLab*

PRACTICE   WATCH   DOWNLOAD   READ   REVIEW

Evaluate each determinant. See Example 1.

1. $\begin{vmatrix} 3 & 5 \\ -1 & 7 \end{vmatrix}$

2. $\begin{vmatrix} -5 & 1 \\ 1 & -4 \end{vmatrix}$

3. $\begin{vmatrix} 9 & -2 \\ 4 & -3 \end{vmatrix}$

4. $\begin{vmatrix} 4 & -1 \\ 9 & 8 \end{vmatrix}$

5. $\begin{vmatrix} -2 & 9 \\ 4 & -18 \end{vmatrix}$

6. $\begin{vmatrix} -40 & 8 \\ 70 & -14 \end{vmatrix}$

7. $\begin{vmatrix} \frac{3}{4} & \frac{5}{2} \\ \frac{1}{6} & \frac{7}{3} \end{vmatrix}$

8. $\begin{vmatrix} \frac{5}{7} & \frac{1}{3} \\ \frac{6}{7} & \frac{2}{3} \end{vmatrix}$

Use Cramer's rule, if possible, to solve each system of linear equations. See Examples 2 and 3.

9. $\begin{cases} 2y - 4 = 0 \\ x + 2y = 5 \end{cases}$

10. $\begin{cases} 4x - y = 5 \\ 3x - 3 = 0 \end{cases}$

11. $\begin{cases} 3x + y = 1 \\ 2y = 2 - 6x \end{cases}$

12. $\begin{cases} y = 2x - 5 \\ 8x - 4y = 20 \end{cases}$

13. $\begin{cases} 5x - 2y = 27 \\ -3x + 5y = 18 \end{cases}$

14. $\begin{cases} 4x - y = 9 \\ 2x + 3y = -27 \end{cases}$

15. $\begin{cases} 2x - 5y = 4 \\ x + 2y = -7 \end{cases}$

16. $\begin{cases} 3x - y = 2 \\ -5x + 2y = 0 \end{cases}$

17. $\begin{cases} \frac{2}{3}x - \frac{3}{4}y = -1 \\ -\frac{1}{6}x + \frac{3}{4}y = \frac{5}{2} \end{cases}$

18. $\begin{cases} \frac{1}{2}x - \frac{1}{3}y = -3 \\ \frac{1}{8}x + \frac{1}{6}y = 0 \end{cases}$

Evaluate. See Example 4.

19. $\begin{vmatrix} 2 & 1 & 0 \\ 0 & 5 & -3 \\ 4 & 0 & 2 \end{vmatrix}$

20. $\begin{vmatrix} -6 & 4 & 2 \\ 1 & 0 & 5 \\ 0 & 3 & 1 \end{vmatrix}$

21. $\begin{vmatrix} 4 & -6 & 0 \\ -2 & 3 & 0 \\ 4 & -6 & 1 \end{vmatrix}$

22. $\begin{vmatrix} 5 & 2 & 1 \\ 3 & -6 & 0 \\ -2 & 8 & 0 \end{vmatrix}$

23. $\begin{vmatrix} 1 & 0 & 4 \\ 1 & -1 & 2 \\ 3 & 2 & 1 \end{vmatrix}$

24. $\begin{vmatrix} 0 & 1 & 2 \\ 3 & -1 & 2 \\ 3 & 2 & -2 \end{vmatrix}$

25. $\begin{vmatrix} 3 & 6 & -3 \\ -1 & -2 & 3 \\ 4 & -1 & 6 \end{vmatrix}$

26. $\begin{vmatrix} 2 & -2 & 1 \\ 4 & 1 & 3 \\ 3 & 1 & 2 \end{vmatrix}$

Use Cramer's rule, if possible, to solve each system of linear equations. See Example 5.

27. $\begin{cases} 3x + z = -1 \\ -x - 3y + z = 7 \\ 3y + z = 5 \end{cases}$

28. $\begin{cases} 4y - 3z = -2 \\ 8x - 4y = 4 \\ -8x + 4y + z = -2 \end{cases}$

29. $\begin{cases} x + y + z = 8 \\ 2x - y - z = 10 \\ x - 2y + 3z = 22 \end{cases}$

30. $\begin{cases} 5x + y + 3z = 1 \\ x - y - 3z = -7 \\ -x + y = 1 \end{cases}$

31. $\begin{cases} 2x + 2y + z = 1 \\ -x + y + 2z = 3 \\ x + 2y + 4z = 0 \end{cases}$

32. $\begin{cases} 2x - 3y + z = 5 \\ x + y + z = 0 \\ 4x + 2y + 4z = 4 \end{cases}$

33. $\begin{cases} x - 2y + z = -5 \\ 3y + 2z = 4 \\ 3x - y = -2 \end{cases}$

34. $\begin{cases} 4x + 5y = 10 \\ 3y + 2z = -6 \\ x + y + z = 3 \end{cases}$

CONCEPT EXTENSIONS

Find the value of x that will make each a true statement.

35. $\begin{vmatrix} 1 & x \\ 2 & 7 \end{vmatrix} = -3$

36. $\begin{vmatrix} 6 & 1 \\ -2 & x \end{vmatrix} = 26$

37. If all the elements in a single row of a determinant are zero, what is the value of the determinant? Explain your answer.

38. If all the elements in a single column of a determinant are 0, what is the value of the determinant? Explain your answer.

Appendix E

An Introduction to Using a Graphing Utility

THE VIEWING WINDOW AND INTERPRETING WINDOW SETTINGS

In this appendix, we will use the term **graphing utility** to mean a graphing calculator or a computer software graphing package. All graphing utilities graph equations by plotting points on a screen. While plotting several points can be slow and sometimes tedious for us, a graphing utility can quickly and accurately plot hundreds of points. How does a graphing utility show plotted points? A computer or calculator screen is made up of a grid of small rectangular areas called **pixels.** If a pixel contains a point to be plotted, the pixel is turned "on"; otherwise, the pixel remains "off." The graph of an equation is then a collection of pixels turned "on." The graph of $y = 3x + 1$ from a graphing calculator is shown in Figure A-1. Notice the irregular shape of the line caused by the rectangular pixels.

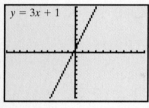

Figure A-1

The portion of the coordinate plane shown on the screen in Figure A-1 is called the **viewing window** or the **viewing rectangle.** Notice the x-axis and the y-axis on the graph. While tick marks are shown on the axes, they are not labeled. This means that from this screen alone, we do not know how many units each tick mark represents. To see what each tick mark represents and the minimum and maximum values on the axes, check the window setting of the graphing utility. It defines the viewing window. The window of the graph of $y = 3x + 1$ shown in Figure A-1 has the following setting (Figure A-2):

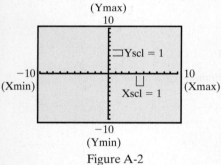

Figure A-2

Xmin $= -10$	The minimum x-value is -10.
Xmax $= 10$	The maximum x-value is 10.
Xscl $= 1$	The x-axis scale is 1 unit per tick mark.
Ymin $= -10$	The minimum y-value is -10.
Ymax $= 10$	The maximum y-value is 10.
Yscl $= 1$	The y-axis scale is 1 unit per tick mark.

By knowing the scale, we can find the minimum and the maximum values on the axes simply by counting tick marks. For example, if both the Xscl (x-axis scale) and the Yscl are 1 unit per tick mark on the graph in Figure A-3, we can count the tick marks and find that the minimum x-value is -10 and the maximum x-value is 10. Also, the minimum y-value is -10 and the maximum y-value is 10. If the Xscl (x-axis scale) changes to 2 units per tick mark (shown in Figure A-4), by counting tick marks, we see that the minimum x-value is now -20 and the maximum x-value is now 20.

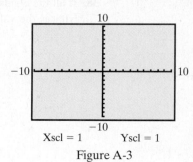

Figure A-3

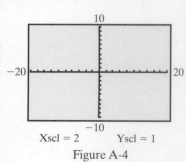

Figure A-4

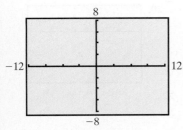

Figure A-5

It is also true that if we know the Xmin and the Xmax values, we can calculate the Xscl by the displayed axes. For example, the Xscl of the graph in Figure A-5 must be 3 units per tick mark for the maximum and minimum x-values to be as shown. Also, the Yscl of that graph must be 2 units per tick mark for the maximum and minimum y-values to be as shown.

We will call the viewing window in Figure A-3 a *standard* viewing window or rectangle. Although a standard viewing window is sufficient for much of this text, special care must be taken to ensure that all key features of a graph are shown. Figures A-6, A-7, and A-8 show the graph of $y = x^2 + 11x - 1$ on three different viewing windows. Note that certain viewing windows for this equation are misleading.

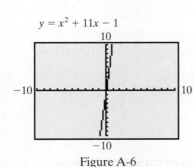

Figure A-6

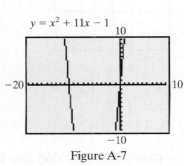

Figure A-7

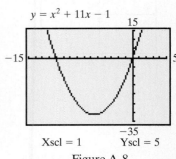

Figure A-8

How do we ensure that all distinguishing features of the graph of an equation are shown? It helps to know about the equation that is being graphed. For example, the equation $y = x^2 + 11x - 1$ is not a linear equation and its graph is not a line. This equation is a quadratic equation and, therefore, its graph is a parabola. By knowing this information, we know that the graph shown in Figure A-6, although correct, is misleading. Of the three viewing rectangles shown, the graph in Figure A-8 is best because it shows more of the distinguishing features of the parabola. Properties of equations needed for graphing will be studied in this text.

VIEWING WINDOW AND INTERPRETING WINDOW SETTINGS EXERCISE SET

In Exercises 1–4, determine whether all ordered pairs listed will lie within a standard viewing rectangle.

1. $(-9, 0), (5, 8), (1, -8)$
2. $(4, 7), (0, 0), (-8, 9)$
3. $(-11, 0), (2, 2), (7, -5)$
4. $(3, 5), (-3, -5), (15, 0)$

In Exercises 5–10, choose an Xmin, Xmax, Ymin, and Ymax so that all ordered pairs listed will lie within the viewing rectangle.

5. $(-90, 0), (55, 80), (0, -80)$
6. $(4, 70), (20, 20), (-18, 90)$
7. $(-11, 0), (2, 2), (7, -5)$
8. $(3, 5), (-3, -5), (15, 0)$
9. $(200, 200), (50, -50), (70, -50)$
10. $(40, 800), (-30, 500), (15, 0)$

Write the window setting for each viewing window shown. Use the following format:

Xmin =	Ymin =
Xmax =	Ymax =
Xscl =	Yscl =

11.

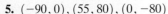

12.

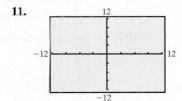

13.

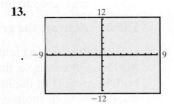

14.

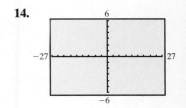

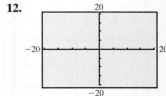

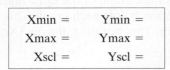

15.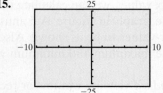

16.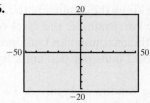

19.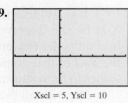
Xscl = 5, Yscl = 10

20.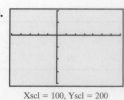
Xscl = 100, Yscl = 200

17.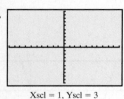
Xscl = 1, Yscl = 3

18.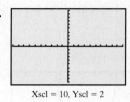
Xscl = 10, Yscl = 2

GRAPHING EQUATIONS AND SQUARE VIEWING WINDOW

In general, the following steps may be used to graph an equation on a standard viewing window.

> **Graphing an Equation in X and Y with a Graphing Utility on a Standard Viewing Window**
>
> **Step 1:** Solve the equation for y.
>
> **Step 2:** Using your graphing utility and enter the equation in the form
> Y = *expression involving x*.
>
> **Step 3:** Activate the graphing utility.

Special care must be taken when entering the *expression involving x* in Step 2. You must be sure that the graphing utility you are using interprets the expression as you want it to. For example, let's graph $3y = 4x$. To do so,

STEP 1: Solve the equation for y.

$$3y = 4x$$
$$\frac{3y}{3} = \frac{4x}{3}$$
$$y = \frac{4}{3}x$$

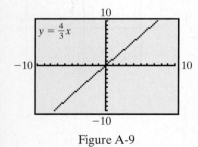

Figure A-9

STEP 2: Using your graphing utility, enter the expression $\frac{4}{3}x$ after the Y = prompt.
In order for your graphing utility to correctly interpret the expression, you may need to enter $(4/3)x$ or $(4 \div 3)x$.

STEP 3: Activate the graphing utility. The graph should appear as in Figure A-9.

Distinguishing features of the graph of a line include showing all the intercepts of the line. For example, the window of the graph of the line in Figure A-10 does not show both intercepts of the line, but the window of the graph of the same line in Figure A-11 does show both intercepts. Notice the notation below each graph. This is a shorthand notation of the range setting of the graph. This notation means [Xmin, Xmax] by [Ymin, Ymax].

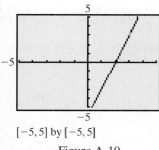

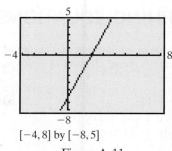

$[-5,5]$ by $[-5,5]$

Figure A-10

$[-4,8]$ by $[-8,5]$

Figure A-11

On a standard viewing window, the tick marks on the y-axis are closer together than the tick marks on the x-axis. This happens because the viewing window is a rectangle, and so 10 equally spaced tick marks on the positive y-axis will be closer together than 10 equally spaced tick marks on the positive x-axis. This causes the appearance of graphs to be distorted.

For example, notice the different appearances of the same line graphed using different viewing windows. The line in Figure A-12 is distorted because the tick marks along the x-axis are farther apart than the tick marks along the y-axis. The graph of the same line in Figure A-13 is not distorted because the viewing rectangle has been selected so that there is equal spacing between tick marks on both axes.

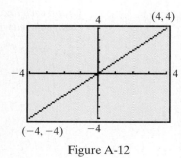

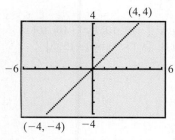

Figure A-12

Figure A-13

We say that the line in Figure A-13 is graphed on a *square* setting. Some graphing utilities have a built-in program that, if activated, will automatically provide a square setting. A square setting is especially helpful when we are graphing perpendicular lines, circles, or when a true geometric perspective is desired. Some examples of square screens are shown in Figures A-14 and A-15.

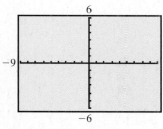

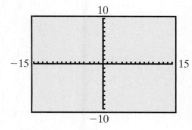

Figure A-14

Figure A-15

Other features of a graphing utility such as Trace, Zoom, Intersect, and Table are discussed in appropriate Graphing Calculator Explorations in this text.

GRAPHING EQUATIONS AND SQUARE VIEWING WINDOW EXERCISE SET

Graph each linear equation in two variables, using the two different range settings given. Determine which setting shows all intercepts of a line.

1. $y = 2x + 12$
Setting A: $[-10, 10]$ by $[-10, 10]$
Setting B: $[-10, 10]$ by $[-10, 15]$

2. $y = -3x + 25$
Setting A: $[-5, 5]$ by $[-30, 10]$
Setting B: $[-10, 10]$ by $[-10, 30]$

3. $y = -x - 41$
Setting A: $[-50, 10]$ by $[-10, 10]$
Setting B: $[-50, 10]$ by $[-50, 15]$

4. $y = 6x - 18$
Setting A: $[-10, 10]$ by $[-20, 10]$
Setting B: $[-10, 10]$ by $[-10, 10]$

5. $y = \dfrac{1}{2}x - 15$
Setting B: $[-10, 10]$ by $[-20, 10]$
Setting B: $[-10, 35]$ by $[-20, 15]$

6. $y = -\dfrac{2}{3}x - \dfrac{29}{3}$
Setting A: $[-10, 10]$ by $[-10, 10]$
Setting B: $[-15, 5]$ by $[-15, 5]$

The graph of each equation is a line. Use a graphing utility and a standard viewing window to graph each equation.

7. $3x = 5y$ **8.** $7y = -3x$ **9.** $9x - 5y = 30$
10. $4x + 6y = 20$ **11.** $y = -7$ **12.** $y = 2$
13. $x + 10y = -5$ **14.** $x - 5y = 9$

Graph the following equations using the square setting given. Some keystrokes that may be helpful are given.

15. $y = \sqrt{x}$ $[-12, 12]$ by $[-8, 8]$
Suggested keystrokes: $\sqrt{}\, x$

16. $y = \sqrt{2x}$ $[-12, 12]$ by $[-8, 8]$
Suggested keystrokes: $\sqrt{}\,(2x)$

17. $y = x^2 + 2x + 1$ $[-15, 15]$ by $[-10, 10]$
Suggested keystrokes: $x^\wedge 2 + 2x + 1$

18. $y = x^2 - 5$ $[-15, 15]$ by $[-10, 10]$
Suggested keystrokes: $x^\wedge 2 - 5$

19. $y = |x|$ $[-9, 9]$ by $[-6, 6]$
Suggested keystrokes: $ABS\,(x)$

20. $y = |x - 2|$ $[-9, 9]$ by $[-6, 6]$
Suggested keystrokes: $ABS(x - 2)$

Graph each line. Use a standard viewing window; then, if necessary, change the viewing window so that all intercepts of each line show.

21. $x + 2y = 30$ **22.** $1.5x - 3.7y = 40.3$

Answers to Selected Exercises

CHAPTER 1 REAL NUMBERS AND ALGEBRAIC EXPRESSIONS

Section 1.2
Practice Exercises
1. 14 sq cm   **2.** 31   **3. a.** $\{6, 7, 8, 9\}$ **b.** $\{41, 42, 43, \dots\}$ **4. a.** true   **b.** true   **5. a.** true   **b.** false   **c.** true   **d.** false
6. a. 4   **b.** $\frac{1}{2}$ **c.** 1   **d.** -6.8 **e.** -4 **7. a.** -5.4 **b.** $\frac{3}{5}$ **c.** -18 **8. a.** $3x$ **b.** $2x - 5$ **c.** $3\frac{5}{8} + x$ **d.** $\frac{x}{2}$ **e.** $x - 14$ **f.** $5(x + 10)$

Vocabulary and Readiness Check 1.2
1. variables   **3.** absolute value   **5.** natural numbers   **7.** integers   **9.** rational number

Exercise Set 1.2
1. 35   **3.** 30.38   **5.** $\frac{3}{8}$ **7.** 22   **9.** 2000 mi   **11.** 20.4 sq. ft   **13.** $10,612.80   **15.** $\{1, 2, 3, 4. 5\}$ **17.** $\{11, 12, 13, 14, 15, 16\}$ **19.** $\{0\}$
21. $\{0, 2, 4, 6, 8\}$ **23.**   **25.**   **27.**
29. answers may vary   **31.** $\{3, 0, \sqrt{36}\}$ **33.** $\{3, \sqrt{36}\}$ **35.** $\{\sqrt{7}\}$ **37.** $\in$ **39.** $\notin$ **41.** $\notin$ **43.** $\notin$ **45.** true   **47.** true
49. false   **51.** false   **53.** true   **55.** false   **57.** answers may vary   **59.** -2 **61.** 4   **63.** 0   **65.** -3 **67.** answers may vary   **69.** 6.2
71. $-\frac{4}{7}$ **73.** $\frac{2}{3}$ **75.** 0   **77.** $2x$ **79.** $2x + 5$ **81.** $x - 10$ **83.** $x + 2$ **85.** $\frac{x}{11}$ **87.** $12 - 3x$ **89.** $x + 2.3$ or $x + 2\frac{3}{10}$ **91.** $1\frac{1}{3} - x$
93. $\frac{5}{4 - x}$ **95.** $2(x + 3)$ **97.** 137   **99.** 69   **101.** answers may vary

Section 1.3
Practice Exercises
1. a. -8 **b.** -3 **c.** 5   **d.** -8.1 **e.** $\frac{1}{15}$ **2. a.** -8 **b.** -3 **c.** -12 **d.** 7.7   **e.** $\frac{8}{21}$ **f.** 1.8   **g.** -7 **3. a.** 12   **b.** -4
4. a. -15 **b.** $\frac{1}{2}$ **c.** -10.2 **d.** 0   **e.** $-\frac{2}{13}$ **f.** 36   **g.** -11.5 **5. a.** -2 **b.** 5   **c.** $-\frac{1}{6}$ **d.** -6 **e.** $\frac{1}{9}$ **f.** 0   **6. a.** 8   **b.** $\frac{1}{9}$
c. -36 **d.** 36   **e.** -64 **f.** -64 **7. a.** 7   **b.** $\frac{1}{4}$ **c.** -8 **d.** not a real number   **e.** 10   **8. a.** 4   **b.** -1 **c.** 10   **9. a.** 2
b. 27   **c.** -29 **10.** 19   **11.** $-\frac{17}{44}$ **12. a.** 67   **b.** -100 **c.** $-\frac{39}{80}$ **13.** 23; 50; 77

Vocabulary and Readiness Check 1.3
1. b, c   **3.** b, d   **5.** b   **7.** 0   **9.** reciprocal   **11.** exponent   **13.** square root

Exercise Set 1.3
1. 5   **3.** -24 **5.** -11 **7.** -4 **9.** $\frac{4}{3}$ **11.** -2 **13.** $-\frac{1}{2}$ **15.** -6 **17.** -60 **19.** 0   **21.** 0   **23.** -3 **25.** 3   **27.** $-\frac{1}{6}$ **29.** 0.56
31. -7 **33.** -8 **35.** -49 **37.** 36   **39.** -8 **41.** $-\frac{1}{27}$ **43.** 7   **45.** $-\frac{2}{3}$ **47.** 4   **49.** 3   **51.** not a real number   **53.** 48   **55.** -1
57. -9 **59.** 17   **61.** -4 **63.** -2 **65.** 11   **67.** $-\frac{3}{4}$ **69.** 7   **71.** -11 **73.** -2.1 **75.** $-\frac{1}{3}$ **77.** $-\frac{79}{15}$ **79.** $-\frac{4}{5}$ **81.** -81
83. $-\frac{20}{33}$ **85.** 93   **87.** -12 **89.** $-\frac{23}{18}$ **91.** 5   **93.** $-\frac{3}{19}$ **95.** 18; 22; 28; 208   **97.** 600; 150; 105   **99.** $\frac{5}{2}$ **101.** $\frac{13}{35}$ **103.** 4205 m
105. $(2 + 7) \cdot (1 + 3)$ **107.** answers may vary   **109.** 3.1623   **111.** 2.8107   **113.** -0.5876 **115.** 15.6%   **117.** 17.7%
119. Long-term. Short-term is very volatile.

Integrated Review
1. 16   **2.** -16 **3.** 0   **4.** -11 **5.** -5 **6.** $-\frac{1}{60}$ **7.** undefined   **8.** -2.97 **9.** 4   **10.** -50 **11.** 35   **12.** 92   **13.** $-15 - 2x$
14. $3x + 5$ **15.** 0   **16.** true

Section 1.4

Practice Exercises

1. $-4x = 20$ **2.** $3(z - 3) = 9$ **3.** $x + 5 = 2x - 3$ **4.** $y + 2 = 4 + \dfrac{z}{8}$ **5. a.** $<$ **b.** $=$ **c.** $>$ **d.** $>$ **6. a.** $x - 3 \leq 5$ **b.** $y \neq -4$

c. $2 < 4 + \dfrac{1}{2}z$ **7. a.** 7 **b.** -4.7 **c.** $\dfrac{3}{8}$ **8. a.** $-\dfrac{3}{5}$ **b.** $\dfrac{1}{14}$ **c.** $-\dfrac{1}{2}$ **9.** $13x + 8$ **10.** $(3 \cdot 11)b = 33b$ **11. a.** $4x + 20y$ **b.** $-3 + 2z$

c. $0.3xy - 0.9x$ **12. a.** $0.10x$ **b.** $26y$ **c.** $1.75z$ **d.** $0.15t$ **13. a.** $16 - x$ **b.** $180 - x$ **c.** $x + 2$ **d.** $x + 9$ **14. a.** $5ab$

b. $10x - 5$ **c.** $17p - 9$ **15. a.** $-pq + 7$ **b.** $x^2 + 19$ **c.** $5.8x + 3.8$ **d.** $-c - 8d + \dfrac{1}{4}$

Vocabulary and Readiness Check 1.4

1. $<$ **3.** $\neq$ **5.** $\geq$ **7.** $-a$ **9.** commutative   **11.** distributive   **13.** terms

Exercise Set 1.4

1. $10 + x = -12$ **3.** $2x + 5 = -14$ **5.** $\dfrac{n}{5} = 4n$ **7.** $z - \dfrac{1}{2} = \dfrac{1}{2}z$ **9.** $7x \leq -21$ **11.** $2(x - 6) > \dfrac{1}{11}$ **13.** $2(x - 6) = -27$

15. $>$ **17.** $=$ **19.** $<$ **21.** $<$ **23.** $<$ **25.** $-5; \dfrac{1}{5}$ **27.** $8; -\dfrac{1}{8}$ **29.** $\dfrac{1}{7}; -7$ **31.** 0; undefined   **33.** $\dfrac{7}{8}; -\dfrac{7}{8}$

35. Zero. For every real number $x, 0 \cdot x \neq 1$, so 0 has no reciprocal. It is the only real number that has no reciprocal because if $x \neq 0$, then $x \cdot \dfrac{1}{x} = 1$

by definition.   **37.** $y + 7x$ **39.** $w \cdot z$ **41.** $\dfrac{x}{5} \cdot \dfrac{1}{3}$ **43.** no; answers may vary   **45.** $(5 \cdot 7)x$ **47.** $x + (1.2 + y)$ **49.** $14(z \cdot y)$

51. 10 and 4. Subtraction is not associative.   **53.** $3x + 15$ **55.** $-2a - b$ **57.** $12x + 10y + 4z$ **59.** $-4x + 8y - 28$ **61.** $3xy - 1.5x$
63. $6 + 3x$ **65.** 0 **67.** 7 **69.** $(10 \cdot 2)y$ **71.** $a(b + c) = ab + ac$ **73.** $0.1d$ **75.** $112 - x$ **77.** $90 - 5x$ **79.** $\$35.61y$ **81.** $2x + 2$

83. $-8y - 14$ **85.** $-9c - 4$ **87.** $4 - 8y$ **89.** $y^2 - 11yz - 11$ **91.** $3t - 14$ **93.** 0 **95.** $13n - 20$ **97.** $8.5y - 20.8$ **99.** $\dfrac{3}{8}a - \dfrac{1}{12}$

101. $20y + 48$ **103.** $-5x + \dfrac{5}{6}y - 1$ **105.** $-x - 6y - \dfrac{11}{24}$ **107.** $(5 \cdot 7)y$ **109.** $6.5y - 7.92x + 25.47$ **111.** no   **113.** 80 million

115. 35 million   **117.** 20.25%

Chapter 1 Vocabulary Check

1. algebraic expression   **2.** opposite   **3.** distributive   **4.** absolute value   **5.** exponent   **6.** variable   **7.** inequality   **8.** reciprocals
9. commutative   **10.** associative   **11.** whole   **12.** real

Chapter 1 Review

1. 21   **3.** 324,000   **5.** $\{-2, 0, 2, 4, 6\}$ **7.** $\varnothing$ **9.** $\{\ldots, -1, 0, 1, 2\}$ **11.** false   **13.** true   **15.** true   **17.** true   **19.** true

21. true   **23.** true   **25.** true   **27.** true   **29.** $\left\{5, \dfrac{8}{2}, \sqrt{9}\right\}$ **31.** $\left\{\sqrt{7}, \pi\right\}$ **33.** $\left\{5, \dfrac{8}{2}, \sqrt{9}, -1\right\}$ **35.** -0.6 **37.** -1 **39.** $\dfrac{1}{0.6}$

41. 1   **43.** -35 **45.** 0.31   **47.** 13.3   **49.** 0   **51.** 0   **53.** -5 **55.** 4   **57.** 9   **59.** 3   **61.** $-\dfrac{32}{135}$ **63.** $-\dfrac{5}{4}$ **65.** $\dfrac{5}{8}$ **67.** -1

69. 1   **71.** -4 **73.** $\dfrac{5}{7}$ **75.** $\dfrac{1}{5}$ **77.** -5 **79.** 5   **81. a.** 6.28; 62.8; 628   **b.** increase   **83.** $-5x - 9$ **85.** $-15x^2 + 6$ **87.** $5.7x + 1.1$

89. $n + 2n = -15$ **91.** $6(t - 5) = 4$ **93.** $9x - 10 = 5$ **95.** $-4 < 7y$ **97.** $t + 6 \leq -12$ **99.** distributive property
101. commutative property of addition   **103.** multiplicative inverse property   **105.** associative property of multiplication

107. multiplicative identity property   **109.** $(3 + x) + (7 + y)$ **111.** $2 \cdot \dfrac{1}{2}$, for example   **113.** $7 + 0$ **115.** $>$ **117.** $=$ **119.** $>$

121. $5; \dfrac{1}{5}$ **123.** 9   **125.** 15   **127.** $\dfrac{1}{11}$ **129.** 1.8, 1.0, 0.4, 0.7, 0.2, 0.7, 1.0

Chapter 1 Test

1. true   **2.** false   **3.** false   **4.** false   **5.** true   **6.** false   **7.** -3 **8.** -56 **9.** -225 **10.** 3   **11.** 1   **12.** $-\dfrac{3}{2}$ **13.** 12   **14.** 1

15. a. 5.75; 17.25; 57.50; 115.00   **b.** increase   **16.** $2(x + 5) = 30$ **17.** $\dfrac{(6 - y)^2}{7} < -2$ **18.** $\dfrac{9z}{|-12|} \neq 10$ **19.** $3\left(\dfrac{n}{5}\right) = -n$

20. $20 = 2x - 6$ **21.** $-2 = \dfrac{x}{x + 5}$ **22.** distributive property   **23.** associative property of addition   **24.** additive inverse property

25. multiplication property of zero   **26.** $0.05n + 0.1d$ **27.** $-6x - 14$ **28.** $\dfrac{1}{2}a - \dfrac{9}{8}$ **29.** $2y - 10$ **30.** $-1.3x + 1.9$

CHAPTER 2 EQUATIONS, INEQUALITIES, AND PROBLEM SOLVING

Section 2.1
Practice Exercises
1. 5 **2.** 0.2 **3.** -5 **4.** -4 **5.** $\dfrac{5}{6}$ **6.** $\dfrac{5}{4}$ **7.** -3 **8.** { } or $\varnothing$ **9.** all real numbers or $\{x \mid x$ is a real number$\}$

Vocabulary and Readiness Check 2.1
1. equivalent **3.** addition **5.** expression **7.** equation **9.** all real numbers **11.** no solution

Exercise Set 2.1
1. 6 **3.** -22 **5.** 4.7 **7.** 10 **9.** -1.1 **11.** -5 **13.** -2 **15.** 0 **17.** 2 **19.** -9 **21.** $-\dfrac{10}{7}$ **23.** $\dfrac{9}{10}$ **25.** 4 **27.** 1 **29.** 5

31. $\dfrac{40}{3}$ **33.** 17 **35.** all real numbers **37.** $\varnothing$ **39.** all real numbers **41.** $\varnothing$ **43.** $\dfrac{1}{8}$ **45.** 0 **47.** all real numbers **49.** 4 **51.** $\dfrac{4}{5}$

53. 8 **55.** $\varnothing$ **57.** -8 **59.** $-\dfrac{5}{4}$ **61.** -2 **63.** 23 **65.** $-\dfrac{2}{9}$ **67.** $\dfrac{8}{x}$ **69.** $8x$ **71.** $2x - 5$ **73.** subtract 19 instead of adding; -3

75. $0.4 - 1.6 = -1.2$, not 1.2; -0.24 **77. a.** $4x + 5$ **b.** -3 **c.** answers may vary **79.** answers may vary **81.** $K = -11$ **83.** $K = -23$

85. answers may vary **87.** 1 **89.** 3 **91.** -4.86 **93.** 1.53

Section 2.2
Practice Exercises
1. a. $3x + 6$ **b.** $6x - 1$ **2.** $3x + 17.3$ **3.** $14, 34, 70$ **4.** \$450 **5.** width: 32 in.; length: 48 in. **6.** $25, 27, 29$

Vocabulary and Readiness Check 2.2
1. $>$ **3.** $=$ **5.** $31, 32, 33, 34$ **7.** $18, 20, 22$ **9.** $y, y + 1, y + 2$ **11.** $p, p + 1, p + 2, p + 3$

Exercise Set 2.2
1. $4y$ **3.** $3z + 3$ **5.** $(65x + 30)$ cents **7.** $10x + 3$ **9.** $2x + 14$ **11.** -5 **13.** $45, 145, 225$ **15.** approximately 1612.41 million acres
17. 2344 earthquakes **19.** 1275 shoppers **21.** 22% **23.** 417 employees **25.** 29.98 million **27.** $29°, 35°, 116°$ **29.** 28 m, 36 m, 38 m
31. 18 in., 18 in., 27 in., 36 in. **33.** 75, 76, 77 **35.** Fallon's zip code is 89406; Fernley's zip code is 89408; Gardnerville Ranchos' zip code is 89410
37. 317 thousand; 279 thousand; 184 thousand **39.** medical assistant: 215 thousand; postsecondary teacher jobs: 603 thousand; registered nurses: 623
thousand **41.** 757-200: 190 seats; 737-200: 113 seats; 737-300: 134 seats **43.** \$430.00 **45.** 41.7 million **47.** $40°, 140°$ **49.** $64°, 32°, 84°$
51. square: 18 cm; triangle: 24 cm **53.** 76, 78, 80 **55.** 40.5 ft; 202.5 ft; 240 ft **57.** Los Angeles: 61.0 million, Atlanta: 74.3 million, Chicago: 62.3 million
59. incandescent: 1500 bulb hours; fluorescent: 100,000 bulb hours; halogen: 4000 bulb hours **61.** height: 48 in.; width: 108 in.
63. a. \$4.9 billion **b.** \$1.23 billion **65.** Russia: 5.6%; China: 19.3%; U.S.: 9.9% **67.** 309 pages **69.** Germany: 11; U.S.: 9; Canada: 7
71. -54 **73.** 155 **75.** 557.424 **77.** answers may vary **79.** $50°$ **81. a.** 2032 **b.** 1015.8 **c.** 3 cigarettes per day; answers may vary
83. 500 boards; \$30,000 **85.** company makes a profit

Section 2.3
Practice Exercises
1. $t = \dfrac{I}{Pr}$ **2.** $y = \dfrac{7}{2}x - \dfrac{5}{2}$ **3.** $r = \dfrac{A - P}{Pt}$ **4.** \$10, 134.16 **5.** 25.6 hr; 25 hr 36 min

Exercise Set 2.3
1. $t = \dfrac{D}{r}$ **3.** $R = \dfrac{I}{PT}$ **5.** $y = \dfrac{9x - 16}{4}$ **7.** $W = \dfrac{P - 2L}{2}$ **9.** $A = \dfrac{J + 3}{C}$ **11.** $g = \dfrac{W}{h - 3t^2}$ **13.** $B = \dfrac{T - 2C}{AC}$ **15.** $r = \dfrac{C}{2\pi}$

17. $r = \dfrac{E - IR}{I}$ **19.** $L = \dfrac{2s - an}{n}$ **21.** $v = \dfrac{3st^4 - N}{5s}$ **23.** $H = \dfrac{S - 2LW}{2L + 2W}$ **25.** \$4703.71; \$4713.99; \$4719.22; \$4722.74; \$4724.45

27. a. \$7313.97 **b.** \$7321.14 **c.** \$7325.98 **29.** $40°C$ **31.** 3.6 hr, or 3 hr and 36 min **33.** 171 packages **35.** 9 ft **37.** 2 gal
39. a. 1174.86 cu. m **b.** 310.34 cu. m **c.** 1485.20 cu. m **41.** 128.3 mph **43.** 0.42 ft **45.** 41.125π ft ≈ 129.1325 ft **47.** \$1831.96
49. $f = \dfrac{C - 4h - 4p}{9}$ **51.** 178 cal **53.** 1.5 g **55.** $-3, -2, -1$ **57.** $-3, -2, -1, 0, 1$ **59.** answers may vary

61. 0.388; 0.723; 1.00; 1.523; 5.202; 9.538; 19.193; 30.065; 39.505 **63.** \$6.80 per person **65.** 4 times a year; answers may vary **67.** 0.25 sec **69.** $\dfrac{1}{4}$

71. $\dfrac{3}{8}$ **73.** $\dfrac{3}{8}$ **75.** $\dfrac{3}{4}$ **77.** 1 **79.** 1

Section 2.4
Practice Exercises

1. a. $(-\infty, 3.5)$ **b.** $[-3, \infty)$ **c.** $[-1, 4)$ **2.** $(4, \infty)$

3. $(-\infty, -4]$ **4. a.** $\left[\frac{2}{3}, \infty\right)$ **b.** $(-4, \infty)$ **5.** $\left[-\frac{3}{2}, \infty\right)$

6. $(-\infty, 13]$ **7.** $(-\infty, \infty)$ **8.** Sales must be $\geq$ \$10,000 per month.   **9.** the entire year 2021 and after

Vocabulary and Readiness Check 2.4

1. d   **3.** b   **5.** $[-0.4, \infty)$ **7.** $(-\infty, -0.4]$ **9.** no   **11.** yes

Exercise Set 2.4

1. $(-\infty, -3)$ **3.** $[0.3, \infty)$ **5.** $[-7, \infty)$ **7.** $(-2, 5)$

9. $(-1, 5]$ **11.** $[-2, \infty)$ **13.** $(-\infty, 1)$ **15.** $(-\infty, 2]$

17. $[8, \infty)$ **19.** $(-\infty, -4.7)$ **21.** $(-\infty, -3]$ **23.** $(-\infty, -1]$ **25.** $(-\infty, 11]$

27. $(0, \infty)$ **29.** $(-13, \infty)$ **31.** $\left[-\frac{79}{3}, \infty\right)$ **33.** $\left(-\infty, -\frac{35}{6}\right)$ **35.** $(-\infty, -6)$ **37.** $(4, \infty)$ **39.** $[-0.5, \infty)$ **41.** $(-\infty, 7]$ **43.** $[0, \infty)$

45. $(-\infty, -29]$ **47.** $[3, \infty)$ **49.** $(-\infty, -1]$ **51.** $[-31, \infty)$ **53.** $(-\infty, -2]$ **55.** $(-\infty, -15)$ **57.** $\left[-\frac{37}{3}, \infty\right)$ **59.** $(-\infty, 5)$

61. $(-\infty, 9)$ **63.** $\left(-\infty, -\frac{11}{2}\right]$ **65.** $(-\infty, \infty)$ **67.** $\varnothing$ **69. a.** $\{x \mid x \geq 81\}$ **b.** A final exam grade of 81 or higher will result in an average of 77 or higher.   **71. a.** $\{x \mid x \leq 1040\}$ **b.** The luggage and cargo must weight 1040 pounds or less.   **73. a.** $\{x \mid x \leq 20\}$

b. She can move at most 20 whole boxes at one time.   **75. a.** $\{x \mid x > 200\}$ **b.** If you make more than 200 calls, plan 1 is more economical.
77. $\{F \mid F \geq 932°\}$ **79. a.** 2011   **b.** answers may vary   **81.** decreasing; answers may vary   **83.** 5.7 gal   **85.** during 2008

87. answers may vary   **89.** 2, 3, 4   **91.** 2, 3, 4, . . .   **93.** 5   **95.** $\frac{13}{6}$ **97.** $\{x \mid x \geq 2\}; [2, \infty)$ **99.** $; (-\infty, 0)$

101. $\{x \mid -2 < x \leq 1.5\};$ **103.** $\{4\}$ **105.** $(4, \infty)$ **107.** answers may vary   **109.** answers may vary   **111.** answers may vary

The Bigger Picture

1. $-\frac{8}{3}$ **2.** 0   **3.** $(-1, \infty)$ **4.** 3   **5.** 6   **6.** $\varnothing$ **7.** $\left(-\infty, \frac{3}{2}\right]$ **8.** all real numbers or $(-\infty, \infty)$

Integrated Review

1. -5 **2.** $(-5, \infty)$ **3.** $\left[\frac{8}{3}, \infty\right)$ **4.** $[-1, \infty)$ **5.** 0   **6.** $\left[-\frac{1}{10}, \infty\right)$ **7.** $\left(-\infty, -\frac{1}{6}\right]$ **8.** 0   **9.** $\varnothing$ **10.** $\left[-\frac{3}{5}, \infty\right)$ **11.** 4.2   **12.** 6

13. -8 **14.** $(-\infty, -16)$ **15.** $\frac{20}{11}$ **16.** 1   **17.** $(38, \infty)$ **18.** -5.5 **19.** $\frac{3}{5}$ **20.** $(-\infty, \infty)$ **21.** 29   **22.** all real numbers

23. $(-\infty, 1)$ **24.** $\frac{9}{13}$ **25.** $(23, \infty)$ **26.** $(-\infty, 6]$ **27.** $\left(-\infty, \frac{3}{5}\right]$ **28.** $\left(-\infty, -\frac{19}{32}\right)$

Section 2.5
Practice Exercises

1. $\{1, 3\}$ **2.** $(-\infty, 2)$ **3.** $\{\ \}$ or $\varnothing$ **4.** $(-4, 2)$ **5.** $[-6, 8]$ **6.** $\{1, 2, 3, 4, 5, 6, 7, 9\}$ **7.** $\left(-\infty, \frac{3}{8}\right) \cup [3, \infty)$ **8.** $(-\infty, \infty)$

Vocabulary and Readiness Check 2.5

1. compound   **3.** or   **5.** $\cup$ **7.** and

Exercise Set 2.5

1. $\{2, 3, 4, 5, 6, 7\}$ **3.** $\{4, 6\}$ **5.** $\{\ldots, -2, -1, 0, 1, \ldots\}$ **7.** $\{5, 7\}$ **9.** $\{x \mid x$ is an odd integer or $x = 2$ or $x = 4\}$ **11.** $\{2, 4\}$

13. $(-3, 1)$ **15.** $\varnothing$ **17.** $(-\infty, -1)$ **19.** $[6, \infty)$ **21.** $(-\infty, -3]$ **23.** $(4, 10)$

25. $(11, 17)$ **27.** $[1, 4]$ **29.** $\left[-3, \frac{3}{2}\right]$ **31.** $\left[-\frac{7}{3}, 7\right]$ **33.** $(-\infty, 5)$ **35.** $(-\infty, -4] \cup [1, \infty)$

37. $(-\infty, \infty)$ **39.** $[2, \infty)$ **41.** $(-\infty, -4) \cup (-2, \infty)$ **43.** $(-\infty, \infty)$ **45.** $\left(-\frac{1}{2}, \frac{2}{3}\right)$ **47.** $(-\infty, \infty)$ **49.** $\left[\frac{3}{2}, 6\right]$

51. $\left(\dfrac{5}{4}, \dfrac{11}{4}\right)$ **53.** $\varnothing$ **55.** $\left(-\infty, -\dfrac{56}{5}\right) \cup \left(\dfrac{5}{3}, \infty\right)$ **57.** $\left(-5, \dfrac{5}{2}\right)$ **59.** $\left(0, \dfrac{14}{3}\right]$ **61.** $(-\infty, -3]$ **63.** $(-\infty, 1] \cup \left(\dfrac{29}{7}, \infty\right)$ **65.** $\varnothing$

67. $\left[-\dfrac{1}{2}, \dfrac{3}{2}\right)$ **69.** $\left(-\dfrac{4}{3}, \dfrac{7}{3}\right)$ **71.** $(6, 12)$ **73.** -12 **75.** -4 **77.** $-7, 7$ **79.** 0 **81.** $2003, 2004, 2005$ **83.** $-20.2° \le F \le 95°$

85. $67 \le$ final score ≤ 94 **87.** $(6, \infty)$ **89.** $[3, 7]$ **91.** $(-\infty, -1)$

The Bigger Picture

1. $[-1, 3]$ **2.** $(-1, 6)$ **3.** 5.1 **4.** $(-\infty, -4)$ **5.** $(-\infty, -3]$ **6.** $(-\infty, -2) \cup (2, \infty)$ **7.** 4 **8.** $[19, \infty)$

Section 2.6
Practice Exercises

1. $-7, 7$ **2.** $-1, 4$ **3.** $-80, 70$ **4.** $-2, 2$ **5.** 0 **6.** $\{ \}$ or $\varnothing$ **7.** $\{ \}$ or $\varnothing$ **8.** $-\dfrac{3}{5}, 5$ **9.** 5

Vocabulary and Readiness Check 2.6
1. C   **3.** B   **5.** D

Exercise Set 2.6

1. $7, -7$ **3.** $4.2, -4.2$ **5.** $7, -2$ **7.** $8, 4$ **9.** $5, -5$ **11.** $3, -3$ **13.** 0 **15.** $\varnothing$ **17.** $\dfrac{1}{5}$ **19.** $|x| = 5$ **21.** $9, -\dfrac{1}{2}$ **23.** $-\dfrac{5}{2}$

25. answers may vary   **27.** $4, -4$ **29.** 0 **31.** $\varnothing$ **33.** $0, \dfrac{14}{3}$ **35.** $2, -2$ **37.** $\varnothing$ **39.** $7, -1$ **41.** $\varnothing$ **43.** $\varnothing$ **45.** $-\dfrac{1}{8}$ **47.** $\dfrac{1}{2}, -\dfrac{5}{6}$

49. $2, -\dfrac{12}{5}$ **51.** $3, -2$ **53.** $-8, \dfrac{2}{3}$ **55.** $\varnothing$ **57.** 4 **59.** $13, -8$ **61.** $3, -3$ **63.** $8, -7$ **65.** $2, 3$ **67.** $2, -\dfrac{10}{3}$ **69.** $\dfrac{3}{2}$ **71.** $\varnothing$

73. answers may vary   **75.** 34% **77.** 39.6 lb   **79.** answers may vary   **81.** no solution   **83.** $|x - 7| = 2$ **85.** $|2x - 1| = 4$ **87. a.** $c = 0$
b. c is a negative number   **c.** c is a positive number

Section 2.7
Practice Exercises

1. $(-2, 2)$ **2.** $(-4, 2)$ **3.** $\left[-\dfrac{2}{3}, 2\right]$ **4.** $\{ \}$ or $\varnothing$ **5.** $(-\infty, -10] \cup [2, \infty)$

6. $(-\infty, \infty)$ **7.** $(-\infty, 0) \cup (12, \infty)$ **8.** 2

Vocabulary and Readiness Check 2.7
1. D   **3.** C   **5.** A

Exercise Set 2.7

1. $; [-4, 4]$ **3.** $; (1, 5)$ **5.** $; (-5, -1)$ **7.** $; [-10, 3]$ **9.** $; [-5, 5]$

11. $; \varnothing$ **13.** $; [0, 12]$ **15.** $; (-\infty, -3) \cup (3, \infty)$ **17.** $; (-\infty, -24] \cup [4, \infty)$

19. $; (-\infty, -4) \cup (4, \infty)$ **21.** $; (-\infty, \infty)$ **23.** $; \left(-\infty, \dfrac{2}{3}\right) \cup (2, \infty)$ **25.** $; \{0\}$

27. $; \left(-\infty, -\dfrac{3}{8}\right) \cup \left(-\dfrac{3}{8}, \infty\right)$ **29.** $; [-2, 2]$ **31.** $; (-\infty, -1) \cup (1, \infty)$

33. $; (-5, 11)$ **35.** $; (-\infty, 4) \cup (6, \infty)$ **37.** $; \varnothing$ **39.** $; (-\infty, \infty)$

41. $; [-2, 9]$ **43.** $; (-\infty, -11] \cup [1, \infty)$ **45.** $; (-\infty, 0) \cup (0, \infty)$ **47.** $; (-\infty, \infty)$

49. $; \left[-\dfrac{1}{2}, 1\right]$ **51.** $; (-\infty, -3) \cup (0, \infty)$ **53.** $; \varnothing$ **55.** $; \dfrac{3}{8}$

57. $; \left(-\dfrac{2}{3}, 0\right)$ **59.** $; (-\infty, -12) \cup (0, \infty)$ **61.** $; [-1, 8]$ **63.** $; \left[-\dfrac{23}{8}, \dfrac{17}{8}\right]$

65. $(-2, 5)$ **67.** $5, -2$ **69.** $(-\infty, -7] \cup [17, \infty)$ **71.** $-\dfrac{9}{4}$ **73.** $(-2, 1)$ **75.** $2, \dfrac{4}{3}$ **77.** $\varnothing$ **79.** $\dfrac{19}{2}, -\dfrac{17}{2}$ **81.** $\left(-\infty, -\dfrac{25}{3}\right) \cup \left(\dfrac{35}{3}, \infty\right)$

83. $\dfrac{1}{6}$ **85.** 0 **87.** $\dfrac{1}{3}$ **89.** -1.5 **91.** 0 **93.** $|x| < 7$ **95.** $|x| \le 5$ **97.** answers may vary   **99.** $3.45 < x < 3.55$

The Bigger Picture

1. -8 **2.** $-13, 21$ **3.** $(-\infty, 6]$ **4.** $(-7, 5]$ **5.** $-\dfrac{13}{2}$ **6.** $\varnothing$ **7.** -50 **8.** -5 **9.** $\left[-\dfrac{9}{5}, 1\right]$ **10.** $(\infty, -13) \cup (-9, \infty)$ **11.** $-3, \dfrac{23}{9}$

12. $-11, -\dfrac{9}{7}$

Chapter 2 Vocabulary Check

1. compound inequality   **2.** contradiction   **3.** intersection   **4.** union   **5.** identity   **6.** formula   **7.** absolute value   **8.** solution
9. consecutive integers   **10.** linear inequality in one variable   **11.** linear equation in one variable

Chapter 2 Review

1. 3   **3.** $-\dfrac{45}{14}$ **5.** 0   **7.** 6   **9.** all real number   **11.** $\varnothing$ **13.** -3 **15.** $\dfrac{96}{5}$ **17.** 32   **19.** 8   **21.** $\varnothing$ **23.** -7 **25.** 52

27. 940.5 million   **29.** no such integers exist   **31.** 258 mi   **33.** $W = \dfrac{V}{LH}$ **35.** $y = \dfrac{5x + 12}{4}$ **37.** $m = \dfrac{y - y_1}{x - x_1}$ **39.** $r = \dfrac{E - IR}{I}$

41. $g = \dfrac{T}{r + vt}$ **43. a.** \$3695.27   **b.** \$3700.81   **45.** length: 10 in.; width: 8 in.   **47.** $(3, \infty)$ **49.** $(-4, \infty)$ **51.** $(-\infty, 7]$ **53.** $(-\infty, 1)$

55. more economical to use housekeeper for more than 35 pounds per week   **57.** 9.6   **59.** $\left[2, \dfrac{5}{2}\right]$ **61.** $\left(\dfrac{1}{8}, 2\right)$ **63.** $\left(\dfrac{7}{8}, \dfrac{27}{20}\right]$ **65.** $\left(\dfrac{11}{3}, \infty\right)$

67. 5, 11   **69.** $-1, \dfrac{11}{3}$ **71.** $-\dfrac{1}{6}$ **73.** $\varnothing$ **75.** $5, -\dfrac{1}{3}$ **77.** ←———(———)———→ $\left(-\dfrac{8}{5}, 2\right)$ **79.** ←———————→ $(-\infty, -3) \cup (3, \infty)$
                                                                        $-\frac{8}{5}$ 2 -3 3

81. ←———+———→ $\varnothing$ **83.** ←——)———)——→ $(-\infty, -27) \cup (-9, \infty)$ **85.** 2   **87.** China: 137 million; USA: 102 million; France: 93 million
          0   -27 -9

89. $h = \dfrac{3V}{\pi r^2}$ **91.** 58 mph   **93.** $(2, \infty)$ **95.** $(-\infty, \infty)$ **97.** $3, -3$ **99.** $-10, -\dfrac{4}{3}$ **101.** $\left(-\dfrac{1}{2}, 2\right)$

Chapter 2 Test

1. 10   **2.** -32 **3.** $\varnothing$ **4.** all real numbers   **5.** $-\dfrac{80}{29}$ **6.** $\dfrac{29}{4}$ **7.** $1, \dfrac{2}{3}$ **8.** $\varnothing$ **9.** $-4, -\dfrac{1}{3}$ **10.** $\dfrac{3}{2}$ **11.** $y = \dfrac{3x - 8}{4}$ **12.** $g = \dfrac{S}{t^2 + vt}$

13. $C = \dfrac{5}{9}(F - 32)$ **14.** $(5, \infty)$ **15.** $\left(-\infty, -\dfrac{11}{3}\right]$ **16.** $\left(\dfrac{3}{2}, 5\right]$ **17.** $(-\infty, -2) \cup \left(\dfrac{4}{3}, \infty\right)$ **18.** $(3, 7)$ **19.** $[5, \infty)$ **20.** $[4, \infty)$

21. $\left[1, \dfrac{11}{2}\right)$ **22.** $(-\infty, \infty)$ **23.** 9.6   **24.** 230,323 people   **25.** approximately 8 hunting dogs   **26.** more than 850 sunglasses
27. \$3542.27   **28.** New York: 21.8 million; Seoul: 23.1 million; Tokyo: 33.4 million

Chapter 2 Cumulative Review

1. a. $\{101, 102, 103, \ldots\}$ **b.** $\{2, 3, 4, 5\}$; Sec. 1.2, Ex. 3   **3. a.** 3   **b.** $\dfrac{1}{7}$ **c.** -2.7 **d.** -8 **e.** 0; Sec. 1.2, Ex. 6   **5. a.** -14

b. -4 **c.** 5   **d.** -10.2 **e.** $-\dfrac{5}{21}$; Sec. 1.3, Ex. 1   **7. a.** 3   **b.** 5   **c.** $\dfrac{1}{2}$ **d.** -6 **e.** not a real number; Sec. 1.3, Ex. 7   **9. a.** 33   **b.** -18

c. $\dfrac{1}{12}$; Sec. 1.3, Ex. 12   **11. a.** $x + 5 = 20$ **b.** $2(3 + y) = 4$ **c.** $x - 8 = 2x$ **d.** $\dfrac{z}{9} = 9 + z$; Sec. 1.4, Ex. 1   **13.** $5 + 7x$; Sec. 1.4, Ex. 9

15. 2; Sec. 2.1, Ex. 1   **17.** all real numbers; Sec. 2.1, Ex. 9   **19. a.** $3x + 3$ **b.** $12x - 3$; Sec. 2.2, Ex. 1   **21.** 23, 49, 92; Sec. 2.2, Ex. 3

23. $y = \dfrac{2x + 7}{3}$ or $y = \dfrac{2x}{3} + \dfrac{7}{3}$; Sec. 2.3, Ex. 2   **25.** $b = \dfrac{2A - Bh}{h}$; Sec. 2.3, Ex. 3   **27. a.** ←——[——→ ; $[2, \infty)$ **b.** ←——)——→ ; $(-\infty, -1)$
                                                                                                                       2   -1

c. ←—(———]——→ ; $(0.5, 3]$; Sec. 2.4, Ex. 1   **29.** $\left[\dfrac{5}{2}, \infty\right)$; Sec. 2.4, Ex. 5   **31.** $(-\infty, \infty)$; Sec. 2.4, Ex. 7   **33.** $\{4, 6\}$; Sec. 2.5, Ex. 1
       0.5   3

35. $(-\infty, 4)$; Sec. 2.5, Ex. 2   **37.** $\{2, 3, 4, 5, 6, 8\}$; Sec. 2.5, Ex. 6   **39.** $(-\infty, \infty)$; Sec. 2.5, Ex. 8   **41.** $2, -2$; Sec. 2.6, Ex. 1

43. $24, -20$; Sec. 2.6, Ex. 3   **45.** 4; Sec. 2.6, Ex. 9   **47.** $[-3, 3]$; Sec. 2.7, Ex. 1   **49.** $(-\infty, \infty)$; Sec. 2.7, Ex. 6

CHAPTER 3 GRAPHS AND FUNCTIONS

Section 3.1
Practice Exercises

1.

a. Quadrant IV   **b.** y-axis   **c.** Quadrant II   **d.** x-axis   **e.** Quadrant III   **f.** Quadrant I
2. yes, no, yes   **3. a.** $4200   **b.** more than $9000

4. $y = -3x - 2$ 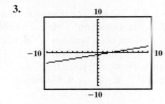   **5.** 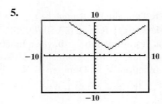   **6.** $y = 2x^2$ 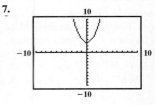   **7.** $y = -|x|$

Graphing Calculator Explorations 3.1

1.   **3.**   **5.**   **7.**

Vocabulary and Readiness Check 3.1

1. $(5, 2)$ **3.** $(3, 0)$ **5.** $(-5, -2)$ **7.** $(-1, 0)$ **9.** QI   **11.** QII   **13.** QIII   **15.** y-axis   **17.** QIII   **19.** x-axis

Exercise Set 3.1

1. Quadrant I   **3.** Quadrant II   **5.** Quadrant IV   **7.** y-axis   **9.** Quadrant III

 $(3, 2)$ $(-5, 3)$ $\left(5\frac{1}{2}, -4\right)$ $(0, 3.5)$ $(-2, -4)$

11. Quadrant IV   **13.** x-axis   **15.** Quadrant III   **17.** no; yes   **19.** yes; yes   **21.** yes; yes   **23.** yes; no   **25.** yes; yes

27. linear   **29.** linear   **31.** linear   **33.** not linear   **35.** linear   **37.** not linear

     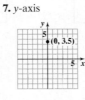   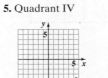   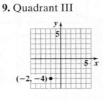

39. not linear   **41.** linear   **43.** linear   **45.** not linear   **47.** not linear   **49.** not linear

51. linear   **53.** linear   **55.** -5 **57.** $-\frac{1}{10}$ **59.** $(-\infty, -5]$ **61.** $(-\infty, -4)$ **63.** b   **65.** b   **67.** c

69. 1991   **71.** answers may vary   **73.**   **75. a.** 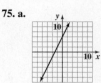   **b.** 14 in.   **77.** $7000   **79.** $500

81. Depreciation is the same from year to year.   **83.** ; answers may vary   **85.** answers may vary

87. $y = -3 - 2x$;   **89.** $y = 5 - x^2$; 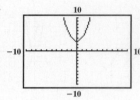   **91.** 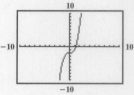   **93.**

Section 3.2

Practice Exercises

1. a. Domain: $\{4, 5\}$; Range: $\{1, -3, -2, 6\}$ **b.** Domain: $\{3\}$; Range: $\{-4, -3, -2, -1, 0, 1, 2, 3, 4\}$ **c.** Domain: $\{$Administrative Secretary, Game Developer, Engineer, Restaurant Manager, Marketing$\}$; Range: $\{27, 50, 73, 35\}$ **2. a.** yes, a function   **b.** not a function   **c.** yes, a function
3. yes, a function   **4.** yes, a function   **5. a.** yes, a function   **b.** yes, a function   **c.** no, not a function   **d.** yes, a function   **e.** no, not a function
6. a. Domain: $[-1, 2]$; Range: $[-2, 9]$; yes, a function   **b.** Domain: $[-1, 1]$; Range: $[-4, 4]$; not a function
c. Domain: $(-\infty, \infty)$; Range: $(-\infty, 4]$; yes, a function   **d.** Domain: $(-\infty, \infty)$; Range: $(-\infty, \infty)$; yes, a function
7. a. 1   **b.** 6   **c.** -2 **d.** 15   **8. a.** -3 **b.** -2 **c.** 3   **d.** 1   **e.** -1 and 3   **f.** -3 **9.** $35 billion   **10.** $57.224 billion

Graphing Calculator Explorations 3.2

1. 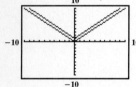   **3.** 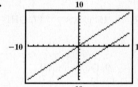   **5.**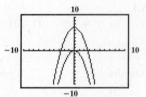

Vocabulary and Readiness Check 3.2

1. origin   **3.** $x; y$ **5.** V-shaped   **7.** relation   **9.** domain   **11.** vertical

Exercise Set 3.2

1. domain: $\{-1, 0, -2, 5\}$; range: $\{7, 6, 2\}$; function   **3.** domain: $\{-2, 6, -7\}$; range: $\{4, -3, -8\}$; not a function

5. domain: $\{1\}$; range: $\{1, 2, 3, 4\}$; not a function   **7.** domain: $\left\{\dfrac{3}{2}, 0\right\}$; range: $\left\{\dfrac{1}{2}, -7, \dfrac{4}{5}\right\}$; not a function

9. domain: $\{-3, 0, 3\}$; range: $\{-3, 0, 3\}$; function   **11.** domain: $\{-1, 1, 2, 3\}$; range: $\{2, 1\}$; function   **13.** domain: $\{$Iowa, Alaska, Delaware, Illinois, Connecticut, New York$\}$; range: $\{5, 1, 19, 29\}$; function   **15.** domain: $\{32°, 104°, 212°, 50°\}$; range: $\{0°, 40°, 10°, 100°\}$; function
17. domain: $\{0\}$; range: $\{2, -1, 5, 100\}$; not a function   **19.** function   **21.** not a function   **23.** function   **25.** not a function   **27.** function
29. domain: $[0, \infty)$; range: $(-\infty, \infty)$; not a function   **31.** domain: $[-1, 1]$; range: $(-\infty, \infty)$; not a function   **33.** domain: $(-\infty, \infty)$; range: $(-\infty, -3] \cup [3, \infty)$; not a function   **35.** domain: $[2, 7]$; range $[1, 6]$; not a function   **37.** domain: $\{-2\}$; range: $(-\infty, \infty)$; not a function
39. domain: $(-\infty, \infty)$; range: $(-\infty, 3]$; function   **41.** answers may vary   **43.** yes   **45.** no   **47.** yes   **49.** yes   **51.** yes   **53.** no

55. 15   **57.** 38   **59.** 7   **61.** 3   **63. a.** 0   **b.** 1   **c.** -1 **65. a.** 246   **b.** 6   **c.** $\dfrac{9}{2}$ **67. a.** -5 **b.** -5 **c.** -5 **69. a.** 5.1
b. 15.5   **c.** 9.533   **71.** $(1, -10)$ **73.** $(4, 56)$ **75.** $f(-1) = -2$ **77.** $g(2) = 0$ **79.** $-4, 0$ **81.** 3   **83.** infinite number
85. a. $17 billion   **b.** $15.592 billion   **87.** $15.54 billion   **89.** $f(x) = x + 7$ **91.** 25π sq cm   **93.** 2744 cu in.   **95.** 166.38 cm
97. 163.2 mg   **99. a.** 106.26; per capita consumption of poultry was 106.26 lb in 2006.   **b.** 108.54 lb   **101.** $5, -5, 6$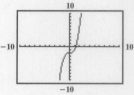

103. $2, \dfrac{8}{7}, \dfrac{12}{7}$

105. $0, 0, -6$

107. yes; 170 m   **109.** false   **111.** true   **113. a.** $-3s + 12$ **b.** $-3r + 12$
115. a. 132   **b.** $a^2 - 12$ **117.** answers may vary

Section 3.3
Practice Exercises

1.

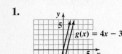
$g(x) = 4x - 3$
$f(x) = 4x$

2.

$g(x) = -2x + 5$
$f(x) = -2x$

3. a. $\left(0, -\dfrac{2}{5}\right)$ **b.** $(0, 4.1)$

4.

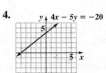
$4x - 5y = -20$

5.

$y = -3x$
$(-1, 3)$
$(0, 0)$
$(1, -3)$

6. $x = -4$

7.

$y = 4$

Graphing Calculator Explorations 3.3

1. $y = \dfrac{x}{3.5}$

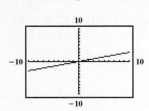

3. $y = -\dfrac{5.78}{2.31}x + \dfrac{10.98}{2.31}$

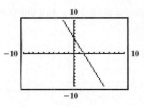

5. $y = |x| + 3.78$

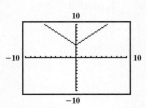

7. $y = 5.6x^2 + 7.7x + 1.5$

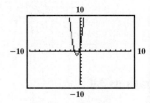

Vocabulary and Readiness Check 3.3

1. linear   **3.** vertical; $(c, 0)$ **5.** y; $f(x)$; x

Exercise Set 3.3

1.
$y = -2x$
$(-1, 2)$
$(0, 0)$
$(1, -2)$

3.
$(-1, 5)$ $y = -2x + 3$
$(0, 3)$
$(1, 1)$

5.
$y = \dfrac{1}{2}x$
$(2, 1)$
$(0, 0)$
$(-2, -1)$

7.
$y = \dfrac{1}{2}x - 4$
$(0, -4)$ $(4, -2)$
$(2, -3)$

9. C   **11.** D   **13.**

15.

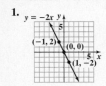

17.

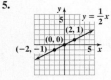

19.

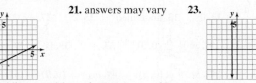

21. answers may vary

23.

25.

27.

29. C   **31.** A   **33.** The vertical line $x = 0$ has y-intercepts.

35.

$x + 2y = 8$

37.

$3x + 5y = 7$

39.

41.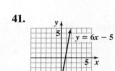

43.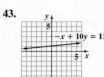

45.

47.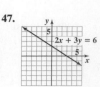

49. $x = -3$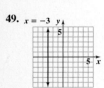

51.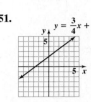

53.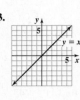

55.

57.

59. $x = -3$

61. $9, -3$ **63.** $(-\infty, -4) \cup (-1, \infty)$ **65.** $\left[\dfrac{2}{3}, 2\right]$ **67.** $\dfrac{3}{2}$ **69.** 6 **71.** $-\dfrac{6}{5}$

73. a. $(0, 500)$; if no tables are produced, 500 chairs can be produced   **b.** $(750, 0)$; if no chairs are produced, 750 tables can be produced   **c.** 466 chairs

75. a. \$64   **b.**   **c.** The line moves upward from left to right.   **77. a.** \$2855.12   **b.** 2012   **c.** answers may vary

79.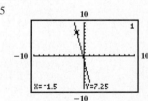

81.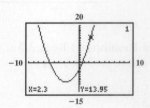

83. a. a line parallel to $y = -4x$ but with y-intercept $(0, 2)$ **b.** a line parallel to $y = -4x$ but with y-intercept $(0, -5)$ **85.** B   **87.** A

Section 3.4
Practice Exercises

1. $m = -\dfrac{1}{2}$;   **2.** $m = \dfrac{3}{5}$; 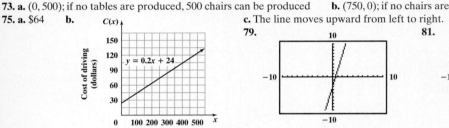   **3.** $m = -4$ **4.** $m = \dfrac{2}{3}$; y-intercept: $(0, -3)$ **5.** \$81.84   **6.** undefined

7. $m = 0$ **8. a.** perpendicular   **b.** parallel

Graphing Calculator Explorations 3.4

1. 18.4 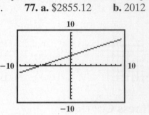   **3.** -1.5 **5.** $14.0; 4.2, -9.4$

Vocabulary and Readiness Check 3.4

1. slope   **3.** $m; (0, b)$ **5.** horizontal   **7.** -1 **9.** upward   **11.** horizontal

Exercise Set 3.4

1. $\dfrac{9}{5}$ **3.** $-\dfrac{7}{2}$ **5.** $-\dfrac{5}{6}$ **7.** $\dfrac{1}{3}$ **9.** $-\dfrac{4}{3}$ **11.** 0 **13.** undefined   **15.** 2 **17.** -1 **19.** l_2 **21.** l_2 **23.** l_2 **25.** $m = 5; (0, -2)$

27. $m = -2; (0, 7)$ **29.** $m = \dfrac{2}{3}; \left(0, -\dfrac{10}{3}\right)$ **31.** $m = \dfrac{1}{2}; (0, 0)$ **33.** A   **35.** B   **37.** undefined   **39.** 0 **41.** undefined

43. answers may vary   **45.** $m = -1; (0, 5)$ **47.** $m = \dfrac{6}{5}; (0, 6)$ **49.** $m = 3; (0, 9)$ **51.** $m = 0; (0, 4)$ **53.** $m = 7; (0, 0)$

55. $m = 0; (0, -6)$ **57.** slope is undefined, no y-intercept   **59.** neither   **61.** parallel   **63.** perpendicular   **65.** answers may vary

67. $\dfrac{3}{2}$ **69.** $-\dfrac{1}{2}$ **71.** $\dfrac{2}{3}$ **73.** approximately -0.12 **75. a.** \$50,139   **b.** $m = 694.9$; The annual income increases \$694.90 every year.

c. y-intercept: $(0, 43,884.9)$; At year $x = 0$, or 2000, the annual average income was \$43,884.90.   **77. a.** $m = 33$; y-intercept: $(0, 42)$

b. The number of WiFi hotspots increases by 33 thousand for every 1 year.   **c.** There were 42 thousand WiFi hotspots in 2003.

79. a. The yearly cost of tuition increases \$291.5 every 1 year.   **b.** The yearly cost of tuition in 2000 was \$2944.05.   **81.** $y = 5x + 32$

83. $y = 2x-1$ **85.** $m = -\dfrac{20}{9}$ **87.** $-\dfrac{5}{3}$ **89.** $-\dfrac{7}{2}$ **91.** $\dfrac{2}{7}$ **93.** $\dfrac{5}{2}$ **95.** $-\dfrac{2}{5}$

97. a. $(6, 20)$ **b.** $(10, 13)$ **c.** $-\dfrac{7}{4}$ or -1.75 yd per sec   **d.** $\dfrac{3}{2}$ or 1.5 yd per sec   **99.** 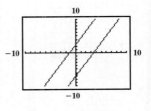   **c.** true

101. a. 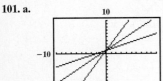   **b.**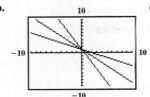

Section 3.5
Practice Exercises

1. $y = -\dfrac{3}{4}x + 4$ **2.** 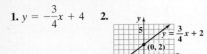   **3.** 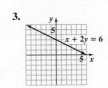   **4.** $y = -4x - 3$ **5.** $f(x) = -\dfrac{2}{3}x + \dfrac{4}{3}$ **6.** $2x + 3y = 5$ **7.** 12,568 house sales

8. $y = -2$ **9.** $x = 6$ **10.** $3x + 4y = 12$ **11.** $f(x) = \dfrac{4}{3}x - \dfrac{41}{3}$

Vocabulary and Readiness Check 3.5

1. $m = -4$, y-intercept: $(0, 12)$ **3.** $m = 5$, y-intercept: $(0, 0)$ **5.** $m = \dfrac{1}{2}$, y-intercept: $(0, 6)$ **7.** parallel   **9.** neither

Exercise Set 3.5

1. $y = -x + 1$ **3.** $y = 2x + \dfrac{3}{4}$ **5.** $y = \dfrac{2}{7}x$ **7.**   **9.** 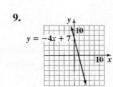   **11.** 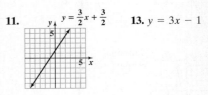   **13.** $y = 3x - 1$

15. $y = -2x - 1$ **17.** $y = \dfrac{1}{2}x + 5$ **19.** $y = -\dfrac{9}{10}x - \dfrac{27}{10}$ **21.** $f(x) = 3x - 6$ **23.** $f(x) = -2x + 1$ **25.** $f(x) = -\dfrac{1}{2}x - 5$

27. $f(x) = \dfrac{1}{3}x - 7$ **29.** $f(x) = -\dfrac{3}{8}x + \dfrac{5}{8}$ **31.** $2x + y = 3$ **33.** $2x - 3y = -7$ **35.** -2 **37.** 2

39. -2 **41.** $y = -4$ **43.** $x = 4$ **45.** $y = 5$ **47.** $f(x) = 4x - 4$ **49.** $f(x) = -3x + 1$ **51.** $f(x) = -\dfrac{3}{2}x - 6$ **53.** $2x - y = -7$

55. $f(x) = -x + 7$ **57.** $x + 2y = 22$ **59.** $2x + 7y = -42$ **61.** $4x + 3y = -20$ **63.** $x = -2$ **65.** $x + 2y = 2$ **67.** $y = 12$

69. $8x - y = 47$ **71.** $x = 5$ **73.** $f(x) = -\dfrac{3}{8}x - \dfrac{29}{4}$ **75. a.** $P(x) = 12,000x + 18,000$ **b.** \$102,000   **c.** end of the ninth yr

77. a. $y = -1000x + 13,000$ **b.** 9500 Fun Noodles   **79. a.** $y = 14,220x + 150,900$ **b.** \$278,880   **c.** every year, the median price of a home

increases by \$14,220.   **81. a.** $y = 20.2x + 387$ **b.** 568.8 thousand people   **83.** $(-\infty, 14]$ **85.** $\left[\dfrac{7}{2}, \infty\right)$ **87.** $\left(-\infty, -\dfrac{1}{4}\right)$ **89.** true

91. $-4x + y = 4$ **93.** $2x + y = -23$ **95.** $3x - 2y = -13$ **97.** answers may vary   **99.**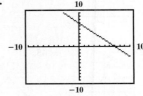
101.   **103.**

Integrated Review

1.   **2.**   **3.**   **4.**   **5.** 0 **6.** $-\dfrac{3}{5}$ **7.** $m = 3$; $(0, -5)$ **8.** $m = \dfrac{5}{2}$; $\left(0, -\dfrac{7}{2}\right)$

9. parallel   **10.** perpendicular   **11.** $y = -x + 7$ **12.** $x = -2$

13. $y = 0$ **14.** $f(x) = -\dfrac{1}{2}x - 8$ **15.** $f(x) = -5x - 6$

16. $f(x) = -4x + \dfrac{1}{3}$ **17.** $f(x) = \dfrac{1}{2}x - 1$ **18.** $y = 3x - \dfrac{3}{2}$

19. $y = 3x - 2$ **20.** $y = -\dfrac{5}{4}x + 4$ **21.** $y = \dfrac{1}{4}x - \dfrac{7}{2}$ **22.** $y = -\dfrac{5}{2}x - \dfrac{5}{2}$ **23.** $x = -1$ **24.** $y = 3$

Section 3.6
Practice Exercises

1. $f(4) = 5; f(-2) = 6; f(0) = -2$ **2.**   **3.**   **4.**   **5.**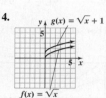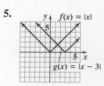

6. 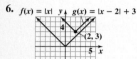   **7.**

Vocabulary and Readiness Check 3.6
1. c   **3.** d

Exercise Set 3.6

1.   **3.** 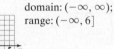   **5.**   **7.**   **9.** domain: $(-\infty, \infty)$; range: $[0, \infty)$

11. domain: $(-\infty, \infty)$; range: $(-\infty, 5)$ **13.** domain: $(-\infty, \infty)$; range: $(-\infty, 6]$ **15.** domain: $(-\infty, 0] \cup [1, \infty)$; range: $\{-4, -2\}$

17.   **19.**   **21.**   **23.**   **25.**   **27.**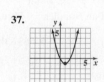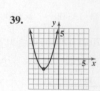

29.   **31.**   **33.**   **35.** 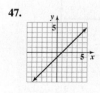   **37.**   **39.**

41. 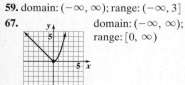   **43.**   **45.** 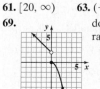   **47.** 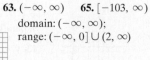   **49.** A   **51.** D   **53.** answers may vary   **55.** 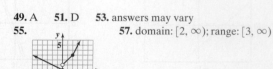   **57.** domain: $[2, \infty)$; range: $[3, \infty)$

59. domain: $(-\infty, \infty)$; range: $(-\infty, 3]$ **61.** $[20, \infty)$ **63.** $(-\infty, \infty)$ **65.** $[-103, \infty)$ **67.** domain: $(-\infty, \infty)$; range: $[0, \infty)$ **69.** domain: $(-\infty, \infty)$; range: $(-\infty, 0] \cup (2, \infty)$

Section 3.7
Practice Exercises

1. $3x + y < 8$

2.

3. 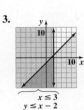 $x \leq 3$ $y \leq x - 2$

4.

Exercise Set 3.7

1. $x < 2$

3. $x - y \geq 7$

5. $3x + y > 6$

7. $y \leq -2x$

9. $2x + 4y \geq 8$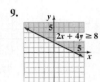

11. $5x + 3y > -15$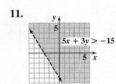

13. answers may vary

15. $x = 3$ $y = -2$

17. $y = 4$ $x = -2$

19. $x - y = 3$ $x = 4$

21.

23.

25.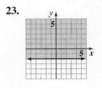

27.

29.

31.

33.

35.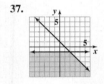

37.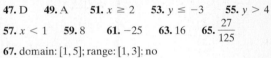

39.

41.

43.

45.

47. D **49.** A **51.** $x \geq 2$ **53.** $y \leq -3$ **55.** $y > 4$

57. $x < 1$ **59.** 8 **61.** -25 **63.** 16 **65.** $\dfrac{27}{125}$

67. domain: $[1, 5]$; range: $[1, 3]$; no

69. $x \leq 20$ and $y \geq 10$.

71.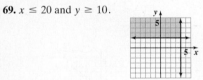

Chapter 3 Vocabulary Check

1. relation **3.** linear inequality **5.** range **7.** slope-intercept **9.** slope **11.** y **13.** linear function **15.** point-slope

Chapter 3 Review

1.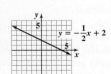

3. no, yes **5.** yes, yes **7.** linear $y = 3x$

9. linear $3x - y = 4$

11. nonlinear $y = |x| + 4$

13. linear $y = -\dfrac{1}{2}x + 2$

15. linear $y = 2x - 1$

17. linear $y = -1.36x$

19. domain: $\left\{-\frac{1}{2}, 6, 0, 25\right\}$; range: $\left\{\frac{3}{4} \text{ or } 0.75, -12, 25\right\}$; function   **21.** domain: $\{2, 4, 6, 8\}$; range: $\{2, 4, 5, 6\}$; not a function

23. domain: $(-\infty, \infty)$; range: $(-\infty, -1] \cup [1, \infty)$; not a function   **25.** domain: $(-\infty, \infty)$; range: $\{4\}$; function   **27.** -3 **29.** 18

31. -3 **33.** 381 lb   **35.** 0   **37.** $-2, 4$ **39.**   **41.** 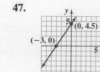   **43.** A   **45.** D   **47.**

49.   **51.**   **53.**   **55.** -3 **57.** $\frac{5}{2}$ **59.** $m = \frac{2}{5}, b = -\frac{4}{3}$ **61.** 0   **63.** l_2 **65.** l_2

67. a. $m = 0.3$; The cost increases by $0.30 for each additional mile driven.
b. $b = 42$; The cost for 0 miles driven is $42.   **69.** parallel

71.   **73.**   **75.** $x = -2$ **77.** $y = 5$ **79.** $2x - y = 12$ **81.** $11x + y = -52$ **83.** $y = -5$

85. $f(x) = -x - 2$ **87.** $f(x) = -\frac{3}{2}x - 8$ **89.** $f(x) = -\frac{3}{2}x - 1$

91. a. $y = \frac{17}{22}x + 43$ **b.** 52 million

93.   **95.**   **97.** $(-3, -1)$ **99.**   **101.**

103.   **105.**   **107.**   **109.** $x = -7$ **111.** $y = \frac{3}{4}x + 2$ **113.** $y = -\frac{3}{2}x - 8$

115.   **117.** $(2, 0)$

Chapter 3 Test

1. A: quadrant IV   B: x-axis   C: quadrant II   **2.**   **3.**   **4.**

5.   **6.** $-\frac{3}{2}$ **7.** $m = -\frac{1}{4}, b = \frac{2}{3}$ **8.** $y = (x - 1)^2$ **9.** $y = |x| + 2$ **10.** $y = -8$
11. $x = -4$
12. $y = -2$
13. $3x + y = 11$

14. $5x - y = 2$ **15.** $f(x) = -\frac{1}{2}x$ **16.** $f(x) = -\frac{1}{3}x + \frac{5}{3}$ **17.** $f(x) = -\frac{1}{2}x - \frac{1}{2}$ **18.** neither

19.   **20.** $2x - y > 5$ **21.**   **22.** domain: $(-\infty, \infty)$; range: $\{5\}$; function
23. domain: $\{-2\}$; range: $(-\infty, \infty)$; not a function
24. domain: $(-\infty, \infty)$; range: $[0, \infty)$; function
25. domain: $(-\infty, \infty)$; range: $(-\infty, \infty)$; function
26. a. $25,193   **b.** $32,410   **c.** 2015   **d.** The average yearly earnings for high school graduates increases $1031 per year.   **e.** The average yearly earnings for a high school graduate in 2000 was $25,193.

27.   domain: $(-\infty, \infty)$;
range: $(-3, \infty)$

28.

29.

domain: $(-\infty, \infty)$;
range: $(-\infty, -1]$

30.

Chapter 3 Cumulative Review

1. 41; Sec. 1.2, Ex. 2   **3. a.** true   **b.** false   **c.** false   **d.** false; Sec. 1.2, Ex. 5   **5. a.** -6 **b.** -7 **c.** -16 **d.** 20.5

e. $\dfrac{1}{6}$ **f.** 0.94   **g.** -3; Sec. 1.3, Ex. 2   **7. a.** 9   **b.** $\dfrac{1}{16}$ **c.** -25 **d.** 25   **e.** -125 **f.** -125; Sec. 1.3, Ex. 6

9. a. $>$ **b.** $=$ **c.** $<$ **d.** $<$; Sec. 1.4, Ex. 5   **11. a.** $\dfrac{1}{11}$ **b.** $-\dfrac{1}{9}$ **c.** $\dfrac{4}{7}$; Sec. 1.4, Ex. 8   **13.** 0.4; Sec. 2.1, Ex. 2

15. { } or $\varnothing$; Sec. 2.1, Ex. 8   **17. a.** $3x + 3$ **b.** $12x - 3$; Sec. 2.2, Ex. 1   **19.** 86, 88 and 90; Sec. 2.2, Ex. 7   **21.** $\dfrac{V}{lw} = h$; Sec. 2.3, Ex. 1

23. $\{x | x < 7\}$ or $(-\infty, 7)$;   ; Sec. 2.4, Ex. 2   **25.** $\left(-\infty, -\dfrac{7}{3}\right]$; Sec. 2.4, Ex. 6   **27.** $\varnothing$; Sec. 2.5, Ex. 3

29. $\left(-\infty, \dfrac{13}{5}\right] \cup [4, \infty)$; Sec. 2.5, Ex. 7   **31.** $-2, \dfrac{4}{5}$; Sec. 2.6, Ex. 2   **33.** $\dfrac{3}{4}, 5$; Sec. 2.6, Ex. 8   **35.** $\left[-2, \dfrac{8}{5}\right]$; Sec. 2.7, Ex. 3

37. $(-\infty, -4) \cup (10, \infty)$; Sec. 2.7, Ex. 5   **39.** solutions: $(2, -6)$, $(0, -12)$; not a solution $(1, 9)$; Sec. 3.1, Ex. 2   **41.** yes; Sec. 3.2, Ex. 3

43. a. $\left(0, \dfrac{3}{7}\right)$ **b.** $(0, -3.2)$; Sec. 3.3, Ex. 3   **45.** $\dfrac{2}{3}$; Sec. 3.4, Ex. 3   **47.** $y = \dfrac{1}{4}x - 3$; Sec. 3.5 Ex. 1   **49.**   Sec. 3.7; Ex. 1

CHAPTER 4 SYSTEMS OF EQUATIONS

Section 4.1

Practice Exercises

1. a. yes   **b.** no   **2. a.** infinite number of solutions of the form $\{(x, y) | 3x - 2y = 4\}$ or $\{(x, y) | -9x + 6y = -12\}$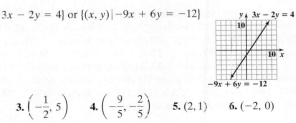

2. b. solution: $(1, 5)$ **c.** no solution   **3.** $\left(-\dfrac{1}{2}, 5\right)$ **4.** $\left(-\dfrac{9}{5}, -\dfrac{2}{5}\right)$ **5.** $(2, 1)$ **6.** $(-2, 0)$

7. $\varnothing$ or { }   **8.** $\{(x, y) | -3x + 2y = -1\}$ or $\{(x, y) | 9x - 6y = 3\}$

Graphing Calculator Explorations 4.1

1. $(2.11, 0.17)$ **3.** $(0.57, -1.97)$

Vocabulary and Readiness Check 4.1

1. B   **3.** A

Exercise Set 4.1

1. yes   **3.** no   **5.** no   **7.** $(2, -1)$ **9.** $(1, 2)$ **11.** $\varnothing$ **13.** No; answers may vary

15. $(2, 8)$ **17.** $(0, -9)$ **19.** $(1, -1)$ **21.** $(-5, 3)$ **23.** $\left(\dfrac{5}{2}, \dfrac{5}{4}\right)$ **25.** $(1, -2)$ **27.** $(8, 2)$ **29.** $(7, 2)$ **31.** $\varnothing$ **33.** $\{(x, y)\,|\,3x + y = 1\}$

35. $\left(\dfrac{3}{2}, 1\right)$ **37.** $(2, -1)$ **39.** $(-5, 3)$ **41.** $\{(x, y)\,|\,3x + 9y = 12\}$ **43.** $\varnothing$ **45.** $\left(\dfrac{1}{2}, \dfrac{1}{5}\right)$ **47.** $(9, 9)$ **49.** $\{(x, y)\,|\,x = 3y + 2\}$

51. $\left(-\dfrac{1}{4}, \dfrac{1}{2}\right)$ **53.** $(3, 2)$ **55.** $(7, -3)$ **57.** $\varnothing$ **59.** $(3, 4)$ **61.** $(-2, 1)$ **63.** $(1.2, -3.6)$ **65.** true   **67.** false   **69.** $6y - 4z = 25$

71. $x + 10y = 2$ **73.** 5000 DVDs; \$21   **75.** supply greater than demand   **77.** $(1875, 4687.5)$ **79.** makes money

81. for x-values greater than 1875   **83.** answers may vary; One possibility: $\begin{cases} -2x + y = 1 \\ x - 2y = -8 \end{cases}$

85. a. Consumption of red meat is decreasing while consumption of poultry is increasing.   **b.** $(35, 103)$ **c.** In the year 2035, red meat and poultry consumption will each be about 103 pounds per person.   **87.** $\left(\dfrac{1}{4}, 8\right)$ **89.** $\left(\dfrac{1}{3}, \dfrac{1}{2}\right)$ **91.** $\left(\dfrac{1}{4}, -\dfrac{1}{3}\right)$ **93.** $\varnothing$

Section 4.2

Practice Exercises
1. $(-1, 2, 1)$ **2.** $\{\ \}$ or $\varnothing$ **3.** $\left(\dfrac{2}{3}, -\dfrac{1}{2}, 0\right)$ **4.** $\{(x, y, z)\,|\,2x + y - 3z = 6\}$ **5.** $(6, 15, -5)$

Exercise Set 4.2
1. a, b, d   **3.** Yes; answers may vary   **5.** $(-1, 5, 2)$ **7.** $(-2, 5, 1)$ **9.** $(-2, 3, -1)$ **11.** $\{(x, y, z)\,|\,x - 2y + z = -5\}$ **13.** $\varnothing$
15. $(0, 0, 0)$ **17.** $(-3, -35, -7)$ **19.** $(6, 22, -20)$ **21.** $\varnothing$ **23.** $(3, 2, 2)$ **25.** $\{(x, y, z)\,|\,x + 2y - 3z = 4\}$ **27.** $(-3, -4, -5)$
29. $\left(0, \dfrac{1}{2}, -4\right)$ **31.** $(12, 6, 4)$ **33.** 15 and 30   **35.** 5   **37.** $-\dfrac{5}{3}$ **39.** answers may vary   **41.** answers may vary   **43.** $(1, 1, -1)$
45. $(1, 1, 0, 2)$ **47.** $(1, -1, 2, 3)$ **49.** answers may vary

Section 4.3

Practice Exercises
1. a. 2037   **b.** yes; answers may vary   **2.** 12 and 17   **3.** Atlantique: 500 kph; V150: 575 kph   **4.** 0.95 liter of water; 0.05 liter of 99% HCL
5. 1500 packages   **6.** $40°, 60°, 80°$

Exercise Set 4.3
1. 10 and 8   **3. a.** Enterprise class: 1101 ft; Nimitz class: 1092 ft   **b.** 3.67 foot ball fields   **5.** plane: 520 mph; wind: 40 mph   **7.** 20 qt of 4%; 40 qt of 1%   **9.** United Kingdom: 32,071 students; Italy: 24,858 students   **11.** 9 large frames; 13 small frames   **13.** -10 and -8 **15.** 2007
17. tablets: \$0.80; pens: \$0.20   **19.** B737: 450 mph; Piper: 90 mph   **21. a.** answers may vary but notice the slope of each function   **b.** 1991
23. 28 cm; 28 cm; 37 cm   **25.** 600 mi   **27.** $x = 75; y = 105$ **29.** 625 units   **31.** 3000 units   **33.** 1280 units   **35. a.** $R(x) = 450x$
b. $C(x) = 200x + 6000$ **c.** 24 desks   **37.** 2 units of Mix A; 3 units of Mix B; 1 unit of Mix C   **39.** 5 in.; 7 in.; 10 in.   **41.** 18, 13, and 9
43. 143 free throws; 177 two-point field goals; 121 three-point field goals   **45.** $x = 60; y = 55; z = 65$ **47.** $5x + 5z = 10$ **49.** $-5y + 2z = 2$
51. 1996: 1,059,444; 2006: 1,085,209   **53. a.** $(112, 137)$ **b.** June 2019   **55.** $a = 1,\ b = -2,\ c = 3$
57. $a = 0.28,\ b = -3.71,\ c = 12.83$; 2.12 in. in Sept.

Integrated Review
1. C   **2.** D   **3.** A   **4.** B   **5.** $(1, 3)$ **6.** $\left(\dfrac{4}{3}, \dfrac{16}{3}\right)$ **7.** $(2, -1)$ **8.** $(5, 2)$ **9.** $\left(\dfrac{3}{2}, 1\right)$ **10.** $\left(-2, \dfrac{3}{4}\right)$ **11.** $\varnothing$

12. $\{(x, y)\,|\,2x - 5y = 3\}$ **13.** $\left(1, \dfrac{1}{3}\right)$ **14.** $\left(3, \dfrac{3}{4}\right)$ **15.** $(-1, 3, 2)$ **16.** $(1, -3, 0)$ **17.** $\varnothing$ **18.** $\{(x, y, z)\,|\,x - y + 3z = 2\}$

19. $\left(2, 5, \dfrac{1}{2}\right)$ **20.** $\left(1, 1, \dfrac{1}{3}\right)$ **21.** 19 and 27   **22.** $70°; 70°; 100°; 120°$

Section 4.4

Practice Exercises
1. $(2, -1)$ **2.** $\varnothing$ **3.** $(-1, 1, 2)$

Vocabulary and Readiness Check 4.4
1. matrix   **3.** row   **5.** false   **7.** true

Exercise Set 4.4
1. $(2, -1)$ **3.** $(-4, 2)$ **5.** $\varnothing$ **7.** $\{(x, y)\,|\,3x - 3y = 9\}$ **9.** $(-2, 5, -2)$ **11.** $(1, -2, 3)$ **13.** $(4, -3)$ **15.** $(2, 1, -1)$ **17.** $(9, 9)$
19. $\varnothing$ **21.** $\varnothing$ **23.** $(1, -4, 3)$ **25.** function   **27.** not a function   **29.** -13 **31.** -36 **33.** 0   **35.** c   **37. a.** end of 1984
b. black-and-white sets; microwave ovens; The percent of households owning black-and-white television sets is decreasing and the percent of households owning microwave ovens is increasing; answers may vary   **c.** in 2002   **d.** no; answers may vary   **39.** answers may vary

Section 4.5
Practice Exercises

1.

2.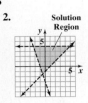

3.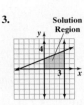

Vocabulary and Readiness Check 4.5

1. system **3.** corner

Exercise Set 4.5

1.

3.

5.

7.

9.

11.

13.

15.

17.

19.

21. C **23.** D **25.** 9 **27.** $\frac{4}{9}$ **29.** 5 **31.** 59

33. the line $y = 3$ **35.** answers may vary

Chapter 4 Vocabulary Check

1. system of equations **3.** consistent **5.** inconsistent

Chapter 4 Review

1. $(-3, 1)$ **2.** $\left(0, \frac{2}{3}\right)$ **3.** $\varnothing$ **4.** $\{(x, y) \mid 3x - 6y = 12\}$ **5.** $\left(3, \frac{8}{3}\right)$ **6.** 1500 backpacks **7.** $(2, 0, 2)$ **8.** $(2, 0, -3)$

9. $\left(-\frac{1}{2}, \frac{3}{4}, 1\right)$ **10.** $(-1, 2, 0)$ **11.** $\varnothing$ **12.** $(5, 3, 0)$ **13.** $(1, 1, -2)$ **14.** $(3, 1, 1)$ **15.** 10, 40, and 48 **16.** 63 and 21

17. 58 mph; 65 mph **18.** width: 37 ft; length: 111 ft **19.** 20 L of 10% solution; 30 L of 60% solution **20.** 30 lb of creme-filled; 5 lb of chocolate-covered nuts; 10 lb of chocolate-covered raisins **21.** 17 pennies; 20 nickels; 16 dimes **22.** larger investment: 9.5%; smaller investment: 7.5%

23. two sides: 22 cm each; third side; 29 cm **24.** 120, 115, and 60 **25.** $(-3, 1)$ **26.** $\{(x, y) \mid x - 2y = 4\}$ **27.** $\left(-\frac{2}{3}, 3\right)$

28. $\left(\frac{1}{3}, \frac{7}{6}\right)$ **29.** $\left(\frac{5}{4}, \frac{5}{8}\right)$ **30.** $(-7, -15)$ **31.** $(1, 3)$ **32.** $(2, 1)$ **33.** $(1, 2, 3)$ **34.** $(2, 0, -3)$ **35.** $(3, -2, 5)$ **36.** $(-1, 2, 0)$

37. $(1, 1, -2)$ **38.** $\varnothing$ **39.** **40.** **41.** **42.** **43.**

44. **45.** **46.** **47.** $\left(\frac{7}{3}, -\frac{8}{3}\right)$ **48.** $(10, -4)$ **49.** $\{(x, y) \mid 5x - 2y = 10\}$ **50.** $\varnothing$

51. $(-1, 3, 5)$ **52.** 33 and 94   **53.** 28 units, 42 units, 56 units   **54.**   **55.** 2000

Chapter 4 Test

1. $(1, 3)$ **2.** $\varnothing$ **3.** $(2, -3)$ **4.** $\{(x, y) \mid 10x + 4y = 10\}$ **5.** $(-1, -2, 4)$ **6.** $\varnothing$ **7.** $\left(\dfrac{7}{2}, -10\right)$

8. $\{(x, y) \mid x - y = -2\}$ **9.** $(5, -3)$ **10.** $(-1, -1, 0)$ **11.** 53 double rooms; 27 single rooms   **12.** 5 gal of 10%; 15 gal of 20%

13. 800 packages   **14.** $23°, 45°, 112°$ **15.**

Chapter 4 Cumulative Review

1. a. true   **b.** true; Sec. 1.2, Ex. 4   **3. a.** 6   **b.** -7; Sec. 1.3, Ex. 3   **5. a.** -4 **b.** $-\dfrac{3}{7}$ **c.** 11.2; Sec. 1.4, Ex. 7   **7. a.** $6x + 3y$

b. $-3x + 1$ **c.** $0.7\,ab - 1.4a$; Sec. 1.4, Ex. 11   **9. a.** $-2x + 4$ **b.** $8yz$ **c.** $4z + 6.1$; Sec. 1.4, Ex. 14   **11.** -4; Sec. 2.1, Ex. 3

13. -4; Sec. 2.1, Ex. 7   **15.** 25 cm, 62 cm, 62 cm; Sec. 2.2, Ex. 6   **17.** $[-10, \infty)$ $\xleftarrow{\quad\;\;\;}\underset{-10}{\;\;\vdash\!\!\!\longrightarrow}$; Sec. 2.4, Ex. 3   **19.** $(-3, 2)$; Sec. 2.5, Ex. 4

21. $1, -1$; Sec. 2.6, Ex. 4   **23.** $(4, 8)$; Sec. 2.7, Ex. 2   **25. a.** IV   **b.** y-axis   **c.** II   **d.** x-axis   **e.** III   **f.** I; ; Sec. 3.1, Ex. 1

27. no; Sec. 3.2, Ex. 4   **29. a.** 5   **b.** 1   **c.** 35   **d.** -2; Sec. 3.2, Ex. 7   **31.** ; Sec. 3.3, Ex. 1   **33.** slope: $\dfrac{3}{4}$; y-intercept: $(0, -1)$; Sec. 3.4, Ex. 4

35. a. parallel   **b.** neither; Sec. 3.4, Ex. 8   **37.** $f(x) = \dfrac{5}{8}x - \dfrac{5}{2}$; Sec. 3.5, Ex. 5   **39.** ; Sec. 3.6, Ex. 2   **41. a.** yes   **b.** no; Sec. 4.1, Ex. 1

43. $(-4, 2, -1)$; Sec. 4.2, Ex. 1   **45.** $(-1, 2)$; Sec. 4.4, Ex. 1

CHAPTER 5 EXPONENTS, POLYNOMIALS, AND POLYNOMIAL FUNCTIONS

Section 5.1
Practice Exercises

1. a. 3^6 **b.** x^7 **c.** y^9 **2. a.** $35z^4$ **b.** $-20.5t^6q^8$ **3. a.** 1   **b.** -1 **c.** 1   **d.** 3   **4. a.** z^5 **b.** 3^6 **c.** $9x^4$ **d.** $\dfrac{4a^7}{3}$ or $\dfrac{4}{3}a^7$

5. a. $\dfrac{1}{36}$ **b.** $\dfrac{1}{64}$ **c.** $\dfrac{3}{x^5}$ **d.** $\dfrac{1}{5y}$ **e.** $\dfrac{1}{k^7}$ **f.** $\dfrac{1}{25}$ **g.** $\dfrac{9}{20}$ **h.** z^8 **6. a.** $\dfrac{1}{z^{11}}$ **b.** $7t^8$ **c.** 9   **d.** $\dfrac{b^7}{3a^7}$ **e.** $\dfrac{2}{x^4}$ **7. a.** x^{3a+4} **b.** x^{2t+1}

8. a. 6.5×10^4 **b.** 3.8×10^{-5} **9. a.** 620,000   **b.** 0.03109

Graphing Calculator Explorations 5.1

1. 6×10^{43} **3.** 3.796×10^{28}

Vocabulary and Readiness Check 5.1

1. x **3.** 3   **5.** y^7 **7.** $\dfrac{5}{xy^2}$ **9.** $\dfrac{a^2}{bc^5}$ **11.** $\dfrac{x^4}{y^2}$

Exercise Set 5.1

1. 4^5 **3.** x^8 **5.** m^{14} **7.** $-20x^2y$ **9.** $-16x^6y^3p^2$ **11.** -1 **13.** 1   **15.** -1 **17.** 9   **19.** a^3 **21.** $-13z^4$ **23.** x **25.** $\dfrac{4}{3}x^3y^2$

27. $-6a^4b^4c^6$ **29.** $\dfrac{1}{16}$ **31.** $-\dfrac{1}{27}$ **33.** $\dfrac{1}{x^8}$ **35.** $\dfrac{5}{a^4}$ **37.** $\dfrac{y^2}{x^7}$ **39.** $\dfrac{1}{x^7}$ **41.** $4r^8$ **43.** 1   **45.** $\dfrac{b^7}{9a^7}$ **47.** $\dfrac{6x^{16}}{5}$ **49.** $-140x^{12}$

51. x^{16} **53.** $10x^{10}$ **55.** 6   **57.** $\dfrac{1}{z^3}$ **59.** -2 **61.** y^4 **63.** $\dfrac{13}{36}$ **65.** $\dfrac{3}{x}$ **67.** r^3 **69.** $\dfrac{1}{x^9y^4}$ **71.** $24x^7y^6$ **73.** $\dfrac{x}{16}$ **75.** 625

77. $\dfrac{1}{8}$ **79.** $\dfrac{a^5}{81}$ **81.** $\dfrac{7}{x^3z^5}$ **83.** x^{7a+5} **85.** x^{2t-1} **87.** x^{4a+7} **89.** z^{6x-7} **91.** x^{6t-1} **93.** 3.125×10^7 **95.** 1.6×10^{-2} **97.** 6.7413×10^4

99. 1.25×10^{-2} **101.** 5.3×10^{-5} **103.** 3.44992×10^{11} **105.** 3.5×10^6 **107.** 1.24×10^{11} **109.** 1.0×10^{-3} **111.** 0.0000000036

113. 93,000,000   **115.** 1,278,000   **117.** 7,350,000,000,000   **119.** 0.00000403   **121.** 300,000,000   **123.** \$153,000,000,000   **125.** 100   **127.** $\dfrac{27}{64}$

129. 64   **131.** answers may vary   **133.** answers may vary   **135. a.** x^{2a} **b.** $2x^a$ **c.** x^{a-b} **d.** x^{a+b} **e.** $x^a + x^b$ **137.** 7^{13} **139.** 7^{-11}

Section 5.2
Practice Exercises

1. a. z^{15} **b.** 625   **c.** $\dfrac{1}{27}$ **d.** x^{24} **2. a.** $32x^{15}$ **b.** $\dfrac{9}{25}$ **c.** $\dfrac{16a^{20}}{b^{28}}$ **d.** $9x$ **e.** $\dfrac{a^4b^{10}}{c^8}$ **3. a.** $\dfrac{b^{15}}{27a^3}$ **b.** y^{15} **c.** $\dfrac{64}{9}$ **d.** $\dfrac{b^8}{81a^6}$

4. a. $\dfrac{c^3}{125a^{36}b^3}$ **b.** $\dfrac{16x^{16}y^4}{25}$ **5. a.** $27x^a$ **b.** y^{5b+3} **6. a.** 1.7×10^{-2} **b.** 1.4×10^{10} **7.** 4.2×10^{-6}

Vocabulary and Readiness Check 5.2

1. x^{20} **3.** x^9 **5.** y^{42} **7.** z^{36} **9.** z^{18}

Exercise Set 5.2

1. $\dfrac{1}{9}$ **3.** $\dfrac{1}{x^{36}}$ **5.** $\dfrac{1}{y^5}$ **7.** $9x^4y^6$ **9.** $16x^{20}y^{12}$ **11.** $\dfrac{c^{18}}{a^{12}b^6}$ **13.** $\dfrac{y^{15}}{x^{35}z^{20}}$ **15.** $\dfrac{1}{125}$ **17.** x^{15} **19.** $\dfrac{8}{x^{12}y^{18}}$ **21.** $\dfrac{y^{16}}{64x^5}$ **23.** $\dfrac{64}{p^9}$

25. $-\dfrac{1}{x^9a^9}$ **27.** $\dfrac{x^5y^{10}}{5^{15}}$ **29.** $\dfrac{1}{x^{63}}$ **31.** $\dfrac{343}{512}$ **33.** $16x^4$ **35.** $-\dfrac{y^3}{64}$ **37.** $4^8x^2y^6$ **39.** 64   **41.** $\dfrac{x^4}{16}$ **43.** $\dfrac{1}{y^{15}}$ **45.** $\dfrac{x^9}{8y^3}$

47. $\dfrac{16a^2b^9}{9}$ **49.** $\dfrac{3}{8x^8y^7}$ **51.** $\dfrac{1}{x^{30}b^6c^6}$ **53.** $\dfrac{25}{8x^5y^4}$ **55.** $\dfrac{2}{x^4y^{10}}$ **57.** x^{9a+18} **59.** x^{12a+2} **61.** b^{10x-4} **63.** y^{15a+3} **65.** $16x^{4t+4}$

67. $5x^{-a}y^{-a+2}$ **69.** 1.45×10^9 **71.** 8×10^{15} **73.** 4×10^{-7} **75.** 3×10^{-1} **77.** 2×10^1 **79.** 1×10^1 **81.** 8×10^{-5} **83.** 1.1×10^7

85. 3.5×10^{22} **87.** 2×10^{-3} sec   **89.** 6.232×10^{-11} cu m   **91.** $-3m - 15$ **93.** $-3y - 5$ **95.** $-3x + 5$ **97.** $\dfrac{15y^3}{x^8}$ sq ft   **99.** 1.331928×10^{13}

101. no   **103.** 85 people per sq mi   **105.** 6.4 times   **107.** 31.7%

Section 5.3
Practice Exercises

1. a. 5   **b.** 3   **c.** 1   **d.** 11   **e.** 0   **2. a.** degree 4; trinomial   **b.** degree 5; monomial   **c.** degree 5; binomial   **3.** 5
4. a. -15 **b.** -47 **5.** 290 feet; 226 feet   **6. a.** $3x^4 - 5x$ **b.** $7ab - 3b$ **7. a.** $3a^4b + 4ab^2 - 5$ **b.** $2x^5 + y - x - 9$
8. $6x^3 + 6x^2 - 7x - 8$ **9.** $15a^4 - 15a^3 + 3$ **10.** $6x^2y^2 - 4xy^2 - 5y^3$ **11.** C

Graphing Calculator Explorations 5.3

1. $x^3 - 4x^2 + 7x - 8$ **3.** $-2.1x^2 - 3.2x - 1.7$ **5.** $7.69x^2 - 1.26x + 5.3$

Vocabulary and Readiness Check 5.3

1. coefficient   **3.** binomial   **5.** trinomial   **7.** degree   **9.** $6x$ **11.** $2y$ **13.** $7xy^2 - y^2$

Exercise Set 5.3

1. 0 **3.** 2 **5.** 3 **7.** 3 **9.** 9 **11.** degree 1; binomial **13.** degree 2; trinomial **15.** degree 3; monomial **17.** degree 4; none of these

19. 57 **21.** 499 **23.** $-\dfrac{11}{16}$ **25.** 1061 ft **27.** 549 ft **29.** $6y$ **31.** $11x - 3$ **33.** $xy + 2x - 1$ **35.** $6x^2 - xy + 16y^2$ **37.** $18y^2 - 17$

39. $3x^2 - 3xy + 6y^2$ **41.** $x^2 - 4x + 8$ **43.** $y^2 + 3$ **45.** $-2x^2 + 5x$ **47.** $-2x^2 - 4x + 15$ **49.** $4x - 13$ **51.** $x^2 + 2$ **53.** $12x^3 + 8x + 8$

55. $7x^3 + 4x^2 + 8x - 10$ **57.** $-18y^2 + 11yx + 14$ **59.** $-x^3 + 8a - 12$ **61.** $5x^2 - 9x - 3$ **63.** $-3x^2 + 3$ **65.** $8xy^2 + 2x^3 + 3x^2 - 3$

67. $7y^2 - 3$ **69.** $5x^2 + 22x + 16$ **71.** $\dfrac{3}{4}x^2 - \dfrac{1}{3}x^2y - \dfrac{8}{3}x^2y^2 + \dfrac{3}{2}y^3$ **73.** $-q^4 + q^2 - 3q + 5$ **75.** $15x^2 + 8x - 6$ **77.** $x^4 - 7x^2 + 5$

79. $\dfrac{1}{3}x^2 - x + 1$ **81.** 202 sq in. **83. a.** 284 ft **b.** 536 ft **c.** 756 ft **d.** 944 ft **e.** answers may vary **f.** 19 sec **85.** $80,000

87. $40,000 **89.** A **91.** D **93.** $15x - 10$ **95.** $-2x^2 + 10x - 12$ **97.** a and c

99. $(12x - 1.7) - (15x + 6.2) = 12x - 1.7 - 15x - 6.2 = -3x - 7.9$ **101.** answers may vary **103.** answers may vary

105. $3x^{2a} + 2x^a + 0.7$ **107.** $4x^{2y} + 2x^y - 11$ **109.** $(6x^2 + 14y)$ units **111.** $4x^2 - 3x + 6$ **113.** $-x^2 - 6x + 10$ **115.** $3x^2 - 12x + 13$

117. $15x^2 + 12x - 9$ **119. a.** $2a - 3$ **b.** $-2x - 3$ **c.** $2x + 2h - 3$ **121. a.** $4a$ **b.** $-4x$ **c.** $4x + 4h$

123. a. $4a - 1$ **b.** $-4x - 1$ **c.** $4x + 4h - 1$ **125. a.** 2.9 million **b.** 57.3 million **c.** 247.4 million **d.** answers may vary

127. a. 42.4 million **b.** 29.5 million **129. a.** 4.4 million **b.** 6.2 million

Section 5.4

Practice Exercises

1. a. $6x^6$ **b.** $40m^5n^2p^8$ **2. a.** $21x^2 - 3x$ **b.** $-15a^4 + 30a^3 - 25a^2$ **c.** $-5m^3n^5 - 2m^2n^4 + 5m^2n^3$
3. a. $2x^2 + 13x + 15$ **b.** $3x^3 - 19x^2 + 12x - 2$ **4.** $3x^4 - 12x^3 - 13x^2 - 8x - 10$ **5.** $x^2 - 2x - 15$
6. a. $6x^2 - 31x + 35$ **b.** $8x^4 - 10x^2y - 3y^2$ **7. a.** $x^2 + 12x + 36$ **b.** $x^2 - 4x + 4$ **c.** $9x^2 + 30xy + 25y^2$ **d.** $9x^4 - 48x^2b + 64b^2$
8. a. $x^2 - 49$ **b.** $4a^2 - 25$ **c.** $25x^4 - \dfrac{1}{16}$ **d.** $a^6 - 16b^4$ **9.** $4 + 12x - 4y + 9x^2 - 6xy + y^2$ **10.** $9x^2 - 6xy + y^2 - 25$
11. $x^4 - 32x^2 + 256$ **12.** $h^2 - h + 3$

Graphing Calculator Explorations 5.4

1. $x^2 - 16$ **3.** $9x^2 - 42x + 49$ **5.** $5x^3 - 14x^2 - 13x - 2$

Vocabulary and Readiness Check 5.4

1. b **3.** b **5.** d

Exercise Set 5.4

1. $-12x^5$ **3.** $12x^2 + 21x$ **5.** $-24x^2y - 6xy^2$ **7.** $-4a^3bx - 4a^3by + 12ab$ **9.** $2x^2 - 2x - 12$ **11.** $2x^4 + 3x^3 - 2x^2 + x + 6$
13. $15x^2 - 7x - 2$ **15.** $15m^3 + 16m^2 - m - 2$ **17.** $x^2 + x - 12$ **19.** $10x^2 + 11xy - 8y^2$ **21.** $3x^2 + 8x - 3$

23. $9x^2 - \dfrac{1}{4}$ **25.** $5x^4 - 17x^2y^2 + 6y^4$ **27.** $x^2 + 8x + 16$ **29.** $36y^2 - 1$ **31.** $9x^2 - 6xy + y^2$ **33.** $25b^2 - 36y^2$ **35.** $16b^2 + 32b + 16$

37. $4s^2 - 12s + 8$ **39.** $x^2y^2 - 4xy + 4$ **41.** answers may vary **43.** $x^4 - 2x^2y^2 + y^4$ **45.** $x^4 - 8x^3 + 24x^2 - 32x + 16$ **47.** $x^4 - 625$

49. $9x^2 + 18x + 5$ **51.** $10x^5 + 8x^4 + 2x^3 + 25x^2 + 20x + 5$ **53.** $49x^2 - 9$ **55.** $9x^3 + 30x^2 + 12x - 24$ **57.** $16x^2 - \dfrac{2}{3}x - \dfrac{1}{6}$

59. $36x^2 + 12x + 1$ **61.** $x^4 - 4y^2$ **63.** $-30a^4b^4 + 36a^3b^2 + 36a^2b^3$ **65.** $2a^2 - 12a + 16$ **67.** $49a^2b^2 - 9c^2$ **69.** $m^2 - 8m + 16$
71. $9x^2 + 6x + 1$ **73.** $y^2 - 7y + 12$ **75.** $2x^3 + 2x^2y + x^2 + xy - x - y$ **77.** $9x^4 + 12x^3 - 2x^2 - 4x + 1$ **79.** $12x^3 - 2x^2 + 13x + 5$

81. $a^2 - 3a$ **83.** $a^2 + 2ah + h^2 - 3a - 3h$ **85.** $b^2 - 7b + 10$ **87.** -2 **89.** $\dfrac{3}{5}$ **91.** function **93.** $7y(3z - 2) + 1 = 21yz - 14y + 1$

95. answers may vary **97. a.** $a^2 + 2ah + h^2 + 3a + 3h + 2$ **b.** $a^2 + 3a + 2$ **c.** $2ah + h^2 + 3h$ **99.** $30x^2y^{2n+1} - 10x^2y^n$
101. $x^{3a} + 5x^{2a} - 3x^a - 15$ **103.** $\pi(25x^2 - 20x + 4)$ sq km **105.** $(8x^2 - 12x + 4)$ sq in. **107. a.** $6x + 12$
b. $9x^2 + 36x + 35$; one operation is addition, the other is multiplication. **109.** $5x^2 + 25x$ **111.** $x^4 - 4x^2 + 4$ **113.** $x^3 + 5x^2 - 2x - 10$

Section 5.5

Practice Exercises

1. $8y$ **2. a.** $3(2x^2 + 3 + 5x)$ **b.** $3x - 8y^3$ **c.** $2a^3(4a - 1)$ **3.** $8x^3y^2(8x^2 - 1)$ **4.** $-xy^2(9x^3 - 5x - 7)$ **5.** $(3 + 5b)(x + 4)$
6. $(8b - 1)(a^3 + 2y)$ **7.** $(x + 2)(y - 5)$ **8.** $(a + 2)(a^2 + 5)$ **9.** $(x^2 + 3)(y^2 - 5)$ **10.** $(q + 3)(p - 1)$

Vocabulary and Readiness Check 5.5

1. factoring **3.** least **5.** false **7.** false **9.** 6 **11.** 5 **13.** x **15.** $7x$

Exercise Set 5.5

1. a^3 **3.** y^2z^2 **5.** $3x^2y$ **7.** $5xz^3$ **9.** $6(3x - 2)$ **11.** $4y^2(1 - 4xy)$ **13.** $2x^3(3x^2 - 4x + 1)$ **15.** $4ab(2a^2b^2 - ab + 1 + 4b)$
17. $(x + 3)(6 + 5a)$ **19.** $(z + 7)(2x + 1)$ **21.** $(x^2 + 5)(3x - 2)$ **23.** answers may vary **25.** $(a + 2)(b + 3)$
27. $(a - 2)(c + 4)$ **29.** $(x - 2)(2y - 3)$ **31.** $(4x - 1)(3y - 2)$ **33.** $3(2x^3 + 3)$ **35.** $x^2(x + 3)$ **37.** $4a(2a^2 - 1)$

39. $-4xy(5x - 4y^2)$ or $4xy(-5x + 4y^2)$ **41.** $5ab^2(2ab + 1 - 3b)$ **43.** $3b(3ac^2 + 2a^2c - 2a + c)$ **45.** $(y - 2)(4x - 3)$
47. $(2x + 3)(3y + 5)$ **49.** $(x + 3)(y - 5)$ **51.** $(2a - 3)(3b - 1)$ **53.** $(6x + 1)(2y + 3)$ **55.** $(n - 8)(2m - 1)$ **57.** $3x^2y^2(5x - 6)$
59. $(2x + 3y)(x + 2)$ **61.** $(5x - 3)(x + y)$ **63.** $(x^2 + 4)(x + 3)$ **65.** $(x^2 - 2)(x - 1)$ **67.** $55x^7$ **69.** $125x^6$ **71.** $x^2 - 3x - 10$
73. $x^2 + 5x + 6$ **75.** $y^2 - 4y + 3$ **77.** d **79.** $2\pi r(r + h)$ **81.** $A = 5600(1 + rt)$ **83.** answers may vary **85.** none **87.** a
89. $A = P(1 + RT)$ **91.** $y^n(3 + 3y^n + 5y^{7n})$ **93.** $3x^{2a}(x^{3a} - 2x^a + 3)$ **95. a.** $h(t) = -16(t^2 - 14)$ **b.** 160 **c.** answers may vary

Section 5.6
Practice Exercises
1. $(x + 3)(x + 2)$ **2.** $(x - 3)(x - 8)$ **3.** $3x(x - 5)(x + 2)$ **4.** $2(b^2 - 9b - 11)$ **5.** $(2x + 1)(x + 6)$ **6.** $(4x - 3)(x + 2)$
7. $3b^2(2b - 5)(3b - 2)$ **8.** $(5x + 2y)^2$ **9.** $(5x + 2)(4x + 3)$ **10.** $(5x + 3)(3x - 1)$ **11.** $(x - 3)(3x + 8)$ **12.** $(3x^2 + 2)(2x^2 - 5)$

Vocabulary and Readiness Check 5.6
1. 5 and 2 **3.** 8 and 3

Exercise Set 5.6
1. $(x + 3)(x + 6)$ **3.** $(x - 8)(x - 4)$ **5.** $(x + 12)(x - 2)$ **7.** $(x - 6)(x + 4)$ **9.** $3(x - 2)(x - 4)$ **11.** $4z(x + 2)(x + 5)$
13. $2(x^2 - 12x - 32)$ **15.** $(5x + 1)(x + 3)$ **17.** $(2x - 3)(x - 4)$ **19.** prime polynomial **21.** $(2x - 3)^2$ **23.** $2(3x - 5)(2x + 5)$
25. $y^2(3y + 5)(y - 2)$ **27.** $2x(3x^2 + 4x + 12)$ **29.** $(2x + y)(x - 3y)$ **31.** $2(7y + 2)(2y + 1)$ **33.** $(2x - 3)(x + 9)$
35. $(x^2 + 3)(x^2 - 2)$ **37.** $(5x + 8)(5x + 2)$ **39.** $(x^3 - 4)(x^3 - 3)$ **41.** $(a - 3)(a + 8)$ **43.** $(x - 27)(x + 3)$ **45.** $(x - 18)(x + 3)$
47. $3(x - 1)^2$ **49.** $(3x + 1)(x - 2)$ **51.** $(4x - 3)(2x - 5)$ **53.** $3x^2(2x + 1)(3x + 2)$ **55.** $(x + 7z)(x + z)$ **57.** $(x - 4)(x + 3)$
59. $3(a + 2b)^2$ **61.** prime polynomial **63.** $(2x + 13)(x + 3)$ **65.** $(3x - 2)(2x - 15)$ **67.** $(x^2 - 6)(x^2 + 1)$ **69.** $x(3x + 1)(2x - 1)$
71. $(4a - 3b)(3a - 5b)$ **73.** $(3x + 5)^2$ **75.** $y(3x - 8)(x - 1)$ **77.** $2(x + 3)(x - 2)$ **79.** $(x + 2)(x - 7)$ **81.** $(2x^3 - 3)(x^3 + 3)$
83. $2x(6y^2 - z)^2$ **85.** $2xy(x + 3)(x - 2)$ **87.** $(x + 5y)(x + y)$ **89.** $x^2 - 9$ **91.** $4x^2 + 4x + 1$ **93.** $x^3 - 8$ **95.** $\pm 5, \pm 7$
97. $x(x + 4)(x - 2)$ **99. a.** 576 ft; 672 ft; 640 ft; 480 ft **b.** answers may vary **c.** $-16(t + 4)(t - 9)$ **101.** $(x^n + 2)(x^n + 8)$
103. $(x^n - 6)(x^n + 3)$ **105.** $(2x^n + 1)(x^n + 5)$ **107.** $(2x^n - 3)^2$ **109.** $x^2(x + 5)(x + 1)$ **111.** $3x(5x - 1)(2x + 1)$

Section 5.7
Practice Exercises
1. $(b + 8)^2$ **2.** $5b(3x - 1)^2$ **3. a.** $(x + 4)(x - 4)$ **b.** $(5b - 7)(5b + 7)$ **c.** $5(3 - 2x)(3 + 2x)$ **d.** $\left(y - \dfrac{1}{9}\right)\left(y + \dfrac{1}{9}\right)$

4. a. $(x^2 + 100)(x + 10)(x - 10)$ **b.** $(x + 9)(x - 5)$ **5.** $(m + 3 + n)(m + 3 - n)$ **6.** $(x + 4)(x^2 - 4x + 16)$
7. $(a + 2b)(a^2 - 2ab + 4b^2)$ **8.** $(3 - y)(9 + 3y + y^2)$ **9.** $x^2(b - 2)(b^2 + 2b + 4)$

Vocabulary and Readiness Check 5.7
1. $(9y)^2$ **3.** $(8x^3)^2$ **5.** 5^3 **7.** $(2x)^3$ **9.** $(4x^2)^3$

Exercise Set 5.7
1. $(x + 3)^2$ **3.** $(2x - 3)^2$ **5.** $3(x - 4)^2$ **7.** $x^2(3y + 2)^2$ **9.** $(x + 5)(x - 5)$ **11.** $(3 + 2z)(3 - 2z)$ **13.** $(y + 9)(y - 5)$
15. $4(4x + 5)(4x - 5)$ **17.** $(x + 3)(x^2 - 3x + 9)$ **19.** $(z - 1)(z^2 + z + 1)$ **21.** $(m + n)(m^2 - mn + n^2)$ **23.** $y^2(x - 3)(x^2 + 3x + 9)$
25. $b(a + 2b)(a^2 - 2ab + 4b^2)$ **27.** $(5y - 2x)(25y^2 + 10yx + 4x^2)$ **29.** $(x + 3 + y)(x + 3 - y)$ **31.** $(x - 5 + y)(x - 5 - y)$
33. $(2x + 1 + z)(2x + 1 - z)$ **35.** $(3x + 7)(3x - 7)$ **37.** $(x - 6)^2$ **39.** $(x^2 + 9)(x + 3)(x - 3)$ **41.** $(x + 4 + 2y)(x + 4 - 2y)$
43. $(x + 2y + 3)(x + 2y - 3)$ **45.** $(x - 6)(x^2 + 6x + 36)$ **47.** $(x + 5)(x^2 - 5x + 25)$ **49.** prime polynomial **51.** $(2a + 3)^2$
53. $2y(3x + 1)(3x - 1)$ **55.** $(2x + y)(4x^2 - 2xy + y^2)$ **57.** $(x^2 - y)(x^4 + x^2y + y^2)$ **59.** $(x + 8 + x^2)(x + 8 - x^2)$

61. $3y^2(x^2 + 3)(x^4 - 3x^2 + 9)$ **63.** $(x + y + 5)(x^2 + 2xy + y^2 - 5x - 5y + 25)$ **65.** $(2x - 1)(4x^2 + 20x + 37)$ **67.** 5 **69.** $-\dfrac{1}{3}$ **71.** 0

73. 5 **75.** no; $x^2 - 4$ can be factored further **77.** yes **79.** $\pi R^2 - \pi r^2 = \pi(R + r)(R - r)$ **81.** $x^3 - y^2x; x(x + y)(x - y)$ **83.** $c = 9$
85. $c = 49$ **87.** $c = \pm 8$ **89. a.** $(x + 1)(x^2 - x + 1)(x - 1)(x^2 + x + 1)$ **b.** $(x + 1)(x - 1)(x^4 + x^2 + 1)$ **c.** answers may vary
91. $(x^n + 6)(x^n - 6)$ **93.** $(5x^n + 9)(5x^n - 9)$ **95.** $(x^{2n} + 25)(x^n + 5)(x^n - 5)$

Integrated Review Practice Exercises
1. a. $3xy(4x - 1)$ **b.** $(7x + 2)(7x - 2)$ **c.** $(5x - 3)(x + 1)$ **d.** $(3 + x)(x^2 + 2)$ **e.** $(2x + 5)^2$ **f.** cannot be factored
2. a. $(4x + y)(16x^2 - 4xy + y^2)$ **b.** $7y^2(x - 3y)(x + 3y)$ **c.** $3(x + 2 + b)(x + 2 - b)$ **d.** $x^2y(xy + 3)(x^2y^2 - 3xy + 9)$
 e. $(x + 7 + 9y)(x + 7 - 9y)$

Integrated Review
1. $2y^2 + 2y - 11$ **2.** $-2z^4 - 6z^2 + 3z$ **3.** $x^2 - 7x + 7$ **4.** $7x^2 - 4x - 5$ **5.** $25x^2 - 30x + 9$ **6.** $x - 3$

7. $2x^3 - 4x^2 + 5x - 5 + \dfrac{8}{x + 2}$ **8.** $4x^3 - 13x^2 - 5x + 2$ **9.** $(x - 4 + y)(x - 4 - y)$ **10.** $2(3x + 2)(2x - 5)$ **11.** $x(x - 1)(x^2 + x + 1)$

12. $2x(2x - 1)$ **13.** $2xy(7x - 1)$ **14.** $6ab(4b - 1)$ **15.** $4(x + 2)(x - 2)$ **16.** $9(x + 3)(x - 3)$ **17.** $(3x - 11)(x + 1)$
18. $(5x + 3)(x - 1)$ **19.** $4(x + 3)(x - 1)$ **20.** $6(x + 1)(x - 2)$ **21.** $(2x + 9)^2$ **22.** $(5x + 4)^2$ **23.** $(2x + 5y)(4x^2 - 10xy + 25y^2)$

24. $(3x - 4y)(9x^2 + 12xy + 16y^2)$ **25.** $8x^2(2y - 1)(4y^2 + 2y + 1)$ **26.** $27x^2y(xy - 2)(x^2y^2 + 2xy + 4)$
27. $(x + 5 + y)(x^2 + 10x - xy - 5y + y^2 + 25)$ **28.** $(y - 1 + 3x)(y^2 - 2y + 1 - 3xy + 3x + 9x^2)$ **29.** $(5a - 6)^2$ **30.** $(4r + 5)^2$
31. $7x(x - 9)$ **32.** $(4x + 3)(5x + 2)$ **33.** $(a + 7)(b - 6)$ **34.** $20(x - 6)(x - 5)$ **35.** $(x^2 + 1)(x - 1)(x + 1)$ **36.** $5x(3x - 4)$
37. $(5x - 11)(2x + 3)$ **38.** $9m^2n^2(5mn - 3)$ **39.** $5a^3b(b^2 - 10)$ **40.** $x(x + 1)(x^2 - x + 1)$ **41.** prime   **42.** $20(x + y)(x^2 - xy + y^2)$
43. $10x(x - 10)(x - 11)$ **44.** $(3y - 7)^2$ **45.** $a^3b(4b - 3)(16b^2 + 12b + 9)$ **46.** $(y^2 + 4)(y + 2)(y - 2)$ **47.** $2(x - 3)(x^2 + 3x + 9)$
48. $(2s - 1)(r + 5)$ **49.** $(y^4 + 2)(3y - 5)$ **50.** prime   **51.** $100(z + 1)(z^2 - z + 1)$ **52.** $2x(5x - 2)(25x^2 + 10x + 4)$ **53.** $(2b - 9)^2$
54. $(a^4 + 3)(2a - 1)$ **55.** $(y - 4)(y - 5)$ **56.** $(c - 3)(c + 1)$ **57.** $A = 9 - 4x^2 = (3 + 2x)(3 - 2x)$

Section 5.8
Practice Exercises

1. $-8, 5$ **2.** $-4, \dfrac{2}{3}$ **3.** $-4, -\dfrac{2}{3}$ **4.** $-\dfrac{3}{4}$ **5.** $-\dfrac{1}{8}, 2$ **6.** $0, 3, -1$ **7.** $3, -3, -2$ **8.** 6 seconds   **9.** $6, 8, 10$ units   **10.** $f(x):$ C; $g(x):$ A; $h(x):$ B

Graphing Calculator Explorations 5.8

1. $-3.562, 0.562$ **3.** $-0.874, 2.787$ **5.** $-0.465, 1.910$

Vocabulary and Readiness Check 5.8

1. $3, -5$ **3.** $3, -7$ **5.** $0, 9$

Exercise Set 5.8

1. $-3, \dfrac{4}{3}$ **3.** $\dfrac{5}{2}, -\dfrac{3}{4}$ **5.** $-3, -8$ **7.** $\dfrac{1}{4}, -\dfrac{2}{3}$ **9.** $1, 9$ **11.** $\dfrac{3}{5}, -1$ **13.** 0 **15.** $6, -3$ **17.** $\dfrac{2}{5}, -\dfrac{1}{2}$ **19.** $\dfrac{3}{4}, -\dfrac{1}{2}$ **21.** $-2, 7, \dfrac{8}{3}$

23. $0, 3, -3$ **25.** $2, 1, -1$ **27.** answers may vary   **29.** $-\dfrac{7}{2}, 10$ **31.** $0, 5$ **33.** $-3, 5$ **35.** $-\dfrac{1}{2}, \dfrac{1}{3}$ **37.** $-4, 9$ **39.** $\dfrac{4}{5}$ **41.** $-5, 0, 2$

43. $-3, 0, \dfrac{4}{5}$ **45.** $\varnothing$ **47.** $-7, 4$ **49.** $4, 6$ **51.** $-\dfrac{1}{2}$ **53.** $-4, -3, 3$ **55.** $-5, 0, 5$ **57.** $-6, 5$ **59.** $-\dfrac{1}{3}, 0, 1$ **61.** $-\dfrac{1}{3}, 0$ **63.** $-\dfrac{7}{8}$

65. $\dfrac{31}{4}$ **67.** 1 **69. a.** incorrect   **b.** correct   **c.** correct   **d.** incorrect   **71.** -11 and -6 or 6 and 11 **73.** 75 ft   **75.** 105 units

77. 12 cm and 9 cm   **79.** 2 in.   **81.** 10 sec   **83.** width: $7\dfrac{1}{2}$ ft; length: 12 ft   **85.** 10 in. sq tier   **87.** 9 sec   **89.** E   **91.** F   **93.** B
95. $(-3, 0), (0, 2)$; function   **97.** $(-4, 0), (0, 2), (4, 0), (0, -2)$; not a function   **99.** answers may vary

101. $x - 5 = 0$ or $x + 2 = 0$
            $x = 5$ or $x = -2$
103. $y(y - 5) = -6$
            $y^2 - 5y + 6 = 0$
            $(y - 2)(y - 3) = 0$
            $y - 2 = 0$ or $y - 3 = 0$
            $y = 2$ or $y = 3$
105. $-3, -\dfrac{1}{3}, 2, 5$ **107.** no; answers may vary   **109.** answers may vary
111. answers may vary

The Bigger Picture

1. $-\dfrac{1}{2}, 6$ **2.** $(-7, 3)$ **3.** $-\dfrac{5}{3}$ **4.** $-\dfrac{3}{2}, 6$ **5.** $(-\infty, \infty)$ **6.** $-8, 3$ **7.** $-3, 10$ **8.** $(-\infty, 0]$

Chapter 5 Vocabulary Check

1. polynomial   **2.** factoring   **3.** exponents   **4.** degree of a term   **5.** monomial   **6.** 1   **7.** trinomial
8. quadratic equation   **9.** scientific notation   **10.** degree of a polynomial   **11.** binomial   **12.** 0

Chapter 5 Review

1. 4   **3.** -4 **5.** 1   **7.** $-\dfrac{1}{16}$ **9.** $-x^2y^7z$ **11.** $\dfrac{1}{a^9}$ **13.** $\dfrac{1}{x^{11}}$ **15.** $\dfrac{1}{y^5}$ **17.** -3.62×10^{-4} **19.** 410,000   **21.** $\dfrac{a^2}{16}$ **23.** $\dfrac{1}{16x^2}$

25. $\dfrac{1}{8^{18}}$ **27.** $-\dfrac{1}{8x^9}$ **29.** $\dfrac{-27y^6}{x^6}$ **31.** $\dfrac{xz}{4}$ **33.** $\dfrac{2}{27z^3}$ **35.** $2y^{x-7}$ **37.** -2.21×10^{-11} **39.** $\dfrac{x^3y^{10}}{3z^{12}}$ **41.** 5   **43.** $12x - 6x^2 - 6x^2y$

45. $4x^2 + 8y + 6$ **47.** $8x^2 + 2b - 22$ **49.** $12x^2y - 7xy + 3$ **51.** $x^3 + x - 2xy^2 - y - 7$ **53.** 58   **55.** $x^2 + 4x - 6$
57. $(6x^2y - 12x + 12)$ cm   **59.** $-12a^2b^5 - 28a^2b^3 - 4ab^2$ **61.** $9x^2a^2 - 24xab + 16b^2$ **63.** $15x^2 + 18xy - 81y^2$
65. $x^4 + 18x^3 + 83x^2 + 18x + 1$ **67.** $16x^2 + 72x + 81$ **69.** $16 - 9a^2 + 6ab - b^2$ **71.** $(9y^2 - 49z^2)$ sq units
73. $16x^2y^2z - 8xy^zb + b^2$ **75.** $8x^2(2x - 3)$ **77.** $2ab(3b + 4 - 2ab)$ **79.** $(a + 3b)(6a - 5)$ **81.** $(x - 6)(y + 3)$ **83.** $(p - 5)(q - 3)$
85. $x(2y - x)$ **87.** $(x - 4)(x + 20)$ **89.** $3(x + 2)(x + 9)$ **91.** $(3x + 8)(x - 2)$ **93.** $(15x - 1)(x - 6)$ **95.** $3(x - 2)(3x + 2)$
97. $(x + 7)(x + 9)$ **99.** $(x^2 - 2)(x^2 + 10)$ **101.** $(x + 9)(x - 9)$ **103.** $6(x + 3)(x - 3)$ **105.** $(4 + y^2)(2 + y)(2 - y)$ **107.** $(x - 7)(x + 1)$
109. $(y + 8)(y^2 - 8y + 64)$ **111.** $(1 - 4y)(1 + 4y + 16y^2)$ **113.** $2x^2(x + 2y)(x^2 - 2xy + 4y^2)$ **115.** $(x - 3 - 2y)(x - 3 + 2y)$
117. $(4a - 5b)^2$ **119.** $\dfrac{1}{3}, -7$ **121.** $0, 4, \dfrac{9}{2}$ **123.** $0, 6$ **125.** $-\dfrac{1}{3}, 2$ **127.** $-4, 1$ **129.** $0, 6, -3$ **131.** $0, -2, 1$ **133.** $-\dfrac{15}{2}, 7$ **135.** 5 sec
137. $3x^3 + 13x^2 - 9x + 5$ **139.** $8x^2 + 3x + 4.5$ **141.** -24 **143.** $6y^4(2y - 1)$ **145.** $2(3x + 1)(x - 6)$ **147.** $z^5(2z + 7)(2z - 7)$ **149.** $0, 3$

Chapter 5 Test

1. $\dfrac{1}{81x^2}$ **2.** $-12x^2z$ **3.** $\dfrac{3a^7}{2b^5}$ **4.** $-\dfrac{y^{40}}{z^5}$ **5.** 6.3×10^8 **6.** 1.2×10^{-2} **7.** 0.000005 **8.** 0.0009 **9.** $-5x^3y - 11x - 9$

10. $-12x^2y - 3xy^2$ **11.** $12x^2 - 5x - 28$ **12.** $25a^2 - 4b^2$ **13.** $36m^2 + 12mn + n^2$ **14.** $2x^3 - 13x^2 + 14x - 4$ **15.** $4x^2y(4x - 3y^3)$

16. $(x - 15)(x + 2)$ **17.** $(2y + 5)^2$ **18.** $3(2x + 1)(x - 3)$ **19.** $(2x + 5)(2x - 5)$ **20.** $(x + 4)(x^2 - 4x + 16)$

21. $3y(x + 3y)(x - 3y)$ **22.** $6(x^2 + 4)$ **23.** $2(2y - 1)(4y^2 + 2y + 1)$ **24.** $(x + 3)(x - 3)(y - 3)$ **25.** $4, -\dfrac{8}{7}$ **26.** $-3, 8$

27. $-\dfrac{5}{2}, -2, 2$ **28.** $(x + 2y)(x - 2y)$ **29. a.** 960 ft   **b.** 953.44 ft   **c.** 11 sec

Chapter 5 Cumulative Review

1. a. 3   **b.** 1   **c.** 2; Sec. 1.3, Ex. 8   **3.** 1; Sec. 2.1, Ex. 4   **5.** \$11,607.55; Sec. 2.3, Ex. 4   **7. a.** $\left(-\infty, \dfrac{3}{2}\right]$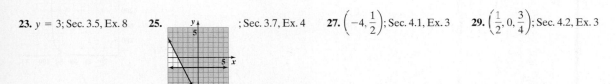

b. $(-3, \infty)$; Sec. 2.4, Ex. 4   **9.** $\left[-9, -\dfrac{9}{2}\right)$; Sec. 2.5, Ex. 5   **11.** 0; Sec. 2.6, Ex. 5   **13.** $\varnothing$; Sec. 2.7, Ex. 4

15. 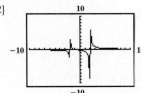 ; Sec. 3.1, Ex. 5   **17.** $(2, -3), (-6, -9), (0, 3)$; Sec. 3.6, Ex. 1   **19.** ; Sec. 3.3, Ex. 6   **21.** 0; Sec. 3.4, Ex. 7

23. $y = 3$; Sec. 3.5, Ex. 8   **25.** ; Sec. 3.7, Ex. 4   **27.** $\left(-4, \dfrac{1}{2}\right)$; Sec. 4.1, Ex. 3   **29.** $\left(\dfrac{1}{2}, 0, \dfrac{3}{4}\right)$; Sec. 4.2, Ex. 3

31. 7, 11; Sec. 4.3, Ex. 2   **33.** $\varnothing$; Sec. 4.4, Ex. 2   **35.** $30°, 40°, 110°$; Sec. 4.3, Ex. 6   **37. a.** 7.3×10^5 **b.** 1.04×10^{-6}; Sec. 5.1, Ex. 8

39. a. $\dfrac{y^6}{4}$ **b.** x^9 **c.** $\dfrac{49}{4}$ **d.** $\dfrac{y^{16}}{25x^5}$; Sec. 5.2, Ex. 3   **41.** 4; Sec. 5.3, Ex. 3   **43. a.** $10x^9$ **b.** $-7xy^{15}z^9$; Sec. 5.4, Ex. 1

45. $17x^3y^2(1 - 2x)$; Sec. 5.5, Ex. 3   **47.** $(x + 2)(x + 8)$; Sec. 5.6, Ex. 1   **49.** $-5, \dfrac{1}{2}$; Sec. 5.8, Ex. 2

CHAPTER 6 RATIONAL EXPRESSIONS

Section 6.1

Practice Exercises

1. a. $\{x \mid x \text{ is a real number}\}$ **b.** $\{x \mid x \text{ is a real number and } x \neq -3\}$ **c.** $\{x \mid x \text{ is a real number and } x \neq 2, x \neq 3\}$

2. a. $\dfrac{1}{2z - 1}$ **b.** $\dfrac{5x + 3}{6x - 5}$ **3. a.** 1   **b.** -1 **4.** $-\dfrac{5(2 + x)}{x + 3}$ **5. a.** $x^2 - 4x + 16$ **b.** $\dfrac{5}{z - 3}$ **6. a.** $\dfrac{2n + 1}{n(n - 1)}$ **b.** $-x^2$

7. a. $\dfrac{-y^3}{21(y + 3)}$ **b.** $\dfrac{7x + 2}{x + 2}$ **8.** $\dfrac{5}{3(x - 3)}$ **9. a.** \$7.20   **b.** \$3.50

Graphing Calculator Explorations 6.1

1. $\{x \mid x \text{ is a real number and } x \neq -2, x \neq 2\}$ 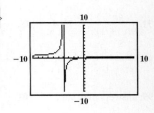   **3.** $\left\{x \mid x \text{ is a real number and } x \neq -4, x \neq \dfrac{1}{2}\right\}$

Vocabulary and Readiness Check 6.1

1. rational   **3.** domain   **5.** 1   **7.** $\dfrac{-a}{b}; \dfrac{a}{-b}$ **9.** $\dfrac{xy}{10}$ **11.** $\dfrac{2y}{3x}$ **13.** $\dfrac{m^2}{36}$

Exercise Set 6.1

1. $\{x \mid x \text{ is a real number}\}$ **3.** $\{t \mid t \text{ is a real number and } t \neq 0\}$ **5.** $\{x \mid x \text{ is a real number and } x \neq 7\}$

7. $\left\{x \mid x \text{ is a real number and } x \neq \dfrac{1}{3}\right\}$ **9.** $\{x \mid x \text{ is a real number and } x \neq -2, x \neq 0, x \neq 1\}$ **11.** $\{x \mid x \text{ is a real number and } x \neq 2, x \neq -2\}$

13. $1 - 2x$ **15.** $x - 3$ **17.** $\dfrac{9}{7}$ **19.** $x - 4$ **21.** -1 **23.** $-(x + 7)$ **25.** $\dfrac{2x + 1}{x - 1}$ **27.** $\dfrac{x^2 + 5x + 25}{2}$ **29.** $\dfrac{x - 2}{2x^2 + 1}$

31. $\dfrac{1}{3x + 5}$ **33.** $-\dfrac{4}{5}$ **35.** $-\dfrac{6a}{2a + 1}$ **37.** $\dfrac{3}{2(x - 1)}$ **39.** $\dfrac{x + 2}{x + 3}$ **41.** $\dfrac{3a}{5(a - b)}$ **43.** $\dfrac{1}{6}$ **45.** $\dfrac{x}{3}$ **47.** $\dfrac{4a^2}{a - b}$

49. $\dfrac{4}{(x + 2)(x + 3)}$ **51.** $\dfrac{1}{2}$ **53.** -1 **55.** $\dfrac{8(a - 2)}{3(a + 2)}$ **57.** $\dfrac{(x + 2)(x + 3)}{4}$ **59.** $\dfrac{2(x + 3)(x - 3)}{5(x^2 - 8x - 15)}$ **61.** $r^2 - rs + s^2$

63. $\dfrac{8}{x^2 y}$ **65.** $\dfrac{(y + 5)(2x - 1)}{(y + 2)(5x + 1)}$ **67.** $\dfrac{5(3a + 2)}{a}$ **69.** $\dfrac{5x^2 - 2}{(x - 1)^2}$ **71.** $\dfrac{10}{3}, -8, -\dfrac{7}{3}$ **73.** $\dfrac{17}{48}, \dfrac{2}{7}, -\dfrac{3}{8}$

75. a. \$200 million   **b.** \$500 million   **c.** \$300 million   **d.** $\{x \mid x \text{ is a real number}\}$ **77.** $\dfrac{7}{5}$ **79.** $\dfrac{1}{12}$ **81.** $\dfrac{11}{16}$

83. b and d   **85.** no; answers may vary   **87.** $\dfrac{5}{x - 2}$ sq m   **89.** $\dfrac{(x + 2)(x - 1)^2}{x^5}$ ft   **91.** answers may vary

93. a. 1   **b.** -1 **c.** neither   **d.** -1 **e.** -1 **f.** 1   **95.** $(x - 5)(2x + 7)$ **97.** $0, \dfrac{20}{9}, \dfrac{60}{7}, 20, \dfrac{140}{3}, 180, 380, 1980;$

99. $2x^2(x^n + 2)$ **101.** $\dfrac{1}{10y(y^n + 3)}$ **103.** $\dfrac{y^n + 1}{2(y^n - 1)}$

Section 6.2

Practice Exercises

1. a. $\dfrac{9 + x}{11z^2}$ **b.** $\dfrac{3x}{4}$ **c.** $x - 4$ **d.** $\dfrac{-3}{2a^2}$ **2. a.** $18x^3 y^5$ **b.** $(x - 2)(x + 3)$ **c.** $(b - 4)^2(b + 4)(2b + 3)$ **d.** $-4(y - 3)(y + 3)$

3. a. $\dfrac{20p + 3}{5p^4 q}$ **b.** $\dfrac{5y^2 + 19y - 12}{(y + 3)(y - 3)}$ **c.** 3   **4.** $\dfrac{t^2 - t - 15}{(t + 5)(t - 5)(t + 2)}$ **5.** $\dfrac{5x^2 - 12x - 3}{(3x + 1)(x - 2)(2x - 5)}$ **6.** $\dfrac{4}{x - 2}$

Vocabulary and Readiness Check 6.2

1. a, b   **3.** c   **5.** $\dfrac{12}{y}$ **7.** $\dfrac{35}{y^2}$ **9.** $\dfrac{-x + 4}{2x}$ **11.** $\dfrac{16}{y - 2}$

Exercise Set 6.2

1. $-\dfrac{3}{xz^2}$ **3.** $\dfrac{x + 2}{x - 2}$ **5.** $x - 2$ **7.** $\dfrac{-1}{x - 2}$ or $\dfrac{1}{2 - x}$ **9.** $-\dfrac{5}{x}$ **11.** $35x$ **13.** $x(x + 1)$ **15.** $(x + 7)(x - 7)$ **17.** $6(x + 2)(x - 2)$

19. $(a + b)(a - b)^2$ **21.** $-4x(x + 3)(x - 3)$ **23.** $\dfrac{17}{6x}$ **25.** $\dfrac{35 - 4y}{14y^2}$ **27.** $\dfrac{-13x + 4}{(x + 4)(x - 4)}$ **29.** $\dfrac{3}{x + 4}$ **31.** 0   **33.** $-\dfrac{x}{x - 1}$

35. $\dfrac{-x + 1}{x - 2}$ **37.** $\dfrac{y^2 + 2y + 10}{(y + 4)(y - 4)(y - 2)}$ **39.** $\dfrac{5(x^2 + x - 4)}{(3x + 2)(x + 3)(2x - 5)}$ **41.** $\dfrac{-x^2 + 10x + 19}{(x - 2)(x + 1)(x + 3)}$ **43.** $\dfrac{x^2 + 4x + 2}{(2x + 5)(x - 7)(x - 1)}$

45. $\dfrac{5a + 1}{(a + 1)^2(a - 1)}$ **47.** $\dfrac{3}{x^2 y^3}$ **49.** $-\dfrac{5}{x}$ **51.** $\dfrac{25}{6(x + 5)}$ **53.** $\dfrac{-2x - 1}{x^2(x - 3)}$ **55.** $\dfrac{b(2a - b)}{(a + b)(a - b)}$ **57.** $\dfrac{2(x + 8)}{(x + 2)^2(x - 2)}$

59. $\dfrac{3x^2 + 23x - 7}{(2x - 1)(x - 5)(x + 3)}$ **61.** $\dfrac{5 - 2x}{2(x + 1)}$ **63.** $\dfrac{2(x^2 + x - 21)}{(x + 3)^2(x - 3)}$ **65.** $\dfrac{6x}{(x + 3)(x - 3)^2}$ **67.** $\dfrac{4}{3}$ **69.** $\dfrac{2x^2 + 9x - 18}{6x^2}$ or $\dfrac{(x + 6)(2x - 3)}{6x^2}$

71. $\dfrac{4a^2}{9(a - 1)}$ **73.** 4   **75.** $-\dfrac{4}{x - 1}$ **77.** $-\dfrac{32}{x(x + 2)(x - 2)}$ **79.** 10   **81.** $4 + x^2$ **83.** 10   **85.** 2   **87.** 3   **89.** 5 m

91. $\dfrac{2x - 3}{x^2 + 1} - \dfrac{x - 6}{x^2 + 1} = \dfrac{2x - 3 - x + 6}{x^2 + 1} = \dfrac{x + 3}{x^2 + 1}$ **93.** $\dfrac{4x}{x + 5}$ ft; $\dfrac{x^2}{(x + 5)^2}$ sq ft   **95.** answers may vary   **97.** answers may vary

99. answers may vary   **101.** $\dfrac{3}{2x}$ **103.** $\dfrac{4 - 3x}{x^2}$ **105.**

Section 6.3
Practice Exercises

1. a. $\dfrac{1}{12m}$ **b.** $\dfrac{8x(x+4)}{3(x-4)}$ **c.** $\dfrac{b^2}{a^2}$ **2. a.** $\dfrac{8x(x+4)}{3(x-4)}$ **b.** $\dfrac{b^2}{a^2}$ **3.** $\dfrac{y(3xy+1)}{x^2(1+xy)}$ **4.** $\dfrac{1-6x}{15+6x}$

Vocabulary and Readiness Check 6.3

1. $\dfrac{7}{1+z}$ **3.** $\dfrac{1}{x^2}$ **5.** $\dfrac{2}{x}$ **7.** $\dfrac{1}{9y}$

Exercise Set 6.3

1. 4 **3.** $\dfrac{7}{13}$ **5.** $\dfrac{4}{x}$ **7.** $\dfrac{9(x-2)}{9x^2+4}$ **9.** $2x+y$ **11.** $\dfrac{2(x+1)}{2x-1}$ **13.** $\dfrac{2x+3}{4-9x}$ **15.** $\dfrac{1}{x^2-2x+4}$ **17.** $\dfrac{x}{5(x-2)}$

19. $\dfrac{x-2}{2x-1}$ **21.** $\dfrac{x}{2-3x}$ **23.** $-\dfrac{y}{x+y}$ **25.** $-\dfrac{2x^3}{y(x-y)}$ **27.** $\dfrac{2x+1}{y}$ **29.** $\dfrac{x-3}{9}$ **31.** $\dfrac{1}{x+2}$ **33.** 2

35. $\dfrac{xy^2}{x^2+y^2}$ **37.** $\dfrac{2b^2+3a}{b(b-a)}$ **39.** $\dfrac{x}{(x+1)(x-1)}$ **41.** $\dfrac{1+a}{1-a}$ **43.** $\dfrac{x(x+6y)}{2y}$ **45.** $\dfrac{5a}{2(a+2)}$ **47.** $xy(5y+2x)$

49. $\dfrac{xy}{2x+5y}$ **51.** $\dfrac{x^2y^2}{4}$ **53.** $-9x^3y^4$ **55.** $-4, 14$ **57.** a and c **59.** $\dfrac{770a}{770-s}$ **61.** a, b **63.** $\dfrac{1+x}{2+x}$ **65.** $x(x+1)$

67. $\dfrac{x-3y}{x+3y}$ **69.** $3a^2+4a+4$ **71. a.** $\dfrac{1}{a+h}$ **b.** $\dfrac{1}{a}$ **c.** $\dfrac{\dfrac{1}{a+h}-\dfrac{1}{a}}{h}$ **d.** $\dfrac{-1}{a(a+h)}$ **73. a.** $\dfrac{3}{a+h+1}$

b. $\dfrac{3}{a+1}$ **c.** $\dfrac{\dfrac{3}{a+h+1}-\dfrac{3}{a+1}}{h}$ **d.** $\dfrac{-3}{(a+h+1)(a+1)}$

Section 6.4
Practice Exercises

1. $3a^2-2a+5$ **2.** $5a^2b^2-8ab+1-\dfrac{8}{ab}$ **3.** $3x-2$ **4.** $3x-2$ **5.** $5x^2-6x+8+\dfrac{6}{x+3}$ **6.** $2x^2+3x-2+\dfrac{-8x+4}{x^2+1}$

7. $16x^2+20x+25$ **8.** $4x^2+x+7+\dfrac{12}{x-1}$ **9.** $x^3-5x+21-\dfrac{51}{x+3}$ **10. a.** -4 **b.** -4 **11.** 15

Exercise Set 6.4

1. $2a+4$ **3.** $3ab+4$ **5.** $2y+\dfrac{3y}{x}-\dfrac{2y}{x^2}$ **7.** $x+1$ **9.** $2x-8$ **11.** $x-\dfrac{1}{2}$ **13.** $2x^2-\dfrac{1}{2}x+5$ **15.** $2x^2-6$

17. $3x^3+5x+4-\dfrac{2x}{x^2-2}$ **19.** $2x^3+\dfrac{9}{2}x^2+10x+21+\dfrac{42}{x-2}$ **21.** $x+8$ **23.** $x-1$ **25.** $x^2-5x-23-\dfrac{41}{x-2}$

27. $4x+8+\dfrac{7}{x-2}$ **29.** $x^6y+\dfrac{2}{y}+1$ **31.** $5x^2-6-\dfrac{5}{2x-1}$ **33.** $2x^2+2x+8-\dfrac{28}{x-4}$ **35.** $2x^3-3x^2+x-4$

37. $3x^2+4x-8+\dfrac{20}{x+1}$ **39.** $3x^2+3x-3$ **41.** x^2+x+1 **43.** $-\dfrac{5y}{x}-\dfrac{15z}{x}-25z$ **45.** $3x^4-2x$ **47.** 1 **49.** -133

51. 3 **53.** $-\dfrac{187}{81}$ **55.** $\dfrac{95}{32}$ **57.** $-\dfrac{5}{6}$ **59.** 2 **61.** 54 **63.** $(x-1)(x^2+x+1)$ **65.** $(5z+2)(25z^2-10z+4)$ **67.** $(y+2)(x+3)$

69. $x(x+3)(x-3)$ **71.** yes **73.** no **75.** a or d **77.** (x^4+2x^2-6) m **79.** $(3x-7)$ in. **81.** (x^3-5x^2+2x-1) cm

83. $x^3+\dfrac{5}{3}x^2+\dfrac{5}{3}x+\dfrac{8}{3}+\dfrac{8}{3(x-1)}$ **85.** $\dfrac{3}{2}x^3+\dfrac{1}{4}x^2+\dfrac{1}{8}x-\dfrac{7}{16}+\dfrac{1}{16(2x-1)}$ **87.** $x^3-\dfrac{2}{5}x$ **89.** $5x-1+\dfrac{6}{x}; x\ne 0$

91. $7x^3+14x^2+25x+50+\dfrac{102}{x-2}; x\ne 2$ **93.** answers may vary **95.** answers may vary

97. $(x+3)(x^2+4)=x^3+3x^2+4x+12$ **99.** 0 **101.** $x^3+2x^2+7x+28$

Section 6.5
Practice Exercises

1. 4 **2.** 7 **3.** { } or $\varnothing$ **4.** -1 **5.** 1 **6.** $12, -1$

Vocabulary and Readiness Check 6.5

1. c **3.** a

Exercise Set 6.5

1. 72 **3.** 2 **5.** 6 **7.** 2, −2 **9.** ∅ **11.** $-\dfrac{28}{3}$ **13.** 3 **15.** −8 **17.** 3 **19.** ∅ **21.** 1 **23.** 3 **25.** −1 **27.** 6 **29.** $\dfrac{1}{3}$

31. −5, 5 **33.** 3 **35.** 7 **37.** ∅ **39.** $\dfrac{4}{3}$ **41.** −12 **43.** 1, $\dfrac{11}{4}$ **45.** −5, −1 **47.** $-\dfrac{7}{5}$ **49.** 5 **51.** length, 15 in.; width, 10 in.

53. 36% **55.** 12–19 **57.** 40,000 students **59.** answers may vary **61.** 800 pencil sharpeners **63.** $\dfrac{1}{9}, -\dfrac{1}{4}$ **65.** 3, 2 **67.** 1.39

69. −0.08 **71.** 1, 2 **73.** −3, $-\dfrac{3}{4}$ **75.**

77.

The Bigger Picture

1. $\left(-2, \dfrac{16}{7}\right)$ **2.** $-2, \dfrac{16}{7}$ **3.** ±11 **4.** 5 **5.** $-\dfrac{8}{5}$ **6.** $(-\infty, 2]$ **7.** $(-\infty, -5]$ **8.** (7, 10] **9.** $(-\infty, -17) \cup (18, \infty)$ **10.** $0, -\dfrac{1}{3}, \dfrac{7}{5}$

Integrated Review

1. $\dfrac{1}{2}$ **2.** 10 **3.** $\dfrac{1 + 2x}{8}$ **4.** $\dfrac{15 + x}{10}$ **5.** $\dfrac{2(x - 4)}{(x + 2)(x - 1)}$ **6.** $-\dfrac{5(x - 8)}{(x - 2)(x + 4)}$ **7.** 4 **8.** 8 **9.** −5 **10.** $-\dfrac{2}{3}$ **11.** $\dfrac{2x + 5}{x(x - 3)}$

12. $\dfrac{5}{2x}$ **13.** −2 **14.** $-\dfrac{y}{x}$ **15.** $\dfrac{(a + 3)(a + 1)}{a + 2}$ **16.** $\dfrac{-a^2 + 31a + 10}{5(a - 6)(a + 1)}$ **17.** $-\dfrac{1}{5}$ **18.** $-\dfrac{3}{13}$ **19.** $\dfrac{4a + 1}{(3a + 1)(3a - 1)}$

20. $\dfrac{-a - 8}{4a(a - 2)}$ or $-\dfrac{a + 8}{4a(a - 2)}$ **21.** $-1, \dfrac{3}{2}$ **22.** $\dfrac{x^2 - 3x + 10}{2(x + 3)(x - 3)}$ **23.** $\dfrac{3}{x + 1}$ **24.** {$x \mid x$ is a real number and $x \neq 2, x \neq -1$} **25.** −1

26. $\dfrac{22z - 45}{3z(z - 3)}$ **27. a.** $\dfrac{x}{5} - \dfrac{x}{4} + \dfrac{1}{10}$ **b.** Write each rational expression term so that the denominator is the LCD, 20. **c.** $\dfrac{-x + 2}{20}$

28. a. $\dfrac{x}{5} - \dfrac{x}{4} = \dfrac{1}{10}$ **b.** Clear the equation of fractions by multiplying each term by the LCD, 20. **c.** −2 **29.** b **30.** d **31.** d **32.** a **33.** d

Section 6.6
Practice Exercises

1. $a = \dfrac{bc}{b + c}$ **2.** 7 **3.** 3000 **4.** $1\dfrac{1}{5}$ hr **5.** 50 mph

Exercise Set 6.6

1. $C = \dfrac{5}{9}(F - 32)$ **3.** $I = A - QL$ **5.** $R = \dfrac{R_1 R_2}{R_1 + R_2}$ **7.** $n = \dfrac{2S}{a + L}$ **9.** $b = \dfrac{2A - ah}{h}$ **11.** $T_2 = \dfrac{P_2 V_2 T_1}{P_1 V_1}$ **13.** $f_2 = \dfrac{f_1 f}{f_1 - f}$

15. $L = \dfrac{n\lambda}{2}$ **17.** $c = \dfrac{2L\omega}{\theta}$ **19.** 1 and 5 **21.** 5 **23.** 4.5 gal **25.** 4470 women **27.** 15.6 hr **29.** 10 min **31.** 200 mph

33. 15 mph **35.** −8 and −7 **37.** 36 min **39.** 45 mph; 60 mph **41.** 5.9 hr **43.** 2 hr **45.** 135 mph **47.** 12 mi **49.** $\dfrac{7}{8}$

51. $1\dfrac{1}{2}$ min **53.** $2\dfrac{2}{9}$ hr **55.** 10 mph; 8 mph **57.** 2 hr **59.** by jet: 3 hr; by car: 4 hr **61.** 428 movies **63.** 6

65. 22 **67.** answers may vary; 60 in. or 5 ft **69.** 6 ohms **71.** $\dfrac{1}{R} = \dfrac{1}{R_1} + \dfrac{1}{R_2} + \dfrac{1}{R_3}; R = \dfrac{15}{13}$ ohms

Section 6.7
Practice Exercises

1. $k = \dfrac{4}{3}; y = \dfrac{4}{3}x$ **2.** $18\dfrac{3}{4}$ inches **3.** $k = 45; b = \dfrac{45}{a}$ **4.** $P = 653\dfrac{1}{3}$ kilopascals **5.** $A = $ kpa **6.** $k = 4; y = \dfrac{4}{x^3}$ **7.** $k = 81; y = \dfrac{81z}{x^3}$

Vocabulary and Readiness Check 6.7

1. direct **3.** joint **5.** inverse **7.** direct

Exercise Set 6.7

1. $k = \dfrac{1}{5}$; $y = \dfrac{1}{5}x$ **3.** $k = \dfrac{3}{2}$; $y = \dfrac{3}{2}x$ **5.** $k = 14$; $y = 14x$ **7.** $k = 0.25$; $y = 0.25x$ **9.** 4.05 lb   **11.** 204,706 tons   **13.** $k = 30$; $y = \dfrac{30}{x}$

15. $k = 700$; $y = \dfrac{700}{x}$ **17.** $k = 2$; $y = \dfrac{2}{x}$ **19.** $k = 0.14$; $y = \dfrac{0.14}{x}$ **21.** 54 mph   **23.** 72 amps   **25.** divided by 4   **27.** $x = kyz$

29. $r = kst^3$ **31.** $k = \dfrac{1}{3}$; $y = \dfrac{1}{3}x^3$ **33.** $k = 0.2$; $y = 0.2\sqrt{x}$ **35.** $k = 1.3$; $y = \dfrac{1.3}{x^2}$ **37.** $k = 3$; $y = 3xz^3$ **39.** 22.5 tons

41. 15π cu in.   **43.** 8 ft   **45.** $y = kx$ **47.** $a = \dfrac{k}{b}$ **49.** $y = kxz$ **51.** $y = \dfrac{k}{x^3}$ **53.** $y = \dfrac{kx}{p^2}$ **55.** $C = 8\pi$ in.; $A = 16\pi$ sq in.

57. $C = 18\pi$ cm; $A = 81\pi$ sq cm   **59.** 9   **61.** 1   **63.** $\dfrac{1}{2}$ **65.** $\dfrac{2}{3}$ **67.** a   **69.** c   **71.** multiplied by 8   **73.** multiplied by 2

75.   **77.**

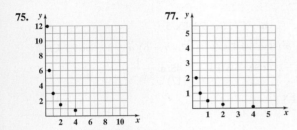

Chapter 6 Vocabulary Check

1. complex fraction   **2.** long division   **3.** directly   **4.** inversely   **5.** least common denominator
6. synthetic division   **7.** jointly   **8.** opposites   **9.** rational expression   **10.** equation, expression

Chapter 6 Review

1. $\{x \mid x \text{ is a real number}\}$ **3.** $\{x \mid x \text{ is a real number and } x \neq 5\}$ **5.** $\{x \mid z \text{ is a real number and } x \neq 0, x \neq -8\}$ **7.** -1 **9.** $\dfrac{1}{x - 1}$

11. $\dfrac{2(x - 3)}{x - 4}$ **13.** $-\dfrac{3}{2}$ **15.** $\dfrac{a - b}{2a}$ **17.** $\dfrac{12}{5}$ **19.** $\dfrac{a - b}{5a}$ **21.** $-\dfrac{1}{x}$ **23.** $60x^2 y^5$ **25.** $5x(x - 5)$ **27.** $\dfrac{4 + x}{x - 4}$

29. $\dfrac{3}{2(x - 2)}$ **31.** $\dfrac{-7x - 6}{5(x - 3)(x + 3)}$ **33.** $\dfrac{5a - 1}{(a - 1)^2(a + 1)}$ **35.** $\dfrac{5 - 2x}{2(x - 1)}$ **37.** $\dfrac{4 - 3x}{8 + x}$ **39.** $\dfrac{5(4x - 3)}{2(5x^2 - 2)}$ **41.** $\dfrac{x(5y + 1)}{3y}$

43. $\dfrac{1 + x}{1 - x}$ **45.** $\dfrac{3}{a + h}$ **47.** $\dfrac{\dfrac{3}{a + h} - \dfrac{3}{a}}{h}$ **49.** $1 + \dfrac{x}{2y} - \dfrac{9}{4xy}$ **51.** $3x^3 + 9x^2 + 2x + 6 - \dfrac{2}{x - 3}$ **53.** $x^2 - 1 + \dfrac{5}{2x + 3}$

55. $3x^2 + 6x + 24 + \dfrac{44}{x - 2}$ **57.** $x^2 + 3x + 9 - \dfrac{54}{x - 3}$ **59.** 3043   **61.** $\dfrac{365}{32}$ **63.** 6   **65.** $\dfrac{3}{2}$ **67.** $\dfrac{2x + 5}{x(x - 7)}$ **69.** $\dfrac{-5(x + 6)}{2x(x - 3)}$

71. $R_2 = \dfrac{RR_1}{R_1 - R}$ **73.** $r = \dfrac{A - P}{Pt}$ **75.** 1, 2   **77.** $1\dfrac{23}{37}$ hr   **79.** 8 mph   **81.** 9   **83.** 2   **85.** $\dfrac{3}{5x}$ **87.** $\dfrac{5(a - 2)}{7}$ **89.** $\dfrac{13}{3x}$

91. $\dfrac{1}{x - 2}$ **93.** $\dfrac{2}{15 - 2x}$ **95.** $\dfrac{2(x - 1)}{x + 6}$ **97.** 2   **99.** $\dfrac{23}{25}$ **101.** 10 hr   **103.** $63\dfrac{2}{3}$ mph; 45 mph   **105.** 64π sq in.

Chapter 6 Test

1. $\{x \mid x \text{ is a real number and } x \neq 1\}$ **2.** $\{x \mid x \text{ is a real number and } x \neq -3, x \neq -1\}$ **3.** $-\dfrac{7}{8}$ **4.** $\dfrac{x}{x + 9}$ **5.** $x^2 + 2x + 4$

6. $\dfrac{5}{3x}$ **7.** $\dfrac{3}{x^3}$ **8.** $\dfrac{x + 2}{2(x + 3)}$ **9.** $-\dfrac{4(2x + 9)}{5}$ **10.** -1 **11.** $\dfrac{1}{x(x + 3)}$ **12.** $\dfrac{5x - 2}{(x - 3)(x + 2)(x - 2)}$ **13.** $\dfrac{-x + 30}{6(x - 7)}$

14. $\dfrac{3}{2}$ **15.** $\dfrac{64}{3}$ **16.** $\dfrac{(x - 3)^2}{x - 2}$ **17.** $\dfrac{4xy}{3z} + \dfrac{3}{z} + 1$ **18.** $2x^2 - x - 2 + \dfrac{2}{2x + 1}$ **19.** $4x^3 - 15x^2 + 45x - 136 + \dfrac{407}{x + 3}$

20. 91   **21.** 8   **22.** $\dfrac{2}{7}$ **23.** 3   **24.** $x = \dfrac{7a^2 + b^2}{4a - b}$ **25.** 5   **26.** $\dfrac{6}{7}$ hr   **27.** 16   **28.** 9   **29.** 256 ft

Chapter 6 Cumulative Review

1. a. $8x$ **b.** $8x + 3$ **c.** $x \div -7$ or $\dfrac{x}{-7}$ **d.** $2x - 1.6$ **e.** $x - 6$ **f.** $2(4 + x)$; Sec. 1.2, Ex. 8   **3.** 2; Sec. 2.1, Ex. 5

5. 2026 and after; Sec. 2.4, Ex. 9   **7.** $\varnothing$; Sec. 2.6, Ex. 7   **9.** -1; Sec. 2.7, Ex. 8   **11.** ; Sec. 3.1, Ex. 4

13. a. function   **b.** not a function   **c.** function; Sec. 3.2, Ex. 2   **15.** ; Sec. 3.3, Ex. 4   **17.** $y = -3x - 2$; Sec. 3.5, Ex. 4

19. ; Sec. 3.7, Ex. 3   **21.** $(0, -5)$; Sec. 4.1, Ex. 6   **23.** $\varnothing$; Sec. 4.2, Ex. 2   **25.** $30°, 110°, 40°$; Sec. 4.3, Ex. 6

27. $(1, -1, 3)$; Sec. 4.4, Ex. 3   **29. a.** 1   **b.** -1 **c.** 1   **d.** 2; Sec. 5.1, Ex. 3   **31. a.** $4x^b$ **b.** y^{5a+6}; Sec 5.2, Ex. 5

33. a. 2   **b.** 5   **c.** 1   **d.** 6   **e.** 0; Sec. 5.3, Ex. 1   **35.** $9 + 12a + 6b + 4a^2 + 4ab + b^2$; Sec. 5.4, Ex. 9   **37.** $(b - 6)(a + 2)$; Sec 5.5, Ex. 7

39. $2(n^2 - 19n + 40)$; Sec. 5.6, Ex. 4   **41.** $(x + 2 + y)(x + 2 - y)$; Sec. 5.7, Ex. 5   **43.** $-2, 6$; Sec. 5.8, Ex. 1   **45. a.** $\dfrac{1}{5x - 1}$

b. $\dfrac{9x + 4}{8x - 7}$; Sec. 6.1, Ex. 2   **47.** $\dfrac{5k^2 - 7k + 4}{(k + 2)(k - 2)(k - 1)}$; Sec. 6.2, Ex. 4   **49.** -2; Sec. 6.5, Ex. 2

CHAPTER 7 RATIONAL EXPONENTS, RADICALS, AND COMPLEX NUMBERS

Section 7.1
Practice Exercises

1. a. 7   **b.** 0   **c.** $\dfrac{4}{9}$ **d.** 0.8   **e.** z^4 **f.** $4b^2$ **g.** -6 **h.** not a real number   **2.** 6.708   **3. a.** -1 **b.** 3   **c.** $\dfrac{3}{4}$ **d.** x^4 **e.** $-2x$

4. a. 10   **b.** -1 **c.** -9 **d.** not a real number   **e.** $3x^3$ **5. a.** 4   **b.** $|x^7|$ **c.** $|x + 7|$ **d.** -7 **e.** $3x - 5$ **f.** $7|x|$ **g.** $|x + 2|$

6. a. 4   **b.** 2   **c.** 2   **d.** -2 **7.**   **8.**

Vocabulary and Readiness Check 7.1

1. index; radical sign; radicand   **3.** is not   **5.** $[0, \infty)$ **7.** $(16, 4)$ **9.** d   **11.** d

Exercise Set 7.1

1. 10   **3.** $\dfrac{1}{2}$ **5.** 0.01   **7.** -6 **9.** x^5 **11.** $4y^3$ **13.** 2.646   **15.** 6.164   **17.** 14.142   **19.** 4   **21.** $\dfrac{1}{2}$

23. -1 **25.** x^4 **27.** $-3x^3$ **29.** -2 **31.** not a real number   **33.** -2 **35.** x^4 **37.** $2x^2$ **39.** $9x^2$ **41.** $4x^2$

43. 8   **45.** -8 **47.** $2|x|$ **49.** x **51.** $|x - 5|$ **53.** $|x + 2|$ **55.** -11 **57.** $2x$ **59.** y^6 **61.** $5ab^{10}$

63. $-3x^4y^3$ **65.** a^4b **67.** $-2x^2y$ **69.** $\dfrac{5}{7}$ **71.** $\dfrac{x}{2y}$ **73.** $-\dfrac{z^7}{3x}$ **75.** $\dfrac{x}{2}$ **77.** $\sqrt{3}$ **79.** -1 **81.** -3 **83.** $\sqrt{7}$

85. $[0, \infty)$;   **87.** $[3, \infty)$; 0, 1, 2, 3   **89.** $(-\infty, \infty)$;   **91.** $(-\infty, \infty)$; 0, 1, -1, 2, -2

93. $-32x^{15}y^{10}$ **95.** $-60x^7y^{10}z^5$ **97.** $\dfrac{x^9y^5}{2}$ **99.** not a real number   **101.** not a real number   **103.** answers may vary   **105.** 13   **107.** 18

109. 1.69 sq m   **111.** answers may vary   **113.**   **115.**

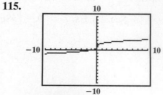

Section 7.2
Practice Exercises
1. a. 6 **b.** 10 **c.** $\sqrt[5]{x}$ **d.** 1 **e.** -8 **f.** $5x^3$ **g.** $\sqrt[4]{3x}$ **2. a.** 64 **b.** -1 **c.** -27 **c.** $\dfrac{1}{125}$ **e.** $\sqrt[9]{(3x+2)^5}$

3. a. $\dfrac{1}{27}$ **b.** $\dfrac{1}{16}$ **4. a.** $y^{10/3}$ **b.** $x^{17/20}$ **c.** $\dfrac{1}{9}$ **d.** $b^{2/9}$ **e.** $\dfrac{31}{x^3y^{11/3}}$ **5. a.** $x^{14/15}-x^{13/5}$ **b.** $x+4x^{1/2}-12$ **6.** $x^{-1/5}(2-7x)$

7. a. $\sqrt[3]{x}$ **b.** $\sqrt{6}$ **c.** $\sqrt[4]{a^2b}$ **8. a.** $\sqrt[12]{x^7}$ **b.** $\sqrt[15]{y^2}$ **c.** $\sqrt[6]{675}$

Vocabulary and Readiness Check 7.2
1. true **3.** true **5.** multiply **7.** A **9.** C **11.** B

Exercise Set 7.2
1. 7 **3.** 3 **5.** $\dfrac{1}{2}$ **7.** 13 **9.** $2\sqrt[3]{m}$ **11.** $3x^2$ **13.** -3 **15.** -2 **17.** 8 **19.** 16 **21.** not a real number **23.** $\sqrt[5]{(2x)^3}$

25. $\sqrt[3]{(7x+2)^2}$ **27.** $\dfrac{64}{27}$ **29.** $\dfrac{1}{16}$ **31.** $\dfrac{1}{16}$ **33.** not a real number **35.** $\dfrac{1}{x^{1/4}}$ **37.** $a^{2/3}$ **39.** $\dfrac{5x^{3/4}}{7}$ **41.** $a^{7/3}$ **43.** x **45.** $3^{5/8}$

47. $y^{1/6}$ **49.** $8u^3$ **51.** $-b$ **53.** $\dfrac{1}{x^2}$ **55.** $27x^{2/3}$ **57.** $\dfrac{y}{z^{1/6}}$ **59.** $\dfrac{1}{x^{7/4}}$ **61.** $y-y^{7/6}$ **63.** $x^{5/3}-2x^{2/3}$ **65.** $4x^{2/3}-9$ **67.** $x^{8/3}(1+x^{2/3})$

69. $x^{1/5}(x^{1/5}-3)$ **71.** $x^{-1/3}(5+x)$ **73.** $\sqrt{x}$ **75.** $\sqrt[3]{2}$ **77.** $2\sqrt{x}$ **79.** $\sqrt{xy}$ **81.** $\sqrt[3]{a^2b}$ **83.** $\sqrt{x+3}$ **85.** $\sqrt[15]{y^{11}}$

87. $\sqrt[12]{b^5}$ **89.** $\sqrt[24]{x^{23}}$ **91.** $\sqrt{a}$ **93.** $\sqrt[6]{432}$ **95.** $\sqrt[15]{343y^5}$ **97.** $\sqrt[6]{125r^3s^2}$ **99.** $25\cdot3$ **101.** $16\cdot3$ or $4\cdot12$ **103.** $8\cdot2$ **105.** $27\cdot2$

107. 1509 calories **109.** 210.1 million **111.** $a^{1/3}$ **113.** $x^{1/5}$ **115.** 1.6818 **117.** 5.6645 **119.** $\dfrac{t^{1/2}}{u^{1/2}}$

Section 7.3
Practice Exercises
1. a. $\sqrt{35}$ **b.** $\sqrt{13z}$ **c.** 5 **d.** $\sqrt[3]{15x^2y}$ **e.** $\sqrt{\dfrac{5t}{2m}}$ **2. a.** $\dfrac{6}{7}$ **b.** $\dfrac{\sqrt{z}}{4}$ **c.** $\dfrac{5}{2}$ **d.** $\dfrac{\sqrt[4]{5}}{3x^2}$ **3. a.** $7\sqrt{2}$ **b.** $3\sqrt[3]{2}$ **c.** $\sqrt{35}$ **d.** $3\sqrt[4]{3}$

4. a. $6z^3\sqrt{z}$ **b.** $2pq^2\sqrt[3]{4pq}$ **c.** $2x^3\sqrt[4]{x^3}$ **5. a.** 4 **b.** $\dfrac{7}{3}\sqrt{z}$ **c.** $10xy^2\sqrt[3]{x^2}$ **d.** $6x^2y\sqrt[5]{2z}$ **6.** $\sqrt{17}\approx4.123$ **7.** $\left(\dfrac{13}{2},-4\right)$

Vocabulary and Readiness Check 7.3
1. midpoint; point **3.** midpoint **5.** false **7.** true **9.** false

Exercise Set 7.3
1. $\sqrt{14}$ **3.** 2 **5.** $\sqrt[3]{36}$ **7.** $\sqrt{6x}$ **9.** $\sqrt{\dfrac{14}{xy}}$ **11.** $\sqrt[4]{20x^3}$ **13.** $\dfrac{\sqrt{6}}{7}$ **15.** $\dfrac{\sqrt{2}}{7}$ **17.** $\dfrac{\sqrt[4]{x^3}}{z}$ **19.** $\dfrac{\sqrt[3]{4}}{3}$ **21.** $\dfrac{\sqrt[4]{8}}{x^2}$ **23.** $\dfrac{\sqrt[3]{2x}}{3y^4\sqrt[3]{3}}$

25. $\dfrac{x\sqrt{y}}{10}$ **27.** $\dfrac{x\sqrt{5}}{2y}$ **29.** $-\dfrac{z^2\sqrt[3]{z}}{3x}$ **31.** $4\sqrt{2}$ **33.** $4\sqrt[3]{3}$ **35.** $25\sqrt{3}$ **37.** $2\sqrt{6}$ **39.** $10x^2\sqrt{x}$ **41.** $2y^2\sqrt[3]{2y}$ **43.** $a^2b\sqrt[4]{b^3}$

45. $y^2\sqrt{y}$ **47.** $5ab\sqrt{b}$ **49.** $-2x^2\sqrt[5]{y}$ **51.** $x^4\sqrt[3]{50x^2}$ **53.** $-4a^4b^3\sqrt{2b}$ **55.** $3x^3y^4\sqrt{xy}$ **57.** $5r^3s^4$ **59.** $\sqrt{2}$ **61.** 2 **63.** 10

65. x^2y **67.** $24m^2$ **69.** $\dfrac{15x\sqrt{2x}}{2}$ or $\dfrac{15x}{2}\sqrt{2x}$ **71.** $2a^2\sqrt[4]{2}$ **73.** 5 units **75.** $\sqrt{41}$ units ≈6.403 **77.** $\sqrt{10}$ units ≈3.162

79. $\sqrt{5}$ units ≈2.236 **81.** $\sqrt{192.58}$ units ≈13.877 **83.** $(4,-2)$ **85.** $\left(-5,\dfrac{5}{2}\right)$ **87.** $(3,0)$ **89.** $\left(-\dfrac{1}{2},\dfrac{1}{2}\right)$ **91.** $\left(\sqrt{2},\dfrac{\sqrt{5}}{2}\right)$

93. $(6.2,-6.65)$ **95.** $14x$ **97.** $2x^2-7x-15$ **99.** y^2 **101.** $-3x-15$ **103.** $x^2-8x+16$ **105.** $\dfrac{\sqrt[3]{64}}{\sqrt{64}}=\dfrac{4}{8}=\dfrac{1}{2}$ **107.** x^7 **109.** a^3bc^5

111. $z^{10}\sqrt[3]{z^2}$ **113.** $q^2r^5s\sqrt[3]{q^3r^5}$ **115.** $r=1.6$ meters **117. a.** 3.8 times **b.** 2.9 times **c.** answers may vary

Section 7.4
Practice Exercises
1. a. $8\sqrt{17}$ **b.** $-5\sqrt[3]{5z}$ **c.** $3\sqrt{2}+5\sqrt{2}$ **2. a.** $11\sqrt{6}$ **b.** $-9\sqrt[3]{3}$ **c.** $-2\sqrt{3x}$ **d.** $2\sqrt{10}+2\sqrt[3]{5}$ **e.** $4x\sqrt[3]{3x}$ **3. a.** $\dfrac{5\sqrt{7}}{12}$

b. $\dfrac{13\sqrt[3]{6y}}{4}$ **4. a.** $2\sqrt{5}+5\sqrt{3}$ **b.** $2\sqrt{3}+2\sqrt{2}-\sqrt{30}-2\sqrt{5}$ **c.** $6z+\sqrt{z}-12$ **d.** $-6\sqrt{6}+15$ **e.** $5x-9$ **f.** $6\sqrt{x+2}+x+11$

Vocabulary and Readiness Check 7.4

1. Unlike   **3.** Like   **5.** $6\sqrt{3}$ **7.** $7\sqrt{x}$ **9.** $8\sqrt[3]{x}$ **11.** $\sqrt{11} + \sqrt[3]{11}$ **13.** $10\sqrt[3]{2x}$

Exercise Set 7.4

1. $-2\sqrt{2}$ **3.** $10x\sqrt{2x}$ **5.** $17\sqrt{2} - 15\sqrt{5}$ **7.** $-\sqrt[3]{2x}$ **9.** $5b\sqrt{b}$ **11.** $\dfrac{31\sqrt{2}}{15}$ **13.** $\dfrac{\sqrt[3]{11}}{3}$ **15.** $\dfrac{5\sqrt{5x}}{9}$ **17.** $14 + \sqrt{3}$ **19.** $7 - 3y$

21. $6\sqrt{3} - 6\sqrt{2}$ **23.** $-23\sqrt[3]{5}$ **25.** $2b\sqrt{b}$ **27.** $20y\sqrt{2y}$ **29.** $2y\sqrt[3]{2x}$ **31.** $6\sqrt[3]{11} - 4\sqrt{11}$ **33.** $4x\sqrt[4]{x^3}$ **35.** $\dfrac{2\sqrt{3}}{3}$ **37.** $\dfrac{5x\sqrt[3]{x}}{7}$

39. $\dfrac{5\sqrt{7}}{2x}$ **41.** $\dfrac{\sqrt[3]{2}}{6}$ **43.** $\dfrac{14x\sqrt[3]{2x}}{9}$ **45.** $15\sqrt{3}$ in.   **47.** $\sqrt{35} + \sqrt{21}$ **49.** $7 - 2\sqrt{10}$ **51.** $3\sqrt{x} - x\sqrt{3}$ **53.** $6x - 13\sqrt{x} - 5$

55. $\sqrt[3]{a^2} + \sqrt[3]{a} - 20$ **57.** $6\sqrt{2} - 12$ **59.** $2 + 2x\sqrt{3}$ **61.** $-16 - \sqrt{35}$ **63.** $x - y^2$ **65.** $3 + 2x\sqrt{3} + x^2$ **67.** $23x - 5x\sqrt{15}$

69. $2\sqrt[3]{2} - \sqrt[3]{4}$ **71.** $x + 1$ **73.** $x + 24 + 10\sqrt{x-1}$ **75.** $2x + 6 - 2\sqrt{2x+5}$ **77.** $x - 7$ **79.** $\dfrac{7}{x+y}$ **81.** $2a - 3$ **83.** $\dfrac{-2 + \sqrt{3}}{3}$

85. $22\sqrt{5}$ ft; 150 sq ft   **87. a.** $2\sqrt{3}$ **b.** 3   **c.** answers may vary   **89.** answers may vary

Section 7.5
Practice Exercises

1. a. $\dfrac{5\sqrt{3}}{3}$ **b.** $\dfrac{15\sqrt{x}}{2x}$ **c.** $\dfrac{\sqrt[3]{6}}{3}$ **2.** $\dfrac{\sqrt{15yz}}{5y}$ **3.** $\dfrac{\sqrt[3]{z^2x^2}}{3x^2}$ **4. a.** $\dfrac{5(3\sqrt{5} - 2)}{41}$ **b.** $\dfrac{\sqrt{6} + 5\sqrt{3} + \sqrt{10} + 5\sqrt{5}}{-2}$ **c.** $\dfrac{6x - 3\sqrt{xy}}{4x - y}$

5. $\dfrac{2}{\sqrt{10}}$ **6.** $\dfrac{5b}{\sqrt[3]{50ab^2}}$ **7.** $\dfrac{x - 9}{4(\sqrt{x} + 3)}$

Vocabulary and Readiness Check 7.5

1. conjugate   **3.** rationalizing the numerator   **5.** $\sqrt{2} - x$ **7.** $5 + \sqrt{a}$ **9.** $-7\sqrt{5} - 8\sqrt{x}$

Exercise Set 7.5

1. $\dfrac{\sqrt{14}}{7}$ **3.** $\dfrac{\sqrt{5}}{5}$ **5.** $\dfrac{2\sqrt{x}}{x}$ **7.** $\dfrac{4\sqrt[3]{9}}{3}$ **9.** $\dfrac{3\sqrt{2x}}{4x}$ **11.** $\dfrac{3\sqrt[3]{2x}}{2x}$ **13.** $\dfrac{3\sqrt{3a}}{a}$ **15.** $\dfrac{3\sqrt[3]{4}}{2}$ **17.** $\dfrac{2\sqrt{21}}{7}$ **19.** $\dfrac{\sqrt{10xy}}{5y}$ **21.** $\dfrac{\sqrt[3]{75}}{5}$

23. $\dfrac{\sqrt{6x}}{10}$ **25.** $\dfrac{\sqrt{3z}}{6z}$ **27.** $\dfrac{\sqrt[3]{6xy^2}}{3x}$ **29.** $\dfrac{3\sqrt[4]{2}}{2}$ **31.** $\dfrac{2\sqrt[4]{9x}}{3x^2}$ **33.** $\dfrac{5a\sqrt[5]{4ab^4}}{2a^2b^3}$ **35.** $-2(2 + \sqrt{7})$ **37.** $\dfrac{7(3 + \sqrt{x})}{9 - x}$ **39.** $-5 + 2\sqrt{6}$

41. $\dfrac{2a + 2\sqrt{a} + \sqrt{ab} + \sqrt{b}}{4a - b}$ **43.** $-\dfrac{8(1 - \sqrt{10})}{9}$ **45.** $\dfrac{x - \sqrt{xy}}{x - y}$ **47.** $\dfrac{5 + 3\sqrt{2}}{7}$ **49.** $\dfrac{5}{\sqrt{15}}$ **51.** $\dfrac{6}{\sqrt{10}}$ **53.** $\dfrac{2x}{7\sqrt{x}}$ **55.** $\dfrac{5y}{\sqrt[3]{100xy}}$

57. $\dfrac{2}{\sqrt{10}}$ **59.** $\dfrac{2x}{11\sqrt{2x}}$ **61.** $\dfrac{7}{2\sqrt[3]{49}}$ **63.** $\dfrac{3x^2}{10\sqrt[3]{9x}}$ **65.** $\dfrac{6x^2y^3}{\sqrt{6z}}$ **67.** answers may vary   **69.** $\dfrac{-7}{12 + 6\sqrt{11}}$ **71.** $\dfrac{3}{10 + 5\sqrt{7}}$

73. $\dfrac{x - 9}{x - 3\sqrt{x}}$ **75.** $\dfrac{1}{3 + 2\sqrt{2}}$ **77.** $\dfrac{x - 1}{x - 2\sqrt{x} + 1}$ **79.** 5   **81.** $-\dfrac{1}{2}, 6$ **83.** $2, 6$ **85.** $\sqrt[3]{25}$ **87.** $r = \dfrac{\sqrt{A\pi}}{2\pi}$ **89.** answers may vary

Integrated Review

1. 9   **2.** -2 **3.** $\dfrac{1}{2}$ **4.** x^3 **5.** y^3 **6.** $2y^5$ **7.** $-2y$ **8.** $3b^3$ **9.** 6   **10.** $\sqrt[4]{3y}$ **11.** $\dfrac{1}{16}$ **12.** $\sqrt[5]{(x+1)^3}$ **13.** y **14.** $16x^{1/2}$

15. $x^{5/4}$ **16.** $4^{11/15}$ **17.** $2x^2$ **18.** $\sqrt[4]{a^3b^2}$ **19.** $\sqrt[4]{x^3}$ **20.** $\sqrt[6]{500}$ **21.** $2\sqrt{10}$ **22.** $2xy^2\sqrt[4]{x^3y^2}$ **23.** $3x\sqrt[3]{2x}$ **24.** $-2b^2\sqrt[5]{2}$

25. $\sqrt{5x}$ **26.** $4x$ **27.** $7y^2\sqrt{y}$ **28.** $2a^2\sqrt[4]{3}$ **29.** $2\sqrt{5} - 5\sqrt{3} + 5\sqrt{7}$ **30.** $y\sqrt[3]{2y}$ **31.** $\sqrt{15} - \sqrt{6}$ **32.** $10 + 2\sqrt{21}$

33. $4x^2 - 5$ **34.** $x + 2 - 2\sqrt{x+1}$ **35.** $\dfrac{\sqrt{21}}{3}$ **36.** $\dfrac{5\sqrt[3]{4x}}{2x}$ **37.** $\dfrac{13 - 3\sqrt{21}}{5}$ **38.** $\dfrac{7}{\sqrt{21}}$ **39.** $\dfrac{3y}{\sqrt[3]{33y^2}}$ **40.** $\dfrac{x - 4}{x + 2\sqrt{x}}$

Section 7.6
Practice Exercises

1. 18   **2.** $\dfrac{3}{8}, -\dfrac{1}{2}$ **3.** 10   **4.** 9   **5.** $\dfrac{3}{25}$ **6.** $6\sqrt{3}$ meters   **7.** $\sqrt{193}$ in. ≈ 13.89

Graphing Calculator Explorations 7.6

1. 3.19   **3.** $\varnothing$ **5.** 3.23

Vocabulary and Readiness Check 7.6

1. extraneous solution   **3.** $x^2 - 10x + 25$

Exercise Set 7.6

1. 8   **3.** 7   **5.** $\varnothing$ **7.** 7   **9.** 6   **11.** $-\dfrac{9}{2}$ **13.** 29   **15.** 4   **17.** -4 **19.** $\varnothing$ **21.** 7   **23.** 9   **25.** 50   **27.** $\varnothing$ **29.** $\dfrac{15}{4}$

31. 13   **33.** 5   **35.** -12 **37.** 9   **39.** -3 **41.** 1   **43.** 1   **45.** $\dfrac{1}{2}$ **47.** 0, 4   **49.** $\dfrac{37}{4}$ **51.** $3\sqrt{5}$ ft   **53.** $2\sqrt{10}$ m

55. $2\sqrt{131}$ m ≈ 22.9 m   **57.** $\sqrt{100.84}$ mm ≈ 10.0 mm   **59.** 17 ft   **61.** 13 ft   **63.** 14,657,415 sq mi   **65.** 100 ft   **67.** 100

69. $\dfrac{\pi}{2}$ sec ≈ 1.57 sec   **71.** 12.97 ft   **73.** answers may vary   **75.** $15\sqrt{3}$ sq mi ≈ 25.98 sq mi   **77.** answers may vary   **79.** 0.51 km

81. function   **83.** function   **85.** not a function   **87.** $\dfrac{x}{4x+3}$ **89.** $-\dfrac{4z+2}{3z}$

91. $\sqrt{5x-1}+4=7$
$\sqrt{5x-1}=3$
$\left(\sqrt{5x-1}\right)^2 = 3^2$
$5x-1=9$
$5x=10$
$x=2$

93. 1   **95. a.–b.** answers may vary   **97.** $-1, 2$ **99.** $-8, -6, 0, 2$

The Bigger Picture

1. -19 **2.** $-\dfrac{5}{3}, 5$ **3.** $-\dfrac{9}{2}, 5$ **4.** $\left[\dfrac{-11}{5}, 1\right]$ **5.** $\left(-\dfrac{7}{5}, \infty\right)$ **6.** 25   **7.** $(-5, \infty)$ **8.** $\varnothing$ **9.** $(-\infty, -13) \cup (17, \infty)$ **10.** $\dfrac{17}{25}$

Section 7.7

Practice Exercises

1. a. $2i$ **b.** $i\sqrt{7}$ **c.** $-3i\sqrt{2}$ **2. a.** $-\sqrt{30}$ **b.** -3 **c.** $25i$ **d.** $3i$ **3. a.** $-1-4i$ **b.** $-3+5i$ **c.** $3-2i$ **4. a.** 20   **b.** $-5+10i$

c. $15+16i$ **d.** $8-6i$ **e.** 85   **5. a.** $\dfrac{11}{10} - \dfrac{7i}{10}$ **b.** $0 - \dfrac{5i}{2}$ **6. a.** i **b.** 1   **c.** -1 **d.** 1

Vocabulary and Readiness Check 7.7

1. complex   **3.** -1 **5.** real   **7.** $9i$ **9.** $i\sqrt{7}$ **11.** -4 **13.** $8i$

Exercise Set 7.7

1. $2i\sqrt{6}$ **3.** $-6i$ **5.** $24i\sqrt{7}$ **7.** $-3\sqrt{6}$ **9.** $-\sqrt{14}$ **11.** $-5\sqrt{2}$ **13.** $4i$ **15.** $i\sqrt{3}$ **17.** $2\sqrt{2}$ **19.** $6-4i$ **21.** $-2+6i$

23. $-2-4i$ **25.** -40 **27.** $18+12i$ **29.** 7   **31.** $12-16i$ **33.** $-4i$ **35.** $\dfrac{28}{25} - \dfrac{21}{25}i$ **37.** $4+i$ **39.** $\dfrac{17}{13} + \dfrac{7}{13}i$ **41.** 63

43. $2-i$ **45.** $27+3i$ **47.** $-\dfrac{5}{2} - 2i$ **49.** $18+13i$ **51.** 20   **53.** 10   **55.** 2   **57.** $-5 + \dfrac{16}{3}i$ **59.** $17+144i$ **61.** $\dfrac{3}{5} - \dfrac{1}{5}i$

63. $5-10i$ **65.** $\dfrac{1}{5} - \dfrac{8}{5}i$ **67.** $8-i$ **69.** 7   **71.** $12-16i$ **73.** 1   **75.** i **77.** $-i$ **79.** -1 **81.** -64 **83.** $-243i$ **85.** $40°$

87. $x^2 - 5x - 2 - \dfrac{6}{x-1}$ **89.** 5 people   **91.** 14 people   **93.** 16.7%   **95.** $-1-i$ **97.** 0   **99.** $2+3i$ **101.** $2+i\sqrt{2}$ **103.** $\dfrac{1}{2} - \dfrac{\sqrt{3}}{2}i$

105. answers may vary   **107.** $6-6i$ **109.** yes

Chapter 7 Vocabulary Check

1. conjugate   **2.** principal square root   **3.** rationalizing   **4.** imaginary unit   **5.** cube root   **6.** index, radicand   **7.** like radicals
8. complex number   **9.** distance   **10.** midpoint

Chapter 7 Review

1. 9   **3.** -2 **5.** $-\dfrac{1}{7}$ **7.** -6 **9.** $-a^2b^3$ **11.** $2ab^2$ **13.** $\dfrac{x^6}{6y}$ **15.** $|-x|$ **17.** -27 **19.** $-x$ **21.** $5|(x-y)^5|$ **23.** $-x$

25. $(-\infty, \infty)$; $-2, -1, 0, 1, 2$ **27.** $-\dfrac{1}{3}$ **29.** $-\dfrac{1}{4}$ **31.** $\dfrac{1}{4}$ **33.** $\dfrac{343}{125}$ **35.** not a real number   **37.** $5^{1/5}x^{2/5}y^{3/5}$ **39.** $5\sqrt[3]{xy^2z^5}$

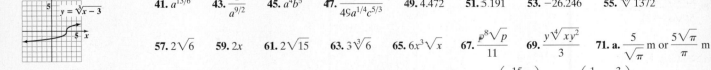

41. $a^{13/6}$ **43.** $\dfrac{1}{a^{9/2}}$ **45.** a^4b^5 **47.** $\dfrac{b^{5/6}}{49a^{1/4}c^{5/3}}$ **49.** 4.472   **51.** 5.191   **53.** -26.246 **55.** $\sqrt[6]{1372}$

57. $2\sqrt{6}$ **59.** $2x$ **61.** $2\sqrt{15}$ **63.** $3\sqrt[3]{6}$ **65.** $6x^3\sqrt{x}$ **67.** $\dfrac{p^8\sqrt{p}}{11}$ **69.** $\dfrac{y\sqrt[4]{xy^2}}{3}$ **71. a.** $\dfrac{5}{\sqrt{\pi}}$ m or $\dfrac{5\sqrt{\pi}}{\pi}$ m

b. 5.75 in.   **73.** $\sqrt{130}$ units ≈ 11.402 **75.** $7\sqrt{2}$ units ≈ 9.899 **77.** $\sqrt{275.6}$ units ≈ 16.601 **79.** $\left(-\dfrac{15}{2}, 1\right)$ **81.** $\left(\dfrac{1}{20}, -\dfrac{3}{16}\right)$

83. $\left(\sqrt{3}, -3\sqrt{6}\right)$ **85.** $2x\sqrt{3xy}$ **87.** $3a\sqrt[4]{2a}$ **89.** $\dfrac{3\sqrt{2}}{4x}$ **91.** $-4ab\sqrt[4]{2b}$ **93.** $x - 6\sqrt{x} + 9$ **95.** $4x - 9y$ **97.** $\sqrt[3]{a^2} + 4\sqrt[3]{a} + 4$

99. $a + 64$ **101.** $\dfrac{\sqrt{3x}}{6}$ **103.** $\dfrac{2x^2\sqrt{2x}}{y}$ **105.** $-\dfrac{10 + 5\sqrt{7}}{3}$ **107.** $-5 + 2\sqrt{6}$ **109.** $\dfrac{6}{\sqrt{2y}}$ **111.** $\dfrac{4x^3}{y\sqrt{2x}}$ **113.** $\dfrac{x - 25}{-3\sqrt{x} + 15}$

115. $\varnothing$ **117.** $\varnothing$ **119.** 16   **121.** $\sqrt{241}$ **123.** 4.24 ft   **125.** $-i\sqrt{6}$ **127.** $-\sqrt{10}$ **129.** $-13 - 3i$ **131.** $-12 - 18i$ **133.** $-5 - 12i$

135. $\dfrac{3}{2} - i$ **137.** x **139.** -10 **141.** $\dfrac{y^5}{2x^3}$ **143.** $\dfrac{1}{8}$ **145.** $\dfrac{1}{x^{13/2}}$ **147.** $\dfrac{n\sqrt{3n}}{11m^5}$ **149.** $4x - 20\sqrt{x} + 25$ **151.** $(4, 16)$ **153.** $\dfrac{2\sqrt{x} - 6}{x - 9}$

Chapter 7 Test

1. $6\sqrt{6}$ **2.** $-x^{16}$ **3.** $\dfrac{1}{5}$ **4.** 5   **5.** $\dfrac{4x^2}{9}$ **6.** $-a^6b^3$ **7.** $\dfrac{8a^{1/3}c^{2/3}}{b^{5/12}}$ **8.** $a^{7/12} - a^{7/3}$ **9.** $|4xy|$ or $4|xy|$ **10.** -27 **11.** $\dfrac{3\sqrt{y}}{y}$

12. $\dfrac{8 - 6\sqrt{x} + x}{8 - 2x}$ **13.** $\dfrac{\sqrt[3]{b^2}}{b}$ **14.** $\dfrac{6 - x^2}{8(\sqrt{6} - x)}$ **15.** $-x\sqrt{5x}$ **16.** $4\sqrt{3} - \sqrt{6}$ **17.** $x + 2\sqrt{x} + 1$ **18.** $\sqrt{6} - 4\sqrt{3} + \sqrt{2} - 4$

19. -20 **20.** 23.685   **21.** 0.019   **22.** 2, 3   **23.** $\varnothing$ **24.** 6   **25.** $i\sqrt{2}$ **26.** $-2i\sqrt{2}$ **27.** $-3i$ **28.** 40   **29.** $7 + 24i$ **30.** $-\dfrac{3}{2} + \dfrac{5}{2}i$

31. $\dfrac{5\sqrt{2}}{2}$ **32.** $[-2, \infty)$;   ; 0, 1, 2, 3   **33.** $2\sqrt{26}$ units   **34.** $\sqrt{95}$ units   **35.** $\left(-4, \dfrac{7}{2}\right)$ **36.** $\left(-\dfrac{1}{2}, \dfrac{3}{10}\right)$

$y = \sqrt{x + 2}$

37. 27 mph   **38.** 360 ft

Chapter 7 Cumulative Review

1. a. $2xy - 2$ **b.** $2x^2 + 23$ **c.** $3.1x - 0.3$ **d.** $-a - 7b + \dfrac{7}{12}$; Sec. 1.4, Ex. 15   **3.** $\dfrac{21}{11}$; Sec. 2.1, Ex. 6   **5.** \$4500 per month; Sec. 2.4, Ex. 8

7. $\varnothing$; Sec. 2.6, Ex. 6   **9.** $(-\infty, -3] \cup [9, \infty)$; Sec. 2.7, Ex. 7   **11.**   ; Sec. 3.1, Ex.7   **13. a.** domain: $\{2, 0, 3\}$; range: $\{3, 4, -1\}$

$y = |x|$

b. domain: $\{-4, -3, -2, -1, 0, 1, 2, 3\}$; range: $\{1\}$ **c.** domain: {Lubbock, Colorado Springs, Omaha, Yonkers, Sacramento}; range: {307, 404, 445, 206, 197};

Sec. 3.2, Ex. 1   **15.**   ; Sec. 3.3, Ex.7   **17.** undefined; Sec. 3.4, Ex.6   **19.** $\left(-\dfrac{21}{10}, \dfrac{3}{10}\right)$; Sec. 4.1, Ex.4   **21. a.** 2^7 **b.** x^{10}

$y = -3$

c. y^7; Sec. 5.1, Ex. 1   **23.** 6×10^{-5}; Sec. 5.2, Ex. 7   **25. a.** -4 **b.** 11; Sec. 5.3, Ex. 4   **27. a.** $2x^2 + 11x + 15$ **b.** $10x^3 - 27x^2 + 32x - 21$;

Sec. 5.4, Ex. 3   **29.** $5x^2$; Sec. 5.5, Ex. 1   **31. a.** $x^2 - 2x + 4$ **b.** $\dfrac{2}{y - 5}$; Sec. 6.1, Ex. 5   **33. a.** $\dfrac{6x + 5}{3x^3y}$ **b.** $\dfrac{2x^2 + 7x - 6}{(x + 2)(x - 2)}$ **c.** 2; Sec. 6.2, Ex. 3

35. a. $\dfrac{x(x - 2)}{2(x + 2)}$ **b.** $\dfrac{x^2}{y^2}$; Sec. 6.3, Ex. 2   **37.** $2x^2 - x + 4$; Sec. 6.4, Ex. 1   **39.** $2x^2 + 5x + 2 + \dfrac{7}{x - 3}$; Sec. 6.4, Ex. 8   **41.** $\varnothing$; Sec. 6.5, Ex. 3

43. $x = \dfrac{yz}{y - z}$; Sec. 6.6, Ex. 1   **45.** constant of variation: 15; $u = \dfrac{15}{w}$; Sec. 6.7, Ex. 3   **47. a.** $\dfrac{1}{8}$ **b.** $\dfrac{1}{9}$; Sec. 7.2, Ex. 3

49. $\dfrac{x - 4}{5(\sqrt{x} - 2)}$; Sec. 7.5, Ex. 7

CHAPTER 8 QUADRATIC EQUATIONS AND FUNCTIONS

Section 8.1
Practice Exercises

1. $-3\sqrt{2}, 3\sqrt{2}$ **2.** $\pm\sqrt{10}$ **3.** $-3 \pm 2\sqrt{5}$ **4.** $\dfrac{2 + 3i}{5}, \dfrac{2 - 3i}{5}$ **5.** $-2 \pm \sqrt{7}$ **6.** $\dfrac{3 \pm \sqrt{5}}{2}$ **7.** $\dfrac{6 \pm \sqrt{33}}{3}$ **8.** $\dfrac{5 \pm i\sqrt{31}}{4}$ **9.** 6%

Graphing Calculator Explorations 8.1

1. $-1.27, 6.27$ 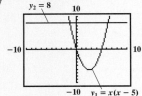 **3.** $-1.10, 0.90$ 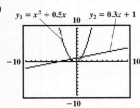 **5.** no real solutions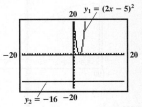

Vocabulary and Readiness Check 8.1

1. $\pm\sqrt{b}$ **3.** completing the square **5.** 9 **7.** 1 **9.** 49

Exercise Set 8.1

1. $-4, 4$ **3.** $-\sqrt{7}, \sqrt{7}$ **5.** $-3\sqrt{2}, 3\sqrt{2}$ **7.** $-\sqrt{10}, \sqrt{10}$ **9.** $-8, -2$ **11.** $6 - 3\sqrt{2}, 6 + 3\sqrt{2}$ **13.** $\dfrac{3 - 2\sqrt{2}}{2}, \dfrac{3 + 2\sqrt{2}}{2}$

15. $-3i, 3i$ **17.** $-\sqrt{6}, \sqrt{6}$ **19.** $-2i\sqrt{2}, 2i\sqrt{2}$ **21.** $1 - 4i, 1 + 4i$ **23.** $-7 - \sqrt{5}, -7 + \sqrt{5}$ **25.** $-3 - 2i\sqrt{2}, -3 + 2i\sqrt{2}$

27. $x^2 + 16x + 64 = (x + 8)^2$ **29.** $z^2 - 12z + 36 = (z - 6)^2$ **31.** $p^2 + 9p + \dfrac{81}{4} = \left(p + \dfrac{9}{2}\right)^2$ **33.** $x^2 + x + \dfrac{1}{4} = \left(x + \dfrac{1}{2}\right)^2$ **35.** $-5, -3$

37. $-3 - \sqrt{7}, -3 + \sqrt{7}$ **39.** $\dfrac{-1 - \sqrt{5}}{2}, \dfrac{-1 + \sqrt{5}}{2}$ **41.** $-1 - \sqrt{6}, -1 + \sqrt{6}$ **43.** $\dfrac{6 - \sqrt{30}}{3}, \dfrac{6 + \sqrt{30}}{3}$ **45.** $\dfrac{3 - \sqrt{11}}{2}, \dfrac{3 + \sqrt{11}}{2}$

47. $-4, \dfrac{1}{2}$ **49.** $-1, 5$ **51.** $-4 - \sqrt{15}, -4 + \sqrt{15}$ **53.** $\dfrac{-3 - \sqrt{21}}{3}, \dfrac{-3 + \sqrt{21}}{3}$ **55.** $-1, \dfrac{5}{2}$ **57.** $-1 - i, -1 + i$ **59.** $3 - \sqrt{6}, 3 + \sqrt{6}$

61. $-2 - i\sqrt{2}, -2 + i\sqrt{2}$ **63.** $\dfrac{-15 - 7\sqrt{5}}{10}, \dfrac{-15 + 7\sqrt{5}}{10}$ **65.** $\dfrac{1 - i\sqrt{47}}{4}, \dfrac{1 + i\sqrt{47}}{4}$ **67.** $-5 - i\sqrt{3}, -5 + i\sqrt{3}$ **69.** $-4, 1$

71. $\dfrac{2 - i\sqrt{2}}{2}, \dfrac{2 + i\sqrt{2}}{2}$ **73.** $\dfrac{-3 - \sqrt{69}}{6}, \dfrac{-3 + \sqrt{69}}{6}$ **75.** 20% **77.** 4% **79.** answers may vary **81.** 8.11 sec **83.** 6.73 sec

85. simple; answers may vary **87.** $\dfrac{7}{5}$ **89.** $\dfrac{1}{5}$ **91.** $5 - 10\sqrt{3}$ **93.** $\dfrac{3 - 2\sqrt{7}}{4}$ **95.** $2\sqrt{7}$ **97.** $\sqrt{13}$ **99.** complex, but not real numbers

101. real solutions **103.** complex, but not real numbers **105.** $-6y, 6y$ **107.** $-x, x$ **109.** 6 in. **111.** 16.2 in. $\times$ 21.6 in.
113. 2.828 thousand units or 2828 units

Section 8.2
Practice Exercises

1. $2, -\dfrac{1}{3}$ **2.** $\dfrac{4 \pm \sqrt{22}}{3}$ **3.** $1 \pm \sqrt{17}$ **4.** $\dfrac{-1 \pm i\sqrt{15}}{4}$ **5. a.** one real solution **b.** two real solutions **c.** two complex, but not real
solutions **6.** 6 ft **7.** 2.4 sec

Vocabulary and Readiness Check 8.2

1. $x = \dfrac{-b \pm \sqrt{b^2 - 4ac}}{2a}$ **3.** $-5; -7$ **5.** $1; 0$

Exercise Set 8.2

1. $-6, 1$ **3.** $-\dfrac{3}{5}, 1$ **5.** 3 **7.** $\dfrac{-7 - \sqrt{33}}{2}, \dfrac{-7 + \sqrt{33}}{2}$ **9.** $\dfrac{1 - \sqrt{57}}{8}, \dfrac{1 + \sqrt{57}}{8}$ **11.** $\dfrac{7 - \sqrt{85}}{6}, \dfrac{7 + \sqrt{85}}{6}$ **13.** $1 - \sqrt{3}, 1 + \sqrt{3}$

15. $-\dfrac{3}{2}, 1$ **17.** $\dfrac{3 - \sqrt{11}}{2}, \dfrac{3 + \sqrt{11}}{2}$ **19.** $\dfrac{-5 - \sqrt{17}}{2}, \dfrac{-5 + \sqrt{17}}{2}$ **21.** $\dfrac{5}{2}, 1$ **23.** $-3 - 2i, -3 + 2i$ **25.** $-2 - \sqrt{11}, -2 + \sqrt{11}$

27. $\dfrac{3 - i\sqrt{87}}{8}, \dfrac{3 + i\sqrt{87}}{8}$ **29.** $\dfrac{3 - \sqrt{29}}{2}, \dfrac{3 + \sqrt{29}}{2}$ **31.** $\dfrac{-5 - i\sqrt{5}}{10}, \dfrac{-5 + i\sqrt{5}}{10}$ **33.** $\dfrac{-1 - \sqrt{19}}{6}, \dfrac{-1 + \sqrt{19}}{6}$

35. $\dfrac{-1 - i\sqrt{23}}{4}, \dfrac{-1 + i\sqrt{23}}{4}$ **37.** 1 **39.** $3 + \sqrt{5}, 3 - \sqrt{5}$ **41.** two real solutions **43.** one real solution **45.** two real solutions

47. two complex but not real solutions **49.** two real solutions **51.** 14 ft **53.** $2 + 2\sqrt{2}$ cm, $2 + 2\sqrt{2}$ cm, $4 + 2\sqrt{2}$ cm

55. width: $-5 + 5\sqrt{17}$ ft; length: $5 + 5\sqrt{17}$ ft **57. a.** $50\sqrt{2}$ m **b.** 5000 sq m **59.** 37.4 ft by 38.5 ft **61.** base, $2 + 2\sqrt{43}$ cm;

height, $-1 + \sqrt{43}$ cm **63.** 8.9 sec **65.** 2.8 sec **67.** $\dfrac{11}{5}$ **69.** 15 **71.** $(x^2 + 5)(x + 2)(x - 2)$ **73.** $(z + 3)(z - 3)(z + 2)(z - 2)$

75. b **77.** answers may vary **79.** $0.6, 2.4$ **81.** Sunday to Monday **83.** Wednesday **85.** 32; yes **87. a.** 8630 stores **b.** 2011

89. answers may vary **91.** $\dfrac{\sqrt{3}}{3}$ **93.** $\dfrac{-\sqrt{2} - i\sqrt{2}}{2}, \dfrac{-\sqrt{2} + i\sqrt{2}}{2}$ **95.** $\dfrac{\sqrt{3} - \sqrt{11}}{4}, \dfrac{\sqrt{3} + \sqrt{11}}{4}$

97. 8.9 sec: 1200   2.8 sec: 200   **99.** two real solutions

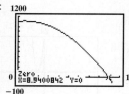 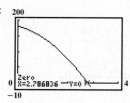

Section 8.3
Practice Exercises

1. 8 **2.** $\dfrac{5 \pm \sqrt{137}}{8}$ **3.** $4, -4, 3i, -3i$ **4.** $1, -3$ **5.** $1, 64$ **6.** Katy: $\dfrac{7 + \sqrt{65}}{2} \approx 7.5$ hr; Steve: $\dfrac{9 + \sqrt{65}}{2} \approx 8.5$ hr

7. to Shanghai: 40 km/hr; to Ningbo: 90 km/hr

Exercise Set 8.3

1. 2 **3.** 16 **5.** $1, 4$ **7.** $3 - \sqrt{7}, 3 + \sqrt{7}$ **9.** $\dfrac{3 - \sqrt{57}}{4}, \dfrac{3 + \sqrt{57}}{4}$ **11.** $\dfrac{1 - \sqrt{29}}{2}, \dfrac{1 + \sqrt{29}}{2}$ **13.** $-2, 2, -2i, 2i$

15. $-\dfrac{1}{2}, \dfrac{1}{2}, -i\sqrt{3}, i\sqrt{3}$ **17.** $-3, 3, -2, 2$ **19.** $125, -8$ **21.** $-\dfrac{4}{5}, 0$ **23.** $-\dfrac{1}{8}, 27$ **25.** $-\dfrac{2}{3}, \dfrac{4}{3}$ **27.** $-\dfrac{1}{125}, \dfrac{1}{8}$ **29.** $-\sqrt{2}, \sqrt{2}, -\sqrt{3}, \sqrt{3}$

31. $\dfrac{-9 - \sqrt{201}}{6}, \dfrac{-9 + \sqrt{201}}{6}$ **33.** $2, 3$ **35.** 3 **37.** $27, 125$ **39.** $1, -3i, 3i$ **41.** $\dfrac{1}{8}, -8$ **43.** $-\dfrac{1}{2}, \dfrac{1}{3}$ **45.** 4

47. -3 **49.** $-\sqrt{5}, \sqrt{5}, -2i, 2i$ **51.** $-3, \dfrac{3 - 3i\sqrt{3}}{2}, \dfrac{3 + 3i\sqrt{3}}{2}$ **53.** $6, 12$ **55.** $-\dfrac{1}{3}, \dfrac{1}{3}, -\dfrac{i\sqrt{6}}{3}, \dfrac{i\sqrt{6}}{3}$ **57.** 5 mph, then 4 mph

59. inlet pipe: 15.5 hr; hose: 16.5 hr **61.** 55 mph, 66 mph **63.** 8.5 hr **65.** 12 or -8 **67. a.** $(x - 6)$ in. **b.** $300 = (x - 6) \cdot (x - 6) \cdot 3$

c. 16 cm by 16 cm **69.** 22 feet **71.** $(-\infty, 3]$ **73.** $(-5, \infty)$ **75.** domain: $(-\infty, \infty)$; range: $(-\infty, \infty)$; function

77. domain: $(-\infty, \infty)$; range: $[-1, \infty)$; function **79.** $1, -3i, 3i$ **81.** $-\dfrac{1}{2}, \dfrac{1}{3}$ **83.** $-3, \dfrac{3 - 3i\sqrt{3}}{2}, \dfrac{3 + 3i\sqrt{3}}{2}$ **85.** answers may vary

87. a. 150.94 ft/sec **b.** 151.49 ft/sec **c.** Bourdais: 102.9 mph; Pagenaud: 103.3 mph

Integrated Review

1. $-\sqrt{10}, \sqrt{10}$ **2.** $-\sqrt{14}, \sqrt{14}$ **3.** $1 - 2\sqrt{2}, 1 + 2\sqrt{2}$ **4.** $-5 - 2\sqrt{3}, -5 + 2\sqrt{3}$ **5.** $-1 - \sqrt{13}, -1 + \sqrt{13}$

6. $1, 11$ **7.** $\dfrac{-3 - \sqrt{69}}{6}, \dfrac{-3 + \sqrt{69}}{6}$ **8.** $\dfrac{-2 - \sqrt{5}}{4}, \dfrac{-2 + \sqrt{5}}{4}$ **9.** $\dfrac{2 - \sqrt{2}}{2}, \dfrac{2 + \sqrt{2}}{2}$ **10.** $-3 - \sqrt{5}, -3 + \sqrt{5}$

11. $-2 + i\sqrt{3}, -2 - i\sqrt{3}$ **12.** $\dfrac{-1 - i\sqrt{11}}{2}, \dfrac{-1 + i\sqrt{11}}{2}$ **13.** $\dfrac{-3 + i\sqrt{15}}{2}, \dfrac{-3 - i\sqrt{15}}{2}$ **14.** $3i, -3i$ **15.** $0, -17$

16. $\dfrac{1 + \sqrt{13}}{4}, \dfrac{1 - \sqrt{13}}{4}$ **17.** $2 + 3\sqrt{3}, 2 - 3\sqrt{3}$ **18.** $2 + \sqrt{3}, 2 - \sqrt{3}$ **19.** $-2, \dfrac{4}{3}$ **20.** $\dfrac{-5 + \sqrt{17}}{4}, \dfrac{-5 - \sqrt{17}}{4}$ **21.** $1 - \sqrt{6}, 1 + \sqrt{6}$

22. $-\sqrt{31}, \sqrt{31}$ **23.** $-\sqrt{11}, \sqrt{11}$ **24.** $-i\sqrt{11}, i\sqrt{11}$ **25.** $-11, 6$ **26.** $\dfrac{-3 + \sqrt{19}}{5}, \dfrac{-3 - \sqrt{19}}{5}$ **27.** $\dfrac{-3 + \sqrt{17}}{4}, \dfrac{-3 - \sqrt{17}}{4}$

28. $10\sqrt{2}$ ft ≈ 14.1 ft **29.** Jack: 9.1 hr; Lucy: 7.1 hr **30.** 5 mph during the first part, then 6 mph

Section 8.4
Practice Exercises

1. $(-\infty, -3) \cup (4, \infty)$ **2.** $[0, 8]$ **3.** $(-\infty, -3] \cup [-1, 2]$ **4.** $(-4, 5]$ **5.** $(-\infty, -3) \cup \left(-\dfrac{8}{5}, \infty\right)$

Vocabulary and Readiness Check 8.4

1. $[-7, 3)$ **3.** $(-\infty, 0]$ **5.** $(-\infty, -12) \cup [-10, \infty)$

Exercise Set 8.4

1. $(-\infty, -5) \cup (-1, \infty)$ **3.** $[-4, 3]$ **5.** $[2, 5]$ **7.** $\left(-5, -\dfrac{1}{3}\right)$ **9.** $(2, 4) \cup (6, \infty)$ **11.** $(-\infty, -4] \cup [0, 1]$

13. $(-\infty, -3) \cup (-2, 2) \cup (3, \infty)$ **15.** $(-7, 2)$ **17.** $(-1, \infty)$ **19.** $(-\infty, -1] \cup (4, \infty)$ **21.** $(-\infty, 2) \cup \left(\dfrac{11}{4}, \infty\right)$ **23.** $(0, 2] \cup [3, \infty)$

25. $(-\infty, -7) \cup (8, \infty)$ **27.** $\left[-\dfrac{5}{4}, \dfrac{3}{2}\right]$ **29.** $(-\infty, 0) \cup (1, \infty)$ **31.** $(-\infty, -4] \cup [4, 6]$ **33.** $\left(-\infty, -\dfrac{2}{3}\right] \cup \left[\dfrac{3}{2}, \infty\right)$

35. $\left(-4, -\dfrac{3}{2}\right) \cup \left(\dfrac{3}{2}, \infty\right)$ **37.** $(-\infty, -5] \cup [-1, 1] \cup [5, \infty)$ **39.** $\left(-\infty, -\dfrac{5}{3}\right) \cup \left(\dfrac{7}{2}, \infty\right)$ **41.** $(0, 10)$ **43.** $(-\infty, -4) \cup [5, \infty)$

45. $(-\infty, -6] \cup (-1, 0] \cup (7, \infty)$ **47.** $(-\infty, 1) \cup (2, \infty)$ **49.** $(-\infty, -8] \cup (-4, \infty)$ **51.** $(-\infty, 0] \cup \left(5, \dfrac{11}{2}\right]$ **53.** $(0, \infty)$

55. 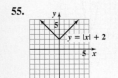   **57.** 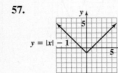   **59.**   **61.**   **63.** answers may vary

65. any number less than -1 or between 0 and 1   **67.** x is between 2 and 11   **69.** 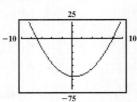   **71.**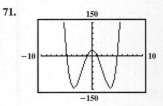

The Bigger Picture

1. $-9, \dfrac{7}{3}$ **2.** $(4, 7)$ **3.** $4, 5$ **4.** $\dfrac{-1 - \sqrt{13}}{6}, \dfrac{-1 + \sqrt{13}}{6}$ **5.** $[-2, 7)$ **6.** $\dfrac{5}{4}$ **7.** $\dfrac{1}{5}, 7$ **8.** $\left(-\infty, -\dfrac{1}{2}\right] \cup [4, \infty)$

9. $(-\infty, -8) \cup (22, \infty)$ **10.** $(7, \infty)$

Section 8.5
Practice Exercises

1. 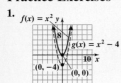   **2.**   **3.** 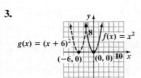   **4.**

5.   **6.** 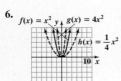   **7.**   **8.**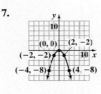

Graphing Calculator Explorations 8.5

1. 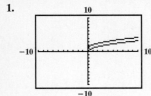   **3.** 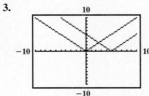   **5.**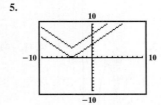

Vocabulary and Readiness Check 8.5

1. quadratic   **3.** upward   **5.** lowest   **7.** $(0, 0)$ **9.** $(2, 0)$ **11.** $(0, 3)$ **13.** $(-1, 5)$

Exercise Set 8.5

1.   **3.**   **5.**   **7.**   **9.**   **11.**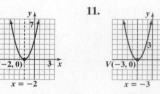

13.   **15.**   **17.**   **19.**   **21.**   **23.**

25.   **27.**   **29.**   **31.**   **33.**   **35.**

37.   **39.** 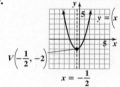   **41.** 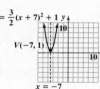   **43.**

45. 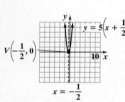   **47.**   **49.** 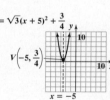   **51.**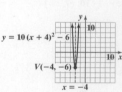

53.   **55.** $x^2 + 8x + 16$ **57.** $z^2 - 16z + 64$ **59.** $y^2 + y + \frac{1}{4}$ **61.** $-6, 2$ **63.** $-5 - \sqrt{26}, -5 + \sqrt{26}$ **65.** $4 - 3\sqrt{2}, 4 + 3\sqrt{2}$ **67.** c   **69.** $f(x) = 5(x - 2)^2 + 3$ **71.** $f(x) = 5(x + 3)^2 + 6$

73.   **75.**   **77.**

Section 8.6
Practice Exercises

1.   **2.**   **3.**   **4.** $(1, -4)$ **5.** Maximum height 9 feet in $\frac{3}{4}$ second

Vocabulary and Readiness Check 8.6

1. (h, k) **3.** 0; 1   **5.** 2; 1   **7.** 1; 1   **9.** down   **11.** up

Exercise Set 8.6

1. $(-4, -9)$ **3.** $(5, 30)$ **5.** $(1, -2)$ **7.** $\left(\dfrac{1}{2}, \dfrac{5}{4}\right)$ **9.** D   **11.** B

13.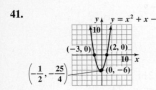

15.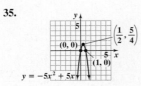

17.

19.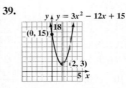

21.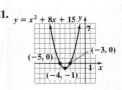

23.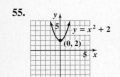

25.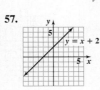

27.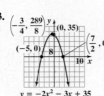

29.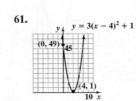

31.

33.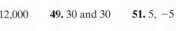

35.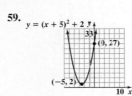

37.

39.

41.

43.

45. 144 ft   **47. a.** 200 bicycles   **b.** \$12,000   **49.** 30 and 30   **51.** 5, -5
53. length, 20 units; width, 20 units

55.

57.

59.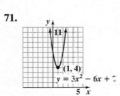

61.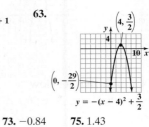

63.

65. minimum value   **67.** maximum value   **69.**

71.

73. -0.84 **75.** 1.43

77. a. maximum; answers may vary   **b.** 2005   **c.** 31,523   **79.**

81.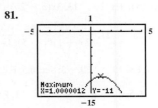

Chapter 8 Vocabulary Check

1. discriminant   **2.** $\pm\sqrt{b}$ **3.** $\dfrac{-b}{2a}$ **4.** quadratic inequality   **5.** completing the square   **6.** $(0, k)$ **7.** $(h, 0)$ **8.** (h, k)
9. quadratic formula   **10.** quadratic

Chapter 8 Review

1. 14, 1 **3.** −7, 7 **5.** $\dfrac{-3 - \sqrt{5}}{2}, \dfrac{-3 + \sqrt{5}}{2}$ **7.** 4.25% **9.** two complex but not real solutions **11.** two real solutions **13.** 8 **15.** $-\dfrac{5}{2}, 1$

17. $\dfrac{5 - i\sqrt{143}}{12}, \dfrac{5 + i\sqrt{143}}{12}$ **19. a.** 20 ft **b.** $\dfrac{15 + \sqrt{321}}{16}$ sec; 2.1 sec **21.** 3, $\dfrac{-3 + 3i\sqrt{3}}{2}, \dfrac{-3 - 3i\sqrt{3}}{2}$ **23.** $\dfrac{2}{3}, 5$ **25.** 1, 125 **27.** −1, 1, −i, i

29. Jerome: 10.5 hr; Tim: 9.5 hr **31.** $[-5, 5]$ **33.** $(5, 6)$ **35.** $(-\infty, -6) \cup \left(-\dfrac{3}{4}, 0\right) \cup (5, \infty)$ **37.** $(-5, -3) \cup (5, \infty)$ **39.** $\left(-\dfrac{6}{5}, 0\right) \cup \left(\dfrac{5}{6}, 3\right)$

41.

43.

45.

47.

49.

51.
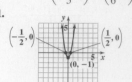

53.
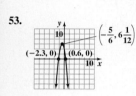
55. The numbers are both 210. **57.** −5, 6 **59.** −2, 2 **61.** $\dfrac{-1 - 3i\sqrt{3}}{2}, \dfrac{-1 + 3i\sqrt{3}}{2}$ **63.** $-i\sqrt{11}, i\sqrt{11}$

65. $-\dfrac{8\sqrt{7}}{7}, \dfrac{8\sqrt{7}}{7}$ **67.** $\left(-\infty, -\dfrac{5}{4}\right] \cup \left[\dfrac{3}{2}, \infty\right)$ **69.** $\left(2, \dfrac{7}{2}\right)$

Chapter 8 Test

1. $\dfrac{7}{5}, -1$ **2.** $-1 - \sqrt{10}, -1 + \sqrt{10}$ **3.** $\dfrac{1 + i\sqrt{31}}{2}, \dfrac{1 - i\sqrt{31}}{2}$ **4.** $3 - \sqrt{7}, 3 + \sqrt{7}$ **5.** $-\dfrac{1}{7}, -1$ **6.** $\dfrac{3 + \sqrt{29}}{2}, \dfrac{3 - \sqrt{29}}{2}$

7. $-2 - \sqrt{11}, -2 + \sqrt{11}$ **8.** −1, 1, −i, i, −3 **9.** −1, 1, −i, i **10.** 6, 7 **11.** $3 - \sqrt{7}, 3 + \sqrt{7}$ **12.** $\dfrac{2 - i\sqrt{6}}{2}, \dfrac{2 + i\sqrt{6}}{2}$

13. $\left(-\infty, -\dfrac{3}{2}\right) \cup (5, \infty)$ **14.** $(-\infty, -5] \cup [-4, 4] \cup [5, \infty)$ **15.** $(-\infty, -3) \cup (2, \infty)$ **16.** $(-\infty, -3) \cup [2, 3)$

17.

18.

19.

20.

21. $(5 + \sqrt{17})$ hr ≈ 9.12 hr
22. a. 272 ft **b.** 5.12 sec **23.** 7 ft

Chapter 8 Cumulative Review

1. a. $5 + y \geq 7$ **b.** $11 \neq z$ **c.** $20 < 5 - 2x$; Sec. 1.4, Ex. 6 **3.** slope: 1;

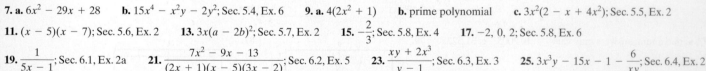

; Sec. 3.4, Ex. 1 **5.** $(-2, 2)$; Sec. 4.1, Ex. 5

7. a. $6x^2 - 29x + 28$ **b.** $15x^4 - x^2y - 2y^2$; Sec. 5.4, Ex. 6 **9. a.** $4(2x^2 + 1)$ **b.** prime polynomial **c.** $3x^2(2 - x + 4x^2)$; Sec. 5.5, Ex. 2

11. $(x - 5)(x - 7)$; Sec. 5.6, Ex. 2 **13.** $3x(a - 2b)^2$; Sec. 5.7, Ex. 2 **15.** $-\dfrac{2}{3}$; Sec. 5.8, Ex. 4 **17.** −2, 0, 2; Sec. 5.8, Ex. 6

19. $\dfrac{1}{5x - 1}$; Sec. 6.1, Ex. 2a **21.** $\dfrac{7x^2 - 9x - 13}{(2x + 1)(x - 5)(3x - 2)}$; Sec. 6.2, Ex. 5 **23.** $\dfrac{xy + 2x^3}{y - 1}$; Sec. 6.3, Ex. 3 **25.** $3x^3y - 15x - 1 - \dfrac{6}{xy}$; Sec. 6.4, Ex. 2

27. a. 5 **b.** 5; Sec. 6.4, Ex. 10 **29.** −3; Sec. 6.5, Ex. 1 **31.** 2; Sec. 6.6, Ex. 2 **33.** $\dfrac{1}{6}$; $y = \dfrac{1}{6}x$; Sec. 6.7, Ex. 1 **35. a.** 3 **b.** $|x|$ **c.** $|x - 2|$

d. −5 **e.** $2x - 7$ **f.** $5|x|$ **g.** $|x + 1|$; Sec. 7.1, Ex. 5 **37. a.** $\sqrt{x}$ **b.** $\sqrt[3]{5}$ **c.** $\sqrt{rs^3}$; Sec. 7.2, Ex. 7 **39. a.** $5x\sqrt{x}$ **b.** $3x^2y^2\sqrt[3]{2y^2}$

c. $3z^2\sqrt[4]{z^3}$; Sec. 7.3, Ex. 4 **41. a.** $\dfrac{2\sqrt{5}}{5}$ **b.** $\dfrac{8\sqrt{x}}{3x}$ **c.** $\dfrac{\sqrt[3]{4}}{2}$; Sec. 7.5, Ex. 1 **43.** $\dfrac{2}{9}$; Sec. 7.6, Ex. 5 **45. a.** $\dfrac{1}{2} + \dfrac{3}{2}i$ **b.** $-\dfrac{7}{3}i$; Sec. 7.7, Ex. 5

47. $-1 + 2\sqrt{3}, -1 - 2\sqrt{3}$; Sec. 8.1, Ex. 3 **49.** 9; Sec. 8.3, Ex. 1

CHAPTER 9 EXPONENTIAL AND LOGARITHMIC FUNCTIONS

Section 9.1
Practice Exercises

1. a. $4x + 7$ **b.** $-2x - 3$ **c.** $3x^2 + 11x + 10$ **d.** $\dfrac{x + 2}{3x - 5}$, where $x \neq -\dfrac{5}{3}$ **2. a.** $50; 46$ **b.** $9x^2 - 30x + 26; 3x^2 - 2$

3. a. $x^2 + 6x + 14$ **b.** $x^2 + 8$ **4. a.** $(h \circ g)(x)$ **b.** $(g \circ f)(x)$

Vocabulary and Readiness Check 9.1
1. C   **3.** F   **5.** D

Exercise Set 9.1

1. a. $3x - 6$ **b.** $-x - 8$ **c.** $2x^2 - 13x - 7$ **d.** $\dfrac{x - 7}{2x + 1}$, where $x \neq -\dfrac{1}{2}$ **3. a.** $x^2 + 5x + 1$ **b.** $x^2 - 5x + 1$ **c.** $5x^3 + 5x$

d. $\dfrac{x^2 + 1}{5x}$, where $x \neq 0$ **5. a.** $\sqrt{x} + x + 5$ **b.** $\sqrt{x} - x - 5$ **c.** $x\sqrt{x} + 5\sqrt{x}$ **d.** $\dfrac{\sqrt{x}}{x + 5}$, where $x \neq -5$

7. a. $5x^2 - 3x$ **b.** $-5x^2 - 3x$ **c.** $-15x^3$ **d.** $-\dfrac{3}{5x}$, where $x \neq 0$ **9.** 42 **11.** -18 **13.** 0

15. $(f \circ g)(x) = 25x^2 + 1; (g \circ f)(x) = 5x^2 + 5$ **17.** $(f \circ g)(x) = 2x + 11; (g \circ f)(x) = 2x + 4$

19. $(f \circ g)(x) = -8x^3 - 2x - 2; (g \circ f)(x) = -2x^3 - 2x + 4$ **21.** $(f \circ g)(x) = |10x - 3|; (g \circ f)(x) = 10|x| - 3$

23. $(f \circ g)(x) = \sqrt{-5x + 2}; (g \circ f)(x) = -5\sqrt{x} + 2$ **25.** $H(x) = (g \circ h)(x)$ **27.** $F(x) = (h \circ f)(x)$ **29.** $G(x) = (f \circ g)(x)$

31. answers may vary; for example $g(x) = x + 2$ and $f(x) = x^2$ **33.** answers may vary; for example, $g(x) = x + 5$ and $f(x) = \sqrt{x} + 2$

35. answers may vary; for example, $g(x) = 2x - 3$ and $f(x) = \dfrac{1}{x}$ **37.** $y = x - 2$ **39.** $y = \dfrac{x}{3}$ **41.** $y = -\dfrac{x + 7}{2}$ **43.** 6 **45.** 4 **47.** 4

49. -1 **51.** answers may vary   **53.** $P(x) = R(x) - C(x)$

Section 9.2
Practice Exercises

1. a. one-to-one   **b.** not one-to-one   **c.** not one-to-one   **d.** not one-to-one   **e.** not one-to-one   **f.** not one-to-one

2. a. no, not one-to-one   **b.** yes   **c.** yes   **d.** no, not a function   **e.** no, not a function

3. $f^{-1}(x) = \{(4, 3), (0, -2), (8, 2), (6, 6)\}$ **4.** $f^{-1}(x) = 6 - x$

5.   **6. a.**   **b.**   **7.** $f(f^{-1}(x)) = f\left(\dfrac{x + 1}{4}\right) = 4\left(\dfrac{x + 1}{4}\right) - 1 = x + 1 - 1 = x$

$f^{-1}(f(x)) = f^{-1}(4x - 1) = \dfrac{(4x - 1) + 1}{4} = \dfrac{4x}{4} = x$

Vocabulary and Readiness Check 9.2
1. $(2, 11)$ **3.** $(3, 7)$ **5.** horizontal   **7.** $x; x$

Exercise Set 9.2

1. one-to-one; $f^{-1} = \{(-1, -1), (1, 1), (2, 0), (0, 2)\}$ **3.** one-to-one; $h^{-1} = \{(10, 10)\}$ **5.** one-to-one; $f^{-1} = \{(12, 11), (3, 4), (4, 3), (6, 6)\}$

7. not one-to-one   **9.** one-to-one;

11. a. 3 **b.** 1 **13. a.** 1 **b.** -1

15. one-to-one   **17.** not one-to-one

19. one-to-one   **21.** not one-to-one

Rank in Population (Input)	1	19	35	4	48
State (Output)	CA	MD	NV	FL	ND

23. $f^{-1}(x) = x - 4$ **25.** $f^{-1}(x) = \dfrac{x + 3}{2}$ **27.** $f^{-1}(x) = 2x + 2$ **29.** $f^{-1}(x) = \sqrt[3]{x}$

31. $f^{-1}(x) = \dfrac{x - 2}{5}$ **33.** $f^{-1}(x) = 5x + 2$ **35.** $f^{-1}(x) = x^3$ **37.** $f^{-1}(x) = \dfrac{5 - x}{3x}$ **39.** $f^{-1}(x) = \sqrt[3]{x} - 2$

41.   **43.**   **45.**   **47.** $(f \circ f^{-1})(x) = x; (f^{-1} \circ f)(x) = x$

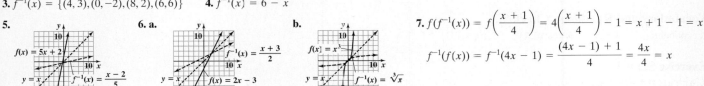

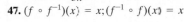

49. $(f \circ f^{-1})(x) = x; (f^{-1} \circ f)(x) = x$ **51.** 5   **53.** 8   **55.** $\dfrac{1}{27}$ **57.** 9   **59.** $3^{1/2} \approx 1.73$ **61. a.** $(2, 9)$ **b.** $(9, 2)$

63. a. $\left(-2, \dfrac{1}{4}\right), \left(-1, \dfrac{1}{2}\right), (0, 1), (1, 2), (2, 5)$ **b.** $\left(\dfrac{1}{4}, -2\right), \left(\dfrac{1}{2}, -1\right), (1, 0), (2, 1), (5, 2)$

c.
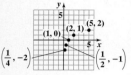

d.

65. answers may vary   **67.** $f^{-1}(x) = \dfrac{x-1}{3}$;

69. $f^{-1}(x) = x^3 - 1$;

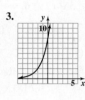

Section 9.3

Practice Exercises

1.
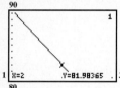

2.
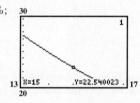

3.
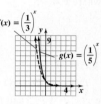

4. a. 2;   **b.** $\dfrac{4}{3}$;   **c.** -4 **5.** \$3950.43   **6.** 60.86%

Graphing Calculator Explorations 9.3

1. 81.98%;

3. 22.54%;

Vocabulary and Readiness Check 9.3

1. exponential   **3.** yes   **5.** yes; $(0, 1)$ **7.** $(0, \infty)$

Exercise Set 9.3

1.

3.

5.

7.

9.

11.

13.

15.

17. C   **19.** B   **21.** 3   **23.** $\dfrac{3}{4}$ **25.** $\dfrac{8}{5}$ **27.** $-\dfrac{2}{3}$ **29.** 4   **31.** $\dfrac{3}{2}$

33. $-\dfrac{1}{3}$ **35.** -2 **37.** 24.6 lb   **39.** 333 bison   **41.** 1.1 g   **43. a.** 658.1 pascals   **b.** 180.0 pascals   **45. a.** 134,342 students   **b.** 840,276 students

47. \$7621.42   **49.** \$4065.59   **51.** 562 million cell phone users   **53.** 4   **55.** $\varnothing$ **57.** 2, 3   **59.** 3   **61.** -1 **63.** answers may vary

65.

67.

69. The graphs are the same since $\left(\dfrac{1}{2}\right)^{-x} = 2x$.   **71.** 24.60 lb;
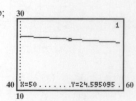

73. 18.62 lb; 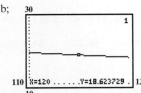   **75.** 50.41 g;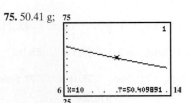

Section 9.4
Practice Exercises

1. a. $3^4 = 81$ **b.** $5^{-1} = \dfrac{1}{5}$ **c.** $7^{1/2} = \sqrt{7}$ **d.** $13^4 = y$ **2. a.** $\log_4 64 = 3$ **b.** $\log_6 \sqrt[3]{6} = \dfrac{1}{3}$ **c.** $\log_5 \dfrac{1}{125} = -3$ **d.** $\log_\pi z = 7$

3. a. 2   **b.** -3 **c.** $\dfrac{1}{2}$ **4. a.** -2 **b.** 2   **c.** 36   **d.** 0   **e.** 0   **5. a.** 4   **b.** -2 **c.** 5   **d.** 4

6. 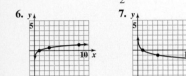   **7.**

Vocabulary and Readiness Check 9.4
1. logarithmic   **3.** yes   **5.** no; none   **7.** $(-\infty, \infty)$

Exercise Set 9.4

1. $6^2 = 36$ **3.** $3^{-3} = \dfrac{1}{27}$ **5.** $10^3 = 1000$ **7.** $9^4 = x$ **9.** $\pi^{-2} = \dfrac{1}{\pi^2}$ **11.** $7^{1/2} = \sqrt{7}$ **13.** $0.7^3 = 0.343$

15. $3^{-4} = \dfrac{1}{81}$ **17.** $\log_2 16 = 4$ **19.** $\log_{10} 100 = 2$ **21.** $\log_\pi x = 3$ **23.** $\log_{10} \dfrac{1}{10} = -1$ **25.** $\log_4 \dfrac{1}{16} = -2$

27. $\log_5 \sqrt{5} = \dfrac{1}{2}$ **29.** 3   **31.** -2 **33.** $\dfrac{1}{2}$ **35.** -1 **37.** 0   **39.** 2   **41.** 4   **43.** -3 **45.** 2   **47.** 81

49. 7   **51.** -3 **53.** -3 **55.** 2   **57.** 2   **59.** $\dfrac{27}{64}$ **61.** 10   **63.** 4   **65.** 5   **67.** $\dfrac{1}{49}$ **69.** 3   **71.** 3   **73.** 1

75.   **77.**   **79.**   **81.**   **83.** 1

85. $\dfrac{x-4}{2}$ **87.** $\dfrac{2x+3}{x^2}$ **89.** $m - 1$ **91. a.** $g(2) = 25$ **b.** $(25, 2)$ **c.** $f(25) = 2$ **93.** answers may vary   **95.** $\dfrac{9}{5}$ **97.** 1

99.   **101.** $y = \left(\dfrac{1}{3}\right)^x$ **103.** answers may vary   **105.** 0.0827

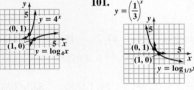

Section 9.5
Practice Exercises

1. a. $\log_8 15$ **b.** $\log_2 6$ **c.** $\log_5(x^2 - 1)$ **2. a.** $\log_5 3$ **b.** $\log_6 \dfrac{x}{3}$ **c.** $\log_4 \dfrac{x^2+1}{x^2+3}$ **3. a.** $8 \log_7 x$ **b.** $\dfrac{1}{4} \log_5 7$

4. a. $\log_5 512$ **b.** $\log_8 \dfrac{x^2}{x+3}$ **c.** $\log_7 15$ **5. a.** $\log_5 4 + \log_5 3 - \log_5 7$ **b.** $2 \log_4 a - 5 \log_4 b$ **6. a.** 1.39   **b.** 1.66   **c.** 0.28

Vocabulary and Readiness Check 9.5
1. 36   **3.** $\log_b 2^7$ **5.** x

Exercise Set 9.5

1. $\log_5 14$ **3.** $\log_4 9x$ **5.** $\log_6(x^2 + x)$ **7.** $\log_{10}(10x^2 + 20)$ **9.** $\log_5 3$ **11.** $\log_3 4$ **13.** $\log_2 \dfrac{x}{y}$ **15.** $\log_2 \dfrac{x^2+6}{x^2+1}$ **17.** $2 \log_3 x$

19. $-1 \log_4 5 = -\log_4 5$ **21.** $\dfrac{1}{2} \log_5 y$ **23.** $\log_2 5x^3$ **25.** $\log_4 8$ **27.** $\log_5 x^3 z^5$ **29.** $\log_4 4$, or 1   **31.** $\log_7 \dfrac{9}{2}$ **33.** $\log_{10} \dfrac{x^3 - 2x}{x+1}$

35. $\log_2 \dfrac{x^{7/2}}{(x+1)^2}$ **37.** $\log_8 x^{16/3}$ **39.** $\log_3 4 + \log_3 y - \log_3 5$ **41.** $\log_4 2 - \log_4 9 - \log_4 z$ **43.** $3\log_2 x - \log_2 y$ **45.** $\dfrac{1}{2}\log_b 7 + \dfrac{1}{2}\log_b x$

47. $4\log_6 x + 5\log_6 y$ **49.** $3\log_5 x + \log_5(x+1)$ **51.** $2\log_6 x - \log_6(x+3)$ **53.** 1.2 **55.** 0.2 **57.** 0.35 **59.** 1.29 **61.** -0.68

63. -0.125 **65.**   **67.** -1 **69.** $\dfrac{1}{2}$ **71.** a and d **73.** false **75.** true **77.** false

Integrated Review

1. $x^2 + x - 5$ **2.** $-x^2 + x - 7$ **3.** $x^3 - 6x^2 + x - 6$ **4.** $\dfrac{x-6}{x^2+1}$ **5.** $\sqrt{3x-1}$ **6.** $3\sqrt{x}-1$

7. one-to-one; $\{(6,-2),(8,4),(-6,2),(3,3)\}$ **8.** not one-to-one **9.** not one-to-one **10.** one-to-one

11. not one-to-one **12.** $f^{-1}(x) = \dfrac{x}{3}$ **13.** $f^{-1}(x) = x - 4$ **14.** $f^{-1}(x) = \dfrac{x+1}{5}$ **15.** $f^{-1}(x) = \dfrac{x-2}{3}$

16. $y = \left(\dfrac{1}{2}\right)^x$ **17.** $y = 2^x + 1$ **18.** $y = \log_3 x$ **19.** $y = \log_{1/3} x$ **20.** 3

21. 7 **22.** -8 **23.** 3 **24.** 2 **25.** $\dfrac{1}{2}$ **26.** 32 **27.** 4 **28.** 5 **29.** $\dfrac{1}{9}$ **30.** $\log_2 x^5$ **31.** $\log_2 5^x$ **32.** $\log_5 \dfrac{x^3}{y^5}$

33. $\log_5 x^9 y^3$ **34.** $\log_2 \dfrac{x^2 - 3x}{x^2 + 4}$ **35.** $\log_3 \dfrac{y^4 + 11y}{y + 2}$ **36.** $\log_7 9 + 2\log_7 x - \log_7 y$ **37.** $\log_6 5 + \log_6 y - 2\log_6 z$

Section 9.6
Practice Exercises

1. 1.1761 **2. a.** -2 **b.** 5 **c.** $\dfrac{1}{5}$ **d.** -3 **3.** $10^{3.4} \approx 2511.8864$ **4.** 5.6 **5.** 2.5649 **6. a.** 4 **b.** $\dfrac{1}{3}$

7. $\dfrac{e^8}{5} \approx 596.1916$ **8.** \$3051 **9.** 0.7740

Vocabulary and Readiness Check 9.6

1. 10 **3.** 7 **5.** 5 **7.** $\dfrac{\log 7}{\log 2}$ or $\dfrac{\ln 7}{\ln 2}$

Exercise Set 9.6

1. 0.9031 **3.** 0.3636 **5.** 0.6931 **7.** -2.6367 **9.** 1.1004 **11.** 1.6094 **13.** 1.6180 **15.** answers may vary **17.** 2 **19.** -3 **21.** 2

23. $\dfrac{1}{4}$ **25.** 3 **27.** -7 **29.** -4 **31.** $\dfrac{1}{2}$ **33.** $\dfrac{e^7}{2} \approx 548.3166$ **35.** $10^{1.3} \approx 19.9526$ **37.** $\dfrac{10^{1.1}}{2} \approx 6.2946$ **39.** $e^{1.4} \approx 4.0552$

41. $\dfrac{4 + e^{2.3}}{3} \approx 4.6581$ **43.** $10^{2.3} \approx 199.5262$ **45.** $e^{-2.3} \approx 0.1003$ **47.** $\dfrac{10^{-0.5} - 1}{2} \approx -0.3419$ **49.** $\dfrac{e^{0.18}}{4} \approx 0.2993$ **51.** 1.5850 **53.** -2.3219

55. 1.5850 **57.** -1.6309 **59.** 0.8617 **61.** 4.2 **63.** 5.3 **65.** \$3656.38 **67.** \$2542.50 **69.** $\dfrac{4}{7}$ **71.** $x = \dfrac{3y}{4}$ **73.** $-6, -1$ **75.** $(2, -3)$

77. $\ln 50$; answers may vary **79.** $f(x) = e^x$ **81.** $f(x) = e^{-3x}$ **83.** 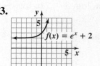 $f(x) = e^x + 2$ **85.** $f(x) = e^{x-1}$ **87.** $f(x) = 3e^x$

89. $f(x) = \ln x$ **91.** $f(x) = -2\log x$ **93.** $f(x) = \log(x+2)$ **95.** $f(x) = \ln x - 3$ **97.** answers may vary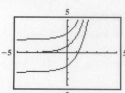

Section 9.7
Practice Exercises

1. $\dfrac{\log 9}{\log 5} \approx 1.3652$ **2.** 33   **3.** 1   **4.** $\dfrac{1}{3}$ **5.** 937 rabbits   **6.** 10 years

Graphing Calculator Explorations 9.7

1. 3.67 years, or 3 years and 8 months   **3.** 23.16 years, or 23 years and 2 months

Exercise Set 9.7

1. $\dfrac{\log 6}{\log 3}$; 1.6309   **3.** $\dfrac{\log 3.8}{2\log 3}$; 0.6076   **5.** $3 + \dfrac{\log 5}{\log 2}$; 5.3219   **7.** $\dfrac{\log 5}{\log 9}$; 0.7325   **9.** $\dfrac{\log 3}{\log 4} - 7$; −6.2075   **11.** $\dfrac{1}{3}\left(4 + \dfrac{\log 11}{\log 7}\right)$; 1.7441

13. $\dfrac{\ln 5}{6}$; 0.2682   **15.** 11   **17.** 9, −9   **19.** $\dfrac{1}{2}$ **21.** $\dfrac{3}{4}$ **23.** 2   **25.** $\dfrac{1}{8}$ **27.** 11   **29.** 4, −1   **31.** $\dfrac{1}{5}$ **33.** 100   **35.** $\dfrac{-5 + \sqrt{33}}{2}$

37. $\dfrac{192}{127}$ **39.** $\dfrac{2}{3}$ **41.** 103 wolves   **43.** 354,000 inhabitants   **45.** 14.7 yr   **47.** 9.9 yr   **49.** 1.7 yr   **51.** 8.8 yr   **53.** 24.5 lb   **55.** 55.7 in.

57. 11.9 lb/sq in.   **59.** 3.2 mi   **61.** 12 weeks   **63.** 18 weeks   **65.** $-\dfrac{5}{3}$ **67.** $\dfrac{17}{4}$ **69.** $f^{-1}(x) = \dfrac{x-2}{5}$ **71.** 2.9%   **73.** answers may vary

75. 6.93   **77.** −3.68   **79.** 1.74   **81.** 0.2

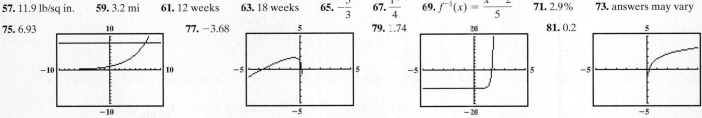

The Bigger Picture

1. $-\dfrac{3}{2}$ **2.** $\dfrac{\log 5}{\log 11} \approx 0.6712$ **3.** $[-5, \infty)$ **4.** $\left[-\dfrac{13}{3}, -2\right]$ **5.** $\left(-\dfrac{6}{5}, 0\right)$ **6.** 6, $-\dfrac{1}{5}$ **7.** $\dfrac{21}{8}$ **8.** $-\dfrac{7}{3}$, 3   **9.** $(-\infty, \infty)$ **10.** −2, 2

11. $-5 + \sqrt{3}, -5 - \sqrt{3}$ **12.** $-\dfrac{1}{4}$, 7

Chapter 9 Vocabulary Check

1. inverse   **2.** composition   **3.** exponential   **4.** symmetric   **5.** Natural   **6.** Common   **7.** vertical; horizontal   **8.** logarithmic

Chapter 9 Review

1. $3x - 4$ **3.** $2x^2 - 9x - 5$ **5.** $x^2 + 2x - 1$ **7.** 18   **9.** −2   **11.** one-to-one;
$h^{-1} = \{(14, -9), (8, 6), (12, -11), (15, 15)\}$ **13.** one-to-one;

Rank in Automobile Thefts (Input)	2	4	1	3
US Region (Output)	W	Midwest	S	NE

15. a. 3   **b.** 7   **17.** not one-to-one
19. not one-to-one   **21.** $f^{-1}(x) = x + 9$

23. $f^{-1}(x) = \dfrac{x - 11}{6}$ **25.** $f^{-1}(x) = \sqrt[3]{x + 5}$

27. $g^{-1}(x) = \dfrac{6x + 7}{12}$ **29.** 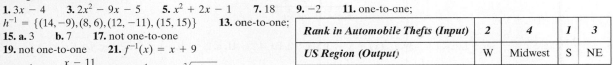   **31.** $f^{-1}(x) = \dfrac{x + 3}{2}$;   **33.** −2   **35.** $\dfrac{3}{2}$ **37.** $\dfrac{8}{9}$ **39.**   **41.**

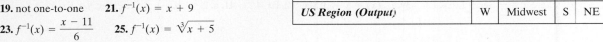

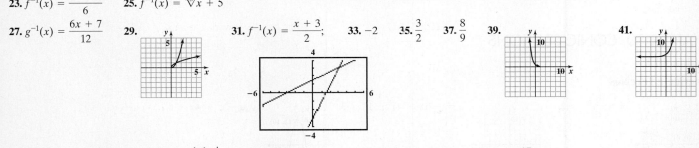

43. $1131.82   **45.** $\log_7 49 = 2$ **47.** $\left(\dfrac{1}{2}\right)^{-4} = 16$ **49.** $\dfrac{1}{64}$ **51.** 0   **53.** 8   **55.** 5   **57.** 4   **59.** $\dfrac{17}{3}$ **61.** −1, 4   **63.**

65. $\log_3 32$ **67.** $\log_7 \dfrac{3}{4}$ **69.** $\log_{11} 4$ **71.** $\log_5 \dfrac{x^3}{(x+1)^2}$ **73.** $3\log_3 x - \log_3(x + 2)$ **75.** $\log_2 3 + 2\log_2 x + \log_2 y - \log_2 z$

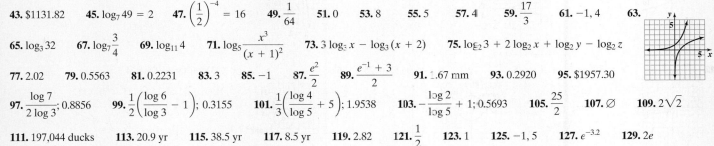

77. 2.02   **79.** 0.5563   **81.** 0.2231   **83.** 3   **85.** −1   **87.** $\dfrac{e^2}{2}$ **89.** $\dfrac{e^{-1} + 3}{2}$ **91.** 1.67 mm   **93.** 0.2920   **95.** $1957.30

97. $\dfrac{\log 7}{2\log 3}$; 0.8856   **99.** $\dfrac{1}{2}\left(\dfrac{\log 6}{\log 3} - 1\right)$; 0.3155   **101.** $\dfrac{1}{3}\left(\dfrac{\log 4}{\log 5} + 5\right)$; 1.9538   **103.** $-\dfrac{\log 2}{\log 5} + 1$; 0.5693   **105.** $\dfrac{25}{2}$ **107.** ∅   **109.** $2\sqrt{2}$

111. 197,044 ducks   **113.** 20.9 yr   **115.** 38.5 yr   **117.** 8.5 yr   **119.** 2.82   **121.** $\dfrac{1}{2}$ **123.** 1   **125.** −1, 5   **127.** $e^{-3.2}$ **129.** $2e$

Chapter 9 Test

1. $2x^2 - 3x$ **2.** $3 - x$ **3.** 5   **4.** $x - 7$ **5.** $x^2 - 6x - 2$

6.   **7.** one-to-one   **8.** not one-to-one   **9.** one-to-one; $f^{-1}(x) = \dfrac{-x + 6}{2}$ **10.** one-to-one; $f^{-1} = \{(0, 0), (3, 2)(5, -1)\}$

11. not one-to-one   **12.** $\log_3 24$ **13.** $\log_5 \dfrac{x^4}{x + 1}$ **14.** $\log_6 2 + \log_6 x - 3 \log_6 y$ **15.** -1.53 **16.** 1.0686 **17.** -1

18. $\dfrac{1}{2}\left(\dfrac{\log 4}{\log 3} - 5\right)$; -1.8691 **19.** $\dfrac{1}{9}$ **20.** $\dfrac{1}{2}$ **21.** 22   **22.** $\dfrac{25}{3}$ **23.** $\dfrac{43}{21}$ **24.** -1.0979

25.   **26.**   **27.** $5234.58   **28.** 6 yr   **29.** 64,913 prairie dogs   **30.** 15 yr   **31.** 1.2%

Chapter 9 Cumulative Review

1. a. 8   **b.** $-\dfrac{1}{3}$ **c.** -0.36 **d.** 0   **e.** $-\dfrac{2}{11}$ **f.** 42   **g.** 0; Sec. 1.3, Ex. 4   **3.** 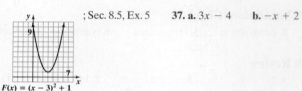 ; Sec. 3.1, Ex. 6

5. $\{(x, y, z) | x - 5y - 2z = 6\}$; Sec. 4.2, Ex. 4   **7. a.** x^3 **b.** 5^6 **c.** $5x$ **d.** $\dfrac{6y^2}{7}$; Sec. 5.1, Ex. 4   **9. a.** $102.60   **b.** $12.60; Sec. 6.1, Ex. 9

11. a. $\dfrac{3x}{2}$ **b.** $\dfrac{5 + x}{7z^2}$ **c.** $x - 7$ **d.** $-\dfrac{1}{3y^2}$; Sec. 6.2, Ex. 1   **13.** $3x^2 + 2x + 3 + \dfrac{-6x + 9}{x^2 - 1}$; Sec. 6.4, Ex. 6   **15.** -1; Sec. 6.5, Ex. 4

17. 6 mph; Sec. 6.6, Ex. 5   **19. a.** 3   **b.** -3 **c.** -5 **d.** not a real number   **e.** $4x$; Sec. 7.1, Ex. 4   **21. a.** $\sqrt[4]{x^3}$ **b.** $\sqrt[6]{x}$

c. $\sqrt[6]{72}$; Sec. 7.2, Ex. 8   **23. a.** $5\sqrt{3} + 3\sqrt{10}$ **b.** $\sqrt{35} + \sqrt{5} - \sqrt{42} - \sqrt{6}$ **c.** $21x - 7\sqrt{5x} + 15\sqrt{x} - 5\sqrt{5}$ **d.** $49 - 8\sqrt{3}$

e. $2x - 25$ **f.** $x + 22 + 10\sqrt{x - 3}$; Sec. 7.4, Ex. 4   **25.** $\dfrac{\sqrt[4]{xy^3}}{3y^2}$; Sec. 7.5, Ex. 3   **27.** 3; Sec. 7.6, Ex. 4   **29.** $\dfrac{9 + i\sqrt{15}}{6}, \dfrac{9 - i\sqrt{15}}{6}$; Sec. 8.1, Ex. 8

31. $\dfrac{-1 + \sqrt{33}}{4}, \dfrac{-1 - \sqrt{33}}{4}$; Sec. 8.3, Ex. 2   **33.** $[0, 4]$; Sec. 8.4, Ex. 2   **35.** ; Sec. 8.5, Ex. 5   **37. a.** $3x - 4$ **b.** $-x + 2$

$F(x) = (x - 3)^2 + 1$

c. $2x^2 - 5x + 3$ **d.** $\dfrac{x - 1}{2x - 3}$, where $x \neq \dfrac{3}{2}$; Sec. 9.1, Ex. 1   **39.** $f^{-1}(x) = x - 3$; Sec. 9.2, Ex. 4   **41. a.** 2   **b.** -1 **c.** $\dfrac{1}{2}$; Sec. 9.4, Ex. 3

CHAPTER 10 CONIC SECTIONS

Section 10.1
Practice Exercises

1. $x = \dfrac{1}{2}y^2$ **2.** $x = -2(y + 4)^2 - 1$ **3.** 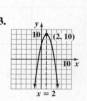 $y = -x^2 + 4x + 6$

4. $x = 3y^2 + 6y + 4$ **5.** $x^2 + y^2 = 25$ **6.** $(x - 3)^2 + (y + 2)^2 = 4$

7. $(x + 2)^2 + (y + 5)^2 = 81$ **8.**

$x^2 + y^2 + 6x - 2y = 6$

Graphing Calculator Explorations 10.1

1. 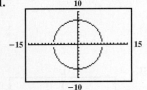 **3.** 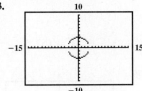 **5.** 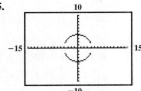 **7.**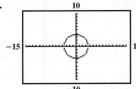

Vocabulary and Readiness Check 10.1

1. conic sections **3.** circle, center **5.** radius **7.** upward **9.** to the left **11.** downward

Exercise Set 10.1

1. **3.** **5.** **7.** **9.**

11. **13.** **15.** **17.** **19.**

21. **23.** **25.** $(x - 2)^2 + (y - 3)^2 = 36$ **27.** $x^2 + y^2 = 3$ **29.** $(x + 5)^2 + (y - 4)^2 = 45$

31. The radius is $\sqrt{10}$. **33.** 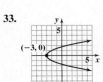 **35.** **37.** **39.**

41. **43.** **45.** **47.** **49.**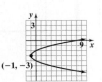

51. $\left(-\dfrac{7}{2}, -\dfrac{25}{4}\right)$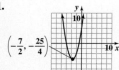

53. $r = 7$ $C(-1, -6)$

55. $(-20, -4)$

57. $r = \sqrt{21}$ $C(0, 5)$

59. $(75, 5)$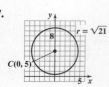

61. $r = \sqrt{5}$ $C(0, 0)$

63. $(2, -4)$

65.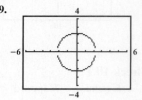

67.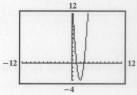

69. $\dfrac{\sqrt{10}}{4}$ **71.** $2\sqrt{5}$

73. a. 67.5 meters **b.** ground level or 0 m **c.** 67.5 meters **d.** $(0, 67.5)$ **e.** $x^2 + (y - 67.5)^2 = (67.5)^2$

75. a. 76.5 m **b.** 7 m **c.** 83.5 m **d.** $(0, 83.5)$ **e.** $x^2 + (y - 83.5)^2 = (76.5)^2$

77. a. $C(0, 0)$ **b.** $x^2 + y^2 = 100$ **c.** 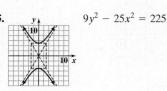 $x^2 + y^2 = 25$

79.

81.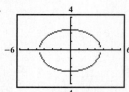

Section 10.2
Practice Exercises

1. 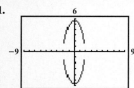 $(-5, 0)$ $(0, 2)$ $(0, -2)$ $(5, 0)$ $\dfrac{x^2}{25} + \dfrac{y^2}{4} = 1$

2. 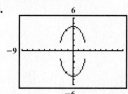 $(0, 3)$ $(-2, 0)$ $(2, 0)$ $(0, -3)$ $9x^2 + 4y^2 = 36$

3. $(4, -1)$ $\dfrac{(x - 4)^2}{49} + \dfrac{(y + 1)^2}{81} = 1$

4. $(-3, 4)$ $(3, 4)$ $(-3, -4)$ $(3, -4)$ $\dfrac{x^2}{9} - \dfrac{y^2}{16} = 1$

5. $9y^2 - 25x^2 = 225$

Graphing Calculator Explorations 10.2

1. **3.** **5.**

Vocabulary and Readiness Check 10.2

1. hyperbola **3.** focus **5.** hyperbola; $(0, 0)$; x; $(a, 0)$ and $(-a, 0)$ **7.** ellipse **9.** hyperbola **11.** hyperbola

Exercise Set 10.2

1. $(0, 5)$ $(-2, 0)$ $(2, 0)$ $(0, -5)$

3. $(0, 1)$ $(-3, 0)$ $(3, 0)$ $(0, -1)$

5. $(0, 6)$ $(-2, 0)$ $(2, 0)$ $(0, -6)$

7. $(0, 2)$ $(-5, 0)$ $(5, 0)$ $(0, -2)$

9. $C(-1, 2)$

11.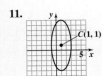

13.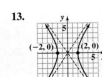

15.

17.

19.

21. answers may vary

23. parabola

25. ellipse

27. hyperbola

29. circle

31. parabola

33. ellipse

35. hyperbola

37. parabola

39. $(-\infty, 5)$ **41.** $[4, \infty)$ **43.** $-2x^3$ **45.** $-5x^4$ **47.** x-intercepts; 6 units   **49.** x-intercepts; 6 units

51. ellipses: C, E, H; circles: B, F; hyperbolas: A, D, G   **53.** A: 49, 7; B: 0, 0; C: 9, 3; D: 64, 8; E: 64, 8; F: 0, 0; G: 81, 9; H: 4, 2

55. A: $\frac{7}{6}$; B: 0; C: $\frac{3}{5}$; D: $\frac{8}{5}$; E: $\frac{8}{9}$; F: 0; G: $\frac{9}{4}$; H: $\frac{1}{6}$ **57.** equal to zero   **59.** answers may vary   **61.** $\dfrac{x^2}{1.69 \cdot 10^{16}} + \dfrac{y^2}{1.5625 \cdot 10^{16}} = 1$

63. $9x^2 + 4y^2 = 36$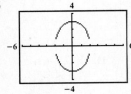

65.

67.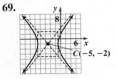

69.

Integrated Review

1.

2.

3.

4.

5.

6.

7.

8.

9.

10.

11.

12.

13.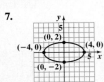

14.

15.

Section 10.3
Practice Exercises

1. $(-4, 3)(0, -1)$ **2.** $(4, -2)$ **3.** $\varnothing$ **4.** $(2, \sqrt{3})$; $(2, -\sqrt{3})$; $(-2, \sqrt{3})$; $(-2, -\sqrt{3})$

Exercise Set 10.3

1. $(3, -4), (-3, 4)$ **3.** $(\sqrt{2}, \sqrt{2}), (-\sqrt{2}, -\sqrt{2})$ **5.** $(4, 0), (0, -2)$ **7.** $(-\sqrt{5}, -2), (-\sqrt{5}, 2), (\sqrt{5}, -2), (\sqrt{5}, 2)$ **9.** $\varnothing$ **11.** $(1, -2), (3, 6)$
13. $(2, 4), (-5, 25)$ **15.** $\varnothing$ **17.** $(1, -3)$ **19.** $(-1, -2), (-1, 2), (1, -2), (1, 2)$ **21.** $(0, -1)$ **23.** $(-1, 3), (1, 3)$ **25.** $(\sqrt{3}, 0), (-\sqrt{3}, 0)$
27. $\varnothing$ **29.** $(-6, 0), (6, 0), (0, -6)$ **31.** 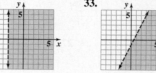   **33.** 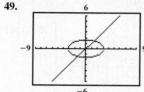   **35.** $(8x - 25)$ in.   **37.** $(4x^2 + 6x + 2)$ m

39. answers may vary   **41.** 0, 1, 2, 3, or 4; answers may vary   **43.** 9 and 7; 9 and -7; -9 and 7; -9 and -7 **45.** 15 cm by 19 cm
47. 15 thousand compact discs price: $3.75   **49.** 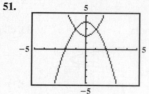   **51.**

Section 10.4
Practice Exercises

1. $\dfrac{x^2}{36} + \dfrac{y^2}{16} \geq 1$ **2.** 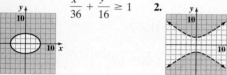 $16y^2 > 9x^2 + 144$ **3.** $\begin{cases} y \geq x^2 \\ y \leq -3x + 2 \end{cases}$ **4.** 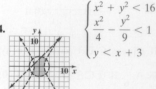 $\begin{cases} x^2 + y^2 < 16 \\ \dfrac{x^2}{4} - \dfrac{y^2}{9} < 1 \\ y < x + 3 \end{cases}$

Exercise Set 10.4

1.   **3.**   **5.**   **7.**   **9.**   **11.**

13.   **15.**   **17.**   **19.** 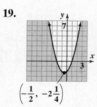   **21.** 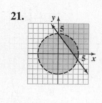   **23.**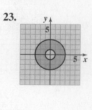

25.   **27.**   **29.**   **31.**   **33.**   **35.**

37. not a function   **39.** function   **41.** 1   **43.** $3a^2 - 2$ **45.** answers may vary   **47.**

Chapter 10 Vocabulary Check

1. circle; center   **2.** nonlinear system of equations   **3.** ellipse   **4.** radius   **5.** hyperbola

Chapter 10 Review

1. $(x + 4)^2 + (y - 4)^2 = 9$ **3.** $(x + 7)^2 + (y + 9)^2 = 11$ **5.**   **7.** 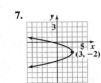 **9.**

11.   **13.** 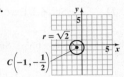 **15.**   **17.**   **19.**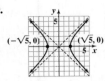

21.   **23.**   **25.**   **27.** $(1, -2), (4, 4)$ **29.** $(-1, 1), (2, 4)$ **31.** $(2, 2\sqrt{2}), (2, -2\sqrt{2})$

33. $(1, 4)$ **35.** 15 ft by 10 ft **37.**   **39.**   **41.**   **43.** $(x + 7)^2 + (y - 8)^2 = 25$

45.   **47.**   **49.**   **51.**   **53.**

55. $(5, 1), (-1, 7)$ **57.**

Chapter 10 Test

1.   **2.**   **3.**   **4.**   **5.**

6.   **7.**   **8.**   **9.** $(-5, -1), (-5, 1), (5, -1), (5, 1)$ **10.** $(6, 12), (1, 2)$

11.   **12.**   **13.**   **14.** height: 10 ft; width: 30 ft

Chapter 10 Cumulative Review

1. $(4 \cdot 9)y = 36y$; Sec. 1.4, Ex. 10   **3.** 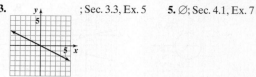 ; Sec. 3.3, Ex. 5   **5.** $\varnothing$; Sec. 4.1, Ex. 7

7. a. $125x^6$ **b.** $\dfrac{8}{27}$ **c.** $\dfrac{9p^8}{q^{10}}$ **d.** $64y^2$ **e.** $\dfrac{y^{14}}{x^{35}z^7}$; Sec. 5.2, Ex. 2   **9.** $-\dfrac{1}{6}$, 3; Sec. 5.8, Ex. 5   **11.** $\dfrac{12}{x-1}$; Sec. 6.2, Ex. 6

13. a. $\dfrac{1}{9xy^2}$ **b.** $\dfrac{x(x-2)}{2(x+2)}$ **c.** $\dfrac{x^2}{y^2}$; Sec. 6.3, Ex. 1   **15.** $2x-5$; Sec. 6.4, Ex. 3   **17.** 16; Sec. 6.4, Ex. 11   **19.** $-6, -1$; Sec. 6.5, Ex. 5

21. $2\dfrac{2}{9}$ hr; no; Sec. 6.6, Ex. 4   **23. a.** 1   **b.** -4 **c.** $\dfrac{2}{5}$ **d.** x^2 **e.** $-3x^3$; Sec. 7.1, Ex. 3   **25. a.** $z - z^{17/3}$ **b.** $x^{2/3} - 3x^{1/3} - 10$; Sec. 7.2, Ex. 5

27. a. 2   **b.** $\dfrac{5}{2}\sqrt{x}$ **c.** $14xy^2\sqrt[3]{x}$;   **d.** $4a^2b\sqrt[4]{2a}$; Sec. 7.3, Ex. 5   **29. a.** $\dfrac{5\sqrt{5}}{12}$ **b.** $\dfrac{5\sqrt[3]{7x}}{2}$; Sec. 7.4, Ex. 3   **31.** $\dfrac{\sqrt{21xy}}{3y}$; Sec. 7.5, Ex. 2

33. 42; Sec. 7.6, Ex. 1   **35. a.** $-i$ **b.** 1   **c.** -1 **d.** 1; Sec. 7.7, Ex. 6   **37.** $-1 + \sqrt{5}, -1 - \sqrt{5}$; Sec. 8.1, Ex. 5

39. $2 + \sqrt{2}, 2 - \sqrt{2}$; Sec. 8.2, Ex. 3   **41.** $2, -2, i, -i$; Sec. 8.3, Ex. 3   **43.** $[-2, 3)$; Sec. 8.4, Ex. 4   **45.** ; Sec. 8.5, Ex. 8

47. $(2, -16)$; Sec. 8.6, Ex. 4   **49.** $\sqrt{2} \approx 1.414$; Sec. 7.3, Ex. 6

CHAPTER 11 SEQUENCES, SERIES, AND THE BINOMIAL THEOREM

Section 11.1
Practice Exercises
1. 6, 9, 14, 21, 30   **2. a.** $-\dfrac{1}{5}$ **b.** $\dfrac{1}{20}$ **c.** $\dfrac{1}{150}$ **d.** $-\dfrac{1}{95}$ **3. a.** $a_n = (2n - 1)$ **b.** $a_n = 3^n$ **c.** $a_n = \dfrac{n}{n+1}$ **d.** $a_n = -\dfrac{1}{n+1}$ **4.** \$2022.40

Vocabulary and Readiness Check 11.1
1. general   **3.** infinite   **5.** -1

Exercise Set 11.1
1. 5, 6, 7, 8, 9   **3.** $-1, 1, -1, 1, -1$ **5.** $\dfrac{1}{4}, \dfrac{1}{5}, \dfrac{1}{6}, \dfrac{1}{7}, \dfrac{1}{8}$ **7.** 2, 4, 6, 8, 10   **9.** $-1, -4, -9, -16, -25$ **11.** 2, 4, 8, 16, 32   **13.** 7, 9, 11, 13, 15

15. $-1, 4, -9, 16, -25$ **17.** 75   **19.** 118   **21.** $\dfrac{6}{5}$ **23.** 729   **25.** $\dfrac{4}{7}$ **27.** $\dfrac{1}{8}$ **29.** -95 **31.** $-\dfrac{1}{25}$ **33.** $a_n = 4n - 1$ **35.** $a_n = -2^n$

37. $a_n = \dfrac{1}{3^n}$ **39.** 48 ft, 80 ft, and 112 ft   **41.** $a_n = 0.10(2)^{n-1}$; \$819.20   **43.** 2400 cases; 75 cases   **45.** 50 sparrows in 2004; extinct in 2010

47.   **49.**   **51.** $\sqrt{13}$ units   **53.** $\sqrt{41}$ units   **55.** 1, 0.7071, 0.5774, 0.5, 0.4472
57. 2, 2.25, 2.3704, 2.4414, 2.4883

Section 11.2
Practice Exercises
1. 4, 9, 14, 19, 24   **2. a.** $a_n = 5 - 3n$ **b.** -31 **3.** 51   **4.** 47   **5.** $a_n = 54{,}800 + 2200n$; \$61,400   **6.** 8, -24, 72, -216 **7.** $\dfrac{1}{64}$ **8.** -192
9. $a_1 = 3$; $r = \dfrac{3}{2}$ **10.** 75 units

Vocabulary and Readiness Check 11.2
1. geometric; ratio   **3.** first; difference

Exercise Set 11.2
1. 4, 6, 8, 10, 12   **3.** 6, 4, 2, 0, -2 **5.** 1, 3, 9, 27, 81   **7.** 48, 24, 12, 6, 3   **9.** 33   **11.** -875 **13.** -60 **15.** 96   **17.** -28 **19.** 1250

21. 31   **23.** 20   **25.** $a_1 = \dfrac{2}{3}$; $r = -2$ **27.** answers may vary   **29.** $a_1 = 2$; $d = 2$ **31.** $a_1 = 5$; $r = 2$ **33.** $a_1 = \dfrac{1}{2}$; $r = \dfrac{1}{5}$ **35.** $a_1 = x$; $r = 5$

37. $a_1 = p$; $d = 4$ **39.** 19   **41.** $-\dfrac{8}{9}$ **43.** $\dfrac{17}{2}$ **45.** $\dfrac{8}{81}$ **47.** -19 **49.** $a_n = 4n + 50$; 130 seats   **51.** $a_n = 6(3)^{n-1}$

53. $486, 162, 54, 18, 6; a_n = \dfrac{486}{3^{n-1}}; 6$ bounces   **55.** $a_n = 4000 + 125(n-1)$ or $a_n = 3875 - 125n$; $5375   **57.** 25 g   **59.** $\dfrac{11}{18}$ **61.** 40   **63.** $\dfrac{907}{495}$

65. $11,782.40, $5891.20, $2945.60, $1472.80   **67.** $19.652, 19.618, 19.584, 19.55$ **69.** answers may vary

Section 11.3
Practice Exercises

1. a. $-\dfrac{5}{4}$ **b.** 360   **2. a.** $\displaystyle\sum_{i=1}^{6} 5i$ **b.** $\displaystyle\sum_{i=1}^{4}\left(\dfrac{1}{5}\right)^i$ **3.** $\dfrac{655}{72}$ **4.** 95 plants

Vocabulary and Readiness Check 11.3
1. infinite   **3.** summation   **5.** partial sum

Exercise Set 11.3

1. -2 **3.** 60   **5.** 20   **7.** $\dfrac{73}{168}$ **9.** $\dfrac{11}{36}$ **11.** 60   **13.** 74   **15.** 62   **17.** $\dfrac{241}{35}$ **19.** $\displaystyle\sum_{i=1}^{5}(2i-1)$ **21.** $\displaystyle\sum_{i=1}^{4} 4(3)^{i-1}$

23. $\displaystyle\sum_{i=1}^{6}(-3i+15)$ **25.** $\displaystyle\sum_{i=1}^{4}\dfrac{4}{3^{i-2}}$ **27.** $\displaystyle\sum_{i=1}^{7} i^2$ **29.** -24 **31.** 0   **33.** 82   **35.** -20 **37.** -2 **39.** $1, 2, 3, \ldots, 10$; 55 trees

41. $a_n = 6(2)^{n-1}$; 96 units   **43.** $a_n = 50(2)^n$; n represents the number of 12-hour periods; 800 bacteria   **45.** 30 opossums; 68 opossums

47. 6.25 lb; 93.75 lb   **49.** 16.4 in.; 134.5 in.   **51.** 10   **53.** $\dfrac{10}{27}$ **55.** 45   **57.** 90   **59. a.** $2 + 6 + 12 + 20 + 30 + 42 + 56$

b. $1 + 2 + 3 + 4 + 5 + 6 + 7 + 1 + 4 + 9 + 16 + 25 + 36 + 49$ **c.** answers may vary   **d.** true; answers may vary

Integrated Review

1. $-2, -1, 0, 1, 2$ **2.** $\dfrac{7}{2}, \dfrac{7}{3}, \dfrac{7}{4}, \dfrac{7}{5}, \dfrac{7}{6}$ **3.** $1, 3, 9, 27, 81$ **4.** $-4, -1, 4, 11, 20$ **5.** 64   **6.** -14 **7.** $\dfrac{1}{40}$ **8.** $-\dfrac{1}{82}$ **9.** $7, 4, 1, -2, -5$

10. $-3, -15, -75, -375, -1875$ **11.** $45, 15, 5, \dfrac{5}{3}, \dfrac{5}{9}$ **12.** $-12, -2, 8, 18, 28$ **13.** 101   **14.** $\dfrac{243}{16}$ **15.** 384   **16.** 185   **17.** -10 **18.** $\dfrac{1}{5}$

19. 50   **20.** 98   **21.** $\dfrac{31}{2}$ **22.** $\dfrac{61}{20}$ **23.** -10 **24.** 5

Section 11.4
Practice Exercises

1. 80   **2.** 1275   **3.** 105 blocks of ice   **4.** $42\dfrac{5}{8}$ **5.** $987,856   **6.** $9\dfrac{1}{3}$ **7.** 900 in.

Vocabulary and Readiness Check 11.4
1. arithmetic   **3.** geometric   **5.** arithmetic

Exercise Set 11.4

1. 36   **3.** 484   **5.** 63   **7.** 2.496   **9.** 55   **11.** 16   **13.** 24   **15.** $\dfrac{1}{9}$ **17.** -20 **19.** $\dfrac{16}{9}$ **21.** $\dfrac{4}{9}$ **23.** 185   **25.** $\dfrac{381}{64}$

27. $-\dfrac{33}{4}$, or -8.25 **29.** $-\dfrac{75}{2}$ **31.** $\dfrac{56}{9}$ **33.** $4000, 3950, 3900, 3850, 3800$; 3450 cars; 44,700 cars   **35.** Firm A (Firm A, $265,000; Firm B, $254,000)

37. $39,930; $139,230   **39.** 20 min; 123 min   **41.** 180 ft   **43.** Player A, 45 points; Player B, 75 points   **45.** $3050   **47.** $10,737,418.23

49. 720   **51.** 3   **53.** $x^2 + 10x + 25$ **55.** $8x^3 - 12x^2 + 6x - 1$ **57.** $\dfrac{8}{10} + \dfrac{8}{100} + \dfrac{8}{1000} + \cdots; \dfrac{8}{9}$ **59.** answers may vary

Section 11.5
Practice Exercises

1. $p^7 + 7p^6 r + 21p^5 r^2 + 35p^4 r^3 + 35p^3 r^4 + 21p^2 r^5 + 7pr^6 + r^7$ **2. a.** $\dfrac{1}{7}$ **b.** 840   **c.** 5   **d.** 1

3. $a^9 + 9a^8 b + 36a^7 b^2 + 84a^6 b^3 + 126a^5 b^4 + 126a^4 b^5 + 84a^3 b^6 + 36a^2 b^7 + 9ab^8 + b^9$ **4.** $a^3 + 15a^2 b + 75ab^2 + 125b^3$

5. $27x^3 - 54x^2 y + 36xy^2 - 8y^3$ **6.** $1,892,352x^5 y^6$

Vocabulary and Readiness Check 11.5
1. 1   **3.** 24   **5.** 6

Exercise Set 11.5

1. $m^3 + 3m^2 n + 3mn^2 + n^3$ **3.** $c^5 + 5c^4 d + 10c^3 d^2 + 10c^2 d^3 + 5cd^4 + d^5$ **5.** $y^5 - 5y^4 x + 10y^3 x^2 - 10y^2 x^3 - 5yx^4 - x^5$
7. answers may vary   **9.** 8   **11.** 42   **13.** 360   **15.** 56   **17.** $a^7 + 7a^6 b + 21a^5 b^2 + 35a^4 b^3 + 35a^3 b^4 + 21a^2 b^5 + 7ab^6 + b^7$
19. $a^5 + 10a^4 b + 40a^3 b^2 + 80a^2 b^3 + 80ab^4 + 32b^5$ **21.** $q^9 + 9q^8 r + 36q^7 r^2 + 84q^6 r^3 + 126q^5 r^4 + 126q^4 r^5 + 84q^3 r^6 + 36q^2 r^7 + 9qr^8 + r^9$
23. $1024a^5 + 1280a^4 b + 640a^3 b^2 + 160a^2 b^3 + 20ab^4 + b^5$ **25.** $625a^4 - 1000a^3 b + 600a^2 b^2 - 160ab^3 + 16b^4$ **27.** $8a^3 + 36a^2 b + 54ab^2 + 27b^3$
29. $x^5 + 10x^4 + 40x^3 + 80x^2 + 80x + 32$ **31.** $5cd^4$ **33.** d^7 **35.** $-40r^2 s^3$ **37.** $6x^2 y^2$ **39.** $30a^9 b$

41.   **43.** 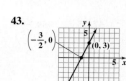 **45.**   **47.** $x^2\sqrt{x} + 5\sqrt{3}x^2 + 30x\sqrt{x} + 30\sqrt{3}x + 45\sqrt{x} + 9\sqrt{3}$
49. 126   **51.** 28   **53.** answers may vary

Chapter 11 Vocabulary Check

1. finite sequence   **2.** factorial of n **3.** infinite sequence   **4.** geometric sequence, common ratio   **5.** series   **6.** general term
7. arithmetic sequence, common difference   **8.** Pascal's triangle

Chapter 11 Review

1. $-3, -12, -27, -48, -75$ **3.** $\dfrac{1}{100}$ **5.** $a_n = \dfrac{1}{6n}$ **7.** 144 ft, 176 ft, 208 ft   **9.** 660,000; 1,320,000; 2,640,000; 5,280,000; 10,560,000; 2010:

10,560,000 infested acres   **11.** $-2, -\dfrac{4}{3}, -\dfrac{8}{9}, -\dfrac{16}{27}, -\dfrac{32}{81}$ **13.** 111   **15.** -83 **17.** $a_1 = 3; d = 5$ **19.** $a_n = \dfrac{3}{10^n}$ **21.** $a_1 = \dfrac{8}{3}, r = \dfrac{3}{2}$

23. $a_1 = 7x, r = -2$ **25.** 8, 6, 4.5, 3.4, 2.5, 1.9; good   **27.** $a_n = 2^{n-1}$, \$512, \$536,870,912   **29.** $a_n = 900 + (n-1)150$ or $a_n = 150n + 750$;

\$1650/month   **31.** $1 + 3 + 5 + 7 + 9 = 25$ **33.** $\dfrac{1}{4} - \dfrac{1}{6} + \dfrac{1}{8} = \dfrac{5}{24}$ **35.** -4 **37.** -10 **39.** $\displaystyle\sum_{i=1}^{6} 3^{i-1}$ **41.** $\displaystyle\sum_{i=1}^{4} \dfrac{1}{4^i}$ **43.** $a_n = 20(2)^n$;

n represents the number of 8-hour periods; 1280 yeast   **45.** Job A, \$48,300; Job B, \$46,600   **47.** 150   **49.** 900   **51.** -410 **53.** 936   **55.** 10

57. -25 **59.** \$30,418; \$99,868   **61.** \$58; \$553   **63.** 2696 mosquitoes   **65.** $\dfrac{5}{9}$ **67.** $x^5 + 5x^4z + 10x^3z^2 + 10x^2z^3 + 5xz^4 + z^5$

69. $16x^4 + 32x^3y + 24x^2y^2 + 8xy^3 + y^4$ **71.** $b^8 + 8b^7c + 28b^6c^2 + 56b^5c^3 + 70b^4c^4 + 56b^3c^5 + 28b^2c^6 + 8bc^7 + c^8$
73. $256m^4 - 256m^3n + 96m^2n^2 - 16mn^3 + n^4$ **75.** $35a^4b^3$ **77.** 130   **79.** 40.5

Chapter 11 Test

1. $-\dfrac{1}{5}, \dfrac{1}{6}, -\dfrac{1}{7}, \dfrac{1}{8}, -\dfrac{1}{9}$ **2.** 247   **3.** $a_n = \dfrac{2}{5}\left(\dfrac{1}{5}\right)^{n-1}$ **4.** $a_n = (-1)^n 9n$ **5.** 155   **6.** -330 **7.** $\dfrac{144}{5}$ **8.** 1   **9.** 10   **10.** -60

11. $a^6 - 6a^5b + 15a^4b^2 - 20a^3b^3 + 15a^2b^4 - 6ab^5 + b^6$ **12.** $32x^5 + 80x^4y + 80x^3y^2 + 40x^2y^3 + 10xy^4 + y^5$ **13.** 925 people; 250 people initially

14. $1 + 3 + 5 + 7 + 9 + 11 + 13 + 15$; 64 shrubs   **15.** 33.75 cm, 218.75 cm   **16.** 320 cm   **17.** 304 ft; 1600 ft   **18.** $\dfrac{14}{33}$

Chapter 11 Cumulative Review

1. a. -5 **b.** 3   **c.** $-\dfrac{1}{8}$ **d.** -4 **e.** $\dfrac{1}{4}$ **f.** undefined; Sec. 1.3, Ex. 5   **3.** \$2350; Sec. 2.2, Ex. 4   **5.** $y = \dfrac{2x}{3} + \dfrac{7}{3}$; Sec. 2.3, Ex. 2

7. a. $15x^7$ **b.** $-9.6x^4p^{12}$; Sec. 5.1, Ex. 2   **9.** $x^3 - 4x^2 - 3x + 11 + \dfrac{12}{x+2}$; Sec. 6.4, Ex. 9   **11. a.** $5\sqrt{2}$ **b.** $2\sqrt[3]{3}$ **c.** $\sqrt{26}$

d. $2\sqrt[4]{2}$; Sec. 7.3, Ex. 3   **13.** 10%; Sec. 8.1, Ex. 9   **15.** 2, 7; Sec. 8.3, Ex. 4   **17.** $\left(-\dfrac{7}{2}, -1\right)$; Sec. 8.4, Ex. 5   **19.** $\dfrac{25}{4}$ ft; $\dfrac{5}{8}$ sec; Sec. 8.6, Ex. 5

21. a. 25; 7   **b.** $x^2 + 6x + 9$; $x^2 + 3$; Sec. 9.1, Ex. 2   **23.** $f^{-1} = \{(1, 0), (7, -2), (-6, 3), (4, 4)\}$; Sec. 9.2, Ex. 3   **25. a.** 4   **b.** $\dfrac{3}{2}$

c. 6; Sec. 9.3, Ex. 4   **27. a.** 2   **b.** -1 **c.** 3   **d.** 6; Sec. 9.4, Ex. 5   **29. a.** $\log_{11} 30$ **b.** $\log_3 6$ **c.** $\log_2(x^2 + 2x)$; Sec. 9.5, Ex. 1

31. \$2509.30; Sec. 9.6, Ex. 8   **33.** $\dfrac{\log 7}{\log 3} \approx 1.7712$; Sec. 9.7, Ex. 1   **35.** 18; Sec. 9.7, Ex. 2   **37.** 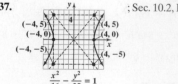 ; Sec. 10.2, Ex. 4

39. $(2, \sqrt{2})$; Sec. 10.3, Ex. 2   **41.** ; Sec. 10.4, Ex. 1   **43.** 0, 3, 8, 15, 24; Sec. 11.1, Ex. 1   **45.** 72; Sec. 11.2, Ex. 3

47. a. $\dfrac{7}{2}$ **b.** 56; Sec. 11.3, Ex. 1   **49.** 465; Sec. 11.4, Ex. 2

APPENDIX A.2 PRACTICE FINAL EXAM

1. $6\sqrt{6}$ **2.** $-\dfrac{3}{2}$ **3.** 5 **4.** $\dfrac{1}{81x^2}$ **5.** $\dfrac{64}{3}$ **6.** $\dfrac{3a^7}{2b^5}$ **7.** $\dfrac{8a^{1/2}c^{2/3}}{b^{5/12}}$ **8.** $3y(x+3y)(x-3y)$ **9.** $2(2y-1)(4y^2+2y+1)$

10. $(x+3)(x-3)(y-3)$ **11.** $-5x^3y-11x-9$ **12.** $36m^2+12mn+n^2$ **13.** $2x^3-13x^2+14x-4$ **14.** $\dfrac{x+2}{2(x+3)}$ **15.** $\dfrac{1}{x(x+3)}$

16. $\dfrac{5x-2}{(x-3)(x+2)(x-2)}$ **17.** $-x\sqrt{5x}$ **18.** -20 **19.** $2x^2-x-2+\dfrac{2}{2x+1}$ **20.** -32 **21.** $1,\dfrac{2}{3}$

22. $4,-\dfrac{8}{7}$ **23.** $\left(\dfrac{3}{2},5\right]$ **24.** $(-\infty,-2)\cup\left(\dfrac{4}{3},\infty\right)$ **25.** 3 **26.** $\dfrac{3\pm\sqrt{29}}{2}$ **27.** 2, 3 **28.** $\left(-\infty,-\dfrac{3}{2}\right)\cup(5,\infty)$ **29.** $\left(\dfrac{7}{2},-10\right)$

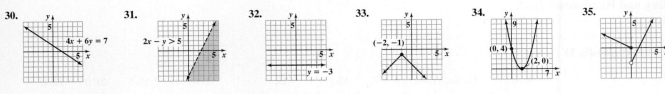

30. **31.** **32.** **33.** **34.** **35.**

36. $f(x)=-\dfrac{1}{2}x$ **37.** $f(x)=-\dfrac{1}{3}x+\dfrac{5}{3}$ **38.** $2\sqrt{26}$ units **39.** $\left(-4,\dfrac{7}{2}\right)$ **40.** $\dfrac{3\sqrt{y}}{y}$ **41.** $\dfrac{8-6\sqrt{x}+x}{8-2x}$

42. New York: 21.8 million; Seoul: 23.1 million; Tokyo: 33.4 million **43.** $(x+2y)(x-2y)$ **44.** 5 **45.** 16 **46.** 7 ft

47. a. 272 ft **b.** 5.12 sec **48.** 5 gal of 10%; 15 gal of 20% **49.** $-2i\sqrt{2}$ **50.** $-3i$ **51.** $7+24i$ **52.** $-\dfrac{3}{2}+\dfrac{5}{2}i$

53. $(g\circ h)(x)=x^2-6x-2$ **54.** $f^{-1}(x)=\dfrac{-x+6}{2}$ **55.** $\log_5\dfrac{x^4}{x+1}$ **56.** -1 **57.** $\dfrac{1}{2}\left(\dfrac{\log 4}{\log 3}-5\right);-1.8691$ **58.** 22

59. $\dfrac{43}{21}$ **60.** $\dfrac{1}{2}$ **61.** **62.** 64,913 prairie dogs **63.** **64.** **65.**

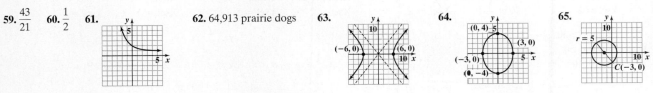

66. $(-5,-1)(-5,1),(5,-1),(5,1)$ **67.** $-\dfrac{1}{5},\dfrac{1}{6},-\dfrac{1}{7},\dfrac{1}{8},-\dfrac{1}{9}$ **68.** 155 **69.** 1 **70.** 10

71. $32x^5+80x^4y+80x^3y^2+40x^2y^3+10xy^4+y^5$

APPENDIX B.3 REVIEW OF VOLUME AND SURFACE AREA

1. $V=512$ cu. cm; $SA=108$ sq. cm **3.** $V=512$ cu. cm; $SA=384$ sq. cm

5. $V=4\pi$ cu. yd ≈ 12.56 cu. yd; $SA=(2\sqrt{13}\pi+4\pi)$ sq yd ≈ 35.20 sq. yd **7.** $V=\dfrac{500}{3}\pi$ cu. in. $\approx 523\dfrac{17}{21}$ cu. in.; $SA=100\pi$ sq. in. $\approx 314\dfrac{2}{7}$ sq. in.

9. $V=48$ cu. cm; $SA=96$ sq. cm **11.** $2\dfrac{10}{27}$ cu. in. **13.** 26 sq. ft **15.** $10\dfrac{5}{6}$ cu. in. **17.** 960 cu. cm **19.** 196π sq. in.

21. $7\dfrac{1}{2}$ cu. ft **23.** $12\dfrac{4}{7}$ cu. cm

APPENDIX C

Exercise Set Appendix C

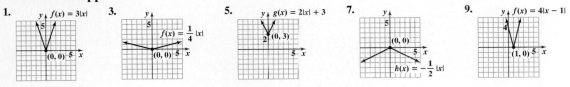

1. **3.** **5.** **7.** **9.**

11. 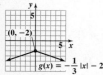   **13.**   **15.**

APPENDIX D

Vocabulary and Readiness Check

1. 56   **3.** −32   **5.** 20

Exercise Set Appendix D

1. 26   **3.** −19   **5.** 0   **7.** $\dfrac{13}{6}$ **9.** (1, 2)   **11.** $\{(x, y)\,|\,3x + y = 1\}$ **13.** (9, 9)   **15.** (−3, −2)   **17.** (3, 4)   **19.** 8   **21.** 0   **23.** 15

25. 54   **27.** (−2, 0, 5)   **29.** (6, −2, 4)   **31.** (−2, 3, −1)   **33.** (0, 2, −1)   **35.** 5   **37.** 0; answers may vary

APPENDIX E AN INTRODUCTION TO USING A GRAPHING UTILITY

Viewing Window and Interpreting Window Settings Exercise Set

1. yes   **3.** no   **5.** answers may vary   **7.** answers may vary   **9.** answers may vary

11. Xmin = −12   Ymin = −12   **13.** Xmin = −9   Ymin = −12   **15.** Xmin = −10   Ymin = −25   **17.** Xmin = −10   Ymin = −30
Xmax = 12   Ymax = 12   Xmax = 9   Ymax = 12   Xmax = 10   Ymax = 25   Xmax = 10   Ymax = 30
Xscl = 3   Yscl = 3   Xscl = 1   Yscl = 2   Xscl = 2   Yscl = 5   Xscl = 1   Yscl = 3

19. Xmin = −20   Ymin = −30
Xmax = 30   Ymax = 50
Xscl = 5   Yscl = 10

Graphing Equations and Square Viewing Window Exercise Set

1. Setting B   **3.** Setting B   **5.** Setting B

7. 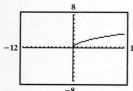   **9.** 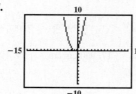   **11.** 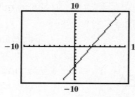   **13.**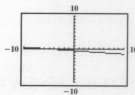

15. 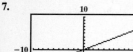   **17.** 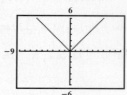   **19.** 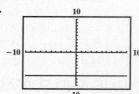   **21.**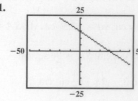

Index

Photo Credits

Martin-Gay's **VIDEO RESOURCES**
Help Students Succeed

MARTIN-GAY'S CHAPTER TEST PREP VIDEO (AVAILABLE WITH THIS TEXT) TEST PREP VIDEO

- Provides students with help during their most "teachable moment"—while they are studying for a test.
- Text author Elayn Martin-Gay presents step-by-step solutions to the exact exercises found in each Chapter Test in the book.
- Easy video navigation allows students to instantly access the worked-out solutions to the exercises they want to review.
- Close captioned in English and Spanish.

NEW MARTIN-GAY'S INTERACTIVE DVD/CD LECTURE SERIES

Martin-Gay's video series has been comprehensively updated to address the way today's students study and learn. The new videos offer students active learning at their pace, with the following resources and more:

- **A complete lecture** for each section of the text, presented by Elayn Martin-Gay. Students can easily review a section or a specific topic before a homework assignment, quiz, or test. Exercises in the text marked with the ⬛ are worked on the video.
- **A new interface** with menu and navigation features helps students quickly find and focus on the examples and exercises they need to review.
- Martin-Gay's "pop-ups" reinforce key terms and definitions and are a great support for multiple learning styles.
- A new **Practice Final Exam Video** helps students prepare for the final exam. This Practice Final Exam is included in the text in Appendix A.2. At the click of a button, students can watch the full solutions to each exercise on the exam when they need help. Overview clips provide a brief overview on how to approach different problem types—just as they will need to do on a Final Exam.
- **Interactive Concept Checks** allow students to check their understanding of essential concepts. Like the concept checks in the text, these multiple choice exercises focus on common misunderstandings. After making their answer selection, students are told whether they're correct or not, and why! Elayn also presents the full solution.
- **Study Skills Builders** help students develop effective study habits and reinforce the advice provided in Section 1.1, Tips for Success in Mathematics, found in the text and video.
- **Close-captioned in Spanish and English**
- Ask your bookstore for information about Martin-Gay's *Intermediate Algebra,* Fifth Edition Interactive DVD/CD Lecture Series or visit www.mypearsonstore.com.

You will find Interactive Concept Checks and Study Skills Builders in the following sections on the Interactive DVD/CD Lecture Series:

Interactive Concept Checks Section		Study Skills Builders Section
1.2	6.5	2.2 Time Management
1.3	6.6	2.3 Are You Familiar with the Resources Available with Your Textbook?
1.4	6.7	
2.1	7.1	3.5 Have You Decided to Complete This Course Successfully?
2.4	7.2	
2.5	7.4	
2.6	7.5	3.7 How Well Do You Know Your Textbook?
2.7	7.6	4.3 Tips for Studying for an Exam
3.1	8.1	4.5 How Are Your Homework Assignments Going?
3.2	8.2	
3.3	8.3	5.5 Doing Your Homework Online
3.4	8.4	5.8 What to Do the Day of an Exam?
3.6	8.6	6.1 Are You Satisfied with Your Performance on a Particular Quiz?
4.1	9.1	
4.2	9.2	6.4 Are You Organized?
4.4	9.3	
5.1	9.5	7.3 Are You Familiar with the Resources Available with Your Textbook?
5.2	9.6	
5.3	10.1	7.7 Have You Decided to Complete This Course Successfully?
5.4	10.2	
5.6	10.3	8.5 How Well Do You Know Your Textbook?
5.7	11.1	9.4 Tips for Studying for an Exam
6.2	11.2	9.7 Are You Satisfied with Your Performance on a Particular Quiz or Exam?
6.3	11.3	
		10.4 What to Do the Day of an Exam?
		11.4 How Are Your Homework Assignments Going?
		11.5 Preparing for Your Final Exam